ZENITH AIRCRAFT
LIBRARY
TECHNICAL LIBRARY
HITCO
DATE RECEIVED
9-14-54
TECHNICAL LIBRARY

HITCO
TECHNICAL LIBRARY

HITCO
LIBRARY

ZENITH PLASTICS COMPANY
ENGINEERING LIBRARY

TECHNICAL

HITCO
TECHNICAL LIBRARY

D1106619

HANDBOOK

OF

EXPERIMENTAL
STRESS ANALYSIS

HANDBOOK

OF

EXPERIMENTAL
STRESS ANALYSIS

Edited by

M. HETÉNYI

Professor of Engineering Mechanics
The Technological Institute
Northwestern University

ZENITH PLASTICS COMPANY
ENGINEERING LIBRARY

BOOK
c. 1

NEW YORK · JOHN WILEY & SONS, INC.
LONDON · CHAPMAN & HALL, LIMITED

Copyright, 1950
By
John Wiley & Sons, Inc.

———

All Rights Reserved

*This book or any part thereof must not
be reproduced in any form without the
written permission of the publisher.*

PRINTED IN THE UNITED STATES OF AMERICA

PREFACE

Experimental science does not receive Truth
from superior Sciences: she is the Mistress and
the other sciences are her servants

ROGER BACON: *Opus Tertium*

Stress analysis has been regarded for some time as a distinct professional branch of engineering, the object of which is the determination and improvement of the mechanical strength of structures and machines. Experimental stress analysis strives to achieve these aims by experimental means. In doing so it does not remain, however, a mere counterpart of theoretical methods of stress analysis but encompasses those, utilizing all the conclusions reached by theoretical considerations, and goes far beyond them in maintaining direct contact with the true physical characteristics of the problems under considerations.

Many factors make the experimental approach indispensable, and often the only means of access, in the investigation of problems of mechanical strength. At our present state of knowledge it is remarkable how quickly we can reach the limit of applicability of mathematical methods of stress analysis, and there is a multitude of comparatively simple, and in practice frequently occurring, stress problems for which no theoretical solutions have yet been obtained. In addition to this, theoretical considerations are usually based on simplifying assumptions which imply certain detachment from reality, and it can be decided only by experimentation whether such idealization has not resulted in an undue distortion of the essential features of the problem. No such doubt needs to enter experimental stress analysis, especially if it is done under actual service conditions, where all the factors due to the properties of the employed materials, the methods of manufacture, and the conditions of operation are fully represented. The advantage of the experimental approach becomes especially obvious if we consider that it is possible to determine experimentally the stress distribution in a machine part in actual operation without knowing the nature of the forces acting on the part under these circumstances, which proposition is clearly inaccessible to any theoretical method of analysis. To these major advantages we may add one more, from the point of view of the average practicing engineer, whose mathematical preparation is not likely to enable him to deal theoretically with some of the complex strength problems which he, nevertheless, is expected to settle satisfactorily. To these men experimental methods constitute a recourse that is more readily accessible and that, with proper care and perseverance, is most likely to furnish the needed information.

Several principal methods and literally hundreds of individual tools and artifices constitute the "arsenal" of the experimental stress analyst. It is interesting to observe, however, that each of these devices, no matter how peculiar it sometimes appears to be, has its characteristic feature and, with it, some unique advantage that may render this tool most suitable for the investigation of a particular problem. The stress analyst cannot afford, therefore, to ignore any of these possibilities. This circumstance, together with the ever-increasing demand on mechanical strength, will always tend to keep experimental stress analysis a distinct entity in the field of technical sciences.

There has been a long-felt need of a comprehensive reference book of this nature, but, at the same time, it was recognized that no one person could possibly write with authority on all the major experimental procedures that are being used at present in the investigation of mechanical strength. It was proposed therefore that the problem could be solved only by a concerted effort which might be initiated most suitably under the aegis of the Society for Experimental Stress Analysis, and the writer was appointed as editor with complete freedom to proceed with the organization of this undertaking. Invitations were sent to thirty eminent engineers and scientists who were best known for their outstanding contributions in one or more of the specific branches of experimental stress analysis. It was most impressive to witness the readiness and understanding with which these men, many of them not even associated with the Society, responded to the request and joined the editor in contributing their work, without remuneration, to the furtherance of the aims of the Society, which thus becomes the sole recipient of all royalties from this publication.

This being the first comprehensive publication in its field, it may be of general interest to say a few words about the method used in the planning and coordination of the material. In inviting the contributors, I first briefly outlined the subject to be covered requesting, in return, from each author a more detailed outline of what he would propose on his respective subject. These authors' outlines were subsequently collected in a booklet, a copy of which was sent to each participant, thus informing him in advance of projected contents of all the other parts of the book. This scheme proved of considerable help in assuring adequate coverage of all matters of interest, without undue overlaps, repetition, or need of frequent cross references. In the final plan, as seen in the table of contents, the main body of the book was divided into 18 chapters, each dealing with either a principal method, from mechanical gages to X-ray analysis, or a major topic of interest, such as residual stresses, interpretation of service fractures, or analogies. In addition to these, an appendix was devoted to the discussion of three theoretical subjects which are of fundamental importance in the planning and interpretation of experimental stress work. In the final outcome, not only the book as a whole but also most of the individual chapters turned out to be pioneering ventures in their own rights, often constituting the first systematic exposition of their respective subject matter. Another innovation was undertaken in the treatment of bibliographical references, where an effort was made to review briefly the contents of each entry, since it was found that the mere titles of technical articles seldom convey a satisfactory picture of their respective contents.   Despite all precautions the book is bound to have errors and shortcomings, and it is the sincere hope of the editor that users of the book will not hesitate to inform him of possibilities of improvement which may be incorporated in a later edition.

In the course of this work the editor was greatly aided by advice from numerous friends and colleagues, among whom he wishes to acknowledge in particular the invaluable help received from B. F. Langer, R. D. Mindlin, W. M. Murray, R. E. Peterson, and G. Pickett.

M. HETÉNYI

Evanston, Illinois
April 1950

CONTRIBUTORS

R. B. ALLNUTT *David W. Taylor Model Basin, Navy Department, Washington 7, D.C.*

CHARLES S. BARRETT, Ph.D. *Professor, Institute for the Study of Metals, University of Chicago, Chicago 37, Illinois*

B. C. CARTER *Professor, Department of Internal Combustion Engines, Indian Institute of Science, Bangalore, India*

C. O. DOHRENWEND, Ph.D. *Professor and Head, Department of Mechanics, Rensselaer Polytechnic Institute, Troy, New York*

THOMAS J. DOLAN *Research Professor of Theoretical and Applied Mechanics, University of Illinois, Urbana, Illinois*

L. H. DONNELL, Ph.D. *Research Professor of Applied Mechanics, Illinois Institute of Technology, Technology Center, Chicago 16, Illinois*

D. C. DRUCKER, PhD. *Associate Professor of Engineering, Graduate Division of Applied Mathematics, Brown University, Providence 12, Rhode Island*

J. R. FORSHAW *Principal Scientific Officer, Ministry of Supply, National Gas Turbine Establishment, Whetstone, Leicester, England*

J. N. GOODIER, Ph.D. *Professor of Mechanics, School of Engineering, Stanford University, Stanford, California*

M. HETÉNYI, Ph.D. *Professor of Engineering Mechanics, The Technological Institute, Northwestern University, Evanston, Illinois*

OSCAR J. HORGER, Sc.D. *Chief Engineer, Railway Division, The Timken Roller Bearing Company, Canton 6, Ohio*

B. F. LANGER *Manager of Structural Engineering, Atomic Power Division, Westinghouse Electric Corporation, Bettis Site, Pittsburgh 30, Pennsylvania*

CHARLES LIPSON, Ph.D. *Consultant, 424 Book Building, Detroit 26, Michigan*

C. W. MacGREGOR, PhD. *Professor of Applied Mechanics, Massachusetts Institute of Technology, Cambridge 39, Massachusetts*

JOSEPH MARIN, Ph.D. *Professor of Engineering Mechanics, The Pennsylvania State College, State College, Pennsylvania*

JOHN L. MAULBETSCH, Ph.D. *Vice-President, Kollmorgen Optical Corporation, 2 Franklin Avenue, Brooklyn 11, New York*

ix

W. R. MEHAFFEY   *Senior Electrical Engineer, Armour Research Foundation, Technology Center, Chicago 16, Illinois*

J. H. MEIER, Sc.D.   *Research Engineer, Bucyrus-Erie Company, South Milwaukee, Wisconsin*

RAYMOND D. MINDLIN, Ph.D.   *Professor of Civil Engineering, Columbia University, New York 27, New York*

F. MINTZ   *Research Engineer, Armour Research Foundation, Technology Center Chicago 16, Illinois*

W. M. MURRAY, Sc.D.   *Associate Professor of Mechanical Engineering, Massachusetts Institute of Technology, Cambridge 39, Massachusetts*

CHARLES H. NORRIS, Sc.D.   *Associate Professor of Structural Engineering, Massachusetts Institute of Technology, Cambridge 39, Massachusetts*

J. ORMONDROYD   *Professor of Engineering Mechanics, University of Michigan, Ann Arbor, Michigan*

R. E. PETERSON   *Manager, Mechanics Department, Westinghouse Research Laboratories, East Pittsburgh, Pennsylvania*

MARIO G. SALVADORI, Dr. Ing.   *Associate Professor of Civil Engineering, Columbia University, New York 27, New York*

W. T. SAVAGE   *Supervisor of Materials of Engineering, Armour Research Foundation, Technology Center, Chicago 16, Illinois*

J. F. SHANNON, Ph.D.   *Gas Turbine Engineering Department, Metropolitan-Vickers Electrical Company, Barton Dock Road, Urmston, Manchester, England*

C. RICHARD SODERBERG   *Professor and Head, Department of Mechanical Engineering, Massachusetts Institute of Technology, Cambridge 39, Massachusetts*

R. D. SPECHT, Ph.D.   *Associate Mathematician, The Rand Corporation, Santa Monica, California*

S. P. TIMOSHENKO, Sc.D.   *Professor of Theoretical and Applied Mechanics, Emeritus, School of Engineering, Stanford University, Stanford University, California*

JOHN B. WILBUR, Sc.D.   *Professor of Civil Engineering, Head, Department of Civil and Sanitary Engineering, Massachusetts Institute of Technology, Cambridge 39, Massachusetts*

CONTENTS

CONTENTS

CHAPTER 1

MECHANICAL PROPERTIES OF MATERIALS

By C. W. MacGregor

A. INTRODUCTION

With the exception of certain elastic constants, the analysis of the state of stress existing in machine parts or structural members, loaded within the elastic range, is carried out without any particular reference to the mechanical properties of the component materials. In the analytical solution of many elasticity problems, even the elastic constants do not enter, whereas in others it is necessary to know the elastic constants in order to effect a solution. In the experimental determination of stresses through elastic strain measurements, it is necessary that the elastic constants be known. When stress calculations are carried out in the plastic range for cold working, metal forming, or creep problems, a knowledge of many more mechanical properties is required than for the elastic range.

After the stresses have been determined through experimental or analytical methods, the engineer is confronted with the problem of assessing the relative importance and significance of the stress values so obtained in relation to the satisfactory performance of the structure or machine parts under consideration. It is in this connection that the mechanical properties of the material play one of their most important roles. In an existing structure or machine

1

part for example, it is necessary to know the mechanical properties of the material in order to determine if the stresses are within allowable limits.   On the other hand, if a member is to be designed, it is essential that the mechanical properties of various materials be known in order to select the proper one to be used.

Many cases exist where the selection of the proper material cannot be based solely on stress considerations. Satisfactory performance may require a limited deflection, a hard surface, capacity to absorb local yielding without excessive stresses, energy absorption, and the like.

It may thus be seen that a knowledge of the mechanical properties of materials is of vital importance to the engineer concerned with stress analysis problems.   This chapter contains a brief discussion of some of those mechanical properties of greatest interest to the stress analyst.   Owing to space limitations, many phases of the subject have to be omitted.   References are given, however, where further information may be obtained.

B. Definitions of Some Basic Concepts

In the following the definitions of a number of basic concepts are given:

1. Stress.   Stress may be defined simply as the internal force per unit of area which resists a change in size or shape of the body.   Since the stress will, in general, vary from point to point in a loaded member, it may be considered as the limit approached by the ratio of the force acting on an elemental area to the area of cross section on which it acts as the area of cross section approaches zero.   Wherever stress is mentioned in this chapter, it is thus understood to be the intensity of stress as previously defined.   The units are usually expressed in pounds per square inch in the United States, but in Europe stress is often reported in tons per square inch, kilograms per square millimeter, and so on.

Two distinct types of stress are of interest: namely, *normal stress* and *shearing stress*.   A *normal stress* is one which acts in a direction perpendicular to the cross-sectional area.   It may be either tensile or compressive, depending on the direction of the stress.   A tensile stress is indicated by an arrow directed away from the plane on which it acts, and its tendency is to resist the action of the external forces to increase the length of the body.   A compressive stress is usually indicated by a vector or arrow directed towards the plane on which it acts, and its tendency is to resist the action of the external forces to decrease the length of the body.   A *shearing stress*, on the other hand, lies in the plane on which it acts.   It resists the action of the external forces tending to make the part of the body above the plane slide over the portion of the body below the plane.   Its action then is similar to that of the friction existing between the individual cards in a stack of playing cards when one presses down on the stack and at the same time gives the top card a displacement in the horizontal direction.   The *resultant stress* acting on any plane in the body is the vector sum of the normal and shearing stresses present.   Experience has shown that the mechanical properties of materials are affected differently by the normal and shearing stresses. Hence, the resultant stress is not very frequently used in engineering problems.

In a uniform prismatic bar loaded axially by a tensile force P, the stress $\sigma = P/A$ is uniformly distributed over the cross section A. If any discontinuity is present such as a hole or a notch, the stress is not uniformly distributed over the cross section through the discontinuity. The stress is considerably increased near the discontinuity, and the factor by which the nominal stress must be multiplied to equal the maximum value present is called the *factor of stress concentration*. This is discussed more fully in other chapters.

In the vast majority of practical applications and in most of the mechanical tests of materials, a two- or three-dimensional state of stress exists rather than the simple one-dimensional or uniaxial type shown in Fig. 1-1a. The

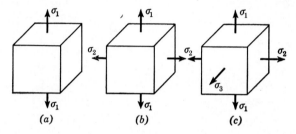

FIG. 1-1. States of Stress

two-dimensional or biaxial state of stress is shown on an element of material in Fig. 1-1b, and the three-dimensional or triaxial state of stress is indicated in Fig. 1-1c. The latter are called states of *combined stress*, and they have a great effect on the strength and ductility of materials. In general, each plane passing through a point of the body will be acted on by both normal and shearing stresses. The problem is, however, greatly simplified if the planes cutting out the element of material are so rotated that only normal stresses appear on the faces of the element. This has been done in Fig. 1-1. It is these normal stresses acting on planes on which no shearing stresses exist which are of the greatest significance in stress analysis problems and in the relation of stress to mechanical properties. Those normal stresses acting on planes containing no shearing stresses are called *principal stresses*. At a point in a stressed body, there are, in general, three principal stresses acting on mutually perpendicular planes. They are designated by σ_1, σ_2, and σ_3 where the subscripts refer to the directions of the stresses. One of these principal stresses is the maximum normal stress for all orientations of planes passing through the point, and one of the others is the minimum normal stress for all such possible planes. The problem of the determination of the directions and magnitudes of these principal stresses in an arbitrarily loaded body is discussed in subsequent chapters of this handbook.

In connection with the yielding of ductile metals, there are two combinations of the principal stresses which are of considerable significance. These

refer to shearing stresses on certain planes through the element shown in
Fig. 1-2. The shearing stresses are maximum on planes inclined by an angle
of 45° to the principal planes (the latter being those on which the principal
normal stresses are acting). If the magnitudes of the principal stresses are
in the order $\sigma_1 > \sigma_2 > \sigma_3$, the *maximum shearing* stress is

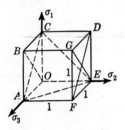

$$\tau_{max} = \frac{\sigma_1 - \sigma_3}{2} \qquad (1)$$

which acts on the planes $ACDF$ and $BGEO$ at 45° to
σ_1 and σ_3 and parallel to σ_2. The other shearing
stress of considerable importance acts on the so-called
octahedral plane (ACE of Fig. 1-2) whose normal
makes equal angles with σ_1, σ_2, and σ_3. This shearing stress is called the *octahedral shearing stress* τ_n,

FIG. 1-2. Maximum   and in terms of the principal stresses it is[2]
Shear and Octahedral
Shear Planes $$\tau_n = \tfrac{1}{3}\sqrt{(\sigma_1 - \sigma_2)^2 + (\sigma_2 - \sigma_3)^2 + (\sigma_3 - \sigma_1)^2} \qquad (2)$$

Equations 1 and 2 are closely related to the maximum shear stress theory
of failure and to the distortion energy theory of failure, respectively.

2. Displacement. The linear change of dimension of a body in a given
direction produced by the action of external forces is called the displacement
or deformation. The displacement is usually expressed in inches in the
United States and in millimeters in Europe.

3. Strain. If the magnitude of the displacement is small compared to the
dimensions of the body, the strain may be defined as the displacement divided

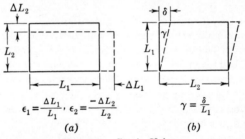

$$\epsilon_1 = \frac{\Delta L_1}{L_1}, \ \epsilon_2 = \frac{-\Delta L_2}{L_2} \qquad\qquad \gamma = \frac{\delta}{L_1}$$

(a)   (b)

FIG. 1-3.   Strain Values

by one of the original dimensions of the body. Strains may be subdivided
into *normal strains* and *shearing strains*. The *normal strain* in any direction
is equal to the displacement in that direction divided by the gage length
measured in the same direction as shown in Fig. 1-3a. The gage length is
the length over which the displacement is measured. The units of normal
strains are thus inches per inch, millimeters per millimeter, and so on. The
shearing strain may be determined by dividing the displacement in a given
direction by a length normal to the direction of the displacement. This is
actually the tangent of the shearing strain angle as indicated in Fig. 1-3b.

Whereas in stress problems various states of uniaxial stresses can exist, in practice it is most uncommon to have a state of purely uniaxial strain. This is due to the lateral strains accompanying a normal strain in any direction. The most common state of strain is the triaxial one shown in Fig. 1-4. As in the discussion of stress, the planes cutting out the element of material have been rotated so that only normal *principal strains* appear on the faces of the element. The *principal strains* are the normal strains acting on the principal planes, the latter undergoing no shearing strain. They are analogous to the principal stresses defined previously and are usually designated by ϵ_1, ϵ_2, ϵ_3 where the subscripts refer to the directions of the strains. One of these principal strains is the maximum normal strain for all directions through a point in the body and one of the others is the smallest normal strain for all such possible directions. The methods used to determine the directions and magnitudes of the principal strains for a given problem are discussed in subsequent chapters.

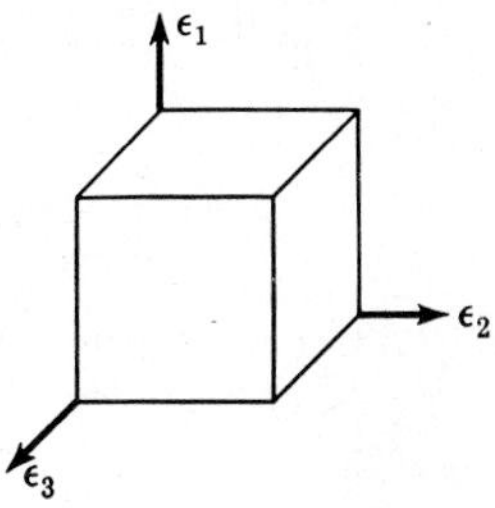

For the yielding of ductile metals, there are two combinations of the principal strains which are of considerable use, especially in conjunction with the stress values given in equations 1 and 2. The *maximum shearing strain* corresponding to the maximum shearing stress of equation 1 is

$$\gamma_{max} = \epsilon_1 - \epsilon_3 \qquad (3)$$

FIG. 1-4. State of Strain

if the principal strains are in the order $\epsilon_1 > \epsilon_2 > \epsilon_3$. The *octahedral shearing strain* corresponding to the octahedral shearing stress of equation 2 is

$$\gamma_n = \tfrac{2}{3} \sqrt{(\epsilon_1 - \epsilon_2)^2 + (\epsilon_2 - \epsilon_3)^2 + (\epsilon_3 - \epsilon_1)^2} \qquad (4)$$

4. Elasticity. The essential characteristic of elasticity is the ability of the material to return to the original dimensions of the body on removal of the externally applied loads. Most materials of engineering interest possess limited ranges of stress throughout which the material may be considered elastic. Within these ranges of stress *Hooke's law* is obeyed. This law states that for a homogeneous and isotropic material stress is proportional to strain as long as the stress does not exceed a limiting value. If a test specimen is loaded in either tension or compression within the elastic range of stress, the ratio of the normal stress to the normal strain in the direction of the applied stress is called the *modulus of elasticity* or *Young's modulus* and is usually designated by the letter E. On the other hand, if the material is tested in shear in a torsion test, the ratio of the shearing stress to the shearing strain within the elastic range of stress is called the *shearing modulus of elasticity* or the *modulus of rigidity* and is designated by the symbol G. The units of both E and G are the same as stress. Table 1-1 lists typical values of E.

5. Poisson's Ratio. When a test bar is loaded in tension or compression, the normal strain in the axial direction is accompanied by a normal strain in the transverse or lateral directions. For tension tests the lateral strain is a contraction, whereas for compression tests the lateral strain is an expansion. The absolute value of the ratio of the lateral strain to the axial strain is known as *Poisson's ratio* and is designated by the symbol μ. Values of Poisson's ratio are listed in Table 1-1 for various materials.

6. Relations between Elastic Constants.   So far three elastic constants have been defined for a homogeneous and isotropic material.   These are the elastic

TABLE 1-1

ELASTIC MODULUS AND POISSON'S RATIO FOR VARIOUS METALS
From M.S. Thesis by R. W. Vose, MIT, 1936

Material	Modulus of Elasticity E, psi	Poisson's Ratio μ
SAE 1045 steel, annealed	29×10^6	0.287
SAE 1045 steel, hot-rolled	28.5×10^6	0.292
SAE 2330 steel, as-rolled	28.6×10^6	0.291
SAE 6150 steel, as-rolled	29.3×10^6	0.289
SAE 6150 steel, water-quenched from 1575°F, drawn 1200°F	30.5×10^6	0.285
Cold-rolled shafting	29.5×10^6	0.287
Cutlery-type stainless steel	30.5×10^6	0.278
18-8 stainless steel	27.6×10^6	0.305
Iso-Elastic steel (Ni 36%, Cr 8%)	26.3×10^6	0.333
Cast iron (no alloying elements)	14.5×10^6	0.211
Cast iron (15% Ni, 2.05% Cr)	13.5×10^6	0.299
Malleable iron	23.6×10^6	0.265
Copper (99.9% pure)	15.6×10^6	0.355
Brass (70-30)	15.9×10^6	0.331
Tobin bronze (Cu 60.3%, Zn 38.1%, Sn 1.56%)	13.8×10^6	0.359
Phosphor bronze (Cu 90%, Zn 6%, Sn 4%)	16.1×10^6	0.349
17ST duraluminum (Cu 3.85%, Mn 0.57%, Mg 0.05%, Al 95.08%)	10.2×10^6	0.330
51ST aluminum alloy (Si 1.07%, Mg. 0.56% Al 98.37%)	9.91×10^6	0.334
Monel metal	25×10^6	0.315

modulus E, the shearing modulus G, and Poissons ratio μ.   It can be shown that these three constants are not independent but are related by the equation,

$$G = \frac{E}{2(1 + \mu)} \tag{5}$$

C. STRESS–STRAIN DIAGRAMS

One of the most common and useful means of determining many of the mechanical properties is to conduct a tension test on the material.   In order to represent the behavior during such a test, it is common practice to plot a stress–strain diagram with stress as ordinate and strain as abscissa.   Since the early development of the subject of the testing of materials, many different forms of stress–strain diagrams have been suggested.   Of these, the ones described herein are *the ordinary stress–strain diagram* and *the true stress–strain diagram.*

7. The Ordinary Stress–Strain Diagram. This is constructed as shown in Fig. 1-5*a* by plotting the stress determined by dividing the axial load P by the original area of cross section A_0 as ordinate versus the strain $\epsilon_0 = \Delta L_0/L_0$ as abscissa where ΔL_0 is the increment of the original gage length L_0. The strain ϵ_0 is thus determined from axial strain measurements by the use of one of the strain gages available commercially. Since both A_0 and L_0 are constants, the resulting diagram has the same shape as one for which the axial load P is plotted versus the deformation ΔL_0. From such a diagram, in addition to the elastic constants, other mechanical properties may be determined as defined in the following. Table 1-2 includes typical values of these properties for various materials.

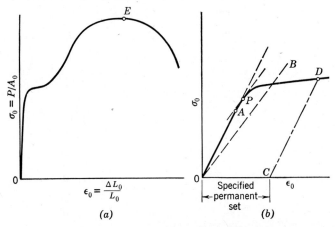

Fig. 1-5. Ordinary Stress–Strain Diagrams

(a) *The Proportional Limit* is usually obtained graphically by determining the point on the stress–strain diagram at which the curve portion departs from the linear elastic part of the curve. Thus, the stress corresponding to point A in Fig. 1-5*b* is the proportional limit. It is defined as the greatest stress intensity for which stress is still proportional to strain.

(b) *The Elastic Limit* is the greatest stress which may be applied to a test specimen without leaving a permanent deformation on complete release of the load. In order to determine the elastic limit, it is necessary to load and unload the bar with increasing values of the load until a permanent set is found after complete unloading. Since this procedure is very time-consuming and the elastic limit so determined differs but little from the proportional limit, the true elastic limit is seldom obtained in actual practice.

(c) *The Johnson's Apparent Elastic Limit* is an arbitrary "elastic limit" devised especially for those materials for which the point of departure from the straight line is not so clearly defined. It is the stress at which the slope of the stress–strain diagram is 50 per cent less than the slope at the origin.

TABLE 1-2

TYPICAL ORDINARY MECHANICAL PROPERTIES FOR VARIOUS METALS AT NORMAL TEMPERATURES

Material	Modulus of Elasticity, psi	Proportional Limit, psi	Yield Strength, psi	Tensile Strength, psi	Per cent Elongation	Reduction of Area, per cent	Hardness No.	Impact Value, ft-lb.	Endurance Limit, psi	Reference
Aluminum 99+ %–2S, extruded	......	......	13,000 (at 0.2 % perm)	15,000	25 (2 in. g.l.)	......	28	......	6,000 (at 500 × 10⁶)	1
Aluminum 99+ %–(2S-0), wrought, annealed	10.3 × 10⁶	......	5,000 (at 0.2 % perm.)	13,000	45 (2 in. g.l.)	......	23	......	5,000 (at 500 × 10⁶)	2
Copper (Cu 99.997 %), oxygen-free, cold-drawn rod ½ in. diam.	17.8 × 10⁶	......	49,400 (at 0.5 % ext.)	51,000	14 (2 in. g.l.)	88	RB 37	......	17,000 (at 300 × 10⁶)	3
Copper (Cu 99.895 %), ¾ in.-diam. rod, ann. ½ hr at 1290°F	......	3,200	......	32,400	56 (2 in. g.l.)	72	47	30	10,000 (at 100 × 10⁶)	4
Brass (Zn 29.92 %, Pb 0.02 %, Fe 0.02), rod ¾ in. diam., ann. 1 hr. at 1100°F, water-quench	14.7 × 10⁶	9,200	......	47,200	55 (8 in. g.l.)	75	RB 11	......	22,500 (at 50 × 10⁶)	5
Brass (same composition), cold-drawn 27 % red.	15.5 × 10⁶	17,800	......	74,100	20 (2 in. g.l.)	58	RB 81	......	22,000 (at 50 × 10⁶)	5
Armco iron (C 0.015 %), hot-rolled	......	21,300	22,700	44,300	47 (2 in. g.l.)	75	83	......	26,200	6
Armco iron (C 0.02 %), annealed	......	16,100	19,000	42,400	48 (2 in. g.l.)	76	69	19	26,000	4
Wrought iron (C 0.017 %, Si 0.122 %, slag 2.24 %), longitudinal	......	......	29,900	47,000	15 (2 in. g.l.)	16	......	42	30,500	7
Wrought iron (same composition), transverse	......	......	28,600	46,800	17 (2 in. g.l.)	16	......	6.5	28,000	7
Low-carbon steel (C 0.10 %, Mn 0.72 Si 0.06), normalized at 1650°F	......	......	36,300 (at 0.1 %)	63,800	37 (2 in. g.l.)	64	......	......	26,900	8
Low-carbon steel (C 0.12 %, Mn 0.84 %, S 0.12 %, P 0.099 %, Si 0.01 %), 1⅛ in. diam. rod, cold-rolled	30,400	......	76,000 (0.001 % perm.)	83,300	18 (2 in. g.l.)	52	V 205	......	......	9
Med.-carbon steel (C 0.35 %, Mn 0.55 %, Si 0.019 %, S 0.030 %, P 0.016 %), annealed at 1280°F	......	......	42,700	68,000	39 (2 in. g.l.)	66	......	30	35,500	7
High-carbon steel (C 1.09 %, Mn 0.33 %, Si 0.028 %), annealed 1 hr at 1475°F, slow-cooled	......	53,000	63,500 (0.01 % perm.)	106,000	28 (2 in. g.l.)	52	......	......	42,500	10

Material	Modulus of elasticity	Proportional limit or yield strength		Ultimate strength	Elongation	Reduction of area	Hardness	Impact	Endurance limit	Ref.
Chromium steel (C 0.037%, Cr 0.050%, Mn 1.14%, Si 0.84%, S 0.033%, P 0.021%) ¾ in. diam., hot-rolled	30 × 10⁶	80,600 (0.005% perm.)	......	125,000	23 (2 in. g.l.)	58	255	13	63,500	11
Chromium steel (C 0.040%, Cr 15.2%, Ni 0.018%) 1 in. diam. bar, 1 hr at 1650°F, water-quenched, drawn at 900°F	......	72,500		164,000	12 (2 in. g.l.)	38	...	...	84,500	12
Cr-Ni steel (C 0.40%, Cr 13.5%, Ni 13.5%, W 2.5%, Si 1.5%), forged	25.0 × 10⁶	......	83,000	134,000	37 (1.5 in. g.l.)	42	260	Iz 50	......	13
Stainless steel (C 0.07%, Cr 18.95%, Ni 7.69%, ¾ in. diam., cold-rolled		13,000	......	143,000	21	......	302	Iz 34	85,000	14
Cast iron (graphite carbon 2.25%, combined carbon 0.63%)	14.8 × 10⁶	......	.. ...	40,900	....	......	189	3	19,600	15
Malleable cast iron (C 1.75–2.30%, Si 0.85–1.20), annealed	25 × 10⁶	37,500	......	57,000	22 (2 in. g.l.)	......	110–145	16	25,000 to 26,500	16
Refined lead-cable sheath, 1 in. O.D. ⅛ in. wall, extruded	....	2,100 (at 0.1 m./in./- min)	......		119 (2.5 in. g.l.)	......	V 4.5	......	380 (at 10 × 10⁶)	17
Magnesium, comm. pure, ½ in. square rod, extruded	6.74 × 10⁶	1,200	......	32,500	6.2 (8 in. g.l.)	4.4	41	2.9	7,800 (at 100 × 10⁶)	18

The values listed would be modified by heat treatment or cold work.

The modulus of elasticity proportional limit, and yield strength for ductile metals in compression will differ little from the tensile values.

Compression strength for ductile metals has little meaning.

Brittle metals usually have compression strengths considerably greater than the tensile strength.

The shear strength for ductile metals is roughly three-fourths the tensile strength.

The endurance limit for nonferrous metals is given at the number of cycles sustained. The latter value is listed as for example (at 100 × 10⁶ cycles).

The gage length is listed for per cent elongation as, for example, 2 in. g.l., meaning a 2-in. gage length.

The yield strength is listed at the specified strain.

The hardness abbreviations are RB, Rockwell B scale; V, Vickers, and where no letter is specified the values shown are Brinell hardness.

The impact values are for the Charpy test unless listed as Iz designating Izod.

References in table:

(1) D. K. Crampton, *Trans. ASM* **25**, 55 (1937); (2) Alcoa Alum. and Alloys, Alum. Co of America, Pittsburgh, 1941; (3) A. R. Anderson, and C. S. Smith *ASTM Proc.*, **41**, 849 (1941); (4) H. F. Moore and T. M. Jasper, *Univ. Illinois Expt. Sta. Bull.*, **152**, (1925); (5) J. B. Kommers, *ASTM Proc.*, **31**, pt. 2, 243 (1931) (6) Same, *ASTM Proc.*, **30**, pt. 2, 368 (1930); (7) H. W. Russell and W. A. Welcher, *ASTM Proc.*, **36**, pt. 2, 118 (1936); (8) W. H. Hatfield, *Metallurgia*, **20**, 107 (1939); (9) H. L. Whittemore *et al.*, *J. Research Natl. Bur. Standards*, **14**, 139 (1935); (10) D. J. McAdam, Jr., and R. W. Clyne, *J. Research Natl. Bur. Standards*, **13**, 527 (1934); (11) W. L. Collins and T. J. Dolan, *ASTM Proc.*, **38**, pt. 2, 157 (1938); (12) D. J. McAdam, Jr., *ASTM Proc.*, **24**, pt. 2, 273 (1924); (13) F. C. Thompson, *Trans. Manchester Assoc. Engrs.*, 311 (1937–38); (14) R. Franks and W. O. Binder, *Trans AIME* **140**, 433 (1940); (15) *Proc. ASTM*, **33**, pt. I, 87 (1933); (16) Prod. Eng. 13, 37 (1942); (17) J. C. Chaston Elec. Comm. 13, 31 (1934); (18) R. R. Moore, *ASTM Proc.* 25, Pt. 2, **66** (1925).

As shown in Fig. 1-5b it is determined by drawing a line $\overline{OB}$ from the origin with a slope 50 per cent less than for the elastic line $\overline{OA}$, followed by moving OB parallel to itself until it is tangent to the curve at P. The stress corresponding to point P is Johnson's apparent elastic limit.

(d) *The Yield Point* has been defined as the stress for which a marked increase in strain occurs without a corresponding increase in stress. For annealed low-carbon steels both an upper and a lower yield point are present. The upper yield point is the stress at which a drop of the beam occurs on gear-driven testing machines or at which the pointer on a hydraulic testing machine begins to drop back. The lower yield point is the lowest stress reached during the drop-back of the load just after the upper yield point has been exceeded. The 1944 ASTM standards E6–36 specify that the term yield point should not be used in connection with a material which shows a gradual transition from the elastic to the plastic range.

(e) *The Yield Strength* is the stress at which the material shows a specified limiting permanent set. This is an arbitrary limit based on an allowable amount of strain and was devised especially to fit the cases in which the stress–strain diagram has a gradual curvature from elastic to plastic states without a natural yield point as, for example, low carbon steel. The magnitude of the specified permanent set varies but is commonly 0.10 or 0.20 per cent of the original gage length. When the value is reported, the amount of permanent set should be specified. The graphical construction is shown in Fig. 1-5b. A straight line $\overline{CD}$ is drawn parallel to $\overline{OA}$ but displaced from it a horizontal distance equal to the specified permanent set. The stress corresponding to point D is the yield strength.

(f)   *The Tensile Strength* is obtained by dividing the maximum axial load observed during the test by the original cross-sectional area of the test specimen. Point E of Fig. 1-5a corresponds to the tensile strength.

(g) *The Per Cent Elongation* after fracture of the specimen is determined by dividing the change in the original gage length by the original gage length and multiplying this ratio by 100. As recommended by the 1944 ASTM Standards E8–42, the original gage length should always be stated in reporting per cent elongation values.

(h) *The Per Cent Reduction of Area* after fracture is the ratio of the change in the original area determined at the smallest cross section to the original area of cross section, this ratio multiplied by 100.

(i) *The Types of Test Specimens* recommended by the ASTM are described under ASTM Designation E8–42 (1944 Standards) to 'which the reader is referred.

8. The True Stress–Strain Diagram.[5] This is constructed by plotting the true stress σ determined by dividing the axial load P by the actual instantaneous area of cross section A as ordinate versus the true strain $\epsilon = \log_e A_0/A$ as abscissa where A_0 is the original area and A the instantaneous area of cross section, respectively, as shown in Fig. 1-6.* To secure the data neces-

---

* This notation is used to agree with the rest of the handbook.   In the specific

sary to construct such a diagram, simultaneous readings of the axial load and the dimension or dimensions required to compute the minimum instantaneous area of cross section are taken throughout the test to fracture. If the test piece is round, the true axial strain ϵ, which is equal to the true reduction in area q', is $2 \log_e d_0/d$ where d_0 is the original diameter and d is the instantaneous diameter. In other words, the true axial strain is determined through diameter measurements. The same diameter measurements serve to evaluate the true axial stress. If the test specimen is of rectangular cross section, where the ratio of width to thickness <6, the instantaneous area of cross section can be obtained from[5]

$$A = \frac{h}{3}(b + 2c) \qquad (6)$$

where A, h, c, and b are the area of cross section, the width at the center of the cross-section parallel to the long side, the thickness parallel to the short side at the center, and the thickness parallel to the short side at the ends of the cross section, respectively. Thus three dimension measurements will establish the cross-sectional area.

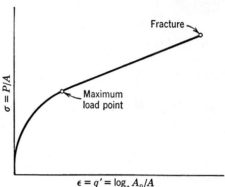

FIG. 1-6.   True Stress–Strain Diagram

An alternate method of plotting the true stress–strain curve, called the *two-load method*, has been suggested.[6] According to this procedure, no strain readings are taken during the test, and only the maximum and fracture loads are noted. A tapered test bar, scribed with fine lateral marks at intervals along its length, is used. The dimension or dimensions governing the areas of cross section are measured at each of these scribed marks both before and after the test is made. It has been shown that these readings are sufficient to construct the complete true stress–strain curve from initial yielding to fracture. The method has been found useful where it is undesirable or difficult to make diameter readings during the test, as in high-speed impact tests or in tests at elevated or subatmospheric temperatures.

Experiments conducted on a wide variety of materials, under various conditions of heat treatment cold work, temperatures, velocities, and the like, have demonstrated that the true stress–strain curve is essentially linear from the point corresponding to the maximum load or shortly thereafter to fracture.

It should perhaps be noted that during local necking after the maximum load has been passed the distribution of the axial stresses across the minimum area of cross section is not strictly uniform. The value P/A is actually the

---

literature on materials testing, the true stress is usually indicated by s and the true strain by q'. They are often called s–q' curves.

average of the true axial stresses. Tests have shown that the average stress value so defined is, in general, not greatly different from the stress which would be present if a necked region had not been allowed to form and the material would have been subjected only to a purely uniform uniaxial state of stress.

From the true stress–strain diagram, in addition to the yield point, or yield strength, as the case may be, the other mechanical properties which may be determined[5] are defined as follows:

(a) *The True Stress at Maximum Load* is equal to the maximum axial load divided by the area of cross section present at the maximum load.

(b) *The True Fracture Stress* is the ratio of the load at fracture to the final fractured area of cross section.

(c) *The Minimum Modulus of Strain Hardening* is the slope of the linear portion of the true stress–strain curve from the maximum load point to fracture.

(d) *The True Fracture Strain* $\epsilon_b = \log_e A_0/A_b$, where A_0 is the original area and A_b is the fractured area of cross section.

(e) *The True Uniform Strain* $\epsilon_\mu = \log_e A_0/A_\mu$, where A_0 is the original area and A_μ is the area of cross section at the maximum load.

(f) *The True Local Necking Strain* $\epsilon_n = \log_e A_\mu/A_b$, where A_μ is the area of cross section at the maximum load and A_b is the fractured area of cross section.

(g) *The Strain Energy per Unit Volume* which the material can absorb before fracture is equal to $\int_0^{\epsilon_b} \sigma \cdot d\epsilon$, or the area under the true stress–strain curve to fracture.

9. Advantages of the True Stress–Strain Diagram. The ordinary type of stress–strain diagram has provided useful data for design purposes. The elastic constants, namely, Poisson's ratio and the modulus of elasticity, are needed in many stress analysis problems. These have been determined for a wide variety of materials and, in general, do not vary much through heat treatment, slight changes in chemical composition, and so on. The proportional limit, although important, depends greatly on the accuracy of the measuring instruments used. The yield strength is consequently of greater value in design. With the exception of the elastic constants and the proportional limit, the remaining mechanical properties determined from the ordinary form of stress–strain diagram are essentially empirical in nature. It is desired that the tension test should provide more information than is disclosed by the elastic properties; otherwise, there would be small incentive today to make many tension tests. Aside from the desirability of having an accurate control of the effects of heat treatment, chemical composition, and such on the mechanical properties, it is important to be able to correlate the tension test with other forms of test such as torsion, impact, and combined stress tests. In addition, the tension test should provide information of use in the metal-forming industries, as in rolling, drawing, and extrusion. In all these and in various connections, the ordinary form of tension test has left much to be desired. It was the realization of the great limitations of the ordinary form of tension test which was responsible for the organization of an extensive research program on the true stress–strain tension test by the present author some dozen years ago at MIT. This research has been carried on continuously since then, and the discussion of this form of test described herein is the result of this research work.

Among the advantages of the true stress–strain tension test may be mentioned:

1. It defines the true stress present during the test rather than the fictitious stress based on the original area of cross section. The area changes greatly during the test.

2. True strain is employed where the change in gage length is referred to the length from which that change is produced, rather than to the original gage length. The ordinary strain definition $\Delta L_0 / L_0$ was inherited from the theory of elasticity where the strains were small.

3. The true stress is related linearly to the true strain from the maximum load to fracture, thus reducing the number of readings necessary to establish this part of the curve.

4. The stress and strain are determined at the most severely deformed part of the test bar. The ordinary strain measured over a 2-in. gage length during local necking has little significance since the strain varies widely along the bar.

5. The stress–strain curve may be determined by the two-load method without strain measurement during the test.

6. The true stress–strain curve is quite sensitive to changes in both metallurgical and mechanical conditions of the material.

7. The true stress–strain curve can be used to correlate tension data with those from other forms of test such as torsion, notched-beam impact, combined stress tests, and metal-forming problems.

8. The ductility of the material, pictured through the true uniform strain ϵ_μ and the true local necking strain ϵ_n, is more accurately determined than by use of the ordinary per cent elongation in 2 in. and the ordinary reduction of area.

10. Relation of the True Stress–Strain Diagram to the Combined Stress Problem for Ductile Metals. In Section B of this chapter the octahedral shearing stress τ_n and the octahedral shearing strain γ_n were defined as

$$\tau_n = \tfrac{1}{3} \sqrt{(\sigma_1 - \sigma_2)^2 + (\sigma_2 - \sigma_3)^2 + (\sigma_3 - \sigma_1)^2}$$

$$\gamma_n = \tfrac{2}{3} \sqrt{(\epsilon_1 - \epsilon_2)^2 + (\epsilon_2 - \epsilon_3)^2 + (\epsilon_3 - \epsilon_1)^2}$$

When the principal stresses σ_1, σ_2, σ_3 and the principal strains ϵ_1, ϵ_2, ϵ_3 are determined from a combined stress test, a curve of τ_n versus γ_n may be constructed.

The τ_n–γ_n curves are useful to represent the results of combined stress tests.[2]

In order to correlate the results for various combined stress ratios or degrees of triaxiality with the results of tension tests, it is obvious that true stresses and strains should be determined. From the true stress–strain tension test, the τ_n–γ_n curve may be constructed by using the relations:

$$\tau_n = \frac{\sqrt{2}}{3}\sigma = \frac{\sqrt{2}}{3}\frac{P}{A}$$
$$\gamma_n = \sqrt{2}\,\epsilon = \sqrt{2}\cdot\log_e\frac{A_0}{A} \tag{7}$$

11. Compression Tests. Although the preceding discussion in Section C of this chapter has related particularly to the tension test, the same general methods apply equally well for compression tests. For ductile metals, the compression strength does not have the same significance as does the tensile strength since the test piece merely decreases in height and flattens out without fracture.

D. FURTHER MECHANICAL PROPERTIES

With the background of basic concepts and stress–strain diagrams described previously, additional mechanical properties determined from test results will now be discussed.

12. Plasticity. This is the property which permits materials to undergo permanent change in shape without fracture. An ideally plastic material is one which undergoes no strain hardening, the latter being measured by the increase in stress necessary to produce further plastic deformation. Almost all metallic materials undergo some strain hardening.

It has been found that no appreciable volume change occurs during the plastic flow of compact ductile metals. In order for such a metal to yield and become plastic under the action of a set of three principal stresses σ_1, σ_2, σ_3, of like sign acting on three perpendicular planes, it is necessary for at least one of the principal stresses to be different in magnitude from the others. Plastic yielding is thus associated with a difference of the principal stresses.

The two conditions governing plasticity in most common use today are the *maximum shearing stress criterion* and the *distortion energy criterion*. If $\sigma_1 > \sigma_2 > \sigma_3$, yielding will occur according to the former if

$$\sigma_1 - \sigma_3 = \pm\sigma_0 \tag{8}$$

and according to the latter if

$$(\sigma_1 - \sigma_2)^2 + (\sigma_2 - \sigma_3)^2 + (\sigma_3 - \sigma_1)^2 = 2\sigma_0^2 \tag{9}$$

where σ_0 is the yield stress in simple tension.

13. Ductility. This is a quantitative measure of the ability of a plastic body to undergo large deformations without fracture. It is common practice to use the per cent elongation in 2 in. and the reduction of area at fracture in the tension test as a measure of this property. More accurate determination of ductility can be made through the use of the true uniform strain ϵ_μ and the true local necking strain ϵ_n discussed in article 8 of this chapter. It should be noted, however, that ductility is a function of the state of stress since a material which is normally ductile under uniaxial tensile stress will behave as a brittle material under a triaxial state of tensile stress. The ductility is likewise affected by temperature and strain rate, as discussed elsewhere.

14. Brittleness. The property of brittleness can be considered as the inverse of ductility. The degree of brittleness is usually reflected in low values of per cent elongation or reduction of area or, if true strain values are used, in low values of ϵ_μ or ϵ_n. It is a relative term since there is no universally accepted value of tensile fracture strain below which a material is considered brittle and above which it is classified as ductile. Extreme cases of brittleness are shown by glass and certain cast irons when subjected to tensile stress. As with ductility, the degree of brittleness exhibited by a given material is greatly affected by the state of stress acting. A material normally brittle under uniaxial tensile stress may behave in a very ductile manner when subjected to compression stresses of different magnitudes in three perpendicular directions.

15. Toughness. This is a term generally associated with the capacity of the material to withstand large values of both stress and strain without fracture. The essential characteristic of high toughness is high energy absorbtion. A measure of this property is the area under the true stress–strain curve.

16. Stiffness. The stiffness of a material is its inherent capacity to resist elastic displacement under stress. The modulus of elasticity is a measure of this property.

17. Hardness. The hardness of a material is most commonly considered to be its resistance to plastic deformation by indentation. Several methods of measuring this property are described later.

E. IMPACT PROPERTIES

Impact testing, as its name implies, includes investigations of material properties under rates of loading which are high compared to those available on the usual tension testing machine. The general effect on the strength and ductility of increasing the rate of straining is directly dependent on the temperature of the test. The result of increasing the strain rate on a standard ASTM tension test specimen is to increase the stress necessary to produce a given strain for most of the metals and testing temperatures. Exceptions to this general rule are tests conducted in the so-called blue-brittle range for certain steels for which, owing to strain aging, higher speeds of testing produce lower stresses at a given strain.[7] In most cases, however, the influence of strain rate on the stress properties for a metal is larger at the elevated temperatures. At room temperature, for example, strain rate variations of the order of 3 to 1 on such metals as copper, aluminum, brass, and steel produce very small effects. Such low-melting metals as tin and lead, however, when tested at room temperature, are very sensitive to increased strain rates, as steels are at elevated temperatures. If the strain rate is very great as with high-speed impact, large effects may be produced even at room temperature for practically all metals.

A recent investigation[7] has shown that there exists a quantitative parallel between the effects of increasing the testing temperature on the one hand and those of decreasing the true strain rate or, vice versa, of decreasing the testing temperature and increasing the true strain rate. A velocity-modified temperature T_m has been suggested[7] which combines the influence of testing temperature and true strain rate in a single variable where

$$T_m = T\left(1 - k \log_e \frac{\dot{\epsilon}}{\dot{\epsilon}_0}\right) \qquad (10)$$

Here T is the testing temperature in degrees absolute, k a constant, $\dot{\epsilon}$ the true strain rate of the test, and $\dot{\epsilon}_0$ a constant. In tension tests conducted at a constant true strain rate, it is shown that the stress $\sigma = f(\epsilon, T_m)$ where ϵ is the true strain.

With a few exceptions, most of the investigations on impact have been conducted on notched-beam specimens stressed in bending. Although such tests provide no stress–strain information which is directly useful in design, the energy to fracture of a standard specimen broken in this manner has proved to be a sensitive indicator of the metallurgical condition of the material. There are two conventional types of notched-beam impact tests widely used in the United States. These are the *Charpy test* and the *Izod test*. In both of these the specimen is struck by a swinging calibrated pendulum, and the energy absorbed in the fracture is determined. Both tests employ low striking velocities (17.5 ft/sec for the Charpy and 11.5 ft/sec for the Izod) compared to those encountered in the impact of projectiles on armor plate.

In the *Charpy test*, the notched bar is placed between two supports with the notch equidistant between them and is struck by the pendulum on the side opposite the notch. Two types of specimens are in common use in the United States: namely, the keyhole-notch specimen and the V-notch specimen.[8] Other shaped specimens are used for special tests, and those used in Europe often differ from those adopted in the United States.

In the *Izod test*, the specimen is held in a vise as a cantilever beam with the center line of the notch on a level with the top surface of the clamping device. The specimen[8] is struck by the pendulum on the notched side 22 mm above the edge of the clamp.

One of the most important features of the notched-beam impact test is its ability to show the tendency toward embrittlement as the temperature of the test is lowered below room temperature. As the testing temperature is lowered from its room-temperature value, most ferritic steels, especially of the unkilled varieties, show a sudden drop in energy absorption over a narrow band of temperatures. At temperatures below this drop-off, the energy absorbed to fracture is only a small fraction of the room-temperature value. Whereas at room temperature the fracture may be of the ductile type, at temperatures below the drop-off the fracture is a brittle one. Some zinc-base die castings show a similar tendency.

For ferritic steels,[9] better low-temperature impact values are obtained, in general, (1) if the steel is fine-grained (a coarse austenitic grain produces low impact values), (2) by full martensitic quenching and proper tempering, (3) by low-carbon content, and (4) by the presence of certain alloying elements such as nickel.

In contrast to the afore-mentioned materials, copper-base alloys and austenitic alloy steels show good energy absorption in the notched-beam impact test at room temperatures and below.

Because of the ease of making low-temperature tests (no clamping being necessary as is in the Izod test), the Charpy test has been favored over the Izod test.

It should be emphasized, however, that both these tests are of an arbitrary nature. Quite different results are obtained by changing the notch radius, the width of the specimen, the over-all size, and similar factors. No good correlation has been found between the results obtained on different shaped notched-beam specimens. Similarly, since the degree of constraint in the standard tests is quite different from those experienced under service conditions in a given structure or machine part, the notched-beam impact test cannot be used to predict the behavior of such structures under service conditions. *Its main function* is to indicate to some arbitrary scale the influence of certain metallurgical conditions on the energy absorption of the material under a fixed and specialized condition of constraint.

The notched-beam impact test has been difficult to correlate with other forms of test. It has shown no correlation with fatigue tests on notched specimens. It has been shown,[11] however, that, if the deformed volume is determined and divided into the total energy to fracture, and thus the energy per unit of deformed volume in the notched bar obtained, essentially the same information portrayed by the Charpy test can be obtained from a static true stress–strain tension test made on a round test specimen containing the same V notch as the Charpy test.

F. CREEP

Under the application of a constant load it has been found that materials, both metallic and nonmetallic, may show a gradual flow or change in dimension. This flow has been called *creep*. Experiment has shown that creep will occur in metals even at stresses below the proportional limit at an elevated temperature.[13]

The creep problem has become of considerable technical importance owing to its influence on the design of equipment for high-temperature service. With the tendency constantly to increase temperatures to effect greater economies in operation, it has been necessary to make elaborate and detailed studies of the creep properties of many different materials.

Creep is a plastic deformation generally associated with slip occurring along crystallographic directions in the individual crystals of the metal together with some flow in the grain-boundary material. In most cases both phenomena take place to different extents in the various metals and are responsible for the resulting deformations. After complete release of load usually a small

fraction of the attained plastic deformation will be recovered with time. Most
of the plastic deformation resulting from creep in metals is not recoverable.

Since the early creep experiments of Andrade[12] in 1910, many different
types of tests have been suggested. The most common ones used today are
the *long-time* creep test under constant load and the *stress-to-rupture* test.
Other forms of test which are used somewhat less frequently but yield information of great value are the *constant-strain-rate test* and the *stress-relaxation test*.

In the *long-time creep test* at constant load the specimen, surrounded by a
furnace held at constant temperature, is loaded by application of a dead
weight at the end of a lever system to which the specimen is attached. The
axial strain over a gage length is read periodically throughout the test, and a
curve is plotted of the strain ϵ as a function of time, as shown in Fig. 1-7.

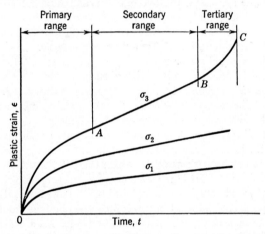

FIG. 1-7.   Typical Creep Curves under Various Constant Loads and at the Same
Temperature

Usually several tests are made for different values of the load at a given
temperature, and a curve of ϵ versus t is plotted for each.   In Fig. 1-7 region
$\overline{OA}$ is called the region of *primary creep*, $\overline{AB}$ the region of *secondary creep*,
and $\overline{BC}$ that of *tertiary creep*.   These are characterized by decreasing, constant, and increasing strain rates $d\epsilon/dt$ or the slopes of the curve. Since, in
the majority of creep applications, the essential information desired by the
designer is the stress which will produce a limiting amount of creep within a
specified time, and these times are much greater than the period of the test,
various extrapolation procedures have been suggested to which the reader is
referred.[14-18]

Experience has shown that various structural changes may occur during
creep tests which alter the metallurgical condition of the metal from its original
state. Some of these changes lead to premature rupture at low values of the
fracture strain, showing an embrittled condition. Tests made at certain elevated temperatures past the so-called equicohesive temperature result in

intercrystalline failure with low fracture strains, as contrasted to transcrystalline failures at lower temperatures with large fracture strains.[19, 20]

The susceptibility of various metals to these conditions is different. The *stress-to-rupture test*[19] is well adapted for investigating this problem. In this, a constant load is applied to a specimen at constant temperature in much the same way as in the long-time creep test discussed previously. The data, however, are analyzed differently. A curve is plotted of the nominal stress versus the time for fracture at constant temperature on a log–log basis, as shown in Fig. 1-8. These are not unlike curves more commonly associated with fatigue tests. The break in the slope of the curve at point P has been related to intergranular oxidation.[19]

In the *constant-strain-rate test* the quantity measured is the stress reaction which is produced by applying a constant strain rate to the specimen. The

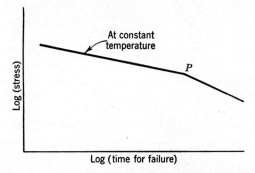

Fig. 1-8.   Typical Curve for Stress-to-Rupture Test

relaxation test is usually performed by maintaining the total strain (elastic + plastic) constant and measuring the decrease of stress as a function of time. It has particular application to the problem encountered in the decrease with time at temperature of the stress in tightened turbine bolts. So far little success has been achieved in using the results obtained from one form of test to predict those that would be determined by another.

Recent investigations have shown that the velocity-modified temperature[1] T_m defined in equation 10 has application to creep tests in a manner similar to its application to slow or fast tension tests.

G. FATIGUE

Fatigue, when applied to the mechanical properties of materials, refers to failure under the action of repeated stresses. It is responsible for most of the failures occurring in machine parts.

From an extensive investigation of the mechanism of fatigue, Gough[21] concludes that fatigue failure is a result of slip occurring along certain crystallographic directions. Under sufficiently high repeated stresses, this slip is apparently accompanied by such local crystal fragmentation that the rupture of the atomic bonds leads to the formation of submicroscopic cracks which grow into visible cracks of a macroscopic type.

Fatigue testing essentially involves the application of periodically varying stresses to a test bar by means of mechanical or magnetic devices. The machines available for this purpose are described in the next chapter. Figure 1-9 shows stress plotted against time for a periodical variation. In fatigue

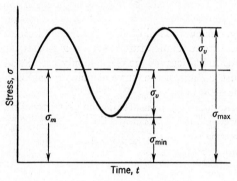

FIG. 1-9.   Periodic Variation of Stress

testing, *the mean stress, σ_m,* which is the average of the maximum stress σ_{max} and the minimum stress σ_{min} for the cycle, may be zero or any positive or negative value. For pure pulsation zero to σ_{max}, σ_m is equal to $\sigma_{max}/2$. For purely alternating stresses between equal positive and negative values σ_m is zero. The *range of stress $2\sigma_v$* is the algebraic difference between the values of σ_{max} and σ_{min}.

18. The Endurance Limit. The endurance limit is the greatest stress that can be applied to a material for an indefinitely large number of times without causing failure. It is determined by making a series of fatigue tests on a number of specimens of the material at different stress values and plotting

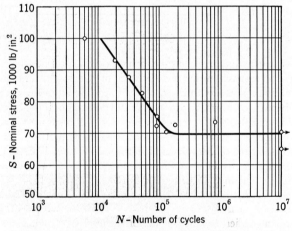

FIG. 1-10.   *S–N* Curve for Fatigue Test under Complete Stress Reversal of Heat-Treated SAE 1045 Steel (Material Quenched from 1525°F in Oil and Drawn at 1200°F for 1½ hr)

the stress endured by each versus the number of cycles to failure. By choosing lower and lower stresses, a value may be found which will not produce failure, regardless of the number of applied cycles. The diagram plotted is called the stress–cycle diagram or briefly the *S–N* diagram. Instead of recording the data on Cartesian coordinates, it has been found convenient to plot either stress versus the logarithm of the number of cycles or both stress and the number of cycles to logarithmic scales. Both types of diagrams show a relatively sharp bend in the curve near the endurance limit. A typical S–N curve is shown in Fig. 1-10.

For most steels it has been found that the endurance limit may be established between 2 and 10 million cycles. Most of the nonferrous metals fail to show clearly defined endurance limits. The ordinates of the S–N curves in these cases show a more or less continuous decrease even for as much as several hundred million cycles. In a manner similar to the arbitrary yield strength definition in tension tests where it was necessary to report both stress and strain values, for nonferrous metals in fatigue both the stress sustained and the number of cycles to which it was carried should be reported. Values of the endurance limit are listed in Table 1-2 for various metals.

19. Influence of the Mean Stress. For tests in which the mean stress σ_m is different from zero, instead of the value of $\sigma_{\max}$ only, which for complete reversal is one-half the range $2\sigma_v$, the values of $\sigma_{\max}$, $\sigma_{\min}$, and the range $2\sigma_v$ are reported. An alternative method which may be used is to give the

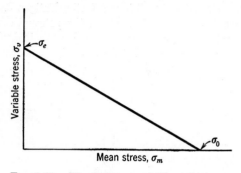

FIG. 1-11. The Influence of Mean Stress on the Variable Stress for Failure by Fatigue

results in the form $\sigma_m \pm \sigma_v$. The influence of different values of the mean stress σ_m on the values of the variable stress σ_v to produce failure has been investigated by various experimenters.[22–24] Several empirical formulas and graphical methods such as the modified Goodman diagram have been developed to show the influence of the mean stress on the stress range for failure.[22–24] Owing to the large amount of experimentation required to establish these relationships, the present knowledge of this phase of the fatigue problem is still quite incomplete. A simple and yet conservative method of representation especially useful in design was suggested some time ago[25] as shown in Fig. 1-11. In this figure, the variable stress σ_v is plotted as ordinate versus the mean stress σ_m as abscissa. At zero σ_m, the ordinate is the endurance limit σ_e under completely reversed stress. Since yielding will occur if the mean stress σ_m exceeds the yield stress σ_0, the value of the variable stress σ_v must be zero for $\sigma_m = \sigma_0$. A straight line is then drawn between σ_e and σ_0. According to the method, the coordinates of any point along this line are values of σ_m and σ_v which may produce failure. The method appears conservative since there is experimental evidence that test points fall above the straight line.

20. Correlation with Other Properties. No very good correlation has been found between fatigue properties and any of the ordinary tensile properties of a material.   Of the latter, the best correlation found so far is between the endurance limit σ_e under completely reversed bending stress and the ordinary tensile strength.   For many ferrous metals the endurance limit σ_e is given approximately by[27]

$$\sigma_e = (0.40 \text{ to } 0.60) \cdot \sigma_{TS} \tag{11}$$

where σ_{TS} is the ordinary tensile strength and the latter is below 200,000 psi. Exceptions to equation 11 are shown by high-yield-strength low-alloy steels where the multiplying factor of equation 11 may be greater than 0.60.[26]   For nonferrous metals it has been found[27] that approximately

$$\sigma_e = (0.20 \text{ to } 0.50) \cdot \sigma_{TS} \tag{12}$$

21. Other Conditions Affecting Fatigue Results.   Among the factors generally tending to lower the fatigue strength may be mentioned stress concentration, rough surfaces, corrosion effects, hydrogen or decarburization in the surface, and overstressing.   Shot peening, nitriding, cold work, and understressing usually improve fatigue properties.   For a discussion of these effects, the reader is referred to reference 24.

H. Hardness

Since the early work of Réaumur[28] in 1722 many attempts have been made to define hardness and to devise apparatus to measure this property.   As yet no completely satisfactory general definition of hardness is available. Perhaps one of the most useful is that hardness is the resistance to permanent indentation.   The various hardness-testing devices are described in the next chapter.   A brief discussion is given here of only a few of the more common methods, together with the relation between hardness and other properties.

22. The Brinell Test.   A hard steel ball 10 mm in diameter is pressed into the flat surface of the test sample under a load of 3000 kg (500 kg for soft metals) and allowed to remain for at least 10 sec (at least 30 sec for other than steel samples).   The diameter of the impression is measured after the load is removed by means of a special microscope.   The hardness is determined by dividing the load P by the spherical area of the impression.   The Brinell hardness number is thus

$$\text{BHN} = \frac{P}{\dfrac{\pi D}{2}\left(D - \sqrt{D^2 - d^2}\right)} \tag{13}$$

where P, D, and d are the load (3000 kg), the diameter of the ball (10 mm), and the diameter of the impression in millimeters at the surface, respectively. A chart is usually available for converting values of d into hardness numbers as shown in Table 1-3.

23. The Rockwell Test.   A small steel ball ($\frac{1}{16}$ in. in diameter) for the Rockwell B test or a conical diamond point for the Rockwell C test is initially pressed against the specimen to be tested under a minor load of 10 kg.   After this a major load of 100 kg for the B test or 150 kg for the C test is applied.

TABLE 1-3

HARDNESS CONVERSION

Approximate Relations Between Brinell, Rockwell, Shore, Vickers, and Firth Hardness Values of SAE Carbon and Alloy Constructional Steels

Brinell		Vickers or Firth Diam. Hardness No.	Rockwell		Shore Sclero-scope No.
Diam. in mm, 3000-kg Load 10-mm Ball	Hardness No.		C 150-kg load, 120° Diamond Cone	B 100-kg load, $\frac{1}{16}$-in.-diam. ball	
2.60	555	633	55	*120*	75
2.65	534	598	53	*119*	72
2.70	514	567	52	*119*	70
2.75	495	540	50	*117*	67
2.80	477	515	49	*117*	65
2.85	461	494	47	*116*	63
2.90	444	472	46	*115*	61
2.95	429	454	45	*115*	59
3.00	415	437	44	*114*	57
3.05	401	420	42	*113*	55
3.10	388	404	41	*112*	54
3.15	375	389	40	*112*	52
3.20	363	375	38	*110*	51
3.25	352	363	37	*110*	49
3.30	341	350	36	*109*	48
3.35	331	339	35	*109*	46
3.40	321	327	34	*108*	45
3.45	311	316	33	*107*	44
3.50	302	305	32	*107*	43
3.55	293	296	31	*106*	42
3.60	285	287	30	*105*	40
3.65	277	279	29	*104*	39
3.70	269	270	28	*104*	38
3.75	262	263	26	*103*	37
3.80	255	256	25	*102*	37
3.85	248	248	24	*102*	36
3.90	241	241	23	100	35
3.95	235	235	22	99	34
4.00	229	229	21	98	33
4.05	223	223	20	97	32
4.10	217	217	*18*	96	31
4.15	212	212	*17*	96	31
4.20	207	207	*16*	95	30
4.25	202	202	*15*	94	30
4.30	197	197	*13*	93	29
4.35	192	192	*12*	92	28
4.40	187	187	*10*	91	28
4.45	183	183	*9*	90	27
4.50	179	179	*8*	89	27
4.55	174	174	*7*	88	26
4.60	170	170	*6*	87	26
4.65	166	166	*4*	86	25
4.70	163	163	*3*	85	25
4.75	159	159	*2*	84	24

TABLE 1-3 (*Continued*)

| Brinell | | Vickers or Firth Diam. Hardness No. | Rockwell | | Shore Sclero-scope No. |
Diam. in mm, 3000-kg Load 10-mm Ball	Hardness No.		C 150-kg load, 120° Diamond Cone	B 100-kg load, $\frac{1}{16}$-in.-diam. ball	
4.80	156	156	*1*	83	24
4.85	153	153		82	23
4.90	149	149		81	23
4.95	146	146		80	22
5.00	143	143		79	22
5.05	140	140		78	21
5.10	137	137		77	21
5.15	134	134		76	21
5.20	131	131		74	20
5.25	128	128		73	20
5.30	126	126		72	
5.35	124	124		71	
5.40	121	121		70	
5.45	118	118		69	
5.50	116	116		68	
5.55	114	114		67	
5.60	112	112		66	
5.65	109	109		65	
5.70	107	107		64	
5.75	105	105		62	
5.80	103	103		61	
5.85	101	101		60	
5.90	99	99		59	
5.95	97	97		57	
6.00	95	95		56	

Figures in italics are an approximation and are to be used only as a guide.
Reproduced from the *Metals Handbook*, 1939 edition, by permission of the American Society for Metals.

On removal of the major load with the minor load still acting, the depth of the indentation made by the application of the major load is measured by a dial gage. The depth of penetration by the major load is the measure of the hardness, which is read on the scale of the dial gage calibrated for both B and C scales. In reporting results both the scale and hardness number are included, as Rockwell B 80 or Rockwell C 35.

A special Rockwell Superficial Tester is available for hard or thin stock.

24. The Vickers Hardness Test. A four-sided diamond pyramid indenter having an apex angle of 136° is pressed into the surface of the metal to be tested. The Vickers hardness number (VHN) is computed in a similar manner to the Brinell test, since it is defined as the load divided by the pyramidal area of the indentation or

$$\text{VHN} = \frac{1.854P}{D^2} \tag{14}$$

where P and D are the load in kilograms and the average length of the two diagonals of the impression in the plane of the surface of the metal measured in millimeters, respectively. Different values of P may be applied by adding weights to a scale pan. The diagonal of the square in the plane of the surface is measured by means of a special microscope. Charts which come with the equipment, prepared according to microscope objective and applied load, are used to read the hardness number corresponding to measured values of the diagonal D.

It has particular application for hard or thin materials or where a spot hardness is desired.

25. Relations between Hardness Values. Table 1-3 shows the relationships between hardness values as determined by the afore-mentioned methods.

26. Hardness and Other Material Properties. It has been shown that a fairly good approximate relationship exists between the Brinell hardness and the ordinary tensile strength of many steels according to equation 15:

$$TS = 500(BHN) \tag{15}$$

where TS is the tensile strength in pounds per square inch and BHN is the Brinell hardness number. Similar formulas can be derived for other hardness tests.

BIBLIOGRAPHY

Basic Concepts

1. S. TIMOSHENKO, *Theory of Elasticity*, McGraw-Hill Book Co., New York, 1934.
2. A. NÁDAI, "Plastic Behavior of Metals in the Strain-Hardening Range," pt 1 and 2, *J Applied Physics*, Mar 1937, pp 205-13. Octahedral shearing stress and strain are developed. Also *Plasticity*, McGraw-Hill Book Co, New York, 1931.

Stress–Strain Diagrams

3. *Standards ASTM*, pt 1 for metals, E6-36 and E8-42, 1944. Discusses ordinary stress–strain diagram and methods.
4. P. LUDWIK, *Elemente der technologischen Mechanik*, Julius Springer, Berlin, 1909.
5. C. W. MACGREGOR, "Relations Between Stress and Reduction in Area for Tensile Tests of Metals," *Metals Technology*, tech publ 805, Apr 1937; also "Differential Area Relations in the Plastic State for Uniaxial Stress," *Stephen Timoshenko 60th Anniversary Volume*, MacMillan Co, New York, 1939; "The Tension Test," *Proc ASTM*, v 40, pp. 508–34, 1940. (The latter paper contains an extensive bibliography on the subject which will not be duplicated here.) "The True Stress–Strain Tension Test—Its Role in Modern Materials Testing," pts 1 and 2, *J Franklin Inst*, v 238, n 2 and 3, pp 111–35 and 159–76, Aug and Sept 1944. Describes the true stress–strain method with applications to various problems.
6. C. W. MACGREGOR, "A Two-Load Method of Determining the Average True Stress–Strain Curve in Tension," *J Applied Mechanics*, v 6, A-156–158, 1939.

Impact Properties

7. C. W. MACGREGOR and J. G. FISHER, "Tension Tests at Constant True Strain Rates," *J Applied Mechanics*, Dec 1945; also "A Velocity-Modified Temperature for the Plastic Flow of Metals," *J Applied Mechanics*, Mar 1945.

Shows the effect of maintaining different constant true strain rates at various temperatures and for various materials on the stress and strain properties. Develops a velocity-modified temperature expression to represent combined effects of strain rate and temperature on material properties and applies it to slow and rapid tension tests, and to creep tests.

8. *Standards ASTM*, 1944, pt 1 for metals, E23-41T. The method and specimen details are given for the Charpy and Izod Impact Tests.
9. H. W. GILLET and F. T. McGUIRE, "Report on Behavior of Ferritic Steels at Low Temperatures," pt 1, ASTM, Dec 1945. A comprehensive discussion of the results of impact tests at low temperatures and their interpretation.
10. "Symposium on Impact Testing," *Proc ASTM*, v 38, pt 2, 1938.
11. C. W. MacGREGOR and J. C. FISHER, "Relations between the Notched-Beam Impact Test and the Static Tension Test," *J Applied Mechanics*, Mar 1944, pp 1–7.

Creep

12. E. N. DA C. ANDRADE, "On the Viscous Flow in Metals and Allied Phenomena," *Proc Royal Soc, (Lond)*, series A, v-84, pp 1–12, (1910).
13. J. J. KANTER and L. W. SPRING, "Long-Time or Flow Tests on Carbon Steels at Various Temperatures with Particular Reference to Stresses below the Proportional Limit," *Proc ASTM*, 1928, v 28, 2, p 80.
14. F. H. NORTON, *Creep of Steel at High Temperatures*, McGraw-Hill Book Co, New York, 1929.
15. *Compilation of Available High-Temperature Creep Characteristics of Metals and Alloys*, ASME—ASTM Joint Research Comm on Effect of Temperature on Properties of Metals, 1938. Many creep curves are given for various metals.
16. A. NÁDAI, "The Influence of Time upon Creep. The Hyperbolic Sine Creep Law," *Stephen Timoshenko 60th Anniversary Volume*, Macmillan Co. New York, 1938.
17. P. G. McVETTY, "Working Stresses for High Temperature Service," *Mech Eng*, v 56, n 3, Mar 1934, p 149.
18. C. R. SODERBERG, "The Interpretation of Creep Tests for Machine Design," *Trans ASME*, v 58, n 8, Nov 1936, pp 733–43.
19. R. H. THIELMANN and E. R. PARKER, "Fracture of Steels at Elevated Temperatures after Prolonged Loading," *Metals Technology*, Apr 1939. Shows results of stress-to-rupture tests on various steels at elevated temperatures with interpretation.
20. W. SIEGFRIED, "Failure from Creep as Influenced by the State of Stress," *J Applied Mechanics*, Dec 1943. Effects of state of stress and relative strengths of crystals and grain boundary material on stress-to-rupture test results.

Fatigue

21. H. J. GOUGH, "Crystalline Structure in Relation to Failure of Metals—Especially by Fatigue," Edgar Marburg Lecture, *Proc ASTM*, v 33, pt 2, 1933. A comprehensive treatment of fatigue as related to crystalline structure.
22. H. F. MOORE and J. B. KOMMERS, *The Fatigue of Metals*, McGraw-Hill Book Co, New York, 1927.
23. H. J. GOUGH, *The Fatigue of Metals*, D. Van Nostrand Co, New York, 1926.
24. *Prevention of the Failure of Metals under Repeated Stress*, Battelle Memorial Institute, John Wiley & Sons, New York, 1941. Includes treatment of nearly all phases of the fatigue problem. An extensive bibliography is given.
25. C. R. SODERBERG, "Working Stresses," *J Applied Mechanics*, v 2, n 3, Sept 1935.
26. H. W. GILLETT, "High-Yield Strength, Low-Alloy Steels," *Metals Handbook*, American Society of Metals, Cleveland, Ohio, 1939, pp 479–83.

27. "The Application of Test Data on Fatigue to the Design of Machine Parts," Special Sheet *Verein deutscher Ingenieure,* n 42, Oct 21, 1933.

Hardness

28. R. A. F. Réaumur, "L'art de convertir le fer forgé en acier, et l'art d'adoucir le fer fondu, ou de faire des ouvrages de fer fondu, aussi finis que le fer forgé," Michel Brunet, Paris, 1722, pp 566–87. Reprinted by F. Cournot, *Revue de metallurgie, mémoires,* 1922, v 19, pp 447–68. Perhaps the earliest recorded development of a hardness measurement method.
29. S. R. Williams, "Hardness and Hardness Measurements," American Society for Metals, 1942, 558 pp. An up-to-date treatment of the hardness problem containing an extensive bibliography.

Miscellaneous

30. J. L. Everhart, W. E. Lindlief, J. Kanegis, P. G. Weissler, and E. Siegel, *Mechanical Properties of Metals and Alloys,* U. S. Govt Printing Office, Washington, D. C., 1943. Gives an extensive list of mechanical properties of metals and alloys at normal, low, and elevated temperatures.
31. *Symposium on Plastics,* American Society for Testing Materials, Feb 1944, 200 pp. The methods of testing of plastics together with numerous mechanical properties are discussed.

CHAPTER 2

TESTING MACHINES

By Joseph Marin

A. INTRODUCTION

In Chapter 1 the mechanical properties of materials are discussed, whereas this chapter deals mainly with the testing machines used to obtain these properties.

Testing machines can be classified into two types, those used to determine (1) the mechanical properties of materials, and (2) the behavior of built-up structural or machine members. Machines used to determine mechanical properties may be classified as to the type of stress, speed of loading, and temperature of the material tested (Table 2-1). There are certain miscellaneous tests of properties, however, such as hardness tests, that cannot be classified in this way (Table 2-2). For all tests, certain specific means of load application and measurement are used. The principles of these methods are discussed before each particular type of machine is considered.

B. METHODS OF APPLICATION OF LOADS

In testing machines, loads are applied to a test specimen by one or a combination of the following methods:

28

TABLE 2-1

MATERIALS-TESTING MACHINES FOR DETERMINATION OF MECHANICAL
PROPERTIES

Classified by Types of Load, Stress, and Temperature

Type of Loading	Temperature	Kind of Stress
Static	Low, normal or elevated	Simple Stresses
		1. Tension
		2. Compression
		3. Bending
		4. Shear
		5. Torsion
		Combined Stresses
		1. Biaxial stresses
		(a) Tension–tension
		(b) Tension–compression
		(c) Compression–compression
		2. Triaxial stresses
Dynamic fatigue	Low, normal, or elevated	Simple stresses (as for static loads)
		Combined stresses—biaxial stresses
Dynamic impact	Low, normal, or elevated	Simple Stresses
		1. Tension
		2. Bending
		3. Torsion

TABLE 2-2

SPECIAL MATERIALS-TESTING MACHINES

1. *Machines for hardness measurement including measurement of resistance to*
   (1) Scratching
   (2) Indentation
   (3) Rebound
   (4) Abrasion and wear
   (5) Machinability
2. *Equipment for determination of material structure including*
   (1) Microstructure
   (2) Macrostructure
3. *Machines for determination of uniformity including*
   (1) Detection of flaws by X Ray and Magnaflux, etc.
   (2) Determination of moisture content
   (3) Determination of porosity
4. *Machines for tests of structural and machine members used to determine*
   (1) Strength
   (2) Resonant frequencies
   (3) Durability—physical and chemical
5. *Equipment for determination of miscellaneous properties as*
   (1) Thermal conductivity and coefficient of expansion
   (2) Electrical and magnetic properties
   (3) Accoustical properties
   (4) Optical properties

1. Weights. Weights of known magnitude can be used directly as a means of applying a tension, compression, or bending load to a specimen. Although this method is limited in application, it was used in some of the early materials testing machines. The main disadvantage of this means of applying loads is that, for most materials, the size of the specimen cross section would be too small, and, therefore, representative properties of the material could not be obtained.

2. Weights and Levers.   A horizontal lever with arms of different lengths, as in a steel yard, is sometimes used for applying loads (Fig. 2-1).   This method of load application is particularly useful in cases where a constant load is to be applied for a long period of time, as for example, in creep tests. If a greater magnification of load is desired, a compound system of levers can be used.

3. Mechanical Gear Systems.   Most mechanical systems for application of tensile or compressive loads consist of a motor-driven horizontal shaft with a screw and gear mechanism for transferring a rotary motion to a translatory

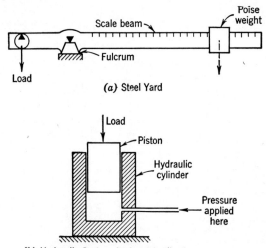

(a) Steel Yard

(b) Hydraulic System for Load Application

Fig. 2-1.   Methods of Application of Loads

motion of the machine head.   In some torsion-testing machines the specimen is rotated directly by a motor with a speed reducer.

4. Hydraulic Systems.   A hydraulic system is often employed to move the head of a testing machine in place of a screw and gear mechanism.   The hydraulic system depends on the movement of a piston in a cylinder by means of oil pressure (Fig. 2-1).   The pressure is usually applied by a motor-driven pump, and valves are used to regulate the rate of application of the load.

In addition to the foregoing methods of applying loads, other special means of load application are used, such as the repeated application of dynamic loads by the inertia force of rotating eccentric weights.   Repeated loads are also applied by an electromagnetic force or by the displacement of a point on a specimen by a mechanically driven eccentric

C. Methods of Load Measurement

When loads are applied to a specimen by a lever system, which is a fixed, variable, or compound system, the load is determined from the known weight applied and the lengths of the lever arms. Instead of the load being calculated, the variable-length arm, to which the balancing weight is applied, can be made self-indicating by means of a scale.

In hydraulic machines the pressure is usually measured by means of manometers or Bourdon tubes. A manometer consists of a glass tube of U shape, usually placed vertically. In this tube a liquid rises to such a level in one arm that it balances the applied pressure acting on the liquid in the other arm. The change in level of the liquid is read on a graduated scale, and the pressure can then be determined. In materials testing the manometer is limited in application because it can be used only for relatively low pressures, even when the liquid used has a high density such as mercury.

The Bourdon tube is generally used for measuring liquid pressures. It consists essentially of a closed curved tube which tends to straighten out as the pressure is increased in the tube (Fig. 2-2). In most Bourdon gages the end movement of the tube as it straightens is magnified mechanically (Fig. 2-2). This motion is transferred into the rotation of a pointer over a scale. The mechanical device used to rotate the pointer consists of a lever, one end of which is attached to the tube, the other end having a ratchet that moves the gear to which the pointer is attached.

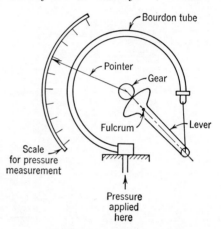

FIG. 2-2. Bourdon Tube for Measurement of Loads

Dynamometers are often employed for measuring loads, and there are several types available for materials testing. One kind of dynamometer consists of a spring balance with a closely wound helical spring. The load to be measured is obtained from the deflection of the spring by calibration. Other types of dynamometers measure the load by determining the elastic deflection of a beam, frame, or ring. The Morehouse proving ring used for calibration of testing machines is an example of the ring-type dynamometer.

A mechanical means, using a dial gage, is a common method of measuring deflections in dynamometers. The deformations can also be measured by using micrometer microscopes or electric strain gages.

I. STATIC TESTING MACHINES

D. Simple Stress Machines

Static testing machines described in this section include those machines used for the determination of mechanical properties of materials when they are subjected to simple static stresses such as tension, compression, bending,

shear, and torsion. Static testing machines are of two main types—universal
testing machines used for tension, compression, bending, and transverse shear
tests, and special machines such as those that can be used only for torsion,
compression, or flexure tests.

5. Universal Testing Machines. The essential parts of a mechanical testing machine are (1) a means of applying the load to a specimen, and (2) a
means of balancing and measuring the applied load. The two parts may be
entirely separate or together, depending on the design of the machine. In

FIG. 2-3. Screw-Gear Universal Machine with Weighing Beam (Courtesy Riehle
Testing Machine Division, American Machines & Metals)

addition to the loading and load-measuring mechanisms, various accessory
parts make up the universal testing machine. These accessory parts include
devices for gripping or supporting the test piece, the power unit, recorders,
speed indicators, and shock absorbers.

The early types of testing machines consisted of a single lever which was
used for both applying and measuring the load. With such machines there
was no means of compensating for the deformation of the specimen. Therefore, the next step in the development was to provide a method of loading
mechanically or hydraulically, independent of the load-measuring mechanism.
The development of universal machines, from the early tests of Galileo to the
present day, is completely described by Gibbons.[6] Most universal machines
now used are of the "screw-gear" or "hydraulic" type.

In universal "screw-gear" testing machines the load is applied mechanically by a screw and gear mechanism. The load in the "hydraulic" universal machine is applied by a hydraulic jack. The power in both types of machines may be supplied by hand or by a motor which operates a gear train or pump.

(a) *Screw-Gear Machines*. A screw-gear machine is shown in Fig. 2-3. The application of the load to the tension or compression specimen is made by the downward movement of a movable crosshead E. The crosshead

FIG. 2-4. Screw-Gear Universal Machine with Pendulum Weighing Device
(Courtesy Tinius Olsen Testing Machine Co)

motion is provided by two or more vertical screws F which have gears attached to their lower ends. The gears attached to the vertical screws in turn mesh with a central gear. The rotation of the central gear is made possible by beveled gears which transfer the rotation of a horizontal shaft H, driven by a motor, to the rotation of the central vertical shaft. Between the beveled gears and motor a system of gears is provided which can be shifted to give various speeds of loading and to reverse the direction of movement of the cross-head.

The load applied to the specimen is measured by a multiple-lever system *L*, as shown in Fig. 2-3. This lever system operates by transferring the load on the bed plate or platen *P* of the machine through a system of levers with knife edges to one end of a scale or weighing beam *W*—the load on the scale beam thereby being reduced. The other end of the scale beam has a poise weight attached which can be moved horizontally until the beam is balanced. The beam has a scale attached which indicates directly the load acting on the specimen. Details regarding operation and variations in design of screw-gear machines are given in manufacturers' catalogs.[12, 13]

Fig. 2-5.   Universal Hydraulic Testing Machine—Type A (Courtesy Riehle Testing Machine Division, American Machines & Metals)

Screw-gear machines in which the weighing beam and poise are replaced by a swinging pendulum and a pointer that moves over a dial are also available.[12] In these machines the load is indicated directly without the balancing of the scale beam being required (Fig. 2-4).

(*b*) *Hydraulic Machines.* Figures 2-5 and 2-6 show two types of hydraulic machines. In type *A* (Fig. 2-5) first built by Amsler of Schaffhausen, Switzerland, the load is applied by a hydraulic press and is measured by the pressure developed within a hydraulic cylinder. The main piston is carefully fitted and lapped, and the load is measured by a pendulum device. Details on the construction and operation of Amsler hydraulic machines can be found in the catalogs of the Riehle and Olsen Companies.[12, 13]

In the type-*B* hydraulic machine (Figs. 2-6*a* and 2-6*b*), the load is applied by a hydraulic press which is separate from the weighing system (Fig. 2-6b). The Southwark-Emery and some Olsen machines are of this type.[11, 13]   A motor-driven pump is used to transmit oil into a cylinder A, thereby producing a pressure against the ram B.   This pressure transmits a compressive force through the compression specimen C to the cross-head E.   The compressive force is then transmitted through the specimen-height adjusting screws F to the lower cross-head G.   The force on the lower cross-head G is in turn trans-

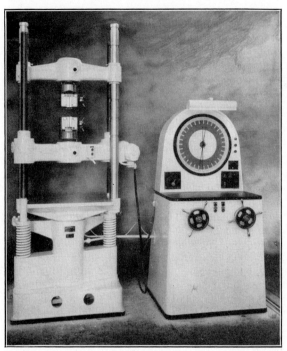

Fig. 2-6a.   60,000-lb Hydraulic Tate-Emery Universal Testing Machine (Courtesy Baldwin Southwark Division, Baldwin Locomotive Works)

mitted to the hydraulic support H.   The hydraulic support H is made up of a shallow cylinder J, a short ram K, and a thin diaphragm L.   The shallow cavity above K is filled with oil and is connected by a pipe to the load-measuring mechanism at the right.   Filling plugs for forcing oil into the capsule are used to provide a means of replacing oil lost by leakage.   Springs M are used to produce an initial load on the hydraulic support to avoid slack motion under small loads.   The oil pressure applied in cylinder J by the movement of the diaphragm L was measured directly by a Bourdon gage in the earlier Baldwin-Southwark machines.   In later machines a load-weighing method, known as the "Tate-Emery" or "null" method, is used (Figs. 2-6a and 2-6b.) By this procedure, oil pressure from the hydraulic support H is transmitted to the Bourdon tube P.   As the tube tends to "straighten out," a baffle Q

which is attached to the tube moves away from the nozzle valve R. By means of a small pump, filtered air under pressure is admitted through an orifice O to the pipe leading to the nozzle valve R. A branch pipe admits air under pressure to the thin corrugated metal bellows S. As the load on the specimen C increases, the baffle Q moves a small distance away from the valve R, and the pressure in the air pipes and bellows decreases. This decrease in pressure pulls the springs T down and stretches the double weighing spring V, thus

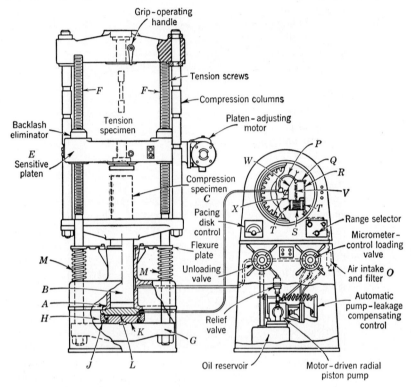

FIG. 2-6b. Hydraulic Testing Machine—Type B, Tate-Emery Universal Testing Machine (Courtesy Baldwin Southwark Division, Baldwin Locomotive Works)

tending to close the space between the baffle Q and valve R. In a very short time equilibrium is established and the stretch of the weighing spring V measures the force acting on the Bourdon tube P. The force measured is proportional to the force acting on the specimen. The elongation of the spring V is measured by the rack pinion X and pointer-scale device W. An autographic record of the load can be obtained by the rack-pinion arrangement X, using a drum and pen or pencil. The drum can be rotated automatically by the strain-measuring apparatus, thereby recording on the drum the complete stress–strain diagram.

Machines are usually equipped with two or more weighing springs for accurately recording different ranges of load. In modern hydraulic machines, various rates of loading can be obtained by the use of an appropriate pump speed or valve setting which controls the flow of oil from the pump to the loading cylinder. Figure 2-6a shows a type-B universal hydraulic machine.

For most purposes the hydraulic-type machine has advantages over the screw-type because of its simplicity of operation and ease of load control and measurement. The screw-gear machine, however, has freedom from leakage of oil and positive control of the rate of motion of the cross-head. The advantages of the balance-beam type of load-weighing mechanism are high accuracy, when carefully balanced, and constancy of calibration. However, the advantages of the self-indicating type of load-weighing device are the elimination of the need to balance the beam and freedom from the personal equation in balancing the beam.

The testing machines described in the foregoing are used, with various modifications, for testing specimens in tension, compression, and bending. The main mechanical properties obtained include the yield strength, ultimate strength for tension and compression (or modulus of rupture in bending), stiffness, and ductility. Bending tests are sometimes made on special small manually operated testing machines, such as bending machines used for the "arbitration test" of cast iron.

A number of auxiliary devices for gripping, supporting, and holding the specimen have been devised for performing tension, compression, and bending tests on materials. For a complete discussion of these devices the reader is referred to references 1, 2, and 3. For tension tests, a gripping device with spherical seats should be provided so that the stress is as uniformly distributed as possible. Similarly, for compression tests, a spherical-seated bearing block makes it possible to apply a uniform stress.

It is important that testing machines be calibrated periodically since the indicated load readings may not continue to be the true values. The Standards of the American Society for Testing Materials[10] give in detail the various methods for calibration of testing machines. In the universal testing machines described in the foregoing, the loading of the specimen is either at a constant (approximately) or variable strain rate. Nádai and Manjoine[58] developed machines which test a specimen in tension at constant rates of load or strain.

6. Torsion-Testing Machines. Torsion tests are most suitable for the determination of shear strength. It is not convenient to adapt the universal testing machine for torsion testing so that special machines for torsion testing have been developed. Both screw-power and hydraulic torsion machines are available. The load in these machines is measured by a pendulum indicator or beam scale. A screw-type, 10,000-in.-lb-capacity Riehle torsion machine is shown in Fig. 2-7. Power is applied by hand through the crank K, or a motor drive on be supplied to apply the force. The specimen S is placed between centering jaws and is gripped between the chucks C so that it is twisted as the crank is turned. As the specimen is twisted, the heavy pendulum P swings out. An arm T, attached to the pendulum, moves an indicator along a scale E a distance a'. The scale E can be graduated to read directly the amount of twisting moment. This direct reading of torque is possible since the twisting moment is the weight of the lever times the distance a, where a = the horizontal movement of the center of gravity of the lever weight. Since the distance a' is proportional to a, the scale E can be used to give the twisting-moment values directly. In testing, a twistmeter which reads the angle of twist for each load increment is attached to the

Fig. 2-7. Screw-Power Pendulum-Type Torsion Machine (Courtesy Riehle Testing Machine Division, American Machine & Metals)

specimen. Most torsion-test specimens are circular in cross section and are either solid or hollow. Fig. 2-8 shows a recent model of the screw-power torsion machine with a dial-pendulum-weighing device.

Torsion machines in which the load is measured by a compound lever system and a weighing scale are also available. In another type, a lever or arm attached to the chuck actuates a hydraulic capsule.

In addition to the torsion-testing machines, other special testing machines for static tests include those used for cold-bend tests to determine ductility,[3] machines for special purposes such as wire or spring testing, machines for flexure tests (usually hand-operated), and machines for compression tests as used in highway laboratories.

E. COMBINED-STRESS MACHINES

Many machine and structural parts are subjected to a combined state of stress or to stresses in more than one direction. Information on material behavior under combined states of stress must be obtained since the values of the mechanical properties for simple stresses no longer apply. A number of special combined stress-testing machines which subject a specimen to combined stresses have been built.

FIG. 2-8. Screw-Power Torsion Machine (Courtesy Baldwin Southwark Division, Baldwin Locomotive Works)

Some of the first experiments on combined stresses were made on solid round cylindrical specimens subjected to torsion combined with bending or torsion combined with axial loading. A nonuniform stress distribution is produced in such specimens and, in order to eliminate this objection, experiments were later made on thin-walled cylindrical tubes subjected to torsion and axial tension, internal pressure and axial tension, or internal pressure and axial compression (Fig. 2-9).

For a thin-walled tube subjected to torsion and axial tensile loading, principal stresses of opposite sign are produced. Their values are

$$\left.\begin{array}{c}\sigma_1\\\sigma_2\end{array}\right\} = \frac{P}{2A} \pm \sqrt{\frac{P^2}{4A^2} + \frac{M_t^2 r^2}{I_p^2}} \tag{1}$$

where A = the cross-sectional area of the tube, r = the outer radius, I_p =

the polar moment of inertia, P = the axial load, and M_t = the twisting moment.

For the thin-walled tube subjected to axial tensile loading and internal pressure (Fig. 2-9), principal stresses of the same sign are produced. Their values are

$$\sigma_1 = \frac{P}{A} + \frac{pd}{4t} \quad \text{and} \quad \sigma_2 = \frac{pd}{2t} \tag{2}$$

where d = the internal tube diameter, t = the tube-wall thickness, P = the axial load, and p = the internal pressure.

In a combined stress test the usual method of loading is to apply both loads simultaneously at a constant ratio so that the ratio of the principal stresses

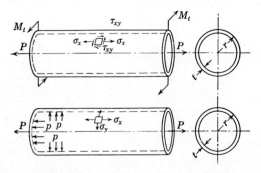

FIG. 2-9. Specimens for Combined Biaxial-Stress Tests

remains essentially constant throughout the test. Another method of loading is to fix one of the loads and to increase the other until rupture occurs. In either method, readings are taken of the strains that accompany loading so that stress–strain diagrams can be plotted and the biaxial mechanical properties such as yield strength, ultimate strength, and ductility can be determined. Experiments on static biaxial stresses have been made by many investigators. Most of the more recent published experimental work and reviews of others' experiments are given by Nádai,[19] Roš and Eichinger,[20] Taylor and Quinney,[21] Lode,[19] Lessels and McGregor,[22] Marin,[9] and Davis.[23]

7. Combined-Tension–Torsion Machines. Figure 2-10 shows special equipment designed for applying a constant strain rate to a specimen in either tension or torsion, or a combination of both. This machine was made by the reconstruction of a 10-ton Amsler testing machine at the suggestion of A. Nádai.[24] With reference to Fig. 2-10, the tensile load is applied to a cylindrical specimen by the Amsler machine and measured on the regular Amsler dial. The torsion load is determined by measuring the deflection of two springs attached to the upper head of the machine. An electric-contact device on the dial of the Amsler load indicator maintains a constant tension when desired. The special strain gage shown is clamped to the shoulders of

FIG. 2-10.   Combined Tension–Torsion Machine (Courtesy Westinghouse Research Laboratories)

the specimen.   The gage consists chiefly of a frame which is clamped to the upper shoulder and a plane disk which is clamped to the lower shoulder. The axial strain is measured by two micrometer heads clamped to the frame in such a manner that the separation between the frame and the plane disk is determined.   The angle of twist is measured by a roller attached to the frame which rolls on the periphery of the disk.   Stress–strain data up to rupture are obtained with this machine. The machine is arranged so that one of the loads can be kept constant as the other is increased, or both loads can be made to vary to give a fixed load ratio.

Another machine for testing thin-walled tubes subjected to combined tension and torsion is described in reference 25. In this machine torsional forces are applied to the vertical test piece through a horizontal disk and the simultaneous axial tensile load by a worm and gear drive. Tensile and torsional loads and deformations are all measured independently.

FIG. 2-11. Combined-Tension–Torsion Machine (Courtesy Chrysler Corp)

A machine for loading a specimen under combined tension and torsion or compression and torsion is shown in Fig. 2-11. Two 20-ton-capacity hydraulic rams provide tensile and compressive loads. The combination of flexible ram locations and a base plate with a gridwork of threaded holes makes possible the application of axial and torsional loads. Two hydraulic pumps located under the bed plate provide fluid pressure to the loading rams, and the knobs shown on the side of the machine are used to release the load. Pressure gages placed on the corner supports measure the load.

8. Combined-Tension–Tension Machines. Most experiments on biaxial stresses have been made on thin-walled tubular specimens subjected to internal pressure and axial tensile loads. Figure 2-12 shows equipment used for applying internal pressure and axial tension to a tubular specimen.[23] By means of special grips the tubular specimen is subjected to an axial tensile load by a standard 30-ton Amsler testing machine. The internal pressure is produced by the high-pressure Amsler pump with a pendulum manometer for load measurement, as shown on the right of Fig. 2-12. The measuring pendulum on the high-pressure pump can be adjusted to a length such that, at full-scale deflection on both the axial testing machine and the high-pressure pump, a given ratio between the principal stresses, defined by equation 1, can be produced. To maintain this ratio during the operation of the test it is necessary to keep the indicating pointers of the machine deflected through the same angle.

Tests on tubes subjected to internal pressures and axial loads have been made using screw-power or various types of hydraulic machines for the application of the axial tensile load. In these tests the internal pressure has sometimes been applied by means of different types of pumps with pressure gages for load measurement in place of the pendulum manometer referred to previously.

Fig. 2-12. Machines for Testing Tubes under Combined Axial Tension and Internal Pressure (Courtesy Westinghouse Research Laboratories)

"Bulge tests" have been made in order to study the plastic behavior of metals subjected to biaxial tensile stresses.[26] In these tests a flat circular or an elliptical plate, clamped at the edge, is subjected to a liquid pressure on one side, thereby deforming the plate in the form of a bulge (Fig. 2-13). The deflections of various points on the specimen are measured with dials, and a grid is marked initially on the specimen to provide reference points for strain measurements. A specimen which is initially circular gives a region of equal biaxial tensile stresses in the plastic range. An elliptical plate produces a stress ratio different from one, of value depending on the relative values of the major and minor axes of the ellipse. The bulge test is valuable for plastic-flow investigations including studies of forming operations. It is not adequate, however, for defining elastic failure.

Equal biaxial tensile stresses can be produced also by subjecting a hemispherical or spherical shell to internal-fluid pressure.[27] The hemispherical type of specimen is of particular value in that it provides a large region of material under essentially the same stresses for a given load. In a tubular specimen there are end restraints which produce bending stresses. If a long specimen is provided, however, the influence of these bending stresses is minimized. Major objections to the use of hemispherical or spherical specimens are the cost of machining the specimen and the limitation in being able to investigate only one ratio of the principal stresses.

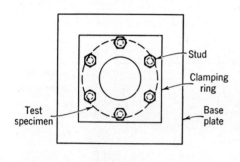

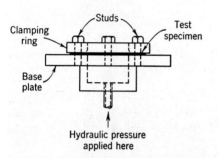

FIG. 2-13. "Bulge" Test of a Circular Plate

Although the foregoing tests are the most common, other combined stress tests have been made as follows:

9. Tension–Compression Tests with the Compression Stress Maximum. In order to investigate biaxial stresses in which the compressive principal stress is greater than the tensile principal stress, Bridgman[28] used a specimen as shown in Fig. 2-14. The central part of the specimen is separated from the ends by two deep and narrow notches. The two ends of the specimen are prevented from rotating, and the center is twisted between the ends by means of keyways. A longitudinal compressive load is applied at the same time as the torque by a small hydraulic ram, in such a way that longitudinal deforma-

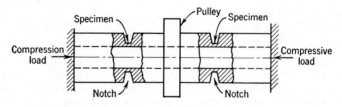

FIG. 2-14. Specimen for Combined Compression–Torsion Testing

tions are free to occur. A central pin provides stability, and the central part of the specimen is attached to a pulley around which a flexible wire cable is wound. The cable from the pulley is wound over a drum which is actuated by a motor with variable gears to give a wide range of speeds. Measurements of angle of twist for various torque values are taken for different values of the compressive loads.

Tension–compression tests have also been made[1] by subjecting a tubular specimen to internal pressure and axial compression, employing equipment similar to that used for the internal-pressure–axial-tension tests. Care must be taken to design the specimen properly so that failure by buckling does not occur under axial compression.

10. Compression–Compression Tests. Biaxial compressive stresses can be applied by subjecting cylindrical specimens to a radial pressure.[19] The radial pressure can be applied by inserting the specimen in a cylinder subjected to internal pressure. A loading frame for applying compressive stresses of different magnitudes was developed by Kamener and Birnbaum[29] in the photoelastic study of a "collar girder." The compressive stresses are applied by a series of small jacks consisting of $3/4$-in. cylinders bored in $1\frac{1}{2}$-in. $\times$ 1-in. $\times$ $3\frac{1}{8}$-in. brass blocks.

11. Triaxial Tests. Thick-walled cylinders subjected to internal pressure and axial loading are under a triaxial state of stress and offer some information on behavior of materials subjected to triaxial stresses.[19] The presence of a nonuniform distribution of stress throughout the cylinder walls, however, introduces error in the evaluation of the results obtained by such tests. Cylindrical specimens subjected to a radial compressive pressure by a hydraulic pump and axial compression by a universal testing machine have yielded much valuable information on the triaxial-compression properties of brittle materials.[19] Strengths of materials under equal triaxial-compressive stresses have been thoroughly studied by Bridgman[30,31] who has developed special equipment to apply the extremely high pressures required for such tests. Pressures up to 100,000 kg/cm^2 have been produced using equipment developed by Bridgman.[31]

F. Creep-Testing Machines

Creep, or continuous plastic deformation with time, occurs in metals at elevated temperatures, in some metals at room temperature, and in nonmetals, such as plastics, at both room and elevated temperatures. Testing machines of different types have been developed for the measurement of creep under various types of stresses.[1, 32, 33]

Most creep testing is done on specimens subjected to simple tension, in machines similar to those shown in Fig. 2-15. Each tension–creep-testing unit consists of a device for applying a fixed load to a specimen by means of a simple lever. In addition, provision must be made for adequate attachment of the specimen, a thermocouple or other type of heating unit, and a micrometer microscope for measurement of creep strains. A series of specimens, each subjected to different stresses, is tested simultaneously and creep-strain readings are usually recorded for a period of 1000 hr.[10]

Automatic creep–tension machines in which creep–time curves are recorded automatically have been developed by Manjoine.[34] One type, a lever-arm creep machine (Fig. 2-16), applies the load using a lever arm and weights.

The temperature is maintained for each specimen by a separate electric furnace and power supply.   The temperature of the furnace is controlled by an expansion rod located near the furnace winding.   The difference between expansion of the rod in the furnace and an Invar rod located outside the furnace is used to operate an electric contact which controls the current in the furnace windings.   The creep strains are measured by an elaborate mechanical and electric device described in detail in reference 34.

For short-time creep–rupture tests another automatic machine was developed by Manjoine.[34]   It is a screw-driven machine as shown in Fig. 2-17. It consists of a stiff spring A in series with the test specimen B which is loaded by a screw-driven jack C.   By keeping a constant deflection of the spring

FIG. 2-15.   Creep–Tension-Testing Machines (Courtesy General Electric Co)

A, the load can be kept constant.   The deflection of the spring is measured by a dial gage with an electric contact which controls the motor.   The motor in turn drives the jack to keep the load constant.   The deformation of the test specimen is measured from the relative motion of the upper head of the machine and the stationary frame.   This motion is magnified through a gear train and drives the pen on the recorder D vertically.   A time clock E drives the pen horizontally so that a continuous creep–time curve is plotted automatically.

Although most creep testing is done with specimens subjected to simple tension, some investigations have been made to determine creep for bending, torsion, and combined stresses.   Creep deflections of steel specimens in bending were measured by E. A. Davis.[35]

Equipment for torsion tests at elevated temperatures is described by Everett.[36] Figure 2-18 shows a four-unit torsion–creep machine used for tests at room temperature.   In this machine the specimen is attached by collets to holders which are supported by bearings.   One end of the specimen is fixed, and the other end has a pulley attached so that torque loads can be applied to the specimen. A series of supports with bearings insures the application of a pure twisting moment to the specimen. Twistmeters attached to the specimen measure the creep angle of twist.

Combined stress–creep tests on steel tubes subjected to axial loading and torsion and lead tubes subjected to combined internal pressure and torsion

Fig. 2-16. Short-Time Creep–Rupture Machine (Courtesy Westinghouse Research Laboratories)

have been made by Bailey.[37] Moore[38] and Norton[39] have made tests on creep of tubular specimens closed at the ends and subjected to internal pressures.

In all the foregoing creep tests the stresses are kept fixed, and the creep deformation is measured with time. However, there are applications in which the creep takes place with a diminishing stress value. The bolted

FIG. 2-17. Automatic Screw-Lever Machine for Tension–Creep Tests (Courtesy
Westinghouse Research Laboratories)

joint is an example of such a stress-relaxation condition. Machines have been built to determine creep under varying stress conditions.[40] Figures 2-19a and 2-19b show apparatus developed by Kanter for making stress-relaxation–creep tests. The stress present on the specimen at any time is obtained from strain measurement on a weighbar at room temperature (Fig. 2-19b). The specimen is placed in a heating unit and subjected to a particular temperature and initial stress. Provision is made for measuring the creep deformation for a specific gage length and the corresponding stress by measuring the deformations of the weighbar. An automatic creep–tension-relaxa-

FIG. 2-18. Four-Unit Creep–Torsion Machine (Courtesy The Pennsylvania State College)

tion machine is shown in Fig. 2-20, in which mechanical and electric controls are used to plot automatically the stress–time relaxation curves.

II. DYNAMIC TESTING MACHINES

In many machines and structures the stresses produced are not always static, as considered in Section I, but they are repeated and vary in magnitude. The load resistance of materials or constructions is less under dynamic loading than under static loading. Many fatigue-testing machines have been developed for evaluating the strength of materials and constructions under these repeated or fatigue loadings. In some cases of dynamic loading the loads applied are not repeated but are impact loads having a high kinetic energy. The resisting properties of materials under such impact loads are different from the properties under static conditions, and various testing machines have been developed for evaluating the mechanical properties of materials under impact stresses.

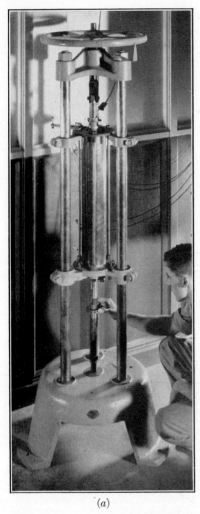

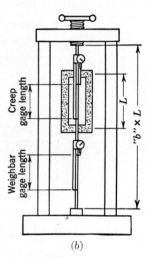

(a)   (b)

FIG. 2-19a. Tension–Stress-Relaxation–Creep Machine (Courtesy Crane Co)
FIG. 2-19b. Stress–Relaxation Machine

G. FATIGUE-TESTING MACHINES

The earliest types of fatigue-testing machines are adequately described by Moore[41] and Gough.[42] The first comprehensive investigation on fatigue testing was made between 1860 and 1870 by Wöhler, who made repeated stress tests in torsion, bending, and direct stress. The main limitation of these testing machines was the slow speed of stress repetitions. A speed of only 72 rpm was used for the rotating-bending tests. However, the machines Wöhler designed were very ingenious, and his original conclusions remain unchallenged.

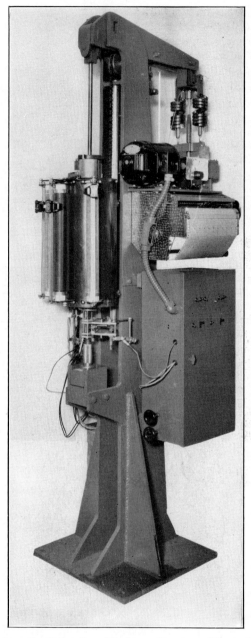

FIG. 2-20. Automatic Relaxation Machine (Courtesy Westinghouse Research Laboratories)

There are numerous kinds of fatigue-testing machines for tests of materials and for fatigue tests of structural and machine members. Only a few of the main types, however, as outlined in Table 2-3 can be discussed in this chapter.

12. Flexure–Fatigue Machines. At the present time the R. R. Moore high-speed fatigue-testing machine (Figs. 2-21a and 2-21b) is the most commonly used. This machine subjects a round specimen to pure bending

Fig. 2-21a. R. R. Moore Reversed-Bending-Fatigue Machine for Speeds of 10,000 rpm (Courtesy Baldwin Southwark Division, Baldwin Locomotive Works)

moments free from transverse shear forces. By rotating the specimen one revolution the stresses at a given point are completely reversed from a tensile stress value to an equal compressive value. This stress variation is accomplished by applying a fixed bending moment to the specimen by means of

TABLE 2-3

CLASSIFICATION OF FATIGUE-TESTING MACHINES

Type	Kinds of Stress

Constant load (dead weights)	(a) *Simple Stresses*
	    1. Pure bending
	    2. Bending and shear
	    3. Tension–compression
	    4. Torsion
	(b) *Combined Stresses* (Biaxial)
	    1. Tension–tension
	    2. Tension–compression

Constant load (inertia forces)	(a) *Simple Stresses*
	    1. Pure bending
	    2. Tension–compression
	    3. Torsion
	(b) *Combined Stresses* (Biaxial)
	    1. Tension–compression
	       (torsion and bending)

Constant deflection	(a) *Simple Stresses*
	    1. Bending
	    2. Tension–compression
	    3. Torsion
	(b) *Combined Stresses* (Biaxial)
	    1. Tension–tension

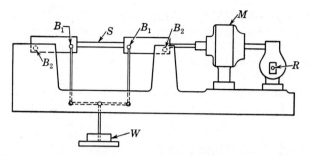

FIG. 2-21b.   R. R. Moore Reversed-Bending-Fatigue Machine

FIG. 2-22.   Fixed-Cantilever Constant-Amplitude Fatigue Machine (Courtesy Krouse Testing Machine Co)

weights W. The specimen S is held at its ends in special holders and loaded by the weights W through two bearings B_1 placed equal distances from the center of the specimen (Fig. 2-22b). Two other bearings B_2, at equal distances from the center of the specimen, provide support for the reactive forces. With such a loading arrangement the vertical transverse shear force on the specimen is zero, or a pure bending stress free from shear stresses is produced.

Cycles of stress variation are provided by the rotation of the specimen by a motor M, and a record of the number of cycles to rupture is given by the revolution counter R. A disengaging device is provided for stopping the motor when the specimen fails. Other rotating-beam-type fatigue machines are described by Moore.[43]

The main advantages of the rotating-beam testing machine are its simple design, low cost, accuracy with which the bending moment can be measured, and the high speed of operation. (Speeds of 12,000 rpm can be provided.) The disadvantages are the limitations on range of stress, shape of specimen cross section, and cost of machining the specimens.

The R. R. Moore machine represents the constant-load type of machine in which the load remains constant during the test. There is another type of fatigue machine, the constant-deflection or constant-amplitude type, in which the specimen is subjected to a constant deflection during the test. Fig. 2-22 shows the fixed cantilever constant-amplitude fatigue machine. In this machine the end of the cantilever specimen A is repeatedly bent back and forth by the variable eccentric B. The stress on the specimen is computed by the beam formula ($\sigma = Mc/I$), where the moment M is obtained by calibration. In calibrating, dead weights are applied in order to produce a given deflection which is measured by a dial gage C. An eccentric is used to produce this same deflection in the fatigue test. The number of cycles of stress is recorded on a counter, and a toggle switch is provided to stop the machine when a specimen fractures. The main advantage of the constant-deflection type machine is that fatigue tests on flat specimens, such as thin sheet metal, can be made. The constant-amplitude type of machine has been found useful in the testing of laminated plastics, and it has been accepted as a tentative method of test for repeated flexural stress tests of plastics.[10] The main disadvantage is that for some materials and stress values the constant deflection method of applying stress may not be sufficiently accurate unless periodic checks are made on the calibration during the test.

Another type of repeated-bending or flexure-fatigue machine applies the load by inertia forces. Figure 2-23 shows the essential features of an inertia machine designed by the Sonntag Scientific Corporation.[11] A specimen A is held by the holder O and attached to a frame C. A platen F, attached to the specimen, moves up and down to produce repeated bending stresses in the specimen. The motion of the platen is produced by the mechanical oscillator D which is driven by the synchronous electric motor I through a flexible drive shaft H. A compensating spring E makes it possible to read directly on the scale adjacent to the revolving eccentric D the force applied to the specimen, irrespective of type of specimen or deflection in the specimen. In running a test, the desired preload on the specimen is applied by a crank and measured by a dial indicator. The superimposed alternating force required is provided for by the proper setting of the eccentric D. The cycles of stress are recorded by a counter T—S, and a microswitch M stops the machine when the specimen ruptures.

The main advantage of this type of machine is that, like the R. R. Moore machine, the value of the load is accurately known. Although the cost of the inertia-type machine may be considered high in comparison to that of other types, it can be used for other kinds of fatigue tests including axial tension and compression, and torsion.

Adaptations and modifications of the foregoing bending-fatigue machines have been developed, for large-size specimens[45] and for high-temperature tests.[55]

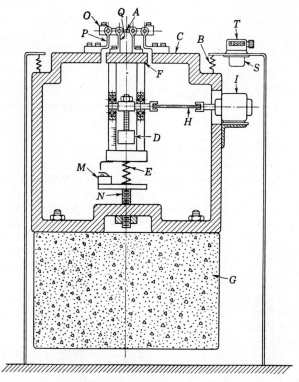

Fig. 2-23. Inertia-Type Flexure Fatigue Machine (Courtesy Baldwin Southwark Division, Baldwin Locomotive Works)

13. Axial-Stress–Fatigue Machines. For fatigue tests in which the stresses are beyond the elastic range a machine which produces axial tension or compression on the specimen permits a more accurate calculation of the stress than flexure machines since the flexure formula does not apply beyond the elastic range.

A constant-deformation spring-type axial fatigue machine developed by Jasper[41] is shown in Fig. 2-24. Cycles of load are applied by a crank and connecting-rod mechanism K. The magnitude of the load is measured by means of the deformation in the spring G to which the specimen S is directly attached. The crank mechanism can be adjusted to give any desired ratio of maximum-to-minimum stress. An improved model of this spring-type machine was developed by Moore and Krouse.[43] Single-, two-, and five-unit axial-stress spring-type fatigue machines are manufactured by the Krouse Testing Machine Company.[47]

A commonly used type of axial-fatigue–stress machine is the a-c magnet type developed by Haigh,[1, 42] and illustrated in Fig. 2-25. This machine

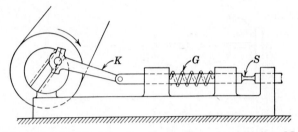

FIG. 2-24.   Constant-Deformation Spring-Type Axial-Fatigue Machine

consists of an armature A which moves rapidly back and forth between two electromagnets M energized by a two-phase alternating current, one phase being connected to each magnet M. The specimen S is subjected to an alternating stress by means of the back and forth motion of the armature head. Flat springs G are used to compensate the force required to accelerate the armature and other vibrating parts, the adjustment being made by four clamps C as shown. By applying suitable initial loads to the flat springs G, different ranges of stress can be produced in the specimen.

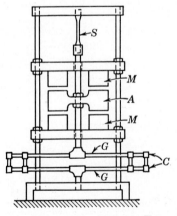

FIG. 2-25.   A-c Magnet-Type Haigh Fatigue Machine

As previously stated, the inertia-type fatigue machine shown in Fig. 2-23 can be used for axial-fatigue tests by means of special fixtures.

14. Torsion–Fatigue Machines. A constant-deflection type repeated-torsion machine, as developed by Moore,[43] is shown in Fig. 2-26. Torsion in the specimen S is produced through a chuck A by a variable-throw cam C. The cam C consists of a double eccentric, and the throw of the eccentric is adjusted by turning the outer eccentric around the inner and clamping in any desired position. The torque is transmitted through the jaw J to a calibrated specimen D. The angle of twist of the specimen D is proportional to the twisting moment and is measured by the dial gages M. The desired range of twisting moment is applied to the specimen by hand-turning the machine and adjusting the throw of the cam C. The initial twisting moment on the bar

D, is applied by screws F which act on a radial arm attached to the left-hand end of the bar D.

Repeated-torsion machines have the same disadvantage as flexure–fatigue machines for tests beyond the elastic range unless a hollow circular specimen with thin walls is used.

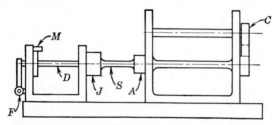

FIG. 2-26.   Constant-Deflection-Type Torsion-Fatigue Machine

15. Combined-Stress–Fatigue Machines.   Repeated combined-stress machines that have been developed are mainly of two types—repeated-torsion–bending or repeated tension–tension.

Fig. 2-27 shows the repeated-torsion–bending-type machine as developed by the National Physical Laboratory.[48]   In this machine a specimen S, of circular cross section, is subjected simultaneously to torsional and bending

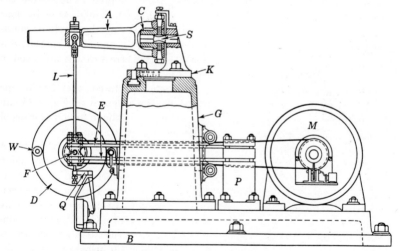

FIG. 2-27.   Combined Torsion–Bending-Fatigue Machine

stresses by application of repeated flexure and torque moments.   The specimen S is clamped in a chuck C at one end and in a bracket K at the other end which is attached to the base plate B.   The bracket K can be rotated to any desired position.   An arm A pivoted about a vertical axis passing through the center of the specimen is attached to the chuck C.   A disk D, carrying the out-of-balance weights W, is mounted on a spindle F and clamped to the ends of springs E. The other ends of the springs are rigidly clamped to a bracket P which is attached to the base plate. The disk D is driven by a synchronous motor M which has a belt drive. The clamps at the left end of the springs E, carrying the spindle F, are connected by links L to the center of percussion of the arm A. The general principle of operation of the machine is the application of an alternating force to the arm A by means of the out-of-balance forces developed at the spindle F of the disk by the rotation of the motor. The speed of the disk is adjusted to the resonant frequency of the moving parts on the outer ends of the springs E by varying the ratio of pulley diameters. This is an important feature of the machine since all inertia forces, except those produced by the out-of-balance weights, are eliminated. In the position shown in Fig. 2-27, cycles of reversed bending are produced on the specimen. By rotating the bracket K and chuck C, bending and twisting moments proportional to the cosine and sine of the angle of rotation are produced, and any desired ratio of the bending to torsional stresses can be obtained.

Although the torsion–bending fatigue test yields valuable information, particularly for shafting and crankshafts subjected to torsion and bending, the nonuniform stress distribution throughout the specimen cross section is a source of error in the interpretation of test results. By modifying the fixture the inertia-type machine in Fig. 2-23 can be used for combined torsion–bending tests.

Repeated stress tests on tubular specimens subjected to fluctuating internal pressure and fluctuating axial stress have been made on the machine shown in Fig. 2-28. By tests of this kind, various ratios of biaxial tensile repeated stresses can be considered. The machine is described in detail in reference 49. The essential features consist of a motor M which drives a gear G. The gear G in turn drives a gear G_2 to which an eccentric is attached. This eccentric gives an up-and-down motion to the lever L_2 which thereby applies a fluctuating axial stress to the tubular specimen S. The internal oil pressure is applied to the specimen by a plunger P which is activated up and down by a lever L_1. The lever L_1 is rotated through a small angle by an eccentric attached to its right end which is operated by a gear G_1. The motion of gear G_1 is synchronized with gear G_2 by means of the pinion gear G. Leakage of oil from the specimen is replaced by an accumulator A which maintains a constant value of the maximum pressure. Two pressure gages equipped with special check valves are used to record the maximum and minimum values of the fluctuating internal pressure. A dynamometer is placed initially at D to determine the maximum and minimum values of the axial load. The stress cycles to failure are recorded on a counter C, and electric controls E_1 and E_2 are used to stop the motor when the specimen fractures. The low rate of application of the stress cycles necessary in this machine (200 per minute) is a major disadvantage. However, various ratios of the maximum biaxial stresses and ranges of stress can be investigated with this machine.

Special dynamic machines, not mentioned under fatigue or impact machines, are used to determine damping constants of materials. Several types of machines and tests have been used to determine the damping capacity. A summary of these tests is given by Von Heydekampf.[51] Recently Lazan[50] developed two inertia-type dynamic machines used for obtaining damping constants in tension and torsion.

Fig. 2-28. Combined Tension–Tension-Fatigue Machine

H. Impact-Testing Machines

The strength, ductility, and toughness of materials are modified when impact loads are used instead of static loads. In particular, toughness may be greatly changed under suddenly applied impact loads and various testing machines have been developed for testing materials under impact loading. There are two main types of impact testing, tests using plain specimens and those using notched specimens. In notched-bar impact testing a triaxial state of stress at the base of a notch is produced. The brittleness of a material under this state of stress is greater than for simple uniaxial stresses, and a more sensitive means of evaluating triaxial-stress brittleness or "notch sensitivity" is provided by the notched-bar test. The energy values for plain or notched specimens do not give a true measure of the toughness since all the energy of a blow is not absorbed by the specimen. Losses of energy occur through friction, deformation of the supports, and striking mass, and by vibration of of machine parts. The energy values obtained are also dependent on the form of specimen used. These values, therefore, are arbitrary and cannot be used directly in design. A classification of impact testing machines is given in Table 2-4.

TABLE 2-4

CLASSIFICATION OF IMPACT MACHINES

Method of Load Application	Kind of Stress	Machine
Swinging pendulum	Tension	Modified Charpy or Izod [11, 12]
	Shear	McAdam[3]
	Bending	Charpy or Izod or combination [11, 12]
Rotating flywheel	Tension	Mann[55]
	Torsion	Carpenter [11, 56]
	Bending	Guillery[2]
Dropped weight (single and repeated blows)	Tension	Olsen[13]
	Compression	Olsen[13]
	Bending	Hatt-Turner[10]

16. Pendulum-Type Impact Machines. The most commonly used impact testing machine is the pendulum type shown in Fig. 2-29. In this machine the specimen S is broken with a single blow by the pendulum P falling a height h. The energy absorbed in the fracture of the specimen is determined by noting the initial position of the pendulum and the highest position h'' that the pendulum reaches after breaking the specimen. If W is the weight of the pendulum, the energy used to fracture the specimen is equal to

$$E_p = Wh - Wh'' \qquad (3)$$

where h = the vertical fall of the center of gravity of the pendulum and h'' = its vertical rise.

The readings of the pointer N measure h and h''. Energy values given by equation 3 are indicative of the relative toughness of various materials subjected to impact loads. Calculations of energy losses produced by air drag and bearing friction are given by Davis.[3]

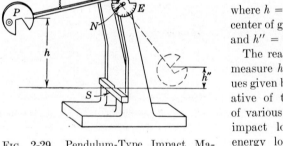

FIG. 2-29. Pendulum-Type Impact Machine

The machine shown in Fig. 2-29 can be used for axial-tension–impact tests on plain specimens. Fixtures are provided for bending tests of notched specimens when using Charpy- or Izod-type specimens (Fig. 2-30). The Charpy specimen is supported at the ends and struck at the middle, whereas the Izod type is supported as a cantilever beam and struck at the free end. Procedures for Charpy-impact tests are standardized by the American Society for Testing Materials.[10]

The *Oxford Impact Machine* is another pendulum-type design in which the specimen is a beam with a constant moment over part of its length (Fig. 2-31). A yoke Y applies the impact blow to two points $1\frac{1}{2}$ in. apart on the specimen. The designers claim[54] that more consistent and reliable results can be obtained since "stray losses" are eliminated by having only normal stresses free from transverse shear. A pendulum-type shear impact machine is manufactured by the Tinius Olsen Testing Machine Company.[13]

17. Rotating-Flywheel-Type Impact Machines. There are several flywheel-type impact machines that use a rotating flywheel as a source of energy for rupturing the specimen. The Guillery machine[2] is of the flywheel type and is designed to break standard Charpy specimens at a velocity of blow = 29 ft/sec. The striking member in this machine is held within the rim of the wheel until the desired rotational speed is reached. The energy used in breaking the specimen is measured by a manometer reading the output pressure of a small turbine coupled to the flywheel. The energy used for rupturing the specimen is obtained by measuring the pressure before and after breaking the specimen.

The *Watertown or Mann flywheel machine,*[55] illustrated in Fig. 2-32, can be used for tension specimens and for speeds up to 1000 ft/sec. In this machine a tup T attaches a specimen S to a pendulum P. With the horns H retracted, the flywheel W is brought up to a selected speed by a motor geared to the supporting shaft. At the desired velocity, measured by means of a tachometer, the external mechanism is tripped, releasing the horns H which strike the tup T, thereby rupturing the specimen S. The angular movement produced in the pendulum is recorded on a dial gage G. The dial-gage reading can then be used to calculate the energy required for rupture.[55] The Carpenter machine[56] is a flywheel-type impact machine used for torsion tests.

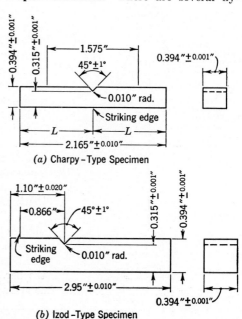

(a) Charpy-Type Specimen

(b) Izod-Type Specimen

FIG. 2-30. Izod–Charpy Impact Specimens

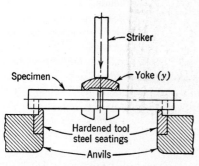

FIG. 2-31. Oxford Impact Machine

18. Dropped-Weight-Type Impact Machines. Impact tests are also made by dropping weights on specimens. The Hatt-Turner machine[1, 53] is used

with either single or repeated blows applied to a specimen subjected to impact
bending. It is a machine that has been found particularly useful for tests on wood and is specified for use in impact tests of wood (ASTM Standards designation D-143-27.) Single-blow impact machines for tension and compression are manufactured by the Tinius Olsen Testing Machine Company.[13]

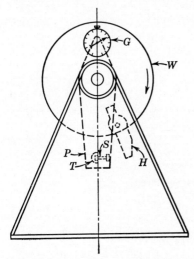

FIG. 2-32. Mann or Watertown Flywheel-Type Tension Impact Machine

The energy necessary to produce rupture of a specimen is determined in the foregoing impact machines. Equipment has been developed to obtain more complete information on properties under impact loadings by providing a means to determine the stress–strain diagram. Clark and Datwyler[57] obtained stress–strain diagrams for impact tension by winding fine constantan wire around a steel bar, the electrical resistance of which changed with the applied force in the bar. A recording oscillograph apparatus for correlating force with time and a means of converting force–time

FIG. 2-33. High-Speed Tension Machine for Tests at Elevated Temperatures
(Courtesy Westinghouse Research Laboratories)

data to force–elongation diagrams were developed to determine the stress–strain relations under impact.

A high-speed tension machine for tests at elevated temperatures (Fig. 2-33) was developed by Manjoine and Nádai.[58] The machine is of the flywheel type, and the stress–strain data are obtained electrically. Hammers applying the impact load hit the anvil attached to the specimen and transmit the force to a force-measuring bar in series with the specimen. Small elastic extensions produced in the force-measuring bar are converted to an electric current impulse which is proportional to the force. When the anvil moves vertically downward, it cuts a light beam falling on a photoelectric cell. The resulting current decrease is proportional to the strain. The two current impulses are combined at right angles on the screen of a standard type cathode-ray oscillograph, and a record of the stress–strain curve is obtained.

Other equipment for obtaining stress–strain diagrams has been developed by Ginns[59] and Itihara.[60] Reference 57 describes several types of impact machines not covered in the foregoing.

III. SPECIAL TESTING MACHINES

There are many special testing machines not covered in section I and II. Machines for tests of structural and machine parts, and hardness-testing machines are discussed briefly in the following.

I. MACHINES FOR TESTS OF STRUCTURAL AND MACHINE MEMBERS

Many new machines have been developed, and standard testing machines have been adapted for determining the performance or strength of machines and structures. The large number of such special machines makes it impossible to discuss them adequately in this chapter, and only a few can be included.

Universal static-testing machines of low and high capacities and special structural-testing machines have been used to test large reinforced-concrete and steel columns, reinforced-concrete arches, frames, bridge rollers, slabs, and many other structural members. Fatigue tests on large beams, box girders, riveted and welded joints, and columns have been made by Templin.[61] The machine shown in Fig. 2-34 is used for fatigue testing of columns. The repeated load is applied through a lever that is moved up and down by an eccentric driven by a motor. For testing welded and riveted joints in fluctuating tension, Wilson[62] developed a machine similar to the one shown in Fig. 2-34.

In the aircraft industry numerous special machines have been built for both static and dynamic tests of airframe and propeller parts. Some of these include machines for testing of wings, fuselages, propeller blades, propeller hubs, crankshafts, and engine mounts. Fig. 2-35 shows a machine used to apply an alternating stress to an aircraft-engine mount. The mount is bolted to a vertical face shown on the left side. A flywheel on the right side has an eccentric bearing connected to the motor ring which subjects the mount to alternating stresses. S-R4 strain gages attached to the various members and a recording oscillograph indicate the stresses produced.

FIG. 2-34. Templin Fatigue Machine for Tests of Columns (Courtesy Aluminum Co of America Research Laboratories)

FIG. 2-35. Fatigue Test of an Aircraft-Engine Mount (Courtesy Timken Roller Bearing Co)

Fig. 2-36. Fatigue-Testing Machine for a Locomotive-Driving Axle (Courtesy Timken Roller Bearing Co)

Fig. 2-37. Vibration-Fatigue Machine (Courtesy Chrysler Corp)

Figure 2-36 shows a machine for fatigue testing of locomotive driving axles.[63] It consists of a double-ended rotating-cantilever-beam-type fatigue machine capable of testing members up to 14 in. in diameter. The machine is driven by a 100-hp variable-speed motor.

A vibration fatigue machine, as shown in Fig. 2-37, is used for testing automobile parts and connections. The vibratory motion in this machine can be produced either vertically or horizontally by two motors. Eccentrics attached to the motor produce the oscillations and vibrations.

Electromagnetic vibrators are now frequently employed to produce resonant vibrations in structural and machine members. Large vibratory loads can be produced by applying alternating current to the magnet at resonant frequencies of the part tested. The same machine can be used for small parts such as compressor valves or larger items such as aircraft crankshafts.

J. HARDNESS-TESTING MACHINES

Hardness of materials has several arbitrary definitions. It may be the resistance to permanent indentation, rebound under impact loads, scratching,

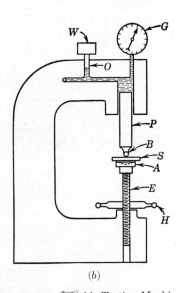

(a)   (b)

FIG. 2-38a.   Brinell-Hardness-Testing Machine (Courtesy Riehle Testing Machine
Division, American Machine & Metals)
Fig. 2-38b.   Brinell-Hardness-Testing Machine

abrasion, or cutting or drilling. In stress analysis and materials testing, tests to determine resistance to permanent indentation are those most commonly considered. Only a brief description of the most commonly used hardness test machines is given here. The reader is referred to reference 64 for a thorough discussion of hardness-testing machines.

The *Brinell machine*, as shown in Figs. 2-38a and 2-38b, consists of an anvil A for supporting the specimen S, an elevating screw E, and a handwheel H for raising the specimen to the desired height. A load of fixed amount is applied to the specimen through the ball B by a plunger P. The plunger is moved down by an oil pressure which is produced by a hand pump. When

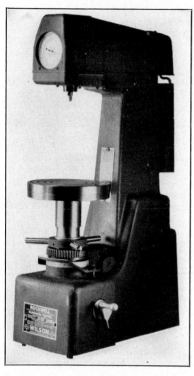

Fig. 2-39. Rockwell-Hardness-Testing Machine (Courtesy Wilson Mechanical Instrument Co; Photo by Harold Haliday Costain)

Fig. 2-40. Scleroscope Used for Hardness Testing of Metals (Courtesy of Shore Instrument & Mfg Co)

the desired load is applied, the balance weight W is lifted by the action of the small piston O which insures that an overload is not applied to the ball. The Bourdon gage G is used only to give a rough indication of the load. The diameter of the indentation on the specimen is measured by a micrometer microscope to obtain a measure of the hardness.

The *Rockwell Testing Machine* shown in Fig. 2-39 differs from the Brinell machine in that the indenters and load values are smaller. The indenter or penetrator is either a steel ball or a conical-shaped diamond. The load is applied to the specimen through a system of weights and levers, and the residual depth of penetration of the indenter is measured by a dial indicator. The hardness is inversely proportional to the depth of penetration. The Rockwell machine is applicable to testing of materials having hardness values beyond the range of the Brinell machine. It is also faster than the Brinell machine since it gives direct readings.

The *Vickers hardness machine*[64] is similar to the Brinell machine except that the penetrator is a square-based diamond pyramid, and a lever system is used to apply the load. A machine used to measure surface hardness is the Scleroscope shown in Fig. 2-40. In this machine the height of bounce of a steel weight (dropped from a given height onto the specimen) is taken as the measure of the hardness.

Naturally only a few of the various types of testing machines can be described in a chapter of this length. The reader is referred in particular to reference 1 for more complete information on the subject.

BIBLIOGRAPHY

General

1. ERICH SIEBEL, *Handbuch der Werkstoffprüfung, Erster Band—"Prüf und Messeinrichtungen,"* Julius Springer, Berlin, 1940. Lithoprinted by Edwards Brothers, Ann Arbor, Mich, 1944, 658 pp. This volume is one of three comprising a handbook on materials testing. Many testing machines, both standard and special, developed in various countries, are thoroughly described.
2. R. G. BATSON and J. H. HYDE, *Mechanical Testing,* v 1, "Testing of Materials of Construction," Chapman and Hall, London; E. P. Dutton & Co., New York, 1922, 413 pp. A book describing many of the early materials testing machines.
3. H. E. DAVIS, G. E. TROXELL, and C. T. WISKOCIL, *The Testing and Inspection of Engineering Materials,* McGraw-Hill Book Co, New York, 1941, 372 pp. Various types of machines and tests (including nondestructive testing) are treated in this text.
4. H. J. GILKEY, G. MURPHY, and E. O. BERGMAN, *A Manual of Materials Testing,* McGraw-Hill Book Co. New York, 1941. A manual for a laboratory course on materials testing.
5. H. F. MOORE, *Materials of Engineering,* McGraw-Hill Book Co. 6th ed, 1941, 454 pp. A chapter on testing machines in this book gives a good description of the main standard testing machines.
6. C. H. GIBBONS, *Materials Testing Machines,* Instruments Publishing Co, Pittsburgh, Pa, 1935, 89 pp. This book covers the development of testing machines, particularly the universal static machine.
7. A. MARTENS, *Handbook of Testing Materials,* (translated by G. C. Henning) John Wiley & Sons, New York, 1899, 2 v. This book is of historical interest.
8. M. O. WITHEY and JAMES ASTON, *Johnson's Materials of Construction,* John Wiley & Sons, New York, 1939, 866 pp. A section on testing machines adequately describes the main standard machines.
9. J. MARIN, *Mechanical Properties of Materials and Design,* McGraw-Hill Book Co, 1942, 273 pp. A book dealing with the interpretation of various types of tests. It briefly describes certain special types of testing machines.
10. *Standards Am Soc Testing Matls,* 1944. Three volumes giving standards and test procedures for various types of tests.
11. *Catalog on Materials Testing Machines,* Baldwin-Southwark Division, Baldwin Locomotive Works, Philadelphia, Pa. Catalog on description of testing machines, strain gages, and auxiliary testing equipment.

12. *Catalogs on Materials Testing Machines*, Riehle Testing Machine Division, American Machines and Metals, East Moline, Ill. Catalogs on description of testing machines, strain gages, and auxiliary testing equipment.

13. *Catalogs on Materials Testing Machines*, Tinius Olsen Testing Machine Co, Philadelphia, Pa. Catalogs on description of testing machines, strain gages, and auxiliary testing equipment.

14. *Catalogs on Materials Testing Machines*, Herman Holz, New York. Catalogs on foreign testing machines.

15. *Metals Handbook*, American Society of Metals, Cleveland, Ohio, 1939, 1800 pp. Describes various types of tests.

16. *Welding Handbook*, American Welding Society, New York, 1938, 1211 pp. Includes information on testing of welds and equipment for these tests.

Static Testing Machines

17. C. H. GIBBONS, "Load-Weighing and Load-Indicating Systems," *ASTM Bul* 100, Oct 1939, pp 7–13.

18. H. F. MOORE, "The Calibration of Testing Machines," *Proc New Int Assn Testing Matl* (1st Congress), Zürich, 1931, v 2, pp 482–91.

19. A. NÁDAI, "Theories of Strength," *Trans ASME*, v 55, 1933. Surveys various types of combined stress experiments and describes equipment used for some combined stress tests.

20. M. RoŠ and A. EICHINGER, "Versuche zur Klärung der Frage der Bruchgefahr," *Proc 2d Int Congress Applied Mechanics*, 1926, p 315; also "Materialprüfungsanstalf," E. T. H. Zürich, n 28, 1928 and n 34, 1929. These papers describe combined stress experiments on tubes subjected to internal pressure and axial loads or torsion and axial loads.

21. G. I. TAYLOR and H. QUINNEY, "Plastic Distortion of Metals," *Trans Royal Soc (Lond)*, series, A, v 23, 1931, p 323. Tests on tubes subjected to combined tension and torsion are reported in this paper.

22. J. M. LESSELLS and C. W. MacGREGOR, "Combined Stress Experiments on a Nickel–Chrome–Molybdenum Steel," *J Franklin Inst*, v 230, 1940, pp 163–81. This paper reports tests on tubes subjected to axial tension and internal pressure.

23. E. A. DAVIS, "Yielding and Fracture of Medium Carbon Steel under Combined Stress," *J Applied Mechanics*, American Society of Mechanical Engineers, Mar 1945, p–A-13–24. Tests are described in which plastic strains are measured to rupture in tubes subjected to axial tension and internal pressure.

24. E. A. DAVIS, "Combined Tension–Torsion Tests on a 0.35 per cent Carbon Steel," *Trans ASME*, v 62, 1940, pp 577–86. A machine for combined tension–torsion loading is described in this paper.

25. J. MARIN and R. L. STANLEY, "Failure of Aluminum Subjected to Combined Stresses," *J Am Welding Soc Supp*, Feb 1940. This paper describes a machine for tests of tubes under combined torsion and tension.

26. G. SACHS, G. ESPEY, and G. B. KASIK, "Bulging of Aluminum Alloy Sheets at Room and Elevated Temperatures," *Trans ASME*, 1946. This paper discusses the technique used in the "bulge" test.

27. W. M. WILSON and J. MARIN, "Tests on Thin Hemispherical Shells Subjected to Internal Hydrostatic Pressure," *Univ Ill Exp Sta Bul* 295, 1937. Tests of hemispherical shells under internal pressure are reported in this bulletin.

28. P. W. BRIDGMAN, "On Torsion Combined with Compression," *J Applied Physics*, v 14, n 6, pp. 273–83. Tests in which specimens are subjected to torsion combined with axial compression are described in this paper.

29. L. KAMENER and M. BIRNBAUM, "A Frame for Uniform Loading," *Proc 14th Semiannual Photoelasticity Conf*, New Haven, Conn, 1941. Describes a frame for applying biaxial-compression stresses.

30. P. W. BRIDGMAN, *The Physics of High Pressures*, Macmillan Co, 1931.　Gives a general survey of high-pressure studies up to 1931, including testing equipment for high-pressure tests.

31. P. W. BRIDGMAN, "Recent Work in the Field of High Pressures," *Am Scientist*, v 31, n 1, 1943.　Discusses devices used to attain high pressures.

32. F. H. NORTON, *Creep of Steel at High Temperatures*, McGraw-Hill Book Co, New York, 1929.　A book on creep of steel at high temperatures describing tests and summarizing test results on creep

33. H. J. TAPSELL, *Creep of Metals*, Oxford Univ. Press, New York, 1931.　A book on creep of metals covering creep tests, machines, and test results.

34. M. J. MANJOINE, "New Machines for Creep and Creep–Rupture Tests," *Trans ASME*, Feb 1945, p 111.　Describes tension creep machine which plots automatically the creep–time relations.

35. E. A. DAVIS, "Creep of Metals at High Temperatures in Bending," *Trans ASME*, v 59, 1937, p A-29.　This paper describes a creep bending test.

36. F. L. EVERETT, "The Strength of Materials Subjected to Shear at High Temperatures," *Trans ASME*, v 53, 1931, p 117.　A machine for torsion creep tests at high temperatures is described in this paper.

37. R. W. BAILEY, "The Utilization of Creep Test Data in Engineering Design," *Proc Inst Mech Engrs (Lond)*, v 131, Nov 1935.　A comprehensive study of the mechanics of creep and some description of tests and equipment used for creep testing.

38. H. F. MOORE, B. B. BETTY, and C. W. DOLLENS, "Investigation of Creep and Fracture of Lead and Lead Alloys for Cable Sheathing," *Univ Ill Eng Exp Sta Bul* 306, 1938.　Creep tests of lead in tension and internal pressure are discussed in this bulletin.

39. F. H. NORTON, "Creep of Tubular Pressure Vessels," *Trans ASME*, v 61, n 3, 1939.　Report on creep tests of tubular specimens closed at the ends and subjected to internal pressure.

40. W. E. TRUMPLER, "Relaxation of Metals at High Temperatures," *J Applied Physics*, v 12, n 3, pp 248–53, 1941.　Describes an automatic-relaxation tension–creep machine.

Dynamic Testing Machines

41. H. F. MOORE and J. B. KOMMERS, *The Fatigue of Metals*, McGraw-Hill Book Co, New York, 1927.　Describes early fatigue-testing machines up to 1927 and the general subject of fatigue.

42. H. J. GOUGH, *The Fatigue of Metals*, D Van Nostrand Co, New York, 1926.　Describes early fatigue-testing machines and fatigue testing.

43. H. F. MOORE and G. N. KROUSE, "Repeated Stress Testing Machines Used in the Materials Testing Laboratory of the Univ of Ill," *Univ Ill Eng Exp Sta Bul* 23, 1934.　This bulletin gives a detailed description of several fatigue machines developed by Prof. Moore.

44. *Bulletins on Sonntag Universal Fatigue Machines*, Baldwin Locomotive Works, Philadelphia, Pa.　These bulletins describe various inertia-type fatigue machines built by the Sonntag Scientific Corp.

45. R. E. PETERSON, "Fatigue Tests of Large Specimens," *Proc ASTM*, v 29, 1929.　Rotating cantilever fatigue machines for testing large-sized specimens are described in this paper.

46. *Catalogs on Vibration Fatigue Machines*, All American Tool and Mfg Co, Chicago, Ill.　Describe testing machines consisting essentially of vibrating tables.

47. *Catalogs of the Krouse Testing Machine Co*, 573 East 11 Ave, Columbus, Ohio.　Various tension and bending constant-deflection-type fatigue machines are described in these catalogs.

48. H. J. GOUGH and H. V. POLLARD, "Strength of Metals under Combined Alternating Stresses," *Proc Inst Mech Engrs (Lond)*, v 131, 1935, p 3. This paper describes a combined torsion–bending fatigue machine.

49. J. MARIN, "Strength of Steel Subjected to Biaxial Fatigue Stresses," *Welding J Research Supp*, Nov 1942. A new machine for biaxial-tension–fatigue tests is described in this paper.

50. B. J. LAZAN, "Some Mechanical Properties of Plastics and Metals under Sustained Vibrations," *Trans ASME*, v 65, 1943, p 87. This paper describes two inertia-type machines for determination of damping constants.

51. G. S. VON HEYDEKAMPF, "Damping Capacity of Materials," *Proc ASTM*, v 31, pt II, 1931, pp 157–71. Describes various types of damping tests.

52. W. P. WELCH and W. A. WILSON, "A New High-Temperature Fatigue Machine," *Proc ASTM*, v 41, 1941. This paper describes a new bending-fatigue machine for tests at high temperature.

53. "Symposium on Impact Testing," *Proc ASTM*, v 38, 1938, pp 21–156. A symposium on impact testing including a brief discussion of impact-testing machines.

54. E. J. WARLOW-DAVIES and R. V. SOUTHWELL, "The Correlation of Impact Tests and the Problem of Standardization," *Proc Instr Mech Engrs (Lond)*, v 134, 1936, pp 507–45. The Oxford impact machine is described in this paper.

55. H. C. MANN, "High-Velocity Tension-Impact Tests," *Proc ASTM*, v 36, 1936, pp 85–109. This paper describes the Mann impact machine.

56. G. V. LUERSSEN and O. V. GREENE, "The Torsion Impact Test," *Proc ASTM*, v 33, 1933, pp 315–33. The Carpenter torsion-impact machine is described in this paper.

57. D. S. CLARK and G. DATWYLER, "Stress–Strain Relations under Tension Impact Loading," *Proc ASTM*, v 38, pt 2, p 98, 1938. Equipment for obtaining stress–strain diagrams for tension at high speeds of loading is described in this paper.

58. M. MANJOINE and A. NÁDAI, "High-Speed Tension Tests at Elevated Temperatures," *Proc ASTM*, v 40, 1940 (pt 1). Pts 2 and 3, *Trans ASME*, v 63, 1941, p A-77. Describes an automatic high-speed tension machine.

59. D. W. GINNS, "The Mechanical Properties of some Metals and Alloys Broken at Ultra-High Speeds," *J Inst Metals*, 61, 1937, p 61. A machine for tension-impact tests in which the stress–strain curves are obtained is described in this paper.

60. M. ITIHARA, "Impact Torsion Tests," *Technology Reports, Tohoku Imperial Univ, Sendai*, Japan, v 11 and 12, 1934 and 1935. Various reports in these references give results of torsion stress–strain data for high speeds of loading at low and high temperatures.

Special Testing Machines

61. R. L. TEMPLIN, "Fatigue Machines for Testing Structural Units," *Proc ASTM*, v 39, 1939. This paper describes various new fatigue machines for fatigue tests of structural members.

62. W. M. WILSON and F. P. THOMAS, "Fatigue Tests of Riveted Joints," *Univ Ill Eng Exp Sta Bul* 302, 1938. This bulletin describes a large–capacity repeated–tension–fatigue machine for tests of riveted joints.

63. T. V. BUCKWALTER, O. J. HORGER, and W. C. SANDERS, "Locomotive Axle Testing," *Trans ASME*, v 60, 1938, p 335. This paper describes fatigue tests of locomotive axles.

64. H. O'NEILL, *The Hardness of Metals and Its Measurement*, Sherwood Press, Cleveland, Ohio, 1934, 292 pp.

CHAPTER 3

MECHANICAL GAGES AND EXTENSOMETERS

By L. H. Donnell and W. T. Savage

A. INTRODUCTION—ADVANTAGES OF VARIOUS METHODS

The problem of accurately measuring minute strains and displacements is a most difficult and fascinating one, which has engaged the attention of engineers and scientists for many years. Since the movements to be studied may be far below the magnitude which can even be detected—much less measured—by the unaided senses, some kind of magnification of their effects is obviously necessary.

The most obvious solution is to magnify the movements directly and mechanically by a system of levers, gears, or similar means. To design such a system to give any desired amplification seems at first glance to be easy. If one lever gives a magnification of ten to one, then a combination of two should give one hundred to one, and so on. But, if we try it out or start to analyze the effects of the various factors which are actually involved, such as friction, lost motion, the weight and inertia and flexibility of the parts, we find it is not so simple to obtain accurate and reliable results in this way. The difficulties increase rapidly with the amount of magnification desired and become still greater when there are rapid changes in the motion, as in studies of impact and vibration.

In their efforts to overcome these difficulties, experimenters early took advantage of the fact that a beam of light can act as an infinitely rigid, weightless, and inertialess pointer, of far greater length than would be practical for mechanical pointers. Most of the optical gages are based on this principle.

Another method of overcoming the difficulties is to transform the movements to be studied into some kind of changes in an electric circuit. This does not necessarily give any magnification in itself, but sensitive equipment is available to measure such small electric changes. Since this equipment can be placed at a distance and connected only by slender wires with the point where the movements occur, there is no limit to its size and complexity. Recent developments in amplification and representation by controlling streams of electrons have made these electrical methods especially useful in cases where there are rapid changes in motion, which make the inertia of mechanical parts a great problem. Electrical methods are also especially useful when the points at which measurements are to be made are enclosed or inaccessible for some reason.

In spite of the advantages of optical and electrical methods, however, purely mechanical devices are still in widespread use, and for many purposes are much more convenient than their competitors. The main advantage of purely mechanical devices probably lies in the fact that they are completely self-contained, and the quantities to be measured are shown on scales or dials which can be conveniently read without the observer having to be in some fixed position. Nonmechanical methods all require supplementary apparatus, or, with some microscope-type optical instruments, the observer's eye must be placed at a certain point, which cannot always be conveniently located.

It is proposed in the following articles to discuss some of the general problems arising in the design of mechanical instruments for measuring strains and small motions. This discussion also applies to the mechanical parts which are frequently used in "optical" and "electric" instruments.

B. Contact Points for Picking up Motion

When the motion of some body or point on a body is to be measured by a dial gage or similar instrument, it is customary to provide the instrument with a rounded contact point, which is constrained to move in a straight line or along an arc relative to the instrument and is forced by a spring against the object whose motion is to be measured.

This is quite satisfactory for most purposes, but it should be remembered that what is really being measured is only the motion, relative to the instrument's case, of the instrument's contact point—its motion of translation if it moves in a straight line, or its angular motion if it moves in an arc. The relation between this motion and the motion of the body being studied may be somewhat complex and difficult to analyze. Thus in Fig. 3-1 this relation evidently depends on the angles between the direction of motion of the contact point, the direction of motion of the body, and the general direction of the body's surface, as well as on the shape of the contact point and the curvature and local irregularities in the shape of the body's surface.

When it is desired to attain great precision with an instrument of very high sensitivity it may be desirable to use some kind of connection which makes this relation more definite and analyzable. Thus in Fig. 3-2, owing to the flexure hinges at A and B, the instrument measures the relative motion, in the direction of the line A-B, between point A (which is fixed rigidly to the body studied) and point B (which is fixed rigidly to the foundation).

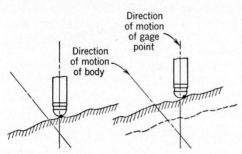

FIG. 3-1. Factors Affecting Measurement of Motion by a Contact Point

When the strains at the surface of a body are to be measured, somewhat different problems arise. Electrical-resistance gages are commonly made in the form of thin semiconducting sheets which are cemented directly to the surface of the body. This is in many ways an ideal arrangement, especially when large accelerations of the body being studied, or rapid variations in the strain, are present. However, even this type of strain gage has its characteristic problems, which are discussed in Chapter 5.

All other common types of strain gages are attached to the specimen at two or more points and measure the relative motion of these points, usually in the direction of the line between them. One of the points of contact or "gage points" of the instrument is commonly fixed to the instrument frame or case, while the motion of the other one is magnified and measured by the instrument. The method of attachment usually consists merely of pressing the gage points against the surface of the specimen, friction being depended on to keep them from slipping on the surface when the specimen strains. The gage points are usually made sharp, and

FIG. 3-2. Accurate Measurement of Relative Motion

their "digging in" to the surface augments the effect of friction, or a scratch or prick punch mark or small hole may be previously made in the surface of the specimen for the points to fit into.

If the sizes of these impressions, scratches, or holes are small compared to the gage length (the initial distance between the gage points) and compared to the important dimensions of the specimen, their presence and the normal and tangential forces which are exerted by the gage and its clamps on the specimen may have a negligible effect on the local and general behavior of the specimen. But, if the specimen is being tested to failure and it behaves in a brittle manner, the stress concentration caused by such notches may have an important effect, or, if the specimen is very small or weak or flexible, the forces associated with the use of the gage may be important.

All this shows the importance of keeping the force required to operate the gage, as well as all other forces associated with its use, *as small as possible.* In this connection also it would be well to remark on the importance of keeping the weight of the gage as small as possible and concentrated as close to the surface as possible, especially when the gage length is small. If the gage is "top heavy," its weight and inertia may produce a strong tendency to tip it and to reduce the pressure on one gage point and increase it on the other. The clamping pressure then has to be increased to keep the *minimum* pressure adequate, and thus the maximum pressure may be very much greater than would otherwise be required to operate the gage.

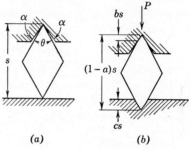

In many gages the point of contact with the specimen is also used as a pivot point, as shown in Fig. 3-3. Besides the obvious fact that rotation of the gage points increases their tendency to slip and, hence, must be limited to very small angles, there are other factors to be considered. The gage points are usually diamond-shaped, with one point of the diamond contacting the specimen and the other

Fig. 3-3.   Diamond Pivot

forming a knife-edge. To this diamond is attached a long mechanical lever or a mirror using a beam of light as a lever.

The smaller the distance s (Fig. 3-3a) is, the greater the magnification will be. As the clamping pressure is increased, the length s will be decreased, owing to compression of the diamond, by a factor such as a (Fig. 3-3b). As the gage point digs into the specimen and the upper point of the knife-edge and the groove in which it operates deform, the effective lever arm will evidently tend to be further decreased by factors b and c. There will also be an undesirable increase in resistance to rotation.

From elementary considerations it can easily be shown that these factors are very roughly

$$a = \frac{2P}{\theta E s t} \log_e \frac{\theta s}{2w}, \quad b = \frac{P}{4\alpha E s t}, \quad c = \frac{P}{\theta S_y s t} \tag{1}$$

where t is the thickness of the diamond perpendicular to the figure, E is the modulus of elasticity of its material, and S_y is the yield point of the specimen's material, θ and α are measured in radians, and w is the very small width of the points of the diamond. If the typical values in pound and inch units are used: $P = 10$, $\theta = 1$, $\alpha = 0.03$, $E = 30{,}000{,}000$, $S_y = 30{,}000$, $s = 0.16$,

$t = 0.06$, $w = 0.0001$, we have

$$a = 0.0005, \quad b = 0.0003, \quad c = 0.035$$

It seems from these figures that deformations of the gage parts themselves are not likely to be important. However, the digging of the gage points into the specimen, in addition to its disadvantages previously discussed, may change the magnification factor by several per cent when the contact point is used as a pivot with a short lever arm. This effect will, in general, vary with the clamping pressure P and other conditions and, hence, cannot very well be allowed for.

The practice of using the contact point as a pivot with a short arm therefore seems definitely undesirable, except perhaps in applications such as optical gages, where the lightness of the parts may make it possible to use very small clamping pressures. The ideal condition is for the movable gage point to move along the line joining the initial positions of the gage points, without rotating.

C. Sensitivity and True Accuracy

Once the motion to be measured has been transferred to the instrument, the next problem is to magnify it sufficiently so that it can be read. In considering the amount of magnification which is required in any given case, a distinction must immediately be made between nominal magnification, or sensitivity, and true accuracy.

Let t represent the *true* movement or strain* being measured, and i be its value as *indicated* by the instrument. The indicated value is usually not read directly from the instrument but is calculated from the reading by use of a calibration factor or a calibration curve or a combination of a factor and a curve. It is of course most convenient if the indicated value can be read directly, and dial gages are usually made to permit this, whereas in strain gages it is usually not attempted.

In any case there are usually consistent errors which can be allowed for by use of a calibration curve, and, if the inconvenience of using such a curve is accepted, the accuracy attainable with the instrument is increased. That is, a gage used without a calibration curve and the same instrument used with one might be regarded as two different instruments, the second version being more accurate but less convenient to use than the first.

The difference between the true and indicated values is the error, e or

$$t - i = e \tag{2}$$

The sensitivity of the instrument is usually measured by the smallest value of i which can be read, i_{min}. This can usually be taken as the value corresponding to from one fifth to one half of the smallest division in the scale (depending

---

* In discussing dial gages, or strain gages having a variable gage length, it is best to talk about the *movement*, but for strain gages having a fixed gage length it may be more convenient to speak in terms of the *unit strain*, that is, the movement divided by the gage length.

on the size of this division, the relative thickness of the pointer, the provisions for avoiding parallax, and so on).

If the maximum errors are less than i_{min}, then i_{min} represents the smallest value which the instrument can measure. But, if the maximum error e_{max} (preferably the maximum found in a considerable number of trials under various conditions and with different observers) is greater than i_{min}, then, e_{max} obviously represents the limiting value which the instrument can measure. The true accuracy of the instrument may, therefore, be measured by the uncertainty u, which is taken equal to i_{min} or e_{max}, whichever is the *larger*. Readings can then be assumed to be accurate to $\pm u$.

Sometimes it is more revealing to measure the accuracy by the *percentage* of the uncertainty to the total movement or strain measured. This is evidently $100u/t$ (or $100u/i$ since t and i differ only slightly). Both u and the percentage $100u/t$ are likely to vary with the magnitude of t or i.

D. MAGNIFICATION REQUIRED

Having defined what is meant by sensitivity and accuracy, let us return to the discussion of means of magnification. In designing an instrument for a given purpose the accuracy required, that is the value of u, will be at least approximately known. If it is assumed that errors can be kept so low that $e_{max} < i_{min}$, then the accuracy is determined by the sensitivity, and this can be computed from purely geometrical considerations. The proposed instrument could then be constructed, the errors measured by careful tests, and refinements undertaken if the errors prove too great.

Such a development is likely to be lengthy and uncertain, and it seems desirable and possible to be more systematic. Consider first the relation between e_{max} and i_{min} and the given value of u. It seems undesirable to have any of these quantities out of proportion to the others. Increasing the magnification used, for instance, decreases i_{min} but is almost certain to *increase* e_{max} at the same time, because the difficulty of keeping down sources of error increases rapidly with the magnification. It would, therefore, seem that the smallest i_{min} and e_{max} and, hence, the smallest uncertainty u would be obtained (for a given type of mechanism, care of manufacture, and so on) if

$$i_{min} = e_{max} = u$$

However, if u has been taken as the maximum uncertainty which can possibly be allowed, it is better to be a little more conservative and to aim for a relation such as

$$i_{min} = e_{max} = \frac{u}{k} \tag{3}$$

where k is a number greater than unity—perhaps 2 or more. This favors ease of reading by making it unnecessary always to read to the limit of perception and gives some factor of safety for errors, so that perfection in the conditions of the test and of the instrument will not always have to be maintained.

E. Factors Affecting Accuracy

It is now possible, by geometrical considerations only, to design a mechanism to give the proper sensitivity or value of i_{min}. To predict theoretically what the value of e_{max} will be is much more difficult, but it seems very important to attempt to do it approximately, and in any case it is obviously important to consider as quantitatively as possible the effect on the error of various types of construction and details of design. In the following an attempt is made to list and discuss the more important factors affecting errors.

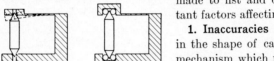

(a)   (b)

Fig. 3-4. Elimination of Lost Motion in Pivots

1. Inaccuracies in mechanism, such as in the shape of cams, gear teeth, or any mechanism which may result in a variable magnification or nonlinear relation between the motion to be measured and the magnified motion read. In positive-drive mechanisms where the indicating hand moves only once over the scale for the entire range of the instrument, a nonlinear scale may be used to correct for the irregularity of the mechanism. In all positive-drive mechanisms, these effects can be largely allowed for and eliminated by calibration charts, but, of course, this may not be desired because of its inconvenience. The effect of inaccuracies can be considered to be independent of the forces present.

2. Lost Motion. The effect of lost motion can also be considered to be independent of the magnitude but not of changes in sign of the forces present. Since most of the forces present change sign when the direction of motion changes, the effect of lost motion could be partly allowed for and eliminated by use of two separate calibration charts for motions in one direction and in the other. This would be very undesirable, both because of the inconvenience and because in many applications it would be difficult to prevent or detect momentary reversals of motion.

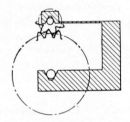

Fig. 3-5. Elimination of Lost Motion in Toothed Gears

Two practical methods for eliminating lost motion seem to be available. One method is to use elements of mechanism which are free from lost motion, such as flexure plates instead of pivots and friction gearing instead of toothed gearing, or to use ordinary elements of tapered or conical form, such that a spring force at right angles to the direction of motion can be used to take up all play. For example pivots can be made as suggested by Figs. 3-4a and 3-4b, and toothed gearing could be made as suggested by Fig. 3-5, a pitch angle of 30° or so being used and a spring to force the two axes towards each other.

The other method for eliminating lost motion, used in most dial gages, is to introduce a spring force at the high-speed end of the system sufficient to drive the system from that end when the motion is in one direction. When the motion is in the opposite direction, the sum of the usual resistance and this spring force must be overcome. With this arrangement the net operating forces are always in the same direction, eliminating most of the lost motion. However, while the operating forces are decreased under some conditions, they are increased, usually by a factor of three or four or more, under the worst conditions. As has been pointed out this is very undesirable for many applications.

3. Effect of Temperature Changes. One effect of temperature changes might be to change the magnification ratio by the resulting dimensional changes in different parts. This effect cancels out if all the parts of the instrument are made of materials having the same coefficient of expansion and is not likely to be important in any case.

More important is the change in the distance between the gage points caused by the expansion or contraction of the instrument or its parts. Materials like brass and aluminum have a coefficient of expansion of about $1/100,000$ per degree Fahrenheit, whereas the coefficient of expansion of steel is about two thirds as great. The apparent unit strain which would be indicated, due to a temperature change of $10°$, with an aluminum gage on a steel specimen or vice versa (if it is assumed the gage and specimen are heated or cooled alike) would, therefore, be about $(\frac{1}{3})(10/100,000) = 1/30,000$. This is the same as the strain produced by a stress of 1000 psi on steel and is hardly unimportant.

It is usually desired to have a strain gage register only the dimensional changes of the specimen due to *stresses* and not to respond to those due to temperature changes. The simplest way to accomplish this is, of course, to have all parts of the gage made of a material having the same coefficient of expansion as the material of the specimen. In some cases it may be sufficient to have the frame of the gage of such a material, but an elaborate analysis may be necessary to show whether this is sufficient.

If different changes in temperature occur in the specimen and in the gage, all such provisions are useless, and serious errors may result, which are difficult to detect and allow for. Currents of warm air from a heating system may cause serious trouble as a result of uneven heating of this sort. If gages and specimens are brought in from different rooms, ample time must be allowed for them to reach a constant temperature before assembling or taking zero readings.

If it is desired to measure absolute movements, whatever their cause, with great precision, it may be desirable to use instruments made of Invar or having temperature-compensating devices such as are used in clocks (sometimes compensation can be achieved by making different parts of different materials) or else to use great care to prevent or allow for temperature changes.

4. Flexure of Parts. This depends of, course, on the forces present, and a study of these forces must be made to understand it. Forces which vary between wide limits are most important in this connection, as the flexure or other type of deformation due to constant forces could easily be allowed for.

5. Slippage and creep in friction drives, when such mechanisms are used, might be mentioned in the same connection as flexure, since its effect also depends on the forces and particularly the variable forces which are present. The possibilities in such drives are frequently disregarded because they are not positive. However, this does not mean that the errors involved will be greater than with other types of instrument. The errors are likely to be cumulative, and such a mechanism would not be suitable for an instrument which is to be used over long periods of time without resetting or rechecking the zero reading. In such use there would be likely to be gradual drift, which might mount up to large proportions.

However, for use in short tests, where the instrument can be reset or a zero reading taken at the beginning of each test, such mechanisms have great possibilities. For example it is possible to obtain a linear amplification of a hundred to one or more in a single stage, with unlimited range, by means of friction gears. The percentage errors during a single use may be kept quite low.

F. The Forces Involved in the Operation of Instruments

These forces are of many kinds. They, of course, do not produce errors of themselves, but they are, as has been discussed, the cause of errors due to flexure and slippage, and are also important for their possible effect on the behavior of the specimen, as has been discussed. They must also be considered in connection with the strength of the instrument parts, although in many cases the dimensions required may be determined by stiffness, to keep down errors due to flexure, rather than by strength.

The most important forces involved might be classified as the *clamping* forces due to attaching the instrument to the specimen or foundation, forces due to the *weight* and *inertia* of the instrument and its parts, *frictional* resistance to the motion of the parts (solid, fluid, and rolling friction), and elastic *spring* forces.

Two radically different kinds of *inertia* forces must be distinguished: (1) inertia forces in the instrument's parts in the direction of and opposing their motions due to rapid changes in the strains or relative motions which the instrument is measuring; (2) those due to accelerations of the specimen and instrument *as a whole*, independent of the strain or relative motion which the instrument is supposed to measure.* This latter type of inertia force would be experienced by a strain gage and all its parts when mounted on a connecting rod or some part of a dive bomber in a dive, even when the strains being measured happen to be zero or constant. The first type involve acceleration in what might be called the "operating motion" of the instrument.

Two kinds of *spring* forces should similarly be distinguished: (1) forces required to bend flexure plates and pivots, which vary between wide limits during an instrument's operation, (2) those due to springs such as shown in

---

* Methods for compensating for errors due to such inertia forces are described in reference 24.

Fig. 3-4, which exert practically constant forces between parts and have no effect on errors except insofar as they increase friction.

It may be illuminating also to consider a different type of classification of forces into (1) those which act in the direction of the operating motion of the instrument, and (2) those which act perpendicular to this direction and which, therefore, affect the motion only indirectly through friction.   The first type is largely produced by friction forces and by the first types of inertia and spring forces, whereas the second type is associated more with weight, clamping forces, and the second types of inertia and spring forces.

G. Effect of Location on Importance of Factors

Now that the various factors which affect errors and the forces associated with them have been enumerated, it is possible to discuss a few broad generalizations which are useful in planning instruments.   In every instrument involving mechanical amplification, whether this concerns a single lever or a complex train of gears and levers, there is a "low-speed" end of the mechanism (the gage points or contact points which pick up the motion to be measured) and a "high-speed" end (at the pointer and scale, where the magnified motion is read) with intermediate speeds between.

Now it is evident that deviations from the desired motion (in the direction of this motion) due to lost motion, flexure of parts, and so on are much more serious when they occur at the *low*-speed end, where their effect on the readings is greatly magnified, than they are if they occur at the high-speed end, where their effect on the readings is unmagnified.   On the other hand, *forces* resisting the motion (which, of course, cause most of the afore-mentioned deviations) are much more serious when they originate at the *high-speed* end, since *their* effect is magnified as we go towards the low-speed end.   This is true whether the forces are due to friction or inertia or other causes.

This means that especial care is necessary to prevent any lost motion (or other irregularities of motion which cannot be balanced out or allowed for) at the low-speed end of the mechanism, whereas this becomes less and less important for parts of the mechanism closer to the high-speed end.   It also means that parts should be made more and more rigid as we approach the low-speed end, both because the operating forces are greater there and because the effects of deformation under these forces are much more serious.

This also means that the increase in inertia forces at the low-speed end, due to the added weight necessary for stiffness there, does little harm.   But inertia forces at the *high*-speed end are very serious, and so the parts at that end should be as *light* as possible.   The resulting flexibility does little harm at that point.

Since the pointer at the reading end is the highest-speed part, a good deal of thought devoted to making it as light as possible may be well repaid.   This indicates that a pointer moving on a fixed scale is generally better than the alternative of a scale moving past a fixed point, since a pointer can be made much lighter than a scale.   Most pointers rotate and, hence, have a higher velocity at the outer end than closer to the axis, and the minimum moment of inertia of the pointer is the object to be aimed at. For instruments measuring motions or strains which vary with time the design of the pointer may be more important than any other detail of the instrument. The use of a very light pointer, even if it is so fragile that it must be protected by a transparent enclosure, may justify itself by permitting a mechanical gage to be employed where optical or electronic devices would otherwise be required.

A study of materials and shapes for mechanical pointers indicates that a solid pointer made of balsa wood, with cross-sectional dimensions of about four thousandths of an inch at the point and a taper of about one in ten, gives the smallest moment of inertia practicable. The moment of inertia of such a pointer may be only 1 or 2 per cent of that of a conventional pointer. Such a pointer is of course very fragile and must be handled with care, but once installed in a protected location it is amply strong and stiff to resist its own very small inertia forces. Balsa wood has rather large pores at intervals in an otherwise fine, even, cellular structure, and such pores must be avoided near the small end of the pointer. Since the wood is cheap and easily cut, a large percentage of rejects can be tolerated. Firm balsa, treated to inhibit decay and warping, can be obtained with a density of less than $\frac{1}{10}$ oz /in.^{3}

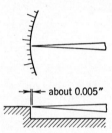

FIG. 3-6. Elimination of Parallax

Parallax in making pointer readings can be avoided by the usual method of providing a mirror behind the pointer and lining up the pointer with its image. A better method, which does not require moving the observer's head to a certain position every time a reading is taken, is to place the pointer flush with the face of the scale, as illustrated in Fig. 3-6. If the dial and pointer mounting are accurate and the width of the pointer is a tenth or less of the width of the scale division, readings can be made consistently to a fifth of one division with this arrangement, even from a considerable viewing angle.

H. MECHANISMS FOR MAGNIFICATION

In the foregoing paragraphs an attempt has been made to discuss the main factors affecting instrumental errors. Another thing which must be considered at an early stage of design is the range of movement which each part of the machanism must undergo. Most mechanisms for mechanical magnification resolve themselves into a series of levers or gearing (toothed or friction). The principles of levers and gears are of course fundamentally similar, but levers are capable of only limited motion, especially if linearity is to be preserved, whereas gears, racks, and pointers operating on full circular scales permit unlimited motions with at least theoretical linearity.

The range of motion required depends both on the purpose for which the instrument is designed and on the part of the instrument considered. Obviously, much more range of motion is required at the high-speed end of an instrument than at the low-speed end, and a type of mechanism suitable at one point may be quite unsuitable at another.

The selection of the type of mechanism to be used at each point can now be made on the basis of the range required and the importance of the various factors affecting errors. Only general statements can be made here on this question. For instance, levers are evidently suitable only for small-range instruments or for the low-speed end of instruments designed for greater range, while toothed or friction gears must be used where unlimited range is required or desirable.

Flexure plates or pivots are, of course, suitable only for use with levers, because of the small angular motion to which they are limited. They are ideally suited for the low-speed end of a gage, because their freedom from lost motion is most important there, and their limited motion and the force required to operate them are of little importance. If more range is required at the low-speed end, then bearings such as shown in Fig. 3-4 are desirable, because they eliminate lost motion, and the increased friction associated with their use is relatively unimportant at that end.

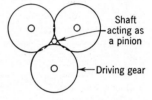

FIG. 3-7.   Friction-Gear Drive

Gearing, using a type of pivot with minimum friction, is particularly suited to the high-speed end of a gage, where great range is required and the backlash and gear-tooth irregularity associated with toothed gearing are relatively harmless. A promising mechanism for the high-speed end of a gage is a friction gear drive using a very small shaft for the pinion, the shaft being rolled between rolls as in centerless grinding, instead of being mounted in ordinary bearings. One of the rolls can act as the driving gear, as indicated in Fig. 3-7.

I. Methods for Calculating Errors

As has been pointed out, elementary principles of geometry or mechanism suffice for designing an instrument to give the required sensitivity or magnification. It is necessary also, however, that the errors be held down to a value commensurate with the sensitivity, if an instrument is to be fully successful. The discussion of the factors affecting errors may suggest ways of keeping the errors down, but there will always be some present, and it is important to calculate their magnitude even if very approximately.

Such a calculation is a problem in mechanics involving the usual principles of statics, dynamics, and strength of materials and can be discussed only in general terms. The calculations should start with the study of the *forces* acting on each part under each of various extreme conditions.

The extreme conditions can be taken as those existing just before and just after the instrument reaches its two extreme positions. The directions of the *friction* forces reverse as we go from just before to just after each extreme position, whereas the directions of the *inertia* and *elastic* forces reverse as we go from one extreme position to the opposite one.   Although it may be necessary to consider these four conditions to determine the maximum changes in forces occurring, it will usually be sufficient to calculate only the two conditions at one extreme position and assume that the forces are equal but opposite at the other extreme position.

After the extremes of forces acting on each part have been calculated, the total error can be computed as the algebraic sum of the errors caused by each *source* of error present.   Individual sources of error can be taken, for instance, as the lost motion at some point due to reversal of the direction of the forces or the distortion of some part due to the maximum *change* in the forces acting on it.   The error due to such a source is the motion of the pointer tip which such a lost motion or distortion would cause.   This is, of course, the actual motion at that point (or rather its component in the direction of the operating motion) times the geometrical magnification between that point and the pointer tip.

Strictly speaking, the directions and magnitudes of the errors which can occur simultaneously between any two of the four extremes conditions should be summed up separately.   Complete calculations of this nature would, of course, be very complicated.   However, if the extreme errors due to each of the main possible sources are computed, without regard to how they may combine together, most of them can usually be disregarded as negligible, and the attention can be fixed on one or two important sources whose possible combinations can be readily seen.   If there are many small errors of about the same magnitude, the total error obviously lies between zero and their *arithmetical* sum, and an estimate of half or two thirds of their arithmetical sum should at least give the right order of magnitude.

Some calculations along these lines, even if very incomplete, should not only give the order of magnitude of the maximum error, but also suggest the most promising methods for substantially reducing it.   The calculations of the extreme forces acting on the different parts are evidently also useful for computing the *strength* of the gage parts, although this is not likely to be critical, as has been mentioned.

J. History of the Development of Mechanical Strain Gages

6. General.   Prior to 1870 very few instruments had been developed for measuring strains accurately, but by 1875 interest in this phase of mechanics was lively.   This interest has continued to the present time with but few lapses and has resulted in a considerable array of equipment for many diverse applications.   For the most part, instruments utilizing mechanical amplification employ wedges, screws, levers (including optical levers), gears, or a combination of these, and these mechanisms were adopted in the order given during the evolution of strain-measuring instruments.

Naturally, interest was first directed to the investigation of tensile and compressive strains in test specimens but was shortly extended to cover strains in actual machines and structures.   Later, means were contrived for recording graphically the behavior of materials under test loading and, eventually, the behavior of structural members in actual service.   Recent endeavors in the development of mechanical instruments have been largely in the nature of refinements of previously established methods.

7. Wedge and Screw Magnification. The wedge gage, Fig. 3-8, was simply a triangular plate with its longer sides related by a 1:10 slope.   When

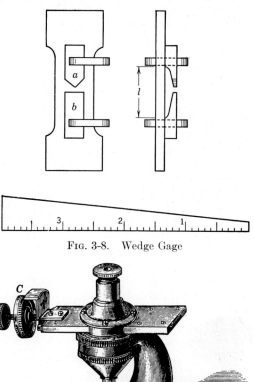

FIG. 3-8.   Wedge Gage

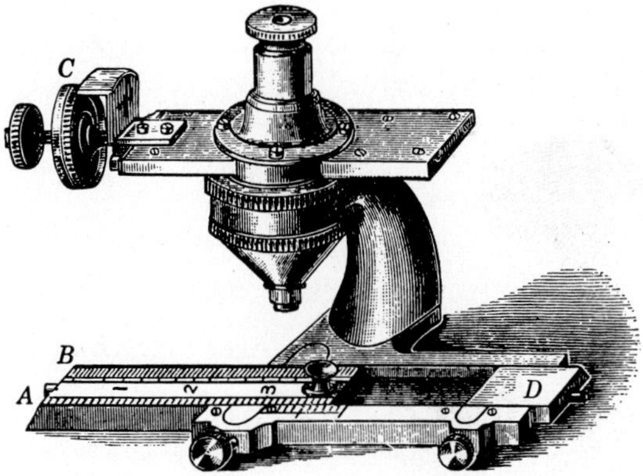

FIG. 3-9.   Unwin's Touch Micrometer

inserted between two shoulders clipped to the test specimen, extensions could be detected to approximately the nearest 0.002 in. Professors Easton Hodgkinson and W. C. Unwin used this method of measurement in about 1856.

Developed by Unwin in 1883, the touch micrometer, Fig. 3-9, was used principally as an extensometer.   Extension was measured by expanding the instrument manually between two reference shoulders firmly clipped to the test specimen.   Scale A and vernier B were affixed to the slide for measuring its motion. Measurements of vernier B were further refined by use of a micrometer microscope. The instrument was graduated to the nearest 0.0001 in. Although no provisions were made to insure uniform contact pressure, an accuracy of 0.0002 in. was claimed.

Many types of extensometers were developed during the period 1870–90, usually employing one or more screw-type micrometers. Pairs of micrometers were generally used alone, whereas single micrometers were used in

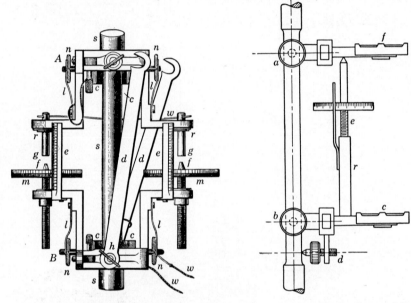

FIG. 3-10.   Double-Screw Micrometer Extensometer

FIG. 3-11.   Single-Screw Micrometer Extensometer

combination with mechanical levers for establishing an average axial-strain value.

Although Professor Thurston, in 1875, was probably the first to employ dual-micrometer screws in an extensometer to measure average axial elongation, one of the most reliable instruments of this type was developed by Hennig and Marshall (Fig. 3-10). Two frames, A and B, carrying contact points and screw micrometers, respectively, were attached to the test specimen, each with a pair of pointed screws. Extension was measured directly with the two screw micrometers. A weak electric circuit, actuating a visual or audible signal, was used to obtain a more uniform micrometer contact. The instrument was graduated to measure to the nearest 0.0001 in. and had a probable accuracy of 0.0002 in.

Other instruments which should be mentioned in this group include Unwin's single-screw extensometer with spirit levels, developed about 1886 (Fig. 3-11), and the extensometer made by the Cambridge and Paul Instrument Co., Ltd.

The strain gage developed by J. E. Howard about 1888 (Fig. 3-12) was one of the pioneer instruments used for measurement of strain in actual structures. The magnification was accomplished solely by a screw micrometer, which measured the relative motion of two coaxial tubes, each provided with a conical contact point. The contact points were inserted in prepared holes

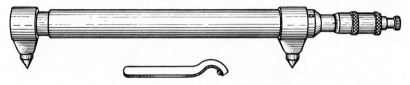

FIG. 3-12.   The Howard Strain Gage

marking a known gage length on the structure. Measurements were determined to the nearest 0.0001 in. and had a probable accuracy of 0.0002 in. under normal operating conditions. Two men were required for most satisfactory operation.

Another application of the screw micrometer is illustrated by Searle's apparatus for measuring extension of wire (Fig. 3-13). The instrument was supported in a level position by identical wires W_1 and W_2. Elongation of W_2 under load P was measured as the micrometer movement required to return spirit level L to its original level position. Wire W_1 served as compensator for the effects of temperature change.

The accuracy of an instrument employing spirit levels depends to a large degree on the sensitivity of the levels. Levels are available with a sensitivity of 5 sec of arc, which is suitable for most applications.

8. Simple Mechanical-Lever Extensometers. The mechanical lever was adopted at an early date for magnification of strains. Two general types may be discerned: (1) instruments in which the lever system was

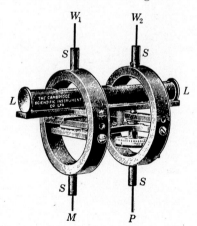

FIG. 3-13.   Searle's Apparatus for Measuring Extension of Wire

actuated through members attached to the specimen, and (2) instruments in which one of the contact points on the specimen served also as a fulcrum, or pivot, of a lever.

Type 1 is illustrated by the instrument shown in Fig. 3-14. This instrument was patented in 1883 and used by Col. W. H. Paine in tests made at the East River Bridge, New York. It utilized a single lever for multiplication of the motion between two sliding bars clipped to the specimen, attained a magnification of 100, and had a probable accuracy of 0.0008 in.

Other instruments of this type are: The Benjamin extensometer (Fig. 3-15) in use about 1895; the Busby Hairline Extensometer (Fig. 3-16) in use about 1907; Strohmeyer's Roller Extensometer, described in 1886; and, those designed by Kennedy, Goodman, Wicksteed, Ashcroft, and Dupuy.

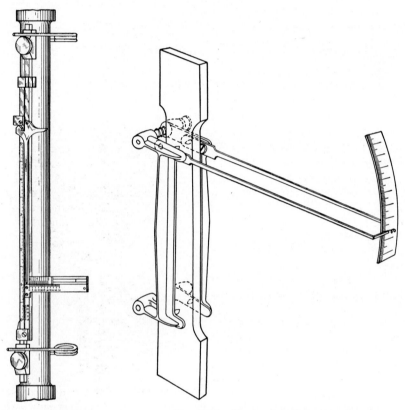

FIG. 3-14. Paine's
Extensometer

FIG. 3-15.   Benjamin's Extensometer

The Strohmeyer instrument, shown in Fig. 3-17, is of interest because of its pioneer applications in the measurement of structural strains resulting from live loads. Bridge members and ship and boiler shells were included in the structures studied. The wire, which was rotated by the relative motion of two frame members attached to the testpiece (being rolled between them) was the basis for the magnification system.

The wire was 0.015 in. in circumference and carried a light pointer which indicated the strain directly on a scale. The scale was graduated in 150 divisions, each corresponding to 0.0001 in. of motion. Apparently considerable difficulty was experienced in the installation and use of the instrument. Some investigators expressed doubts concerning its accuracy.

Instruments of type 2 are illustrated by the extensometer which was designed by Kennedy about 1890 and later modified by Martens. The principles of operation may be seen in Fig. 3-18. The main frame, which is fastened to the testpiece with a pair of pointed screws, supports the graduated scales and two bar springs, which extend parallel to the testpiece. Small rhomb-shaped levers are held firmly against the specimen by the opposite pair of bar springs. Lightweight pointers, attached to the rhombs, indicate strain on the graduated scales, with a magnification of 50:1.

Capp's Multiplying Divider (Fig. 3-19) should be mentioned in this group. Although intended for qualitative indication of yield point rather than quantitative strain measurement, it is of interest for its simplicity. The pointed ends of the short levers are held manually in gage marks spaced 2 in. apart. Strain is magnified 10:1 on the graduated scale.

9. Compound-Magnification Systems. In general, the self-contained mechanical instrument can be installed and used with greater ease than the optical type. To meet the demand for greater sensitivity, while retaining the advantage of relative ease of applying the mechanical gage, compound magnification was introduced.

The Berry strain gage (Fig. 3-20), was developed about 1910. It consisted of a frame with two conically pointed contact points. One point was rigidly

FIG. 3-16. Busby Hairline Extensometer Developed about 1907 (Courtesy Riehle Testing Machine Division, American Machine & Metals)

fixed to the frame, while the other was pivoted from the frame and was integral with a lever arm, which alone magnified the strain about 5:1. A screw micrometer was used to measure the motion of the arm, thus permitting measurements of strain to the nearest 0.0002 in. with a 0.001-in. micrometer. However, variations of micrometer contact pressure and seating of the conical points in holes marking the gage length probably reduced the accuracy to about 0.0006 in.

The Hurst–Tomlinson Extensometer (Fig. 3-21) patented in 1918 is another

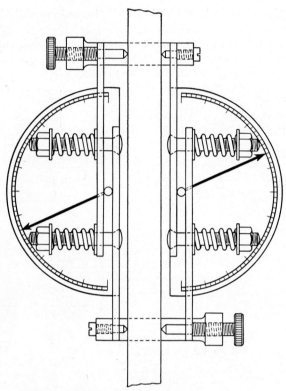

FIG. 3-17.   Strohmeyer's Roller Extensometer.

FIG. 3-18.   Lever Extensometer

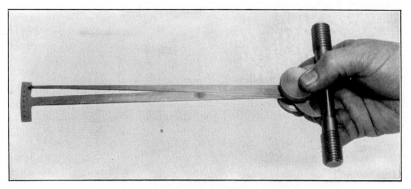

FIG. 3-19. Capp's Multiplying Divider Developed about 1907

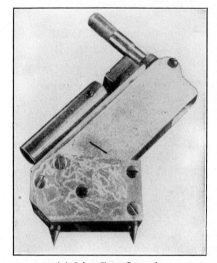

(*a*) 2-in. Gage Length.

(*b*) 8-in. Gage Length.

FIG. 3-20.   Early Models of the Berry Strain Gage Exhibited about 1910 (Courtesy
Prof H. C. Berry)

illustration of a compound system. It consists of frames A and B, which are attached to the specimen's axis, each by a pair of pointed screws; lever G; and dial indicator C. Frames A and B are joined at D and E by an elastic hinge (which is defined as a slender flexible spring offering little resistance to

bending while simultaneously restraining the relative motion between two parts to one or more directions). Elongation of the specimen causes a rotation of B relative to A. Lever G is actuated by the motion of B and, in turn, moves the dial indicator spindle through a distance equivalent to approximately ten times the elongation. An accuracy of 0.00002 in. was claimed for the instrument, but this figure seems questionable.

10. Recording Instruments. Autographic recording of load-deformation relations probably dates to R. H. Thurston's recorder for torsion, described in 1874. Since that time a variety of instruments have been devised for recording data from laboratory test specimens and structures. The early efforts naturally were directed towards laboratory investigations, in which

Fig. 3-21.   Hurst–Tomlinson Extensometer

the interest was primarily concerned with determining the relation between force and deformation. Most of these instruments were designed primarily for use on tension test bars and featured some means for magnifying the strain. Instruments for use on structural members were designed to record strain only.

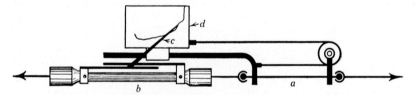

Fig. 3-22.   Kennedy–Ashcroft Autographic Recorder

In 1886 Professor Kennedy and A. G. Ashcroft announced the instrument shown in Fig. 3-22. The load was indicated by the calibrated bar b, whose elongation rotated pointer c in angular proportion to the load. Elongation of test bar a was given a multiplication of 2:1 by means of the chord and pulley arrangement and was recorded as the motion of smoked-glass plate d with respect to pointer c. The recording appeared as a scratched line in the smoke. The load ordinates were necessarily curved. Further magnification was obtained through photographic enlargement of the marked glass plate.

Under the auspices of the American Society of Civil Engineers' special committee on stresses in railroad tracks, the stremmatograph (Fig. 3-23) was developed about 1915. It was patterned to some extent after an instrument developed by Dr. P. H. Dudley about 1898 and was intended primarily for strain measurements in the lower flanges of railroad rails under the action of live loads.

Frames A and B are connected to the lower flange by contact points P_1, P_2, P_3, and P_4 and are prevented from rotation about these points by screws S_1, S_2, S_3, and S_4. The bars N are fixed in frame A with setscrews and terminate in spherical ends which slide in the guide sleeves of frame B. Elastic-hinge plates inserted in bars N maintain the proper contact pressure of the phonograph needle L, against a smoked-glass disk, D, where the strain is recorded without magnification. The disk was rotated by shaft H to correlate the strain magnitude with time. The unique mounting for the phonograph needle was devised to minimize the effect of vibration.

In the early Riehle apparatus shown in Fig. 3-24, the force–deformation relation was recorded on a drum, the load ordinate being vertical, parallel to the drum's axis. Load measurements were transmitted directly from the crank H (which turned the screw moving the balance poise) through bevel gears to screw V, which moved the recording pen vertically. Elongation of the specimen between collars C_1 and C_2 was transmitted from the gear rack on the slide collar C, successively, through pinion P, the shaft, and the universal joints and bevel gears, to appear somewhat magnified as rotation of the drum. The apparatus appearing at the lower right of the figure was designed to control automatically and electrically the motion of the balance poise. Necessarily the results obtained with this apparatus were affected by the inertia of the testing machine's members, particularly the balance beam.

The instrument illustrated in Fig. 3-25 was developed about 1907 by the University of Wisconsin. Designed primarily for obtaining strain–time curves in bridge members, the strain, magnified 50:1 by a simple lever, was recorded on a strip of paper actuated by a clock-driven drum.

The gage length was established between the clamp shown at the left end and a second clamp (not shown) attached to the connecting rod shown on the right end. The connecting rod extended through the instrument and terminated with a hook which caused a rotation of the spindle (see detail at extreme left). A lightweight magnifying arm, which was fixed to the spindle, was thus actuated and in turn moved the pencil along a guide perpendicular to the paper's motion.

The instrument was used for comparing the strains resulting from the live load of a moving train with those observed for the static load of the same train. In this manner, ratios of the effect of moving load to static load were obtained without direct calibration of the instrument.

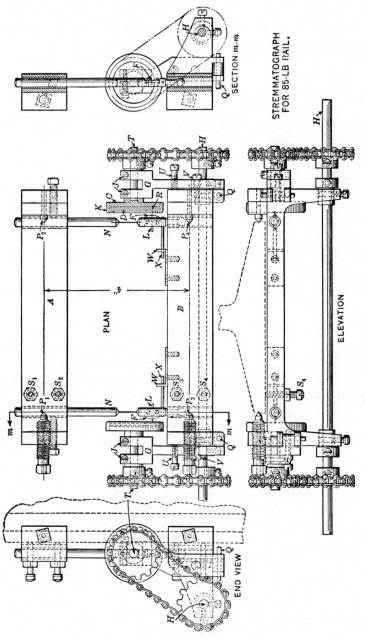

Fig. 3-23.   The Stremmatograph

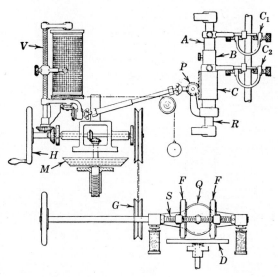

FIG. 3-24.   The Riehle Autographic Recorder (Courtesy Riehle Testing Machine
Division, American Machine & Metals)

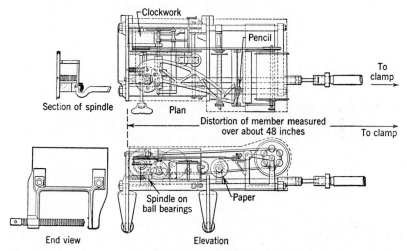

FIG. 3-25.   University of Wisconsin Recording Extensometer (Courtesy Dean
M. O. Withey)

Although the Dalby Stress–Strain Recorder (Fig. 3-26) could be more
properly classed as optical, it is included in this section because of its compact
and self-contained form.   Load measurement is accomplished by means of
the calibrated hollow steel bar W, which is held in the upper head of the testing
machine.   The mirror M, supported at three points, rotates about axis ab
in proportion to the load.   Elongation of the test bar is transmitted through

levers G, L, and link U, appearing as rotation of mirror N about an axis perpendicular to axis ab. Light from source Z passes through prism Q, is reflected from mirror M (which is rotated in proportion to the load), thence is reflected from mirror N (which is rotated in proportion to elongation), and appears on film P as a continuous record of the load–deformation relations. The inertia effect was very small and, it was claimed, could not be detected even in tests performed at such speeds as to be of only a few seconds duration.

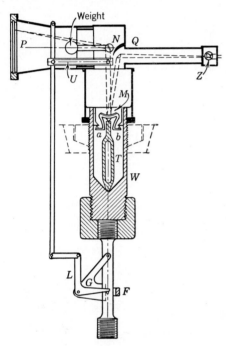

FIG. 3-26. Dalby's Optical Recorder (Courtesy Sir Isaac Pitman & Sons, Ltd)

K. MODERN INSTRUMENTS FOR INDICATING STRAIN AND SMALL MOTION

11. Compound-Lever Magnification. The Huggenberger Tensometer is a lightweight self-contained instrument, relying solely on a compound-lever system for magnification. Five models are available, some for specialized applications, having magnifications of 300 to 2000, depending on the model. The gage length is fixed on most models at either ½ in. or 1 in. but may be extended by means of a bar, carrying a stationary contact point, which is clamped to the gage frame. One model (Fig. 3-27) is provided with a variable gage length controlled by a micrometer screw.

Figure 3-28 illustrates diagrammatically the operation of the instruments. Frame C supports the lever system, including the fixed-contact point a and rhomb b which serves dually as part of the lever system and as a contact point. Rhomb b is integral with the arm h. Its rotation, resulting from the motion Δl, magnifies the motion and transmits it, through link i, to the pointer g, where further magnification occurs. The readings taken from scale z are converted to actual strain values by application of the multiplication factor, which is established for each instrument by calibration. Normal wear or abusive use necessitate recalibration at intervals.

The screw q, by moving the pointer's pivot, provides a means for resetting the pointer during measurement of large strains.

Mounting may be accomplished with clamp, spring, or screw pressure on the frame to hold points a and b in contact with the testpiece. However, a spring pressure mounting is most desirable. Excessive mounting pressure may damage the instrument or cause nicks in the testpiece which might prove detrimental if fatigue stresses are involved. However, sufficient pressure must be provided to prevent slippage of the contact points under the action of operational forces.

Despite elaborate precautions in mounting, a "lag" usually attributed to slippage, is characteristic of the instrument. Although the lag may be of little consequence in large strains, serious errors may result in the measurement of small strains. Vibration of the gage by means of a light buzzer has been recommended to minimize the lag effect. This is important in rosette measurement where an error, in the minimum strain especially, may cause serious error in the calculated results.

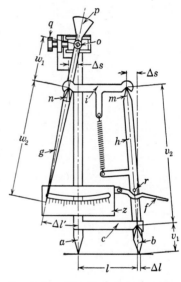

Fig. 3-27. Huggenberger Tensometer with Variable Gage Length (Courtesy Dr A. U. Huggenberger)

Fig. 3-28. The Huggenberger Tensometer Lever System (Courtesy Dr A. U. Huggenberger)

Position of mounting has also been observed to exert an effect on the instrument's accuracy.

In general, excellent results may be obtained, in measurement of static strains, by a skilled operator. Inexperienced operators usually find difficulty in mounting the instrument, which is augmented by its relatively great length perpendicular to the testpiece. Although the instrument's weight is small and the force required to operate its levers is likewise small, its usefulness for measurement of rapidly applied strain is rather limited, particularly if the specimen under study is subject to motion.

In some instruments, the lever system is inclosed and reasonably weatherproofed to permit outdoor application.

TYPICAL SPECIFICATIONS (TYPE-*A* GAGE)

Multiplication: 1200 (approx.)
Gage lengths: 1 in., convertible to ½ in.
Scale: 38 divisions of 0.05 in. each
Strain range: 0.004 in. (without resetting)
Dimensions: 6½ in. × 2¹⁄₁₆ in. width × ⅝ in. depth
Weight: 2½ oz

Dr. Huggenberger has employed the compound-lever system in another instrument, called the *Tensotast*, which permits separation of bending strains from direct strains, by measuring the effect of curvature in the testpiece.

FIG. 3-29.   The Porter-Lipp Strain Gage (Courtesy P. L. Porter)

Another instrument of the general type employing compound levers is the Porter–Lipp gage shown in Fig. 3-29.   For many applications its compactness and extreme light weight would prove advantageous.   It has a self-contained scale and requires calibration.   In mounting and operation it is very similar to the Huggenberger.

SPECIFICATIONS

Gage length: 1 in.
Magnification: 300 (approx.)
Accuracy: 0.000 02 in.*
Range: 0.0004 in. (approx.) without resetting
Dimensions: 1¾ in. length × 2 in. × ⅝ in. depth
Weight: 0.4 oz
* Manufacturer's specification.

12. Magnification by Means of Gears.   A most important class of instruments, employing gear magnification for measuring small motions accurately, has been developed in the form of the dial indicator or dial gage.   Figure 3-30 illustrates the typical mechanism employed.   These instruments have been favored for many applications because of their compactness, ease of application, and accuracy.   For strain measurement, dial indicators have been used frequently in conjunction with lever systems, although many instruments incorporating them depend only on the indicator for magnification.

In general, a dial indicator consists of an encased gear train actuated by a rack cut in the spindle, which follows the motion to be measured.   A spring imposes a spindle force of about 1 to 3 oz to maintain a reasonably uniform and positive contact with the moving part.   The train terminates with a lightweight pointer which indicates spindle travel on a graduated dial. Lost motion in the train is minimized by the positive force of a small coil spring.

The American Gage Design Committee, in cooperation with the U. S. Bureau of Standards, the American Standards Association, and others, has established certain external dimensions as standard, but details of the gage's internal mechanism are left to the choice of the individual manufacturer.

Most manufacturers build dial indicators to conform with specifications for accuracy issued by the Bureau of Standards.   The accuracy generally specified for a gage graduated in 0.0001-in. divisions requires that it read correctly within 1.5 divisions any of several designated increments of spindle travel.   The specifications further require that the reading, on return of the

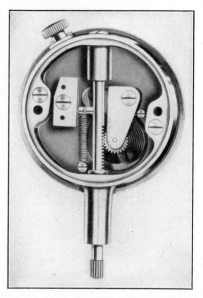

Fig. 3-30.   Dial Indicator Mechanism (Courtesy Standard Gage Co)

spindle, vary less than 0.75 division from the previous one observed at the same increment.   Thus the maximum probable error would be 0.000 225 in. including backlash.

Many excellent gages of this type are available from several companies, including Standard Gage Company, B. C. Ames Company, Federal Products Corporation, and the L. S. Starrett Company.   The term "least graduation" or "least count" is used to describe the smallest division of the scale.   The usual least graduations are 0.001, 0.0005, and 0.0001 in. and the usual range is 0.100 to 0.250 in., although some special gages are available with a range up to 6 in. and a least graduation of 0.001 in.

The "Last Word" Indicator, furnished by the L. S. Starrett Company, has been used considerably in extensometers because of its extreme compactness, light weight (about 1½ oz), and accuracy.   Most models have a range of about 0.02 to 0.03 in. and a least graduation of 0.001 in.   However, one model is graduated to 0.0001 in. with a range of 0.024 in.

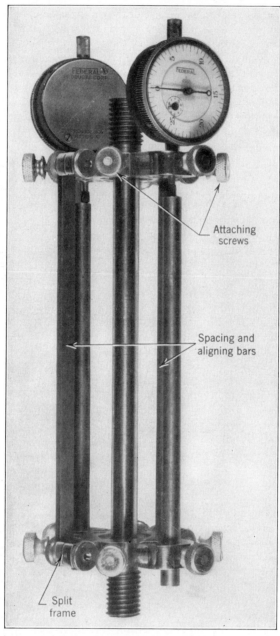

Fig. 3-31.   Dial Indicators Employed for Direct Measurement of Strain (Courtesy Prof P. C. Huntly)

13. Direct Measurement of Strain with Dial Indicators. Many extensometers utilize the dial indicator directly for strain measurement, as illustrated in Fig. 3-31. Such extensometers usually employ two or more dial indicators mounted in a frame which is attached to the testpiece. A second frame is similarly mounted, at a set gage length (usually 8 in.) and their relative motion measured as the strain. The frames usually are secured to the specimen by means of pointed screws or "knife-edge" contacts. Reasonable accuracy in measuring unit strains can be obtained using a 0.0001-in. indicator, because of the relatively large gage length.

Gages mounted in this manner are generally useless for measuring plastic strains, because the rapid decrease in diameter, which accompanies yielding

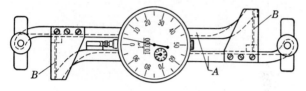

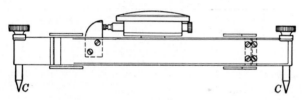

Fig. 3-32. The Whittemore Fulcrum-Plate Strain Gage (Courtesy Baldwin Southwark Division, Baldwin Locomotive Works)

of the specimen, results in loosening of at least one of the frames. This suggests the desirability of a spring force in mounting instruments for measurement of plastic deformation.

The Whittemore gage (Fig. 3-32) is a self-contained instrument consisting essentially of two frame members A bound together by two elastic hinges B for parallel frictionless motion. One 45° conical contact point C is attached to each frame member. For strain measurements, the contact points are inserted into drilled holes defining a predetermined gage length. Motion between the two frame members, or strain, is measured directly with a dial indicator.

In another model, not shown, the frames A have been replaced by two coaxial tubes connected with a pair of elastic hinges, and, since the gage is intended for repeated measurement at a series of stations rather than for fixed mounting at one station, consideration has been given to controlling accidental longitudinal forces which might be applied by the operator. A handle, serving doubly as a shield against temperature change and as an aid to uniform seating of the points, is attached to the gage by means of two elastic hinges. These hinges prevent application of excessive longitudinal forces. A force of about 5 lb is recommended for properly seating the points in the drilled holes. The holes are reamed slightly to an angle of 60°, providing a reasonably definite line of contact with the 45° gage points.

Seating the gage is one of the chief sources of error. Other sources of error arise from the dial indicator, measurement of a chord rather than an arc length, and temperature changes. However, the effect of temperature change is practically eliminated by the use of an Invar tube for the inner tube of the coaxial pair. The use of Invar necessitates a reference reading on a

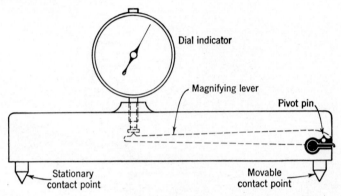

Fig. 3-33.   The Berry Strain Gage (Courtesy Prof H. C. Berry)

standard unstressed bar, placed in the immediate vicinity of each station, with each measurement on the station. Accuracies of 0.00002 unit strain have been reported in field use of the 10 in. gage.

Manufacturer's Nominal Specifications

Gage length: 2 in., 10 in., or to order (above 2 in. length)
Sensitivity: 5:100,000
Accuracy: 0.0002 in. (approx.)
Range: 0.100 in.
Size: $1\frac{3}{4}$ in. $\times$ $3\frac{1}{2}$ in. $\times$ 15 in. (approx.)
Weight: 2 lb (approx.)

The initial instrument was designed for the committee on arch dam investigation of the Engineering Foundation, by Professor H. L. Whittemore of the National Bureau of Standards.

14. Combination of Levers with Dial Gages. The Berry Strain Gage (Fig. 3-33) was one of the first instruments designed primarily for measurements on structures to be widely used and was only an improvement of the original designs shown in Fig. 3-20.

The lever system illustrated is basically identical with that of the original gage developed by Professor H. C. Berry. However, a dial indicator replaces the micrometer. Intended for use at several stations rather than for fixed mounting at one station, the contact points must be inserted in carefully prepared holes marking the gage length. Correction must be made for temperature changes. This is usually accomplished by reference readings on an unstressed bar of similar material to the structure, which is placed in the near vicinity of the measurements. The holes are carefully drilled with a no. 58 drill, spaced at the gage length with close tolerance. They are then countersunk slightly with a 60° conical cutter. Thus a reasonably dependable contact is defined, by the intersection of the drilled hole and the tapered countersink, for seating the gage's conical contact points.

If an indicator graduated to 0.0001 in. is used, strain may be measured to 0.000 01 in. The accuracy of this type of gage, however, depends largely

FIG. 3-34. Special Adjustable Extensometer (Courtesy Tinius Olsen Testing Machine Co)

on the operator's skill and consistency. With exercise of reasonable care, average field measurements should be accurate to 0.0001 in.

Other instruments using this principle are available under other trade names. Longer contact legs are featured on some of the newer instruments to permit measurements on reinforcing bars in concrete.

The Olsen Special Extensometer, Fig. 3-34, is a very compact and convenient instrument for laboratory use. Combining a lever and a Last Word Indicator, the strain in the 2-in. gage length may be read to the nearest 0.0001 in. The lever, visible at the left inside the case, serves also as a knife-edge contact. A fixed knife-edge is provided at the right. It contacts the side of the specimen opposite the lever contact and is spaced a distance of 2 in. axially therefrom. Thus the knife contacts, acting on opposite sides of the specimen, should give an average of the strain values on the two sides with only one gage reading. A cantilever spring acting on the specimen opposite each knife-edge provides the necessary mounting force and contact pressure.

The frame is constructed to permit rapid and easy mounting to the specimen. One available model is adjustable to permit use on specimens ranging from $\frac{1}{16}$ in. to 0.505 in. in diameter. Specifications are:

> Gage length: 2 in.
> Sensitivity: 0.000 05 in.
> Accuracy: 0.0001 in. (approx.)
> Dimensions: $2\frac{3}{8}$ in. $\times$ $1\frac{3}{4}$ in. $\times$ $\frac{7}{8}$ in.
> Weight: 12 oz

15. The Mikrokator. The Mikrokator* (Fig. 3-35), developed by C. E. Johansson, utilizes a principle uncommon in strain gages. The amplification unit is a thin metal strip of rectangular cross section (1) which is twisted

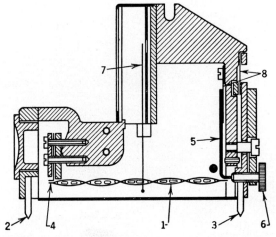

Fig. 3-35.   The Johansson Mikrokator (Courtesy Swedish Gage Co of America)

symmetrically on each side of the pointer attached to its middle and is held at its ends under a tensile force. Variation of the tensile force results in additional twisting or untwisting of the two halves of the strip, with resultant rotation of the pointer. Within reasonable limits, the rotation is proportional to the change in tensile force.

One end of the twisted strip (1) is held by an adjustable bracket (4). The other end is attached to a cantilever spring (5) which applies a continuous tensile force on the strip. Knife-edge (2) is fixed, while edge (3) is mounted to an assembly which is constrained to move parallel to the direction of strain by the elastic hinges (8). Pointer (7) is attached to the twisted strip, and indicates strain values on a calibrated scale. Screw (6) permits adjustment of the tension in the strip.

The instrument is extremely sensitive and essentially frictionless and requires very little force to operate. Necessarily, its working parts are delicate, although it is represented as being protected sufficiently for outdoor

---

* Distributed by the Swedish Gage Company of America.

exposure and as being sufficiently rugged for application to structures such as bridges. In any case its use in the laboratory as a precision instrument for static strain measurement should only be limited by physical dimensions, difficulty of mounting, or its weight. Normally the instrument is held in place by means of a light clamping force. The mounting clamp must have

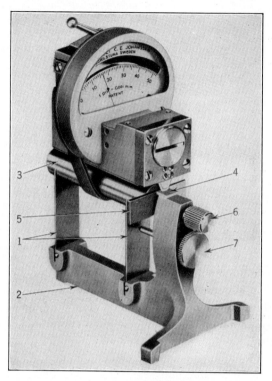

FIG. 3-36.   Method of Calibration with Precision Gage Blocks (Courtesy Swedish Gage Co of America)

sufficient spring action to maintain mounting force despite dimensional changes.

Several models are available, but only the specifications for the least sensitive and the most sensitive of the large size are given here.

MANUFACTURER'S SPECIFICATIONS

	Most Sensitive	Least Sensitive
Gage length	2 in.	2 in.
Least graduation	0.000 01 in.	0.0005 in.
Range	0.0005 in.	0.02 in.

Figure 3-36 shows one of the instruments mounted in a calibration jig and illustrates the method of using precision gage blocks for such calibration.

L. Recording Instruments

16. The DeForest Scratch Recording Strain Gage.   This gage is intended
for recording dynamic strains occurring in structures and moving machine
parts.   No provision is made, within the instrument, for magnification of the
motions, but the record may be examined at a convenient magnification by
means of a microscope.   Several advantages for numerous applications arise

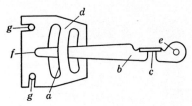

FIG. 3-37a.   The DeForest Scratch Recording Strain Gage (Courtesy Baldwin
Southwark Division, Baldwin Locomotive Works)

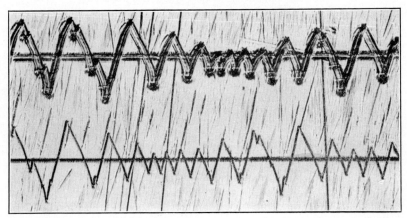

FIG. 3-37b.   Magnified Strain Record (Courtesy Baldwin Southwark Division,
Baldwin Locomotive Works)

from the instrument's light weight, simplicity, ease of installation and operation, and small operational force.

The instrument (Fig. 3-37a) consists of two parts: a target, and a scratch
arm.   These parts may be secured to the test piece by screw, solder, or clamp
applied at g and e.   The target is a small plate with a chromium-plated surface
and includes a raised clip arm a.   The scratch arm b is pivoted at the elastic
hinge c and carries, at f, several grit particles embedded in cured rubber.

Motion between e and g is recorded as scratches made by the grit particles
f on the chromium-plated target.   Propulsion of the scratch arm across the
target is accomplished by the spring action of the elastic hinge c.   The cross
motion is regulated by the pressure of clip a on arm b.   This pressure develops
sufficient static friction to restrain the arm, but cross motion is permitted by

the smaller sliding friction, which results from relative motion of the target and arm as the testpiece is strained.   The rate of the scratch-arm cross travel is a function of the sliding motion occurring, rather than of time.   It can be controlled by variation of the clip pressure and the thickness of the spring hinge.

Figure 3-37*b* illustrates the type of record obtained.   The several grit particles scratch patterns of varying depth, depending on the alignment of target and arm.   Of course, the most clearly defined pattern is used for interpreting the record.   The base line is established by moving the arm across the target while the testpiece is in an unloaded condition.

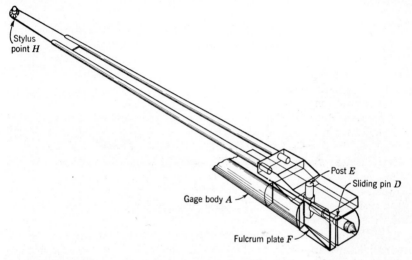

FIG. 3-38.   Recording Strain Gage Employing a Simple Lever (Courtesy Public Roads Administration)

Reliable results are reported at strain rates approaching sonic speed.   The gage seems to be little affected by its own inertia forces.   Readings may be estimated to 0.0001 in.

MANUFACTURER'S SPECIFICATIONS

Gage length: 2 in.
Sensitivity: 0.0001 in.
Accuracy: 0.0002 in. (approx.)
Range: 0.050 in.
Weight: 2 oz

17. Recording Strain Gage Employing a Simple Lever.   Figure 3-38 illustrates Teller's improved model of an instrument developed about 1923, by Goldbeck of the U. S. Bureau of Public Roads.   The instrument was designed particularly for application to concrete roads and structures.   One of the most interesting features of the present instrument is the method used to correct automatically for thermal changes of the concrete testpiece.

The Invar steel gage body A extends to the vicinity of the stylus H where it supports a smoked-glass plate and terminates with a fixed conical point, which firmly contacts a lug set in the concrete. Pin D, which slides in the gage body, is seated firmly against another lug set in the concrete, establishing a 6-in. gage length. Post E is rigidly fixed to the stylus support block and exposes a vertical knife-edge to the horizontal motion of the sliding pin with which it is in contact. The stylus support block, thus actuated by D, rotates about a vertical axis through the elastic hinge F and imparts a magnified motion to stylus H. Strain is recorded on the glass plate. The plate may be moved manually in a longitudinal direction, by means of a capstan nut, to permit recording the results of several loadings.

Correction of measurements for temperature change is accomplished in the stylus support arm. Materials for each of the rods in the arm is such that the difference in the thermal expansion of the two tend to correct for the dimension change in the concrete. However, considerable error still could arise in the event of sudden change in atmospheric temperature, since the metal gage parts would change temperature more rapidly than a relatively large body of concrete.

The magnification obtained with the gage is approximately 60. Further magnification may be obtained by projection of the recording on a screen. For example, a projection ratio of 30 would give an over-all magnification of 1800. The strain could then be measured with reasonable accuracy to the nearest 0.000 03 in. The instrument was tested for accuracy by imposing several successive displacements of 0.0010 in. and checking the scribed record. Ten such check tests indicated a maximum deviation of 5.7 per cent and an average deviation of 1.6 per cent.

18. Goodyear Stress Change Recorder. Instruments which record strain variations by marks on tape or by scratches on targets are suitable for observations lasting a few minutes or at most a few hours. For longer periods, perhaps extending to months and years, the mere interpretation of the miles of records, not to speak of the maintenance, would become prohibitive.

The Goodyear Stress Change Recorder is designed for observation over periods of *any* length, of the stress variations in machines or structures such as aircraft, automobiles, bridges, and ships, subjected to varying and generally unpredictable forces imposed by weather, road conditions, volume and frequency of traffic, wave action, and a variety of other uncontrollable conditions. The instrument records the maximum stresses ever experienced by the member to which it is attached and counts the number of repetitions of stress changes occurring in each of six predetermined ranges. Methods have been developed by which the data so obtained may be applied to prediction of life expectancy of the member.

Essentially, the instrument, Fig. 3-39*b*, consists of a frame and a slide which are attached to the specimen at opposite ends of the gage length as shown. Motion between the slide and the frame, representing strains taking place in the specimen, is magnified by arm r rotating the lever about the pivot. Pawls attached at various points to the lever, thus having different mechanical

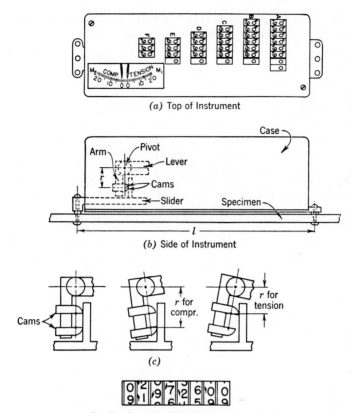

(a) Top of Instrument

(b) Side of Instrument

(c)

Reading from the right end, the arrows show
whether top or bottom figure is to be read when
two complete figures are visible.
Correct reading above is: (0)1,972,600

(d)

Fig. 3-39. The Goodyear Stress Change Recorder (Courtesy Goodyear Aircraft
Corp)

(a) Top of instrument showing maximum tensile and compressive strain indicators and arrangement of counters

(b) Side of instrument

(c) Cam arrangement for weighting the effect of mixed tensile and compressive
stresses

(d) Method for reading the continuous counter

advantages, actuate ratchet wheels (not shown). Each ratchet wheel is connected to a separate counting device and is provided with a friction brake to
prevent backward motion.

The value of the minimum stress change which will operate each counting
device depends on the magnification of the stress and is a function of the
length of the arm (r), the gage length l, the spacing of the ratchet wheel

teeth, the location of the pawl, and the specimen's modulus of elasticity E. This smallest stress change recorded may be expressed as

$$\Delta\sigma = K\left(E\,\frac{r}{l}\right)$$

where K is a constant for each counter, which depends on the pawl location and the ratchet tooth size, having the values given in Table 3-1.

The different ratchet wheels are designed so that each successive value of $\Delta\sigma$ recorded is about 1.5 times the value for the preceding wheel. Each wheel, of course, records the occurrences of not only the minimum stress change for which it was designed but all greater stress changes as well. However, the frequency of each stress change can readily be calculated from the data from all the wheels taken together.

No provision is made for distinguishing tensile from compressive stresses in the total number counted. However, if both tensile and compressive stresses occur promiscuously, compensation may be made for difference in sensitivity of the material to tensile and compressive stresses. Compressive stresses usually exert a smaller effect on fatigue life than tensile stresses of equal value, and they may be weighted, by using a greater arm r length (Fig. 3-39c), so that they will be recorded as equivalent tensile stresses.

A simple gear train operating a continuous counter was employed rather than the ordinary discontinuous type of counter which requires considerably more torque to operate, especially when several numbers are changing simultaneously. The maximum stress recorder incorporated in the instrument utilizes very lightweight sliders or pointers which are pushed only in one direction, in proportion to the strain. Their motion in the opposite direction is prevented by friction. They indicate the maximum tensile and compressive stresses occurring (Fig. 3-39a) since the instrument was installed or reset.

The counting devices for the six different ratchet wheels are designated by letters A to F, inclusive. Descriptive data for the instrument are given in Table 3-1.

Data obtained with this instrument may be prepared for analysis as follows: Let the number of cycles indicated by counters A, B, etc., be designated by N_a, N_b, etc. Since each ratchet wheel records all stress changes larger than the minimum stress change that it was designed to be rotated by, the number of cycles occurring in each range $\Delta\sigma_a$ to $\Delta\sigma_b$, $\Delta\sigma_b$ to $\Delta\sigma_c$, etc. are determined as functions of *differences* in successive counter readings, and are designated as N_{ab}, N_{bc}, etc. N_{ab}, N_{bc}, etc. are defined as the actual number of stress changes having magnitudes between $\Delta\sigma_a$ and $\Delta\sigma_b$, $\Delta\sigma_b$ and $\Delta\sigma_c$, etc., respectively. N_{fm} designates the number of cycles having magnitudes between $\Delta\sigma_f$ and the stress change $\Delta\sigma_m = (\sigma_{m1} - \sigma_{m2})$ given by scales M_1 and M_2. Approximate relations for computing N_{ab}, N_{ac}, etc., are given in Table 3-1. These relations were derived by assuming that the number of cycles are evenly distributed over each interval, and that N_b is small with respect to N_a, etc. The finite differences between the stress changes operating the different counters would be a source of considerable error in measuring fluctuating stresses of nearly constant value, but a high degree of accuracy can be expected when a diverse variety of stress fluctuations is involved, as in applications for which the instrument is intended.

TABLE 3-1

DESCRIPTIVE DATA FOR THE GOODYEAR STRESS CHANGE RECORDER

Counting Device	Number of Cycles Recorded without Repetition	K	Indicated Number of Cycles	Stress Change Which Just Operates Counting Device for: $E = 10^7$ psi, $r = 0.41$ in., $l = 5\frac{1}{2}$ in.	Actual Number of Cycles of Stress Change Between $\Delta\sigma_a$ and $\Delta\sigma_b$, $\Delta\sigma_b$ and $\Delta\sigma_c$, etc., as Indicated by the Brackets
A	10^8	0.008	N_a	$\Delta\sigma_a = 6000$ lb/in.^{2}	$N_{ab} = N_a - 1.3N_b$
B	10^7	0.012	N_b	$\Delta\sigma_b = 9000$ lb/in.^{2}	$N_{bc} = N_b - 1.3N_c$
C	10^6	0.018	N_c	$\Delta\sigma_c = 13,500$ lb/in.^{2}	$N_{cd} = N_c - 1.3N_d$
D	10^5	0.027	N_d	$\Delta\sigma_d = 20,200$ lb/in.^{2}	$N_{de} = N_d - 1.3N_e$
E	10^4	0.041	N_e	$\Delta\sigma_e = 30,700$ lb/in.^{2}	$N_{ef} = N_e - 1.3N_f$
F	10^3	0.062	N_f	$\Delta\sigma_f = 46,400$ lb/in.^{2}	$N_{fm} = N_f - 1$
M_1		0.007	1	$\Delta\sigma_m = (\sigma_{m_1} - \sigma_{m_2})$	
M_2		0.008			

A simple interpretation of the data, sufficiently accurate for most purposes, may be achieved by plotting the quantities:

$$\tfrac{1}{2}(\Delta\sigma_b + \Delta\sigma_a), \quad \tfrac{1}{2}(\Delta\sigma_c + \Delta\sigma_b), \quad \text{etc.}$$

against the quantities:

$$\frac{N_{ab}}{N_{ab}'(\Delta\sigma_b - \Delta\sigma_a)}, \quad \frac{N_{bc}}{N_{bc}'(\Delta\sigma_c - \Delta\sigma_b)}, \quad \text{etc.}$$

N_{ab}' is the number of stress variations of magnitude $\frac{1}{2}(\Delta\sigma_b + \Delta\sigma_a)$, determined from an established S-N fatigue curve, Fig. 3-40a, for the material or type of built-up structure in question which would cause failure, and similarly for N_{bc}', etc. The area under a curve such as shown in Fig. 3-40b, drawn through the seven points thus obtained, should be a good approximation to the *proportion of total fatigue life* which the specimen has undergone at the time the instrument recordings are noted. The fatigue life of the member in question can be computed, in hours of operation time, as the reciprocal of the area under the curve, if the ordinates are calculated using n_{xy} (the number of stress changes per hour in each stress range) rather than N_{xy} (the total number of cycles observed).

Justification for thus superimposing parts of the fatigue life, experienced under various conditions, has been shown by Biezeno and Koch.* This procedure probably would be unjustified if some of the stresses were excessively high and caused appreciable plastic flow. However, a stress condition

* Experiments at Delft by Professor C. B. Biezeno and J. J. Koch, unpublished at the time of reporting.

of this type would be indicated by the maximum stress record and probably would justify redesign.

The instrument may be installed, as shown in Fig. 3-39b, by screwing or riveting directly to the specimen, or may be attached with special jaws or clamps as necessity dictates.   The arm r is adjusted to make the stress changes

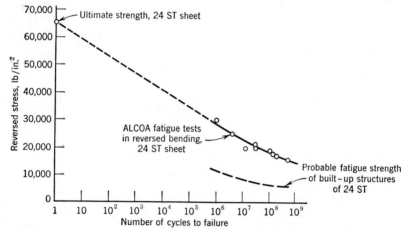

FIG. 3-40a.   S–N Curve (Courtesy Goodyear Aircraft Corp)

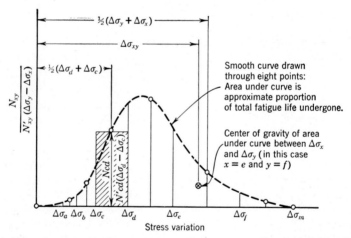

FIG. 3-40b.   Curve for Evaluating Fatigue Life (Courtesy Goodyear Aircraft Corp)

actuating the different counters cover the range of stresses which are expected actually to occur, or which the material can stand.   In installations on mild steel or other materials with a high modulus and low strength, the gage length may also have to be extended somewhat.

In mounting, care should be exercised to locate the movable mounting frame midway of its travel.   The maximum stress-indicating sliders should then be gently pushed into firm contact with their actuater and should appear as in Fig. 3-39a. Usage for measurement on aircraft has indicated that, once mounted properly, the instrument requires little or no attention except for reading, that the instrument's mechanical functioning is satisfactory, and that it is adequately durable. Interpretation of the data generally indicates that the instrument adequately covers the stress range for arriving at reasonably accurate "life" curves. The continuous counters necessitate the exercise of care in reading. Figure 3-39d illustrates the proper method for reading the instrument.

M. Instruments Using Other Mechanical Principles of Magnification

19. Magnification by an Acoustical Method. About 1933 Dr. O. Schaefer devised an instrument which employed vibrating strings. It depends on the

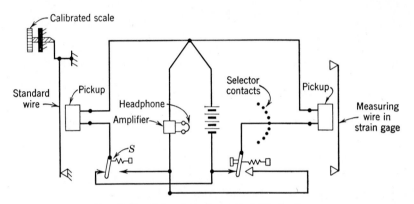

Fig. 3-41. Schaefer's Acoustical Strain Gage

property of strings by which the tensile force on the string governs its frequency of vibration. Figure 3-41 illustrates the operation of such a strain-measuring device.

Essentially, the strain gage is a wire, which is stretched between two supports affixed to the testpiece, and marking a nominal gage length. It also contains a magnetic "pickup" which plucks the wire and then transforms its mechanical vibration into electric impulses. Strain changes in the specimen impose proportional changes in the gage wire's tension. Interpretation is accomplished by comparing the tone, created by vibration of the gage wire, with the tone of a vibrating standard wire. The tension in the standard wire may be adjusted, by means of a calibrated screw, until its tone corresponds with that of the test gage. Matching of the tones is simplified and made more accurate by "tuning out" the beats which result when the vibration frequencies of the two wires are nearly the same.

The apparatus for interpreting the strain values which are indicated by vibration of the gage wires is assembled as a unit. It may be used in conjunction with several gages, successively, by means of a selector switch. It contains: a standard wire attached to a screw, which is calibrated to indicate the wire's tension; a battery, to energize the magnets which pluck the gage wires; a "pickup" unit for plucking the standard wire and transforming its vibrations into electric impulses; an amplifier unit; headphone or loudspeaker, to permit audible comparison of vibrations; and the necessary switches for controlling the circuits.   For convenience, the two switches shown may be incorporated in a double-pole double-throw switch, which in the contact position shown deflects the wires.   Moving the switch to the opposite contacts releases the wires, allowing them to vibrate, and places the audio system in the "pickup" circuit.   Calibration may be checked by placing a standard tuning fork in the circuit.

Although the instrument could not be readily applied to measurement of extremely short-duration stresses, it has been used for studying aircraft and bridge structures.   The average operator, after a little practice, requires 3 to 5 sec to obtain a strain reading.   The instrument's small mass and relative ease of operation after installation recommend it for many applications.   The use of wires having a termal expansion coefficient equal to that of the testpiece minimizes the effect of temperature change.   Instruments having gage lengths of 20, 120 and 150 mm have been used.   Only the specifications for the latter are given:

SPECIFICATIONS

Gage length: 5.9 in. (150 mm)
Calibration: 500 divisions (of 0.000 006 unit strain each)
Sensitivity: $\frac{1}{5}$ division (0.000 0012 unit strain)
Range: 0.0015 in.

20. Magnification by Pneumatic Flow through Orifices.   Pneumatic flow was used first for measurement of strain by Menneson about 1930.   His instrument utilized the pressure differential which exists in an air stream restricted by two successive orifices, one of which varies in size.   The instrument has been described as extremely sensitive, accurate, and easy to operate. Figure 3-42 shows schematically (1) the air supply and manometer, and (2) the extensometer and operation of the variable orifice.

The principle of operation is simple.   Air, under constant pressure H, flows through two orifices placed in series (the first and larger G being called the nozzle, and the second and smaller S being called the exhaust orifice).   The pressure h which prevails between these two orifices is a function of the ratio of their areas.   Consequently, if the nozzle G is of fixed dimensions and the exhaust orifice S is variable, the pressure h serves to measure the dimension of S.

The orifice may be varied in many ways.   For measuring length changes, two methods have been used satisfactorily.   One utilizes the motion being measured to lift a valve, which enlarges or constricts the orifice.   A second method depends on the relative displacement of the orifice, which is set in the end of the discharge tube, and a plate, perpendicular to the tube axis, against which the orifice discharges.

Air at constant pressure is usually furnished by means of a reducing valve. A differential manometer may be installed between the air supply, at pressure H, and the chamber between the orifices G and S, at pressure h, to measure the variation of orifice S. Experience has indicated that a magnification of the order of 100,000 may be obtained with this method under optimum conditions of operation.

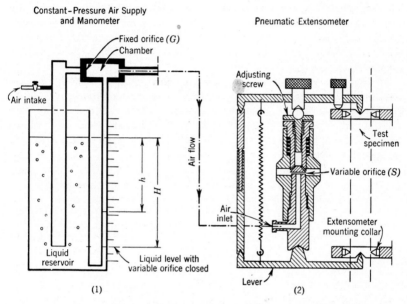

FIG. 3-42.   Extensometer Employing the Pneumatic Principle

The theory utilized in this instrument may be summarized briefly as follows, if air is assumed to be incompressible, and

G = nozzle orifice area

S = discharge orifice area

$C = C_G = C_S$ = coefficient of contraction, assumed to be the same for both orifices

ρ = density of air

g = acceleration of gravity

The flow through each orifice is the same; so:

$$CG \sqrt{2g(H - h)/\rho} = CS \sqrt{2gh/\rho}$$

whence

$$h = \frac{H}{1 + \dfrac{S^2}{G^2}}$$

Obviously, the function $h = f(S)$ is not linear.   However, it has an inflection point when $h/H = \frac{3}{4}$ or $S/G = 0.58$. Hence, for values in this neighborhood, the relation is very nearly linear.

An extensometer employing the pneumatic principle is shown in Fig. 3-42. The orifice S is located between two levers. One end of each of the levers is attached to a collar, which is mounted on the testpiece with a pair of pointed screws. At the opposite end, the levers are spaced apart at a fixed distance. The variable orifice mechanism, set between the two levers at their midspans, thus measures the specimen's elongation, reduced mechanically by a factor of $\frac{1}{2}$. If a nozzle diameter of 1.5 mm and a discharge orifice diameter of 0.45 mm are used, the magnification is greater than 7000. The weight of the complete extensometer is 1.34 oz.

Another application of this principle, for measurement of lateral contraction, attained a magnification of 130,000. The lever system, in this gage, amplified the strain rather than reduced it. It used a nozzle diameter of 1.5 mm and a discharge orifice diameter of 0.2 mm. However, it was found that dust particles may cause trouble by interfering with the flow through such small orifices. The weight of the gage was $\frac{1}{2}$ oz.

BIBLIOGRAPHY

General

1. A. F. C. Pollard, "The Mechanical Amplification of Small Displacements," *J Sci Instr*, v 15, 1938, pp 37–55.
2. F. G. Tatnall, "Strain Gages," *Product Eng*, v 1, n 4, pp 158–59, Apr 1930.
3. A. Thum, O. Swenson, and H. Weiss, "Neuzeitliche Dehnungsmessgeräte," *Forsch Ing-Wes*, v 9, n 5, pp 229–34, 1938.
4. Erich Siebel, *Handbuch der Werkstoffprüfung*, v 1 *Prüf-und Messeinrichtungen*, ch 6 "Messverfahren und Messeinrichtungen für Dehnungsmessungen" by Ernst Lehr, pp 462–571, Julius Springer, Berlin, 1940. Lithoprinted by Edwards Brothers, Ann Arbor, Mich, 1944.
5. E. Lehr, "Messgeräte für statische Dehnungsmessungen," *Archiv für Technisches Messen*, Lieferung 129, T25 and 26, 1942.

Lever Gages

6. H. L. Whittemore, "The Whittemore Strain Gage," *Instruments*, v 1, n 6, pp 299–300, June 1928.
7. T. R. Cuykendall and G. Winter, "Characteristics of Huggenberger Strain Gage," *Civil Eng (New York)*, v 10, n 7, pp 448–50, July 1940.

Dial Gages

8. R. L. Templin, article on errors in dialgages a discussion of the paper "The Strength of Cylindrical Dies," by G. Sachs and J. D. Lubdhn, *J Applied Mechanics*, Dec 1944, p A-246.

Recording Gages

9. M. Greenspan and L. R. Sweetman, "A Transfer Strain Gage for Large Strains," *J Research Nat Bur Standards*, v 34, n 6, pp 595–97, June 1945.
10. A. Friese, "Ritzgeräte zum Aufzeichen Schnellwechselnder Spannungen, Drucke, Kräfte," *Verein deutscher Ingenieure Zeitschrift*, v 82, n 16, pp 457–61, Apr 16, 1938.
11. R. L. Templin, "An Automatic Autographic Extensometer for Use in Tension Tests of Materials," *Proc ASTM*, v 32, pt 2, 1932, pp 783–92.

Acoustic Gages

12. N. DAVIDENKOFF, "The Vibrating-Wire Method of Measuring Deformation," *Proc ASTM*, v 34, pt 2, 1934, pp 847–60.
13. R. S. JERRETT, "The Acoustic Strain Gage," *J Sci Instr*, v 22, n 2, pp 29–34, Feb 1945.
14. "New Maihak Acoustical Strain Gage," *Instruments*, v 1, n 5, pp 251–52, Apr 1928.
15. "Akustischer Ferndehnungsmesser," *Zeitschrift Verein deutscher Ingenieure*, v 72, n 49, p 1810, Dec 8, 1928.
16. H. HOFFMANN, "Genaue Dehnungs-und Spannungs-messungen," *Bauingenieur*, v 11, n 18, pp 312–15, May 2, 1930.

Pneumatic Gages

17. H. De LEIRIS, "Sur la mesure des constantes élastiques par amplification pneumatique des déformations," *Proc 5th Int Congress Applied Mechanics*, Cambridge, Mass, 1938, pp 193–97.
18. G. RIBAND, "Micrométre pneumatique différential," *Mécanique*, v 26, 1942, pp 215–17.
19. L. LEINERT, "Feinmessgerät am Strömungsgrundlage," *Werkstattstechnik*, v 36, 1942, pp 228–31.
20. M. RAUM, "Das pneumatische Prüfverfahren," *Zeitschrift für Technische Physik*, v 24, 1943, pp 46–53.

Calibration of Gages

21. R. L. TEMPLIN, "The Calibration of Extensometers," *Proc ASTM*, v 28, pt 2, 1928, pp 714–27.
22. A. H. STANG and L. R. SWEETMAN, "An Extensometer Comparator," *J Research Nat Bur Standards*, v 15, n 3, paper RP882, p 199, Sept 1935.
23. B. L. WILSON, "Proposed Method for Verification and Classification of Strainometers," *ASTM Bul* 117, Aug 1942, pp 83–5.

Methods for Eliminating Errors

24. WM. M. BLEAKNEY, "Compensation of Strain Gages for Vibration and Impact," *J Research Nat Bur Standards*, v 18, p 723.
25. P. J. McCULLOUGH, "Eliminating Error with Spherical Points on Strain Gage Instruments," *Instruments*, v 1, n 6, June 1928.

CHAPTER 4

OPTICAL METHODS OF STRAIN MEASUREMENT

By John L. Maulbetsch *

* The assistance of Mr. Arnold Reitman, of the Kollmorgen Optical Corporation engineering staff, in the preparation of the drawings is gratefully acknowledged.

A. INTRODUCTION

This chapter is divided into four sections. First, definitions and elements of optical theory are stated, without the details which would be of interest mainly to the lens designer or the builder of industrial instruments. The facts stated are sufficient for an understanding of the functioning of optical systems used in engineering investigations and for help in the building of experimental systems used in the analysis of strength of materials. Several books have been recently published which give details about lens aberrations and the theory of optics, and for those interested in pursuing the subject further a list of these is given in the bibliography.[1-4] For practical laboratory technique in the handling of optical instruments, Strong[5] and Dévé[6] give many useful procedures; for the theoretical aspects and explanations of optical phenomena, Wood[7] and Monk[8] are recommended. The analysis of lens aberrations is extensively treated by Conrady,[9] Czaspki,[10] and Gardner.[11]

In the second section, the various optical elements are described, mainly from the point of view of the engineer who is to give specifications for the making or the purchase of an element to be used in an optical setup. Information regarding the manufacture of optical glasses and the manufacture of optical elements will be found in Wright,[12] Twyman,[13] and Dévé.[6]

In parts III and IV instruments and optical systems, respectively, are described. Instruments which can be commercially purchased are mentioned without referring to the names of manufacturers, as most can be obtained from several different firms.

I. DEFINITIONS AND ELEMENTS OF OPTICAL THEORY

B. LENSES

The refracting surfaces of lenses are usually spherical, sometimes cylindrical. Aspheric surfaces are difficult to generate and are not of practical significance at the present time except in the case of parabolic mirrors, which are corrected by hand, or aspheric condensers and reflectors, which are molded to shape without regard to obtaining a true optical surface. Some molded plastic lenses with aspheric surfaces have been made, but they are still in the development stage and are not yet produced on a commercial basis.

A *single* lens is made from one piece of glass only; a *doublet* is a lens made of two single lenses cemented together, or, in some cases, a doublet may be "air-spaced" when the two elements are not cemented but are separated by a thin metal spacer. A *compound* lens is made up of combinations of three or more single lenses, which may be cemented together or may be air-spaced (Fig. 4-1).

The material used to cement lenses together is usually Canada balsam. During the last 5 years synthetic cements were developed, and these are now used in the optical industry when lenses are submitted to temperatures above 130°F or are subjected to rapid changes in temperature.

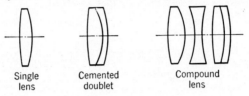

Single lens   Cemented doublet   Compound lens

FIG. 4-1.   Lens Elements

C. Focal Length and Principal Points (Fig. 4-2)

The line joining the centers of the spherical surfaces of a lens is called the *optical axis*. A bundle of parallel rays incident on the lens and parallel to the optical axis will, after being refracted through the lens, converge to a point called *focal point F_2*. The plane normal to the optical axis at F_2 is the focal plane. A similar point F_1 is determined by parallel rays incident to the other side of the lens. The usual convention is to assume that the light travels from left to right. F_1 is then called the *front or first focal point* and F_2, the *back or second focal point*. For a bundle of parallel rays oblique to the optical axis, there will be one ray which will emerge from the lens parallel to its original direction. The intersection of the entering ray with the optical

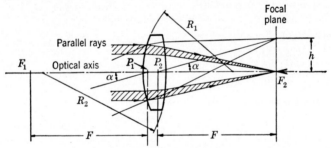

FIG. 4-2.   Effect of Lens on Parallel Rays of Light

axis determines the first principal point P_1, and the intersection of the emerging ray with the optical axis determines the second principal point P_2. The distance P_2F_2, is called the focal length of the lens and is designated by F. In the case of compound lenses or a single thick lens, this distance is called *"equivalent focal length"* and is designated by EF.

The focal length can also be defined as the length F which is a characteristic of a lens, such that when a bundle of parallel rays enters the lens at an angle α from the optical axis, it will converge to a point located at the distance h from the optical axis (Fig. 4-2) so that

$$h = F \times \tan \alpha \tag{1}$$

D. Power of a Lens

The power of a lens, designated by ϕ, is usually expressed in diopters and is the inverse of the focal length expressed in meters:

$$\phi = \frac{1}{F_{\text{in meters}}} = \text{power in diopters} \qquad (2)$$

It is to be noted that a lens of 1000 mm (about 40 in.) has a power of 1 diopter.

A lens is said to be converging, or positive, when it converges an incident bundle of parallel rays. Such a lens is thicker at the center than at the periphery (Fig. 4-3).

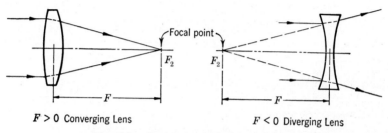

$F > 0$ Converging Lens $F < 0$ Diverging Lens

Fig. 4-3.   Positive and Negative Lenses

A lens is said to be diverging, or negative, when it diverges an incident bundle of parallel rays. Such a lens is thicker at the periphery.

E. Lens Specifications

For manufacturing purposes the following data are required:

1. Radii of curvature of the surfaces.
2. Central thickness.
3. Diameter.
4. Type of glass.

Radii with very close tolerances should be selected after consulting the manufacturer, because, when a radius value with close tolerances is specified and a manufacturer does not have the tools for this dimension, expensive tools have to be made before the lens can be produced. It is best to consult the lens manufacturer or to give him large enough tolerances so as to permit him to select radii for which he is already tooled up.

Commercial tolerances on the central thickness are ± 0.004 in. and on the diameter ± 0.002 in. The central thickness should be so chosen that the edge thickness should never be less than about 0.040 in., or more in case the curvatures are steep. The central thickness of a positive lens, or the edge thickness of a negative lens, if accurate surfaces are to be made, should be at least one-eighth the diameter of the lens, and the central thickness of the negative lens should never be less than 1 mm for small lenses of up to $\frac{1}{2}$ in. and correspondingly thicker for lenses of larger diameters.

There is quite a variety of optical glasses available, but it is always advisable to check with the lens manufacturer to determine those readily obtainable from stock. The most common type of glass for single lenses or for optical windows and mirrors is ordinary crown, with an index of refraction $N_d = 1.523$ and a dispersion $V = 58.6$. For prisms of long glass path, borosilicate crown is frequently used because of its clearness and low light absorption.

F. Thin Lenses

For most optical systems used in experimental work, it is sufficient to consider *thin lenses* only. A thin lens is considered to have no thickness; the vertex of the refracting surfaces and the principal points P_1 and P_2 (Fig. 4-2) are considered to be at the same point on the optical axis. The power of a single thin lens in air* is, expressed in diopters,

$$\phi = 1000 \left(\frac{n-1}{R_1} + \frac{n-1}{R_2} \right) \tag{3}$$

where n is the index of refraction of the lens material, R_1 and R_2 are the radii of curvature of the refracting surfaces in millimeters, taken as positive if a surface is convex, and negative if concave.

If two lenses of power ϕ_1 and ϕ_2 are separated by a distance d, the resultant power of the combination is given by

$$\phi = \phi_1 + \phi_2 - d \times \phi_1 \times \phi_2 \tag{4}$$

It is seen that for lenses in contact the powers are simply additive.

A compound lens, such as a photographic lens or projection objective, can be treated as a thin lens by determining the locations of the principal points of the lens and by taking the midpoint between these as the location for the thin lens. This is an approximation only, but sufficiently accurate in most cases since the distance between the principal points is usually small.

G. Aperture of Lenses (Speed)

The ratio of the focal length to the opening or free aperture of the lens is a useful characteristic number. This ratio, called the "f ratio," is well known for photographic lenses and is significant in optical design. The smaller it is, the larger the diameter is compared to the focal length, and the more light enters the lens, but also the more difficult it is to bring all rays to a common focal point. Values commonly used are given in part II for the various types of lens elements.

H. Field of Lens

Let α (Fig. 4-2) be the angle an oblique bundle of rays makes with the optical axis. Then the *angular field* designates the largest value of α for bundles admitted into the lens and used in the optical system. Care should be taken, when specifying angles of field, to state whether the *half field* α is

---

* For the use of lenses in other media and for the theory of optical path in substances other than air, see references 1–3.

meant or whether the *full field* (which is represented by twice the angle) is specified.

It can easily be realized that lenses which must bring to convergence bundles of large diameters and are required to image large fields are the most difficult type to produce.

I. OBJECT AND IMAGE (FIG. 4-4)

If an object is at a finite distance p from a lens, the location of the image produced by the lens will be at a distance q, satisfying the relation:

$$\frac{1}{p} + \frac{1}{q} = \frac{1}{F} \tag{5}$$

When the light is taken to travel from left to right, p is positive if the object is on the left side of the lens; negative if on the right side.   Distance q is positive if on the right side of the lens; negative if on the opposite side. F is

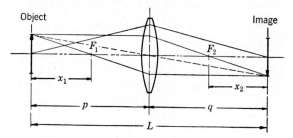

FIG. 4-4.   Formation of Image by a Lens

positive for converging or positive lenses; negative for diverging or negative lenses.   Another useful relation is

$$x_1 \times x_2 = F^2 \tag{6}$$

where x_1 is the distance of the object from F_1 and is taken as positive if the object is at left of F_1. x_2 is distance of image from F_2, taken as positive if the image is at right of F_2.

Magnification is the ratio of the size of the image to the size of the object. It is designated by M and can be computed as follows:

$$M = \frac{q}{p} = \frac{F}{x_1} = \frac{x_2}{F} \tag{7}$$

If the distance from the object to the image is given and is designated by L and the magnification M is specified, the focal length of the lens will be

$$F = \frac{M \times L}{(M + 1)^2} \tag{8}$$

Inversely, given the focal length F and the distance L, the magnification M is obtained by solving equation 8.

J. Depth of Focus

If the object is in one plane normal to the optical axis, the image (excluding lens aberrations) will also be in a plane normal to the optical axis. If the object has depth, or if several objects located at various distances from the lens are simultaneously observed, it is possible to obtain a satisfactory image at some average image plane, provided the aperture or f ratio of the lens is kept small. In general, the lower the magnification, the greater the depth of focus will be.

K. Parallax

Parallax is found in optical systems where the image of an object is brought to focus on a focal plane where a reticule is placed. If the locations on the optical axis of the image plane and of the reticule do not coincide exactly, the system is said to have parallax. It can readily be observed in a telescope provided with cross-wires; if one moves the eye up and down, it will be noted that the image produced by the telescope has an apparent movement relative to the cross-wire.

L. Diaphragms

The size of the bundles of rays can be limited by the lens apertures or by other apertures placed throughout the optical system. These are known as *aperture diaphragms*. If a limiting aperture is at a focal plane it becomes a *field diaphragm*, since at this location it limits the field of the system.

M. Reflections, Antireflection Coating of Lenses

Modern lenses are usually provided with an antireflection coating. This is a hard deposit of a material, the index of refraction of which has a value between the index of refraction of glass and air. The most common material is magnesium fluoride which is evaporated under high vacuum until the optical thickness of the deposit on the lens surface is about one quarter of a wave length thick. By various methods this coating is hardened so that lenses coated at the present time do not need any special care other than the usual precautions taken with any highly polished surface. These coatings reduce stray light caused by reflection at lens surface which interferes with the optical quality of the image.

A good optical system should always be so diaphragmed that only those rays which actually form the image reach the focal plane. To prevent internal reflections, the inside surface of the metal parts should have a dull-black finish.

N. Mirrors

Mirrors are optically flat elements which are used to change the direction of a beam of light. The angle of reflection i' is always equal to the angle of incidence i (Fig. 4-5). If the reflecting surface is a nonconductor, such as glass, some light will be transmitted through the plate, and some will be reflected, and this reflected beam will be polarized. Maximum polarization takes place for crown glass when the angle i is about 57° or more specifically for any glass when $i = $ arc tan n, where n is the index of refraction. This fact is used in constructing simple polariscopes.

O. PRISMS

Prisms are glass elements which are also used to deflect a beam of light. In many cases, a mirror or a prism may be used. Mirrors are to be preferred for experimental work, since they are more easily obtainable. The more common types are described in the article on prisms in section II.

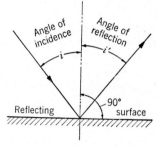

FIG. 4-5. Reflection at a Surface

P. PYRAMIDAL ERROR AND DEVIATION OF PRISMS (FIG. 4-6)

If a ray of light enters the prism normal to the first face, it should emerge normal to the last face. Any angular deviation from this direction is due to an error in the construction of the prism. The error measured in a plane normal to the reflective surface and containing the normal to the exit face is known as *deviation*. The error measured perpendicularly to the same reference plane is called *pyramidal error*. These errors are commercially held within a tolerance of 10 min; for precision optics to less than 5 min. The

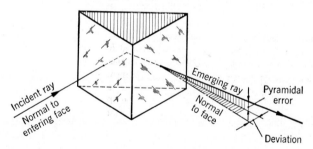

FIG. 4-6.   Prism Errors

greater the number of reflections which take place within the prism, the more difficult it is to keep these limits.

Q. ERECTION OF IMAGE

As seen looking at the ground glass of a camera, the image formed by the lens is completely inverted. In order to bring it back to normal, the image on the ground glass should be imaged by another lens to another focal plane. Because of the inversions caused by the second lens, the image on this second focal plane will be erect. Inversions are also caused by reflections. A single reflection by a mirror or a prism causes an inversion in one direction only. When an optical setup is made, consideration should be given to the number of focal planes and the number of reflections used in order to determine whether the orientation of the final image will be satisfactory.

R. Care of Optical Elements

Polished surfaces are easily scratched. In cleaning them the dirt or grit accumulated on the surface should be gently removed by means of a brush (preferably camel's hair), after which the surface may be lightly wiped with a clean linen towel or a piece of lens tissue, moistened with alcohol or lens-cleaning fluid. If the lens does not have finger marks or grease on its surface, water may be sufficient. A final cleaning can be accomplished by breathing on the lens to deposit some moisture and then drying the surface with a dry clean linen towel or lens tissue.

If the lens is scratched by accident, no attempt should be made to remove the blemish, for a scratched lens will perform satisfactorily, whereas a lens whose surface has been deformed and is not a true sphere may produce severe imagery defects.

II. ELEMENTS OF OPTICAL INSTRUMENTS

S. Objective Lenses

The lens nearest the object in an optical system is designated as the *objective lens;* it is generally a positive lens, which forms a real image. In an optical system, the objective lens is the most critical of its elements, and poor design or workmanship will easily render the system useless. The simplest form of an objective is an *achromatic doublet,* generally cemented and corrected for color, spherical aberration, and coma. Such a lens will give good results for moderate speeds up to $f10$ and for fields not exceeding 10° full field.

Since the quality of the optical characteristics depends so much on the objective, it is usually advisable to select a lens which can easily satisfy the requirements of speed and field to be obtained. There is a wide choice of objectives available, if use is made of those manufactured for various commercial instruments such as cameras, movie cameras, telescopes, projectors, and microscopes. It will often be found more convenient to purchase a camera lens or a projection lens for use where a doublet lens would be satisfactory, than to purchase a doublet which would have to be specially made.

The requirements to consider in selecting objectives are, first:

1. Focal length.
2. Angular field.
3. Aperture ratio (or speed).

As previously stated, large fields and high speeds lead to complicated lenses. In experimental engineering work, when large fields are required, large apertures can be avoided by increasing the illumination of the object. Large fields can be avoided by proper selection of the dimensions of the system. The other requirements which will lead to the proper selection of the objectives are:

1. Definition at the center of the field.
2. Definition at the edge of the field.
3. Distortion.
4. Photographic or visual use.

Before listing the various classifications of objectives, these last factors will first be briefly discussed. Concerning definition, most photographic objectives will resolve when used at their rated speed, a minimum of 40 lines per millimeter at the center of the focal plane; the better ones will resolve up to 140 lines per millimeter. At the edge of the field, also for the rated speed and the rated field, the resolving power is approximately 50 per cent of the value at the center. The resolving power is also controlled by diffraction which becomes important for objectives of small diameter.* If the image of the objective is to reproduce on a photographic plate or film, the sensitivity of the emulsion to be used should be ascertained. Common photographic emulsions will resolve 40 lines per millimeter. Emulsions for process plates are rated up to 60 lines per millimeter, and emulsions for microfilms up to 140 lines per millimeter. Special emulsions used in spectrographic work can be obtained to resolve up to 500 lines per millimeter. Complete data on photographic materials and their use are given in reference 14.

It will be found that most lenses show up to about 2 to 3 per cent distortion at the edges of the rated field. It is an error which, in general, is not serious, but, if the requirements for lack of distortion must be met, an objective should be selected so that it will be used only at a fraction of its rated field. Lenses especially designed to be free of distortion are those used in photographic mapping and are not easily obtainable.

If the optical system is to be used both visually and photographically, a lens corrected for photographic use should always be selected unless monochromatic light in the visual range is used. In this case, as well as for visual work, the color correction of any commercial objective will usually give satisfactory results. For various requirements, the following objectives are suggested:

1. Maximum Total Field 10°; Maximum Speed f10. Suggested type: Achromatic Doublets. Doublets in various focal lengths up to a diameter of $1\frac{1}{2}$ in. can be obtained from most manufacturers. Above $1\frac{1}{2}$ in., it is best to inquire which focal lengths can be obtained from stock. Diameters between $2\frac{1}{2}$ and 6 in. can usually be obtained without too much difficulty but will in most instances require special orders. Above 6 in. the lenses become quite expensive, and their use should be avoided as much as possible.

2. Maximum Total Field 20°; Maximum Speed f3.5. Suggested type: Projection Anastigmats. These lenses are commercially obtainable in focal lengths from 2 to about 7 in. For longer focal lengths, the maximum speed is usually about f 4.5. These lenses are corrected for the visual range of the spectrum and give good central definition. Most of these lenses are used

---

* The theoretical resolving power of an objective is, if D is expressed in inches, $5.5/D$ sec of arc. (See Jacobs,[2] p 178).

for slide projectors and can be obtained from dealers handling projection equipment.

3. Maximum Total Field 30°; Maximum Speed *f*2. Suggested type: Professional Projection Anastigmats. Most lenses of this type are commercially obtainable in focal lengths from 2 to 5 in. in steps of ¼ in. The more expensive ones are flat and give good definition at the center and at the edges, although for the longer focal lengths they should be used for total fields not exceeding 20°. Lenses used in 16- and 8-mm motion-picture projectors can be used for shorter lengths (1 to 2 in.), with a speed for these short focal length of *f*1.6.

4. Maximum Total Field 45° to 50°; Maximum Speed *f*4.5. Suggested type: Photographic Anastigmats.* Lenses used in commercial cameras can be obtained in focal lengths from 2 to 8 in. Those for motion-picture cameras will offer a choice of focal lengths between ½ to 2 in. For longer focal lengths, process lenses up to 25 in. focal length are manufactured. Although they should be used for reproduction of near objects only, they may be found satisfactory for longer ranges also. For visual use, some anastigmats recommended in article 2 may be used for these wider angles.

5. Special Requirements. (*a*) *High-Speed Lenses*. The lenses previously described are only the more commonly found where a wide choice of focal lengths is available. Photographic high-speed lenses (*f* 2 or faster) are found only in short focal lengths up to 2 in., such as those used in motion-picture cameras.

(*b*) *Wide-Angle Lenses*. For angles above 50° of total field, wide angle lenses are required, but the choice of focal lengths is limited.

(*c*) *Near Works*. For reproduction of objects at close distances—that is, a small multiple of the focal length of the lens—most of the afore-mentioned lenses can be satisfactorily used at the expense of a loss in definition and optical quality. If the requirements are strict, lenses used in photographic enlargers are recommended, and they will be found available in focal lengths from 2 to about 7 in. Process lenses can be used for the longer focal lengths.

(*d*) *Large Magnification*. For large magnification of objects placed very close to the lens, lenses of very short focal length are required, for which microscope objectives may be selected.

T. Eyepieces (Magnifiers)

As the name implies, an eyepiece is a lens which is usually placed near the eye of the observer. Its function is to collect bundles of rays coming from all points of an object or of an image on a focal plane and so to refract these bundles that they will converge to a common region (eye point) where the pupil of the observer's eye can be placed (Fig. 4-7). In order for the observer to be able to focus the bundles of rays entering his eye, it is necessary that these bundles consist of rays nearly parallel to each other. This condition requires that the object be placed at the front focal point F_1 of the eye lens. The manner in which the bundles of rays pass through the lens shows a striking

* A complete list of photographic lenses is given on pp 53–66 of reference 14.

difference for the optical requirements of a lens used as an eyepiece compared to one used as an objective. In an eyepiece, each bundle of rays strikes a different portion of the lens, whereas, in general, in an objective all bundles use the full opening of the lens (Fig. 4-2). Because of this difference, the aperture ratio of eyepiece lenses is much higher than the aperture ratio of objective lenses (the aperture ratio for each individual bundle of an eyepiece is small).

It is also seen that there is no functional difference between an eyepiece and a magnifier. The latter is used to observe objects, whereas the former is used in optical instruments to magnify the image of a focal plane. It is, therefore, quite satisfactory in experimental work to use magnifiers as eyepieces for optical systems. The only requirement is that the bundles of rays coming through the system are so directed that they will enter the lens (see section U paragraph 3). The path of the bundles can easily be determined

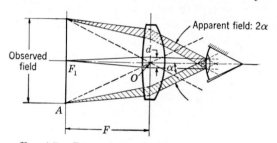

FIG. 4-7.   Diagram Showing Eyepiece Principle

by calculation, using the formula shown in part I and tracing a few simple diagrams of the optical system.

The requirements for an eyepiece usually are that the focal length be as short as possible and, generally, that the field of view be as large as possible. Unfortunately, short focal lengths (which mean large magnification) also imply small dimensions of the observed object. The relation between field and focal length is easily derived. Because of the condition that a ray passing through the center of the lens emerges at the same angle as the entering ray, it is seen that ray AO in Fig. 4-7 gives the direction of the extreme bundle of the apparent field. Angle α will then be determined by

$$\tan \alpha = \frac{\overline{AF_1}}{\overline{OF_1}} = \frac{\overline{AF_1}}{F} \tag{9}$$

Since in ordinary eyepieces α rarely exceeds 25°, the maximum dimensions of the observed field will be

$$2 \times \overline{AF_1} = 0.94 \times F \tag{10}$$

That is, the linear field is proportional to the focal length of the eyepiece.

The magnification of an eyepiece is commonly measured by the ratio of the apparent size of the object, as seen by the observer through the eyepiece, to the apparent size of the same object as seen from a distance of 10 in. In

Figure 4-8, β is measure of the apparent size of the object seen through the eyepiece, and β_0 is the apparent size as seen from 10 in. We have the relation,

$$M = \frac{\tan \beta}{\tan \beta_0} = \frac{h/F}{h/10 \text{ in.}} \tag{11}$$

which gives

$$M = \frac{10 \text{ in.}}{EF \text{ in inches}} \tag{12}$$

Using equation 10 and this last relation, the values of magnification and size of field for various focal lengths will be as shown in Table 4-1.

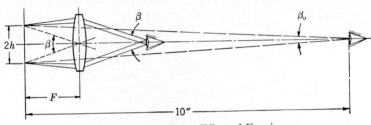

FIG. 4-8.   Magnifying Effect of Eyepieces

TABLE 4-1

Focal Length, in.	Magnification	Appr. Size of Field, in.*
1	10×	0.9
2	5×	1.9
3	3.3×	2.8
5	2×	4.7

* These values are obtainable only with well-corrected magnifiers.

The different types of eyepieces (or magnifiers) commercially available can be classified as follows:

6. Single Lenses (Fig. 4-9a). Single lenses are used mostly as reading glasses, made usually for magnifications of 2× and 3×. Short focal lengths cannot be used because of color aberrations, which become too noticeable at higher powers, and because of distortion, which limits the field. The flatter surface should be turned toward the object to reduce distortion.

7. Doublets (Fig. 4-9b). These are obtainable as achromatic magnifiers and are made up to magnifications of 10×. The field is also limited because of distortion.

8. Ramsden Eyepiece (Fig. 4-9c). By combining two single lenses, it is possible to correct substantially the color aberration and also to increase the field of view. These lenses are commonly used in magnifiers made for powers up to 6×. A clear glass plate is sometimes placed between the lenses to act as a semireflector for the purpose of illuminating the object on the scale. This type is called "Gauss eyepiece" and is commercially available.

9. Kellner Eyepiece (Fig. 4-9d). This is the most common type of eyepiece used in optical systems but is not usually obtainable commercially as a magnifier. This type of eyepiece can be obtained from optical firms in focal lengths varying between ¾ and 2 in.

10. High-Power Magnifiers (Figs. 4-9e and f). The better types of magnifiers found commercially for magnifications between 6× to 20× are of the compound type. To use these lenses as eyepieces, it is necessary, frequently, to place another lens near the focal plane in order to direct the bundles of rays into the magnifier. These magnifiers are corrected for color and distortion over a large field and are corrected for good definition.

11. Compound Eyepieces (Fig. 4-9g). This type of eyepiece, which is similar to the Ramsden eyepiece but consisting of doublets instead of single lenses, is found in the better types of instruments. It can be used equally

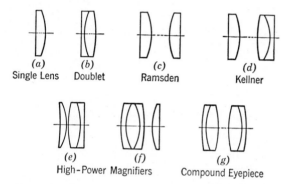

FIG. 4-9.   Representative Eyepieces and Magnifiers

well as a magnifier and is likely to be most suitable for a wide variety of uses. Focal lengths available vary between ⅝ to 2 in.; a focal length of 1 in., giving 10× magnification, is recommended for general-purpose use.

12. Other Types of Eyepieces. In the types discussed previously the focal plane lies outside the lens. The Huygens eyepiece, consisting of two single elements with the focal plane between them, has better color correction than the simple Ramsden eyepiece but is not suitable for general experimental and engineering purposes because of the difficulty in placing a scale or cross-line between the lenses.

Eyepieces with an apparent field of view larger than 45° are usually not commercially available; for a discussion of these (as well as for other special types) see references 1–3.

U. COLLECTING LENSES

It often happens that bundles of rays diverge from each other, such as bundles A and B of Fig. 4-10, when it would be convenient to have them converge so as to limit the size of the lenses or because of space limitations. Bundles A and B emerge from lens 1 and are focused on focal plane 2; and it is desired, for instance, to form an image of plane 2 on plane 3. The ratio of the sizes of the images on planes 3 and 2 determines the location of the lens in accordance with equation 7, and the focal length of the lens is determined by equation 8. The location of plane 4 is then determined.

The size of the lens must then be large enough to accommodate all the rays of bundles A and B which would require a large aperture. This aperture can be made smaller by placing a positive lens at 2 to change the direction of bundles A and B and to make them converge, thus reducing the size of lens 4. A lens used in this manner is called a *collecting lens* or *collector* and is always placed at or preferably near a focal plane so as not to disturb the optical characteristics of the other lenses of the system.

Collecting lenses are usually single lenses made of ordinary crown glass, and their aperture ratio should be limited to speeds not exceeding $f5$. Positive

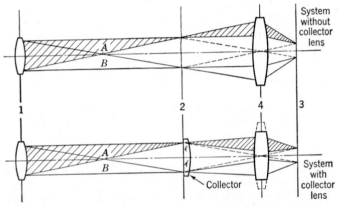

FIG. 4-10.   Action of Collector Lens in Reducing Lens Size

spectacle lenses or reading glasses can be satisfactorily used as collectors in experimental systems. Negative spectacle lenses can be used if it is desired to make the bundles of rays diverge.

V. RETICLES

These elements, on which lines or measuring scales are provided, are placed at the focal plane to be used as reference markers or measuring devices being superimposed on the image formed by the optical system. These lines are usually etched in glass. Lenses provided with cross-lines or single lines can readily be obtained from optical firms. However, since these lenses are placed at the focal plane and are themselves visible with the image, the glass used must be especially free from defects, and the surfaces must be polished to the highest degree possible. These lenses are, therefore, expensive, and for experimental purposes the cost can be reduced by relaxing the specifications on allowable defects. The optical manufacturer should be so advised, and the design should be limited to straight lines only, in order to reduce the cost.

Etched lines can be obtained in widths between 0.0008 and 0.004 in.; thinner lines or wider lines will also increase the cost. Various standard scales used in "measuring eyepieces" and other instruments can be commercially obtained, and their adaptation is recommended rather than the designing of a special scale.

Another method satisfactory for laboratory use is reproducing the scale on a photographic plate by photographing a drawing of the design. The only disadvantages in this method are that there will be some loss in the light transmission of the system and the scale will not be so clean as an optical reticle made of etched glass.

It should be noted that reticles often are given refracting power for use as collecting lenses.

W. Lens Cells

It is advisable to buy lenses already assembled in metal mounts, for then the matching of the optical axis with the mechanical axis of the mount is taken care of by the manufacturer. This facilitates the optical line-up of the system, usually a matter of considerable importance. If a lens is to be mounted for an experimental setup, a simple mount such as that illustrated in Fig. 4-11 can easily be made. It consists of the cell proper, where the inside diameter is accurately machined to run true with the outside diameter. The inside diameter is made large enough to provide an easy sliding fit

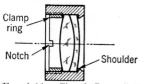

Fig. 4-11. Simple Lens Cell

for the lens. The lens is held in place by a threaded clamp ring which can be secured by means of a drop of shellac placed on the threads. The shoulder of the main cell must be clean and free of burrs so as to provide a uniform resting surface for the lens; the same applies to the inside surface of the clamp ring. Notches are provided to tighten the clamp ring, which should be tightened only sufficiently to hold the lens in place, for if too much pressure is exerted the lens will be deformed, thus losing the true spherical shape of its surfaces. Too much pressure on cemented lenses may cause the components to separate.

To build up compound lenses, each lens can be assembled in a cell, and, in turn, the various cells can be assembled in a common cell, or tube, to hold them in their proper locations. This method provides accurately centered optical systems and is recommended for laboratory work.

X. Mirrors

Mirrors can be classified as back-surface mirrors, front-surface mirrors, and semireflecting mirrors (Fig. 4-12).

13. Back-Surface Mirrors have good reflecting properties (the loss of light amounts to about 5 per cent) but, because some reflection also occurs at the front surface of the mirror, double images will result unless the mirrors are used where the bundles consist of parallel rays. Because of the development of front-surface mirrors which are more stable and less sensitive to handling than those available heretofore, the need for back-surface mirrors in experimental work has considerably diminished.

In ordering a back-surface mirror, it is advisable to indicate where the mirror is to be used so that the manufacturer can determine the quality of surface required and the degree of parallelism desired between the two surfaces. Mirrors can be made to a parallelism of 2 sec of arc between the two faces but are expensive. Angles of 10 to 20 sec are common and commercially available. The reflecting surface is usually silvered, copper-plated, and lacquered to protect the silver from deterioration.

14. Front-Surface Mirrors require optical accuracy only on one side of the mirror and are, therefore, much cheaper to manufacture. Their main drawback was that those with good reflecting material could not be adequately protected and the surface deteriorated rapidly, and those with resistant coatings had poor reflecting properties. Recent developments have lead to the manufacture of front-surface mirrors, with good reflecting properties, the coating of which is as resistant to handling as any optical polished surface. Loss in light caused by the reflection is somewhat higher than for back-surface mirrors but does not exceed 12 per cent. These mirrors are commercially available in almost any size up to about 10 in., and the only requirement, if good surfaces are required, is that the thickness of the mirror should be at least one-tenth to one-eighth of the longest dimension. Mirrors used near an objective should have a surface quality comparable to the quality of the surface of the objective lens; if they are used near a collecting lens or an eye-piece, the surface quality is not so important.

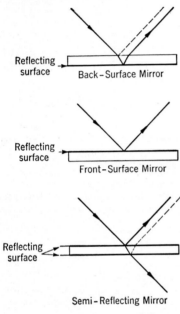

Fig. 4-12.   Reflection by Mirrors

15. Semireflecting Mirrors. If the reflecting surface of a mirror is coated with a substance which allows some of the light to be reflected and some to pass through, splitting of beams of light can be accomplished. This type of mirror suffers the same drawback of double reflection as the back-surface mirror, and, unless employed in parallel light or for the splitting of rays used for illumination only, it should be avoided. Splitting prisms should then be used. Mirrors which transmit and reflect approximately equal percentages of light are now available, with coatings which will withstand ordinary handling. Coatings which give various ratios of transmitted light to reflected light can be made but are rather delicate to handle, and usually the color of the reflected beam is not the same as the color of the transmitted beam. The simplest type of semireflecting mirror is a glass plate which reflects about 10 per cent, probably more, of the incident light and which is used in various instruments to illuminate the reticle. Thin membranes, which act as semi-reflecting mirrors are also made and are commercially available; they are fragile, however.

Strong[5] gives an extensive description of the making and use of mirrors.

Y. SPECIAL MIRRORS

Various instruments use other types of mirrors which can be found useful. For instance, galvanometer mirrors are very small (as little as $\frac{1}{8}$ in.) and also very thin (as little as 0.015 in.). They are used where the mass and the moment of inertia must be as small as possible. These mirrors are commercially available in various sizes.

Convex and concave reflectors can easily be made by using positive or negative lenses, the surface of which can be coated as a front-surface mirror, or for some purposes, back-surfaced.

Z. MOUNTING OF MIRRORS

A perfectly good mirror can be rendered useless by the method in which the mirror is held in place. The most accurate method is to provide a flat bearing surface which touches the mirror around the edges of the back surface only and to provide three flexible clamps which press the mirror against the bearing surface. If a frame is placed over the mirror, some layers of paper should be interposed between the frame and the mirror to equalize the pressure, and the frame should not be pressed too tightly against the mirror. In any case, it should be held in such a way that no bending moment is applied to the mirror.

AA. PRISMS

The two most common types of prisms are the 90° prism (Fig. 4-13), with one reflecting surface, and the Penta prism, which deflects a beam of light to a direction perpendicular to the direction of incidence and has two reflecting surfaces. Prisms or top-surface mirrors must be used when a beam of light consisting of convergent or divergent bundles is reflected. The 90° prism is fairly common and can be commercially obtained in dimensions up to 5 in. for the entering and exit faces. To order a prism, the size of one face only need be given, and the tolerances desired for deviation and pyramidal error should be specified (see section P). Prisms commonly available are usually made of borosilicate crown or ordinary crown.

A roof-edge prism (Fig. 4-13) is a prism, the reflecting surface of which is replaced by two surfaces which must be at exactly 90° to each other within a tolerance of a few seconds. The 90° prism produces an inversion in one plane only, whereas the 90° roof-edge prism completely inverts the image. Roof-edge prisms are usually avoided in optical instruments because of their high cost, caused by the accuracy required in the making of the roof.

There is a variety of other types of prisms, but they are not commonly used in engineering research.*[1-3]

* For applications of Nicol prisms used in photoelasticity, see chapter 17.

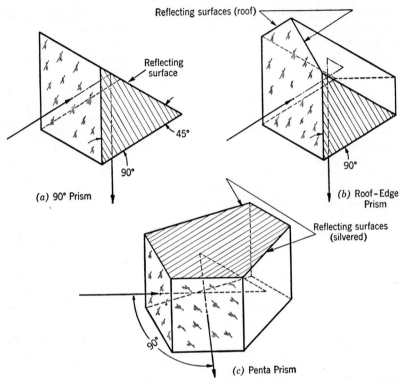

FIG. 4-13.   Types of Prisms Frequently Used

BB. SPLITTING BLOCKS AND PRISMS

By using two 90° prisms cemented together after the reflecting face of one of them has been provided with a semireflecting coating, a splitting block is obtained.   These are used to split beams of converging or diverging rays to avoid double reflections.   Splitting or coincidence prisms are made similarly but by using various types of prisms.

Prisms giving various ratios of reflected to transmitted light can be obtained by varying the density or the composition of the semireflecting coating.

CC. CONDENSERS

Condensers are strong positive elements used to obtain proper illumination by directing bundles of light.   They are similar to collecting lenses except that the requirements for fine optical correction and sphericity of surfaces are, in general, not necessary.   Their speed, therefore, is high, may reach $f1$. The optical quality of their surfaces cannot be compared to the quality of lenses used in systems forming well-defined images and often are only molded to shape with a "fire polish."

They are commercially available in various diameters, up to about 8 in.;

in the smaller diameters there is a wide choice of focal lengths. The larger diameters are usually one-half to two-thirds of the focal length.

Cylindrical lenses are used as condensers when it is desired to elongate a bundle of light in one direction and are found mostly in recording instruments and for slit illumination.

DD. Optical Windows

Parallel plates whose surfaces are finished to an optical quality are used as windows in optical systems either to protect these from dirt or fumes or for observation into pressure vessels. The quality of the surface is determined by the location of the window and must be as good as the quality of the nearest lens surface.

In passing through a window whose surfaces are out of parallel by an angle δ, a ray of light will change its direction by an angle $(n - 1)\delta$, or approximately $\delta/2$ (valid for angles δ less than $1°$). This deviation may become important in front of high-power systems, and the order of parallelism desired should be specified in ordering windows. Commercial tolerances are of the order of 30 sec. For windows subjected to gas pressure, round windows are preferable because of the regularity of deformation under pressure. Sealing is accomplished by means of gaskets of rubber or synthetic material which also distributes more evenly the force exerted by the window frame, and prevents points of stress concentration.

With a window properly mounted and free of scratches or pits on the side subjected to tension, a glass window can be made to withstand a pressure of several hundred pounds per square inch. Glass does not appear to have an ultimate strength, and the allowable stress depends on the length of time the load is to be supported.[37] Very little is known about the action of repeated loads. An allowable stress of 1500–2000 psi in tension offers a factor of safety for extended periods of loading. Precautions should, however, be taken in case of failure of the window.

Irrespective of strength considerations, optical window thickness should be one-tenth to one-eighth of the largest dimension if good optical surfaces are required.

III. OPTICAL INSTRUMENTS

EE. Condensing Systems—Sources of Illumination

Because optical tolerances for condenser lenses are not high, the general belief exists that condensing systems can easily be made by placing a few condenser lenses back of a light source. For low-speed systems and low utilization of the light available, this assumption is substantially correct; however, for high-speed systems and high efficiency, the designing of a condensing system is not a simple task.

Commercially, various instruments designed especially as sources of illumination are available, and it will be found advantageous to utilize these whenever possible, rather than to attempt the design of a system.

Condensing systems can be classified into two broad groups: those designed for uniform illumination of a surface, and those required to produce uniform illumination and parallel bundles of light, or "collimated light."

16. Uniform Illumination. In order to obtain uniformity of illumination in an optical system it is necessary that light furnished by the condensing system enter and be transmitted by the optical system. For instance, in Fig. 4-14, A is the front aperture of an optical instrument. At location E_1, it receives all bundles furnished to object A by the condensing system. If the aperture were placed at E_2 all the light would not enter the optical system and also more light would be cut off from the edges of the image than at the center, thus preventing any possibility of obtaining uniformity of illumination in the system.

It is seen that uniform illumination of an object depends both on the optical system used and on the condensing system and source of light. Knowing

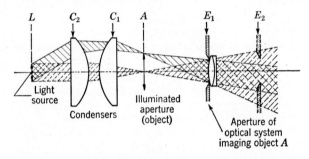

FIG. 4-14.   Condensing System

the size and orientation of the bundles of rays which will pass through the optical system, the following procedure should be used to obtain the proper illumination. By refracting the objective bundles by condensers C_1 and C_2, it can be determined whether these bundles strike a source of light, which should be of uniform illumination, and whether all bundles strike it in a uniform manner.

For maximum utilization of the light source, it can be noted that the condensers image the source in the aperture of the optical system. This is an ideal condition, rarely realized, as the source of light (usually the filament of an electric bulb) is not perfectly uniform in illumination and the sizes available cannot always be matched to the size of the aperture of the optical instrument. Also, in most optical instruments, the bundles from the edges of the object have a smaller area than the bundles from the center. This condition, known as "vignetting," also prevents uniform illumination.

Lamps which will be found useful in experimental work and are commercially obtainable are:

1. Lamps used in surgical and industrial recording instruments. These occupy little space and use low voltage, but give low intensity of illumination.

2. Lamps used in projectors provide filaments distributed over a rectangular or square area of various sizes. To equalize the light over this area a

reflector is used on the back side of the lens to provide rays of light into the spaces between the filament. They require 110 volts alternating current and are available up to 1000 watts. These lamps generate a great deal of heat. The height and orientation of the filament is determined by special sockets and "prefocused" bases.

3. Lamps having a narrow straight filament are used as exciter lamps in motion-picture projectors. They are useful for illumination of a slit, require 4 to 6 volts, and are usually less than 10 watts.

Besides sources of illumination which are commercially available as such, well-designed condensing units can be obtained by using condensing units from motion-picture and slide projectors to illuminate areas up to 1½ in. in diameter. The 8-mm projector covers ¼ in., the 16-mm, ½ in.; slide projectors, 1½ in. Light tubes used in sound projectors can be employed to obtain uniformly illuminated slits. In 35-mm sound projectors the slit is

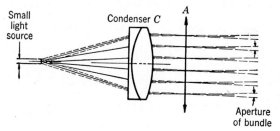

FIG. 4-15.   Collimated Light

0.001 × 0.084 in., and in 16-mm sound projectors the slit is 0.0005 × 0.072 in. The speed of these systems is approximately $f2$.

17. Collimated Light. If it is desired to observe a surface A (Fig. 4-15) by means of parallel bundles of small aperture, a source of illumination providing *collimated light* must be used. Such systems are used in photoelastic polariscopes and in comparators (see section HH). Such a source consists of a lens C and a small source of light placed at its front focal point. The better the correction of the lens, the more parallel the rays will be; and, the smaller the source is, the smaller the aperture of each bundle will be.

Point sources of very high intensity and specially designed for this purpose are commercially available. The recently developed "concentrated-arc" lamps[16] give the smallest source with the highest intensity. A special power supply must be used with these lamps.

For sources of monochromatic light, such as are required for interferometers and photoelastic polariscopes, mercury and sodium lamps convenient to use are available. They can be operated on 110-volt a-c supply by means of a control unit.

For engineering work where observations are made both visually and photographically, the green light from a mercury lamp or the yellow light of a sodium lamp is preferred. These colors are in the range of maximum visual acuity of the human eye, most photographic emulsions are sensitive to these wave lengths, and the correction of optical instruments and lenses is well suited to these colors. To obtain green light with mercury lamps, the other colors must be eliminated by means of filters, obtainable as accessories of the lamps.

FF. TELESCOPES

A telescope consists of an objective lens forming a real image which is observed and magnified by means of an eyepiece (Fig. 4-16). If an object subtends an angle α measured from the objective, it will be seen by the

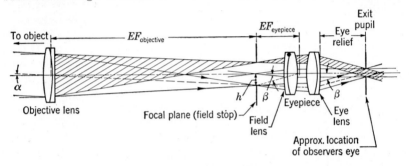

FIG. 4-16.   Inverting Telescope

observer at an apparent angle β. The height of the image on the focal plane corresponding to angle α is

$$h = EF_{\text{OBJ.}} \times \tan \alpha = EF_{\text{eyepiece}} \times \tan \beta \qquad (13)$$

By definition, the magnification of a telescope is

$$M = \frac{\tan \beta}{\tan \alpha} \qquad (14)$$

and from equation 13 it is seen that: *the magnification is the ratio of the focal length of the objective to the focal length of the eyepiece.* Also, as can be seen from equation 14, the *true field of view of a telescope is approximately the maximum apparent field of the eyepiece divided by the magnification.*

The telescope illustrated in Fig. 4-16 is an inverting telescope. An erecting telescope can be made by re-imaging the objective focal plane to a second focal plane by means of lenses known as "erector" lenses and using this erected focal plane for observation by means of an eyepiece. Other erecting telescopes, such as are used in surveying instruments, combine the erector lens with the eyepiece to form a combination known as the "terrestrial eyepiece."

Prisms can be used to erect the image as, for instance, in binoculars. For measuring purposes, the prism erecting telescope is not satisfactory as the eyepiece is mechanically offset from the body of the telescope, which causes difficulty in finding the target when high power is used.*

* Erecting telescopes of the "Galilean type" are not considered here as they do not have a real focal plane and cannot be used for sighting.

The only high-power commercial erecting telescopes provided with lines of reference at the focal plane are surveying-instrument telescopes, which are available with magnifications of $10\times$ to $30\times$. Generally, adjustment for focusing on a near object is obtained by means of a negative lens which can slide between the objective and the focal plane. This construction is known as "internal focusing." In the simpler types of surveying telescopes, the focusing is done by changing the distance of the objective to the focal plane. For powers up to $20\times$ they can be used for focusing an object located as close as 6 ft from the telescope; higher powers, up to about $30\times$, will focus to 9 or 10 ft. The focal plane of these instruments is small because the equivalent focus of a terrestrial eyepiece is short (of the order of $\frac{1}{2}$ in.) and they do not lend themselves easily to the placing of a scale at the focal plane for measuring purposes.

Inverting telescopes are used in various optical instruments such as spectrometers and are available commercially.

If the power of the types available is not satisfactory, a telescope with the desired power can be made with component parts. The main requirement is good alignment of the objective, reticle, and eyepiece. Powers above $40\times$ are not recommended. Focusing can be accomplished by mounting the objective in a cell sliding inside of the main body of the telescope. High-power telescopes of this type can be constructed to focus to very short distances to permit observation at ranges which are too great for microscopes and too short for surveying instruments.

To measure dimensions of the image at the focal plane, a micrometer eyepiece can be provided. This type of eyepiece can be moved with the reticule across the focal plane by means of an accurately calibrated screw carrying a drum which permits measuring of the distance traveled. "Gauss" eyepieces for scale illumination can also be obtained.

GG. Microscopes and Other Instruments

The optical principle of microscopes is the same as that of telescopes, except that the working distance (distance of object to image) is very small and the image on the focal plane is a magnification of the object. The higher the magnification, the shorter the working distance. There are many different types of microscopes commercially available; for stress analysis, microscopes provided with a measuring eyepiece are the most practicable. Magnification should be kept below $100\times$; as higher powers do not have sufficient depth of focus.

Various special-purpose instruments used by physicists and metallurgists and instruments developed for shop measurements may be used in stress analysis. They consist, in general, of a telescope (or microscope) mounted on a carriage, the displacement of which can be accurately measured to determine distances or angular displacements. For inspecting the condition of internal surfaces of tubes and parts, but not to make accurate measurements, *boroscopes* are available.

HH. Collimators

A collimator consists of a reticle placed at the focal plane of an objective (Fig. 4-17). The teticle is provided with reference lines or a measuring scale, and, to facilitate observation, it is artificially illuminated. A simple collimator does not have an eyepiece; its main function is to provide bundles of parallel

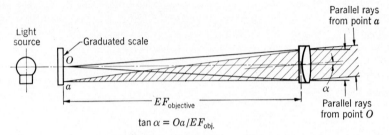

$$\tan \alpha = Oa/EF_{obj.}$$

Fig. 4-17.   Elements of Collimator

rays. By fastening the collimator to the part to be tested, an angular motion of this part can be followed by means of a telescope which focuses the rays of the collimator and thereby images the collimator scale on the telescope's focal plane. A relative displacement of the image of the collimator relative to the telescopes scale indicates and measures the angular displacement of the col-

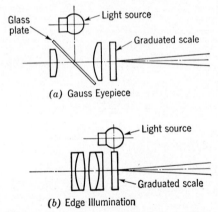

(a) Gauss Eyepiece

(b) Edge Illumination

Fig. 4-18.   Two Methods of Scale Illumination

limator and of the test part relative to the telescope. Another use is illustrated in Fig. 4-24 and is discussed in Section KK.

An *autocollimator* is a collimator provided with an observing eyepiece and an illuminated reticle. Illumination can be supplied in two ways, as shown in Fig. 4-18. One method is by means of a Gauss eyepiece, which will show the reticle lines as dark lines in a light background; in the other method, where the bulb is placed at the edge of the reticle, the lines will appear brightly illuminated in a dark field, provided the instrument is used in a darkened space to prevent outside light entering through the objective. The parallel bundles of the collimator are reflected back into its objective, which is then used as a telescope objective. The reflected image is observed through the eyepiece, and its displacement on the scale gives the measurements of the angular deflections caused on the bundles by the reflection which has taken place.

If the autocollimator is set to reflect the "O point" of the scale back to itself when mirror A (Fig. 4-19) is in its normal position, the reflected image will move to point a of the scale when the mirror is tilted through an angle α. The linear displacement on the scale will be

$$h = 2 \cdot \alpha \cdot EF_{\text{OBJ.}} \text{ (small values of } \alpha) \qquad (15)$$

Collimators and autocollimators, in order to be of any value, must have a well-corrected objective so that all the rays of a bundle are parallel within a very close tolerance. A low-speed objective and a small field of view are indicated for high accuracy which limits somewhat their use. If objective sizes or fields are desired other than those available, a collimator can easily be built by means of component parts.

The most difficult part of the construction is the proper setting of the scale at the focal plane of the objective. This can be done by using the collimator

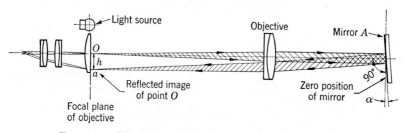

Fɪɢ. 4-19.   Diagram Showing Principle of Autocollimation

as a telescope, sighting on a distant object and focusing the objective until all trace of parallax disappear. The higher the power and the longer the focal length of the objective, the farther away the object should be. Another more accurate method is to use the principle of autocollimation and to reflect from an optically flat mirror the image of the scale back into the telescope. When there is no parallax between the scale and its reflected image, the scale will be exactly at the focal plane of the objective.

The use of collimators and autocollimators are discussed in part IV.

II. Optical Flats and Interferometers

The measuring of displacements by means of interference fringes is used whenever the displacements to be measured are very small, for instance, of the order required for the accurate determination of Poisson's ratio or Young's modulus for small stress values.

The use of interference fringes involves a rather delicate technique and requires proper laboratory conditions. The sensitivity of the method is such that the slightest change in the test conditions will distort the results and introduce errors. The principle is illustrated in Fig. 4-20. Monochromatic light is used, and the reflection coming from two surfaces nearly parallel is observed. Interference between the light waves of the two reflections will produce black and illuminated fringes. A black fringe will appear if the distance is a multiple of $\lambda/2$ (λ being the wave length of the light used), and a light fringe will appear for odd multiples of $\lambda/4$. Optical flats made to an accuracy of a fraction of a wave length must be used. These are commercially available and are sold in sets for use in the inspection and testing of gages.

A typical application is the measuring of the difference in size of two cylinders illustrated in Fig. 4-20. A and C are optical flats; B is a plano-parallel plate in optical contact with A and of such thickness that a small air space is left between B and C. By using monochromatic light, interference fringes will be seen, and the slope of C relative to A can be determined from the number of fringes appearing over a certain distance. If the slope is known, the difference in size between A and B can be computed. The direc-

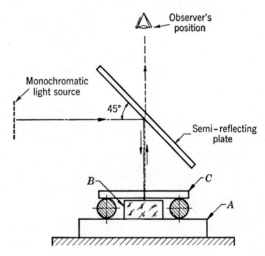

FIG. 4-20.   Optical System for Observing Interference Fringes

tion of this slope can be determined by slightly tilting plate C on one side. An increase in the number of fringes indicates the slope is in the direction of the tilt.

Another application of interference fringes is the measurement of changes of distances. For instance, if plate C (Fig. 4-20) is slowly lifted, dark and light fringes will alternately appear at every point as the distance changes by multiples of $\lambda/4$. By counting the number of changes at any point, the changes in distance can be measured. This principle is used in interferometers and has been used in one type of strain gage (section LL). The principle of interference fringes and interferometers is extensively discussed in references 1, 7, and 8. Application of interference methods, especially the measurement of slopes as shown in Fig. 4-20, is exceedingly useful for laboratory measurements, such as calibration of gages, but will be found too sensitive for most engineering investigations. Unless conditions are very favorable, fringes move too rapidly, rendering observations practically impossible.

IV. OPTICAL SYSTEMS

JJ. CLASSIFICATION OF STRAIN GAGES AND RELATED INSTRUMENTS

The variety of optical systems used to measure elongations and deflections, either linear or angular displacements, can ordinarily be classified into two groups as follows:

1. Instruments using the optical-lever principle.
2. Instruments using mechanical levers.

In instruments using the optical lever, the lever consists of a short mechanical arm holding a mirror which reflects a beam of light. The reflected beam is the other arm of the lever, which, because of the law of reflection, moves twice as fast as the short arm. The angular movement of the reflected beam is magnified by an optical system or measured at a large distance from the pivot point of the system, thus magnifying the displacement of the end of the short arm. In instruments classified under the mechanical-lever principle, the magnification is obtained by solid levers. At the end of the long arms, reference marks are provided. The relative movement of these points can then be measured by optical or other means. In general, from the optical point of view, the optical-lever system requires the measuring of an angle, whereas in the mechanical system, a length is observed.

The type of optical system to choose is determined by the magnitude of the quantities to be measured and the degree of accuracy desired. Assuming that a quantity A is to be measured to an accuracy ϵ, it will be sufficient to have an optical system of such magnification that ϵ will be magnified so as to be just resolved or evaluated by the observer. This statement holds for single measurements and does not take into consideration the possibility of obtaining increased accuracy of measurements by means of repeated observations. In stress analysis, an accuracy of 1 per cent in the measurement should be considered accurate enough. If the quantities to be measured are known, for instance, given 30,000 psi maximum stress and a required accuracy of

TABLE 4-2

Magnification	Max. Length to Be Measured	Examples of Application
None, or small; optical system used for convenience or by necessity	$\frac{1}{4}$ in. to several inches	Deflection of structures, rails, bridges; plastic deformations
$10\times$ to $20\times$	0.020 to $\frac{1}{4}$ in.	Deflection of beams, small parts; creep of metals
$20\times$ to $100\times$	0.005 to 0.020 in.	Strain gages with gage length of several inches; small deflections; vibrations of structures
$100\times$ to $1000\times$	0.0005 to 0.005 in.	Strain gages with gage length of 1 to 2 in.; small deflections
$1000\times$ to $10,000\times$	0.0001 to 0.0005 in.	Strain gages with short gage length

1 per cent, the smallest quantity to be resolved will be 300 psi. A stress of this magnitude will, in some cases, produce deflections which can be seen with the naked eye. At the other extreme, there will be cases where a thousand-fold magnification will be required. This wide range requires, therefore, a wide variety of optical systems. For any particular test, the selection of the system will depend on the magnification required. For ease of operation, the system which has sufficient magnification, but no more, will be the most economical and the most practicable to use.

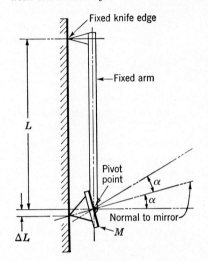

FIG. 4-21.   Diagram of Single-Mirror Extensometer

Table 4-2 indicates, approximately, the ranges of magnifications for different magnitudes of quantities to be measured.

KK. INSTRUMENTS USING THE OPTICAL-LEVER-PRINCIPLE SINGLE-MIRROR SYSTEM

The original and best-known system working according to this principle is the single-mirror system, of which the Martens extensometer is an example. A fixed scale (Figs. 4-21 and 4-22) is observed through a telescope by means of the tilting mirror M which is fastened to a rotatable knife-edge whose pivot point is rigidly held by a fixed arm. The other end of this arm is fastened to

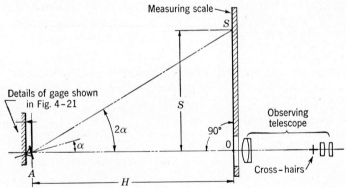

FIG. 4-22.   Principle of Single-Mirror System

the specimen by the fixed knife-edge. As the specimen is elongated, the measuring knife-edge will rotate about its pivot point, thereby tilting the mirror. As the mirror tilts, different portions of the scale are seen, giving a reading S which is a measure of the angle of tilt. S is a magnified value of the quantity to be measured ΔL.   The magnification M is

$$M = \frac{S}{\Delta L} = \frac{H \tan 2\alpha}{r \sin \alpha} \qquad (16)$$

For small angles the magnification is approximately

$$M = \frac{2H}{r} \qquad (17)$$

It is well known that this system is subject to many errors.   The gage, test specimen and testing machine, or equipment being tested, must have no movement relative to the telescope and scale; or, at least, if there is any motion, its magnitude must be smaller than the smallest scale division used.   The scale must be in the plane of travel of the reflected beam, and, if the preceding formulas are used, it must be perpendicular to the line of sight of the telescope.   If the distance OA is increased, the magnification is increased, but the main advantage obtained is that linear displacements of the mirror become small relative to the scale graduations. There is no advantage in using a finely divided scale at a large distance, and, as the telescope and scale are placed far from the tested parts, the chances of error arising from relative angular movement increase.

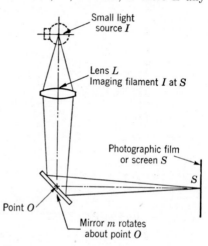

FIG.   4-23.   Simple   Mirror   in   "Galvanometer System"

Another error may arise in the focusing of the telescope.   Since the telescope is focused on a near object, and this distance varies, it will have to be refocused during the test, especially if a high-power telescope is used.   Movement of the objective or of the reticule to adjust the image distance should be parallel to the line of sight to a close tolerance.   Also to reduce the linear displacement of the mirror and resulting errors, the reflecting surface should be as close to the pivot point as possible.

In spite of its inherent errors the single mirror offers a convenient means for testing purposes and should be used where small magnifications are required.

Single mirrors are also used to measure angular deflection, and the system shown in Fig. 4-23 illustrates the so-called "galvanometer system."   A small electric lamp I (a lamp with a condensing system and a small diaphragm can be used) acts as a point source of light; L is a lens imaging the source of light onto a photographic film, or a screen, after being reflected by the mirror m.

Particular problems arising because of the size of the mirror are discussed by Hardy.[1] The geometry of the curve obtained and of the errors arising if the mirror moves in two directions are investigated by Dejuhasz.[17] He extensively describes the use of the system in pressure indicators and gives drawings of indicators which have been built.

The same principle, using many such systems to determine the deflection characteristics of a structure at its various joints, has been employed by Donnell and collaborators.[18, 19] In their tests they did not use a telescope but instead used a peephole to fix the eye of the observer at the same location for every measurement.

The use of collimated light, by means of either a collimator or autocollimator, eliminates the error caused by linear displacement of the mirror in front of

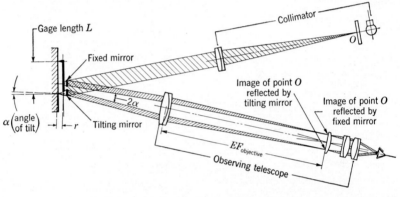

$$\text{Apparent linear magnification of system} = \frac{20}{r_{in.}} \times \text{magnification of telescope}$$

FIG. 4-24.   Double-Mirror System with Collimator

the telescope, but the error caused by an angular tilt of the gage as a whole remains. Since collimated light will limit the maximum tilt of the mirror (the rays must strike the objective of the telescope), the use of the instrument is thus limited to the measurement of very small rotations, for which it is not well suited. Collimated light can be put to better advantage in the "two-mirror" system.

18. Two-Mirror Systems. To remove errors caused by relative angular motion of the measuring system and testing equipment, a fixed reference mirror can be fastened to the body of the gage. By measuring the angular tilt of the reference mirror a correction can be applied to the readings of the measuring mirror. This method requires two telescopes, two scales, and usually two observers. The error due to linear displacement of the mirror remains. A better system is obtained when collimated light is used.

Because of the variety of test conditions encountered, many different types of gages have been developed, especially in the direction of making gages with gage lengths as short as possible. All these gages differ, not in principle, but in their mechanical construction. Several different designs are described by Lehr;[15] one in particular, developed for the Junkers Company, has a gage length of 0.060 in. and a magnification of 10,000. It is not stated whether consistent and reliable results were obtained.

By using a fixed reference mirror and collimated light, the two principal sources of error are removed, and the system can be used for very large magnification. When the magnification is great, however, the field of view of the telescope is small, and the observer is apt to lose the reflected images during a test. The setting to zero is also quite delicate, and small vibratory motions, if present, will affect the image. The systems becomes accurate, but difficult to operate.

The magnification of this system (Fig. 4-24) is computed as follows: The movement at the focal plane magnifies the displacement of the knife-edge by

$$M = \frac{EF_{\text{TEL. OBJ.}} \times \tan 2\alpha}{r \times \sin \alpha} \tag{18}$$

Since the image is further magnified by the eyepiece, this magnification is multiplied by 10 in./EF of eyepiece (equation 12), and, since the magnification of a telescope is the ratio of the focal length of the objective to the focal length of the eyepiece, and also since the angle measured is very small, one obtains, for the apparent magnification of the system,

$$M = \frac{20}{r \text{ (in inches)}} \times M_{\text{TEL.}} \tag{19}$$

For instance, with a pivot radius of $\frac{1}{4}$ in. and a telescope of $30\times$, the magnification is $2,400\times$. If it is assumed that the eye can estimate relative displacements of 0.004 in., the smallest distance that could then be estimated would be 1.7×10^{-6}. Instruments designed for the testing of gages to this order of accuracy and using this principle are described in the literature.[20, 21]

19. Three-Mirror System. An improvement over the two-mirror system has been made by Tuckerman.[22] The principle of his gage is shown in Fig. 4-25. It was shown previously that, when the beam of light is reflected on the fixed mirror also, the reflected image will not be affected by movements common to both mirrors but will measure only the changes of the angle between them. By using this principle in two perpendicular directions it is possible to stabilize the gage against tilt in all directions and avoid the inconvenience of losing the image during a test period. It is done by replacing the fixed mirror with a roof-edge prism giving a double reflection in a plane normal to the gage, thus obtaining stabilization in that direction. Since the gage is not sensitive to a tilt normal to the plane swept by the reflected beam, it becomes necessary to obtain an indication of the relative inclination of the collimating system to that plane. This is done by providing a flat surface at the bottom of the roof, which then acts with the tilting mirror as an unstabilized two-mirror system which reflects an image sensitive to the inclination of the collimator.

The observer sees, through the eyepiece of the autocollimating telescope T, the image of the index line, reflected by the three-mirror system. The index line consists of an 0 line and a vernier scale, and the location of its image in the focal plane is measured by means of a scale placed in the focal plane. If the orientation of the telescope is close to the plane of the gage, the observer will also see a faint reflection of the same index line, produced by surface F (flash surface) and the tilting mirror. As long as this image is seen, the relative inclination of the collimator is small, and the error caused thereby can be neglected. It is also only because of the stability of the image which is

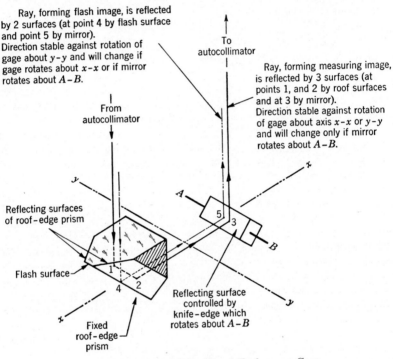

FIG. 4-25. Optical Principle of Tuckerman Gage

unaffected by vibration or small shifts of the gage that it is possible to provide a vernier with the index line.

The characteristics of this gage have been recently carefully investigated by Wilson,[23] who found it to have an average deviation of only 2×10^{-6} in. He found that the readings are proportional to the changes in length of the gage length, and that the material of the specimen does not influence the calibration, provided the gage is properly attached. He also investigated the influence of the clamping force and found that best results were obtained when the force holding the knife-edge against the specimen did not exceed 1 lb.

This type of gage appears to be the most convenient to use with the optical-lever system if very large magnifications are desired; it is commercially available in gage lengths of $1/4$ to 2 in.

LL. Strain Gages Using Mechanical Levers

Only those gages which use an optical system for observation of the readings are discussed in this chapter. All of them have been designed for very large magnifications, principally to reduce the gage length to permit the measuring of stresses in regions of high stress gradient.

20. Instruments with Optical Magnification. If a movement is magnified by mechanical levers, the magnified movement of the end of the levers can be further magnified if it is observed through a microscope. Such an instrument has been built and used by Peterson and Wahl.[24] The gage length of their instrument is 0.1 in., and the long arm of the levers is made of hollow aluminum tubing. The two levers are held together by means of two springs which permit the two arms to rotate relative to each other without altering their relative distance at point O, which acts as the pivot point.

By using a microscope of $100\times$ and a mechanical magnification of 50, the total magnification can reach 5000. The disadvantage of this method is that the focusing of a high-power microscope is always quite critical, and, in order to keep the ends of the arms in the field of the microscope and in sharp focus, a complicated fixture is required to keep the microscope properly aligned. Peterson and Wahl obtained good results with their instrument and claim an accuracy of $1\frac{1}{2}$ per cent. Hill[25] also used a similar instrument but does not give any data concerning its accuracy or ease of operation.

21. Instruments with Electronic Magnification. Instead of observing the movement of the levers, it is possible to record their relative movement by means of a variable slit which they actuate. A beam of light is passed through the slit and directed to a photoelectric cell. As the gap opening changes, the amount of light reaching the cell varies, causing a varying intensity in the current generated by the cell. The intensity is electronically amplified and measured. Pochapsky and Mase[26] used this method to study damping of forks at high temperatures. The magnification of their instrument is not given. Gadd and Van Degrift,[27] instead of using one gap, placed gratings of alternate transparent and opaque points (120 per inch) at the end of the levers in such a way that one grating moved in front of the other. In this manner, they obtained a large number of slits varying in identical manner. This system has the advantage of using a wider beam which can be uniformly distributed over the whole surface of the cell. A magnification of 30,000 is claimed for this system, and the gage lengths used were $1/16$, $1/8$, and $1/4$ in. A German design, based on the same principle, was developed by E. Lehr.[15] The gage lengths used were 0.040, $1/16$ and 0.080 in.; the mechanical magnification was 50 and the total magnification 50,000.

This type of gage seems to offer great possibilities. Optically, it requires an optical system which is carefully designed to provide uniform illumination over the variable gap.

22. Strain Gages with Interference Fringes. By placing optical flats at the end of the levers the variation in distance between the arms can be measured by interference fringes. Adjustments must be provided to bring the flats nearly parallel at the zero position so as to reduce the number of fringes caused by a relative tilt of the surfaces. As was mentioned in the article on interference fringes, this system is too sensitive for usual research work. This system was used by Vose[28] to measure the change in thickness of stress bakelite models in photoelastic testing. Gages to measure Young's modulus and to determine Poisson's ratio are described by B. Chalmers[4] and Lehr.[15]

MM. CALIBRATION OF GAGES

Of the several designs discussed in the preceding article, few appear to have been given thorough tests to determine their reliability and accuracy. These many designs indicate only a constant search for better means to measure very small displacements so as to permit the use of very small gage lengths. It is questionable whether present gages giving computed magnifications higher than 4000× will increase the accuracy of the measurements and permit observation of quantities which cannot already be accurately measured with magnifications of 2000 to 4000×. With the exception of the Tuckerman gage, which was tested by Wilson,[23] no optical gage designed for stress analysis with a small gage length has as yet been thoroughly tested.

Before the results are accepted, the reliability of the measurements must be determined by tests on specimens with known stress distributions. Peterson and Wahl[24] used sections of a beam where the stress was uniform and could be computed; Gadd and Van Degrift[27] followed a similar procedure with standard ASTM specimens. The gage should be used in actual tests under conditions identical to those which existed during calibration. Wilson[23] has investigated the influence of temperature, position of the gage, and mounting pressure and has shown that all of these factors may influence the results. Vose[29] had already shown that the mounting force is a critical factor by making tests on Huggenberger strain gages.

NN. OTHER INSTRUMENTS

For measurements requiring magnifications of less than 100×, measuring microscopes, comparators, and telescopes mounted on micrometer slides are used for direct readings. A portable comparator was designed by W. Klemperer for the Zeppelin-Goodyear Corporation.* The method consisted in accurately stamping, with a "marker," two reference lines approximately 10 in. apart on the parts investigated and in observing the relative displacement of these two marks by means of an optical instrument calibrated to the "marker." The comparator consists of two microscope objectives which form images of the reference lines on the focal plane of an eyepiece, bringing the image of one line to one side of the field and the other on the opposite side of the field by means of a splitting prism. When the testpiece is under

* This information was received from Dr. L. H. Donnell, formerly of the Good-Corporation, now at the Illinois Institute of Technology.

stress and the comparator is brought above the reference marks, their relative displacement is measured by means of a scale placed in the focal plane.

For observation of plastic deformations, Nádai[30] used the Schlieren method of illumination to make Lueder's lines visible; this method is described in section PP. A recent method, the "photogrid" method, has been developed by Brener[31] to measure plastic deformations in various stages of development. A photographic emulsion is applied to the surface of the part to be tested, and a fine grid of lines is printed thereon, and after development the emulsion is hardened into a coating strongly resistant to abrasion. When the part is plastically deformed, the grid lines follow the deformation of the surface, and the plastic flow can be analyzed by measuring the relative displacements of the grid.[32] Gerard[33] proposes a type of coating different from that used by Brener, which he states has superior properties and is easier to handle.

OO. Photoelastic Polariscopes

For accurate photoelastic work, the requirement is that a ray entering the specimen at point A (Fig. 4-26) should also pass through all points having

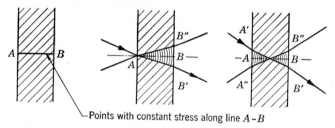

Points with constant stress along line $A-B$

Fig. 4-26. Path of Light Rays through Photoelastic Model

the same stress conditions, emerging at point B. Since images are formed by bundles of rays instead of single rays, there will be several rays passing through point A which will then be affected, not by the stress conditions along $A-B$, but by conditions within the circular cone $AB'B''$. If the rays intersect in the middle of the specimen, the stress conditions within the double cone $A'A''$ $B'B''$ will influence the direction of polarization of the bundle. To obtain a true image of the stress conditions the size of the cone must be as small as possible to give good definition of fringes closely spaced, as in the case of steep stress gradients. Since this condition must be satisfied at every point of the model, well-corrected collimated light must be used.

Collimation of the light or limitation of the bundles can be done in two ways: either by the optical system used to illuminate the specimen, which means a source of illumination with collimated light (section EE) or by the objective system which forms the image of the testpiece; that is, by an objective system properly diaphragmed. This last method is shown in Fig. 4-27. A diaphragm is shown at D, and, if it is placed at the focal point of the collecting lens $C-2$, only collimated bundles will be used for formation of the image. For ease of operation, a combination of the two methods is advisable.

The source of illumination is made to provide accurately collimated light with the aperture of the bundles somewhat large (Fig. 4-28).   On the objective side a variable diaphragm is placed so as to vary the aperture.   It is then possible to set the model with the objective diaphragm wide open, giving strong illumination at the expense of definition of the fringes but still retaining accuracy in their location.   Then the aperture of the diaphragm on the objective side is reduced, thus sharpening the fringes to record the picture under better conditions.

If Nicol prisms are used, in view of their small size, they should be placed near the diaphragms.   With polarizing plates the question of size is not so important, and they may be placed close by the model.   The function of the various lenses is as follows:

Lens C_1 is a collecting lens which should be corrected for spherical aberrations in order to give parallel bundles.   A single planoconvex lens with the

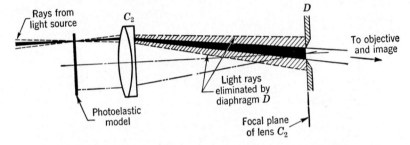

FIG. 4-27.   Method of Collimating Light on Objective Side

plano side turned toward the light source will be fairly satisfactory provided its speed is not more than $f10$ and the objective system is accurately diaphragmed.   A doublet lens will permit better correction and better matching of the collimated light emerging from the illuminating system with the collimation of the objective side.   Lens C_2 is also a collecting lens, and it should always be well corrected for spherical aberrations in order to collimate properly the system and to prevent distortion of the image.   It has two functions: (1) refracting of the bundles and (2) it is part of the objective system which forms an image of the model on the screen S.   Its speed should not exceed $f8$, less is preferable.

Lens O_1 is an objective lens which focuses the bundles and forms an image of the model at location I.   If the screen is to be placed at I as shown in Fig. 4-28, the image of the model will be inverted.   Lens O_1 should be a well-corrected lens.   If Nicol prisms are not used, the best solution is obtained by placing a photographic lens with iris diaphragm in place of diaphragm D and using the iris diaphragm of the lens as the collimating aperture.   A process-type lens is satisfactory.   Its focal length can be approximately determined by means of equation 3 by using distance DM for the object distance and DS for the image distance.

In a system designed to give an image on the screen in a normal position

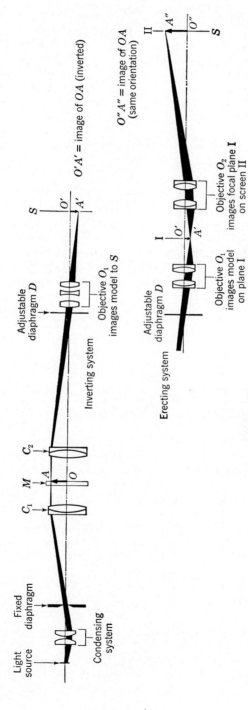

FIG. 4-28. Optical Elements of Photoelastic Polariscope

(that is, erect), focal plane I must be re-imaged on plane II by lens O_2. In this case, in order to keep the size of lens O_2 small without using a condensing lens at focal plane I, lens O_1 should be placed after diaphragm D. Photographic lenses are not usually designed for refracting bundles entering the lens in this manner. A well-corrected compound eyepiece would be satisfactory, or a high-speed projection lens can be used. The focal length of this objective should be small so as not to make the focal plane too large. To image plane I to the screen, a similar type of lens should be used. Selection of various focal lengths will give different-size images. In locations O_1 and O_2, if projection lenses are used, the back of the lens should be toward plane I; if eyepiece-type lenses are used, plane I should be considered as the focal plane of the eyepiece.

With a well-corrected system, and with the diaphragm D set for low speed, it should be possible to move the test model along the optical axis between lenses C_1 and C_2 with only a loss in sharpness in the extreme locations but with the size of the image remaining constant throughout the range.

Because of the low apertures used, fringe images can easily be obtained by lenses of secondary quality, which are sufficient for demonstration purposes; but, for accurate experimental work, all lenses should be chosen for the specific work they have to perform.

PP. Other Optical Systems Using Collimated Light

It has been shown that for the optical system used in the polariscope it is possible to obtain an image whose magnification of the object is independent of the location of the object in the space contained between lenses C_1 and C_2 (Fig. 4-28). This principle is used in *contour projectors*, where the magnification of the object must be independent of the accuracy of focussing.[35] Such systems are used to magnify objects up to 100×. Reflected collimated light is also used to obtain magnified contour lines of machined surfaces in the inspection of surface finish.[36]

An interesting application of collimated light is the inspection of surface irregularities and of irregularities inside of transparent materials by the *Schlieren method*. Barnes and Bellinger[34] give a description for its application to air-flow analysis; their article gives a complete bibliography on the subject. Figure 4-29 shows the principle of this method as applied to the inspection of a surface. If S is illuminated by collimated light and S is perfectly uniform, all the light will be reflected as a beam of collimated light. To observe the surface, the bundles are made to converge to point E, where a diaphragm is placed. When the observer places his eye behind the small opening E, he will receive light from all points of the surface, which will appear of uniform brightness. If there are irregularities on surface S, some of the bundles will be reflected at a different angle and will then not be refracted to point E and, therefore, will not enter the observer's eye. To the observer, therefore, the irregularity will appear as a dark spot on surface S. A camera objective can be placed back of E for the purpose of taking pictures of the surface observed.

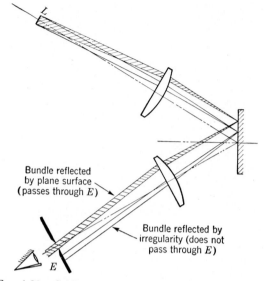

Bundle reflected
by plane surface
(passes through E)

Bundle reflected by
irregularity (does not
pass through E)

E

FIG. 4-29.   Schlieren Method for Surface Examination

BIBLIOGRAPHY

1. A. C. HARDY and F. H. PERRIN, *The Principles of Optics*, McGraw-Hill Book Co, 1st ed, New York, 1932.
2. D. H. JACOBS, *Fundamentals of Optical Engineering*, McGraw-Hill Book Co, 1st ed, New York, 1943.
3. J. P. C. SOUTHALL, *Mirrors, Prisms, and Lenses*, Macmillan Co, 1st ed, New York, 1933.
4. B. CHAMBERS, *The Physical Examination of Metals*, v 1 *Optical Methods*, Longmans, Green & Co, 1939.
5. J. STRONG and others, *Procedures in Experimental Physics*, Prentice-Hall, 1st ed, New York, 1939.
6. C. DÉVÉ, *Optical Workshop Principles*, translated by T. L. Tippel, Adam Hilger, 1st ed, London, 1943.
7. R. W. WOOD, *Physical Optics*, Macmillan Co, 1st ed, New York, 1934.
8. G. S. MONK, *Light, Principles, and Experiments*, McGraw-Hill Book Co, 1st ed, New York, 1937.
9. A. E. CONRADY, *Applied Optics and Optical Design*, v, Oxford Univ Press, London, 1929.
10. S. CZAPSKI and O. EPPENSTEIN, *Grundzüge der Theorie der optischen Instrumente*, Johann A. Barth, 3d ed, Leipzig, 1924.
11. I. C. GARDNER, "Application of Algebraic Aberrations Equations to Optical Design," *Sci Papers U. S. Bur Standards*, U. S. Govt Printing Office, Washington, D. C., v 22, n 550, 1927.
12. F. E. WRIGHT, "The Manufacture of Optical Glass and of Optical Systems," *U. S. Ordnance Dept Doc* 2037, 1st ed, U. S. Govt Printing Office, Washington, D. C., 1921.
13. F. TWYMAN, "Prism and Lens Making," Adam Hilger, 1st ed, London, 1942.
14. K. HENNEY and B. DUDLEY, *Handbook of Photography*, Whittlesey House, McGraw-Hill Book Co, 1st ed, New York, 1939.
15. E. SIEBEL, *Handbuch de Werkstoffprüfung*, Julius Springer, Berlin, 1941, 3 v. Lithoprinted by Edwards Brothers, Ann Arbor, Mich, 1944.

16. W. D. Buckingham and C. R. Deibert, "Characteristics and Applications of Concentrated-Arc Lamps," *J Soc Motion Picture Engrs*, v 47, n 5, pp 376–99, Nov 1946.
17. K. J. Dejuhasz, "On the Geometry of Optical Indicators," *J Franklin Inst*, v 229, pp 53–80, 1940.
18. L. H. Donnell, E. L. Shaw, and W. C. Potthoff, "Stress Model of a Complete Airship Structure," *J Applied Mechanics*, v 5, pp A-67–77, June 1938.
19. E. L. Shaw, "Some Phases of Structural Research at Goodyear Aircraft Corporation," *Proc Soc Exp Stress Analysis*, v 1, n 2 pp 90–100, 1944.
20. S. H. Hemsley, *Optical Instruments in Engineering*, Paul Elek, 1st ed, London, 1945.
21. A. Turner and F. H. Rolt, "End Gage Comparator," *Mech Eng*, v 60, p 767, Oct 1938. Review of article published in *Engineering*, 1938.
22. L. B. Tuckerman, "Optical Strain Gages and Extensometers," *Proc ASTM*, v 23, pt 2, pp 602–10, 1923.
23. B. L. Wilson, "Characteristics of the Tuckerman Strain Gage," *Proc ASTM*, v 44, pp 1017–26, 1944.
24. R. E. Peterson and A. M. Wahl, "Two- and Three-Dimensional Cases of Stress Concentration and Comparison with Fatigue Tests," *J Applied Mechanics*, v 3, pp 15–22, Mar 1936.
25. H. N. Hill, "Some Experiences in Experimental Stress Determination at the Aluminum Research Laboratories," *Proc Soc Exp Stress Analysis*, v 1, n 1, p 27, 1945.
26. T. G. Pochapsky and W. J. Mase, "A Photoelectric Method of Measuring Damping in Metal Forks at Elevated Temperatures," *J Applied Mechanics*, v 13, pp 157–61, June 1946.
27. C. W. Gadd and T. C. Van Degrift, "A Short Gage Length Extensometer and Its Application to the Study of Crankshaft Stresses," *J Applied Mechanics*, v 9, pp A-15–20, Mar 1942.
28. R. V. Vose, "An Application of the Interferometer Strain Gage in Photo-elasticity," *J Applied Mechanics*, v 2, pp 99–102, Sept 1935.
29. R. W. Vose, "Characteristics of the Huggenberger Tensometer," *Proc ASTM*, v 34, pt 2, p 862, 1934.
30. A. Nádai, "The Phenomenon of Slip in Plastic Materials," *Proc ASTM*, v 31, pt 2, pp 11–46, 1931.
31. G. A. Brener, "Measurement of Strain in the Plastic Range," *Proc Soc Exp Stress Analysis*, v 1, n 2, pp 105–15, 1944.
32. C. P. O'Haven and J. E. Harding, "Studies of Plastic Flow Research by Photo Grid Methods," *Proc Soc Exp Stress Analysis*, v 2, n 2, pp 59–70, 1945.
33. G. Gerard, "Photogrid Strain Analysis of Formed Parts," *Proc Soc Exp Stress Analysis*, v 3, n 2, pp 110–20, 1946.
34. N. F. Barnes and S. L. Bellinger, "Schlieren and Shadowgraph Equipment for Airflow Analysis," *J Optical Soc of America*, v 35, pp 497–509, Aug 1945. Extensive bibliography.
35. H. F. Kurtz, "Optical Projection," *Mech Eng*, v 60, pp 469–73, June 1938.
36. G. Schlesinger, *Surface Finish*, Institution of Production Engineers, 36 Portman Square, London W. 1, 1942. American ed, American Society of Mechanical Engineers, New York, 1942.
37. G. W. Morley, *The Properties of Glass*, Rheinhold Publishing Corp. 1st ed, New York, 1938.
38. C. D. Hodgmen and H. N. Holmes, *Handbook of Chemistry and Physics*, Chemical Rubber Publishing Co, 30th ed, Cleveland, Ohio, 1947. This reference is included because of its value in furnishing data on the optical properties of glass and other materials.
39. C. Mylonas and M. Greek, "The Optical System of Polariscopes as Used in Photoelasticity," *J Sci Instr*, v 25, n 3, pp 77–81, Mar 1948.

40. H. T. JESSOP, "The Optical System in Photoelastic Observations," *J Sci Instr*, v 25, n 4, pp 124–6, Apr 1948. These last two articles have appeared since the writing of this chapter and will be found useful to those who wish to build their own polariscope in conjunction with the outline given in Section OO of this chapter.

41. R. WELLER and B. M. SHEPARD, "Displacement Measurement by Mechanical Interferometry," *Proc Soc Exp Stress Analysis*, v VI, n 1, pp 35–8, 1948. This article shows an interesting use of the Schlieren system, whereby a photographic record is taken of the displacement of a set of lines engraved on a transparent testpiece and is measured by reference to another set of parallel lines engraved on a fixed surface held parallel and close to the model.

CHAPTER 5

ELECTRICAL-RESISTANCE GAGES AND CIRCUIT THEORY

By C. O. Dohrenwend and W. R. Mehaffey

A. INTRODUCTION

The theory of the resistance type of gage is to express a displacement as the function of a resistance change produced by the displacement. The resistance change is usually measured by a determination of the change in potential produced in an electric circuit, called the gaging circuit. When the displacement to be measured is a strain, the gage is called a resistance-type strain gage. In general, there are three methods by which a change in resistance may be coupled with a change in displacement. The first is the common variable potentiometer that has its resistance ratio changed by a physical variation of the contact point of the potentiometer; the variation of the contact point is controlled by the displacement. The second is the common type of variable pressure resistor, composed of nonmetallic material such as the carbon-pile resistor. In this case the resistance change, or potential variation of the gaging circuit, is coupled to the displacement by a variation of pressure controlled by the displacement. The third type operates by varying the stress in a metal wire as a function of the displacement to be measured.

Each of the methods mentioned for controlling the potential in the gaging circuit with an imposed displacement in the mechanical system to which the gage is attached has applications that are limited by the nature of the phenomena to be measured. The selection of the type of gage to be used depends on the magnitude of the over-all displacement, and the precision to which it is to be measured. All of the afore-mentioned methods have been used in a variety of places and with a large number of variations.

It is apparent that, if the measured displacements are small quantities, the resistance changes accompanying them will be small quantities. Such cases will require careful measuring methods for their determination, such as a good bridge circuit, or a high-fidelity amplifier.

Amplifiers are necessary for any dynamic measurements since the time for balancing a bridge is not available, and a much higher output than that of the gaging circuit is necessary for the operation of the oscilloscope or meter. On the other hand many applications can be made where the resistance change is large enough without amplification and where static conditions allow a direct measurement with a galvanometer.

The general use of resistance-type gaging methods may require the use of four separate circuits or units. The first is the supply circuit which may be either a simple d-c supply or an a-c oscillator circuit. The second is the gaging circuit, which has the function of relating the displacement to be measured to the potential difference caused by the displacement. The third is the amplifier circuit, which has the function of increasing the magnitude of the signal from the gaging circuit without distorting or warping the signal. The amplification is necessary in order to magnify the signal to the point where it will operate the recording mechanism, or oscilloscope. Whether the amplifier is essential or not depends on the phenomena to be measured, type of recording, and gage to be used. The fourth is the recording or metering circuit. This in turn may be divided into two parts. The first is a circuit which has the function of giving an indication of the direction of the displacement, that is, the sign of the displacement. This circuit is sometimes called a discriminator. The second is the recording circuit proper, which may include a meter, a galvanometer, or a cathode-ray oscilloscope.

A block diagram showing the various units is shown in Fig. 5-1. This diagram shows all the types of circuits that may be necessary for a resistance-

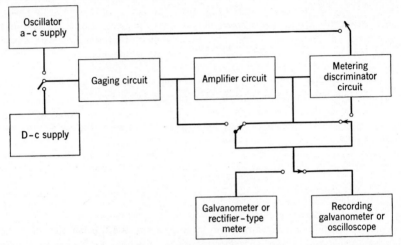

FIG. 5-1. Block Diagram of the Essential Circuits Used in Electrical-Gaging Measurements

type displacement measurement. In any particular application some of the units are not used, but those necessary may be selected to fit the problem.

In the discussion that follows the subject matter is divided into three major parts. The first deals with the resistance type of gage, and the second with the electric circuits used in electrical-gaging operations, while the third deals with principles of electronics and their application to the gaging problem. The second and third parts have a double objective: they aim to be basic enough for those whose knowledge and experience with electric circuits, especially electronics, is very limited, and at the same time sufficiently detailed to be of use to those very familiar with electric circuits and their use in electrical gaging.

For the convenience of the reader all symbols are defined when first encountered.

I. TYPES OF ELECTRICAL-RESISTANCE GAGES

There are a number of possible types of electrical-resistance gages. It is not the purpose of this section to discuss in detail all the forms and types in which such gages can be made and used, as there is practically an endless number of possibilities. It is rather the purpose to discuss in detail the three main types referred to in the introduction: namely, the variable potentiometer, the nonmetallic pressure resistor, and the metallic wire gage.

B. Varying Potentiometer Resistance Gages

This gage simply consists of applying the principle of the slide-wire potentiometer to the measurement of displacement with time. The variable point of the slide wire is attached to one of the members which is undergoing relative displacement with respect to another member which has the main body of the resistor attached to it. The type of resistor that may be used in this case, as in all application problems, depends on the particular application. If large displacements are to be measured, the slide-wire potentiometer may be used

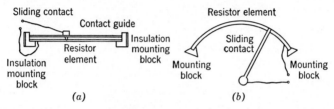

Fig. 5-2a.   Illustration of Slide-Wire Variable Potentiometer for Linear-Displacement Measurements

Fig. 5-2b.   Illustration of Slide-Wire Variable Potentiometer for Angular-Displacement Measurements

in the simple form of sliding the variable-contact point along the wire. If smaller displacements are to be measured, the resistor may be composed of a close-wound wire resistor of the sliding-contact type, and a mechanical multiplier which increases the displacement motion at the resistor may be added. The contact point must be very small and the wires of the resistor quite fine, depending on the range to be covered. The main factor in the design of such a gage is the size requirement, and the diameter of the wound-coil resistor is often controlled by this factor alone. It is desirable to have the resistor of such a size that the resistance change produced by the smallest change in displacement that one wishes to detect is large enough to operate the metering circuit with no amplification. This can be done when the displacements are quite large.

The physical design of the resistor may take on nearly any shape. It is not necessary for the displacement to be rectilinear, as the resistor may be made in the shape of a circular arc so that angular displacements can also be recorded. The method has limitations as to the smallest displacement that it is practical to measure by this means. This is controlled by the size of the contact point and by the size of the wire that may be used to wind the resistor. Displacements of a range of over $\frac{1}{4}$ in. are easily measured by this means with no mechanical magnification of contact resistor motion. Examples of this type would be the dynamic displacements of long-span girders, bridges, cranes, large flexible couplings, large vibratory motions, etc.   The gages of this type are particularly useful for the determination of the position of a piston with time and are often used to obtain indicator cards in engines and pumps. Several potentiometer gages of this type are illustrated in Fig. 5-2.

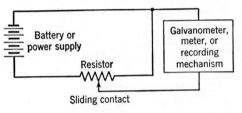

FIG. 5-3.   Simple Circuit for Varying Poten-tiometer Resistance-Gage Measurements

The circuit requirements for a varying potentiometer type of resistance gage are very simple and, in general, may be similar to that shown in Fig. 5-3.

C. NONMETALLIC RESISTANCE GAGES

The nonmetallic type of resistance gages may be divided into two classes: the unbonded and the bonded gages.   The first is a mechanically actuated gage that contains a resistance element so arranged that when one part of the gage is displaced with respect to another there is developed a change in pressure on the measuring element of the gage.   This change in pressure changes the resistance of the element which may be recorded by electrical means.   The second type is a simplification of the first in that the resistance element is bonded directly to the material—hence, its name—and the strain in the material changes the pressure or the dimensions of the element bonded to it and thus couples the displacement to change in resistance.   This second type is very suitable for strain measurements.

1. Unbonded Nonmetallic Resistance Gages.   This principle is best described by studying a particular application.   A gage of this type was developed in 1923 and 1924 by Burton McCollum and O. S. Peters.[4]   This gage is composed of a series of carbon plates arranged in a stack.   The stack is so adjusted that a displacement of one part of the gage relative to another changes the pressure on the stack of plates.   This pressure must be so regulated that the plate stack behaves like an elastic body.

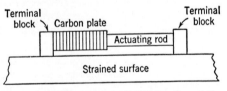

FIG. 5-4.   Diagrammatic Illustration of the Principle of Carbon Strain Gage

The gage arrangement as proposed by McCollum and Peters is as shown in Fig. 5-4.   It can be seen that the terminal blocks in Fig. 5-4 are so arranged that, when the strain is applied in the structure to which the gage is attached, the change in length is communicated to the carbon-plate stack.   This change in length requires a change in pressure in the stack, and the resistance of the stack changes.   This gage was given the name of the electric telemeter.

The change in pressure in the stack of carbon plates controls the resistance in two ways: (1) With an increase in pressure, the areas of contact between the plates are enlarged and new areas will come into contact, thus decreasing the resistance of the element; (2) if the pressure is released, the areas of contact are reduced, and some of the areas in contact will lose contact, thus increasing the resistance of the element. As long as the points of contact between the plates are not disturbed, and remain absolutely the same, the results of the gage are very good. If, however, the pressure becomes excessive,

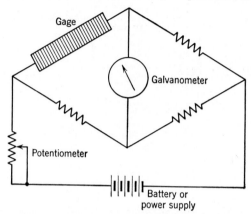

Fig. 5-5.   Diagram Showing Principle of Connecting Single-Element Resistor in Wheatstone Bridge

so that the elastic limit of the carbon in the gages is exceeded or the carbon is even crushed, or if the plates are allowed to shift in the lateral direction with respect to each other, the results become very erratic. This erratic result is due to the change in the number and size of points in contact. Any construction of the gage must be such as to avoid the occurrence of these

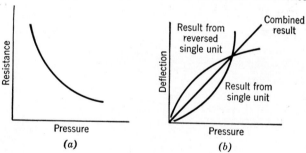

Fig. 5-6a.   Characteristic Relations between Pressure and Resistance of Single Unit

Fig. 5-6b.   Combination of Two Units, One on Each Side of the Bridge

things. Besides these difficulties, there is a further defect of mechanical friction and hysteresis in the mechanical parts of the gage.

It is advantageous to place the unit in a bridge circuit as shown in Fig. 5-5. In order to make the response of the unit, which is somewhat like the curve shown in Fig. 5-6a, more linear, it is advisable to place two units in the bridge circuit, with one unit undergoing a decrease in pressure while the other unit is undergoing an increase in pressure. Figure 5-7 shows how this can be arranged from mechanical considerations, and Fig. 5-6b shows how the two response curves add to give a nearly linear variation of resistance with displacement.

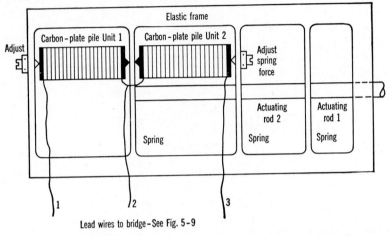

Lead wires to bridge—See Fig. 5-9

FIG. 5-7.   Method of Mounting Double-Resistor Type of Strain Gage

The use of these gages is rather cumbersome, and the elements are somewhat delicate. The gage lengths are rather long, and the units fairly heavy. Figure 5-8 shows the attachment of this type gage to a tension member. Figure 5-9 shows the circuit used by McCollum and Peters. The instrument is held into the stressed member by the use of steel points similar to most

FIG. 5-8.   Strain Gage Clamped on Member under Test.

mechanical gages. The force required to operate the gage is rather high and may be as much as 10 lb. The ratio of the displacement in the stressed member to that of the resistor is 10 to 1. There is some change in the initial value of the resistance with time especially when the resistor is new. The apparent reason for this aging of the new resistors is that the end pieces, pivot bearings, threads, and carbon stacks all go through a slow and permanent deformation process, or a bedding into each other, which tends toward a reduction in the set pressure in the carbon stack and a resulting increase in resistance. This may amount to a resistance change of a few per cent. The gages appear to be fairly stable with time, it having been reported that they changed in resistance in 1½ years by about 1 per cent. The gage is subjected to a temperature effect primarily from the expansion and contraction difference of the frame which holds the carbon stacks and of the carbon stacks themselves. This expansion or contraction difference changes the pressure on the stacks and, thus, its resistance.

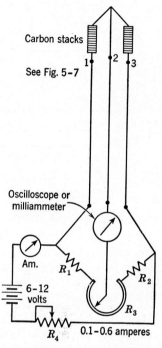

Gages of this kind have been used to determine displacements, loads and strains in flexible cables, airplanes, bridges, vibrating members, dynamometers, and pressure gages. With a single instrument the range of sensitivity is rather large. The bridge current can be varied from 0.1 to 0.6 amperes, which gives a ratio of 6 to 1, and the ratio of the carbon-stack displacement to the stressed-member displacement may be varied mechanically, which makes the total change of sensitivity as much as 20 to 1.

In the past these units have been used with a good measure of success. However, the development of other types of electrical gaging methods which are less cumbersome and more reliable has reduced its usefulness materially.

Fig. 5-9. Diagram of the Electric Circuit for Telemeter as Proposed by McCollum and Peters

2. Bonded Nonmetallic Resistance Gages.

The direct bonding of nonmetallic resistor elements to a material in which the strain was to be measured is probably due to A. Bloch, who reported in a note appearing in the August 10, 1935 issue of *Nature Magazine* that he had prepared a carbon coating which could be applied directly to the surface of a structure to be tested (in metallic structures the surface was first coated with a nonconducting material). If the underlying surface of such a coating was stretched, the carbon particles moved apart, and, if the undercoating was compressed, the particles moved closer together, and the resistance changed in the same manner as the resistance of a microphone. If the coatings are properly prepared, they behave in a sufficiently stable manner and also give a linear response without hysteresis. Bloch found that an ordinary two-stage amplifier was adequate for the operation of the coating.

The development of this coating by Bloch was a forerunner of the impregnated-plastic resistor developed at Hamilton Standard Division of United

Aircraft Corporation by Kearns*   These impregnated-plastic gages are prepared by the impregnation of colloidal carbon particles in plastic sheets.
These sheets are cut into strips about ¼ in. wide and 1 in. long.   Each
little strip has a silver band plated to each end so that lead wire may be
attached and forms one gage unit.   A sketch of one of these gage units is
shown in Fig. 5-10a.   The gage is bonded directly to the surface to be strained

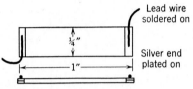

FIG.   5-10a.   Bonded-Carbon   Impregnated-Plastic Strip Gage

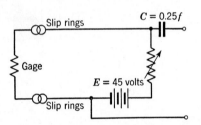

FIG. 5-10b.   Conventional Gage Circuit
Used by Hamilton Standard for Control
Carbon Strip Gage

with a common glue.

The carbon gages developed at
Hamilton Standard had a resistance
which varied between 15,000 and
35,000 ohms.   The high resistance
of the gage minimizes the trouble
from interference induced from slip-
ring applications and allows a relatively high energizing potential without excessive currents.   The wide
variation of the resistance makes it
nearly impossible to use fixed bridge
circuits and amplifier units.   The
sensitivity and resistance of the
gages are affected by temperature
and humidity.   The width of the
gage induces a resistance change
due to the lateral stress; this is
termed cross sensitivity.†   The ratio of transverse sensitivity to axial
sensitivity is called cross-sensitivity
factor.   For these gages the cross-sensitivity factor is high.   This high
cross-sensitivity factor can be materially reduced by bonding only the
ends of the gage to the surface of measurement.   These gages have the
center of the strain-sensitive element about 0.02 in. above the strained surface.
This is not a serious objection except when the measurements are made on
thin sheets which are subjected to bending stresses.   In such case the error
may be quite large.   The gages have been used when applied with a bakelite
cement to temperatures of 300°F.   The gage, in general, is rather rugged and
can stand very rough handling compared to most resistance-type gages.

The conventional gage circuit used with these gages by Hamilton Standard
is shown in Fig. 5-10b.   These cages have been used very successfully for
the measurement of stresses in the propellers of aircraft while in flight.   For
many applications the gage has been replaced by the bonded wire strain gage.

D. Metallic Resistance Gages

The metallic resistance gage may be divided into the same two classes as
the nonmetallic gage: namely, those gages in which the measuring element

---

* Information on carbon strip strain gage furnished by Hamilton Standard
Division of United Aircraft Corporation, D. E. Richards.
† See page 175.

is a metallic wire whose resistance is controlled by motion of the mechanical parts of a gage, and those which have the element bonded directly to the material in which the strain is to be measured.

3. Unbonded Metallic Gages. The physicist has known and used the change in resistance of metals with a change in external forces for some time. However, the first engineering application of this phenomenon appears to be in an electrical-resistance wire strain gage employed in the measurement of strains in concrete structures. This first device appears to have been designed by R. W. Carlson[2] and reported in the *Engineering News Record* by E. C. Eaton[1] in the October 15, 1930, issue.

The principle of the Carlson resistance gage is based on the change in electrical resistance of an elastic steel wire due to the change in tension of the wire. The breaking strength of the wire used is reported as 700,000 psi, with an elastic limit of 300,000 psi. Eaton reported that the change in resistance due to the change in tension on the wire was about four times the per cent change in length due to the

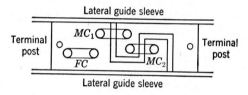

FIG. 5-11.   Coil Arrangement in Carlson Gage

tension, and that the resistance changed 0.35 per cent per degree centigrade. The gage that was constructed was sensitive to 10 psi and 0.25°C.

The gage was constructed by winding wire in three coils, the first providing a coil unaffected by the gage motion, and the other two having tensions altered by the gage motion, each in an opposite manner: for example, one had its tension increased and the other had its tension reduced by a given gage displacement (see Fig. 5-11). The fixed coil is marked FC in the schematic sketch of the gage, and the movable coils are marked as MC_1 and MC_2. The whole unit is mounted in a sleeve that allows only longitudinal movement. The coils are placed under initial tension. The electrical arrangement of the coils allows each to be checked against the standard coil or neutral coil. In such an arrangement, the gage under strain shows each coil with an equal but opposite resistance change with respect to the fixed coil.

In the gage constructed by Carlson only a small portion of the Wheatstone bridge is made variable. The larger portion of the arm and all the other arm were buried in paraffin and not disturbed.

The effect of temperature to the nearest 0.5° could be determined from the combined resistance of the two coils of the strain meter. This is possible since the increase in strain of one is offset by an almost equal decrease in strain in the other. The operation of the gage required a force of about 1 lb to cause a strain of 0.0005 in. in the gage length. The main application of this type of gage was for the measurement of strains in the interior of concrete structures and slab displacements in concrete at the joints, as well as shrinkage strains.

An elaboration of the wire-resistance principle as developed by Carlson in the unbonded form has been carried out by Statham Laboratories.[5] Los

Angeles, Calif.   These units have been incorporated into accelerometers and pressure pickups and promise much in a new approach to the measurement of force, pressure, acceleration, and movement.

4. Bonded Metallic Gages.   The idea of bonding the resistance element directly to the material was conceived at California Institute of Technology in the application to a tension impact test.   This application was made by Simons and reported by Clark and Datwyler.[6]   In this case approximately 14 ft of no. 40 constantan wire was laid longitudinally on four successive faces of a bar in zigzag fashion and coated with glyptal as a binder.   The wire was protected by Scotch tape.   The complete unit was used as a dynamometer in impact testing.

Ruge at Massachusetts Institute of Technology at about the same time conceived the idea of bonding the wire to a paper and then bonding the paper with a common glue to the material where the strain is to be measured.

This bonded-wire type of electrical-resistance strain gage consists of a gird of fine alloy wire bonded to a paper base.   In use this gage is cemented to the surface of the structural member to be tested.   Two constructions of the gage are shown in Fig. 5-12.   The strain-sensitive wires are about 0.001 in. in diameter.   These fine alloy wires are soldered or welded to heavier copper lead wires.   This type of gage is typified by the SR-4 gage manufactured by Baldwin–Southwark.

Since each incremental length of wire is bonded by the cement, the wires cannot buckle and need not be preloaded.   The cement gives enough support so that the gage will respond to compression as well as tension.

The principle of operation is based on the formula for the resistance of a conductor.

$$R = \rho \frac{L}{A} \tag{1}$$

where
R = resistance of conductor
ρ = specific resistance
L = length of conductor
A = cross-sectional area of conductor

If a wire is stretched, its length L will increase, and its area of cross section A will decrease; this will result in a change of its resistance R.   From experimental observations the changes in resistance R are found to be larger than would be predicted from the pure geometrical changes owing to elastic straining.   In order to determine the unit change in resistance per unit strain, equation 1 is differentiated with all terms considered variable, and the result is shown as follows:

$$dR = \frac{\rho A \, dL + LA \, d\rho - L\rho \, dA}{A^2} \tag{a}$$

Let the volume of the wire be written as $V = AL$.   Then,

$$dV = A \, dL + L \cdot dA \tag{b}$$

For a given strain the expression for dV may also be written as

$$dV = L(1 + \epsilon)A(1 - m\epsilon)^2 - LA$$

where ϵ is the unit longitudinal strain and m Poisson's ratio and $dV = L \cdot A\epsilon(1 - 2m)$ if the strain is small so that second-order terms of ϵ may be neglected. The unit strain ϵ may be written dL/L, and dV then becomes

$$dV = A \cdot dL(1 - 2m) \tag{c}$$

Equations b and c may be equated, and then

$$A\,dL + L \cdot dA = A \cdot dL - 2mA \cdot dL$$

or

$$L \cdot dA = -A \cdot dL \cdot 2m \tag{d}$$

This expression d may be substituted in equation a.

$$dR = \frac{\rho A(dL) + LA(d\rho) + \rho A(dL)2m}{A^2}$$

and

$$dR = \frac{\rho\,dL(1 + 2m)}{A} + \frac{L\,d\rho}{A} \tag{e}$$

Now divide equation e by equation 1 and

$$\frac{dR}{R} = \frac{dL}{L}(1 + 2m) + \frac{d\rho}{\rho} \tag{f}$$

Equation f may be written as

$$\frac{dR/R}{dL/L} = 1 + 2m + \frac{d\rho/\rho}{dL/L} \tag{g}$$

The factor $\dfrac{dR/R}{dL/L}$ is called the gage factor and is written as K_s, and

$$K_s = 1 + 2m + \frac{d\rho/\rho}{dL/L} \tag{2}$$

The term $\dfrac{d\rho/\rho}{dL/L}$ is positive for most materials and nearly zero for some; in a few cases it is negative. Values of the gage factor K_s taken from the literature are shown with source for the common gage wires in Table 5-1, and for other materials in Table 5-2.

The choice of wire to be used in wire-resistance measurements is based primarily on the gage factor K_s. However, the change of resistance with temperature is also an important factor. The temperature coefficient of resistance is shown in Table 5-3.

The change in resistance per degree of temperature change for a gage may be considerably larger than the temperature coefficient of resistance of an unbonded wire. This is due to the differential coefficient of expansion between gage wire and the base metal to which the gage is bonded. The magnitude of this effect for the common gage wire (Advance and Iso Elastic) gages mounted on various metals is listed in Table 5-4. Another disturbing factor, the thermal electromotive force is important when d.c amplifiers are used in the controlling circuits and the junctions are not at the same temperature. In most applications both copper-alloy junctions will be at the same temperature, and this effect can be neglected, but it should be guarded against. The

TABLE 5-1
COMMONLY USED GAGE MATERIAL

Material	K_s	Observer	Remarks
Advance*	2.12	J. H. Meier	Tested as a single-wire gage on test bar of steel
	2.1	A. V. DeForest	Method not stated
	2.12	TMB Report† R-212	Tested as an unbonded wire
	2.05	W. R. Campbell NACA Technical Note 954	Tested on tensile testpiece as a standard gage
	2.04	Baldwin-Southwark	Tested as a gage on beam
Iso Elastic*	3.56	J. H. Meier	Tested as a single-wire gage on cold-rolled steel
	3.6	A. V. DeForest	Method not stated
	3.53	Baldwin Southwark	Tested as a gage on beam
	3.6	TMB Report R 212	Tested as an unbounded wire
Nichrome*	2.55	J. H. Meier	Single-wire gage on celluloid beam
	2.1	A. V. DeForest	Method not stated
	2.63	TMB Report R 212	Tested as an unbonded wire

* These are trade names for these materials. Their actual composition is approximately as follows:

Advance: 54–55% copper
44–46% nickel

Iso Elastic: 36% Nickel
8% chromium
4% (manganese silicon and molybdenum)
Remainder iron
Small amts. carbon and vanadium

Nichrome: 75% nickel
12% iron
11% chromium
2% manganese

† Taylor Model Basin.

thermal electromotive force when joined to copper lead wires is shown in Table 5-5.

The mechanical properties of the gage wire are important in that the yield point of the wire should be high compared to that of the base member to which the gage is attached. This is nearly always the case for the common gage wires.

From Table 5-1 and Table 5-2 it will be observed that tests of K_s for com-

TABLE 5-2

SPECIAL MATERIALS

Material	K_s	Observer	Remarks
5% iridium	5.1	De Forest	Method not stated
Platinum	5.83	J. H. Meier	Tested as single-wire gage
Monel*	1.9	De Forest	Method not stated
Platinum	4.12	J. H. Meier	Tested on beam as a single-wire gage
	6.1	TMB Report R 12	Unbonded wire
Chromel C*	2.5	L. M. Ball	Tested as a gage on steel
Manganin*	0.47	De Forest	Method not stated
	0.5	TMB Report R 212	Tested as unbonded wire
	0.47	J. H. Meier	Single-wire gage on steel
Palladium	4.0	J. H. Meier	Tested as single-wire gage
Gold	3.22	J. H. Meier	
Phosphor bronze*	1.93	J. H. Meier	
Nickel	−12 to −20	J. H. Meier	As a single-wire gage
	−12	De Forest	Method not stated
Constantan*	1.79	J. H. Meier	As a single-wire gage

* These are trade names for these materials. Their actual composition is approximately:

Monel:	Chromel C:	Manganin:	Phosphor Bronze:	Constantan:
⅓ copper	60% nickel	9–18% manganese	5% tin	60% copper
⅔ nickel	24% iron	1½–4% nickel	0.1–1% phosphorus	40% nickel
	16% chromium	Remainder copper	Trace lead Remainder copper	

TABLE 5-3

TEMPERATURE COEFFICIENT OF RESISTANCE PER DEGREE CENTIGRADE

Copper	0.003 93
Advance*	0.000 01
Constantan*	0.000 01
Manganin*	0.000 01
Monel*	0.002
Nichrome*	0.000 4
Nickel	0.006
Palladium	0.003 3
Phosphor bronze*	0.0018
Platinum	0.003
Iso Elastic*	0.000 47

* For composition of these materials see footnotes to Tables 5-1 and 5-2.

plete grid-type gages are considerably lower than for unbonded wire or single-wire bonded gages. This is due to the loss of effectiveness of part of the wire when the end loops are used. This wire at the end loops results in a cross sensitivity to strain at right angles to the principal axis of the gage. The K_s value given for SR 4 gages is based on a $m = 0.285$ for the calibrating

TABLE 5-4

Base Material	Apparent Stress per °C	Source of Data
Advance Gages		
On Steel	−30	A. V. de Forest
	−66	L. R. Ball
On aluminum	46	L. R. Ball
Iso Elastic Gages		
On steel	1930	L. R. Ball
	5000	A. V. de Forest
On Aluminum	755	L. R. Ball

TABLE 5-5

THERMOELECTRIC ELECTROMOTIVE FORCES

Type of Junction	Microvolts per °C
Copper Advance*	43
Copper Iso Elastic*	3.0
Copper Nichrome*	22
Copper Manganin*	2.0

* For composition of these materials see footnotes to Tables 5-1 and 5-2.

TABLE 5-6

SR 4* Type	K_c, %
A-1	2
A-3	2
A-5	3.5
A-6	1.75
A-7	−1
A-8	−2
A-9	Negligible
A-11	0.5
A-12	1
A-13	−0.75
A-14	−0.75
A-15	−0.75
A-18	−2
C-1	1.75
C-5	4
C-7	1
C-8	−2
C-10	0.75
C-11	2
C-14	0.75

* Trade name—Baldwin-Southwark Wire Resistance Strain Gages, manufactured by the Baldwin Locomotive Company, the Baldwin-Southwark Division.

beam material. The cross sensitivity is defined as

$$K_{\text{cross}} = \frac{\text{transverse sensitivity}}{\text{axial sensitivity}}$$

Table 5-6* gives the value of K_c for SR 4 gages. For additional data on this effect consult the chapter on strain rosettes pp. 407—10.

The low values of cross sensitivity for A_7, A_8, and C_7 are due to a different method of construction in which a flat helical winding is used instead of a

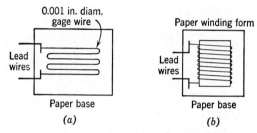

FIG. 5-12a. Bonded-Wire Strain-Gage Flat Grid
FIG. 5-12b. Bonded-Wire Strain-Gage Helical Coil

flat grid. The end loops are arranged in a direction normal to the surface of the number (see Fig 5-12b).

The values of the gage factor K_s for wire strain gages has been shown by William R. Campbell[9] to be slightly different in tension and compression. Table 5-7 is taken from his work.

TABLE 5-7

COMPARISON OF AVERAGE CALIBRATION FACTORS IN TENSION AND IN COMPRESSION

Average Calibration Factors

Gage Type	Tension, $K_s(t)$	Compression, $K_s(c)$	$\left[1 - \dfrac{K_s(t)}{K_s(c)}\right]100$
A	2.027	2.024	−0.1
B	2.083	2.082	0.0
C	2.034	2.035	0.0
D	2.058	2.063	0.3
E	2.104	2.067	−1.8
F	2.037	2.033	−0.2
G	2.314	2.357	1.8
I	2.149	2.127	−1.0
J	2.088	2.070	−0.9
K	2.170	2.134	−1.6
L	2.243	2.331	3.8
M	1.980	1.959	−1.1
N	3.480	3.461	−0.5
O	2.086	2.089	0.1

* Taken from reference 8.

E. Bonding of Gages to Strain Surface

The usual practice in bonding a gage to the material in which the strain is to be measured is to use a commercially prepared fast-drying cement (such

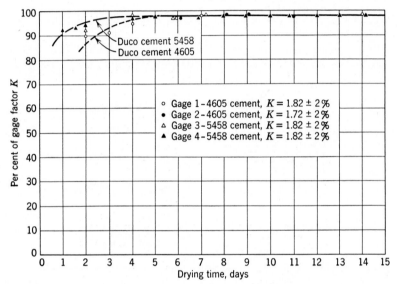

FIG. 5-13.   Gage Factor versus Drying Time for Two Commercial Nitrocellulose Cements.   Normal Temperature and Humidity Drying.   SR-4-Type Strain Gages

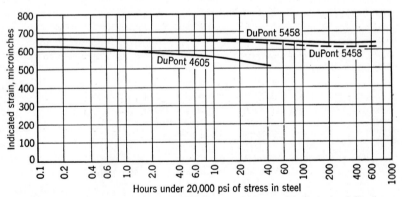

FIG. 5-14.   Performance of A-8 SR-4 Strain Gages under Sustained Strain

as DuPont Company's Duco Cement).   The question often arises as to the creep in the cement under sustained strain and also the effect on the measurement of the length of time from which the gages are first applied to the time of straining.   The results of tests run at the Caterpillar Tractor Company's research laboratory on this effect are shown in Fig. 5-13 and Fig. 5-14.

Figure 5-13 shows the effect of drying time as a function of per cent gage factor, and Fig. 5-14 shows the effect of sustained strain. It can be seen that the effects are small. The indication is, however, that the Duco-type cements should be allowed to set one day.

F. Slip Rings and Sliding Contacts

Often it is necessary to use the strain gage on a moving part, such as a shaft. In order to get the signal from the gage to the recording mechanism, some form of slip ring or sliding contact must be used. If these contact points are

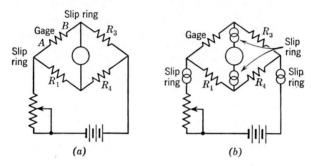

FIG. 5-15a. Slip Rings in Bridge Circuit Avoided when Possible
FIG. 5-15b. Slip Rings in Exciting Circuit Preferred when Possible

enclosed in the bridge circuit proper, as indicated by points A and B in Fig. 5-15a, slight variations in resistance of the contact points may be as large as the signal from the gage, and poor results are obtained unless this difficulty can be overcome. If the contact points can be outside the bridge circuit (Fig. 5-15b), the variation of resistance is not of so much importance. This requires that the complete bridge circuit be mounted on the moving part, which in some cases is possible. If the shaft has pure torsion, and there is no space limitation, all arms of the bridge can be made to record strain and, thus, give a better gain. However, if the moving part does not have a homogeneous stress, the four arms of the bridge cannot be used as measuring arms, and the placing of the complete bridge circuit on the moving part becomes more involved since three of the arms must not suffer any change during stressing. It is necessary under any condition to use as much care as possible in holding the resistance change at the slip rings to a minimum. Some idea of an adequate device may be obtained from Fig. 5-16. The effect of variation in resistance in the exciting circuit compared to that in the bridge circuit is discussed in detail in Article 7.

G. Gage Calibration

Since the bonded type of gage is not generally usable more than once, it is desirable to calibrate the gage without actually attaching it to a calibrating bar and testing it. This can be done by measuring the resistance of the gage proper and then using the gage factor K_s of the material of the gage:

FIG. 5-16a. Strain-Gage Slip-Ring Assembly Cover not Shown

FIG. 5-16b. Partially Dismantled Strain-Gage Slip-Ring Assembly

$$K_s = \frac{\Delta R/R}{\Delta L/L} = \frac{\Delta R/R}{\epsilon} \quad \text{or} \quad \epsilon \doteq \frac{\Delta R}{RK_s}$$

and the instrument need only be calibrated against known ΔR values. In practice, it is very convenient to produce a known ΔR by shunting a resistance

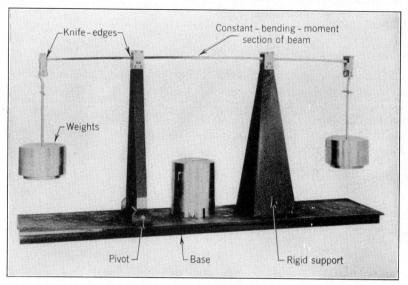

Knife-edges

Constant-bending-moment section of beam

Weights

Pivot · Base · Rigid support

FIG. 5-17. Strain-Gage Beam Calibrator

across the strain gage and noting the change in output. If R_s is the resistance of calibration resistor, and R_2 the gage resistance, then

$$\Delta R_2 = R_2 - \frac{R_2 R_s}{R_2 + R_s}$$

and

$$\epsilon = \frac{R_2}{K_s(R_2 + R_s)}$$

If this resistance is shunted across the compensating gage, it will correspond to tension. This method of course, requires a linear amplifying system.

However, if the gages are standard, such as each type of SR-4, and if electronic units are used in the circuit, a direct calibration of each type rather than each gage by mechanical means is preferred. A common method of calibration is by the use of a beam in bending as shown in Fig. 5-17. In this case a beam that is of rectangular section at least six times as wide as its depth should be used. The equation of strain in terms of the bending moment is given then, if the bar is assumed to remain with no anticlastic curvature, so that radius of curvature in that direction is ∞ and

$$\epsilon_x = \frac{M_x(1 - m^2) \dfrac{h}{2}}{EI}$$

This value of ϵ_x may then be determined as a function of meter reading and the instrument calibrated.

II. RESISTANCE MEASUREMENTS AND ELECTRONIC PRINCIPLES FOR ELECTRICAL GAGING

H. Theory of Resistance Measurements

In order to use the electrical-resistance type of gage it is necessary to understand the methods by which the change of resistance set up in the gage by the displacements can be measured. The basic circuits for registering the potential difference caused by the change in the resistance have been called the gaging circuits. These circuits are of two kinds, the potentiometer type and the bridge type.

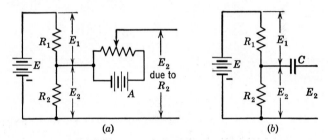

(a) (b)

Fig. 5-18a.   Potentiometer Circuit with Auxiliary Electromotive Force
Fig. 5-18b.   Potentiometer Circuit with Capacitor

5. The Potentiometer Circuit. Circuits of this type are shown in Fig. 5-18. Let it be required to measure the change in voltage ΔE_2 that would be produced by changing the resistance R_2 by ΔR_2, as shown in Fig. 5-18. The voltage E_2 will be large compared to ΔE_2.

If the change in voltage ΔE_2 is to be put into an amplifier, the voltage E_2 must be reduced to zero. This may be done in one of two ways. The first, as shown in Fig. 5-18a, may be used when the coupling is to be to a direct-coupling amplifier or when steady-state conditions are to be measured. The balancing is obtained from an auxiliary source of voltage applied at A. The second way, as shown in Fig. 5-18b, may be used if the conditions in the circuit are dynamic or transient; then the voltage E_2 is eliminated by the use of a coupling condenser.

The magnitude of ΔE_2 as a function of R_1, ΔR_2, R_2, and E may be found in the following manner.

Let R_2 be the resistance that is to be varied by a displacement by the amount ΔR_2 and R_1 a constant or ballast resistor.

E is the impressed voltages on the circuit by the battery.

$E = E_1 + E_2$ where E_1 is voltage across resistance R_1 and E_2 voltage across resistance R_2.

$$E_1 = IR_1, \qquad E_2 = IR_2$$

$$\therefore \frac{E_1}{E_2} = \frac{R_1}{R_2}$$

$$E_2 = \frac{R_2}{R_1} E_1 \quad \text{but} \quad E_1 = E - E_2 \quad \therefore E_2 = \frac{R_2}{R_1}(E - E_2)$$

$$E_2 = \frac{R_2/R_1}{1 + \dfrac{R_2}{R_1}} = \frac{ER_2}{R_1 + R_2} \tag{3}$$

Now let R_2 change by an amount ΔR_2 and E_2 will change by an amount ΔE_2, and, by differentiation,

$$dE_2 = \frac{E(R_1 + R_2)\, dR_2 - E_2 R_2\, dR_2}{(R_1 + R_2)^2}$$

or

$$dE_2 = \frac{ER_1\, dR_2}{(R_1 + R_2)^2} \tag{4}$$

Then, $\Delta E_2 = ER_1 \dfrac{\Delta R_2}{(R_1 + R_2)^2}.$ This equation is good only for small changes in ΔR_2. This may be demonstrated in the following manner.

If R_2 changes by an amount ΔR_2, then, E_2 will change in the following manner:

$$E_2 = \frac{E(R_2 + \Delta R_2)}{[R_1 + (R_2 + \Delta R_2)]} - \frac{ER_2}{(R_1 + R_2)}$$

Let $(R_1 + R_2) = R$;

Then,

$$\Delta E_2 = \frac{E(R_2 + \Delta R_2)}{(R + \Delta R_2)} - \frac{ER_2}{R} = \frac{E}{R} \frac{R_2 + \Delta R_2}{\left(1 + \dfrac{\Delta R_2}{R}\right)} - \frac{ER_2}{R}$$

$$= \frac{E}{R}\left(\frac{R_2 + \Delta R_2 - R_2 - \dfrac{\Delta R_2}{R} R_2}{\left(1 + \dfrac{\Delta R_2}{R}\right)}\right) = \frac{ER_1}{R}\left(\frac{\dfrac{\Delta R_2}{R}}{1 + \dfrac{\Delta R_2}{R}}\right)$$

This may be expanded in series form by division.

$$\Delta E_2 = E \frac{R_1}{R} \frac{\Delta R_2}{R}\left[1 - \frac{\Delta R_2}{R} + \left(\frac{\Delta R_2}{R}\right)^2 - \left(\frac{\Delta R_2}{R}\right)^3 + \left(\frac{\Delta R_2}{R}\right)^4 - \cdots\right] \tag{5}$$

A first approximation is to assume $(\Delta R_2/R)^2$ is negligible compared to $\Delta R_2/R$.

Then $\Delta E_2 = E \dfrac{R_1 \Delta R_2}{(R_1 + R_2)^2}$, the same as equation 4. Since $i = E/R_1 + R_2$,

this may be written as $\Delta E_2 = iR_1 \dfrac{\Delta R_2}{R_1 + R_2}$, and, if $R_1 = R_2$ as when the

gages are matched, then, $\Delta E_2 = \frac{1}{2}i\,\Delta R_2$.

6. The Bridge Type of Circuit. The bridge circuit is a well-known method for establishing the values of resistances and change in resistances. The

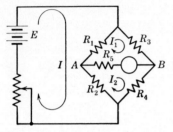

simple type of dc bridge circuit is shown in Fig. 5-19.

In this circuit the basic relation is to have the current in resistance R_5 be equal to zero. This requires no potential across the bridge from point A to point B. The problem is, therefore, to find the relation between resistances R_1, R_2, R_3, R_4 to make $I_5 = 0$. This is called balancing the bridge.

Fig. 5-19. D-C Bridge Circuit
Currents I are taken as $(+)$ in
clockwise direction as shown

The condition necessary to balance the bridge is obtained by applying the principles that the sum of the potential drops taken around a closed loop is zero (Kirchhoff's second law) and the current in any conductor which is common to two meshes is the difference between the two mesh currents (Maxwell's Artifice of hypothetical cyclic currents). The currents are assumed positive as shown in Fig. 5-19.

Applying these principles, let the current in the closed mesh be positive if it is clockwise in that mesh. The following equations result:

$$E = (R_1 + R_2)I - R_1I_1 - R_2I_2 \tag{a}$$

$$0 = -R_1I + (R_1 + R_3 + R_5)I_1 - R_5I_2 \tag{b}$$

$$0 = -R_2I - R_5I_1 + (R_2 + R_4 + R_5)I_2 \tag{c}$$

and $I_2 = I_1 + I_5$. $I_5 =$ current in resistance R_5.
Then,

$$E = -R_2I_5 - (R_1 + R_2)I_1 + (R_1 + R_2)I \tag{d}$$

$$0 = -R_5I_5 + (R_1 + R_3)I_1 - R_1I \tag{e}$$

$$0 = (R_2 + R_4 + R_5)I_5 + (R_2 + R_4)I_1 - R_2I \tag{f}$$

If determinants are used, I_5 may be expressed as

$$I_5 = \frac{\begin{vmatrix} E, & -(R_1 + R_2), & (R_1 + R_2) \\ 0, & (R_1 + R_3), & -R_1 \\ 0, & (R_2 + R_4), & -R_2 \end{vmatrix}}{\Delta} = \frac{E}{\Delta}(R_1R_4 - R_2R_3) \tag{6}$$

where

$$\Delta = \begin{vmatrix} -R_2, & -(R_1 + R_2), & (R_1 + R_2) \\ -R_5, & (R_1 + R_3), & -R_1 \\ (R_2 + R_4 + R_5), & (R_2 + R_4), & -R_2 \end{vmatrix} \tag{6a}$$

If I_5 is to be zero then

$$R_1 R_4 = R_2 R_3 \quad \text{or} \quad \frac{R_1}{R_2} = \frac{R_3}{R_4} \tag{7}$$

the condition for the bridge to be in balance, and, if R_2 is unknown, $R_2 = \dfrac{R_4}{R_3} R_1$.

In a measurement then where R_2 is given an increment ΔR_2 and R_1, R_3, and R_4 are constant, this increment ΔR_2 may be determined by adjusting R_1 until the bridge is again in balance as follows:

$$R_2 + \Delta R_2 = \frac{R_4 + \Delta R_4}{R_3} R_1$$

$$\Delta R_2 = \frac{R_4}{R_3} R_1 + \frac{R_1}{R_3} \Delta R_4 - \frac{R_4}{R_3} R_1 = \frac{R_1}{R_3} \Delta R_4 = \text{constant } \Delta R_4$$

$$\therefore \Delta R_2 \text{ is determined by knowing } \Delta R_4$$

If the value of displacement as a function of ΔR_2 is known, then the value of the displacement is determined by balancing the bridge.

This method would require that the value be constant long enough to allow the bridge to be balanced. This is often not only inconvenient or undesirable but also impossible. It is helpful to know the change in resistance as a function of the galvanometer reading so that the deflection of the galvanometer indicates the displacement of the gage.

$$I_5 = \frac{E}{\Delta} (R_1 R_4 - R_2 R_3) \text{ when bridge is unbalanced.}$$

Now, let R_2 change by a small amount ΔR_2. Then,

$$I_5 + \Delta I_5 = \frac{E}{\Delta'} (R_1 R_4 - (R_2 + \Delta R_2) R_3)$$

$$= \frac{E}{\Delta'} (R_1 R_4 - R_2 R_3 - \Delta R_2 R_3)$$

and, since $\Delta \doteq \Delta'$ for small values of ΔR_2,

$$\Delta I_5 = \frac{E}{\Delta} R_3 \cdot \Delta R_2 = \text{constant} \cdot \Delta R_2 \tag{8}$$

$$\therefore \text{ Galvanometer reading is proportional to } \Delta R_2.$$

If we extend this to an a-c bridge, then equation 6 becomes replacing resistances R by impedance Z where $Z = (R + jX)$.

$$X = \text{reactance}$$

j indicates that its contribution is added 90° out of phase with the contribution for R.

$$\therefore I_5 = \frac{E}{\delta} (Z_1 Z_4 - Z_2 Z_3)$$

$$\text{where } \delta = \begin{vmatrix} -Z_2 & , & -(Z_1 + Z_2), & (Z_1 + Z_2) \\ -Z_5 & , & (Z_1 + Z_3), & -Z_1 \\ (Z_2 + Z_4 + Z_5), & (Z_2 + Z_4), & -Z_2 \end{vmatrix}$$

The condition for the bridge to be in balance is, then, as before,

$$Z_1 Z_4 = Z_2 Z_3$$

or
$$(R_1 + jX_1)(R_4 + jX_4) = (R_2 + jX_2)(R_3 + jX_3)$$

Remembering that $j^2 = -1$, we have

$$(R_1 R_4 - X_1 X_4) + j(R_1 X_4 + R_4 X_1) = (R_2 R_3 - X_2 X_3) + j(R_2 X_3 + R_3 X_2)$$

If these terms are to be equal, and since they are 90° out of phase, then,

$$(R_1 R_4 - X_1 X_4) = (R_2 R_3 - X_2 X_3) \tag{9}$$

and
$$(R_1 X_4 + R_4 X_1) = (R_2 X_3 + R_3 X_2) \tag{10}$$

Since we have in this instance more terms than in the d-c bridge, the balance may be obtained in a number of ways.

If, for example, equation 9 is written

$$R_1 R_4 = R_2 R_3 + X_1 X_4 - X_2 X_3$$

and the resistances and reactances are arranged so that

$$R_1 R_4 = R_2 R_3, \quad \text{and} \quad X_1 X_4 = X_2 X_3$$

equation 9 is satisfied.

These conditions may be substituted in equation 10 in the following manner:

$$R_4 = \frac{R_2 R_3}{R_1} \qquad X_4 = \frac{X_2 X_3}{X_1}$$

Then, equation 10 becomes

$$R_1 \frac{X_2 X_3}{X_1} + X_1 \frac{R_2 R_3}{R_1} = R_2 X_3 + R_3 X_2$$

$$R_1{}^2 X_2 X_3 + X_1{}^2 R_2 R_3 = R_1 R_2 X_1 X_3 + R_3 R_1 X_1 X_2$$

$$R_2 X_1 (X_1 R_3 - R_1 X_3) = R_1 X_2 (X_1 R_3 - R_1 X_3)$$

$$R_2 X_1 = R_1 X_2$$

∴ the equations 9 and 10 are both satisfied if

$$\frac{R_1}{R_2} = \frac{R_3}{R_4}; \quad \frac{X_1}{X_2} = \frac{X_3}{X_4}; \quad \frac{R_1}{R_2} = \frac{X_1}{X_2}$$

or
$$\frac{R_1}{R_2} = \frac{R_3}{R_4} = \frac{X_1}{X_2} = \frac{X_3}{X_4} \tag{11}$$

One way in which balance may be obtained.

If now the resistance R_2 is changed a small amount ΔR_2 without any of the other factors being changed,

$$I_5 + \Delta I_5 = \frac{E}{\delta'} [Z_1 Z_4 - (Z_2 + \Delta Z_2) Z_3]$$

$$\delta' \doteq \delta \text{ for small values of } \Delta R_2 \text{ or } \Delta Z_2$$

$$\Delta E_5 = Z_5 \Delta I_5 = \frac{E}{\delta} Z_3 \cdot \Delta Z_2 \cdot Z_5 = \text{constant } \Delta Z_2$$

where $Z_5 = $ impedance of detector. But $\Delta Z_2 = \Delta R_2$ here, and detector reading is proportional to ΔE_5.

∴ Detector reading is proportional to ΔR_2.

7. Bridge Circuits in Strain Measurements. A simple bridge circuit is shown in Fig. 5-19 where the resistance R_2 is the strain-measuring element.

Either or both resistors R_1 and R_3 may be made variable. If R_1 is variable, then the change $\Delta R_2 = k_1 \Delta R_1$ where $k_1 = R_4/R_3$, and if R_3 is variable, then $\Delta R_2 = k_2 \Delta R_3$ where $k_2 = \dfrac{R_4}{R_1} \Delta R_3$.

If both R_1 and R_3 are varied, then

$$\frac{(R_1 + \Delta R_1) R_4}{(R_3 + \Delta R_3)} - R_2 = \Delta R_2$$

$$\frac{R_1 R_4}{R_3 + \Delta R_3} + \frac{\Delta R_1 R_4}{R_3 + \Delta R_3} - R_2 = \Delta R_2$$

$$R_1 R_4 + \Delta R_1 R_4 - \frac{R_1 R_4}{R_3} (R_3 + \Delta R_3) = \Delta R_2 (R_3 + \Delta R_3)$$

$$R_1 R_4 + \Delta R_1 R_4 - R_1 R_4 - \frac{R_1 R_4}{R_3} \Delta R_3 = R_2 (R_3 + \Delta R_3)$$

$$\left(R_4 \cdot \Delta R_1 - \frac{R_1 R_4}{R_3} \Delta R_3 \right) \frac{1}{R_3 + \Delta R_3} = \Delta R_2$$

if ΔR_3 is small compared to R_3.

$$\Delta R_2 \doteq \frac{R_4}{R_3} \Delta R_1 - \frac{R_1 R_4}{R_3} \Delta R_3 = C_1 \Delta R_1 - C_2 \Delta R_3 \tag{12}$$

In any case where the resistance in the bridge is varied, the contact resistance must be carefully controlled since a small change in the contact resistance would be of the same order of magnitude as the change in resistance due to strain.   This contact-resistance difficulty may be avoided by arranging the bridge as shown in Fig. 5-20.

In this case the arm R_3 has a variable resistor R_6 connected in parallel.

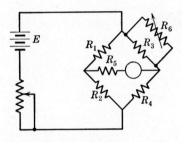

The resistance of the arm then becomes R_3' and $R_3' = \dfrac{R_3 R_6}{R_3 + R_6}$.   It is apparent that a small change in R_6 makes a smaller change in R_3'.   To illustrate this, give R_6 an increment ΔR_6; then R_3' gets an increment $\Delta R_3'$, or, by differentiation, the relation between the error due to contact resistance without R_6 and with R_6 is given by

$$dR_3' = \frac{R_3{}^2 \, dR_6}{(R_3 + R_6)^2} \qquad (13)$$

FIG. 5-20.   Varying a Bridge-Arm Resistance by Using a Shunting Circuit

$\therefore$ if R_6 is the same order of magnitude as R_3 the error is reduced to $\frac{1}{4}$ of its value.   Usually R_6 is greater than R_3.

The strain in this bridge is proportional to ΔR_2, and

$$\Delta R_2 = \text{constant } \Delta R_3'$$

For large values of ΔR_2 the relation to be used is found as follows:

$$\Delta R_3' = \frac{R_3(R_6 + \Delta R_6)}{R_3 + (R_6 + \Delta R_6)} - \frac{R_3 R_6}{R_3 + R_6}$$

$$R_3 + R_6 = R$$

$$\Delta R_3' = \frac{R_3}{R} \frac{\left(R_6 + \Delta R_6 - R_6 - \dfrac{\Delta R_6}{R} R_6 \right)}{\left(1 + \dfrac{\Delta R_6}{R} \right)} = \frac{E R_3}{R} \left(\frac{\dfrac{\Delta R_6}{R}}{1 + \dfrac{\Delta R_6}{R}} \right)$$

$$\Delta R_3 = \frac{R_3}{R} \frac{\Delta R_6}{R} \left[1 - \frac{\Delta R_6}{R} + \left(\frac{\Delta R_6}{R} \right)^2 - \cdots \right] \qquad (14)$$

$\therefore \Delta R_2 = \text{constant (nonlinear function of } \Delta R_6)$.   This method, then, requires that it is necessary to work from a calibration or set of curves in order to evaluate the strain resistance ΔR_2.

Another method of getting around the contact problem in these gage circuits is by using the circuit in Fig. 5-21a.   In this case the resistance contact at point C is not in the bridge circuit, and, thus, it has no influence on the values of resistance measured.

Then both R_1 and R_3 are varied so that ΔR_2 is given by applying equation 13 in the form:

$$R_2 - R_2' = R_4 \left(\frac{R_1}{R_3} - \frac{R_1'}{R_3'} \right) = \Delta R_2$$

8. Deflection of a Galvanometer as a Measure of Strain (Example). If the deflection of a galvanometer is to be used as a measure of the strain, it is convenient to calibrate the galvanometer in terms of strain on the gage. This method is more rapid than the null method owing to the time required to balance the circuit. If the galvanometer gives a linear relation, the problem of using the deflection as a measure of the strain is simplified. It is of importance to determine the sensitivity of the galvanometer to be used. This may be best illustrated by the following problem:

Let the voltage applied be represented by $E = 6$ volts.

Let the resistance of the bridge arms be $R_1 = R_2 = R_3 = R_4 = 120$ ohms.

Let the maximum strain to be recorded be 0.001.

Let the resistance of the galvanometer be $R_5 = 500$ ohms.

Let R_2 represent the resistance of the strain gage.

Let ΔR_2 be the change in resistance due to a strain of 0.001.

Let the gage be of Advance wire; gage factor from Table 5-1 be 2.1

$$\therefore \frac{\Delta R_2/R_2}{\Delta L/L} = 2.1 \quad \frac{\Delta R_2/120}{0.001} = 2.1 \quad \Delta R_2 = 0.25 \text{ ohm}$$

I_5 is the current through the galvanometer and is given by the equation, $I_5 = \dfrac{E}{\Delta} R_3 \cdot \Delta R_2$, Δ from equation 6a:

$$\Delta = \begin{matrix} -120, & -240, & 240 \\ -500, & 240, & -120 \\ 740, & 240, & -120 \end{matrix} = 35.7 \times 10^6$$

$$\therefore I_5 = \frac{6 \times 120 \times 0.25 \times 10^{-6}}{35.7} = 5.04 \times 10^{-6} \text{ ampere for maximum strain}$$

If the instrument is to have 5.04×10^{-6} ampere for full scale, and if the least strain that is to be read is 0.00002 per division, 50 divisions are necessary, and each division should have a sensitivity of $\dfrac{5.04 \times 10^{-6}}{50} = 0.1 \times 10^{-6}$ ampere.

Such a galvanometer requires a level position and isolation from vibration and shock. Since it is a sensitive instrument, a galvanometer is easily damaged by transportation. Further, the period of a galvanometer is long and may be as great as 4 to 5 sec. This makes the instrument difficult to use in the field.

In order to eliminate the use of sensitive galvanometers, the d-c excitation may be replaced with an alternating voltage. The frequency of the voltage depends on the phenomena to be measured and may range from as low as 60 cps to several thousand. In this case the output of the bridge is placed into an amplifier with a rectifier and a milliammeter used to indicate the off-balance. This system is much less sensitive to shock and vibration, and the sensitivity can be controlled through varying the gain of the amplifier.

9. Simplified Bridge Theory. The afore-mentioned treatment of an a-c bridge, although rigorous, is difficult to apply. Since the amplifier circuit can be designed to have a very high input impedance, R_5 of Fig. 5-19 can be assumed to be infinite, and the signal voltage then becomes the differential between two potentiometer voltages. This is shown in Fig. 5-21b.

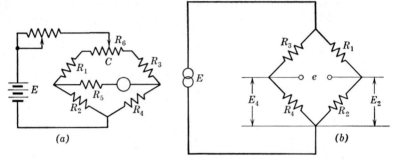

(a)   (b)

FIG. 5-21a and b.   Method of Varying R_1/R_3 and Keeping Contact Resistance in External Circuit

If R_2 represents an active strain gage and R_1, R_3, and R_4 represent fixed arms, from the analysis of a potentiometer circuit the following equation can be obtained:

$$e = E_4 - (E_2 + \Delta E_2) \quad \text{but} \quad \Delta E_2 = \frac{ER_1\,\Delta R_2}{(R_1 + R_2)^2}$$

Since $E_4 = E_2$ at balance,

$$e = \Delta E_2 = E\,\frac{R_1\,\Delta R_2}{(R_1 + R_2)^2} \quad \text{approximately}$$

Now, if two arms are active,

$$e = (E_4 + \Delta E_4) - (E_2 + \Delta E_2)$$

$$e = \Delta E_4 - \Delta E_2$$

Thus, if ΔE_4 and ΔE_2 have the same sign, they will cancel, but, if they have opposite signs, the output will be twice that for a single gage.

In a similar manner, it can be shown that, if all four arms are active, the output signal will be four times that of a single gage, providing the signs of the strains are opposite in adjacent bridge arms.

This simplified analysis assumes that the bridge is first balanced to remove all capacitance unbalance and that capacitance unbalance is independent of resistance unbalance. From the rigorous solution capacitance unbalance will actually vary somewhat as the resistance balance changes with strain, but this error should be small for the incremental changes in resistance corresponding to actual strain measurements.

10. Theory of the Carrier Amplifier System. If a-c bridge excitation is used and a dynamic strain is observed, a modulated wave will result. When the bridge is initially balanced the carrier will be suppressed. The following analysis is of value in determining the side bands and distortion terms which will be present in the output signal from the bridge.

Referring to the bridge circuit shown in Fig. 5-21b, let ΔR_2 vary in a sinusoidal manner,

$$R_2 + \Delta R_2 = R_2(1 + m \cos \omega_s t)$$

where

$$m = \left(\frac{1}{2}\right) \frac{R_{\max} - R_{\min}}{R_0}$$

$$= \left(\frac{1}{2}\right) \frac{(R_2 + \Delta R_2) - (R_2 - \Delta R_2)}{R_2} = \frac{\Delta R_2}{R_2}$$

$$E_4 = E_{\max} \cos \omega_c t \, \frac{R_4}{R_3 + R_4}$$

$$E_2 = E_{\max} \cos \omega_c t \, \frac{R_2(1 + m \cos \omega_s t)}{R_1 + R_2(1 + m \cos \omega_s t)}$$

where
f_c is the frequency of the bridge excitation and f_s is the frequency of the sinusoidal strain.

$$\omega_c = 2\pi f_c$$

$$\omega_s = 2\pi f_s$$

$$e = E_2 - E_4$$

$$= E_{\max} \cos \omega_c t \, \frac{R_2(1 + m \cos \omega_s t)}{R_1 + R_2(1 + m \cos \omega_s t)}$$

$$e = E_2 - E_4$$

$$= E_{\max} \cos \omega_c t \left[\frac{R_2(1 + m \cos \omega_s t)}{R_1 + R_2(1 + m \cos \omega_s t)} - \frac{R_4}{R_3 + R_4} \right]$$

Now, for a balanced bridge $R_2 = R_4$, and $R_1 = R_3$.

$$e = E_{\max} \cos \omega_c t \left(\frac{R_1 R_2}{R_1 + R_2} \right) \left(\frac{m \cos \omega_s t}{R_1 + R_2 + m \cos \omega_s t} \right)$$

Let

$$\frac{R_1}{R_2} + 1 = h \quad \text{and} \quad \frac{R_1 R_2}{R_1 + R_2} = R_T$$

then

$$e = E_{\max} \frac{R_T}{R_2} \cos \omega_c t \left(\frac{m \cos \omega_s t}{h + m \cos \omega_s t} \right)$$

By division,

$$e = \frac{R_T E_{\max}}{R_2} \left(\cos \omega_c t \frac{m}{n} \cos \omega_s t - \frac{m^2}{h^2} \cos^2 \omega_s t + \frac{m^3}{h^3} \cos^3 \omega_s t \right.$$

$$\left. - \cdots + (-1)^{n+1} \frac{m^n}{h} \cos^n \omega_s t \right)$$

$$e = \frac{R_T E_{\max}}{R_2} \left\{ \begin{array}{ll} - \dfrac{m^2}{2h^2} \cos \omega_s t & \text{(Carrier term)} \\[2mm] + \dfrac{3m^3}{8h^3} + \dfrac{m}{2h} \cos (\omega_c + \omega_s)t & \text{(Useful term)} \\[2mm] - \dfrac{m^2}{4h^2} \cos (\omega_c + 2\omega_s)t & \text{(Distortion term)} \\[2mm] + \dfrac{m^3}{8h^3} \cos (\omega_c + 3\omega_s)t & \text{(Distortion term)} \\[2mm] + \ldots \ldots \ldots \ldots & \\[2mm] + \dfrac{3}{8} \dfrac{m^3}{h^3} + \dfrac{m}{2h} \cos (\omega_c - \omega_s)t & \text{(Useful term)} \\[2mm] - \dfrac{m^2}{4h^2} \cos (\omega_c - 2\omega_s)t & \text{(Distortion term)} \\[2mm] + \dfrac{m^3}{8h^3} \cos (\omega_c - 3\omega_s)t & \text{(Distortion term)} \\[2mm] + \ldots \ldots \ldots \ldots & \end{array} \right.$$

Upper Side Band

Lower Side Band

The carrier term indicates that as the bridge is unbalanced as R_2 varies, a carrier voltage appears which is proportional to the magnitude of ΔR_2.

The distortion terms are small in magnitude compared to the useful side-band terms.

If the bridge is slightly unbalanced by one of the arms being adjusted, a larger carrier term can be introduced. This initial unbalance should be selected so that slightly less than 100 per cent modulation results for the largest expected strain.

The foregoing analysis is based on the use of cosines instead of sines in order to be valued at zero frequency and for the result to be obtained as a series of cosine terms instead of a mixture of sine and cosine terms.

The analysis assumes that the bridge consists of nonreactive elements.

When the carrier frequency is very low, this condition is approximately realized, but, when the high carrier frequencies are employed, the capacitance unbalance will result in additional terms.

11. Choice of the Bridge Ratio. The choice of the ratio of R_1/R_2 for a bridge circuit depends on the conditions selected. If ΔR_2 and E are fixed, the ratio should be unity for a maximum signal output.

$$e = \Delta E_2 = E\,\Delta R_2 \frac{R_1}{(R_1 + R_2)^2}$$

Let

$$E\,\Delta R_2 = K$$

Then,

$$e = K \frac{R_1}{(R_1 + R_2)^2}$$

$$\frac{de}{dR_1} = K\left[\frac{(R_1 + R_2)^2 - 2R_1(R_1 + R_2)}{(R_1 + R_2)^4}\right]$$

$$= K\left[\frac{(R_1 + R_2) - 2R_1}{(R_1 + R_2)^3}\right]$$

Now,

$$(R_1 + R_2) - 2R_1 = 0$$

$$R_2 = R_1$$

Now,

$$\Delta E = K \frac{R_1}{(R_1 + R_2)^2}$$

Let

$$n = \frac{R_1}{R_2}$$

Then, $R_1 = nR_2$

$$= K \frac{R_2 n}{(R_2 n + R_2)^2} = K \frac{R_2 n}{R_2^2 n^2 + 2R_2^2 n + R_2^2}$$

$$= E \frac{\Delta R_2}{R_2} \frac{n}{n^2 + 2n + 1} = E \frac{\Delta R_2}{R_2} \frac{n}{(n + 1)^2}$$

$$\Delta E = \frac{\Delta R_2}{R_2}\left(\frac{n}{n^2 + 2n + 1}\right)$$

A curve giving the relation of n to $\dfrac{n}{(n + 1)^2}$ is shown in Fig. 5-21c.

When any value of E is employed, merely multiply the value shown by E to obtain the proper value of $\dfrac{n}{(n + 1)^2}$.

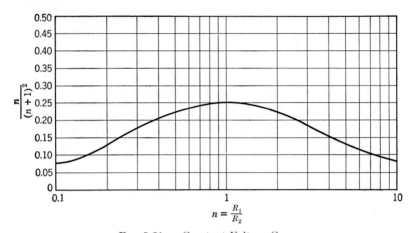

Fig. 5-21c.   Constant-Voltage Curve

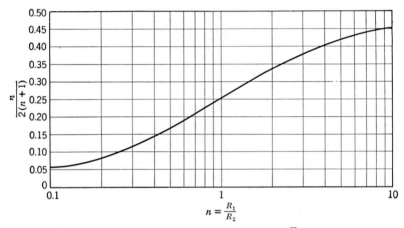

Fig. 5-21d.   Constant Current $I = \dfrac{E}{2R_2}$

If E is varied proportional to n so that a constant current is maintained,

$$i = \frac{E_0}{R_1 + R_2} = \frac{E_0}{2R_2} = \frac{E}{R_2(1 + n)}$$

$$E = E_0\left(\frac{1 + n}{2}\right)$$

where E_0 is bridge voltage corresponding to condition $n = 1$

Since

$$\Delta E = E\frac{\Delta R_2}{R_2}\left(\frac{n}{n^2 + 2n + 1}\right)$$

$$\Delta E = E_0 \left(\frac{1+n}{2}\right) \frac{\Delta R_2}{R_2} \left(\frac{n}{n^2 + 2n + 1}\right) = E_0 \frac{\Delta R_2}{R_2} \frac{n}{2(n+1)}$$

This relation is presented in Fig. 5-21d. The voltage required for constant current is shown in Fig. 5-21e.

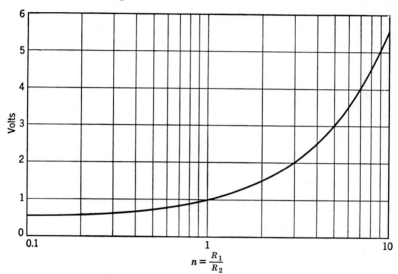

FIG. 5-21e. Voltage Corresponding to a Constant Current $I = \dfrac{E}{2R_2}$. Multiply Voltage from Curve by Actual Bridge-Excitation Voltage

From these curves it is evident that increasing the ratio n above the unity value can result in increased signal, but the required excitation voltage increases at a greater rate than the signal developed.

When this analysis is extended to a carrier system, the required power will usually dictate a ratio near unity.

III. PRINCIPLES OF ELECTRONICS AND THEIR APPLICATION TO ELECTRICAL-GAGING PROBLEMS

I. THE VACUUM TUBE

If a filament is heated in an evacuated tube, it becomes the source of electrons, and, if a plate is inserted in the tube and positively charged, electrons will flow from the hot filament to the plate, and a current will flow in the circuit. If the polarity of the circuit is reversed, no current will flow (Fig. 5-22). This simple tube is called a diode. If now a third electrode is introduced into the tube so that it is midway between the filament and the plate, it would have a greater effect on the flow of electrons than the plate since it is nearer the filament than the plate. Therefore, a small positive charge on this electrode would pull over as many electrons as a larger positive charge on the plate, and a small negative charge on the electrode would repel some of the electrons, and, thus, a smaller number of electrons would reach the plate.

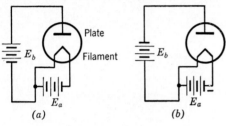

FIG. 5-22. Simple Diode Tubes
(a) Current flows in circuit
(b) Current does not flow

If this electrode were to be made solid, it would theoretically block the flow of electrons to the plate. In order that it only control and not block the flow of electrons to the plate, the electrode is made with openings and is called the grid.

Since this grid controls the flow of electrons by very small potential changes placed on it, it is possible to control the flow of large plate currents by means of small potential changes on the grid. This three-element tube is called a triode; Fig. 5-23 shows this tube and the variation of current in the plate circuit produced by potential differences placed on the grid.

The grid with a low negative charge will not cut off all the electrons so that cutoff is not symmetrical to signal, and, thus, when the signal to the tube is varied, the current from the tube is not varied in the same manner. This may be overcome by adjusting the negative potential on the grid so that the tube will cut off as soon as the signal voltage becomes negative. This is obtained by the battery source E_c in Fig. 5-23a.

12. Characteristics of Vacuum Tubes. The important feature about vacuum tubes is their characteristics. The basic principle is that the heated filament or cathode discharges electrons which are attracted to a positively charged plate and made to flow in the plate circuit. To investigate the characteristics of the tubes we plot plate current as a function of plate voltage when the filament current is kept constant. These curves are called characteristic curves.

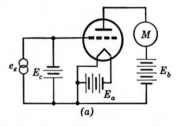

(a)

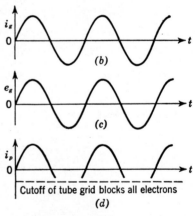

Cutoff of tube grid blocks all electrons
(d)

FIG. 5-23. Operation of Triode Tube
(a) Simple circuit
(b) Input current
(c) Input voltage
(d) Current in plate circuit

The characteristic curve for the diode is as shown in Fig. 5-24. It may be noticed that the portion of the curve AB is practically a straight line and that the two ends of the graph are curved. The curve at the low end is due to a space charge, consisting of a cloud of electrons which gather around the filament and repel the new electrons being emitted. After the potential on the

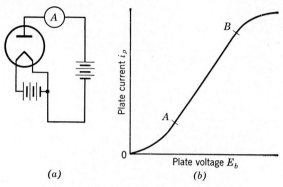

(a)   (b)

FIG. 5-24.   Characteristic Curve of Diode
(a) Simple circuit
(b) Plate current versus plate voltage, characteristic curve

plate is increased, the number of electrons reaching the plate is increased until at B nearly all those emitted by the cathode reach the plate, so that further increases in voltage do not materially increase the number of electrons reaching the plate—and, thus, only very little increase in current results

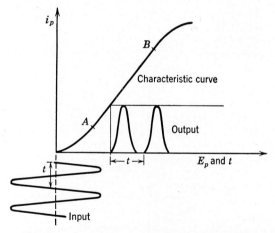

FIG. 5-25.   Rectification by the Use of a Diode

with further increase in voltage. The space charge effect may be reduced by making the plate-to-cathode distance quite small. The effect is illustrated in Fig. 5-25, which shows rectification by use of a diode, as well.

The characteristic curves of the triode are as shown in Fig. 5-26. Two

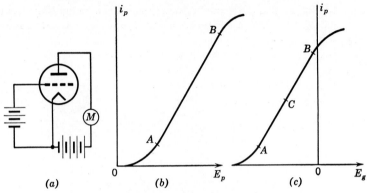

Fig. 5-26.   Characteristic of Triode Tubes
(a) Simple circuit
(b) Characteristic i_p versus E_p
(c) Characteristic i_p versus E_g

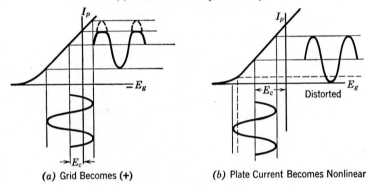

(a) Grid Becomes (+)   (b) Plate Current Becomes Nonlinear

(c) Proper Grid Bias

Fig. 5-27.   Effect of Grid Bias on Output of a Triode Tube
(a) Graph showing the effect of too little grid bias
(b) Graph showing the effect of too much grid bias
(c) Proper grid bias

characteristic curves are plotted: (1) plate current as a function of plate voltage for a given grid potential (Fig. 5-26b), and (2) plate current as a function of grid voltage for a given plate potential (Fig. 5-26c).

In this case as in the case of the diode the portion of the curve AB is a straight line. A point C is taken between these two points on the I_p–E_g curve, and it is called the operating point or quiescent point. The grid is usually operated at a bias voltage corresponding to point C. This is usually

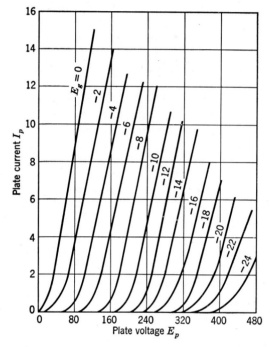

FIG. 5-28.   Family of Plate Characteristic Curves.   6J5 Triode.

a fixed direct voltage to which the signal input is added. The effect of having this voltage C too high or too low is shown in the plots of Fig. 5-27.

This characteristic curve is for a given voltage between plate and filament E_p. If E_p is changed and we again plot the grid voltage E_g as a function of plate current I_p, we get a second curve resembling the first and lying parallel to it. In such a manner a family of characteristic curves may be obtained (Fig. 5-28).

In a like manner the characteristic family of curves of E_p as a function of I_p for a given E_g value is shown in Fig. 5-29.

All the curves we have discussed have been with the tube with no load on the tube, and these are called static characteristic curves. Actually, the output of a tube feeds into a load, such as the primary coil of a coupling transformer. If we show this load as resistance R_L in the diagram of Fig.

5-30 and plot the curves anew, we get characteristic curves that are better representative of the operating conditions of the tubes. Such curves are

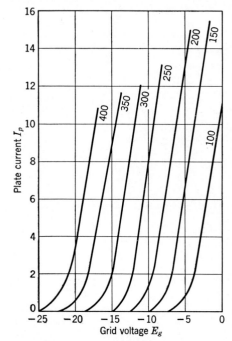

called dynamic curves. The static curve is nearly always steeper than the dynamic curve. It can be noted that the curves cross in the region of point C. This is the same point noted C in Fig. 5-30.

When the tube is operating at no load (static), the plate-to-cathode potential is constant regardless of plate current. If, however, there is a resistance R_L in the plate circuit, there is a drop in potential across the resistance R_L; thus the plate-to-cathode potential is reduced by $I_p R_L$. Therefore, the changing plate current causes corresponding changes in plate-to-cathode potential, and the dynamic curve differs from the static curve.

The point where the curves cross indicates a condition where the characteristics are the same under load conditions and no-load condition, and this may be taken as the operating point.

Figure 5-31 shows the effect of

FIG. 5-29. Family of Transfer or Mutual Characteristic Curves. 6J5 Triode

different resistance loads on the characteristic curves of a triode.

The characteristic curves tell the interrelation of grid bias, voltage, plate voltage, and plate current. Thus, if we apply a grid voltage of 8 volts, a

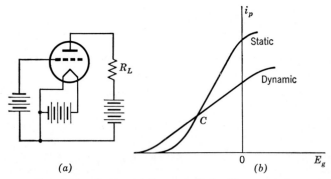

FIG. 5-30. Static and Dynamic Tube Characteristics
    (a) Simple circuit
    (b) Characteristic dynamic and static curves

250 voltage on the plate, we can determine the current that will flow in the plate circuit at this value of E_p (see Fig. 5-31).

The tube has three important characteristics: amplification factor, plate resistance, and transconductance.

(a) The amplification factor is the ratio between the increase in plate voltage and the increase in grid voltage and is defined by

$$\mu = -\frac{\partial e_p}{\partial e_g} \qquad di_p = 0$$

If, for example, the plate voltage increased 10 volts when the grid voltage is increased only 0.1 volt, the amplification is then 100.

(b) The plate resistance is the a-c internal resistance of a vacuum tube; that is, the resistance of the path between plate and cathode. Therefore, it is the ratio between a small change in plate voltage and the corresponding change in plate current, and is defined by:

$$r_p = \frac{\partial e_p}{\partial i_p} \qquad de_g = 0$$

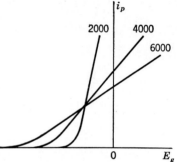

Fig. 5-31. Effect of Increasing the Load on the Characteristic Curve of a Triode Tube

(c) The transconductance is the ratio between a small change in plate current and a small change in grid potential, with plate potential remaining constant, and is defined by

$$g_m = \frac{\partial i_p}{\partial e_g} \qquad de_p = 0$$

These three factors are interrelated since,

$$r_p \times g_m = \frac{de_p}{de_g} = \mu$$

13. Amplification of a Stage. The circuit of the vacuum tube as shown in Fig. 5-32a can be represented by its equivalent circuit shown in Fig. 5-32b. This is called a stage of an amplifier. Let the signal voltage be e_g and applied to the grid, and R_L is the resistance of the load, and μ is amplification factor.

$$\text{Since} \quad I = \frac{E}{R} = \frac{\mu e_g}{r_p + R_L} \qquad e_p = IR = \frac{R_L \mu e_g}{r_p + R_L}$$

$$\therefore \frac{\mu R_L}{r_p + R_L} = \frac{e_p}{e_g} = A_0$$

where A_0 is the amplification of the stage.

This equation for A_0 is only satisfactory for small input signals. When these signals are large, the nonlinear characteristic of the tube becomes important, and a graphical solution is to be preferred. To illustrate this, the following graphical solution is given. The family of characteristic curves with plate current as a function of plate voltage is used as the basis of the solution (Fig. 5-33). These are curves for a triode tube.

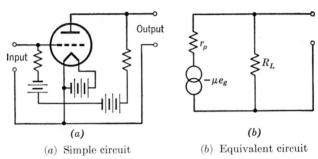

(a)	(b)
(a) Simple circuit	(b) Equivalent circuit

Fig. 5-32.   Triode Amplifier Stage

The dynamic load impedance is given by $R_2 = R_L R_g/(R_L + R_g)$

In general, the slope of load line may be determined on this graph from $1/R_2 = I_p/E_p$, and the no-load slope may also be determined from $1/R_L$. In addition, the maximum point of plate supply voltage is known as E_b. From point E_b the no-load slope is first drawn $\theta_1 = -1/R_L$. Next it is necessary to know, or select, the bias voltage at which the tube is to operate. This value is called E'_p, and a vertical line is drawn through this point. The

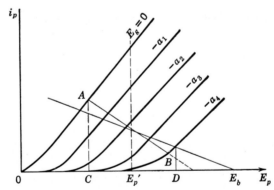

Fig. 5-33.   Determination of Best Value for Grid Bias and Corresponding Amplification Factor

intersection of this point with the no-load line is then the operating point. Through this point the load line is drawn at angle $\theta_2 = -1/R_2$. This line cuts the various e_g curves, and the limits of operation must be in the linear portion of these curves, such as AB on the graph. This fixes the grid swing e_g that may be used. Vertical lines through A and B fix the value of e_L so that the amplification $A_0 = e_L/e_g$ is thus determined by

$$\frac{(E_p)_D - (E_p)_C}{(E_g)_B - (E_g)_A} = A_0$$

J. The A-C Vacuum-Tube Amplifier (Introduction)

The vacuum tube a.c amplifier is usually divided into two major classes. The first class, called audio-frequency amplifiers, is used to amplify currents whose frequencies are between 30 and 15,000 cps. The second, called radio-frequency amplifiers, is used to amplify from 15 kc to over 300 megacycles. If the amplifier is designed to give a magnified reproduction of the input signal without regard to the power delivered, it is called a voltage amplifier, and, if it is designed to deliver a large amount of power to some load, it is called a power amplifier.

Generally speaking, the last stage of any amplifier system is a power stage, and the intermediate stages are called voltage-amplifier stages. A good amplifier must be capable of amplifying signal voltages whose frequencies lie within the range of use for which the amplifier was designed. This must be done insofar as possible to exactly the same degree for all frequencies.

K. Classes of Amplifiers

Amplifiers are commonly classified as A, AB, B, and C, according to the portion of cycle during which plate current flows. These classes are defined as follows:

Class A amplifiers are those in which grid-bias and alternating grid voltage are such that plate current in the tube, or each tube of a push–pull stage, flows at all times.

Class AB amplifiers are those in which the grid-bias and alternating grid voltages are such that plate current in the tube, or each tube of a push–pull stage, flows for more than half but less than the entire electric cycle.

Class B amplifiers are those in which the grid bias is about equal to cutoff value, so that the plate current is approximately zero when no exciting grid voltage is applied. This means that plate current in the tube or each tube of a push–pull* stage flows for about half the electric cycle.

Class C amplifiers are those in which the grid bias is greater than cutoff value, and plate current flows for less than half the electric cycle.

Sometimes a suffix 1 or 2 may be added to the letter or letters of class identification. The suffix 1 denotes that grid current does not flow during any part of the electric cycle, and 2 denotes that grid current does flow for some part of the cycle.

In strain-gage work it is important to keep distortion to a minimum, and all amplifiers are class A.

L. Distortion in an Amplifier

As mentioned previously, it is the aim of an amplifier to produce an output whose form coincides with that of the signal input; therefore, any tendency

* See Fig. 5-48 for a push–pull amplifier circuit.

for distortion must be cut to a minimum. There are three basic types of distortion which may be present in any amplifier: amplitude distortion, frequency distortion, and phase distortion. These may be present singly or together.

Amplitude distortion is defined as the production of new frequencies within the device so that a Fourier analysis of the output wave form will differ from that of the input wave form. Frequency distortion is unequal amplification of various frequencies due to the variation of input and output impedance with frequency. Phase-shift distortion is the change in the relative phase between the various components of a complex wave in passing through the amplifier. In most amplifiers both amplitude frequency and phase distortion will be found because of the change in amplification and phase shift with frequency.

The production of new frequencies is due to the nonlinear nature of a vacuum tube. In general, the plate current can be represented by a power series which means that there will always be some amplitude distortion since the new frequencies are always present. In practice, the signal is kept small in order to limit the production of new frequencies. In power-output stages where large output voltages are necessary considerable distortion may result.

The type of distortion that takes place in the tube itself may be caused by improper selection of grid bias, forcing the tube to operate under conditions represented by the nonlinear portion of the characteristic curve as shown in Fig. 5-27. This shows the effect of grid bias on tube output. It is called nonlinear distortion. When the grid bias is too low, the top of the output signals are flattened.

Distortion may also be caused by overloading the amplifier. If the grid bias is correct, but if a signal comes in that produces too great a swing of the grid potential, the grid may be driven positive on the positive half-cycle, causing a grid current to flow, and on the negative half-cycle the operation is forced into the nonlinear portion of the plate characteristic. This results in the flattening of the tops and bottoms of the output signal. This distortion may be eliminated in a simple manner by choosing a tube of longer straight-line characteristic or else using an input signal reduced in swing or inverse feedback discussed later. This distortion is controlled by the load in the plate circuit. As shown in Fig. 5-31, the higher the load resistance, the less the characteristic curve is bent, and the greater the straight-line portion of the curve.

In any given amplifier the voltage output is a function of frequency. This is dependent to some extent on the method of coupling the various stages of the amplifier. The variation with frequency is shown in Fig. 5-34.

It may be noted that there is a marked decrease in the gain of the amplifier at low and high frequencies. At some arbitrary value, say 0.707 of full gain, the amplifier is said to cut off, and the corresponding low and high frequency values are called the cutoff frequencies. These points also correspond approximately to the 45° phase-shift points. The phase-shift curve is shown in Fig. 5-35. The phase shift on the high-frequency end is shown as lagging because of the 180° phase shift for each stage of the amplifier. These phase relations are important in predicting the behavior of an amplifier with inverse feedback.

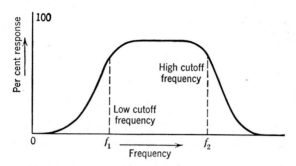

FIG. 5-34. Typical Frequency-Response Curve

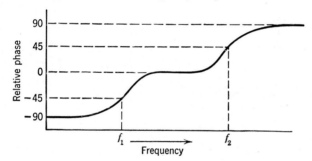

FIG. 5-35. Typical Phase-Shift Frequency Curve

In order to determine the frequency response of the amplifier the equivalent circuits for low, medium, and high-frequency ranges are used. The equivalent-circuit changes with frequency are due to the relative importance of the coupling condenser and cathode bypass condensers in low frequencies, and the lowering of the effective load impedance by the input capacitance and stray-wire capacitance of the successive stages in high frequencies.

For low-frequency range of the given amplifier, the equivalent diagram is as shown in Fig. 5-36, and the relation between frequency and response is given by equation A. Here μ is amplification factor, R_L is the plate-load resistance, R_g is the resistance of the next stage, C_1

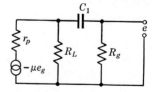

FIG. 5-36. Triode Equivalent Circuit at Low-Frequency Input

is the coupling condenser and ω is the circular frequency and is equal to $2\pi f$ where f is the frequency. Here the loss of low-frequency response is due to the increase of reactance of the coupling condenser. The grid voltage is divided between the grid resistor R_g and the coupling condenser X_c.

$$A = \frac{e}{e_g} = \frac{R_L R_g \mu}{R_L r_p + R_L R_g + R_g r_p - j \, \dfrac{R_L + r_p}{\omega C_1}} \tag{A}$$

The value of C_1 contributes to the capacitance reactance, which is given by

$$X_c = \frac{1}{2\pi f C}$$

For medium frequency of the given triode amplifier, the equivalent diagram is shown in the Fig. 5-37. In this case the capacitance reactance is nearly zero, as shown by Equation B. Thus, it is apparent that frequency does not influence the output, either as to gain or phase shift.

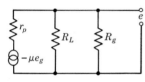

FIG. 5-37. Triode Equivalent Circuit at Medium-Frequency Input

$$A = \frac{e}{e_g} = \frac{\mu}{1 + r_p \left(\dfrac{R_L + R_g}{R_L R_g} \right)} \tag{B}$$

The equivalent circuit for the amplifier in the high-frequency end of the response curve is shown in Fig. 5-38 together with the equation for gain, equation C. The loss of high-frequency response is due to the shunting effect of the capacitance across the plate load. This capacitance is due to the plate-to-cathode capacitance plus the input capacitance of the next stage. The relative gain and phase shift as a function of the ratio R_L to X_{C_p} is shown in Fig. 5-40.

$$A = \frac{e}{e_g} = \frac{\mu}{1 + r_p \left(\dfrac{R_L + R_g}{R_L R_g} \right) + j \omega C r_p} \tag{C}$$

C includes C_{input} and C_{pf} for the stage.

The input capacitances of a triode tube operated with a resistance load is given by the following equation:

$$C_{\text{input}} = C_{gf} + C_{gp}(1 + A_0) + C_{\text{stray}}$$

C_{gf} = grid-cathode capacitance
C_{gp} = grid-plate capacitance
A_0 = amplification of stage

This equation illustrates that, when a triode tube is operated with a resistance load in the plate circuit, the input capacitance is increased

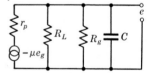

FIG. 5-38. Triode Equivalent Circuit at High-Frequency Input

by the factor $C_{gp}(1 + A_0)$. This is often called the "Miller Effect" and is of importance in cascaded amplifier stages using triode tubes.

The importance of C_{input} depends on R_L, and the choice of R_L is determined by the high-frequency response and by the per cent of amplification factor that can be used.

The high-frequency response requires a low value of R_L, and the lower R_L, the higher the frequency response. The dependency of R_L on per cent μ is shown in the graph of Fig. 5-39.

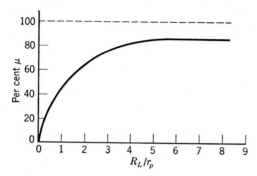

FIG. 5-39.   Dependency of A_o on R_L. E_b (the supply voltage) is Increased to Keep a Reasonable Plate Voltage

M. Multiple-Stage Amplifiers (Triode)

When single-stage amplifiers are cascaded, the over-all gain is equal to the produce of the gain of individual stages, and the over-all phase shift is equal to the algebraic sum of the individual phase shifts.

As in the case of a single stage, the low-frequency response is determined by the coupling condensers and grid resistors. The high-frequency response must be calculated on the basis of the shunting effect of the input capacitance of the second stage. The total capacitance is, therefore,

$$C_L = C_{pf_1} + C_{gf_2} + C_{stray} + C_{gp_2}(1 + A_2)$$

where C_L = capacitance shunting R_L

$\quad C_{pf_1}$ = plate-cathode capacitance tube 1

$\quad C_{gf_2}$ = grid-cathode capacitance tube 2

$\quad C_{gp_2}$ = grid-plate capacitance tube 2

$\quad C_{stray}$ = 10 to 25 $\mu\mu$f. (This depends on circuit wiring and layout and for good design should not exceed 20 $\mu\mu$f.)

$\quad A_2$ = gain of stage 2

N. Procedure for Amplifier Design

The first step is to select the desired gain and output voltage and then select the cutoff points f_1 and f_2. From the lower cutoff frequency, the coupling condenser can be calculated.

$$R_g = X_c \qquad X_c = \frac{1}{2\pi f C}$$

$$\therefore C = \frac{1}{w R_g}$$

The plate-load resistor R_b for each stage should next be determined by referring to the equation for gain at middle frequencies, equation b. This first-trial load resistance may not be satisfactory for high-frequency response.

Now, start at the last stage and compute the high-frequency gain, taking account of the capacitance of the output cables, etc. From this gain compute the C_L for the next to the last stage from equation 1. Then from C_L the gain for the next to the last stage can be found, if it is remembered that at f_2 the high-frequency cutoff, $R_L = X_{C_L}$, and the response will be 0.707 of the middle-frequency value.

$$X_{C_L} = \frac{1}{2\pi f_2 C_L}$$

$$f_2 = \frac{1}{2\pi X_{C_L} \cdot C_L}$$

Now if this f_2 is not the desired value, there are three possible corrective means:

1. Use less gain per stage.
2. Use tubes having lower interelectrode capacitances.

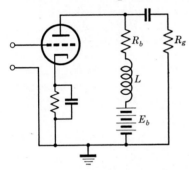

3. Apply high-frequency correction networks.

The use of less gain per stage will mean lower values of R_L; therefore, f_2 will occur at a higher frequency.

The new miniature series of tubes have definite advantages in providing fair gain possibilities with low interelectrode capacitances.

A simple approximate method of high-frequency compensation is shown in Fig. 5-40.

For essentially flat response to a given frequency f_{2_1}, use a value of R_b which is equal in ohms to the reactance of the shunting capacitance C_L, and make $X_L = (\frac{1}{2})X_{C_L}$.

FIG. 5-40. A Method for High-Frequency Compensation

O. INVERSE FEEDBACK

If a portion of the voltage output of an amplifier is introduced or fed back into the input, the amplifier performance will be improved. These improvements are primarily reduction of noise and distortion and increase of stability and frequency response. The feedback may be one of two types of negative feedback—current feedback and voltage feedback.

14. Current Feedback. The current feedback can be introduced into the amplifier circuit by omitting the bypass condenser C_c as shown in Fig. 5-41. The voltage across R_c will be 180° out of phase with the applied signal e. This is equivalent to reducing the effective signal voltage applied to the amplifier grid. The feedback factor in this case is given by the following formula:

$$\beta = -\frac{R_c}{R_L} \quad \text{approx.}$$

The gain with feedback is equal to the gain without feedback divided by $(1 - A_0\beta)$.

$$A = \frac{A_0}{1 - A_0\beta}$$

In this type of feedback circuit the effective plate resistance is increased.
If r_p = plate resistance without feedback
  r_p' = plate resistance with feedback
  μ = amplification factor
then the change r_p' may be expressed in one of three ways according to assumption; all give values that are in fair agreement. (3) is probably the simplest to use.

$$r_p' = r_p + (1 - \mu_c R) \qquad (1)$$

$$r_p' = r_p(1 + R_c Gm) - R_c \qquad (2)$$

$$r_p' = r_p + \mu R_c \qquad (3)$$

Since Z_L instead of R_L controls the value of β at high frequencies, and Z_L will change with frequency, the current-feedback circuit does not improve frequency response.

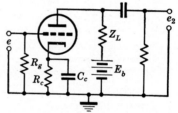

Fig. 5-41. Triode-Tube Circuit. Inverse Current Feedback by Removing Capacitor C_c

There are several worth-while benefits from current feedback: reduction of noise and distortion introduced by the plate circuit of the tube, and reduction of the changes in gain with replacement of tubes.
If D' = distortion and noise with feedback
  D = distortion and noise without feedback
  K = per cent change in gain for a given change in line voltage without feedback
  K' = per cent change in gain for a given change in line voltage with feedback
then the relation between distortion and gain with and without feedback is given by

$$D' = \frac{D}{1 - A_0\beta} \qquad K' = \frac{K}{1 - A_0\beta} \qquad (4)$$

If the resistor R_C is shunted by C_c, then C_c is selected so that, at the low-frequency "cutoff" f, X_c does not exceed 10 per cent of R_c. In practice, this requires a very large condenser for C_1. If C_c is eliminated, the advantages stated in the preceding paragraph will be obtained.

With current feedback any heater cathode leakage will cause hum to be introduced into the amplifier-grid circuit; therefore, all tubes in low-level stages must be checked for heater cathode leakage.

15. Voltage Feedback. The second type of inverse feedback is the voltage-feedback circuit, in which a portion of the voltage developed across the load impedance is introduced into the grid circuit. This feedback circuit is shown in Fig. 5-42. In general, the voltage feedback will be 180° out of phase with the signal, and, thus, it will tend to reduce the effective input signal so that larger input signals will be required for the same output.

C_f = feedback blocking condenser
R_1 = feedback resistor
R_2 = feedback resistor
μ = amplification factor

$$\beta = -\frac{R_2}{R_1 + R_2}$$

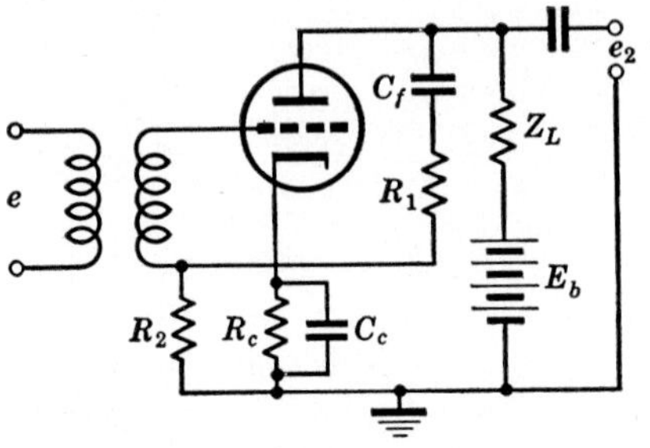

FIG. 5-42.   Voltage Inverse Feedback
C_f = feedback blocking capacitor
R_1 = feedback resistor
R_2 = feedback resistor
μ = amplification factor

when $X_{C_f} << (R_1 + R_2)$

$$A = \frac{A_0}{1 - \beta A_0}$$

This type of feedback lowers the effective plate impedance by shunting it with a fictitious resistance given by $1/Rg_m$. It can be shown that $r_p' = \frac{r_p}{1 - \beta\mu}$. If there is a change in gain of K per cent for a given change in supply voltage, the change with feedback will be reduced.

$$K' = \frac{K}{1 - \beta A_0}$$

If there is noise and distortion without feedback of D per cent, with feedback this will be reduced.

$$D' = \frac{D}{1 - \beta A_0}$$

If f_1 and f_2 are the two frequencies at which the gain without feedback is reduced to 0.707 of the maximum mid-frequency gain, f_1' and f_2' are the frequencies with feedback.

$$f_1' = \frac{f_1}{1 - \beta A_0} \tag{5}$$

$$f_2 = f_2(1 - \beta A_0) \tag{6}$$

It should be pointed out that these equations 5 and 6 hold only for single-stage feedback.

In general, it is desirable to use as large a β as possible and still have the required gain. With modern high-μ tubes considerable feedback can be used. For high values of β the gain is essentially independent of tubes and circuit-voltage fluctuations.

It is no trouble to use any value of β up to unity for single-stage feedback since the feedback voltage cannot shift in phase through 360° which would be required for positive feedback or oscillation.

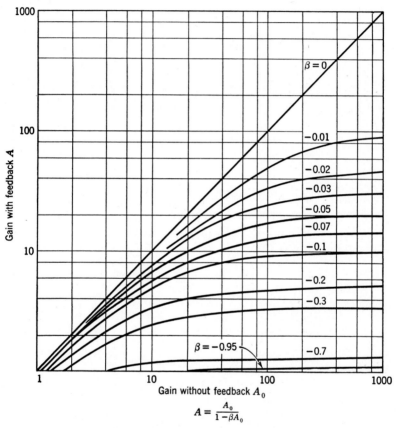

$$A = \frac{A_0}{1 - \beta A_0}$$

Fig. 5-43. Variation of Gain with Feedback

When feedback is to be used in amplifiers for measurement purposes, it is a good policy to use single-stage feedback instead of attempting multiple-stage feedback.

When for simplicity or saving of parts multiple-stage feedback is used, it should be remembered that each tube introduces 180° phase shift, and so for two stages the feedback voltage must be introduced into the cathode circuit of the first tube or reversed in phase by a transformer.

A two-stage amplifier with feedback over the two stages is likely to oscillate at high and low frequencies where the phase shift can approach 180° plus 180° for one amplifier stage making 360° and a possibility of oscillation.

A three-stage amplifier is almost certain to oscillate at high and low frequencies unless at least one stage is made extremely flat in respect to gain versus frequency.

A convenient graph of the gain versus feedback relations is shown in Fig. 5-43; its use saves a considerable amount of time.

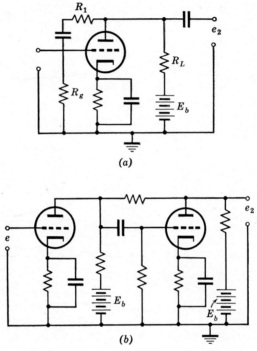

(a)

(b)

Fig. 5-44.   Special Feedback Circuits

The circuits of Fig. 5-44 require very few parts.   In Fig. 5-44a R_g in parallel with R_L, and r_p of the preceding tube represents the resistance R_2 shown in Fig. 5-42.

16. Multiple-Stage Feedback.   If feedback is arranged over two stages having identical frequency response $A_0\beta$ must be less than -2 or oscillation may occur at high and low frequencies where the over-all phase shift equals 360° and the feedback becomes positive.

If feedback is introduced over three stages, oscillation will occur unless one stage has a much broader frequency response than the other two stages. If F_1 for this broad response stage is made equal to $\frac{1}{10}$ of F_1 for the other two stages, and F_2 for the flat stage is equal to $10F_2$ for the other two stages, $A_0\beta$ can be made any value less than -2 without oscillation.

It should be pointed out that single-stage feedback over individual stages has the advantage that a higher over-all $A_0\beta$ can be safely applied without fear of oscillation.

₁P. The Tetrode and Pentode Tubes

Many desirable characteristics can be attained in vacuum tubes by the use of more than one grid. The most common types of multigrid tubes are the tetrode and the pentode. These are four- and five-electrode types of thermionic tubes containing an anode, a cathode, a control electrode, and one or two additional electrodes that are ordinary grids. The need for more grids is brought about by the necessity of reducing the capacitance between

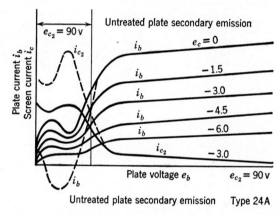

Fig. 5-45.   Typical Screen-Grid Tetrode Plate Characteristics

the grid and the plate of the triode. If a second grid is placed between the control grid and plate, this capacitance is reduced. This second grid is called a screen grid, and the complete tube is called a tetrode. These tubes can be designed to have the same transconductance as that of an equivalent triode and very much higher amplification factor and plate resistance. Figure 5-45 shows a family of plate characteristics for a seven-grid tetrode, type 24A.

Tubes of this type gives rise to an undesirable effect when operated with high plate voltages in that the electrons strike the plate with velocities high enough to generate secondary emission from the plate. Because the screen is at a higher voltage than the plate, the screen draws these secondary electrons to it, thus reducing the net plate current. If the plate is not treated to reduce secondary emission, the number of secondary electrons leaving the plate may exceed the number of primary electrons that strike the plate, and so the plate current may reverse in direction. This is shown by the dashed curve in Fig. 5-45. These effects of secondary emission can also be reduced or eliminated by preventing the secondary electrons emitted by the plate from going to the screen. This can be done by placing between screen grid

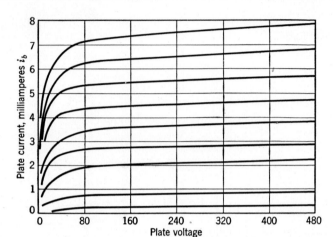

FIG. 5-46.   Typical Plate Characteristic of Voltage Pentode

and plate a third grid, called the suppressor grid.   Figure 5-46 shows the characteristics of a tube of this kind.

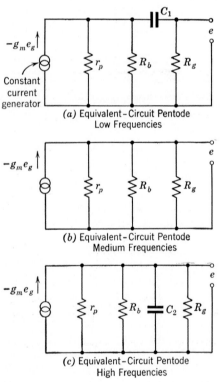

FIG. 5-47.   Equivalent Circuits Pentode Tubes

Q. PENTODE AMPLIFIER STAGES

Tubes of this kind are used in amplifiers in a manner similar to triode tubes.   The pentode amplifiers have equivalent circuits, and the gain as a function of frequency is illustrated in a like manner.   These equivalent circuits are shown in Fig. 5-47, and the equations A, B, and C are equations for the gain.

Amplification at low frequencies

$$= \frac{A'}{\sqrt{1 + \left(\dfrac{X_{c_1}}{R}\right)^2}}$$

Amplification at high frequencies

$$= \frac{A'}{\sqrt{1 + \left(\dfrac{R_e}{X_{c_2}}\right)^2}}$$

Amplification at medium frequencies $= G_M R_e = A'$

$$\text{where } R_e = \frac{r_p R_b R_g}{r_p R_g + R_b r_p + R_b R_g}$$

$$\text{and } R = R_g + \frac{R_b r_p}{R_b + r_p}$$

X_{c_1} = reactance of coupling condenser

X_{c_2} = reactance of capacitance shunting-plate load $C_2 = C_{pf} + C_{\text{stray}} + (1 + A_2)C_{gP}$

A_2 = amplification of next stage

R = resistance of R_g in series with r_p and R_b in parallel

R_L = resistance of parallel combination of R_b, R_g, and r_p

17. Effect of Screen Grid. The screen grid must be effectively at cathode potential for the signal frequency. This is accomplished by the use of a relatively large bypass condenser whose reactance at the signal frequency will be very low. If we define N as the gain reduction factor for a given bypass condenser relative to the infinite value of C_s,

$$N = \sqrt{\frac{P^2 + P^2 R_s^2 w^2 C_s^2}{(P + R_s)^2 + P^2 R_s^2 w^2 C_s^2}}$$

Now

$$P = \frac{\mu_1}{G_m} \cdot \frac{i_p}{i_s} \frac{1 + \frac{Z_L}{r_p}}{1 - \frac{\mu_1}{\mu_2}}$$

$$P = \frac{\mu_1}{gm} \cdot \frac{i_p}{i_s} \text{ approx.}$$

C_s = screen bypass condenser

R_s = screen dropping resistor

G_m = pentode mutual conductance

μ_1 = triode amplification factor

μ_2 = pentode amplification factor

r_p = pentode plate resistance

i_p = plate current

i_s = screen current

$\omega = 2\pi f$

f = frequency at which N is to be calculated

18. Cathode Bias Resistor. The cathode bypass condenser must be employed, for pentode amplifiers, like triode amplifiers or current feedback, will decrease the gain of the stage.

If S is the ratio of gain with a given value of cathode bypass condenser to the gain with an infinite bypass condenser:

$$S = \sqrt{\frac{1 + (\omega C_c R_c)^2}{(1 + W A_0 R_c)^2 + (\omega C_c R_c)^2}}$$

where $W = \dfrac{1}{A_0(R_L + r_p)} + \dfrac{1}{R_L}$

$\omega = 2\pi f$

f = frequency at which S is desired

C_c = cathode bypass condenser

R_c = cathode resistor

A_0 = gain at medium frequency

R_L = load resistor

r_p = plate resistance

A close approximation is to make $wC_c = 2.2\,G_m$ for which $S = 0.8$.

19. Amplification of a Pentode Amplifier. Actual amplification = $A_0 S N$ where A_0 is the gain of the amplifier at the given frequency if both screen and cathode were bypassed by infinite large condensers so that their reactance was approximately zero.

20. Advantages of Pentode Amplifiers. The gain which can be obtained per stage of amplification is considerably higher with pentode tubes than with triodes. This makes it feasible to use feedback and still have the same over-all gain as would be obtained with the same number of stages of triode amplifier without feedback.

The high-frequency response is considerably improved for the same value of plate load since the C_{gp} of a pentode is very small, and, therefore, C_2 (the capacitance shunting the plate load) is small.

R. Power-Output Stages

In many applications of amplifiers it is necessary to deliver a considerable amount of power to the load. Typical examples of loads requiring power are

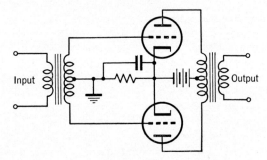

Fig. 5-48.   Push–Pull Amplifier Stage

magnetic oscillographs, rectifier-type output meters, and loudspeakers. In some cases a single-ended output using a single tube will be satisfactory. In this case the tube will normally be of the power-output type. Since the tube-plate characteristic curve is nonlinear, considerable distortion may occur for large input signals. This distortion can be reduced by using a large amount of inverse feedback.

If the power required is much greater than the rated power output of a single tube, push–pull circuits should be used (see Fig. 5-48).

In this circuit the input signal is applied to the grids of two tubes. Because of the connections in the input transformer, the applied signals are 180° out of phase. The plates of the two tubes are connected to the ends of a center-tapped primary winding of the output transformer, and the plate supply voltage is connected to the center tap of the winding. One feature of this circuit is that even harmonics generated in the plate circuit, owing to the nonlinearity of the tube characteristic, will be much less than for a single tube. In general, from two to three times the power output for the same percentage even-harmonic distortion can be obtained from push-pull amplifiers. The input transformer may be eliminated if the input voltage is obtained by a phase-inverter circuit.

S. Phase-Inverter Circuit

In this circuit R_2 and R_L are equal, and the outputs 1 and 2 are out of phase by 180° (see Fig. 5-49). The gain is very low, even less than unity,

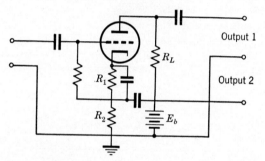

Fig. 5-49. Phase-Inverter Circuit

owing to the high degree of current feedback. In practical cases the stage gain is about 0.9. The advantages over a transformer are that the distortion and the cost are considerably less. The frequency response will, in general, be better with the phase inverter than with an ordinary push–pull input transformer.

T. Oscillators

In some of the strain-gage systems a source of audio-frequency voltage or power is required. Two types of oscillators are readily constructed from commercial parts: the resistance-tuned and the phase-shaft oscillators.

The resistance-tuned oscillator consists of a two-stage resistance-coupled amplifier whose output is coupled to its input by means of a frequency-selective network (see Fig. 5-50a).

If a voltage E_1 of variable frequency is applied to the circuit shown in Fig. 5-50a, the output voltage E_2 will vary as shown in Fig. 5-50b. It may be noticed that this curve appears much like a resonance curve except that it is very broad.

A circuit of an oscillator is shown in Fig. 5-51. Since there are two stages, there will be a total phase shift of 360°, and, therefore, positive feedback or regeneration will occur, owing to the path consisting of the selective network. The output of the second stage is also fed back into the cathode circuit of the first stage. This will result in negative feedback or degeneration, and the amount of negative feedback is determined by the feedback factor. The

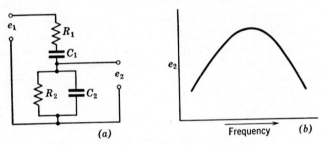

FIG. 5-50.   Frequency-Selective Network
(a) Circuit
(b) Response curve

cathode resistor of the first stage is a tungsten-filament 3-watt mazda lamp, which has a cold resistance of some 200 ohms and a hot resistance of about 2000 ohms. Thus the feedback factor will depend on the tube current and feedback path current. The result of using this 3-watt mazda lamp is that a high degree of amplitude stability is attained.

The combination of a broadly tuned circuit having a maximum at the operating frequency and regeneration at the operating frequency together

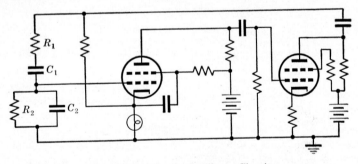

FIG. 5-51.   Simple Oscillator Circuit

with degeneration at all frequencies results in the equivalent of an oscillator with a sharply tuned resonant circuit.

The oscillator frequency is given by the following formula:

$$f = \frac{1}{2\pi R_1 C_1}$$

when $R_1 C_1 = R_2 C_2$.

The frequency stability is primarily determined by the two resistors and two condensers, R_1R_2 and C_1C_2, which must be temperature-stable. It is recommended that silver mica capacitors and temperature-stable resistors be used.

The circuit diagram for a single-frequency oscillator of this type for approximately 1000 cps is shown in Fig. 5-51.

U. Phase-Shift Oscillator

A simple oscillator is the so-called phase-shift oscillator in which a single tube and a phase-shift network are used. The circuit is shown in Fig. 5-52. In this circuit 180° phase shift is provided by the tube and the other 180° by a three-section RC filter. It can be shown that a gain of 29 is required for oscillation.

If $R_b \ll R$ the frequency will be given by the following formula:

$$f = \frac{1}{2\pi \sqrt{6}\, RC}$$

A 6AC7 tube is very suitable, giving ample gain with a low value of R_b.

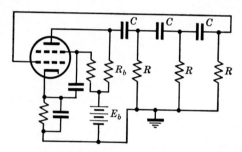

Fig. 5-52.   Phase-Shift Oscillator

Both the phase-shift oscillator and the resistance-tuned type require a buffer amplifier for best results. For most applications a single 6F6 or 6V6 with a high percentage of feedback will be satisfactory. In certain applications distortion must be minimized, and so a phase inverter and a push–pull amplifier should be used.

V. Discriminators—Circuits for Indicating the Sign of the Strain

When an a-c bridge is followed by an amplifier, some circuit for indicating phase between the oscillator voltage and bridge unbalance voltage must be provided in order to show the sign of the strain. In general, there is a 180° phase shift in going through balance. Most of the circuits are based on comparison of a voltage from the oscillator with the amplified unbalance voltage from the bridge circuit.

In the circuit shown in Fig. 5-53a the copper oxide bridge is used. The amplified unbalance voltage is applied across two opposite corners of the bridge, and the reference signal from the oscillator is applied across the other two corners. This is a full-wave rectifier circuit in which voltages are either in phase or 180° out of phase. If they are in phase, the rectified currents will add, but, if they are 180° out of phase, the rectified currents will subtract. When the bridge is off balance the polarity of the direct voltage acting on the meter depends on whether the voltage unbalance from the bridge circuit is in phase or 180° out of phase with the reference voltage.

In Fig. 5-53b a Lissajou figure is employed to show the sign of the strain. This is a very simple method and convenient in balancing of dynamic strain-gage bridges where a cathode-ray oscilloscope must be provided for photographic recording. The procedure is simply to note which way the ellipse is inclined for tension and for compression on a known test bar; then the sign of an unknown strain can be readily determined by observing the direction of inclination of the ellipse due to the strain.

The circuit shown in Fig. 5-53c is an electronic mixer in which a local signal from the oscillator is added to the second grid of a dual tube having both

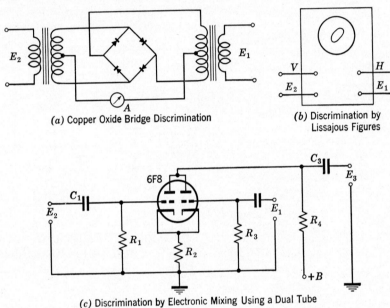

(a) Copper Oxide Bridge Discrimination

(b) Discrimination by Lissajous Figures

(c) Discrimination by Electronic Mixing Using a Dual Tube

FIG. 5-53a, b and c.   Three Methods for Indicating Direction of Bridge Unbalance

plates coupled together. The plate current will depend on the sign of the bridge output signal. This, of course, requires that a phase-shift network is provided for adjusting the phase of the oscillator voltage so that it is either in phase with the voltage unbalance or 180° out of phase with this unbalance voltage. This circuit has many advantages such as elimination of special transformers, copper oxide rectifiers, and so on. The only disadvantage is the necessity of using a phase-shift network for initial phase adjustment.

Another circuit which is used in several commercial instruments is shown in Fig. 5-53d. In this circuit the local oscillator signal is applied by the use of a center-tapped transformer. The two ends of this winding are connected by two equal resistors which are in series. The signal voltage is rectified by copper oxide or diode rectifiers. The unbalance voltage from the bridge circuit is amplified and applied between the center tap of the transformer winding and the junction of the two resistors.

The operation of this circuit is as follows: When the phase of the signal is such that point G is $+$ in respect to point F, point H will be $-$ in respect to point F. The direct voltage drop from C to D and D to E will be equal and opposite for successive half-cycles. Since the meter has a long period compared with the time of a half-cycle, the meter will not deflect. Now if a voltage is applied from A to B of the same frequency and either in phase or 180° out of phase with the voltage G to F, there will be a definite voltage E_{CE} applied to the meter. If the phase of E_{AB} is reversed, E_{CE} will also reverse, causing the meter to read in the opposite direction. The reference voltage should be at least twice as large as the maximum amplified unbalance voltage in order to keep the meter reading proportional to the unbalance of the bridge circuit.

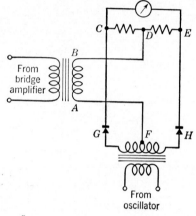

Fig. 5-53d. Discrimination by Copper Oxide Rectification

W. D-C Amplifiers

When static strain must be measured, a direct-coupled amplifier may be used. This type amplifier has poor stability, and the zero will usually drift with time. This drift is due to random conditions at the cathode of low-level stages and to small changes in emission caused by tube aging, supply voltage, and the like.

Direct-coupled amplifiers employing four cascaded push–pull stages have been constructed with a gain of 10,000 and a frequency response of 0 to 30,000 cycles. This amplifier will produce a deflection of 2 in. on a 3-in. cathode-ray tube for an alternating strain of 300 μin. when type C-1 strain gages are used.

The drift is minimized by using the push–pull stages which are coupled directly from plates of one stage to grids of the next. Any changes in plate supply voltage will tend to cancel if both tubes are identical. The cathodes are tied together and returned to ground by means of a common resistor.

The circuit diagram of the first two stages is shown in Fig. 5-54, and the block diagram of the amplifier is given in Fig. 5-55.

It was found that very good regulated voltage supplies were required for these amplifiers and a regulated filament supply as well. Forced-draft ventilation was provided to shorten the time required for reaching temperature equilibrium.

The circuit diagram of the last two stages is very similar to that of the first two stages except that two separate tubes were used in the output instead of a dual tube.

In general d-c amplifiers can be constructed, but the problems of aging tubes, tube selection, and adjusting the amplifier are very difficult. This is

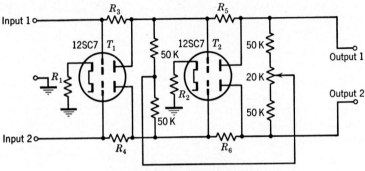

R_1 is adjusted to give desired bias on T_1
R_2 is adjusted to give desired bias on T_2
$R_3 = R_4$ feedback resistances
$R_5 = R_6$ feedback resistances

FIG. 5-54.   First Two Stages, D-C Amplifier

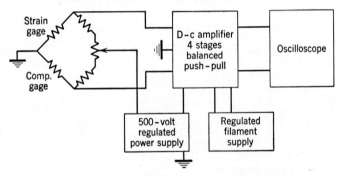

FIG. 5-55.   Block Diagram, D-C Amplifier System

the primary reason that manufacturers have hesitated to build a commercial
unit.

X. CARRIER SYSTEM

When low-frequency dynamic strain must be measured, a carrier system is
the best means of measurement.   This system is less critical to construct and
use than a d-c amplifier.   A carrier amplifier equipped with system for indicating tension and compression is shown in Fig. 5-56.   Like the d-c amplifier
it can be readily calibrated by dead loading.   The carrier frequency can be
selected between 60 and 10,000 cps.   Sixty cycles per second is very satisfactory for dynamic strains of 6 cps.   As a general rule, the carrier frequency
should be at least ten times the highest desired modulation frequency.   For
many strain measurements on large structures such as bridges and steam
shovels a carrier of 500 to 1000 cps will give good results.   The amplifier
should be designed to pass a limited band of frequencies since the noise level
is determined by the band width.

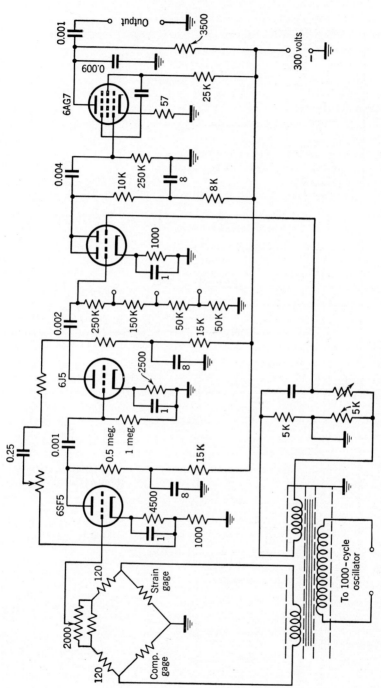

Fig. 5-56. Carrier Amplifier Circuit Equipped with System for Indicating Tension and Compression

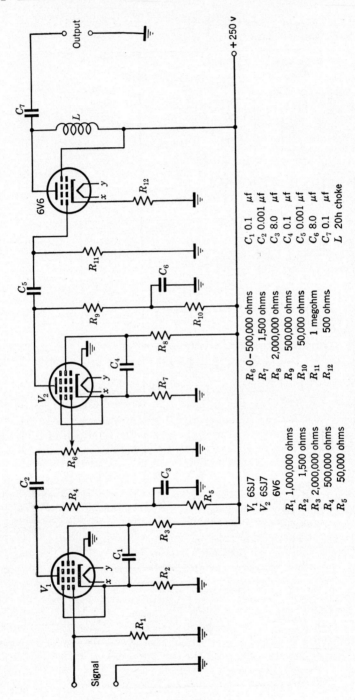

Fig. 5-57. Circuit Diagram of a Simple Three-Stage Pentode Amplifier

For certain applications in laboratory measurements, the leads to the strain-gage bridge can be kept very short, and 10,000-cycle carrier systems can be used.

Figure 5-57 shows the circuit diagram of a simple three-stage pentode amplifier having a response curve as shown in Fig. 5-58. The coupling condensers are much smaller in value than would normally be used in a public-address or similar amplifier. Current feedback is employed in order to improve stability and decrease the effect of the variations between tubes. A regulated power supply is used in order to further improve stability.

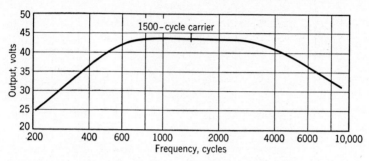

FIG. 5-58. Frequency Response Curve of the Amplifier Shown in Fig. 5-57

A step attenuator can be used to give the amplifier four ranges, in steps of 1, 2, 5, and 10. If the attenuator is used, it can be installed in place of R_6.

Y. DESIGN OF AN AMPLITUDE-MODULATION STRAIN-GAGE AMPLIFIER

The first step in the design of an amplitude-modulation strain-gage system is to determine the signal output from the bridge circuit. In Fig. 5-59 the output in millivolts per volt of bridge excitation as a function of the strain is presented in graphical form. This curve is constructed for type A-1 strain gages. The signal to be obtained can be determined by multiplying the value from the curve by the number of volts of bridge excitation to be used.

The maximum safe bridge voltage depends on the thermal conductivity of the base member to which the gage is attached. When the gage is mounted on metal, a bridge voltage of 6 volts can be applied: when the gage is mounted on wood, concrete, plastic, or similar materials, a bridge voltage of 1 to 2 volts can be employed without excessive creep.

The second step in the design is to determine the output voltage required. If a cathode-ray oscilloscope is to be used, the deflection sensitivity can be obtained from the data by the tube manufacturer. A typical 3-in. tube will require about 75 direct volts per inch of deflection. Since the signal applied to the output stage is a sinusoidal carrier modulated by the strain, the output signal will be 150 volts peak to peak for a 2 in. peak-to-peak deflection. This output can be obtained by a 6AG7 video output pentode with a signal of approximately 4 volts peak to peak.

The third step is to determine the required gain of the remaining stages by taking the ratio of the 4 volts to the bridge signal. The circuit component values required for the amplifier can be determined from the amplifier analysis shown in previous sections or by referring to the audio-amplifier section of the RCA tube manual.

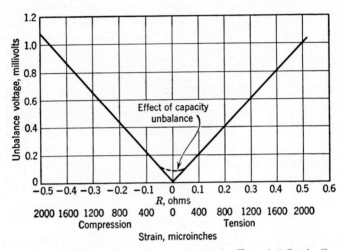

FIG. 5-59. Unbalance Voltage versus Strain for Type A-1 Strain Gages

In Fig. 5-56 the circuit of a special amplifier is shown. This amplifier has a circuit for indicating the sign of the strain. In Fig. 5-60 the initial offset corresponding to zero strain results in a deflection of 1 in. A compressive strain corresponding to 500 μin. will produce a deflection of approximately zero, and a tension strain of 500 μin. will produce a deflection of 2 in. This

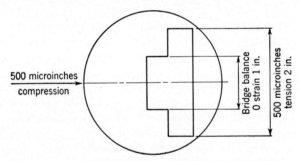

FIG. 5-60. Schematic Representation of Strain versus Time by Showing Balance, Tension, and Compression in Carrier System

is accomplished by the use of the mixer circuit shown in Fig. 5-53c. In this circuit a carrier-frequency signal is applied to one grid of the 6SN7 tube, and the amplifier-bridge unbalance signal is applied to the other. The phase-shifting network is provided so that the initial place can be adjusted to be either 180° out of phase or in phase with the signal. Since the bridge will result in a 180° phase shift in going from a tension to a compression strain, the pattern of Fig. 5-60 will result.

A step attenuator for adjusting the magnitude of the signal applied to the signal grid of the mixer is provided. Since this attenuator does not affect

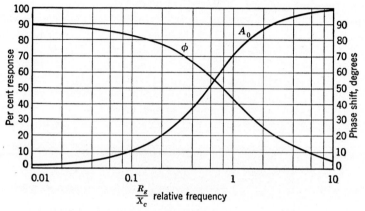

FIG. 5-61. Effect of Coupling Condenser on Amplifier Response

the reference signal applied to the other grid, changing amplifier ranges will not change the offset or reference deflection. If this offset were produced by initially unbalancing the bridge in a tension or compression direction, it would change with the amplifier sensitivity range.

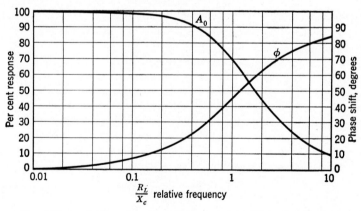

FIG. 5-62. Effect of Shunting Capacitance across Plate Load on Amplifier Response

The optimum plate-load resistor R in Fig. 5-56 depends on tube characteristics but should be about 5000 to 10,000 ohms.

A feedback loop is provided over the first two stages and used as an initial gain adjustment.

The curves shown in Fig. 5-61 and Fig. 5-62 will be of considerable value in designing amplifier circuits. It should be remembered that the gain of a multiple-stage amplifier is the product of the gains of the individual stages, and the phase shift is the sum of the phase shifts of the individual stages.

Z. RECORDING METHODS

There are three recording systems which are commonly used for recording dynamic-strain versus time curves. The first system is the cathode-ray oscilloscope in which the electron beam is deflected in one direction by the voltage from the output of a strain-gage amplifier. The time axis is provided by photographing the cathode-ray trace with a continuous-motion-film camera. The line trace is at right angles to the direction of film travel. This system is capable of recording low or high frequencies, depending only on the optical system and film exposure time. Figure 5-63 shows this type of recording.

FIG. 5-63. Typical Record of Moving-Film Type of Recording. Amplitude-Modulated Method. Strain Measurement on Press Break

This is a high-impedance recording system and can be connected to voltage-amplifier circuits.

The second method of recording is to apply a sawtooth time trace to the oscilloscope instead of providing the time axis by a moving film. If a single-sweep type of circuit is employed, the camera lens can be left open during the measurement and closed after the single sweep has occurred. Figure 5-64 shows more records made by this type of recording. This system of recording has the advantage that any camera with a suitable lens can be employed. It is best to use a lens with a speed of f2 or higher if high-frequency dynamic strains are to be measured. Another advantage of this type of recording is that the only film used is the single frame, whereas in the continuous-drive film system many feet of film are wasted. For all photographic recordings from the cathode-ray tubes, type P11 cathode-ray-tube screens should be used.

The third method of recording is the magnetic oscillograph. These oscillographs are available in multichannel models for recording on films or paper. The oscillograph consists of a galvanometer and light source, optical system, and recording film. A typical magnetic oscillograph recording on paper, showing a damped vibration in aluminum is demonstrated by Fig. 5-65. The galvanometers are of two general types, the moving-coil and the bifilar type. The moving-coil types are very similar to a D'Arsonval galvanometer of the reflecting type.

The moving-coil types are limited to low-frequency measurements since there is considerable mass to the moving system. They are capable of a high degree of current sensitivity and can be readily matched to an amplifying system. Since the galvanometers are current-operated, they require less voltage amplification than cathode-ray oscillographs. This is a decided advantage for field work or low-frequency strain, acceleration, and so on.

The bifilar system consists of a hairpin-shaped strip of metal with a mirror mounted across the hairpin. The deflection of this system in a magnetic field is directly proportional to the current. Since the mass of the moving

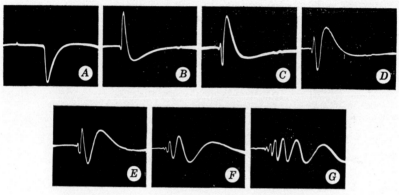

FIG. 5-64. Typical Records

Single sweep type of circuits. Bending disturbances as functions of the distance from impact point. Illustrated by impact on a beam of rectangular cross section. x is the distance from impact point. h is the depth of beam. Gage length $\frac{1}{4}$ in.

Point	x/h	Point	x/h	Point	x/h
A	0	D	24	F	48
B	8	E	32	G	96
C	16				

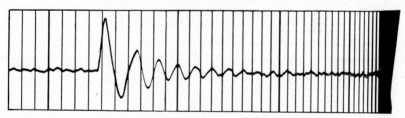

FIG. 5-65. Typical Magnetic-Oscillograph Recording on Paper. Damped Vibration in Aluminum Strip

system is very small, the frequency response can be extended to several thousand sinusoidal cycles. The sensitivity is considerably less than the moving-coil type. This bifilar type has a low impedance and is usually transformer-coupled to an amplifier.

AA. FILTER CIRCUITS

When carrier systems are employed, it is advantageous to use filter circuits to eliminate unwanted frequencies, such as 60-cycle interference due to induction from nearby electric-power systems, and 120-cycle voltage emanating from power-supply ripple. In the elimination of such interference and in performing many other functions in electric networks, several types of circuit structure are available. In the following, filters are described which may be broadly classified as:

1. RC filters.⎫ These are standard notations. RC stands for Resistance ×
2. LC filters.⎭ Capacitance and LC stands for Inductance × Capacitance.
3. Filters inserted in a feedback loop.

Each of these basic systems is briefly described, and basic design formulas are included.

21. RC Filter Circuits. Fig. 5-66 illustrates simple RC filters as used in the design of resistance-coupled amplifiers. The attenuation at the undesired

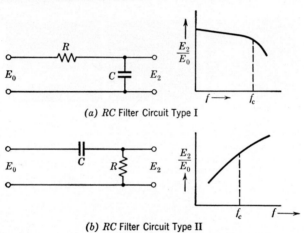

(a) RC Filter Circuit Type I

(b) RC Filter Circuit Type II

Fig. 5-66.   Simple RC Filter Circuits

frequencies is too low for real effective elimination in these circuits. The cutoff frequency f_c and the frequency of desired network response are given for these circuits by

$$f_c = \frac{1}{2\pi RC} \qquad f = f_c \sqrt{\left(\frac{E_0}{E_2}\right)^2 - 1}$$

where f_c = cutoff frequency ($|X_c| = |R|$)
    f = desired network response frequency

22. LC Filters. LC filters may, of course, be constructed in any of several basic circuit forms, one of the most common being the "ladder-type" network, so called because of its formation from several "T" or "π" sections. A "T" section is shown in Fig. 5-67a. The series impedance Z_1 is divided into two equal arms on either side of the shunting impedance Z_2. The other basic circuit or filter section is a "π" section; the schematic configuration of which is shown in Fig. 5-67b. Low-pass, high-pass, band-pass, and band-elimination filters are commonly constructed of several of these sections connected together. These so-called composite filters come under two different headings:

1. The constant-K filter.
2. The M-derived filter.

The constant-K type filter is one constructed of "T" or "π" sections in which Z_1 and Z_2 are constants. This type of filter is of much simpler design than the M derived type; however, it is not so flexible. In addition, there are two features which make difficult its use in exacting filtering requirements. First, the "characteristic" or "surge" impedance does not approximate a constant value over the transmission range; and, second, the transmission range boundaries are not so

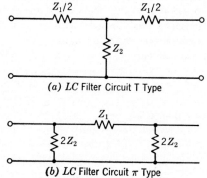

(a) LC Filter Circuit T Type

(b) LC Filter Circuit π Type

Fig. 5-67. Simple LC Filter Circuits

TABLE 5-8
DESIGN DATA FOR CONSTANT-K FILTERS

Constant-K Filter			
Type	Series Arm (Z_1)	Shunt Arm (Z_2)	Notation
Low pass	$L = \frac{R}{\pi f_c}$	$C = \frac{1}{\pi f_c R}$	f_c = cutoff frequency R = terminating impedance
High pass	$C = \frac{1}{4\pi f_c R}$	$L = \frac{R}{4\pi f_c}$	f_c = cutoff frequency R = terminating impedance
Band pass	$L_1 = \frac{R}{\pi(f_2-f_1)}$; $C_1 = \frac{f_2-f_1}{4\pi f_1 f_2 R}$	$L_2 = \frac{f_2-f_1}{4\pi f_1 f_2}R$ $C_2 = \frac{1}{\pi(f_2-f_1)R}$	f_2 = upper cutoff frequency f_1 = lower cutoff frequency
Band elimination	$L_1 = \frac{f_2-f_1}{\pi f_1 f_2}R$; $C_1 = \frac{1}{4\pi(f_2-f_1)R}$	$L_2 = \frac{R}{4\pi(f_2-f_1)}$ $C_2 = \frac{f_2-f_1}{4 f_1 f_2 R}$	f_2 = upper cutoff frequency f_1 = lower cutoff frequency

sharp or abrupt as they should be. However, in many instances these shortcomings can be easily overlooked, and, in view of the simple design procedure and simpler circuit arrangements, this type of filter is often the more practical.

The M-derived filter is a composite ladder-type filter constructed of several "T" or "π" type structures. The design is rather complicated and is beyond the scope of this discussion. Let it suffice to say that filters of very sharp cutoff and widely varying transmission characteristics can be constructed.

Table 5-8 is one that may be used in designing a constant-K filter. The fundamental data required are the impedance into which the filter is to work R, and the cutoff frequency (in the case for the low-pass or high-pass filter) or the frequency limits (in the case of a band-pass or band-elimination filter).

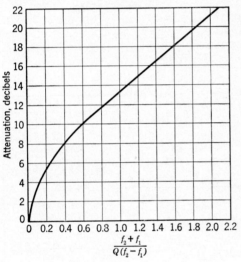

FIG. 5-68. Alternation at Cutoff Frequencies
f_1 and f_2

The table gives values for the series impedance Z_1 and the shunt impedance Z_2; these values are arranged in either "T" or "π" form as shown in the diagrams.

All of the formulas assume dissipationless elements. In a practical filter the coils have an appreciable resistance and, therefore, this dissipation must be corrected by adding the coil Q.

$$Q = \frac{\omega L}{r}$$

where Q = figure of merit of the coil

$\omega = 2\pi f$

r = coil resistance

The attenuation of the band-pass filter at the mid-band frequency is given by the following formula (for dissipationless coils):

$$\cosh a = I + \frac{Z_1}{ZZ_2}$$

From the literature on filters, if Q is greater than 20:

$$\frac{Z_1}{ZZ_2} = \frac{Z}{Q^2}\left(\frac{f_m}{f_2 - f_1}\right)^2$$

$$a = \frac{17.3}{Q} \cdot \frac{f_m}{f_2 - f_1} \quad \text{decibels approx.}$$

The attenuation at the cutoff frequencies f_2 and f_1 can be obtained from the curve in Fig. 5-68

BB. Filters Inserted in a Feedback Loop

The desired narrow-band characteristic can be obtained by inserting a band rejection RC filter in the feedback loop of a three-stage feedback amplifier. The block diagram of this system is shown in Fig. 5-69a. Figure

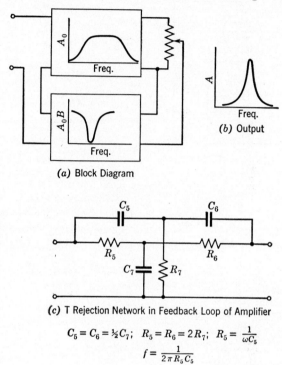

(a) Block Diagram

(b) Output

(c) T Rejection Network in Feedback Loop of Amplifier

$$C_5 = C_6 = \tfrac{1}{2}C_7; \quad R_5 = R_6 = 2R_7; \quad R_5 = \frac{1}{\omega C_5}$$

$$f = \frac{1}{2\pi R_5 C_5}$$

Fig. 5-69.   Narrow-Band-Pass Circuit

5-69c shows the narrow-band pass circuit obtained by inserting equivalent "T" rejection network in feedback loop of amplifier.

CC. The Cathode Follower

The problem of connecting low-impedance cables to high-impedance amplifier circuits can be solved by the use of a circuit called a cathode follower. The circuit is shown in Fig. 5-70.

In this circuit, the resistance is common to both grid and plate circuits. This circuit will be recognized as a special form of the current-feedback circuit in which the usual plate-circuit load resistance has been transferred to the cathode circuit.

The gain of this circuit is given by the following equation:

$$A = \frac{\mu R_{c_1}}{r_p + R_{c_1}(1 + \mu)}$$

where μ = amplification factor

r_p = plate resistance

This circuit gain will always be less than unity.

The input resistance is given by the following equation:

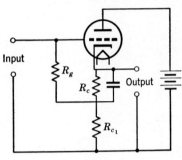

Input

FIG. 5-70. Cathode-Follower Circuit

$$R = \frac{R_g}{1 - A}$$

The input capacitance is given by

$$C = C_{gp} + \frac{C_{gk}}{1 + g_m R_{c_1}}$$

The output impedance is given by the following relation:

$$R_{\text{output}} = \frac{r_p}{1 + \mu} \quad \text{or approx.} \quad \frac{1}{g_m}$$

The cathode followers are of advantage for the following purposes:

1. To match a high-impedance device to a low-impedance transmission line.

2. As a coupling device in wide-band amplifiers, to prevent the "Miller effect" from lowering the frequency response of preceding stages. This makes it feasible to use triode stages coupled by cathode followers instead of pentode amplifiers.

3. As a wide-band electronic attenuator which is relatively free of frequency or phase distortion.

DD. REGULATED POWER SUPPLIES

The simplest form of regulated power supply is the voltage-regulator tube. These tubes are designed to maintain a reasonable constant-voltage drop over a considerable range of load current. They are fairly satisfactory for regulating the voltage for voltage-amplifier stages. The low-output voltage limits the number of applications of these tubes. This type of regulation is shown in Fig. 5-71.

23. Series-Tube Regulators. The series-tube regulator consists of a tube in series with the load. The grid-bias voltage for the series

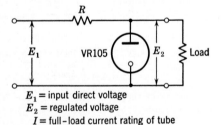

E_1 = input direct voltage
E_2 = regulated voltage
I = full-load current rating of tube

FIG. 5-71. Voltage-Regulator Tube Circuit

tube is derived from the amplified differential between the output voltage and a reference voltage. The bias for the series tube will tend to maintain a constant-output voltage for reasonably large fluctuations of load. The circuit is shown in Fig. 5-72.

By adjusting the screen voltage of the 6SJ7 tube, the power-supply regulation can be adjusted so that the output voltage is constant over broad fluctuations of load or line voltage.

Several variations of this circuit can be employed such as obtaining screen voltage from the output side. A simple *RC* filter in the grid circuit of the

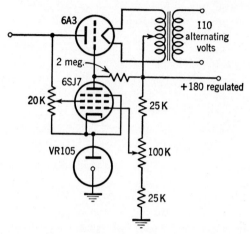

FIG. 5-72. Series-Tube Voltage Regulator

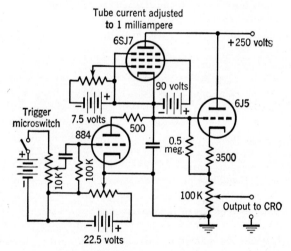

FIG. 5-73. Single-Sweep Circuit

pentode tube is sometimes employed to delay the response and minimize overshooting.

The resistance *R* should be designed for about 10 per cent of the full-load rating of the *VR* tube.

24. Single-Sweep Circuits. Commercial cathode-ray oscilloscopes are normally equipped with continuous-sweep circuits. Although these can be modified to give a single sweep, it is usually better to provide an external single-sweep generator. A suitable circuit is shown in Fig. 5-73.

The condenser is normally charged and is discharged when a pulse is applied to the grid of the gas tube. The condenser then charges at constant current through the pentode tube. The cathode-follower amplifier is provided to furnish a low-impedance output so that several oscilloscopes can be connected in parallel.

Although a microswitch triggering circuit is shown in the diagram, photoelectric triggering systems can be readily adapted.

The same triggering pulse can be used to trip a one-shot multi-vibrator circuit for producing a square-wave brightening pulse for brightening the cathode-ray trace during the sweep.

EE. Application of Resistances Strain Gages to the Measurement of Other Physical Qualities

Where it is possible to relate other physical quantities, such as pressures, accelerations, displacements, forces, and temperatures, to a strain, it is possible to use the electrical-resistance type of strain measurement as a measure of these other mechanical quantities. In each case, it is only necessary to arrange for a known relation to exist between the strain and the quantity to be measured. This sometimes can be done by direct measurement on part of a machine or structure or by using the strain gage as part of a pickup unit which it is necessary to add in order to establish the desired relation. There is a large number of different arrangements that can be made for these purposes, and only a few of the very simple ones are shown here to illustrate the possibilities of adapting this type of equipment for a broader measurement use. Naturally, in constructing these instruments, the same principles of design must be followed as in using any other type of mechanism for measuring mechanical quantities.

In the case of the accelerometer, several simple arrangements are indicated in Fig. 5-74a. The first is simply a cantilever beam with a mass attached to the end and gages placed so as to measure the bending of the beam. The bending becomes proportional to the acceleration of the instrument when the natural frequency of the instrument is higher than the frequency of the phenomenon to be measured. Naturally, some means of damping has to be added in the same manner as in the design of any accelerometer pickup, and the instrument cannot be used to measure accelerations of high frequencies, since the instrument itself has a low natural frequency, and the highest frequency of the measured acceleration should not be greater than a third of the natural frequency of the instrument. Since the displacements of the mass in this type of instrument to produce bending may be fairly large, successful magnetic damping may be possible. Figure 5-74d shows the circuit for use with this type of gage application. If it is desirable to increase the frequency response of the accelerometer, the arrangement shown in Fig. 5-74c may be used. This consists of a thin-walled tube with a series of gages arranged longitudinally around the cylinder circumference. Although this structure can be designed to have very high natural frequency, its sensitivity may not be too large, and it is practically impossible to attain suitable damping.

Following the well-known principles of mechanics, the device suggested in Fig. 5-74a as an accelerometer will, of course, act as a displacement meter for frequencies considerably higher than the natural frequency of the instrument.

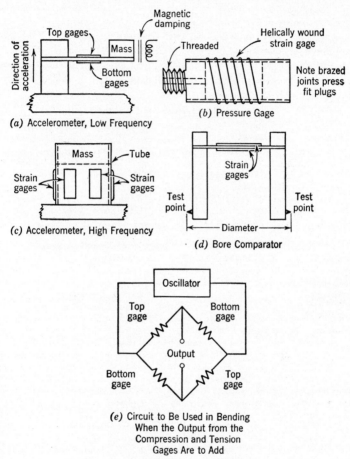

FIG. 5-74.   Application of Resistance-Type Strain Gages for Physical Measurements

In order to measure pressures, a gage may be placed so as to measure the variation of strain with pressures in a diaphram or thin-walled tube.   One method for doing this is shown in Fig. 5-74b.   This kind of setup allows for remove indication of pressure changes.   However, in devices of this kind, the gage should be bonded with Bakelite.   Many applications of the resistance-wire-gage principle have been made for weighing and measuring objects in the industrial plants by simply measuring the strains in various parts of equipment such as in the hooks and attachments for cranes and on the shafts and connecting rods of various rotating equipment. A common use is in dynamometer bars to measure drawbar pull on various types of equipment. For force and direct-pressure measurement an unbonded type of pickup such as the Statham pickup units is often used. Force plates have been designed to weigh dynamically various vertical and horizontal loads such as might be exerted by aircraft on the apron during the warm-up periods. There are a number of ways in which the wire-resistance gage can be adapted to measurements of particular physical quantities. All that is required is a little thought and care in the design. In all these cases the electronic equipment necessary for control is similar to that indicated in the preceding discussions throughout the chapter.

BIBLIOGRAPHY

1. E. C. EATON, "Resistance Strain Gage Measures Stresses in Concrete," *Eng News-Rec*, v 107, Oct 15, 1931, pp 615–16. A description of one of the first types of resistance-type strain gages; of historical importance only.
2. R. W. CARLSON, "Five Years' Improvement of the Elastic–Wire Strain Meter," *Eng News-Rec*, v 114, May 16, 1935, pp 696–97. A description of improvement of the Eaton gage; has an historic importance only.
3. R. FANNING and W. V. BASSETT, "Measurement of Impact Strains by a Carbon–Strip Extensometer," *J Applied Mechanics*, v 7, n 1, Mar 1940. A description of the application of a carbon-strip extensometer to impact problems.
4. B. McCOLLUM and O. S. PETERS, "A New Electrical Telemeter," *U. S. Bur Standards Technologic Papers* 221–47, v 17, 1922–24, pp 737–77, A description of the nonmetallic type of resistance gage, unbonded, Discusses at length the construction and operation of such types of gases; primarily of historic importance.
5. R. D. MEYER, "Application of Unbonded-Type Resistance Gages," *Instruments*, v 19, n 3, pp 136–39, Mar 1946. A description of the Statham application of unbonded forms of wire-resistance gages.
6. D. S. CLARK and G. DATWYLER, "Stress–Strain Relations under Tension Impact Loadings, *Proc ASM*, v 38, 1938, pp 98–111. A description of the first application made by Simons of the bonded type of wire-resistance gage.
7. A. BLOACH, "New Methods for Measuring Mechanical Stresses at Higher Frequencies," *Nature*, Aug 19, 1935, pp 223–24. A description of the application of bonded resistance coating to surface and strain measurements; of historic interest.
8. R. BAUMBERGER and F. HINES, "Practical Reduction Formulas for Use on Bonded Wire Strain Gages in Two-Dimensional Stress Fields," *Proc Soc Exp Stress Analysis*, v 2, n 1. A discussion of and information about cross sensitivity.
9. WM. R. CAMPBELL, "Performance Tests of Wire Strain Gages; II Calibration Factors in Compression," *Nat Advisory Commit for Aeronautics Tech Note* 978, Washington, D. C., Sept 1947. Information about gage factors.
10. A. V. DE FOREST, "Characteristics and Aircraft Applications of Wire Resistance Strain Gages," *Instruments*, v 15, n 4, pp 112–14 and 136–37, Apr 1942. Discusses the characteristics of various types of wire for use as a wire-resistance-type strain gage as well as some dynamic applications of strain measurement.
11. C. C. DOHRENWEND and W. R. MEHAFFEY, "Measurement of Dynamic Strain," *J Applied Mechanics*, Mar 1943. A description of various types of circuits used with SR4 strain equipment.

12. H. C. ROBERTS, "Electric Gaging Methods for Strain, Movement, Pressure, and Vibration," *Instruments*, v 17 and 18, Apr 1944 to Dec 1945. A series of 20 articles dealing with all problems of electric gaging methods; primarily descriptive.

13. R. S. GLASGOW, *Principles of Radio Engineering*, McGraw-Hill Book Co, 1936. A standard textbook with a good treatment of the design of audio amplifiers.

14. F. L. SMITH, *The Radiotron Designer's Handbook*, RCA, 1940. This handbook deals with design data on audio amplifiers. The material is in a condensed form.

15. F. E. TERMAN and WEN-YOUN PAN, "Employing Negative Feedback," *Communications*, Mar 1939. The first treatment of multiple-stage inverse feedback in amplifiers.

16. F. E. TERMAN, "Feedback Amplifier Design," *Electronics*, Jan 1937. A good survey of the problem in simple feedback amplifier circuits.

17. W. RICHTER, "Cathode Follower Circuits," *Electronics*, Nov 1943. This Paper is a comprehensive survey of cathode follower circuits. The phase-inverter circuits are also treated.

18. W. A. LYNCH, "Video Amplifier Low Frequency Correction," *Communications*, Apr 1943. A very complete analysis of plate circuit compensation for improving the low-frequency response of amplifiers.

19. A. PRIESMAN, "Square Wave Analysis," *Communications*, Mar 1942. A good treatment of the technique for measuring the low-frequency performance of amplifiers by the use of a square-wave test signal.

20. E. J. RHOAD, "Design of Resistance Coupled Amplifiers," *Communications*, Jan 1938. A very useful series of design charts for determination of circuit values. These charts cover the range of frequencies normally encountered in strain-gage work.

21. L. R. MALLING, "Zero Phase Shift Amplifier Design," *Electronics*, Mar 1945. This paper shows a method of high-frequency compensation which is equivalent to inductive compensation but simpler to design and fabricate.

23. B. HAGUE, *Alternating Current Bridge Methods*, Pitman Publishing Co, 1938. This book deals with the a-c bridge and is very useful. It considers a-c bridges in which resistance and reactive balances are independent.

24. H. HOLUBOW, "Attenuation Charts for Band Pass and Band Rejection Filters," *Electronics*, Aug 1942. An excellent treatment of the loss correction in wave filters.

25. T. E. SHEA, *Transmission Networks and Wave Filters*. This book is well known as the standard reference for filter design.

26. W. R. MEHAFFEY, T. N. VAN SCOYOC, and D. S. SCHOUER, "A Direct-coupled Amplifier for Recording Dynamic Strain," *Proc Soc Exp Stress Analysis*, v 6, n 1.

CHAPTER 6

ELECTRIC-INDUCTANCE GAGES

By B. F. Langer

A. DEFINITION. GENERAL TYPES

An electric-inductance gage is a device in which the mechanical quantity to be measured produces a change in the magnetic field, and, hence, in the impedance, of a current-carrying coil. The impedance of a coil depends on its inductance and on its effective resistance, and either or both of these quantities can be made sensitive to the mechanical quantity being measured. The inductance which is changed can be either the self-inductance of the coil or its mutual inductance with respect to another coil.

The self-inductance of an air-core coil depends on its shape, dimensions, and number of turns. Since these are properties which are not easily changed by mechanical force or displacement, air-core coils are not often used in electric gages. The exception is the type of device in which the mutual inductance between two air-core coils is changed by changing their relative position. The inductance of an iron-core coil depends principally on the number of turns and on the reluctance in the magnetic circuit. Its resistive component of impedance depends principally on the losses in the magnetic circuit. Reluctance and loss can easily be made a function of force or position, and so iron-core coils are well suited for use as electric gages.

Electric-inductance gages can be classified according to the method they use for varying impedance.

1. Variable-air-gap gages (Fig. 6-1a) are gages in which the reluctance of the magnetic circuit is varied by changing the air gap.

2. Movable-core solenoid gages (Fig. 6-1b) are gages in which the reluctance of the magnetic circuit is varied by changing the position of the iron core in the coil.

3. Eddy-current gages (Fig. 6-1c) are gages in which the losses in the magnetic circuit are varied by changing the thickness or position of a high-loss element inserted in the magnetic field.

4. Magnetostriction gages Fig. 6-1d are gages in which the reluctance of the magnetic circuit is varied by changing the stress in the magnetic core of the coil.

B. FUNDAMENTAL RELATIONSHIPS

The impedance of a coil to the passage of alternating current is given by the expression,

$$Z = \sqrt{(2\pi fL)^2 + R^2} \qquad (1)$$

where Z = impedance in ohms, f = frequency of current in cycles per second, L = inductance of coil in henrys, R = resistive component in ohms.

In a coil of high "quality factor," q, $2\pi fL$ is large compared to R and the impedance varies almost in proportion to the inductance.

The action of the variable-air-gap gage is shown by the expression for the inductance of an iron-core coil, the magnetic core of which contains a small air gap.

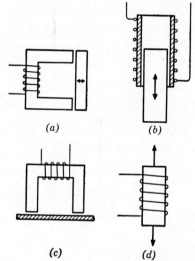

(a)   (b)

(c)   (d)

FIG. 6-1. Basic Forms of Electric-Inductance Gages
(a) Variable air gap
(b) Moving-core solenoid
(c) Eddy current
(d) Magnetostriction

$$L = \frac{3.19N^2}{\dfrac{l_i}{\mu a_i} + \dfrac{l_a}{a_a}} \times 10^{-8} \qquad (2)$$

where L = inductance in henrys, N = number of turns, l_i = length of iron magnetic circuit in inches, l_a = length of air gap in inches, μ = permeability of magnetic material at the maximum alternating flux density, a_i = cross section of iron in square inches, a_a = cross section of air gap in square inches.

If the permeability of the iron μ is sufficiently high, almost all the reluctance of the magnetic circuit is in the air gap and $l_i/\mu a_i$ is very small relative to l_a/a_a. Equation 2 then reduces to

$$L = \frac{a_a}{l_a} \times 3.19N^2 \times 10^{-8} \qquad (3)$$

The expression a_a/l_a is called the permeance of the air gap.   Permeance is the reciprocal of reluctance.

The relationship between the voltage applied across a coil and the flux density in its core is

$$E = 4.44BaNf \times 10^{-8} \tag{4}$$

where E = voltage, B = flux density in lines per square inch, N = number of turns, a = cross section of core in square inches, and f = frequency in cycles per second of the applied voltage.

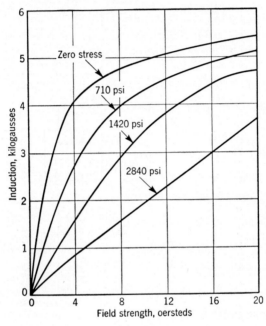

FIG. 6-2a.   Effect of Tensile Stress on the Magnetization Curve of Nickel[17]

From the foregoing it may be seen that under ideal conditions the impedance of an iron-core coil varies inversely with the length of the air gap in the magnetic circuit.   If the motion to be measured is a large percentage of the initial air gap, very large changes in impedance can be produced, and large amounts of electric energy become available.   Therefore, the variable-air-gap gage is one of the best-known methods of converting small motions into high-energy electric signals.

The inverse linear relationship between permeance and length of gap holds only for cases where the length of the gap is small relative to its cross-sectional dimensions.   For larger gaps the fringing flux becomes important, and a point is finally reached where further increase in length produces negligible decrease in impedance.   For larger motions it is possible to make use of the direct linear relationship between permeance and gap area by moving one part of the gage in a direction perpendicular to the flux lines in the air gap. This arrangement has the disadvantage that it is difficult to guide the motion with sufficient accuracy to prevent changes in the length of the gap. For large motions it is more advisable to use the moving-core solenoid.

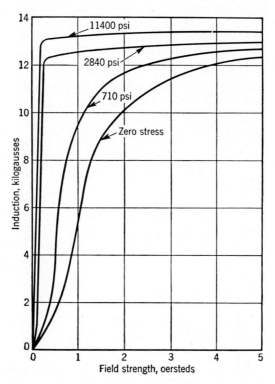

Fig. 6-2b. Effect of Tensile Stress on the Magnetization Curve of "68 Perm-alloy"[17]

The inductance of a long solenoid of small cross section a sq. in. filled through l in. of its length with magnetic material of permeability μ is approximately

$$L = 3.19ln^2\mu a \times 10^{-8} \qquad (5)$$

where n in this case is turns per inch of length. Therefore, to a first approximation, the inductance increases linearly as the core enters the coil. This formula shows the principles involved but is not sufficiently accurate for use in designing a solenoid. For accurate design work it is necessary to determine the reluctance of the air path inside and outside the coil by means of graphical flux-mapping methods.

Eddy-current gages find application in special fields, such as the measurement of motion and of the thickness of nonferrous sheets. The impedance of an a-c electromagnet, particularly its resistive component, depends on the currents generated by the alternating flux in the iron core and in any other conducting material through which the flux passes. These currents are known as eddy currents, and the power dissipated by them depends on the resistivity and thickness of the material in which they occur.

Magnetostriction gages depend for their action on the fact that the magnetic properties of ferromagnetic materials are affected by their state of stress. The effect is small in most commercial magnetic irons but is large in nickel and some nickel–iron and cobalt–iron alloys. Nickel exhibits what is known as negative magnetostriction since tension decreases its permea-

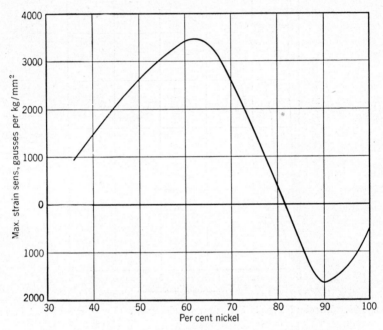

FIG. 6-2c.   Maximum Strain Sensitivity of Iron–Nickel Alloys[17]

bility, as shown in Fig. 6-2a. Compression has an opposite but smaller effect. One of the most strain-sensitive materials is "68 Permalloy", an alloy of nickel and iron containing 68 per cent nickel. As shown in Fig. 6-2b it exhibits positive magnetostriction. A stress of 11400 psi increases its maximum permeability by a factor of 20. The strain sensitivity of any material may be defined as the gausses change at constant magnetomotive force per pound per square inch of stress. It varies with both stress and induction and reaches a maximum usually at some low value of stress and an induction somewhat over half of saturation. Values of maximum strain sensitivity for various nickel–iron alloys are shown in Fig. 6-2c.

A change in stress changes the value of permeability μ in equations 2 and 5 and, hence, changes the inductance of the coil. The effect is not completely reversible under all conditions, and so special means must usually be provided for reducing hysteresis.

C. Types of Pickup

1. Variable Air Gap. The simplest type of electric-inductance gage (Fig. 6-1*a*) consists of a laminated iron **U** or **E** core carrying a coil on one or more legs and a laminated armature which moves relative to the core to form the variable air gap. Figure 6-3 shows a commercially available form of this gage. It has a gage length of 2 in. and is energized with a few watts of 2000-cycle current. For deflections of the order of 0.001 in. it will provide enough energy output to operate indicating instruments and oscillographs without the use of any amplifiers. Smaller gages of the same type are also made, but they require electronic amplification of the output signal.

FIG. 6-3. Hathaway Type-MS-2 Electric Strain Gage. Single Gap, 2-in. Gage Length

Owing to flux leakage and other factors, single-gap gages are not linear in their response, except over small portions of their ranges or when used with very special circuits. In order to improve linearity, and also to provide other advantages described later, it is often advantageous to go to the more

FIG. 6-4. Westinghouse Magnetic Strain Gage. Double Gap, 3-in. Gage Length

complicated double-gap gage. An example of this gage is shown in Fig. 6-4. Here two **E** cores are attached to a common base, and the armature moves between them, increasing the gap of one core by the same amount

that it decreases the gap of the other core.   This arrangement has been called
the inductance-ratio type because its output is determined by the ratio of
the inductances of the two coils.

The single gap and the double gap gage are the basic forms of the variable-
gap type, but innumerable variations are possible.   Figure 6-5 shows some
of the arrangements which have been devised for special puposes.   (a) and
(b) are the basic types, already mentioned; (c) is an adaptation of type (b)
to the measurement of angular displacement; (d) is an adaptation of type (b)
to the measurement of lateral motion of a rotating shaft; (e) and (f) are simple
forms of the variable-coupling type in which one coil is energized and measurement is made of the voltage generated in the other coil; (g), (h), and (i) are

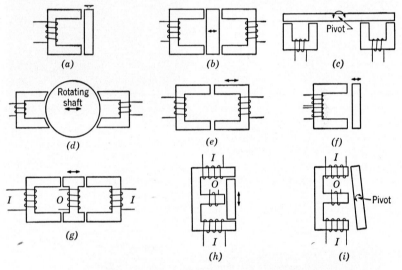

FIG. 6-5.   Forms of Variable-Air-Gap Gages

improved variable-coupling types with two air gaps and three coils.   In each
case, alternating current is supplied to the two input coils, labeled I.   When
the movable armature is in its neutral position the voltage generated in the
output coil O is zero, but when motion of the armature destroys the symmetry
of the gaps a voltage appears in the output coil.   The magnitude of this
voltage is proportional to the magnitude of the armature displacement, and
the phase of the voltage is determined by the direction of the displacement.
The input and output coils can be reversed, in which case power is applied
to the center coil O and the sum of the voltages of coils I is measured.

2. Moving-Core Solenoid.   Various forms of moving-core solenoids are
shown schematically in Fig. 6-6.   (a) is the basic type.   In (b) the core is
tapered and always extends beyond the coil on both ends.   It is useful for
measuring very large motions with a short coil.   (c) is an adaptation of the
inductance-ratio principle to the solenoid type of construction.   (d) is an
application of the variable-coupling type and is similar in its action to Figs.

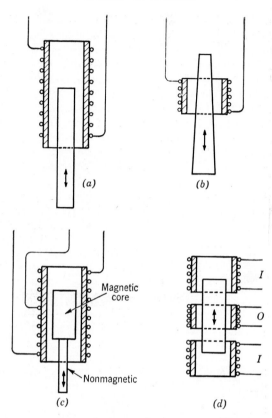

Fig. 6-6.   Forms of Moving-Core-Solenoid Gages

Fig. 6-7.   Variable-Coupling Solenoid with Core Removed (Baldwin-Southwark "Microformer")

6-5*h* and 6-5*i*. Figure 6-7 shows a variable-coupling solenoid of the type of Fig. 6-6*d* designed for measuring small displacements.

3. Eddy-Current. Figure 6-8 shows two forms of eddy-current gage. In Fig. 6-8*a* the coil impedance is sensitive to both the thickness and the proximity of the nonmagnetic sheet. Thus, it can be used to measure the thickness of nonmetallic coatings or else the thickness of uncoated sheets. As a coating-thickness gage it will also work with magnetic sheets, since it acts then as a variable air-gap type. It is not satisfactory for measuring the thickness of magnetic sheets because the alternating flux does not penetrate solid magnetic material. In Fig. 6-8*b* the impedance of the solenoid is sensitive to the axial position of the metal tube, since the tube acts like a short-circuited secondary coil in a transformer.

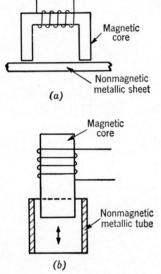

(a)

(b)

Fig. 6-8. Forms of Eddy-Current Gages

4. Torquemeters. Electric-inductance gages are well suited to the measurement of strains in rotating members since it is not difficult to energize them through slip rings and brushes. Certain limitations must be noted, however. The gage and its mounting must be rigid enough so that centrifugal force will not distort it in such a way as to produce an erroneous reading. The brushes must run smoothly on the rings with a fluctuation in contact resistance which is small compared to the impedance of the rest of the circuit. As long as the brushes maintain contact, it is not difficult to keep the contact resistance sufficiently low, since the gage circuit is mostly reactive impedance and the contact drop is resistive, and, thus, the two add in quadrature. Good results have been obtained with both brass and silver rings, using either graphite or silver–graphite brushes. Two or more brushes should be used on each ring to assure continuity of contact. Brush pressures higher than those used in industrial practice are often employed. Industrial brushes usually operate below 5 psi, whereas in temporary strain-gage setups it is often found advantageous to go to 50 or 100 psi. The most important factor in the successful operation of slip rings with strain gages is the roundness and concentricity of the rings themselves.

Many special devices have been built for the specific purpose of measuring torque in a rotating shaft. Use is made of the torsional deflection of the shaft itself, which usually has a section with reduced diameter to provide sufficient angle of twist. Figure 6-9 shows a straightforward application of inductance gages and slip rings for this purpose. In most devices of this type two or more gages are equally spaced around the periphery of the shaft in order to cancel out the effects of axial stress and bending.

The "Magnetic Coupled Torquemeter" uses the principles of the inductance gage but succeeds in eliminating all need for slip rings. The arrangement is shown schematically in Fig. 6-10. Elimination of the slip rings is achieved by locating the point of transition from the stationary to the rotating elements in the magnetic circuit instead of the electric circuit. Magnetic rings with axially extending teeth are attached to collars on the shaft, and the air gaps between the teeth on adjacent rings vary with the twist of the shaft. Stationary coils surround the rotating shaft and feed magnetic flux into the toothed rings.

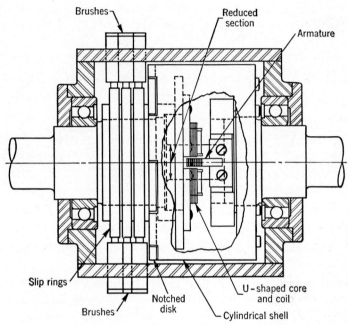

Fig. 6-9. Electromagnetic Torquemeter[11] (Courtesy General Electric Co)

Another interesting method of measuring twist in a rotating shaft is that which uses two a-c generators spaced at some distance from each other along the shaft. The phase difference between the generated voltages is a measure of shaft twist. The disadvantage of this method, compared to those just mentioned, is that it requires a comparatively large angle of twist. It also has attractive advantages. For one thing it requires no slip rings or brushes. It is also easily adaptable to the direct measurement of either torque or horse-power, since the generated voltages can be made either proportional to shaft speed or independent of speed over a limited range. At zero speed no voltage is generated, and the device becomes inoperative. Therefore, it cannot be calibrated statically.

Magnetostriction has been used occasionally for the measurement of torque in a rotating shaft. It has the advantage that the pickup is very simple, consisting merely of a stationary coil surrounding the shaft but not touching it. The practical difficulties which arise from hysteresis and temperature error are so great, however, that very little use has been made of this method.

5. Pressure Gages. Inductance gages of the types described in the foregoing are used for the measurement of pressures in both gases and liquids. The usual method is to transmit the pressure to a flexible diaphragm and then measure the deflection of the diaphragm. For obtaining sufficient motion

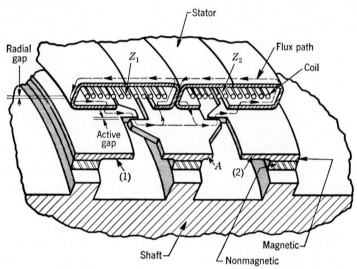

FIG. 6-10. Magnetic-Coupled Torquemeter[12-14] (Courtesy Westinghouse Electric Corp)

with small pressure, use is sometimes made of a sylphon bellows. Magnetostriction gages can be used for pressure measurement by transmitting the force on a diaphragm or piston directly to a nickel rod.

D. STRUCTURAL DETAILS

Attention to mechanical details is important in the design of any strain gage, and the following section discusses some points which are of particular importance in the design of inductance gages of the variable-air-gap type.

The single-gap gage of Fig. 6-3 is built in two separate pieces, one carrying the laminated **E** core and coil, and the other carrying the laminated armature. Because of its nonlinearity of response the air gap must be adjusted after the gage is attached to the test member to exactly the same value that it had when the gage was calibrated. To facilitate this adjustment a cam is provided by which the armature can be moved through very small amounts.

The gage of Fig. 6-3 is quite satisfactory for tests in which the member being studied remains essentially stationary, but, if the member is subjected to large acceleration or centrifugal force, this overhung construction of each half allows too much distortion of the gage. Attempts have been made to use sliding surfaces as guides, but they result in friction and binding which prevent the motion being measured from being transmitted to the air gap. A good solution to the problem is the use of flat parallel springs such as are used in the gage of Fig. 6-4. These act as frictionless guides between the two halves of the gage.

Attachment of the gage to the test member is usually effected by means of machine screws or clamps which push hardened knife-edges into the test member at the gage points. Knife-edges are necessary for accurate determination of the gage length, since if two smooth surfaces are bolted together the exact effective point of attachment is inde-

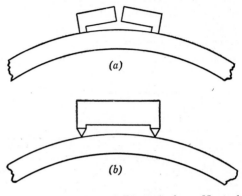

FIG. 6-11. Effect of Distance from Neutral Axis

terminate by an amount somewhat greater than the diameter of the bolt. This may be a considerable percentage of the total gage length.

Particular care must be used in the interpretation of the results of tests in which bending stresses are being measured. The air gap of an inductance gage is not at the same distance from the neutral axis of the beam as is the surface to which the gage is attached. Therefore, if the mounting is such that

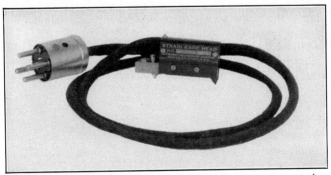

FIG. 6-12. Hathaway Type MS-1-B1 Electric Strain Gage

each half of the gage rotates with the gage point to which it is attached (see Fig. 6-11a), it will magnify strains due to bending. The magnitude of the error is proportional to the ratio between the height of the gage and the distance to the neutral axis of the beam or plate. When strains are to be measured on a surface close to the neutral axis it is necessary to use a gage in which the two halves are guided with respect to each other to form a rigid unit and in which the points of attachment allow some rocking of the knife-edges (see Fig. 6-11b). A small gage designed specifically for this purpose is shown in Fig. 6-12.

Errors which occur owing to inertia of the gage itself can also be minimized by proper design and mounting. The construction of Fig. 6-11a, for example, is not well suited for use on rotating members because each half will bend as a cantilever beam owing to its own inertia. The construction of Fig. 6-11b is somewhat better because the gage bends as a simply supported beam instead of as a cantilever. This is still not the best that can be done, however. If the knife-edges are located on the level of the center of the air gap (see

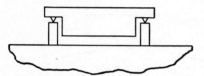

Fig. 6-13), bending of the gage itself will result in opening the top half of the gap and closing the bottom half, so that the gage can bend a considerable amount without changing the total gap reluctance.

Fig. 6-13. Neutral-Axis Mounting to Eliminate Error from Inertia Forces

The mechanical construction of a variable-air-gap gage can have an important effect on its accuracy under varying temperature conditions. If the ambient temperature varies rapidly, it is necessary to provide thermal insulation to reduce the temperature differential between the gage and the testpiece. Even if there are no temperature gradients at any moment, the reading can be changed by slowly varying temperature due to the different rates of expansion of the magnetic laminations, the nonmagnetic frame of the gage, and the testpiece. For any given testpiece material, however, it is possible to construct a gage which is unaffected by temperature variations, provided the effective points of attachment between the various members can be controlled. The simple case of the single-gap gage illustrates the principles involved. In Fig. 6-14, A_1A_2 is the gage length over which strain is being measured. B_1 and B_2 are the effective points of attachment between the magnetic laminations and the nonmagnetic base plates. If α_1, α_2, and α_3 are the thermal-expansion coefficients of the testpiece, the nonmagnetic base plate, and the magnetic laminations, respectively, there will be no error due to differential expansion if the distance B_1B_2 is made to satisfy the equation,

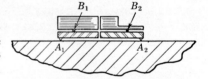

Fig. 6-14. Construction to Eliminate Error from Differential Thermal Expansion

$$B_1B_2 = A_1A_2\left(\frac{\alpha_1 - \alpha_2}{\alpha_3 - \alpha_2}\right) \qquad (6)$$

E. Magnetic Forces

When an inductance gage is used to measure the strain in a structure, the stiffness of the structure is usually so great compared to the magnetic forces in the gage that the magnetic forces can be neglected. When a gage is used to measure deflections in a flexible system, however, occasions arise where the magnetic forces cannot be neglected. An example of this is the use of an inductance gage as the pickup element in a seismic vibration recorder.

The attractive force between the core and armature of a single-air-gap gage (Fig. 6-1a) is

$$\text{Instantaneous force in psi of gap area} = \frac{B_m{}^2}{144} - \frac{B_m{}^2}{144} \cos 2\omega t \qquad (7)$$

where B_m = peak flux density in kilolines per square inch, $\omega = 2\pi \times$ frequency of power supply in cycles per second, t = time in seconds.

The force consists of a steady pull plus an oscillatory component. The steady pull, in terms of root-mean-square flux density B is $B^2/72$. The frequency of the oscillatory component is double that of the electric-power supply. It is important to make sure that this frequency does not resonate with a natural frequency of the structure on which the gage is mounted. The flux density B is inversely proportional to the air gap for any given excitation current. Since the force is proportional to B^2, the relationship between air gap and force is approximately an inverse-square law. Considerable deviation from the inverse-square law can occur, however, depending on the characteristics of the circuit into which the coil is connected. If the circuit is such that the voltage remains constant when the air gap varies, the current will decrease as the air gap becomes smaller, owing to the increase in inductance. Thus the force will increase more slowly than it would in a constant-current circuit.

For any given armature position the force is proportional to the square of the excitation voltage. Therefore, the easiest way to reduce the magnetic force to an acceptable value is to lower the voltage. This, of course, decreases the sensitivity of the gage. If the lower sensitivity is not acceptable, a better condition can be obtained by using a larger gage. A larger gage gives a higher ratio between sensitivity and magnetic pull because the sensitivity is proportional to the total flux. Thus sensitivity is proportional to $B \times$ gap area, whereas total magnetic pull is proportional to $B^2 \times$ gap area. If the gap area is doubled and the flux density halved, the sensitivity will be the same, but the total magnetic pull will be halved. Another way to increase the ratio between sensitivity and magnetic pull is to raise the frequency of the electric-power supply to the gage. The amount of improvement obtained in this way depends on how well the eddy-current losses in the gage can be controlled at the higher frequency. If the losses can be kept small, say by using thinner laminations, the decrease in magnetic pull can be proportional to the increase in frequency.

The same principles can be applied to the case of the double-gap gage, except that here the magnetic forces are comparatively small when the armature is midway between the cores since it is being pulled both ways. It is in unstable equilibrium, however, and owing to the inverse-square relationship between air gap and force the net force increases rapidly as the armature moves away from the center of the gap.

In the simple solenoid the magnetic force acts to pull the core to a central position in the coil. The force is a maximum when the core is halfway into the coil. The magnitude of this maximum force can be estimated from the formula,

$$\text{Force} = \frac{NIa}{100l} \text{ lb} \tag{8}$$

where N = number of turns, I = instantaneous amperes of current, a = square inches cross section of core and l = inches length of coil.

F. TYPICAL CIRCUITS

6. Simple Circuits. The simplest method of measuring the impedance of a coil is to apply a known alternating voltage to it and measure the current which flows (see Fig. 6-15). If the voltage is kept constant the a-c ammeter gives a continuous indication of the displacement being measured. When used with a variable-coupling gage the a-c instrument may be a voltmeter which measures the voltage induced in the secondary coil (see Fig. 6-16).

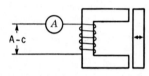

FIG. 6-15. Simple Ammeter Circuit

The main disadvantage of such simple circuits is that only part of the scale of the indicating instrument is used. The current flowing in the instrument is an indication of the *total* impedance of the coil whereas the useful measurement is the *change* of impedance. Few inductance gages change their coil impedances by a factor of more than two over the operating range, and in many cases the change is only a few per cent. Some improvement in scale length can be obtained by using a suppressed-zero instrument, in which a certain amount of current is required to bring the pointer up off the lower stop on to the scale. The improvement is mostly illusory, however, because the coil and spring of the instrument must still be designed for the total current which flows. Another disadvantage of the circuit is that the reading is very sensitive to fluctuations in supply voltage and frequency. Say, for

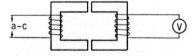

FIG. 6-16. Simple Voltmeter Circuit

example, we have a coil which changes its impedance by 33 per cent over the working range. The useful scale length is one third of the total scale length. If the supply voltage varies 1 per cent the total current varies 1 per cent, but the error in the deflection reading is 3 per cent of the range of the strain gage.

7. Bridge Circuits. The usual method of eliminating the foregoing disadvantages is to measure the impedance of the gage in some form of bridge circuit. The basic form of this circuit is shown in Fig. 6-17. Here the gage coil of impedance Z_1 is one leg of a four-leg network. The reading of the instrument is proportional to the expression $Z_1Z_4 - Z_2Z_3$. By suitable adjustment of the remaining three legs it is possible to obtain zero reading on the instrument for any desired value of gage impedance. The *total* instrument current is then proportional to the *change* in gage impedance.

The bridge circuit is well suited for use with the double-coil gage, in which one coil increases its impedance at the same time that the other coil decreases. In Fig. 6-17, Z_1 is the active coil. If the second active coil is placed at either Z_2 or Z_3, the effects of impedance changes in the coils will be additive at the instrument. At the same time, certain parasitic effects which change the impedances of both gage coils in the same direction will tend to cancel themselves out of the instrument reading. An example of such a parasitic effect is the effect of temperature on the resistivity of the coil. The same advantage can be obtained in the single-coil gage by making Z_2

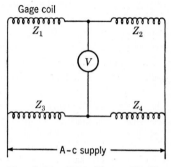

Fig. 6-17. Basic Form of Bridge Circuit

or Z_3 a dummy coil of the same characteristics as the gage and keeping it at the same temperature as the gage.

A further obvious extension of the bridge circuit is to make all four coils active and connect them in such a way that the impedance changes due to deflection of the gage are additive at the meter. A possible application is to the measurement of angular displacement (see Fig. 6-18). Clockwise

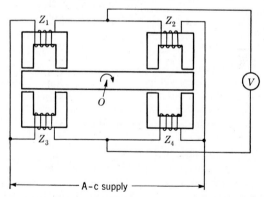

Fig. 6-18.   Circuit for Measurement of Angular Displacement

rotation of the armature about point O increases Z_1 and Z_4 and decreases Z_2 and Z_3, so that the effect is additive at the instrument. Upward displacement of the armature, however, increases Z_1 and Z_2 and decreases Z_3 and Z_4, which produces no unbalance of the bridge.

The advantages of the bridge circuit can be obtained in variable-coupling pickups by means of the arrangement of the pickup elements themselves.

The principle is illustrated in Fig. 6-5g and has already been explained in the description of the pickup.

8. Linear Circuits for Single-Gap Gages. It has been stated in section C of this chapter that one advantage of the double-gap gage over the single-gap gage is its better linearity of response. The nonlinearity of the single-gap gage is due to the departure from the inverse relationship between air gap and impedance. This departure is due to (1) reluctance of the iron, (2) impedance in the external measuring circuit, and (3) leakage flux, which becomes more and more important with increasing air gap. These effects are additive. In the double-gap gage the nonlinearities of the two coils are balanced against each other to give an essentially linear response over a much larger range of displacements. Circuits have been devised, however, with which it is possible to improve the linearity of a single-gap gage. One method is to use a capacitor in series with the gage coil to neutralize the leakage reactance. Another method is shown in Fig. 6-19. The capacitor C is chosen with a value such that the total current I in the metering circuit has a leading power factor. This reverses the relationship between air gap and current and makes I increase with decreasing air gap. What is more important is that it is now possible to buck the nonlinearity due to the impedance of the external circuit Z against the nonlinearity due to leakage. Accurate adjustment of linearity is obtained by adjustment of the external impedance

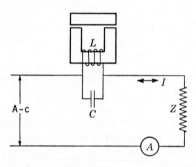

FIG. 6-19.   Linear-Response   Circuit
for Single-Gap Gage[8]

Z. A detailed explanation of this device and its application to bridge-type circuits is given in U. S. patent 2,361,173.

9. Deflection-Type Bridge Circuits. Most electric-inductance gages use some form of bridge circuit, but there is considerable variety in the methods used to measure the unbalance of the bridge. Most methods can be classified as either deflection methods or null-balance methods. In the deflection methods the bridge is allowed to remain out of balance when the gage is deflected and the degree of unbalance is measured with a voltmeter or an ammeter. All circuits used with oscillographs for recording rapid variations in strain are of the deflection type. In the null-balance methods, adjustments are made either manually or automatically to bring the bridge back into balance, and the reading is obtained by noting the amount of adjustment required to produce balance.

The simplest deflection-type bridge circuit is that shown in Fig. 6-17, where the voltmeter is a repulsion-iron or electrodynamometer type. These types of voltmeter are inefficient, however, since the magnetic field of the instrument must be built up and maintained with energy taken from the current which is being measured. D-c instruments of the permanent-magnet, moving-coil (d'Arsonval) type are much more efficient, by a factor of over 1000 in terms of power consumed for full pointer movement.   Therefore it is advantageous to rectify the a-c output of the bridge and take the reading on a d-c instrument, even if a large fraction of the a-c power output is lost in the rectifier.   The rectifier can be of the copper-oxide, selenium, or vacuum-tube type.

Various methods have been used for adjusting the initial balance of the bridge circuit.   Sometimes with single-gap gages the only provision for adjusting the bridge is in the air gaps of the active and dummy gages.   Figure 6-20 shows the circuit commonly used with such gages.   In the double-gap gage the exact setting of the air gaps is not so critical, because of its better linearity, and the initial balance can be adjusted with an external potentiometer (see Fig. 6-21).   The resistance of the potentiometer makes the circuit inefficient, however, as is shown in section G.   Greater power output to the instrument can be obtained by replacing

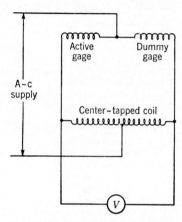

FIG. 6-20.   Typical Circuit Used with Single-Gap Gage

the potentiometer with a variable autotransformer, as shown in Fig. 6-22. The autotransformer balances the reactive components of the circuit, and it is sometimes necessary to add a resistance balance as shown.   Instrument response as a function of gage displacement with and without resistance balance is shown in Fig. 6-23.   If the operating range is kept sufficiently far

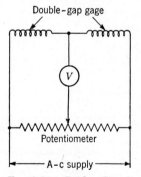

FIG. 6-21.   Bridge Circuit with Resistance Balance

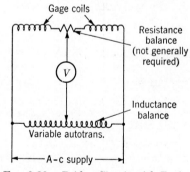

FIG. 6-22.   Bridge Circuit with Resistance and Inductance Balance

away from the balance point, the resistance balance is not required.   Figure 6-24 shows a method which is useful where fine adjustment is required over a narrow range.   This can be combined with a tap-changing switch to provide both coarse and fine adjustment over a wide range.

10. Deflection-Type Bridge Circuits with Phase Sensitivity. The curves of Fig. 6-23 disclose a basic weakness of the simple bridge circuits which have been described so far. The a-c voltmeter can detect the amount of bridge unbalance, but it cannot detect the phase of the unbalance voltage. The phase of the unbalance voltage reverses when the bridge passes through the

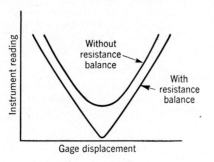

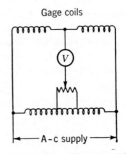

FIG. 6-23.   Response Curves   FIG. 6-24.   Bridge Circuit with Fine Balance Adjustment

balance point, but the voltmeter is unable to indicate this change. Therefore, in order to measure both amount and direction of a displacement it is necessary to set the bridge initially off the balance point and determine direction by noting whether the reading increases or decreases. With such an arrangement, zero strain at the gage does not correspond to zero current in

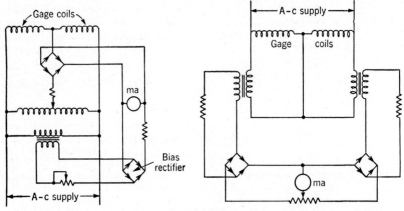

FIG. 6-25.   Bridge Circuit with D-C   FIG. 6-26.   Phase-Sensitive Circuit with
                    Bias   Two Rectifiers

the voltmeter, and it is not possible to adjust the gage sensitivity without also affecting the zero-strain setting. Therefore adjustment to a definite sensitivity requires a series of manipulations of the two controls.

When the voltmeter is of the rectifier type, it is possible to correct this difficulty by applying a d-c bias to the instrument, as shown in Fig. 6-25.

Additional resistors must be used as shown to provide adjustment of the bias current and to prevent the bias rectifier from shunting too much signal current around the milliammeter. Another double-rectifier arrangement which gives a reading sensitive to direction of unbalance is shown in Fig. 6-26. Here the balance adjuster is located in the d-c end of the circuit. Similar arrangements have been used with the balance adjuster in the a-c bridge.

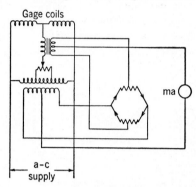

FIG. 6-27. Phase-Sensitive Circuit with One Rectifier

Figure 6-27 is an example of one of the best types of phase-sensitive rectifier arrangements. It has been widely used with resistance gages as well as with inductance gages. Only one set of rectifier plates is used, but the current in the d-c milliammeter is directly proportional to the strain being measured, in both magnitude and direction.

A quite different method of obtaining phase sensitivity is to use an a-c wattmeter as an indicator. The field coils of the wattmeter are energized from the a-c power supply, and the moving coil is energized by the unbalance current of the bridge. The torque on the instrument pointer is sensitive to both the magnitude and the phase of the bridge unbalance. No rectifiers are required. A disadvantage is that the sensitivity is proportional to the square of the line voltage.

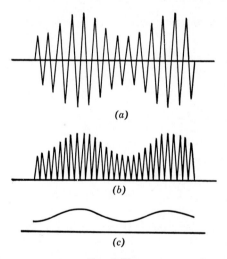

FIG. 6-28.
(a) Oscillogram of modulated a-c bridge output
(b) Same as a with addition of full-wave rectification
(c) Same as b with addition of filter

11. Circuits for Use with Oscillographs. Any of the deflection-type circuits mentioned in the foregoing can be used for the measurement of rapidly varying strains with a cathode-ray or magnetic oscillograph. The oscillographs themselves are discussed in section H of this chapter. It is quite possible to use an oscillograph to measure the a-c unbalance of the bridge directly. The record is then an a-c carrier wave modulated by the strain which is being measured. This method is seldom used, however, because the edge of an envelope is harder to read than a single line, and a large portion of the record is covered by the carrier wave, which serves no useful purpose. Also, the oscillograph element must be capable of following carrier frequency. The usual method is to replace the d-c milliammeter in one of the circuits previously described with a filter and an oscillograph. Figure 6-28 shows the type of record obtained with each arrangement. The output of a full-wave rectifier is a direct current which pulsates at twice the frequency of the a-c supply voltage. The filter must, of course, pass the frequency of the vibration which is being measured. In order to eliminate ripple on the record, the filter must be designed primarily to block a frequency double that of the carrier. It must also block, although to a lesser extent, the carrier frequency and several of its harmonics. The carrier frequency appears in the rectifier output if the two halves of the full-wave rectifier are not perfectly matched.

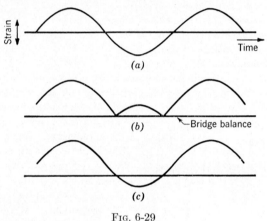

Fig. 6-29

(a) True picture of strain
(b) Fictitious record from overmodulated bridge circuit
(c) True record from phase-sensitive circuit

Higher harmonics appear due to the nonsinusoidal wave shape of the signal current after it has been modulated and rectified.

Two general types of filter have been used successfully. One is the low-pass type, which can be designed to pass up to one-fourth carrier frequency with good accuracy and reject everything from carrier frequency on up. The other consists of band-rejection filters which are tuned to block the carrier frequency and its second harmonic. In many cases the oscillograph will not follow frequencies higher than the second harmonic of the carrier, and higher harmonics can be ignored.

The subject of phase or direction sensitivity has already been discussed in connection with indicating instruments, and it is of equal importance in oscillograph work. In a simple bridge circuit, if the strain is large enough to reverse the direction of bridge unbalance, a condition known as overmodulation exists, and the record will be fictitious, as shown in Fig. 6-29. If a phase-sensitive circuit such as that of Fig. 6-27 is used, there is no danger of overmodulation, as shown in Fig. 6-29c. Other advantages are that the bridge balance and sensitivity adjusters can be made independent, zero strain can be made to correspond to zero galvanometer current, and the maximum galvanometer deflection for a given amplitude of record can be reduced by at least 50 per cent. Phase-sensitive circuits also provide linearity near the balance position, whereas the output voltage of ordinary circuits is nonlinear near the balance position owing to resistance unbalances.

12. Circuits for Use with Ratio Instruments. The deflection-type circuits described in the foregoing are all sensitive to fluctuations in the a-c supply voltage and require manual or automatic regulation of the supply voltage. The use of a d-c ratio instrument instead of a conventional milliammeter eliminates the necessity for voltage regulation when slowly varying strain is measured. A d-c ratio instrument consists of a permanent-magnet instrument movement with two coils set at a wide angle to each other on the shaft of the moving element, which carries the pointer. Connections are made to the moving coils through soft-gold conducting spirals instead of the conventional springs, and the resultant spring restraint is negligible. When each coil is made to carry current, the position which the pointer will assume is determined by the resultant magnetic field of the two coils, and the instrument scale is marked to show the ratio of current flowing in the "forward" coil to that flowing in the "reverse" coil. In the application to electric gages, the "forward" coil carries a direct current proportional to gage deflection and the "reverse" coil is energized from the supply voltage through a rectifier. If the currents in the two coils are both proportional to line voltage, the reading of the instrument is independent of line voltage.

Some work has also been done with an a-c type of ratio instrument which has a movement resembling that of a wattmeter with the spring removed. The stationary coil of the instrument is energized directly from the supply voltage, and the moving coil is connected to the bridge output. Current is conducted to the moving coil through soft-gold spirals, and the moving element comes to rest when the inphase component of the voltage induced in the coil is equal to and opposes the bridge output voltage.

A third type of ratio instrument, suitable for operation on either alternating or direct current, uses two stationary coils which set up fields at an angle to each other. A moving-magnetic vane lines up with the resultant field. This instrument eliminates the errors introduced by the stiffness of the gold spirals but takes more energy from the current being measured.

13. Null-Balance Circuits. Null-balance methods differ from deflection methods in that instead of the amount of unbalance being measured directly, adjustments are made to bring the unbalance current to zero, and the reading is obtained by noting the amount of adjustment required. Null-balance methods are used for precision measurements of slowly varying quantities. Their advantages over deflection measurements are: (1) The reading is essentially independent of fluctuations in supply voltage; (2) a longer scale length can be obtained; and (3) the errors inherent in electric-current-measuring instruments are eliminated.

Almost any of the deflection-type circuits previously described can be used as null-balance circuits by employing a sensitive indicating instrument and putting a graduated scale on the balance adjuster. Even the simple circuits of Figs. 6-21, 6-22, and 6-24 acquire direction sensitivity when used in this way because the direction in which the balance adjuster must be moved depends on the direction of the gage displacement. Even so, reference to the curves of Fig. 6-23 shows that a phase-sensitive circuit such as that of Fig.

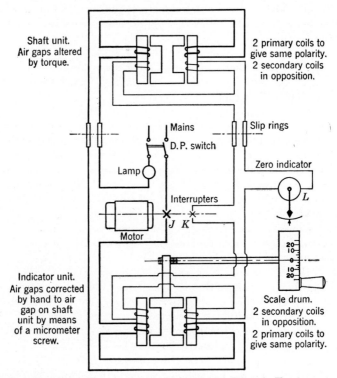

Fig. 6-30.   Schematic Arrangement of McNab Electric Torsionmeter

6-26 or 6-27 is preferable in order to avoid the "flat spot" which occurs near the balance point of the bridge. When copper-oxide or selenium rectifiers are used, this flat spot is accentuated by the current–voltage characteristic of the rectifier itself, which is nonlinear in the region near zero current.

Figure 6-30 shows a manually operated null-balance system of the variable-coupling type which has been used in marine torsion meters. An interesting feature is the use of direct supply voltage and a motor-driven interrupter. The interrupter "chops" the direct current in the primary circuit to give it an alternating component, and at the same time cuts out alternate half-cycles of the secondary current so that a d-c indicator can be used.

Most automatic null-balance systems require electronic amplification of the unbalance current to produce sufficient power to operate the rebalancing motor. A typical arrangement is shown in Fig. 6-31. The motor operates the potentiometer to rebalance the bridge and at the same time operates an indicator, recording pen, or some control function. The motor has two identical windings 90 electrical degrees apart. The operation is similar to that

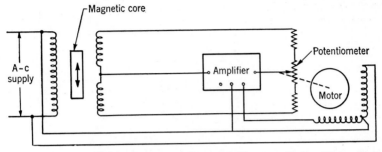

FIG. 6-31. Automatic Null-Balance System[16] (Courtesy Bailey Meter Co.)

of a two-phase motor, and the direction of rotation is determined by the phase relation of the currents in the two windings.

14. Frequency-Modulation Circuits. A different type of circuit, not related to any of those described in the foregoing, is that in which the reactance change of an inductance gage is used to vary the frequency of an oscillator. This type of circuit is more frequently used with capacitance gages than with inductance gages, but it has been used with the latter in telemetering systems. The output from the oscillator is used to modulate a radio transmitter.

G. THEORY OF THE A-C BRIDGE

The basic impedance bridge used in many inductance-gage circuits is shown in Fig. 6-32. Certain features of the theory associated with this network are important in the understanding of electric gages.

Z_1, Z_2, Z_3, and Z_4 are the impedances of the gage coils and balancing elements. Z_5 is the impedance of the instrument circuit. In order to reduce the voltage across Z_5 to zero, both the resistive and the reactive components of the bridge legs must be balanced. Both of the following conditions must be fulfilled:

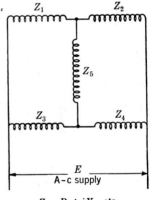

$Z_1 = R_1 + jX_1$, etc.

FIG. 6-32. Basic Impedance-Bridge Circuit

$$\frac{R_1}{R_2} = \frac{R_3}{R_4}$$

and

$$\frac{X_1}{X_2} = \frac{X_3}{X_4}$$

(9)

This shows why two separate adjustments are required to produce perfect balance. Often the R's are negligible or else sufficiently well balanced owing to symmetry of construction, and they can be ignored. In some cases notice must be taken of the third harmonic which appears across Z_5 as a result of nonlinearity of the iron magnetization curve.

When the bridge is out of balance the instrument current I_5 is

$$I_5 = \frac{\left[\dfrac{Z_1 Z_4 - Z_2 Z_3}{(Z_1 + Z_2)(Z_3 + Z_4)} \right] E}{Z_5 + \dfrac{1}{\dfrac{1}{Z_1} + \dfrac{1}{Z_2}} + \dfrac{1}{\dfrac{1}{Z_3} + \dfrac{1}{Z_4}}} \tag{10}$$

The numerator of this expression may be considered the unbalanced voltage of the bridge and the denominator the impedance through which this voltage forces the useful current. The Z_5 of the instrument itself is usually largely resistive, but the rest of the denominator is made up of terms which can be made largely reactive. Therefore, a capacitor placed in series with Z_5 will cancel out a large part of the denominator and considerably increase the instrument current. This is known as resonating the bridge.

Maximum power to the instrument is obtained when $I_5{}^2 R_5$ is a maximum. If we let

$$Z_5 = R_5 + jX_5$$

and

$$\frac{1}{\dfrac{1}{Z_1} + \dfrac{1}{Z_2}} + \frac{1}{\dfrac{1}{Z_3} + \dfrac{1}{Z_4}} = A + jB$$

maximum power will be obtained when

$$R_5 = A \tag{11}$$

and

$$X_5 = -B \tag{12}$$

The condition $X_5 = -B$ is satisfied by the use of the capacitor mentioned previously. The condition $R_5 = A$ may be satisfied by a correct choice of the instrument or else by using a matching transformer to operate the instrument circuit. If it is necessary to use an instrument for which $R_5 = nA$, the transformer ratio should be $\sqrt{n}$. If a resonating capacitor is used, it should be on the high-voltage side of the matching transformer to make its size as small as possible.

Further examination of equation 10 shows that maximum sensitivity is obtained when Z_3 and Z_4 are as small as possible, if it is assumed that Z_1 and Z_2 are the gage coils. This can be carried to the limit by using an auto-transformer for Z_3 and Z_4 so that the same flux will thread both coils and they will have a large mutual inductance. If the transformer has negligible resistance and leakage reactance, then equation 10 becomes

$$I_5 = \frac{\left[\dfrac{Z_1\sqrt{Z_4} - Z_2\sqrt{Z_3}}{(Z_1 + Z_2)(\sqrt{Z_3} + \sqrt{Z_4})}\right]E}{Z_5 + \dfrac{1}{\dfrac{1}{Z_1} + \dfrac{1}{Z_2}}} \tag{13}$$

The voltage output of a double-gap gage over the middle 60 per cent of its total possible travel, if a center-tapped autotransformer is used for the other two legs of the bridge, is approximately

$$E_5 = 0.65\frac{E}{2}\left(\frac{l_1 - l_2}{l_1 + l_2}\right) \tag{14}$$

where l_1 and l_2 are the lengths of the two air gaps. The 0.65 is an empirical factor to account for fringing flux, iron reluctance, coil resistance, iron losses of the gage and autotransformer, and the resistance and leakage inductance of the autotransformer. This factor may vary a good deal with different gages. The value 0.65 was determined in tests on the double-gap gage shown in Fig. 6-4. The voltage given by equation 14 is the open-circuit voltage, that is, as measured with a very high-impedance voltmeter. If the impedance of the external measuring circuit is equal to the internal impedance of the bridge (usually a little more than one-half the impedance of one coil when the armature is in mid-position) then the output voltage will be only one-half the value given by the previous formula. Thus the inductance bridge acts just like a generator having an electromotive force given by equation 14 and a definite internal impedance.

Figure 6-33 shows a typical set of energy-output measurements on a large double-gap gage with 0.010 in. total gap and deflected 0.002 in. The cross section of the magnetic path of each coil was 0.7 sq. in. The advantages of the resonant bridge with proper impedance matching are obvious.

The energy output available from a gage with a given cross section of magnetic path is proportional to the frequency of the power supply used, provided the thickness of the core laminations can be reduced as the frequency is raised. The reason is that $Z_1 \cdots Z_4$ of equation 10 increase with the frequency, and the allowable E for a given flux density also increases. The Z_5 for ideal impedance matching should also be increased, and, thus, I_5 remains constant. Therefore the instrument current remains constant, but the instrument voltage and power increase with frequency. This rule cannot be applied above a few thousand cycles per second because the eddy-current losses become too large even with the thinnest practical laminations.

It is obvious that, unless the gage cores are saturated, the instrument current increases in direct proportion to the applied voltage. Therefore, the available energy output increases as the square of the voltage.

The effect of fluctuations in the frequency of the supply voltage on the accuracy of the reading depends on the impedance matching of the circuit. If R_5 is much larger than A (see equation 11) fluctuations in supply frequency will cause no appreciable error. If R_5 is equal to or smaller than A, there will be considerable error. Therefore, in order to obtain a system which is not dependent on accurate frequency control it is advisable to mismatch the gage and indicator by using a high resistance in the instrument circuit. Frequency compensation can also be obtained by the insertion in series with

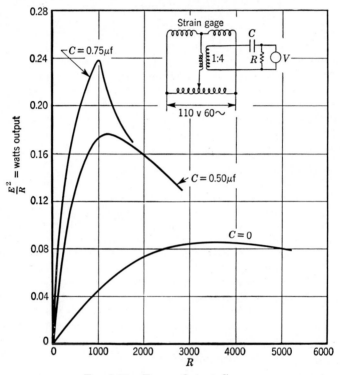

FIG. 6-33. Energy Output Curves

Z_5 of a capacitor which has a frequency response equal and opposite to that of the rest of the circuit.

H. AUXILIARY EQUIPMENT

15. Power Supply. The operation of an electric-inductance gage requires a supply of a-c power. The amount of power required is usually of the order of a few watts, seldom less than 1 watt or more than 20. For low-energy-level gages, where the output signal is electronically amplified, the power taken by the gage is very small, but the amplifier requires several watts.

The frequency of the power supply is determined by various conditions which have already been discussed, such as the frequency of strain fluctuation, the required power output, and the limitation on magnetic force. When the strain fluctuations are slow and the limitations on gage size are not stringent, it is always advisable to consider the use of 60-cycle power because of its convenience in most locations. The voltage from central-station power can be very easily regulated with good accuracy by using various commercially available regulators.

When 60-cycle excitation is not suitable, use must be made of one of the many forms of frequency-changing equipment. For frequencies up to about 2000 cps the best economy of weight and size is obtained with rotating equipment. Motor-generator sets can be built up for converting any available power source into whatever voltage and frequency are desired, although it is often difficult to find the generator. Inverted rotary converters are used for changing direct current into alternating current. The use of 400-cycle power on aircraft has led to the development of many types of small machines for converting 24-volt direct current into 400 cycles. Regulation of voltage and frequency in small generating apparatus is something of a problem. Carbon pile, saturated reactor, and electronic devices have been used, but they frequently approach the size and weight of the generator itself. Good results have been obtained by one or two manufacturers with centrifugal governors.

Vibrator–inverters can be used for changing direct current into frequencies up to 180 cps. Small commercial units are available for frequencies of 60, 105, 120, and 180 cycles. In these devices a vibrating reed acts as a voltage-reversing switch to convert direct current into alternating current. The output is not sinusoidal but can be filtered and regulated. Reliability and contact life depend very greatly on adjusting the unit for the power factor of the load with which it is to be used.

The trend in recent years has been away from rotating machines and toward electronic-power supplies for electric-gaging systems. An oscillator and power amplifier is bulkier than a rotating machine of equal output, but it is easier to obtain, more flexible as to frequency and voltage, and more easily stabilized, particularly with respect to frequency. Some of the carrier systems developed for use with resistance gages have sufficient output to operate inductance gages also. Power supplies developed specifically for general experimental use with inductance gages are commercially available.

16. Amplifiers and Carrier Systems. Electric inductance gages are generally used without any amplification of the output signal because their chief reason for existence is their high energy level and consequent freedom from the difficulties encountered in amplifying low-voltage signals. Amplifiers are used, however, in automatic null-balance systems and in cases where the size of the pickup is severely restricted. The carrier systems and signal amplifiers used with small low-energy gages are the same as those described in Chapter 5, sections F to I.

17. Indicating and Recording Instruments. The choice of an instrument for obtaining the readings from an electric-gaging system depends on the following considerations: (1) Whether a visual indication is satisfactory or a permanent record is required. (2) The frequency of strain fluctuation which must be followed. (3) The electric energy available for operation of the instrument. (4) The scale length and accuracy required. Figure 6-34 shows the approximate frequency response of the various available types of instruments.

Self-balancing or manual-balancing potentiometers, of the type ordinarily used for the measurement and control of temperature are well suited for high-precision low-speed work. The gage signal must be reduced to direct current, and the voltage drop of this current passing through a fixed resistor is measured with the potentiometer. A-c null-balance systems should also be included in this classification. These devices can be made either indicating or recording or both. Frequency response varies widely in different types, some taking

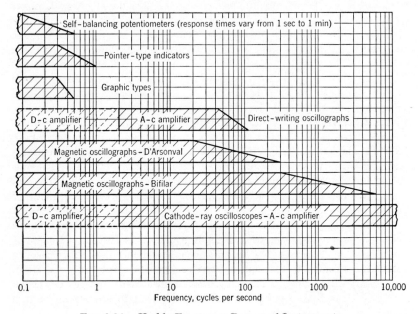

Fig. 6-34. Usable Frequency Ranges of Instruments

about a minute and others taking as little as a second to travel from one end of the scale to the other. The readings can be either continuous or intermittent. The energy required from the gaging circuit is small but should not be ignored. If a galvanometer is used to measure the voltage drop across a resistor, the resistor must be small enough to give the galvanometer adequate damping for stable operation. For example, one instrument of this type with a 10-millivolt scale takes a maximum resistance of about 50 ohms. The energy required is therefore $0.010^2/50$ or 2×10^{-6} watt. Electronic devices can be made several times as sensitive.

Pointer-type indicators are suitable for visual readings up to a frequency of about 1 cps. Their accuracy is seldom better than $\frac{1}{2}$ per cent of full scale. Sensitive d-c types can operate on as little as 1×10^{-6} watt, although the commoner types require about 1×10^{-4} watt. When they are used with a rectifier as an a-c instrument the energy required is about ten times as great, to allow for a resistor to swamp out the variable resistance of the rectifier itself. Straight a-c instruments such as the repulsion-iron type require of the order of 0.2 watt.

Graphic instruments which produce ink records on moving charts have movements similar to the pointer-type indicators but require much more energy to overcome pen friction. A typical d-c recorder takes about 0.05 watt at full scale and can follow up to about $\frac{1}{2}$ cps. Straight a-c types absorb as much as 10 to 15 watts of power, which is seldom available in a gaging system. Special devices such as the Westinghouse "Pilotel" and the General Electric "Photo-Electric Recorder" use amplification to obtain ink records at the energy level of an indicating instrument. The amplifier does not introduce any lower limit of frequency response because the amplification is applied to the torque on the pointer and not to the signal current itself.

Direct-writing oscillographs can be used for frequencies up to the order of 100 cps. These are essentially graphic instruments in which the frequency response is raised by making the pen or stylus very light and supplying several watts of energy to the pen from an amplifier. The Brush oscillograph uses the piezoelectric effect of Rochelle salt to actuate the pen. Other types, developed primarily for medical use, employ d'Arsonval movements. The lower limit of frequency response is dependent on the type of amplifier, since most a-c amplifiers will not respond below 2 cps.

A new development in direct-writing oscillographs is the Brush direct-inking magnetic oscillograph which can be operated with or without an amplifier. Without amplifier it has a flat frequency response from zero to 30 cps and draws 0.2 watt power for its maximum displacement of 2 in. With a specially designed amplifier its response is uniform from 0.5 to 100 cps.

Magnetic oscillographs with photographic recording are widely used in experimental stress analysis with electric gages. These devices might best be described as a d'Arsonval movement with the pointer replaced by a small mirror and light beam. The mirror, coil, and suspension are made as light as possible in order to give a high natural frequency. The bifilar type developed by Duddell consists of a single loop of wire stretched across fixed supports between the poles of a permanent magnet (see Fig. 6-35). A small mirror attached to the loop reflects a light beam to a viewing screen or sensitized paper. The tension on the loop affects both the sensitivity and the natural frequency. The sensitivity is inversely proportional to the tension, and the natural frequency is directly proportional to the square root of the tension. Therefore, all manufacturers supply galvanometers with various characteristics, some designed for high sensitivity at the expense of frequency response, and some designed for high-frequency response and lower sensitivity. Table 6-1 gives typical examples of available oscillograph galvanometers. Usable frequency is that at which the response has dropped to about 90 per cent of the d-c response. A complete oscillograph contains, in addition to the galvanometers, an optical system and a film-drive mechanism. Some also contain numerous accessories such as timing devices, viewing screens, attenuators, and special devices for automatic and remote control. Most

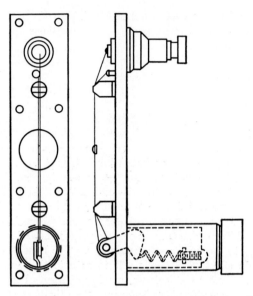

FIG. 6-35. Bifilar Oscillograph Element (Courtesy Hathaway Instrument Co)

models can take several simultaneous records on a single film, which is very valuable in studying phase relationships between various vibration phenomena. Film speeds can be varied from a fraction of an inch per second to several feet

TABLE 6-1

EXAMPLES OF AVAILABLE OSCILLOGRAPH GALVANOMETERS

Manufacturer	Type	Sens., amperes/ inch	Usable Freq., cps	Gal. Resistance, ohms	Power req. at 1 in. defl., watts
Westinghouse	S877443	0.285	5000	2.2	0.180
	S492484	0.150	3500	0.8	0.018
	S492485	0.025	2000	1.5	0.00094
	S577706	0.0023	900	5.5	0.00003
Gen. Electric	5310680-G5	0.190	6500	0.9	0.033
	5310680-G1	0.059	2500	0.9	0.0031
	5310680-G6	0.0028	700	9.0	0.00007
Hathaway	OC-1 Gr. 1	0.140	2700*	.....	....
	OA-2	0.354	6000*	1	0.125
	OA-2	0.0014	360*	12	0.000024
	OD	0.00014	36*	....	....
Cambridge	Low freq.	0.076	1900	....	....
	High freq.	0.076	5400	....	....
Heiland	Type D	0.127	2400	7	0.113
	Type A	0.000035	24	35	0.043×10^{-6}
Consolidated	7-102	0.100	1200	3.0	0.03
Eng. Co.	7-112	0.000033	60	38	0.038×10^{-6}

* Assumed to be 60 per cent of undamped natural frequency.

per second. Figure 6-36 shows a 12-element portable oscillograph designed primarily for strain recording in the field.

Cathode-ray oscilloscopes are not used so extensively with inductance gages as are magnetic oscillographs. The chief advantage of the cathode ray is its high-frequency response, and this can seldom be utilized with an inductance gage because of the frequency limitations of the gage itself. For multielement recording the cathode ray is quite feasible, but completely developed systems

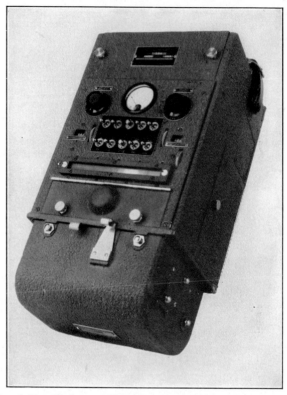

Fig. 6-36.   Hathaway, Type S12-A, 12 Element Oscillograph

are not commercially available in the United States. A single-tube oscilloscope is very useful in any strain-gage laboratory, however, for making quick observations of the operation of a gaging system, for studying periodic phenomena which can be synchronized with the horizontal sweep of the electron beam, and for studying wave forms and phase relationships in a gaging system. The tube is essentially a voltage-measuring device in which the spot on a fluorescent screen is deflected in accordance with the voltage applied to the deflector plates. Commercial units contain a-c or, in special cases, d-c amplifiers so that voltages as low as several millivolts can be measured with no appreciable power absorption from the gage circuit. A fuller discussion of cathode-ray oscilloscopes is given in Chapter 8.

I. APPLICATIONS AND LIMITATIONS

Each type of electric gage has its own advantages and limitations, and the choice of the correct type for any particular investigation requires a thorough knowledge of these factors. The properties of electric-inductance gages which are discussed in the following paragraphs are the ones which are apt to be of importance in the choice of a gaging system.

18. Frequency Response. When an electric gage is energized with alternating current, the frequency of strain fluctuation which it records must be considerably lower than the frequency of the power supply. This is true of any electric gage but is of particular importance with inductance gages because the flux variations produced by the motion of the armature induce a voltage in the gage coil which can be a source of error. The magnitude of the error depends on the ratio between the carrier frequency and the vibration frequency and also on the per cent modulation which the vibration imposes on the carrier wave. The author does not know of any adequate study which has been made of this subject, but D. V. Wright of the Westinghouse Research Laboratories has found that, for a 4:1 ratio between the carrier and vibration frequencies and 50 per cent modulation, the amplitude error in a rectified and filtered record is less than 2 per cent and the phase error is negligible. Owing to iron losses, inductance gages are seldom used with carrier frequencies higher than 5000 cps and 2000 cps is much more common.

19. Stability. The long-time stability of an inductance-gage system is inherently better than that of most other electric gages because (1) the gage parts themselves are not stressed and, therefore, not apt to creep; (2) the magnetic properties of the gage cores can be made quite stable by proper choice of material and proper heat treatment; (3) the permeability of the air gap is not affected by the presence of nonmetallic particles, moisture, or oil; and (4) the high energy level of the system eliminates many sources of trouble found in low-energy systems, such as leakage currents due to moisture, deterioration of insulation, and pickup from stray fields. In inductance-gage systems it is only in the exceptional case that any thought need be given to insulation resistance, lead resistance, lead capacitance, stray fields, or the aging of electronic components. Usually the rectifier is the least stable element of the system, and this can sometimes be eliminated. Most inductance gages contain no sliding surfaces and, therefore, never wear out.

20. Sensitivity. Sufficient sensitivity can be obtained from an inductance gage without electronic amplification for most practical purposes. Amplification factors of 10^4 are easily obtained with ordinary equipment, and amplification by a factor of 10^5 is quite possible. (Amplification factor is the ratio between the amplitude of the final record or pointer motion and the amplitude of the strain being measured.)

21. Effect of Temperature. The most important temperature effect in an electric-inductance gage is that due to differential expansion. This is discussed in section D of this chapter. Temperature also affects the resistance of the windings, the permeability of the cores, and the resistivity of the core material. These can be reduced to a small amount by designing the coils for a large ratio between reactance and resistance. The permeability of the iron should be high, its resistivity should be high, its laminations should be thin, and the wire size of the coils should be large. Use should also be made of a double-coil gage or a single-coil gage with a dummy gage held at the same temperature as the active gage.

In some cases it is necessary to resort to temperature-compensating elements in the control circuit consisting of special materials with high temperature coefficients of resistance. Nickel, iron, and some of their alloys have large positive temperature coefficients of resistance. Carbon and some specially developed materials have negative temperature coefficients. Special resistance wires such as Advance and Manganin are available with extremely low temperature coefficients, and the gage coils themselves are occasionally wound with these materials instead of copper.

22. Size of Pickup. Inductance gages are inherently larger and heavier than most resistance and capacitance gages and should not be used where a small pickup is of great importance. One exception to this rule is telemetering systems which involve a radio or transmission-line link between the point at which the strain occurs and that at which it is measured. In such cases, a large signal output is required at the location of the gage, and the total equipment required to produce this signal is lighter and smaller for an inductance gage than for a resistance gage. Some of the difficulties encountered due to the size and weight of inductance gages are described in section D of this chapter.

BIBLIOGRAPHY

General

1. H. C. ROBERTS, *Mechanical Measurements by Electrical Methods*, Instruments Publishing Co, 1946. An exhaustive treatise on all types of electric gages and associated apparatus. Particularly valuable for its brief descriptions of a large variety of devices.
2. H. C. ROTERS, *Electromagnetic Devices*, John Wiley & Sons, New York, 1941. A thorough treatise written for the designer of electromagnets. Gives formulas and methods for the calculation of permeance, magnetic pull, power requirements, etc., and data on magnetic properties.

Descriptions of Inductance Gages and Circuits

3. B. F. LANGER, "Design and Applications of a Magnetic Strain Gage," *Proc Soc Exp Stress Analysis*, v 1, n 2, p 82, 1944. Description of the inductance gage illustrated in Fig. 6-4, its theory of operation, and uses.
4. M. A. RUSHER and J. W. MATTHEWS, "The Electric Strain Gage," *G E Rev*, v 42, Apr 1939, p 176. A description of single-gap gages, their characteristics in conjunction with standard circuits, and their uses.
5. C. M. HATHAWAY and E. S. LEE, "The Electric Gage," *Mech Eng*, v 59, n 9, p 653, Sept 1937. Common applications of inductance gages are described. Variable-gap and eddy-current types are especially considered.
6. R. J. COX, "A Note on Electromagnetic Induction Micrometers, Including a Novel Circuit Incorporating Metal Rectifiers," *J Sci Instr (Lond)*, v 19, n 8, p 117, Aug 1942. Describes a double-gap inductance gage and its characteristics with various phase-sensitive circuits.
7. H. RENO, "Instruments for Aircraft Strain Analysis," *Proc Soc Exp Stress*

Analysis, v 2, n 2, p 106, 1945.   Describes electromagnetic gages, amplifiers, power supplies, and oscillographs manufactured by Hathaway Instrument Co.

8. *Strain Measuring System,* U. S. Patent 2,361,173, issued to T. E. Browne, assignor to Westinghouse Elec and Mfg Co, Oct 24, 1944.   Describes method of obtaining linear response from a single–gap gage.

9. H. SCHAEVITZ, "The Linear Variable Differential Transformer," *Proc Soc Expl Stress Analysis,* v 4, n 2, p 79, 1947.   Gives description and data on a variable-coupling moving-core solenoid gage of the type shown in Fig. 6-6d.

10. W. H. PICKERING, "Reluctance Gages for Telemetering Strain Data," *Proc Soc Expl Stress Analysis,* v 4, n 2, p 74, 1947.   Discusses relative advantages of different types of gage for telemetering purposes and describes some inductance gages which have been used.

11. M. W. HIVELY and D. F. LIVERMORE, "Electromagnetic Torquemeter," *Trans ASME,* Oct 1946.   Description of the torquemeter illustrated in Fig. 6-9.

12. F. W. GODSEY, JR., and B. F. LANGER, "Aircraft-Engine Torque Instruments," *Trans AIEE,* v 63, Sept 1944, p 686.

13. B. F. LANGER, "Measurement of Torque Transmitted by Rotating Shafts," *J Applied Mechanics (Trans ASME),* v 12, n 1, p A-39, Mar 1945.

14. B. F. LANGER and K. L. WOMMACK, "The Magnetic-Coupled Torquemeter," *Proc Soc Exp Stress Analysis,* v 2, n 2, p 11, 1945.
    Items 12, 13, and 14 give brief descriptions of various torque-measuring devices and more detailed descriptions of the "magnetic-coupled" torquemeter.

15. W. H. TAIT, "An Instrument for Measuring the Thickness of Coatings on Metal," *J Sci Instr (Lond),* v 14, n 10, p 341, Oct 1937.   Description of a magnetic instrument for measuring the thickness of nonferrous coatings on ferrous bases.

16. P. S. DICKEY and A. J. HORNFECK, "Electronic–Type Instruments for Industrial Processes," *Trans ASME,* v 67, n 5, p 393, July 1945.   Descriptions of automatic null-balance instruments manufactured by Bailey Meter Co.

Magnetostriction

17. R. M. BOZORTH and H. J. WILLIAMS, "Effect of Small Stresses on Magnetic Properties," *Rev Modern Physics,* v 17, n 1, p 72,   Jan 1945.   Discusses the general subject of strain sensitivity of magnetic materials and its explanation by domain theory.   Also gives test results on materials subjected to small stresses.

18. F. D. SMITH and C. A. LUXFORD, "Stress Measurement by Magnetostriction," *Proc Instn Mech Engrs (Lond),* v 143, n 1, p 56, Apr 1940.   Gives magnetostriction data on nickel for both tension and compression.   Describes a pressure gage which uses magnetostriction of nickel.

Oscillographs

19. V. S. THOMANDER, "Characteristics of the Oscillograph Galvanometer," *J Franklin Inst,* v 213, Jan 1932, p 41.   The characteristics of oscillograph galvanometers are described, and equations involving vibrator sensitivity, resonance, inertia, tension, and damping are given.

20. K. R. GIESER and J. E. HANCOCK, "The Latest in Magnetic Oscillographs," *G E Rev,* v 46, May 1943, p 289.   A complete description of a modern magnetic oscillograph.   The various components are considered in more or less detail.

CHAPTER 7

ELECTRIC-CAPACITANCE GAGES

By B. C. Carter and J. R. Forshaw and J. F. Shannon

A. INTRODUCTION

This chapter relates mainly to developments for which the contributors have been responsible, and some of the work in the field of capacitance measurement is listed in the references. The methods described deal with the use of elements for measuring displacement and strain using changes in capacitance from 0 to 20 $\mu\mu$f employing carrier frequencies from 1 to 2.5 megacycles per second.

The main advantage of capacitance gages is the opportunity afforded for mechanical design, but for the applications described in the chapter the use of a high-frequency carrier, which permits static calibration, introduces difficulty in the installation and use of the strain elements. Resistance-wire strain gages and inductive elements responding to velocity and with low values of the carrier frequency can be used with less effort. In some applications capacitance gages designed to meet conditions of the application give more accurate information and amply justify the additional effort required.

Each type of strain gage has a field of application in which it is most suited, and if possible amplifiers and recording equipment should be used that can be connected to the outputs of various precircuits with associated elements for example, resistance, electromagnetic capacitance or induction.

The capacitance of a capacitor may be varied by changing either the gap or the effective area of the electrodes. Thus, in general, two bases of design are available, depending on variation of gap and variation of area respectively.

I. VARYING GAP PICKUPS

B. Pressure Indicators

Contributed by M. O. W. Wolfe

For a parallel-plate capacitor the relationship between capacitance and the separation between the plates is given by

$$C = \frac{ak}{3.6\pi t}$$

where C = capacitance in micromicrofarads
a = area of plate in square centimeters
t = separation between the plates in centimeters
k = dielectric constant (unity for air)

Simple pressure indicators based on this principle may be designed for a wide variety of applications, and, when they are used in conjunction with modern carrier-frequency circuits, steady or fluctuating pressures up to frequencies of 20 or 30 kc may be indicated with accuracy.

Devices of this type consist of a fixed insulated plate mounted close to an elastic diaphragm which is arranged to deflect and vary the gap under the influence of applied pressure.

Since the relationship between capacitance and the separation between the plates is hyperbolic, it is necessary to use very small gaps and a small range of movement to obtain an approximately linear relationship. It is not feasible in practice to use smaller gaps than 0.001 in. However, the linearity and sensitivity may be improved by introducing into the gap a disk of material of high dielectric constant such as mica which is arranged partially to fill the gap.

The influence of the mica is to make the "equivalent" air gap smaller which increases the sensitivity and permits a reduced range of diaphragm movement, thereby improving the linearity.

In practice, the relative dimensions of total gap and mica are determined experimentally. The curves drawn in Fig. 7-1 illustrate the method employed. Curve A represents the condition where the ratio of mica to air in the gap is too great (in this case the mica is being compressed by the diaphragm); curve B represents the ideal ratio of mica to air; and curve C represents the condition where the ratio of mica to air is too small.

A further advantage of mica is that it minimizes a possible breakdown of insulation between the plates due to the presence of small particles of conducting material.

A typical indicator of this type is shown in Fig. 7-2 which has been designed for the indication of pressure ranges varying from 0–50 psi to 0–6000 psi with diaphragms of appropriate stiffness. This pickup is suitable for various applications falling within these ranges, provided that large cyclic variations in temperature do not occur in the measured fluid.

The diaphragm movement range is of the order of 10^{-4} in., and for large variations in temperature this may be comparable with the movements produced by differential thermal expansions in the elastic supports. For this reason it is necessary to insure in the design of the pickup that the thermal expansion paths are as small as possible, but for very extreme applications, such as the indication of internal-combustion

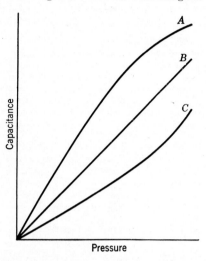

FIG. 7-1. Curves Showing Effect of Mica Dielectric in Capacitor Pressure Pickups

engines, it is necessary to resort to artificial cooling of the pickup element.

Figures 7-3 and 7-4a show a water-cooled instrument which has been developed for the indication of reciprocating internal-combustion engines. This consists essentially of two diaphragms connected together by a small pillar

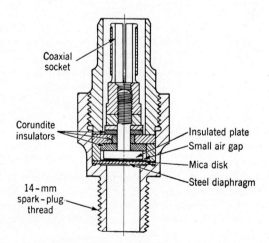

FIG. 7-2. Typical Capacitance-Type Pressure Element

formed on the inner member between which the water is passed. The water is circulated round the whole of the inside of the pickup so that the working portion is maintained at a steady temperature. Figure 7-4b shows two records of combustion pressures in a typical piston-engine cylinder. One indicates the presence of a detonating disturbance at a frequency of approximately 7000 cps and the other indicates a nondetonating cycle.

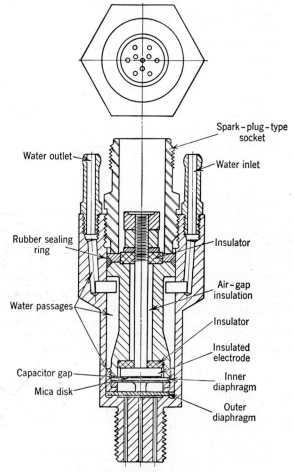

FIG. 7-3. Water-Cooled Capacitance-Type Engine Indicator

1. Design Considerations. The dynamic characteristics of the elastic system of a pressure indicator have an important influence on the accuracy of indication and must be taken into account. The most important of these is the natural frequency of the system and the amount of damping present.

The fundamental requirements are that the displacements of the system should be proportional to and in phase with the applied pressure, and there should be no relative distortion of the harmonic components up to the highest component it is desired to measure. It is, therefore, necessary to design so that the natural frequency of the elastic system will give a value for the ratio of the forcing frequency to the natural frequency less than unity and low

FIG. 7-4a. Water-Cooled Capacitance-Type Engine Indicator

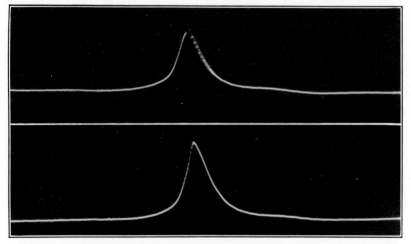

FIG. 7-4b. Typical Engine-Indicator Diagrams
Top—Detonating cycle
Bottom—Nondetonating cycle

enough to provide a working range over the asymptotic portion of the resonance characteristic.

In practice, the value of this ratio should not be greater than 0.3.

Damping is important insofar as it reduces the free vibrations of the system. Its influence on the phase angle between the applied force and the movements of the system up to values of the natural frequency ratio of 0.3 is small and for the amount of damping normally present its effect may be ignored. Some damping is provided by the presence of the water in the engine-indicator pickup.

To achieve a high natural frequency it is necessary to choose a stiff diaphragm. The stiffness is limited, however, by the range of movement necessary to provide an adequate sensitivity.

Two series of semiempirical curves have been derived from experiments made on single-diaphragm types. From these it is possible to choose appropriate dimensions for the pickup system for particular frequency and sensitivity requirements.

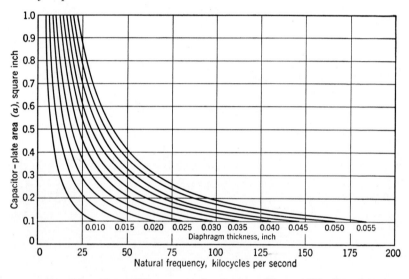

FIG. 7-5. Natural Frequencies for Pressure-Element Diaphragms

2. Natural-Frequency Curves. The first of these (Fig. 7-5) is a family of curves giving the natural frequencies for various areas and thickness of diaphragm. For convenience of reference, the area of the insulated capacitor plate a has been taken as one parameter, the area of the corresponding diaphragm may be taken as $\frac{\pi}{4}(D + 0.06)^2$ where D is the diameter of the capacitor plate and 0.06 the diameteral clearance necessary to maintain a low capacitance between the diaphragm fixing and the perimeter of the insulated capacitor plate.

The natural frequency of a circular plate fixed at its perimeter is given by

$$f = \frac{\alpha}{r^2}\sqrt{\frac{gD}{\rho h}}$$

where
f = natural frequency

α = a dimensionless constant (its value is 10.21 for the fundamental mode)
g = acceleration due to gravity
ρ = density of material of diaphragm
h = thickness of diaphragm
r = radius of diaphragm

$$D = \frac{Eh^3}{12(1 - \mu^2)}$$

μ = Poisson's ratio
E = modulus of elasticity

For steel this relationship may be expressed as

$$f = 1.934 \times 10^6 \frac{h}{A}$$

where
A = area of diaphragm (all dimensions in inches)

From natural-frequency measurements made on various diaphragms in actual pressure pickups it has been determined that for such fixing conditions the relationship is given approximately by

$$f = 0.460 \times 10^6 \frac{h}{A}$$

The curves have been plotted on this basis.

3. Sensitivity of Pressure Pickup. From the relationship among the capacitance, area of plate, and plate separation for a parallel-plate capacitor, that is,

$$C = \frac{a}{t} K$$

the sensitivity is given by

$$\frac{dC}{dt} = \frac{-a}{t^2} K \tag{1}$$

where
a = area of plate
t = separation between the plates
K = constant

(for a mixed dielectric of mica and air, t may be considered the equivalent air gap).

For a circular plate fixed at its periphery the deflection δ produced at the center by a uniform pressure q is given by

$$\delta \propto \frac{qA^2}{h^3} \tag{2}$$

where
A = area of diaphragm
h = thickness of plate

Effect of curvature of the diaphragm is neglected, from equations 1 and 2 the change of capacitance for a uniform pressure q is proportional to

$$\frac{a}{t^2} \times \frac{qA^2}{h^3} \tag{3}$$

Experience has shown that the best results are obtained if a total gap of 0.001 in. and a thickness of mica of 0.00075 in. are used and the range of movement at the center of the diaphragm is limited to approximately 0.0002 in.

For these conditions a series of tests have been made on several diaphragms of different thickness and area from which the following empirical relationship

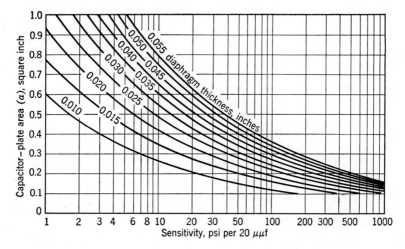

Fig. 7-6. Curves of Sensitivities for Capacitance-Type Pressure Elements

has been derived for the inverse sensitivity expressed as pounds per square inch for 20 $\mu\mu$f change of capacitance

$$\text{Inverse sensitivity } Q = \frac{4.64 \times 10^{-3}h^{1.8}}{aA^2}$$

The fact that Q varies as $h^{1.8}$ instead of as h^3 over the range of diaphragms considered is thought to be due to the effect of yielding at the diaphragm fixing.

From this relationship the inverse sensitivity curves given in Fig. 7-6 have been derived, and these curves considered in conjunction with the frequency curves of Fig. 7-5 may be used to determine the best combination of diaphragm area, diaphragm thickness, and capacitor-plate area for any stipulated natural-frequency and inverse-sensitivity requirements within the limits of the ranges considered.

C. Strain Element for Measuring Forces Transmitted through Feet of Aircraft Engine

This strain element is an application of a parallel-plate capacitor where the ratio $\dfrac{\text{change of gap}}{\text{gap}}$ is very small, which gives a practically linear relationship between change of capacitance and change of load.   This application required a very stiff strain element (a) to eliminate any resonant frequency in the mounting system below 15,000 cycles per minute and (b) to reduce to negligible quantities the inertia forces resulting from movements of the supports.   The

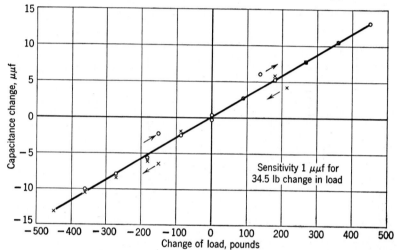

Fig. 7-7.   Calibration Curve of Strain Element for Measuring Forces Transmitted through Feet of Aircraft Engine

area of the capacitor plates was 2.5 sq. in., gap 0.001 in., with air as dielectric. The portion of the strain element over which the strain is measured is equivalent to a steel block 8.5 sq. in. cross-sectional area, 1.875 in. long, subjected to a compressive load.   A typical calibration curve of capacitance change plotted against change of load is shown in Fig. 7-7.   The strain element as shown in Fig. 7-8 comprises a block of steel 7 in. by 2½ in. by 1.75 in. cut into two parts A and B to facilitate manufacture.   The center portion of A is the grounded capacitor plate, and the other plate D is attached to block B through the "Mycalex" insulator C.   Cover plates E and F seal the strain element after special precautions are taken with cleaning.   Attached to cover is a low-capacitance socket G the center connection of which is attached to the capacitor plate D.   The engine is attached to part A with distance pieces as shown, to eliminate any bending of part A in the region of the capacitor plates and to ensure a compressive load is applied to the block.   The capacitor plates and contact surfaces of the block were ground to the best finish possible.

The relatively irregular finish of the ground surface caused a change in contact area at the joint in the block with increase in load. Thus the over-all stiffness of the block varied with mean load on the joint, but with continued use bedding of the two surfaces occurred and the over-all stiffness tends to a constant value. The calculated stiffness of an equivalent solid block is 101×10^6 lb/in. with sensitivity 218 lb/$\mu\mu$f. Table 7-1 gives value of inverse sensitivities and stiffnesses obtained from calibrations and calculation of capacitance from equation 4, article 6 if it is assumed that the gap is 0.001 in.

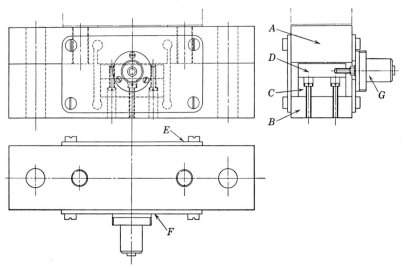

Fig. 7-8.   Strain Element for Measuring Forces Transmitted through Feet of Aircraft Engine

and $\eta = 1$ Values are given for the first assembly of the strain element and for a reassembly after 10 hr running of the engine and check calibration after a further 2 hr running.

TABLE 7-1

Strain Element	First Assembly		Reassembly after 10 hr Running		Check Calibration after 12 hr Running	
	Inverse Sensitivity	Stiffness	Inverse Sensitivity	Stiffness	Inverse Sensitivity	Stiffness
1	31.7	14.65×10^6	88.1	41.2×10^6	89	41.6×10^6
2	34.5	16×10^6	214	99×10^6	214	99×10^6
3	48.6	22.5×10^6	114	53.8×10^6	116	54.7×10^6
4	26	12×10^6	153	73.2×10^6	158	75.5×10^6

Inverse Sensitivities in. lb per $\mu\mu$f.
        Stiffness   in. lb per   in.

Strain element 2 has sensitivity and stiffness approximately equal to the design value, but the accuracy of the manufacture is not known. Element 1 differs most from the design values, the sensitivity being high by a factor

2.4, but it is not known if the gap was a little less than design value or if flexibility was introduced at the joint in the block.

Figure 7-9 shows a design of a strain element by J. T. Mair for a similar application which is at present under construction. There is no joint in the

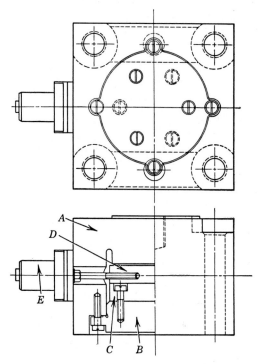

Fig. 7-9.   Strain Element for Measuring Forces Transmitted through Feet of Aircraft Engine (Improved Design)

strained section of the element. The figure is lettered corresponding to Fig. 7-8.

II. VARYING AREA PICKUPS

Three types are described under this heading: (4) the tangent type, (5) the multiple-plate tangent type, and (6) the serrated-capacitor type.

D. TANGENT TYPE

In this type a tangent strip is wrapped in some degree round a circular arc on an electrode from which the strip is insulated by a thin layer of mica.   A single unit of this form is shown in Figs. 7-10 and 7-11.   The tangent spring, of length X, is moved a distance Y towards the arc of a circle of radius R, on the surface of which is the dielectric.   The angle subtended by a change in arc of contact is equal to the angle between the extreme tangents; hence, for small movements,

$$\frac{\text{Increase in arc of contact}}{\text{Movement of point of contact}} = \frac{R}{X}$$

Thus, the movement is transformed into a linear change of capacitance.

A six-unit element 0.75 in. wide embodying this principle is shown in Fig. 7-12. This has a sensitivity of 10 micromicrofarads ($\mu\mu$f) per 0.001 in. of movement and a linear range of 0.0016 in.

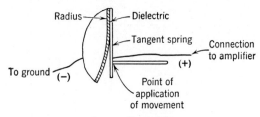

Fig. 7-10. Single Element

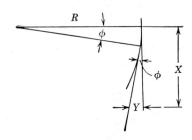

Fig. 7-11. Tangent Capacitor for Strain Measurement

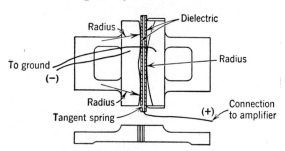

Fig. 7-12. Typical Multiple Element

E. MULTIPLE-PLATE TANGENT TYPE

Further developments led to the type shown in Fig. 7-13. This consists of two pressure plates with faces of 16 in. radius, a flexible adjusting ring B, and the multiple-plate element C. This element consists of two pairs of flat springs D and E, clamped at their ends in the slots of the ring B by means of a wedge W. There is a layer of mica 0.001 in. thick between the pressure plates and the outer springs and also between the springs. The inner springs and the pressure plates are grounded, and the two outer springs are connected in parallel, thus forming four capacitor units. A resilient member is inserted between two inner springs.

The pressure plates transmit the strain between the gage points G to the multiple-plate element, which is thereby compressed and consequently curves round the circular arc. The capacitance change is approximately 7 $\mu\mu$f per 0.001 in. deflection, and the range of linearity is 0.005 in. Figure 7-14 shows a typical calibration curve.

The capacitance change is practically equal on all four pressure faces of the electrode springs. The purpose of the flexible adjusting ring B is to enable

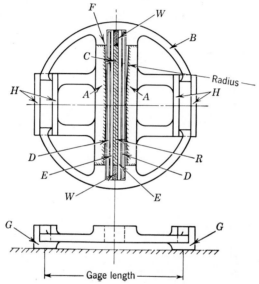

Fig. 7-13. Multiple-Plate Capacitance-Type Strain Gage

the gage to be set at any desired position on the linear part of the calibration and yet be able to operate freely about that position. Thus, the gages can be set and calibrated on a test bar before being affixed to the surface on which the strain is to be measured.

The gage may be attached by any suitable cement such as "Durofix" or De Khotinsky's. These cements have proved satisfactory in centrifugal fields up to 3000g, and experiments have shown that the total hysteresis effect of the gage and cement is less than 5 per cent. For high-temperature applications, the gage can be spot-welded to the surface, and temperature compensation can be obtained by the use of similar material for the gage and the member to which it is attached. The gage can be sealed with a cap to exclude moisture and oil vapor.

A gage of ⅝ in. over-all diameter has been constructed and has given

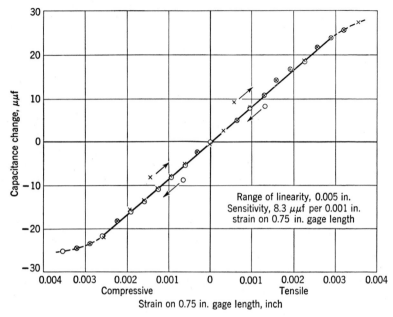

Range of linearity, 0.005 in.
Sensitivity, 8.3 $\mu\mu f$ per 0.001 in.
strain on 0.75 in. gage length

Fig. 7-14.   Calibration Curve of Multiple-Plate Capacitance Strain Gage

Fig. 7-15.   Multiple-Plate Tangent-Type Capacitance Strain Gage

satisfactory results.   Figure 7-15 shows another unit with an over-all diameter of $\frac{7}{8}$ in.

F. SERRATED-CAPACITOR TYPE

The effective area of the capacitor is varied by sliding one capacitor element relative to the other while maintaining a constant gap, as in the Kelvin variable capacitor.   In the present instance, however, the capacitor elements have fine serrations athwart the direction of relative movements in order to make them sensitive to extremely small movements.

A strain-gage pickup unit was made in which a slide, having fine transverse serrations, moved parallel to corresponding serrations in the surrounding member.   After a certain amount of development work had been done on the strain gage, it became evident that basic data for the design of serrated capacitors having fine serrations and air gaps could be obtained with greater facility by making observations of capacitance change on *cylindrical* elements than on *flat* elements (because it is easier to obtain true surface and known air gaps with the former type).   An experimental unit was accordingly made.

4. Serrated-Capacitor Pickup (Twist Type).   As there was need for an improved torsiograph pickup unit, the cylindrical pickup was designed for signaling instantaneous twist in a length of shafting: it was arranged to fit into the pinion-driving shaft of an aircraft engine.

The capacitor gap was made very small at first and then increased in stages by grinding after observations of capacitance change with angular displacement had been made in the calibrating rig.

In Fig. 7-16 the pickup unit is shown fitted in the pinion-driving shaft, the bore of which is 1.5625 in.   Tubular member A is of mild steel and has fine longitudinal internal serrations in the region of the smaller bore.   These serrations are formed by cutting rectangular slots, a small slotting machine having an accurate indexing arrangement being used.   The inner tubular member B is also of mild steel and has corresponding external serrations, formed by using a milling cutter (Fig. 7-17).

Member B (Fig. 7-16) is secured to the central hollow shaft C through the medium of the insulating member D and is connected electrically to the screened signal lead shown.

Between A and B there is a fine gap which is maintained by preloaded ball bearings, and these members constitute a capacitor, the capacitance of which changes with relative angular displacement of the members (Fig. 7-17) Member A (Fig. 7-16) is registered to the angular position of station PP in the pinion-driving shaft by the differential thread expanding grip shown, and member B is registered similarly to station QQ.   Under the full mean torque the twist of the shaft between PP and QQ is represented by a circumferential displacement of approximately 0.0025 in. at the capacitor gap.   The sensitivity of the apparatus must be such that the change of capacitance caused by displacements of this order of magnitude shall give a fairly large deflection in the oscillograph record.   This presents no difficulty, and only moderate amplification is required.

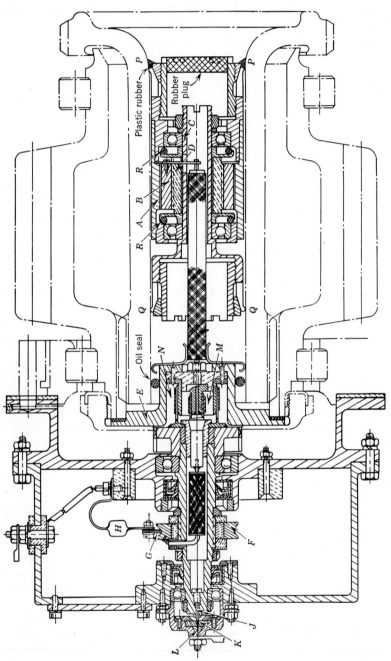

FIG. 7-16. Assembly of Capacitance-Type Twist Pickup

It is clearly very desirable that the sensitivity shall be constant over the full range of movement owing to shaft twist at the most pronounced critical vibration.   That is to say, the capacitance–displacement relationship should be linear over this range; this condition can be met by designing the serrations suitably.   Whereas, with the usual variable-gap capacitor, excessive movement will cause contact of capacitor elements (or of corresponding stops), the capacitor under discussion is not limited mechanically as regards allowable movement, and thus it requires no stops.   The pickup unit is normally fitted

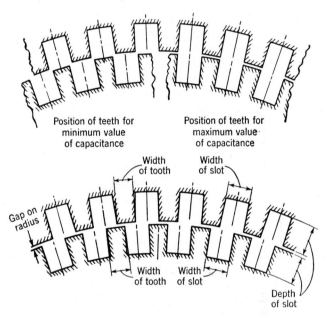

Position of teeth for
minimum value
of capacitance

Position of teeth for
maximum value
of capacitance

Width
of tooth

Width
of slot

Gap on radius

Width
of tooth

Width
of slot

Depth
of slot

Approximate position of teeth for value of capacitance
given at center of linear portion of calibration curve

FIG. 7-17.   Enlarged View of Serrations of Royal Aircraft Establishment Condenser Torsiograph

so that inner and outer teeth half overlap when the shaft is transmitting approximately full mean torque; this gives the fullest range of linearity on either side of such torque.

Rubber sealing rings R prevent the ingress of oil vapor to the capacitor, and so the gap remains filled with the dry air present under the conditions chosen for assembly—with the pinion-driving shaft out of the engine and in a dry place.

The drive for the slip ring and the ground connection is taken from an adapter E securely attached at the front of the gear case, and the electric connections M and N are made by standard low-capacity sockets.   The plug of socket M on the driving adapter is connected to the screened lead from the inner capacitor cylinder B by sweating a wire to the center of the socket on assembly.   In order to exclude oil, a rubber ring is placed between the adapter for driving the slip rings and the pinion-driving shaft; the other end of the torsiograph is plugged with a rubber stopper and sealed with plastic rubber.

5. Slip Rings and Ground Connections.   For transferring the vibration signal, a phosphor-bronze ring F of 1.25 in. diameter, with a 90° groove, was used in conjunction with the copper flexible-wire brush G (Fig. 7-16) which is held against the ring by a flexible holder made of phosphor bronze and of such form as to give universal flexibility.

The instrument could not be grounded satisfactorily by connection to the engine body because variations of resistance and capacitance at the oil films between rotating and stationary parts produce the effect of spurious signals. Furthermore, the grounded parts of the pickup unit itself require to be interconnected suitably, as indicated in Fig. 7-16.

The ground connection is made by means of the "Nichrome" spindle J, shaped to a needle point and secured in the end of the shaft.   The point just perforates a leather diaphragm K which seals some mercury L in a small container having three mounting screws for adjustment.   This arrangement combines true running of the needle with minimum relative velocity of needle and mercury.   These refinements in making the connections are the outcome of experimental development and have proved to be satisfactory.   During a running time exceeding 2 hr no spurious signals appeared on the cathode-ray tube, and the brushes did not require attention.

Another application was later made to a multiple-crankshaft engine in which the torsiograph was built into the engine in an early stage in the assembly.   The signal was taken through the rotating needle and the ground signal passed through the brushes.   Good results were obtained.

6. Theory.   The capacitance of a long plain annular capacitor is proportional to the dielectric constant, the area, and the logarithm of the ratio of outer to inner radius; but the radial gap is such a small fraction of the gap radius for the capacitors concerned here that the curvature of the capacitor surfaces can be ignored, and calculations can thus be based on the simple plate-capacitor formula.   By introducing an empirical coefficient to take account of end-effect distortions of the electrostatic field associated with the serrations, we have

$$\text{Capacitance of serrated-capacitor, } \mu\mu\text{f} = \frac{\eta k A}{3.6\pi t} \tag{4}$$

where k is the dielectric constant (unity for air), A the overlap area of the elements in square centimeters, t the gap in centimeters between elements at the overlap (that is, the radial gap), and η a coefficient which is unity when the gap is extremely small and which decreases as the gap increases.

If the charge distributed itself uniformly, the change of capacitance with relative position of the teeth would be linear, but, owing to end effects, the actual sensitivity and range of linearity remain to be determined by experiment.

7. Results with 180-Tooth Elements.   Calibrations were obtained with an element of 1.26 in. diameter having 180-tooth elements, 0.008 in. wide, and slots 0.0135 in. wide by 0.010 in. deep.   The radial gap corresponded to a diametral clearance of 0.0015 in.*   The sensitivity was found to be 28 $\mu\mu$f. per 0.001 in. of movement at capacitor face, and the range of linear response was 0.006 in.

In order to find the effect of width of gap on the sensitivity, the diametral clearance was increased progressively to 0.003 in., 0.004 in., and 0.005 in.; the calibration curves for 0.003 in. and 0.004 in. are given in Fig. 7-18.   The calibration curves were found to repeat at different relative angular positions of the cylinders, and the sensitivities measured were the same for increase and decrease in capacitance.

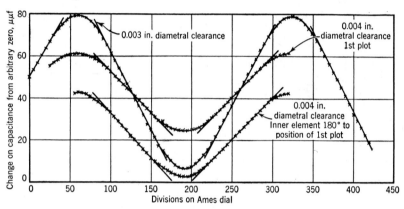

FIG. 7-18.   Calibration of Torsiograph Pickup Unit

12.2 clock divisions = 0.001 in. movement at capacitor face 180 teeth, 0.008 in. wide

Slot 0.0135 in. wide, 0.010 in. deep for 0.0015 in. gap
Diametral clearance 0.003 in., range 0.0055 in.
Sensitivity 8.75 $\mu\mu$f per 0.001 in. movement at capacitor face
Diametral clearance 0.004 in., range 0.0055 in.
Sensitivity 4.85 $\mu\mu$f per 0.001 in. movement at capacitor face

The values of the sensitivities obtained from the calibration and by calculation, if the previous formula is used with $\eta = 1$, are given in Table 7-2 and plotted in Fig. 7-19.

The percentage of actual to calculated sensitivity is given in column 10 of Table 7-2 and plotted in Fig. 7-19; the range of linearity of response is given in column 11.   The range is only slightly affected by change of gap, but the ratio of actual to calculated sensitivities decreases with the increase of gap. This shows that for gaps of the order tried, a capacitor element formed by two teeth and adjacent gaps cannot be considered to have the properties of a capacitor with infinite area in the central region of the overlap associated with distortion at each side due to the termination of the plates.   This would

* Diametral clearance is given because this value is known accurately, whereas the gap on the radius may not be exactly half the afore-mentioned value, owing to very slight error in concentricity.

result in the agreement of actual and calculated sensitivities and in the reduction of range of linearity with increase in gap: hence, the effect of the small breadth of each capacitor element on the field of the capacitor is to distort the whole of the lines of force in the field. This distortion increases with width of gap.

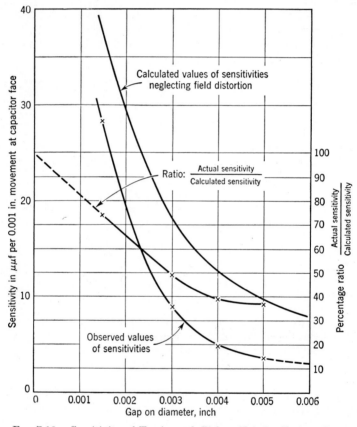

Fig. 7-19.   Sensitivity of Torsiograph Pickup Unit for Various Gaps

8. Results with 90- and 60-Tooth Elements. Two sets of values for different capacitor elements of 90 and 60 teeth have been included in Table 7-2. There are readings for elements with 0.003-in. diametral clearance for 180 and 90 teeth, respectively. The ratios of actual to calculated sensitivities are 48 and 56 per cent for corresponding values of 5.33 and 12.65 for the ratios of tooth width to mean radial gap. This indicates that, although the ratio of tooth width to gap has an effect, the most important factor in the design is the radial gap.

The last set of values in Table 7-2 is for an element of 60 teeth and a gap of 0.006 in. This shows that the ratio of actual to calculated sensitivities is tending to become constant with increase of gap at a value of about 30 per cent.

The element selected for the tests mentioned was the one with 90 teeth and 0.003 in. diametral clearance, because of its large range of linearity combined with adequate sensitivity. Full mean torque of the engine corresponds to 0.0025 in. movement at the capacitor face. The large range facilities correct setting of the pickup unit when assembling it in the shaft.

9. Running Experience with the Torsiograph. For making observations, the electronic apparatus was housed in a test cubicle so located as to require about 25 ft total length of cable lead. Repeat observations gave consistent results; during certain tests, the instrument was removed from the engine, stripped, reassembled, and replaced three times, and the same torsiograph results were obtained.

The instrument was designed to have a very high natural frequency, and the tests confirmed this amount to be well beyond the range of usual forcing frequencies. It was found that vibrations of frequency as high as 80,000 cycles per minute (twice per reduction-gear tooth engagement) can be recorded with ease.

Low-amplitude vibrations of higher frequency than this were recorded, but it was not established that these were genuine: they may have been due to microphony of the electronic recording apparatus.

The slip rings were not found

TABLE 7-2

ROYAL AIRCRAFT ESTABLISHMENT SERRATED-CAPACITOR TORSIOGRAPH

Details of Serrations and Sensitivities

Number of Teeth	Length of Teeth, in.	Diametral Clearance, in.	Width of Slot, in.	Depth of Slot in Inner Element, in.	Width of Tooth, in.	Ratio of Width of Tooth to Mean Gap on Radius	Sensitivity ($\mu\mu f$ per 0.001 in. Movement at Capacitor Face)		Actual / Calculated %	Range of Linearity: Movement at Capacitor Face
							Actual	Calculated		
180	0.75	0.0015	0.0135	0.010	0.008	10.65	28.05	37.57	74.6	0.006
180	0.75	0.003	0.0135	0.009 25	0.008	5.33	8.75	18	48.6	0.0055
180	0.75	0.004	0.0135	0.008 75	0.008	4	4.85	12.62	38.4	0.0055
180	0.75	0.005	0.0135	0.008 25	0.008	3.2	3.65	9.8	37.3	0.005
90	0.75	0.003	0.025	0.030	0.019	12.65	5.4	9.61	56.2	0.014
60	1.57	0.006	0.035	0.030	0.031	10.33	5.5	15.8	34.8	Too large to calibrate

to require frequent cleaning. Subsequent experience has shown that silver rings and silver morganite brushes prove satisfactory. Phosphor-bronze rings and copper-morganite brushes also gave good results. It is important to ground the brush holders by a suitable flexible connection.

A typical record is shown in Fig. 7-20. Time and shaft revolution signals are also recorded on the film used.

10. Other Developments. A larger unit has been made for use in a shaft of much larger bore. Another, a serrated capacitor unit has been made which fits round the outside of an aircraft-engine propeller shaft. This straddles a very short length of shafting, and, although the mean deflection at the capacitor face at full engine power is only 0.0005 in., calibration tests have confirmed that the design sensitivity is adequate. The data given in Table 7-2 constitute, in fact, a satisfactory basis of design for new applications.

11. Serrated Capacitor Pickups (Seismic Types). For observing irregularity of shaft rotation, a small torsiograph was designed and made. The

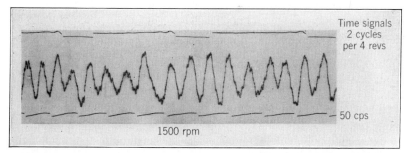

Fig. 7-20.   Typical Record of Royal Aircraft Establishment Capacitance-Type
Torsiograph, taken on Merlin-II, Blade Angle 22.5° at 42 in. Station

central shaft is so driven that it has the irregular motion to be studied; it is mounted in the (stationary) outer casing. The inner serrated element is fixed to this shaft through the medium of a "Mycalex" insulating member, and the outer serrated element is embodied in a floating flywheel member mounted on ball bearings on the shaft. The flywheel is driven by strip springs, and buffer stops are provided to limit the relative movement to $\pm 7°$. Provision is made for adjusting the mean relative position of the capacitor teeth by inserting special tools through the casing.

The capacitor is 1.5 in. long by 1 in. in diameter and the pitch of the serrations is 24°. The tooth width is 1.4 in., and the diametral clearance is 0.003 in. Approximately 11° of relative movement gives linear response. Grounding is effected by two silver-morganite brushes, set at 90°, pressing into a chromium-plated groove. The signal from the capacitor passes through a Nichrome needle, rotating with its point in a small mercury cup, and, thence, through a standard adapter and along a low-capacity screened lead.

The torsiograph has been calibrated dynamically on a laboratory flywheel system, and it has been used on engines with satisfactory results. The sensitivity is 26 $\mu\mu$f. per degree of relative displacement.

The serrated capacitor principle has been applied also to obtain small seismic pickups of high sensitivity, for recording linear vibrational displacements in space.

III. AMPLIFIER CIRCUITS FOR VARIABLE-CAPACITANCE GAGES

Contributed by C. H. W. Brookes-Smith and J. A. Colls

G. INTRODUCTION

A considerable number of circuits for use with variable capacitance gages for measuring pressure, force, strain, and the like, with a cathode-ray oscillograph have from time to time been published by various workers. These circuits fall into two main classes: (*a*) those in which the gage is polarized with a steady source of potential, and (*b*) those that make use of some sort of high-frequency circuit. Both have certain advantages not possessed by the other, and both, therefore, have their uses. Generally speaking, the former is the simpler and has a considerably higher upper-frequency response limit, whereas the latter has the outstanding advantage of being able to work down to zero frequency corresponding to sustained pressures or forces, thus, among other things, greatly facilitating the whole problem of calibration. Examples of the two different types of circuit are given in the following paragraphs.

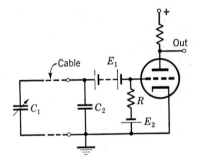

H. D-C POLARIZATION

For this circuit a potential of usually about 100 volts derived from a battery or rectified alternating supply voltage is applied through a high resistance to the variable-capacitance gage, and a large capacitor is connected in parallel

FIG. 7-21.   D-C Polarization

with the gage. There are several possible arrangements, but that shown in Fig. 7-21 is one of the simplest. In this the gage C_1 and shunt capacitor C_2 are charged by the battery E_1, and the feed resistance R and grid-bias battery E_2 serve to hold the grid of the valve on the midpoint of its operating characteristic. The output voltage is directly proportional to the gage capacitance changes so long as the time period of the event under measurement is short compared with the time constant of the circuit. In practice, a compromise must be found between two conditions, namely, the time constant of the system and the total amplification. Any increase in shunt capacitance to obtain a longer time constant reduces the output voltage for a given capacitance change and, hence, requires higher amplification. A limit is set to this process at the point where valve microphony becomes intolerable, especially where the apparatus has to work under conditions of severe mechanical vibration.   Any attempt to raise the time constant by increasing the feed resistance is limited by leakage in the shunt capacitor and cable and the grid resistance of the valve.   The combined effect of these factors sets the lower limit of frequency at a few cycles per second and completely precludes the possibility of recording very slow capacitance changes or of effecting static calibration.   The upper-frequency limit, however, is not restricted by the time constant of the circuit but by the amplifier.   By omitting the shunt capacitor and reducing the value of the feed resistance, an output proportional to the rate of change of capacitance is obtained so that measurements, for example, of velocity instead of movement or displacement can be made.   If desired, the integration process can then be made at a later stage in the amplifier instead of the large shunt capacitor being used.   From the foregoing it may be seen that d-c polarization has considerable utility where rapidly fluctuating phenomena are to be indicated and is of special value where very short-period transient phenomena have to be recorded.   A simple d-c polarizing circuit followed by a wide-band *RC* coupled amplifier and cathode-ray tube is capable of recording extremely short mechanical shock waves.

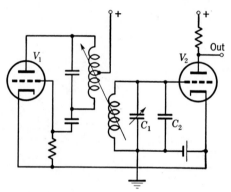

Fig. 7-22.   High-Frequency Variable-Amplitude System

I. High-Frequency Circuits

The high-frequency circuits used with variable-capacitance gages can be divided into two classes: (*a*) variable amplitude, and (*b*) variable frequency.   In the former the variation of capacitance causes a change in the amplitude of a signal fed from a fixed-frequency oscillator to a rectifying circuit.   This can be achieved by connecting the variable capacitance in one arm of a bridge or balanced T network, but the output so obtained is small and requires considerable amplification unless a high-power oscillator is employed.   On the other hand the variable capacitance may form part of the tuning capacity of a resonant circuit in which the magnification of the circuit allows a much higher output to be obtained.   Figure 7-22 shows a simplified circuit where V_1 is the oscillator and V_2 either an anode-bend or diode rectifier.   In this arrangement the working point is on the side of the resonance curve and should be set near the point of inflection to obtain maximum linearity.   The main disadvantages are the possibility of using the wrong side of the resonance curve, the necessity of backing off the unwanted d-c component and the limitation of gage cable length set by the capacity of the cable.   Nevertheless, the circuit, which is comparatively simple to set up, has given very useful service.

J. Frequency-Modulated Circuits

In the variable-frequency or frequency-modulated system the variable-gage capacitance forms part of the oscillator tuning circuit. The variable frequency from the oscillator is fed to a frequency-discriminating circuit where it is converted to a change of amplitude. The frequency discrimination may be obtained by working on one side of a simple resonance circuit, but a more satisfactory arrangement is to use one of the more complex frequency discriminators giving zero output at the mid-operating point and, hence, necessitating no backing-off voltage. A simple form of frequency discriminator is shown in Fig. 7-23.

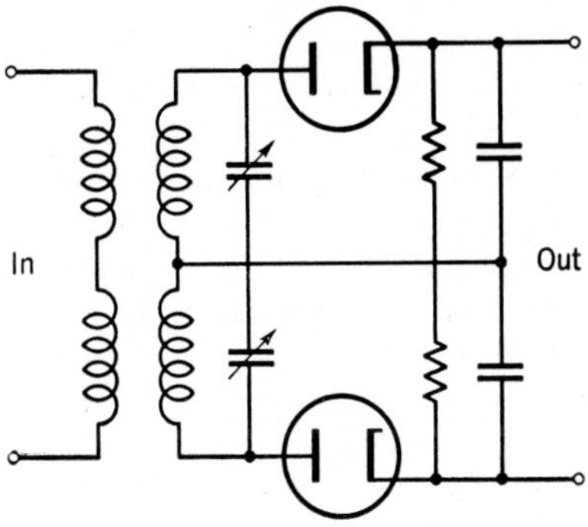

Fig. 7-23. Frequency Discriminator

It consists of two resonant circuits tuned to slightly different frequencies. The outputs from the two circuits are separately rectified, and the difference between the two rectified voltages appears across the output terminals. The resulting relation between input frequency and output voltage is shown in Fig. 7-24. By correct design the central portion of the curve can be made very linear and forms the working portion of the characteristic, there being no ambiguity as in the case of the simple tuned circuit. The

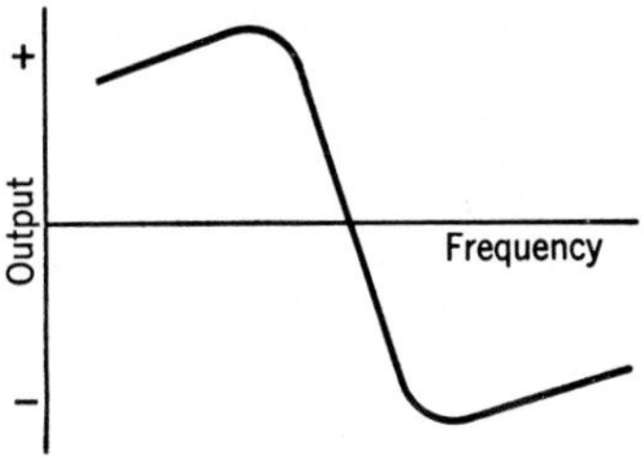

Fig. 7-24. Frequency Discriminator Characteristic

chief advantage of this variable-frequency system is that the variable-capacitance gage and oscillator, which can be quite small, can be situated at a distance and connected to the discriminator circuit by a low-impedance cable several hundred yards in length if required. Limiting amplifiers are provided before the discriminator to insure that amplitude changes have no effect on the output. A block-schematic diagram of this arrangement is shown in Fig. 7-25.

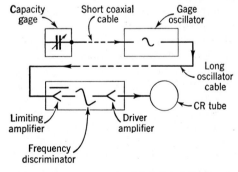

Fig. 7-25. Frequency-Modulated System

A choice of carrier frequency over a fairly wide range can be made to suit different purposes, a figure of about 1 or 2 megacycles being convenient. Either of the high-frequency circuits described previously can be designed without difficulty to work with incremental variable capacitances of 20 $\mu\mu$f. and to give an output of about 1 volt per micromicrofarad. Used with a single-stage direct-coupled driver–amplifier sufficient output is obtained to operate a cathode-ray tube. The over-all system, therefore, has the effect of being direct coupled throughout, and static calibrations as well as measurements down to very low frequencies can be carried out. The upper limit of frequency response depends on the carrier frequency and the high-frequency circuit design and, hence, can be varied over fairly wide limits. With a 2-megacycle-per-second carrier, the upper limit is in the neighborhood of 20–30 kc which, however, is ample for the vast majority of mechanical applications.

K. Calibration

The process of calibration is greatly simplified by having a calibrated variable capacitor connected in parallel with the gage in the variable-amplitude system and in parallel with each half of the frequency-discriminator tuning condenser in the case of the frequency-modulated system. The effect of increase or decrease of gage capacitance under load is counterbalanced by adjustment of this calibrating condenser whose readings are noted. A point-by-point calibration may thus be obtained and later transferred to the photographic record of the event under measurement.

This calibrating method is not entirely free from error on account of the inevitable curvature of the frequency–capacitance scale but, in the case of the frequency-modulated system and under favorable conditions, does not exceed 1 per cent where the incremental capacitance of the gage is not more than about 3 per cent of the total capacitance in the oscillator circuit.

An important consideration in connection with the calibration of variable-capacitance gages is that the high-frequency systems enable point-by-point static calibration readings to be taken with both ascending and descending loads and hence reveal hysteresis inherent in the gage. This aspect is frequently glossed over in systems only capable of dynamic calibration, and, as load, pressure, and other gages, which must be regarded as "mechanisms," sometimes have hysteresis figures of 10 per cent or more, considerable errors can arise. This aspect should not be lost sight of if variable-capacitance gages are to be used with d-c polarization, and provision must be made to carry out the gage calibrations with a high-frequency circuit or an equivalent arrangement.

IV. COMMENTS ON THE USE OF ELECTRIC-CAPACITANCE GAGES

L. Installation of the Strain Elements

The use of high-carrier frequencies necessitates dielectrics having low power factors at these frequencies. Such dielectrics comprise mica, ebonite, mycalex, and the synthetic insulators: polystrene, distrene, ethene, and so on. Mycalex is useful on account of its good dielectric properties, its ability to withstand heat, and the constancy of its dielectric properties with temperature changes. Changes in the capacitance to ground outside the strain element are recorded as strains, and, as the signal may be produced by changes of capacitance less than 20 $\mu\mu$f. out of a total of 600 $\mu\mu$f., special care must be taken with all leads. They must be insulated with a good-quality dielectric having a grounded screen outside the insulation.   The smaller the capacitance per unit length of lead between conductor and screening, the longer is the lead that may be used between the strain element and the recording apparatus when amplitude-modulated circuits are used.

There are several special low-capacity cable leads which fulfill the condition that the central wire shall remain at an almost invariable distance from the grounded screen in spite of a reasonable amount of flexing.   In an instance where severe vibratory movement of cable proved troublesome, the difficulty was overcome by installing a short length of standard Ministry of Aircraft Production "Uniflexmet" cable.   Only short lengths of this cable can be used, because it has a relatively high capacity per unit length: it has adequate flexibility, and at the same time the radial stiffness is such as to prevent the capacity from changing appreciably.

For some applications leads may be built up on a metal surface, plastic dielectrics being used, in which case the grounded screen may be obtained by using a conducting paint such as "Aquadag."

Change in temperature alters the capacity of all the above leads; and, if the temperature is changing, a drift in the steady value of the strain will result.   This change is too slow to affect the usual alternating readings.   If necessary, this drift can be avoided by using a fine wire stretched taut along the center of a grounded tube with insulator supports at intervals: the wire may be tuned by modifying the tension and the spacing of the supports to have a frequency outside the range of important vibration frequencies of the adjacent structure.

M. Applications and Limitations

It will be appreciated that the use of capacitance-type pickups does involve special care with details of the circuit.   Moreover, it has been found that extra special care is required in damp atmospheres.

However, this type of pickup has served extremely well for pressure measurement, and in the torsiograph applications it has given results quite beyond the scope of the Royal Aircraft Establishment optical torsiographs.

The strain-gage pickup units described were developed before the advent of the wire-resistance type of strain gage, and they still have useful application for special purposes, notably in cases where the temperature is beyond the limit for wire-resistance gages.   In the capacitance-type pickups, the range of linearity is not intimately associated with the properties of a material, as in the wire-resistance gage, and thus the capacitance type may serve for measurements under extreme conditions where the wire-resistance type would be overstrained.

N. Acknowledgement

The authors wish to thank the Ministry of Supply and Aircraft Production for permission to contribute this chapter, and in doing so they have to state that they are solely responsible for the opinions expressed therein. The RAF official Crown copyright is reserved for Figs. 7-4a, 7-4b, 7-15, and 7-20.

BIBLIOGRAPHY

1. E. M. Dodds and C. H. Sprake, "Cathode–Ray Oscillograph Engine Indicator," *Engineering*, v 140, n 3632, 3639, and 3643; 1935.
2. E. M. Dodds, "The Metro–Vickers–Dodds Engine Indicator," *Auto Engr*, v 25, 1935.
3. E. M. Dodds, "Development and Application of Cathode–Ray Engine Indicator," *J Soc Automotive Engrs*, v 39, 1936, pp 487–95.
4. M. Bacelin, "Méthode d'enregistrement de faibles déplacements," *Revue générale des chemins de fer*, v 56, 1936, pp 353–55.
5. C. H. W. Brookes–Smith and J. A. Colls, "Measurement of Pressure, Movement, Acceleration, and Other Mechanical Quantities by Electrostatic Systems," *J Sci Instr (Lond)* v 14, 1939, pp 361–66.
6. F. D. Smith, "Basic Principles in Design of Cathode–Ray Oscillograph Engine Indicators," *J and Proc Instn Mech Engrs* v 143, 1940, pp 48–56.
7. L. C. Roess, "Condenser Type High Speed Engine Indicator," *Rev Sci Instr* v 11, 1940, pp 183–95.
8. B. C. Carter, J. F. Shannon, and J. R. Forshaw, "Measurement of Displacement and Strain by Capacity Methods," *Proc Instn Mech Engrs*, v 152, 1945, pp 215–21.
9. G. M. Foley, "Testing of Precision–Lathe Spindles," *Trans ASME* v 67, 1945, pp 553–56.
10. Howard C. Roberts, *Mechanical Measurements by Electrical Methods*, Instruments Publishing Co, 1946.

CHAPTER 8

MOTION MEASUREMENTS

By J. Ormondroyd, R. B. Allnutt, F. Mintz, and R. D. Specht

I. STEADY-STATE MOTIONS

A. Fatigue Stresses and Steady-State Vibrations

1. General Considerations. Steady-state motions can be described mathematically for all time (times which are longer than and include the entire time of observation) by equations which contain a small number of constant parameters. The following types of steady-state motions illustrate this:

$$x = x_0 \tag{1}$$

$$x = x_0 + \dot{x}_0 t \tag{2}$$

$$x = x_0 + \dot{x}_0 t + \tfrac{1}{2}\ddot{x}_0 t^2 \tag{3}$$

$$x = x_0 + \sum_1^N x_n \sin (n\omega t + \phi_n); \quad \omega = \frac{2\pi}{T};$$

$$T = \text{period of lowest harmonic} \tag{4}$$

Similar equations can be written for y and z components of motion. If the time of observation is made long enough, it will be found that no steady-state motions actually exist.

Fatigue stresses are associated with periodic motions of type 4. The fatigue limits of steel and other common materials of construction usually lie well below the elastic limit of the material. For this reason the classical theories of elasticity and vibration are applicable to the study of fatigue stresses.

Dangerous fatigue stresses usually are present only when parts of the structure are at resonance. At resonance the particular harmonic of the periodic motion to which the structure is resonating is the only one of great importance. At and near resonance the vibrating motion is almost a pure simple-harmonic motion.

The danger of a fatigue stress depends on (a) the amplitude of the resonant-vibration harmonic stress and (*b*) on the average constant stress which exist at the stressed section. Goodman diagrams* are used by engineers to estimate the probable danger associated with combinations of fluctuating and constant stresses.

The time in which failure may occur depends on the frequency of the vibration. The *S–N* diagram† is used by engineers to form judgments on this score.

2. Displacement and Stress.   The relationship between the vibration displacements of points in elastic systems and the associated stresses which exist at these points is given here from the theory of elasticity for several common cases.

For beams, bars, and shafts in simple longitudinal vibration:

$$\sigma = E\,\frac{\partial u}{\partial x} \qquad \text{(Compression or tension)} \tag{5}$$

For beams, bars, and shafts in simple torsional vibration:

$$\tau = Gr\,\frac{\partial \phi}{\partial x} \qquad \text{(Shear)} \tag{6}$$

For beams, bars, and shafts in bending vibration:

$$\sigma = Ez\,\frac{\partial^2 v}{\partial x^2} \qquad \text{(Compression or tension)} \tag{7}$$

For plates, panels and slabs in bending vibration:

$$\sigma_x = \frac{Ez}{1 - \nu^2}\left(\frac{\partial^2 v}{\partial x^2} + \nu\,\frac{\partial^2 v}{\partial y^2}\right)$$

$$\sigma_y = \frac{Ez}{1 - \nu^2}\left(\frac{\partial^2 v}{\partial y^2} + \nu\,\frac{\partial^2 v}{\partial x^2}\right) \tag{8}$$

$$\tau = -\frac{Ez}{1 + \nu}\,\frac{\partial^2 v}{\partial x\,\partial y}$$

In these equations

σ = tensile stress in pounds per square inch

τ = shear stress in pounds per square inch

E = Young's modulus of the material in pounds per square inch

G = shear modulus of the material in pounds per square inch

ν = Poisson's ratio of the material

u = longitudinal displacement of a section whose undisturbed position is at x

ϕ = angle of rotation of a section whose undisturbed position is at x

* See Chapter 10, p. 452; Chapter 11, p. 523.
† See Chapter 1, p. 20.

v = deflection of the neutral axis at positions x or x, y

z = distance of stressed point from neutral axis, measured normal to the neutral axis in inches

r = distance of stressed point from twist axis, measured normal to the axis of twist in inches

In general u, v, and ϕ are functions of position and time. For instance, $u = f_1(x)f_2(t)$. The maximum stresses, in the simple cases mentioned previously, all occur when the time functions are at maxima (and minima). Therefore, we are interested only in the amplitudes of u, v, and ϕ. The amplitudes are functions of position. In the previous example the amplitude of u is $u_{max} = f_1(x)$, if it is assumed that $f_2(t)$ is a simple-harmonic function. Thus, in straight tension or compression $\sigma = E \dfrac{df_1(x)}{dx}$ and the maximum stress amplitude occurs when $\dfrac{d}{dx} f_1(x)$ is a maximum, thus:

$$\sigma_{max} = E \left[\frac{d}{dx} f_1(x) \right]_{max} \tag{9}$$

Equations 5 to 8 indicate that the distribution of amplitudes of motion over the vibrating member is the important feature in estimating stresses caused by vibration. Stresses depend on relative motions between parts indicated by the occurrence of first and second space derivatives of amplitudes in equations 5 to 8. The first space derivatives of amplitudes are always largest at nodes which are sections with zero displacement at all times and the second space derivatives or amplitudes are always largest at antinodes which are sections of maximum displacement when the body is vibrating at resonance.

The stresses calculated from the vibration-amplitude distribution by means of equations 5 to 8 are superimposed on the steady or average stresses at the same points.

Stresses inferred from vibration amplitudes cannot be gotten with any high degree of accuracy. This is not so much due to any limitations of vibration-amplitude measurements as to the great difficulties encountered in obtaining accurate first and second derivatives from numerical or graphical test data.

Vibration-measuring instruments are usually so large, even if probes are used as the means of connecting the instrument to the vibrating body, that it is impossible to get direct evidence of stress concentrations by vibration measurements. If stress concentrations do exist, they must be inferred by the use of theory—the vibration measurements giving only fair estimates of the average fluctuating stresses in the neighborhood of the concentration.

In order to obtain space derivatives of vibration amplitudes the motion must be measured at several stations (x or x, y) simultaneously. If the number of vibration instruments available does not permit this, the motion at several stations (x or x, y) can be measured successively with one instrument, provided the frequency and amplitudes of the motion are maintained constant throughout the measurement.

A common procedure to avoid multiple-vibration measurements is to calculate (or assume from previous experience) the spatial relative amplitude distribution at resonance. This is known as the "normal elastic" curve of the system. If the "normal elastic" curve is used, a single measurement of amplitude at some convenient point in the system will serve to establish the scale of the curve and its derivatives.

3. Acceleration and Stress. In view of the difficulty of differentiating amplitude-position data, acceleration-position measurements can be considered. If a vibrating beam is taken as an example, the following procedure can be used:

Since
$$\frac{d^2 M_x}{dx^2} = \frac{w_x a_x}{g} \tag{10}$$

and
$$\sigma_x = \frac{M_x z_x}{I_x} \tag{11}$$

$$\sigma_x = \frac{Z_x}{I_x} \left[\int_0^x \int_0^x \frac{w_x a_x}{g} \, dx \, dx + S_0 X + M_0 \right] \tag{12}$$

where S_0 = shear at $x = 0$, M_0 = moment at $x = 0$,
and M_x = maximum bending moment at section located at x
  w_x = loading rate in pounds per inch at x
  a_x = maximum acceleration at x
  g = acceleration of gravity
  σ_x = maximum bending stress at x
  z_x = distance between outermost fiber and neutral axis at x
  I_x = rectangular moment of inertia of the cross section at x

This procedure leads to the use of an integration process which is inherently more accurate than the differentiating processes demanded by equations 5 to 8.

4. Bending Stresses in a Vibrating Ship. In order to estimate the possible stresses which might occur in the plating of a ship under the action of unbalanced forces in the engine, variable hydrodynamic forces at the propeller, and violent waves during storms, a ship can be subjected to controlled vibrations produced by a vibration generator.*

Figure 8-1 shows the distribution of vertical vibrations for the 4-noded critical speed of a ship 250ft long, 43ft beam, 27 ft deep, 2000 tons displacement. The ship was floating in calm water when the test was made. The vibration generator was attached firmly to the center of the deck at the bow of the ship. It generated vertical vibrations. The 4-noded mode of motion occurred at 565 cycles per minute. At this speed the vibration generator produced a simple harmonic force with an amplitude of 390 lb. A General Radio crystal accelerometer pickup† feeding into an amplifying integrating circuit was used to make readings at 27 stations regularly spaced along the

* See article 29.
† See item 2, Table 8-4.

center line of the deck while the vibration generator was run constantly at 565 rpm.

If the ship is treated as a simple beam the average maximum stress in the deck plating, ignoring the stress concentrations at hatch corners and deckhouse attachments, is given by equation 13:

$$\sigma = Ez\,\frac{\partial^2 v}{\partial x^2} \tag{13}$$

The maximum value of $\partial^2 v/\partial x^2$ occurs amidships at the central antinode over the machinery space. For the purpose of estimating the magnitude of $\partial^2 v/\partial x^2$ the amplitude curve between the two central nodes can be considered

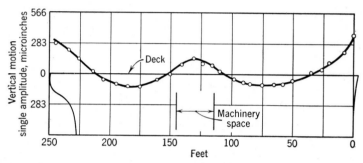

Fig. 8-1.   Profile of the Amplitudes of Vertical Vibration at 565 cpm Measured along the center line of the main deck

as a sine wave $v = v_0 \sin 2\pi \dfrac{x}{l}$ and $\dfrac{\partial^2 v}{\partial x^2} = -\dfrac{4\pi^2 v_0}{l^2}\sin 2\pi \dfrac{x}{l}.$ The maximum value of $\partial^2 v/\partial x^2$ at the central antinode is $\left|\dfrac{4\pi^2 v_0}{l^2}\right|.$

$$v_0 = 142 \times 10^{-6}\text{ in.}; \quad l = 1100\text{ in.}; \quad E = 30 \times 10^6\,\frac{\text{lb}}{\text{in.}^2}; \quad z = 162\text{ in.}$$

$$\sigma = 27\text{ psi}$$

As long as the ship vibrates within the elastic limit of the ship plating, the amplitude at any station in the normal elastic curve of Fig. 8-1 will be proportional to the amplitude of the exciting force at the bow. To produce a stress of 27 psi required a force amplitude of 390 lb at 565 cycles. Therefore, to produce a stress of 10,000 psi at the central antinode, a force amplitude of 145,000 lb would be needed at the bow at the frequency of 565 cycles per minute.

While the ship is vibrating elastically at resonance, the energy per cycle put into the vibrating ship by the vibration generator is

$$W/\text{cycle} = \pi P_1 v_1$$

P_1 is the amplitude of the vertical force generated by the vibration generator. v_1 is the amplitude of motion of the ship at the vibration-generator position. If the vibration generator is attached to some other position x, on the ship the work per cycle at that position would be

$$W/\text{cycle} = \pi P_x v_x$$

If, for a given mode of motion, the force amplitude P_x is adjusted to give

$$\pi P_x v_x = \pi P_1 v_1$$

then,

$$P_x = \frac{v_1}{v_x} P_1$$

The amplitudes at the bow, central antinode, and the stern in Fig. 8-1 are in the ratios 1.00:0.37:0.93. Therefore, it would take 1050 lb amplitude at

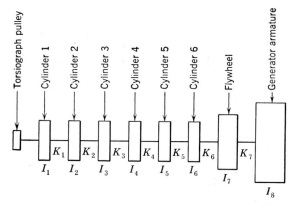

Fig. 8-2. Equivalent Flywheel–Torsional-Spring System for a 6-Cylinder Diesel Engine Directly Coupled to an Electric Generator

the central antinode and 420 lb amplitude at the stern to produce 27 psi stress at the central antinode, and 392,000 lb amplitude at the engine space and 156,000 lb amplitude at the stern to produce 10,000 psi stress at the central antinode. Since neither the engine nor the propeller under the very worst of conditions can produce such force amplitudes at 565 cycles per minute the ship is in no danger of cracking from fatigue stresses alone.

5. Shear Stresses in a Vibrating Crankshaft. A 4-cycle 6-cylinder (in line) Diesel engine rated at 500 hp driving an electric generator, operating at 300–900 rpm, had a severe critical speed in the running range. The main bearings of the engine are 5 in. in diameter, and the shaft connecting the electric generator to the flywheel of the engine is 6 in. in diameter. The alloy steel of the crankshaft has a fatigue limit in shear of about 60,000 psi, and the steel of the generator shaft has a fatigue limit in shear of about 35,000 psi. The drawings of the engine indicate that the rotating and reciprocating parts have the equivalent flywheel moments of inertia as shown in

Fig. 8-2, and the dimensions and elasticity of the crankshaft and generator shaft give torsional spring constants* as shown in Fig. 8-2.

In order to estimate the average stresses in the crankshaft and generator shafts, equation 14 is used.

$$\tau = Gr \frac{\partial \phi}{\partial x} \tag{14}$$

A torsiograph† belted to a pulley, attached to the free end of the crankshaft, showed a one-noded critical speed at 640 rpm having 6 cycles per revolution

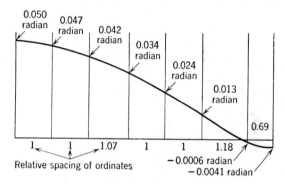

FIG. 8-3.   Distribution of Torsional Vibration Amplitude in One-Noded Mode of Motion of Diesel-Generator Drive

and an amplitude of 0.05 radian (approximately 3°).   A "normal elastic" curve was constructed by using the equation:‡

$$\phi_{n+1} = \phi_n - \frac{\sum\limits_{1}^{n} I_m p^2 \phi_m}{k_n} \tag{15}$$

where $\phi_1 = 0.05$ radian

$$p^2 = \left(2\pi \frac{640 \times 6}{60}\right)^2 = (128\pi)^2 = 161{,}000 \frac{\text{rad}^2}{\text{sec}^2}$$

Figure 8-3 shows the calculated amplitude distribution for the one-noded mode of torsional vibration.

Table 8-1 shows the successive calculation of the amplitudes ϕ_n and the twists $\phi_n - \phi_{n+1}$ from equation 15.

In Table 8-1 the stations 1 to 8 in column 1 are considered at the center lines of the cylinders, the center line of the flywheel, and the center line of the generator.   Column 4 gives the calculated amplitudes of the flywheels

* See reference 3, pp 270–73.
† See Table 8-7.
‡ See reference 3, p 261, eqs *f*, *g*, and *h*.

TABLE 8-1

1	2	3	4	5	6	7	8
					$\sum_{1}^{n} I_m p^2 \phi_m$		Twist, Col. 6
	I_m	$I_m p^2$	ϕ_m	$I_m p^2 \phi_m$		k_m	$\overline{\text{Col. 7}}$
m	lb-in. sec^2	lb-in.	rad	lb-in.	lb-in.	lb-in./rad.	rad
1	16.5	2.66×10^6	0.0500	13.30×10^4	13.30×10^4	48×10^6	0.0028
2	16.5	2.66×10^6	0.0472	12.55×10^4	25.85×10^4	48×10^6	0.0053
3	16.5	2.66×10^6	0.0419	11.13×10^4	36.98×10^4	45×10^6	0.0083
4	16.5	2.66×10^6	0.0336	8.95×10^3	45.93×10^4	48×10^6	0.0096
5	16.5	2.66×10^6	0.0240	6.39×10^4	52.32×10^4	48×10^6	0.0109
6	16.5	2.66×10^6	0.0132	3.51×10^4	55.83×10^4	40.8×10^6	0.0137
7	512.0	82.50×10^6	-0.00055	-4.53×10^4	51.30×10^4	145×10^6	0.0035
8	780.0	125.5×10^6	-0.00407	-51.1×10^4	$.20 \times 10^4$		

in the system. This amplitude distribution is shown in Fig. 8-3. The total twist in each section of shaft between the flywheels is given in column 8.

Table 8-2 shows the calculation of the stresses between the various stations by means of equation 14.

TABLE 8-2

1	2	3	4	5	6	7	8
Station m	$\dfrac{\sum_{1}^{h} I_m p^2 \phi_m}{k_m}$	Equivalent Length, l_m	$\dfrac{\partial \phi}{\partial x} = \dfrac{\phi_m - \phi_{m+1}}{l_m}$	Equivalent Diameter, d_m	$r = \dfrac{\partial \phi}{\partial x} = \dfrac{d_m}{2}\dfrac{\phi_m - \phi_{m+1}}{l_m}$	τ average $Gr\dfrac{\partial \phi}{\partial x}$	$3 \times T_{\text{avg}}$
1	0.0028	15.4''	0.00018'	5''	0.00045	5,450	16,350
2	0.0053	15.4	0.00034	5	0.00085	10,300	30,900
3	0.0083	16.5	0.00050	5	0.00125	15,000	45,000
4	0.0096	15.4	0.00062	5	0.00155	18,600	55,800
5	0.0109	15.4	0.00071	5	0.00177	21,200	63,600
6	0.0137	18.15	0.00076	5	0.00190	22,600	67,800
7	0.0035	10.6	0.00033	6	0.00099	12,000	36,000
8							

In Table 8-2 the total twists are given again in column 2, and the equivalent length of twisted shaft is given in column 3. In column 4 an average value of $\dfrac{\partial \phi}{\partial x} = \dfrac{\phi_m - \phi_{m+1}}{l_m}$ is calculated. Column 7 shows the average shear stress in each section of shaft.

Column 8 shows the shear stress under the assumption of a stress-concentration factor of 3. This is a reasonable assumption for crankshafts. The constant load stress was 2500 psi (or 7500 psi if multiplied by 3). The possible stresses between stations 4–5, 5–6, and 7–8 are all potentially dangerous since the engine would give 6,000,000 stress cycles in 24 hr of operation at 640 rpm.

B. VIBRATION-MEASURING INSTRUMENTS

6. General Observations. All vibration instruments have the same functional parts: (1) a mechanical system which responds to the motion being measured frequently called a "pickup" system; (2) an indicating or recording system which is actuated by the response of the mechanical "pickup" system; if the instrument makes a record it also has (3) a drive which moves the recording surface at a constant speed during the time in which the record is being taken; and (4) a timing mechanism which marks on the record at predetermined equal intervals of time.[4, 5]

7. Pickup Systems of Vibration Instruments. Two different types of "pickup" systems are used. Both are mechanical in nature. These are: (1) "directly connected" systems, and (2) seismic systems.

A "directly connected" pickup system consists of a casing from which a probe protrudes. The probe can move axially relative to the casing in guide bearings which are carried by the case. The end of the probe which is inside the case is usually connected to the case through a spring which holds the probe against a stop when the instrument is not in use. In use the free end of the probe is put in contact with the vibrating body, and the case is pushed down toward the contact point releasing the probe from the stop and distorting the spring so that the probe is held against the moving body by the spring force. The case is then attached to some neighboring body which is not vibrating, or it is held in the hand. The probe in some instruments is a spring-loaded lever arm which protrudes from the case. If the free end of the probe or lever actually stays in contact with the vibrating body and the case is actually held immovable in space, there is a relative movement between the probe and the case which is an exact reproduction of the motion being measured.

"Seismic" pickup systems get their name from the fact that they are constructed on the principles of the seismographs used to measure earthquake motions. This type of instrument consists of a case containing a mass which is suspended from the case by springs. The motion of the mass relative to the case is usually guided mechanically in the direction of the motion to be measured. The case of the seismic instrument is firmly attached to the vibrating body and moves with it. The end of the mass-suspension spring moves with the case, and this excites the suspended mass into motion. The relative motion between the vibrating case and the spring-suspended mass is related to the motion being measured in a definite way.

If the mass is heavy enough, the suspension spring soft enough, and the frequency of the measured vibration high enough $(\omega/p > 4; n < 0.1)$,* the mass almost stands still in space, and the relative motion between the case and the mass is almost an exact reproduction of the motion being measured.

If the mass is light enough, the suspension spring stiff enough, and the frequency of the measured vibration low enough $(\omega/p < 0.7; 0.6 < n < 0.7)$, the mass almost follows the motion of the case. The small relative motion that exists between the case and the mass is almost exactly proportional to the instantaneous acceleration of the case.

8. Indicating, Recording, and Magnifying Systems of Vibration Instruments. The *input* or stimulus of any vibration instrument is the motion being measured or some aspect of that motion. The *output* or response of any vibration instrument is the relative motion between the two physical bodies which form the main parts of the "pickup" unit. The relative motion is transmitted to an indicating or recording device and is usually amplified or magnified in the transmitting mechanism.

Vibration instruments have various methods of transmitting, magnifying,

* ω, p and n defined in Article 21.

and indicating or recording the relative motion between the two mechanical elements of the "pickup." These fall into three general categories: mechanical, optical, and electrical.

Mechanical transmissions make use of levers and gears. They have the advantage of requiring little or no accessory equipment. The parts are generally rugged, and the indications or records attained are immediately available for inspection. They usually are limited to use on fairly low frequencies.

Optical transmissions make use of mirrors on spindles with the main amplification in the optical levers. They combine relative freedom from accessory equipment and high amplification but lack, in general, the versatility of electrical methods and the rugged construction associated with mechanical methods.[6, 8] *

The electrical methods make use of changing resistance, inductance, or capacitance by the relative motion between the pickup members. In crystal-type pickups the relative motion squeezes the crystal and produces charges on its surfaces.[9–14]

Records of vibration instruments are made in many different ways such as by (1) steel points scratching on metal, celluloid, and carbon or wax-covered paper; (2) metallic points writing on prepared paper; (3) stylus writing with ink on paper; (4) stylus emitting high-voltage sparks which cut holes in paper; (5) light beams writing on photographic film or sensitized paper; (6) electron beams writing on fluorescent surfaces.

The recording surface is moved at constant speed, usually controllable, in the proper direction by spring motors which can be wound up or by synchronous electric motors which require an a-c power supply. Indications are made with pointers moving over scales.

Since many modern motion-measuring instruments use electric transmission and amplification with final photographic recording, the electromagnetic oscillograph and the cathode-ray oscillograph are described here.

9. The Electromagnetic Oscillograph. Figure 8-4 shows the essential elements of a modern recording electromagnetic oscillograph. The galvanometer or electromagnetic oscillograph is a device that records variable electric currents by the use of a Duddell electromagnetic galvanometer in conjunction with a light source and a moving strip of photographic film or paper. The Duddell galvanometer consists of a wire loop, with a small mirror attached, suspended between the poles of a strong magnet. Owing to the interaction between the field produced by a current flowing in the loop and the field of the permanent magnet, the mirror rotates, the angle of rotation being proportional to the current. The rotation of the mirror causes a deflection of the light beam which is reflected from the mirror. The movement of the light beam is recorded on photographic film or light-sensitive paper.

The sensitivity of this type of galvanometer is inversely proportional to the square of the natural frequency. Galvanometers are available with natural frequencies as high as 20,000 cps and as low as about 10 cps.

* See reference 7, pp 608, 609.

Electrodynamic oscillographs are generally used at frequencies below the natural frequency of the galvanometer so that $0 < \dfrac{\omega}{p} < 0.7$. The wire loop with the mirror attached is enclosed in a glass tube which is filled with a

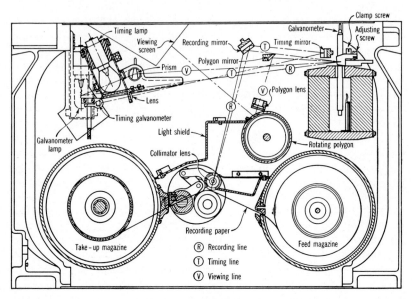

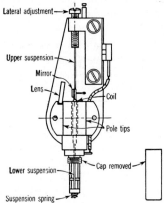

Fig. 8-4.   Cross Section of Recording Electromagnetic Oscillograph

damping fluid of such viscosity that $n \approx 0.65$. Sensitivities are obtained as high as 1 in. deflection on the film for about 40 microamperes of current in the lowest-frequency range. Multichannel oscillographs are available with as many as 24 galvanometers recording simultaneously.

The electromagnetic galvanometer has essentially a low impedance and, therefore, generally requires relatively high-power input. The amplifiers used with galvanometer oscillographs are of the type known as "current amplifiers"; that is, they have a low-impedance output and are capable of putting out fairly high currents, even though the actual voltage amplification may not be high.

10. The Cathode-Ray Oscillograph. Figure 8-5 shows the essential elements of a cathode-ray tube which is the basic part of a cathode-ray oscillograph. The cathode ray oscillograph responds to variations in voltage and has a high input impedance, requiring little power output but considerable voltage amplification, much of which may be in the amplifying circuit built into the oscillograph. The basic element of the oscillograph is the cathode-ray tube, which is essentially an electron gun in a vacuum tube with a fluorescent screen at one end of the tube. Two sets of mutually perpendicular deflection plates in the tube determine the direction of the stream of electrons and, thereby, the point at which the electrons impinge on the screen. By this means, any electric potential may be indicated on the screen (and recorded photographically) either on a time base or as a function of any other electric potential. Since the electrons act as practically an inertialess pointer, signals of extremely high frequency may be recorded, the limitations being determined by the frequency response of the associated electric circuits and the brilliance of the trace on the screen.

11. Timing Devices. These may be separate accurate clocks which send out electric impulses at regular intervals. The electric impulses actuate a marker which marks the record. Or they may be spring-mass systems vibrating at their natural frequencies which write directly on the record or interrupt a light beam at each swing. These systems can be excited continuously or intermittently.

12. Common Vibration Instruments. There is a wide variety of vibration instruments currently available and in common use. The basic principle of all is the same, but they utilize widely diversified methods of detection and recording. The number of instruments that are commercially available is too great to permit including them all in a brief discussion. Those discussed here were chosen as representative reliable instruments embodying various methods of recording, and they are, in general, readily available commercially; the chief criterion for their inclusion was the fact that the present authors have had personal experience in their use.

It should be remembered that all seismic instruments respond only to acceleration. The classification of instruments given here is that which is current in engineering circles. Instruments for the measurement of steady state vibration may be conveniently considered in three basic groups: accelerometers, vibrometers (indicating vibration meters), and vibrographs (recording vibration meters). The latter two groups may be subdivided further; (indicating) vibrometers may be classified as amplitude indicating and frequency indicating, and recording vibrographs may be classified as linear vibration recording and torsional vibration recording. The basic data concerning these instruments are presented in Tables 8-3 to 8-7. These tables

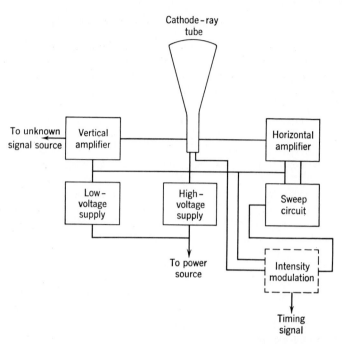

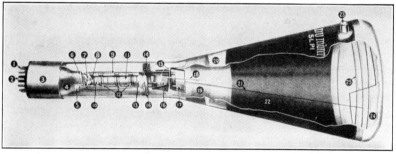

Fig. 8-5. A Typical High-Vacuum Hot-Cathode Low-Voltage Electron-Lens-Focus Cathode-Ray Tube

1—Base pins
2—Alignment key
3—Base collar
4—Stem
5—Getter
6—Press
7—Heater leads (heater inserted inside the cathode tubing)
8—Cathode support collar (Cathode inserted inside the grid tubing)
9—Ceramic supports (two supports diametrically opposed)
10—Control electrode
11—Focusing electrode
12—Support collar

13—Accelerating electrode
14—Mount supports
15—Mica deflection plate support rings
16—Deflection plate pair D_3–D_4
17—Deflection-plate pair D_1–D_2
18—Spring contact (makes contact with static shield)
19—Static shield
20—Glass envelope
21—Electron beam
22—Intensifier electrode
23—Intensifier terminal
24—Fluorescent screen material
25—Pattern traced by beam

314

list all the information required to determine the suitability of the instruments for measuring a particular type of vibration such as frequency range, amplitude range, and sensitivity; as well as other pertinent characteristics, such as weight, dimensions, and recording method. Every instrument is illustrated with a photograph and, where necessary, a schematic diagram; the number of the figure showing the instrument is listed in the tables.

In these tables the extremes of the amplitude and frequency ranges are not, in general, concurrent. At high frequencies the allowable maximum amplitude may be lower than the maximum stated, which applies at low frequencies. Conversely, at low frequencies the minimum measurable amplitude may be higher than the listed value, which applies at higher frequencies.

The recording instruments listed in Tables 8-3 to 8-7 can also be used to measure transient motions, provided the user realizes that the records need special interpretation as outlined later in section F.

C. INTERPRETATION OF VIBRATION RECORDS

13. General Considerations. The frequency or frequencies of vibration indicate the possible sources of excitation. The amplitude of vibration is a measure of its importance as a source of trouble (magnitude of fatigue stress, magnitude of dynamic forces).

Figure 8-26 shows a record from a 3-component linear accelerometer.

14. Frequency Determination in Records of Simple Harmonic Motion. The record will have time marks distributed along its length at equal time intervals. If the recording surface is moving at a constant velocity v, time will be increasing in the direction opposite to v, and the time signals (dots, scratches, or some uniformly shaped mark) will be spaced at equal length intervals. The time intervals are known from the clock or the natural period of the timer elastic pendulum.

If the recording-surface velocity v is *not* constant the length z_1 between two adjacent time signals is measured. The known time interval t_1 divided by z_1, $t_1/z_1 = s_z = $ *seconds per inch* over the interval measured. This time scale is used in the same interval on the motion record. In some mechanical instruments the recording is not made in line with the time marks; this must be taken into account when v is not constant. If v is constant, the length z_1 is used over a convenient number n of time intervals. Then $s_z = nt_1/z_1$.

In the time interval for which s_z has been determined, the length z_2 is measured between two peaks of the recorded simple harmonic motion, m complete cycles apart. m/z_2 then gives the number of complete cycles per inch.

The frequency in cycles per second is given by $\dfrac{1}{s_z}\dfrac{m}{z_2}$. If the recording surface velocity is constant and given in inches per second, $s_z = 1/v$ and $f = vm/z_2$.

In Fig. 8-26 $s_z = \dfrac{2\ \text{sec}}{4.64\ \text{in.}}$ and $\dfrac{m}{z_2} = \dfrac{9\ \text{cycles}}{3.67\ \text{in.}}$. Therefore, $\dfrac{1}{s_z}\cdot\dfrac{m}{z_2} = \dfrac{4.64}{2}\cdot\dfrac{9}{3.67}$

$= 5.7\ \dfrac{\text{cycles}}{\text{sec}} = 342\ \dfrac{\text{cycles}}{\text{min}}$.

TABLE 8-3

Instrument	Brush Crystal Accel., BL-301	Jacklin Accelerometer			Statham Accel. 50 g Unit	Westinghouse Crys. Accel.
		Angular Elements	Linear Elements			
			Low Freq.	High Freq.		
Practical frequency range, cps	Low frequency dependent on input impedance of amplifier. Square law output to approx. 2000 cps	35–55 cps	75–90 cps	175–200 cps	0–200	10–5000
Practical amplitude range, g's single	0.001–10	0.1–30 R/sec^2	0.01–2g	0.05–8g	±50	10–5000
Sensitivity	30V/0.001 in. at 500 cps or about 80 mv per g	$\frac{1}{8}$ to $\frac{1}{16}''$/R/sec^2	$\frac{3}{4}$ to $1\frac{1}{4}''$/g	$\frac{1}{8}$ to $\frac{3}{8}''$/g	20 mv full scale open circuit, 90 μa full scale closed circuit	0.62×10^{-12} coulombs per g
Direction of vibration	Perpendicular to large face. Can be oriented in any direction	About vert. and 2 horizontal axes	Along same three axes, mutually at right angles		Any one	Any one
Method of detection	Piezo elec. crystal (in bending)	Mechanical and optical levers			Strain-sensitive filament suspension	Piezoelec. crystal (in compression)
Method of recording	Oscillograph	Photographic			Oscillograph	Oscillograph
Natural frequency of element, cps	1500	50–75 cps	100–120 cps	250–300 cps	300	15,000

Weight, lb	0.4	Recorder (with 6 components) 45–50, control 30	⅛	0.6
Over-all dimensions, in.	3 × 1⅛	Recorder 8½ × 11 × 14¼ Control 11 × 5½ × 12	1 23/32 × 1 13/16 × 23/32	1D × 2
Power required	110 alternating volts	12 direct volts	8 direct or alternating volts at 40 ma	110 alternating volts for power amplifier
Accessory equipment required	Standard oscillograph equipment and filter	None	Standard oscillographic equipment	Standard oscillographic equipment and filter, voltage and power amplifier
Method of mounting	Clamped to or held against structure under test	Bolted or clamped to structure under test	Bolted or clamped to structure under test	Mounted on ½ in. 13 stud
General information			Units available from 0.6 to 500 g	
Method of clamping	None	Viscous—oil film between stationary and moving surfaces. Damping coeff. of 0.5 to 0.7 of critical over temperature range of 45–50°.	Organosilicone fluid	None
Figure	8-6	8-7	8-8	8-9
Manufacturer	The Brush Development Co, 3405 Perkins Ave., Cleveland, Ohio	H. M. Jacklin, 1436 W. 27th St, Indianapolis 73, Ind	Statham Laboratories, 9328 Santa Monica Blvd, Beverly Hills, Calif	Westinghouse Electric Corp, Electronics and X-Ray Division, 2516 Wilkins Ave. Baltimore 3, Md.

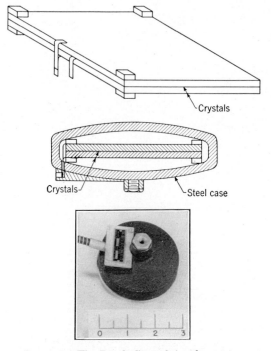

FIG. 8-6.   The Brush Crystal Accelerometer

The Brush crystal accelerometer utilizes the sensitive piezoelectric nature of Rochelle salt crystals.   As shown in the schematic diagram, two flat crystals, separated by a flat conducting strip, are supported on three corners, the fourth corner being unsupported.   Accelerations along an axis normal to the crystal faces causes bending of the crystals, which owing to the piezoelectric effect develop a voltage between their extreme faces.

As Rochelle salt is weak structurally and has a low melting point, the pickup should not be subjected continuously to accelerations greater than 10 g or temperatures higher than about 120°F.   Because of the sensitivity and compactness of this type of transducer, a similar pickup, used with a portable amplifier and meter, serves as a sensitive-vibration indicator (See the General Radio Vibration Meter, Fig. 8-11).

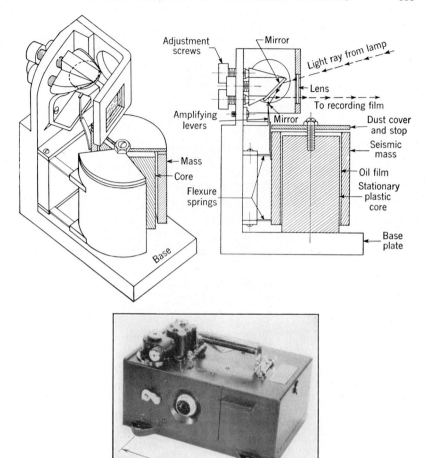

FIG. 8-7.   Jacklin Accelerometer

The Jacklin accelerometer is a medium-frequency instrument for recording simultaneously linear accelerations along and rotational accelerations about three mutually perpendicular axes.   The six acceleration records and a timing trace are obtained on photographic paper 4 in. wide, traveling at a speed of about 3 in./sec.   100-ft rolls of paper are accommodated in the paper magazine

The method of magnification of the motion of the element involves the use of a unique double-reed mechanical magnifying lever, shown in the schematic diagram of a linear element.   The motion of the mirror, attached at the juncture of the reeds, is in turn amplified by the light-beam–lens system comprising the optical lever.   The sensitivity of the instrument is such that it is suitable for recording the usual mechanical vibrations

A control box somewhat smaller than the accelerometer proper is used to provide motor drive for the paper and to control the taking of records

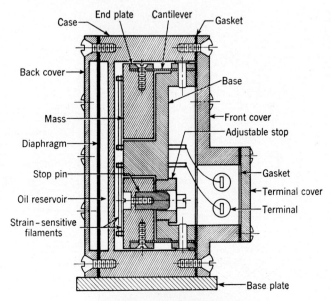

FIG. 8-8. The Statham Accelerometer

In the Statham accelerometer high sensitivity is attained by allowing the strain-sensitive wire to serve as a spring. In this manner, a high ratio of strain to imposed acceleration is attained. Although the sensitivity is high for a resistance-type pickup, it is generally necessary to use an amplifier to obtain optimum performance

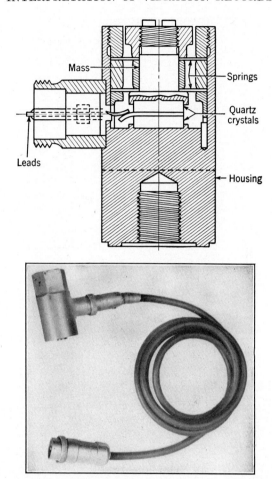

FIG. 8-9. The Westinghouse Crystal Accelerometer

This is a piezoelectric type of pickup, utilizing the relatively insensitive but mechanically strong quartz crystals as detector elements. Because of its high natural frequency and sturdy construction, this pickup is suitable for measurement of high accelerations and high-frequency vibrations. As this pickup has no damping, it is generally used with a low pass filler, especially in the measurement of shock, to eliminate the high-frequency "hash" due to the free vibrations of the sensitive element

TABLE 8-4

Instrument	Cordero Vibrometer	General Radio Vibration Meter and Shure Crystal Pickup	Westinghouse Hand Vibrometer	Askania Vibrograph
Practical frequency range, cpm	960–3000	120–30,000	600–6000	30–6000
Practical amplitude range, mils single	0.5–15	0.016–30,000	1–50	1–200
Direction of vibration	Any one	Any one	Any one	Any one
Method of detection	Mechanical lever	Piezocrystal pickup and integrating circuits	Direct measurement of motion of seismic weight relative to base with dial gage	Spring loaded pickup probe, probe attached to mechanical lever
Method of indication	Vibrating arm on scale	Amplitude is read on meter	Dial gage	Records with stylus on wax paper
Natural frequency of element, cpm	About 300	90,000	About 400	300
Weight, lb	2	Pickup 0.8, meter 23	4	3.2
Over-all dimensions, in.	6 × 2½ × 1	Pickup 2½ × 2½ × 2, meter 13 × 9 × 13	4D × 3	7 × 5 × 3
Power required	None	Self-contained batteries	None	Flashlight battery for timer
Method of applying to structure	Held against vibrating structure	Held or clamped against vibrating structure	Held against or set on vibrating structure	Hand-held with probe against vibrating structure
General remarks		Pickup is accelerometer. Integrating circuits in meter case permit reading of displacements. May be used with GR analyzer	Hand-held operation preferable	Capable of recording deflection up to inch if acceleration is less than 20 g
Figure	8-10	8-11	8-12	8-13
Manufacturer	American Instrument Co, 8020 Georgia Ave, Silver Spring, Md	General Radio Co, Cambridge, Mass	Westinghouse Electric Corp, Electronics & X-Ray Division, 2516 Wilkins Ave, Baltimore 3, Md.	(Manufacturer) U. S. Navy (Design based on German model)

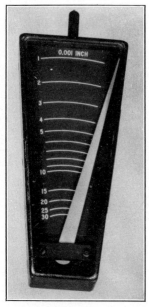

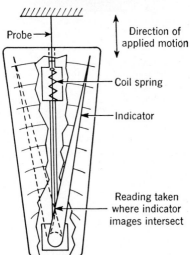

Fig. 8-10.   The Cordero Vibrometer

The cordero vibrometer is a hand-held amplitude-indicating instrument.   When it is held in the hand, with the probe kept in contact with the vibrating body, part of the arm as well as the instrument case, acts as a seismic mass.   The probe acts against a compression spring and is connected to the indicating pointer by a simple mechanical magnifying lever.   The amplitude of vibration is read on the radially graduated scale as the point of intersection of the adjacent sides of the two extreme positions of the indicator as seen owing to persistence of vision

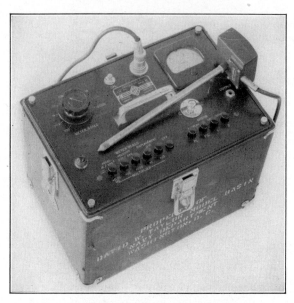

FIG. 8-11.   General Radio Vibration Meter

This is a portable general-purpose vibration-indicating outfit comprising a Rochelle salt-crystal pickup similar to that shown in Fig. 8-6 and a compact unit containing an amplifier, integrating circuits, and a sensitive voltmeter.   The pickup is sensitive to acceleration, and the amplitude of acceleration, velocity, or displacement may be read on the meter by use of the appropriate circuits, which are switched by pressing suitable button switches

This instrument is useful only for relatively steady vibrations.   It may, however, be used for recording vibrations by feeding its output into an oscillograph. In general, the acceleration velocity and displacement readings obtained with this instrument are not directly comparable, as small amplitude high-frequency vibrations predominate in the acceleration readings, whereas the lower-frequency vibrations of large amplitude predominate in the displacement readings

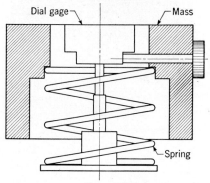

FIG. 8-12.   Westinghouse Hand Vibrometer

This instrument is the commercial prototype of a number of simple homemade vibration indicators that are widely used in field work for quick approximate measurements.   Hand vibrometers, in general, use the inertia of the hand as part of the seismic weight.   The suspended weight of this instrument is fairly heavy so that it may be set on a vibrating object and act seismically without the necessity of being held in the hand.   It is, however, preferable to use it held in the hand

The double amplitude of the vibration is indicated by the band swept out by the dial-gage pointer

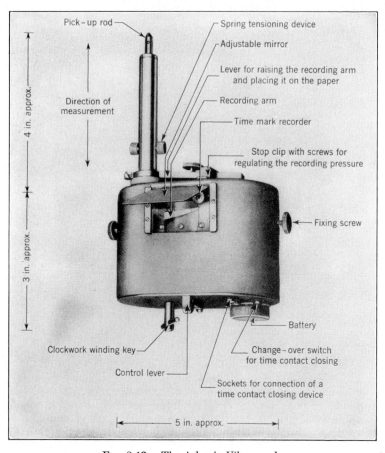

FIG. 8-13. The Askania Vibrograph

This is a hand-held instrument which records. The pickup rod is held against the vibrating body, and the main body of the instrument is held by one or both hands

TABLE 8-5

Instrument	Frahm's Reeds	Westinghouse Reed Vibrometer	General Radio Strobotac
Practical frequency range, cpm	Various frequency ranges from 800 to 30,000 (e.g. 800–1400, 1500–3000, etc.)	500–20,000	600–14,500
Method of detection	Resonant vibration of a reed at its natural frequency	Adjustment of length of reed to give proper frequency	Variable-frequency flashing light. Stroboscope principle
Method of indication	Reed with largest amplitude indicates correct frequency	Resonant vibration of reed at properly adjusted position	Flashing frequency indicated on scale
Weight, lb	(Each assembly of reeds) about 2	About ½	9½
Over-all dimensions, in.	(Other dimensions available) about 6 × 2 × 4	9¼ × 1¾ × 1¼	7½ × 8½ × 9½
Power required	None	None	105–125 alternating volts
Method of applying to structure	Set on or near or held against vibrating structure	Held against vibrating structure	Held in hand or set on convenient base
Remarks		Amplitude at vibration of end of reed gives rough indication of actual vibration; amplitude magnification 300–500	Dim surroundings required for effective use
Figure	8-14	8-15	8-16
Manufacturer	James C. Biddle Co, 1316 Arch St, Philadelphia, 7, Pa	Westinghouse Electric Corp, Electronics and X-Ray Division, 2516 Wilkins Ave, Baltimore 3, Md.	General Radio Co, Cambridge, Mass

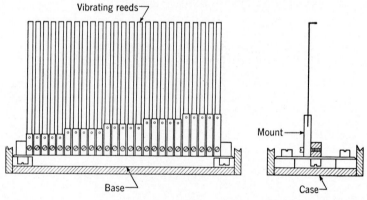

FIG. 8-14.   Frahm's Reeds

This instrument contains a series of cantilever reeds, accurately tuned to frequencies separated by definite even intervals, generally about 1 per cent of the average frequency.   Because of inherently low damping, the tuning of the reeds is rather sharp, and there is no difficulty in determining the proper frequency at moderate amplitudes of vibration.   By careful observation and interpolation vibration frequencies may be determined with an error less than the interval between the indicated frequencies.   Frahm's reeds are widely used in the determination of the rotational speeds of motors and other rotating equipment, which usually generate enough vibration to indicate on this instrument

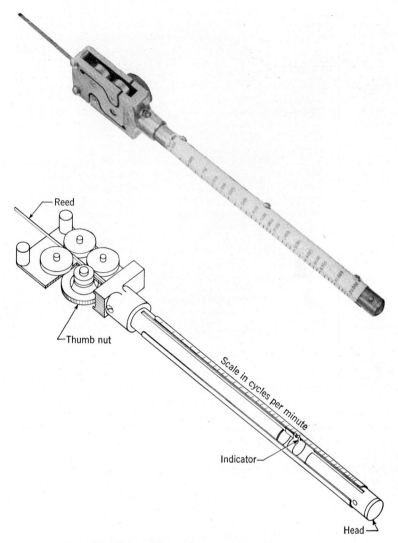

FIG. 8-15. Westinghouse Reed Vibrometer

The Westinghouse reed vibrometer is based, like the Frahm's reeds, on the determination of frequency by resonant vibration of a cantilever reed. This instrument, however, uses a single reed, continuously variable in length, moving in a cylindrical tube rather than a set of fixed reeds. The frequency is indicated on a scale by an indicator line that moves with the enclosed end of the reed. The advantage of this method is apparent—the entire band of mechanical frequencies ordinarily found is covered in one instrument. This is counterbalanced to a certain extent by the time and difficulty sometimes encountered in accurately determining a frequency, particularly when the vibration is unsteady

FIG. 8-16.   Strobotac

The Strobotac is a portable adjustable-frequency stroboscope for determining vibration frequencies and rotational speeds, as well as for the inspection by "stopping" motion of rotating shafts and other members.   As its light output is relatively low, it must be used in rather dim light to be effective or in conjunction with higher-intensity flashing-light sources

TABLE 8-6

Instrument	Cox Vibr. Recorder	Consolidated Type-4-102 Velocity Pickup	TMB Pallograph	Westinghouse LE Vibrograph	Cambridge Universal Vibrograph
Practical freq. cpm	400–5000,	Flat ±7%, 420–12,000; flat ±5%, 480–12,000; for amplitudes ≤0.050 in.	40–1800	600–6,000	400–3000 cpm linear; 200–5000 cpm torsional
Practical ampl. range, mils single	2–350	Vertical 700, horizontal 1000	1–250	0.1–15	1:1 stylus 2–300 mils single linear, 0.05°–5° torsional
Sensitivity or magnification	Adj. about 1, 2, 4, or 8	110 mv/in./sec ±5% up to 300 mils; decreases with increasing amplitude	Adjustable 2, 4, or 6	8½ mech. 40 with microscope	1:1 and 5:1, 0.035 in./deg
Direction of vibration	Vertical or horizontal (separate adapters required)	Any direction	Vertical	Any one	Vertical or horizontal or torsional (spring added for vertical)
Method of detection	Motion of seismic wt. transmitted by bell crank	Seismically mounted magnet moving along a coil	Seismic pendulum with mech. lever	Seismic weight with mechanical lever	Seismic weight with mechanical transmission of motion
Method of recording	Stylus on waxed paper	Oscillographic	Stylus on waxed paper	Stylus on celluloid film	Stylus on celluloid film, 10 ft long 20 mm wide, 4 speeds 3, 9, 15, and 21 mm/sec
Method of damping	Friction of stylus on wax	Fluid, $n = 0.64$	Air dashpot, adj.	Friction of stylus on celluloid	Friction of stylus on celluloid
Natural freq. of element, cpm	About 280	540 (with damping fluid)	20	400	220 horizontal, 270 vertical, 420 torsional
Weight, lb	29	⅝	65	10	12.8 with torsional unit 20.5
Over-all dimensions, in.	12 × 10 × 9	2¾ × 11 15/16 D	18½ × 14½ × 9½	7½ × 5 × 4¾	6.5 × 3.5 × 4.75
Power required	110 alternating volts and 6 direct volts	110 alternating volts	110 alternating volts	None	6 direct volts for timer
Accessory equip. required	None	Standard oscillographic equipment	Synchronous timer	None	None

TABLE 8-6 (*Continued*)

Instrument	Cox Vibr. Recorder	Consolidated Type-4-102 Velocity Pickup	TMB Pallograph	Westinghouse LE Vibrograph	Cambridge Universal Vibrograph
Method of mounting on vibrating structure	Set on, clamped or bolted	Set on, clamped or bolted	Set on, clamped or bolted	Same as others or may be held in hand and used with probe held against vibrating structure	Set on, clamped, or bolted
General information	This is the Cox torsiograph adapted for linear vibration	Pickup impedance d-c coil resistance 900 ohms, non-inductive at 50 cps, output changes $+ 1\%$ per 14°F	Horizontal model with similar characteristics also available		Adapter added to convert vibrograph to torsiograph. Instrument may be used as hand-held instrument with probe for spot-vibration recording. If hand-held, should not be used below 450 cpm. As probe instrument it is capable of recording deflections up to $\frac{3}{4}$ in. as long as the acceleration is less then $6\frac{1}{4}g$
Figure		8-18	8-19	8-20	8-21
Manufacturer	Commercial Research Laboratories, 20 Bartlett Ave, Detroit, Mich	Consolidated Engineering Corp, 620 North Lake Ave, Pasadena 4, Calif	David Taylor Model Basin, U. S. Navy Dept, Washington, D. C.	Westinghouse Electric Corp, Electronics and X-Ray Division, 2516 Wilkins Ave, Baltimore, 3, Md.	Cambridge Instrument Co, Grand Central Station, New York 17

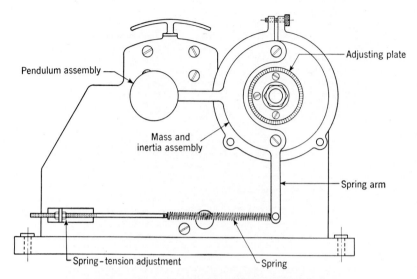

Pendulum assembly

Adjusting plate

Mass and
inertia assembly

Spring arm

Spring-tension adjustment

Spring

FIG. 8-17.   Cox Vibration Recorder

This is the Cox Torsiograph (see Fig. 8-22) modified to record linear vibrations
by the addition of a weight to the pulley plus a balancing spring, converting it to
a horizontal pendulum, for measuring vertical vibrations.   Conversion to a horizontal vibrograph is accomplished by adding a similar weight without the balancing
spring, so that the pendulum arm is vertical

The ready convertibility of this instrument to recording linear vibrations, both
vertical and horizontal, as well as torsional vibrations, is one of its many com-
mendable features

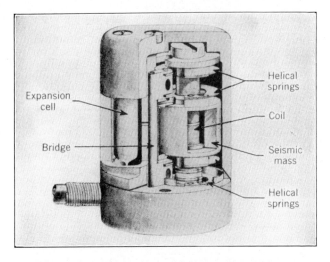

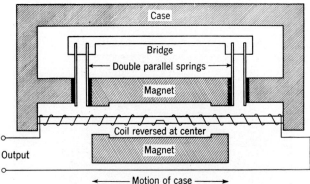

FIG. 8-18.   The Consolidated Type 4-102 Velocity Pickup

The open-circuit voltage of this pickup is proportional to the *relative* velocity between the magnet and the coil fixed to the case.   Only under certain conditions is this proportional to the absolute velocity of the case

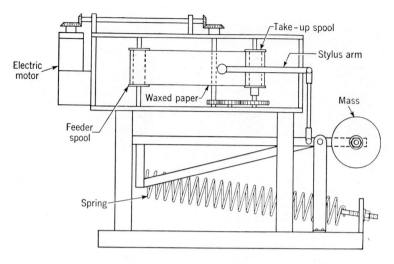

FIG. 8-19.   Taylor Model Basin Pallograph

The pallograph is intended for the measurement on shipboard of vertical vibrations which cover a frequency range of approximately 60 to 2000 cpm.   For this reason, the type-V pallograph, illustrated above, has the exceptionally low natural frequency, for a portable instrument, of 20 cpm; this frequency is attained by utilizing the principle of instability.   The choice of three magnification factors permits recording of small as well as large amplitudes of vibration with reasonable precision.   The type-H pallograph, which is used to record horizontal vibrations, is similar to the Type V, although it has a somewhat higher natural frequency

FIG. 8-20.   Westinghouse L. E. Vibrograph

The L. E. vibrograph is a compact portable instrument for recording practically all linear vibrations ordinarily encountered in mechanical systems.   Although the upper limit of amplitude is rather low, the high mechanical magnification obtained (8X) partially compensates for this.   The built-in reed timer is a convenience affording complete independence of external power

The records obtained are generally analyzed by use of a special microscope furnished with the vibrograph.   It is occasionally inconvenient to use this method, particularly when the record obtained does not approximate a pure sine wave

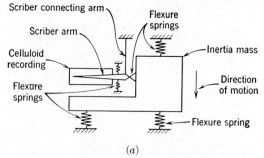

(a)

FIG. 8-20a.   Westinghouse L. E. Vibrograph, Schematic Representation

As shown, the instrument records the relative motion between the case and the inertia mass.   Provision is also made for locking the inertia mass to the case; the instrument can then be hand-held and the scriber connecting arm, after being detached from the case, is used as a probe and is held against the vibrating body.

Fig. 8-21.   Cambridge Universal Vibrograph

In this view the instrument is shown arranged to measure horizontal vibrations. It can be changed to measure vertical vibrations.   Another attachment makes the instrument suitable for the measurement of torsional vibrations.   It can also be rigged to be used as a directly connected instrument

The recording surface, celluloid, receives the record by plastic flow under a needle with a rounded point.   The record can be viewed through a microscope or projection viewer

TABLE 8-7

Instrument	Cox Torsiograph	General Motors Mechanical Torsiograph	Sperry–MIT Torsional Vibration Pickup	Phase-Shift Torsiograph
Practical frequency range, cpm	600–5000	1000–20,000	900–60,000	500–50,000
Practical amplitude range, degrees single	0.03–3.5	0.05–2.5	0.075–5	Depends on pickup gear and engine speed about 0.03–5
Sensitivity or magnification	About 0.4 in. per degree (max)	About 0.3 in. per degree	About 1.2 mv per degree per second	Depends on pickup gear about ½ in. on oscillograph screen per degree
Method of detection	Inertia element, bell-crank transmission	Inertia element, mechanical lever	Inertia element, magnet rotating about coil	Phase shift in gear-tooth carrier wave
Method of recording	Stylus on waxed paper	Stylus on sensitized paper	Oscillographic	Oscillographic
Natural frequency of element, cpm	About 300	480	600	
Method of damping	Friction of stylus on wax	Inherent mechanical friction	Dry friction	No mechanical damping required electrical damping in detector unit
Weight, lb	28½	9½	3½	Detectors 12½ and 24½, pickups variable
Over-all dimensions, in.	12 × 9¼ × 9½	6¼D × 10	3D × 5	Detector 14 × 8 × 8 Power supply 16 × 9 × 6
Power required	110 alternating volts and 6 direct volts	None	110 alternating volts	110 alternating volts
Accessory equipment required	None	Measuring scale	Sperry calibrator, amplifier, and string oscillograph	Cathode-ray oscillograph and camera
Method of attaching to shaft	Attached by belt on a pulley	Fastened to end of shaft with collet adapter	Fastened to end of shaft with set of screws or collet adapter	Pickup depends on job pickup gear designed for job—may be welded anywhere along shaft
General information	Amplitude range and sensitivity may be varied by use of pulleys of different diameter		Pickup measures torsional-vibration velocity, used with integrating circuit	Principal component of instrument is detector unit. See explanation under figure
Figure	8-22	8-23	8-24	8-25
Manufacturer	Commercial Research Laboratories, 20 Bartlett Ave, Detroit 3, Mich	General Motors Corp, Research Laboratories Div, Department ME-6, Detroit, Mich	Consolidated Eng Corp, 620 North Lake Ave, Pasadena 4, Calif	General Motors Corp, Research Laboratories Div, Department ME-6, Detroit, Mich

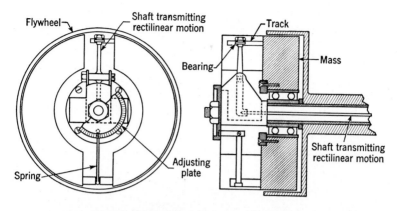

FIG. 8-22. The Cox Torsiograph

The Cox instrument is a modernized version of the Geiger torsiograph, which was one of the most versatile and well-designed of the early vibration instruments and still ranks high among mechanical instruments. The bell-crank arrangement, shown in the sketch, converts the relative rotational displacement between the seismic mass and the pulley into linear motion of the transmitting shaft. This motion in turn is imparted to, and magnified by, the stylus, which records on waxed paper

In recording torsional vibrations, the pulley is connected to the test shaft by a belt either of cloth or of thin steel strip. This belt is made as short as possible to reduce the errors introduced by the flexibility of the belt. The addition of an eccentric weight to the seismic weight converts it to a pendulum, permitting measurement of linear vibrations (see Fig. 8-17)

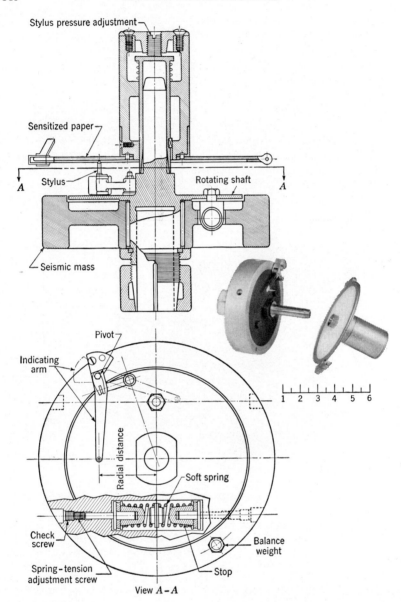

FIG. 8-23.   The G. M. Mechanical Torsiograph

This mechanical torsiograph is a relatively heavy pickup that is clamped to the end of the shaft by a collet adapter. The recording means is a stylus writing on specially sensitized paper. The vibration is recorded in polar-diagram form; this permits immediate determination of the order of vibration without harmonic analysis, but the speed of the engine must be accurately determined independently

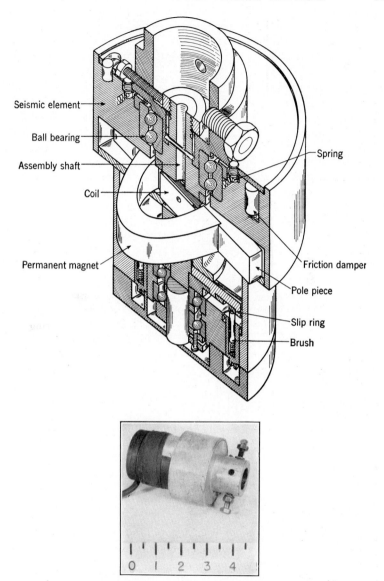

Seismic element

Ball bearing

Assembly shaft

Coil

Permanent magnet

Spring

Friction damper

Pole piece

Slip ring

Brush

0   1   2   3   4

Fig. 8-24.   The Sperry–MIT Torsional Vibration Pickup
This is a velocity-type pickup similar in principle to the Sperry–MIT linear pickups. The relative motion between the seismically suspended mass and the shaft of the pickup causes rotation of a coil fixed to the shaft with respect to a radial magnetic field. The voltage developed is proportional to the velocity of this motion; an integrating circuit is generally used to obtain records in terms of the amplitude of torsional vibration

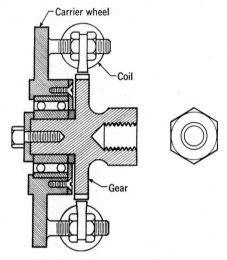

FIG. 8-25.   The Phase-Shift Torsiograph

The phase-shift torsiograph consists of a group of basic members which may be adapted for many different applications in the measurement of torsional vibrations. These members are a steel gear which is attached to the shaft, two iron-core coils and the detector unit with power supply.   The gear may be mounted anywhere along the shaft and the two coils are rigidly supported, close to the gear teeth, at the opposite ends of a diameter.   Passage of the gear teeth by the coils generates a high-frequency voltage; any deviating of the shaft, and thereby the gear, from uniform angular velocity such as that due to torsional vibration, causes a shift in the phase of successive cycles.   By means of an ingenious detecting circuit, this phase shift is used to indicate the torsional vibration on the screen of a cathode-ray oscillograph

The pickup shown was made up by the authors for use on the end of the shaft of a small engine.   In this pickup, the coil-supporting disk rides on ball-bearings, and is snubbed to prevent it from rotating

15. Amplitude Determination in Records of Simple Harmonic Motion.
When the record has a clear-cut line and is at one level on the recording surface, the fine straight-line envelope of the peaks is drawn first touching the tops above several complete cycles.   A lower straight-line envelope is drawn through the inside of the valleys, again touching the top of the record lines. The distance between these envelopes is the double amplitude of the record. If this distance is x_1, the amplitude is $A = x_1/2$.   The actual amplitude of the motion measured is $A = x_1/2\mu$.   Where μ is the magnification or amplification of the recording mechanism, μ is determined by the calibration process

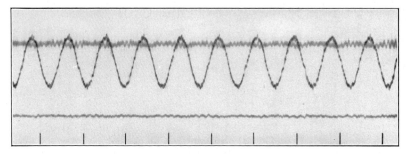

FIG. 8-26.   Record from Three-Component Linear Accelerometer
Top trace—Longitudinal vibration
Center trace—Transverse vibration
Bottom trace—Vertical vibration
Undamped natural frequency = 100 cps

$$\text{Undamped } p^2 = 390{,}000 \ \frac{\text{rad}^2}{\text{sec}^2}$$

$$n = 0.6$$

Time scale $\frac{1}{5}$ sec per mark
Amplitude scale 1.3 in./g

or is calculated from the known kinematic, optical, or electrical characteristics of the instrument.

In an acceleration record the measured double amplitude is x_1 in.   The single amplitude is $x_1/2$.   The calibration scale is $s_x \dfrac{\text{in./sec}^2}{\text{in.}}$.   In Fig. 8-26 $x_1 = \dfrac{1}{2}$ in.; $\dfrac{x_1}{2} = \dfrac{1}{4}$ in.; $s_x = 297 \ \dfrac{\text{in./sec}^2}{\text{in.}}$.   Therefore, the amplitude of the measured acceleration is $\dfrac{s_x x_1}{2} = \dfrac{297}{4} = 74.2$ in./sec^2.

If the record wanders up and down on the recording surface a fine straight line is drawn below the record parallel to the direction of the known or expected zero line.   From this line the vertical distance to the under edge of the valleys (lower peaks) of several successive cycles are measured, $x_1, x_2, \cdot \cdot \cdot x_n$, and the vertical distances to the under edge of the upper peaks between are measured x_1', x_2' $\cdots$ x_n'. The double amplitude is $x = \dfrac{\displaystyle\sum_{1}^{n}(x_m' - x_m)}{n}$. Even

if the record does not wander vertically, but the successive amplitudes are not exactly alike and average double amplitudes are desired, this expression can be used.

16. Harmonic Analysis of Periodic-Motion Records. If the record shows periodic motion which is not simple harmonic motion, harmonic analysis of the record will indicate the amplitudes and phase relationships of the component simple-harmonic motion. A typical section of the record is selected

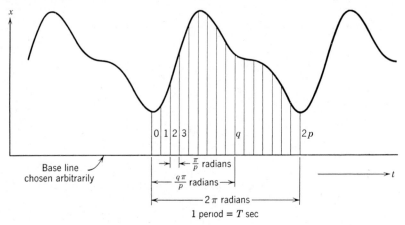

FIG. 8-27. Typical Record Prepared for Fourier Analysis

for analysis. The section should be magnified photographically or by projection until it is large enough for accurate measurements. Figure 8-27 shows a typical section prepared for analysis. The record is to be replaced by the analytical expression:

$$x = a_0 + \sum_{n=1}^{n=p} a_n \cos n\theta + \sum_{n=1}^{n=p-1} b_n \sin n\theta$$

The typical cycle chosen can start and end at any two similar phases. The length of one cycle is 2π radians for the fundamental harmonic and represents $2\pi n$ radians for the nth harmonic. The length of one cycle is divided accurately into an even number of intervals $2p$ in number. Each interval represents π/p radians for the fundamental. A base line accurately parallel to the zero line of the record (or the envelope of the record) is placed at any convenient position below the record. Ordinates are erected perpendicular to the base line at the $2p$ equal intervals. These ordinates are measured in inches between upper (or lower) edge of the base line and the upper (or lower) edge of the record trace giving a series of values x_1, x_2, $\cdots$ x_{2p}. Then,

$$a_0 = \frac{1}{2p} \sum_{q=1}^{q=2p} x_q \tag{16}$$

$$a_n = \frac{1}{p} \sum_{q=1}^{q=2p} x_q \cos n\frac{q\pi}{p}, \quad (n = 1, 2, \cdots, p-1) \tag{17}$$

$$a_p = \frac{1}{2p} \sum_{q=1}^{q=2p} x_q \cos q\pi \tag{18}$$

$$b_n = \frac{1}{p} \sum_{q=1}^{q=2p} x_q \sin n\frac{q\pi}{p} \tag{19}$$

The accuracy of a_n and b_n decreases as $n \to p$. In order to achieve fair accuracy in the coefficients the number of ordinates $2p$ chosen for the analysis should be $4n_{max}$ where n_{max} is the highest harmonic desired in the analysis.

$$a_n \cos n\theta + b_n \sin n\theta = \sqrt{a_n{}^2 + b_n{}^2} \sin\left(n\theta + \tan^{-1}\frac{a_n}{b_n}\right)$$

Also

$$a_n \cos n\theta + b_n \sin n\theta = \sqrt{a_n{}^2 + b_n{}^2} \cos\left(n\theta - \tan^{-1}\frac{b_n}{a_n}\right)$$

It should be noted that

$$\sin\left(n\theta + \tan^{-1}\frac{a_n}{b_n}\right) \text{ has the value 0 and positive slope}$$

when
$$\theta = -\frac{1}{n} \tan^{-1}\frac{a_n}{b_n}$$

and that $\cos\left(n\theta - \tan^{-1}\frac{bn}{an}\right)$ has the value 1 when

$$\theta = +\frac{1}{n} \tan^{-1}\frac{b_n}{a_n}$$

although the expressions just given are the basis of all numerical harmonic analysis, the calculations indicated are long and tedious. Many rapid methods of calculating harmonic coefficients have been devised.

12-*Ordinate Schemes.* If only the three lowest harmonics in a record are of interest a 12-ordinate scheme will give good accuracy. In this scheme $2p = 12$, $2\pi/2p = 30°$, and

$$a_0 = \frac{1}{12} \sum_{q=1}^{q=12} x_q$$

$$a_n = \tfrac{1}{6} \sum_{q=1}^{q=12} x_q \cos nq \times 30°$$

$$b_n = \tfrac{1}{6} \sum_{q=1}^{q=12} x_q \sin nq \times 30°$$

$a_0 = \tfrac{1}{12}[x_1 + x_2 + x_3 + x_4 + x_5 + x_6 + x_7 + x_8 + x_9 + x_{10} + x_{11} + x_{12}]$

$a_1 = \tfrac{1}{6}[0.866(x_1 - x_5 - x_7 + x_{11}) + 0.500(x_2 - x_4 - x_8 + x_{10})$
$$+ 1.000(x_{12} - x_6)]$$

$b_1 = \tfrac{1}{6}[0.500(x_1 + x_5 - x_7 - x_{11}) + 0.866(x_2 + x_4 - x_8 - x_{10})$
$$+ 1.00(x_3 - x_9)]$$

$a_2 = \tfrac{1}{6}[0.500(x_1 + x_5 + x_7 + x_{11} - x_2 - x_4 - x_8 - x_{10})$
$$+ 1.000(x_6 + x_{12} - x_3 - x_9)]$$

$b_2 = \tfrac{1}{6}[0.866(x_1 + x_2 + x_7 + x_8 - x_4 - x_5 - x_{10} - x_{11})]$

$a_3 = \tfrac{1}{6}(x_4 + x_8 + x_{12} - x_2 - x_6 - x_{10})$

$b_3 = \tfrac{1}{6}(x_1 + x_5 + x_9 - x_3 - x_7 - x_{11})$

12-ordinate schemes and 24-ordinate schemes for rapid calculation of harmonic coefficients are given by Whittaker and Robinson.[15]

Runge's 48-ordinate scheme is given by Den Hartog.*

Beevers and Lipson[17] have devised strips of cardboard on which are printed values of $C \cos mnx/p$ for various values of $C = 1, 2, 3, \cdots 100$ and various values of m and n. These strips carry out much of the computation needed in harmonic analysis. A method of applying Beevers and Lipson strips is described by Rose.[18]

Errors in Calculating Fourier Coefficients. If the probable error in measuring the ordinates x_1, x_2, $\cdots x_n$ is e in., then the probable error in any linear combination of these ordinates $\lambda_1 x_1 + \lambda_2 x_2 + \cdots + \lambda_n x_n$ is $(\lambda_1{}^2 + \lambda_2{}^2 + \cdots + \lambda_n{}^2)^{1/2}e$. In the linear combinations of x_1, x_2, $\cdots x_n$ given previously in the schedule for a 12-ordinate calculation, the λ's are all equal to 1. Therefore if all the ordinates are measured with a scale with divisions of $\frac{1}{10}$ in., the error in reading each ordinate can easily be ±0.02 in. The percentage probable error in a_0 is then $\dfrac{100 \sqrt{12} \times 0.02}{12 a_0} \% = \dfrac{0.58}{a_0} \%$. If the calculated value $a_0 = 0.58$ in., the percentage probable error is 1 per cent. The probable error in a_3 under the same conditions is $\dfrac{100 \sqrt{6} \times 0.02}{6 a_3} \% = \dfrac{0.815}{a_3} \%$. If the calculated value $a_3 = 0.4$ in., the probable error is 2 per cent. A discussion of probable error in calculating Fourier coefficients is given by Whittaker and Robinson.†

* See reference 16, p 25.
† See reference 15, p 280.

Other errors in calculation can arise from uneven spacing of the ordinates, from the ordinates being erected slightly off the vertical to the base line, and from the base line being laid off not exactly parallel to the true zero line of the record.

The only way to avoid these errors is to use enlarged records, microscope length measurement, and machine-like accuracy in spacing and erecting ordinates and in drawing the measuring base line.

If the record has been magnified m times the true value of a_n and b_n for the records are those found previously divided by m. If the instrument has a magnifying factor of μ, these values must be divided again by μ to get the actual values of the amplitudes of the harmonics of the motion being measured.

17. Instrumental Dynamic Errors in Records of Periodic Motion. Dynamic errors occur when parts of the transmitting, magnifying, and recording

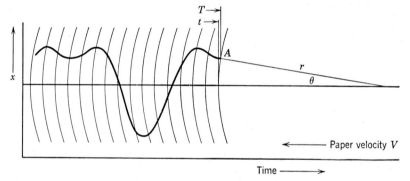

FIG. 8-28.   The Effect of a Pivoted Pen on Record Distortion

system get near to or into resonance with the frequency being measured. Calibration reveals these resonances, and the true magnification at these frequencies can be corrected by the calibration factor.

18. Pivoted Pen Recording Errors. Figure 8-28 shows the basis for kinematic errors on records made by pivoted pens or styli.

The correct value of the ordinate is $X = r\theta$. A vertical ordinate passed through the record measured from the true zero line of the record is $X_1 = r \sin \theta = r \sin \dfrac{X}{r} \approx X\left[1 - \dfrac{1}{6}\left(\dfrac{X}{r}\right)^2\right]$. This is not a source of serious error since $\dfrac{X_1}{X} = 0.99$ even if $X_1 = \dfrac{r}{4}$. The error in time is far more important. The apparent time T for the vertical ordinate X_1 is related to the true time t which should be associated with point A as follows:

$$T = t + \frac{r}{v}\left(1 - \cos\theta\right) = t + \frac{r}{v}\left(1 - \cos\frac{X}{r}\right) \approx t + \frac{1}{2}\frac{r}{v}\left(\frac{X}{r}\right)^2$$

A series of ordinates erected at equal time intervals would cut the record at points not actually associated with the time instants indicated by the position of the ordinate. A series of ordinates which actually passed through the record at points equally spaced in time would not be equally spaced on the true zero line of the record. In a harmonic analysis based on equally spaced ordinates X the errors in amplitude and phase relationship become greater as the frequency of the harmonic increases. The errors in time may easily become very large in comparison with the period T of the higher harmonics.

Correcting faulty analysis due to pivoted-pen errors is a useless process which can be avoided by laying circular arcs equally spaced along the true center line (the line traced by the pivot of the stylus) with radii equal to the radius of the stylus. This will give the correct time for each point on the record trace. Vertical ordinates measured from any arbitrarily chosen base line parallel to the true zero line will be equal to $a_0 + X\left[1 - \dfrac{1}{6}\left(\dfrac{X}{r}\right)^2\right]$ or to $a_0 + X$ to within an accuracy of 1 per cent for $X = r/4$. In this equation a_0 is the vertical distance between the true zero line and the arbitrarily chosen base line. Chords measured from the intersection of the arc on the true zero line and the record yield $X\left[1 - \dfrac{1}{24}\left(\dfrac{X}{r}\right)^2\right]$ or X to within an accuracy of 1 per cent for $X = \frac{1}{2}r$.

D. Calibration of Vibration Instruments

19. General Technique of Calibration. All steady-state vibration motions consist of a combination of one or more simple harmonic motions having different amplitudes and different phase angles.

$$X = a_0 + \Sigma a_n \cos \omega_n t + \Sigma b_n \sin \omega_n t$$

For this type of motion it is only necessary to calibrate the instruments by subjecting them to a simple-harmonic motion of known and controllable amplitude and frequency.

The purposes of calibration are:

1. To ascertain or check the magnification or amplification factor of the transmitting and indicating or recording elements.

2. To check the linearity of the magnification—that is, to locate kinematic and dynamic distortions of the magnification due to backlash, clearances, or nonlinear elements in the mechanical transmitting system or to feedback and electric or mechanical resonances in the mechanism or circuits.

3. To ascertain the distortion of the indication or record due to vibratory motions in directions other than that being measured. An ideal calibration would subject the instrument to linear vibration along all three of its principal axes and to torsional vibration around all three principal axes, indicating the corrective measures to be taken.

4. To ascertain the dynamic characteristics of the pickup units—its natural frequencies and damping constants.

A calibrator which creates simple-harmonic motion will suffice to calibrate displacement, velocity, and acceleration meters for steady-state vibration.

If the motion of the calibrator is $x = x_0 \sin \omega t$, the velocity will be $\dot{x} = x_0\omega \cos \omega t$, and the acceleration will be $\ddot{x} = -x_0\omega^2 \sin \omega t$.

20. Calibration of Directly Connected Instruments. The micrometer dial gage (Fig. 8-29) is the most commonly used directly connected vibration instrument. Its "finger" or probe is pressed down on the vibration

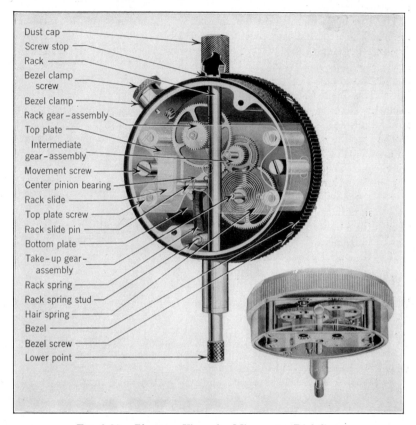

Dust cap
Screw stop
Rack
Bezel clamp
    screw
Bezel clamp
Rack gear – assembly
Top plate
Intermediate
gear – assembly
Movement screw
Center pinion bearing
Rack slide
Top plate screw
Rack slide pin
Bottom plate
Take – up gear –
    assembly
Rack spring
Rack spring stud
Hair spring
Bezel
Bezel screw
Lower point

FIG. 8-29.   Phantom View of a Micrometer Dial Gage

The micrometer dial gage is designed to measure static deflections or very slow variable deflections.   For many years it has been used by engineers to measure vibration amplitudes.   It is only useful on simple harmonic motions.   The width of the blur made by the vibration indicating hand gives the double amplitude of the simple-harmonic motions being measured

body, the body of the gage is held fixed in space, and the blur of the hand on the dial face indicates the double amplitude of the motion. This procedure involves four assumptions: (1) that the finger stays in contact with the vibrating body, (2) that the body or case of the gages is held motionless, (3) that the motion of the needle is not distorted by kinematic errors of the internal mechanism (backlash clearance in the gearing of the gage) or dynamical distortions of the hand or internal mechanism, and (4) that the motion being measured is simple-harmonic motion.

The ordinary micrometer dial gage is designed for use under static conditions or on surfaces which are moving slowly. It is not surprising that it develops errors in reading when used to measure amplitudes on bodies which are vibrating rapidly. Weiss[19] discusses these errors and their detection.

The two main sources of error in dial-gage-vibration amplitude readings are backlash error and "jumping."[19] Backlash errors appear when the inertia forces of the moving parts of the gage overcome the torque of the small hairspring which ordinarily takes up the backlash clearance. These errors appear at a definite frequency for each type of dial gage and are independent of the initial tension in the main gage spring. They can only be eliminated by using the gage below the definite frequency or by introducing a stiffer hairspring into the gage.

The amplitude and frequency limitations of dial gages can be determined on a calibrating table by listening for the audible chattering which develops when contact between the finger and the table is broken.

If p = the natural circular frequency of the dial gage in radians per second

ω = the circular frequency of the simple-harmonic motion being measured in radians per second

x = the amplitude of the simple-harmonic motion at audible loss of contact in inches

Δ = the initial total compression of the gage spring in inches

$\delta = \dfrac{\text{constant friction force of dial-gage mechanism}}{\text{spring constant of dial gage}}$

Then the gage readings are accurate until

$$\frac{x}{2(\Delta + \delta)} = \frac{p^2}{\omega^2 - p^2} \tag{20}$$

which can be expressed in terms of frequency ratio as

$$\frac{\omega^2}{p^2} = 1 + \frac{2(\Delta + \delta)}{x} \tag{21}$$

If, on the calibrator, audible separation occurs at an amplitude x_1 at a circular frequency ω_1 and occurs again for a smaller amplitude x_2 at a higher frequency ω_2 while Δ is maintained at a constant value, then

$$p^2 = \frac{x_1\omega_1{}^2 - x_2\omega_2{}^2}{x_1 - x_2} \tag{22}$$

and

$$2(\Delta + \delta) = \frac{x_1x_2\,(\omega_2{}^2 - \omega_1{}^2)}{x_1\omega_1{}^2 - x_2\omega_2{}^2} \tag{23}$$

$\Delta = \Delta_1 + \Delta_0$ where Δ_1 is the known additional compression introduced into the finger spring and Δ_0 is an unknown amount of spring compression existing when the finger is extended to the dial-gage finger stop.   The magnitude of Δ_0 can be determined by a process indicated by Weiss.[19]   Weiss also indicates another procedure for determining δ experimentally.

21. Theory of the Ideal Seismic Pickup.   The relationship between x, the relative motion between the seismic mass and the case, and the motion y for an ideal seismic pickup with lumped constants is

$$\ddot{x} + 2np\dot{x} + p^2 x = -\ddot{y} \tag{24}$$

where y = motion being measured
$\quad x$ = relative displacement between mass and case
$\quad m$ = mass of seismic weight
$\quad k$ = spring constant of spring
$\quad c$ = equivalent viscous damping constant
$\quad c_c = 2\sqrt{km}$, the critical damping constant
$\quad n = \dfrac{c}{c_c}$, the damping ratio
$\quad p^2 = \dfrac{k}{m}$, the square of the natural circular frequency of the pickup

When
$$y = y_0 \sin \omega t \tag{25}$$
the steady-state solution is

$$x = y_0 \frac{\omega^2/p^2}{\sqrt{4n^2 \dfrac{\omega^2}{p^2} + \left(1 - \dfrac{\omega^2}{p^2}\right)^2}} \sin\left(\omega t - \tan^{-1} \frac{2n\dfrac{\omega}{p}}{1 - \dfrac{\omega^2}{p^2}}\right) \tag{26}$$

If $\omega/p \geq 4$ and $n < 0.1$,
$$x \approx -y_0 \sin \omega t \tag{27}$$

and the pickup is a displacement meter.
   If $\omega/p \leq 0.6$ and $n \approx 0.65$,

$$x \approx \frac{1}{p^2} y_0 \omega^2 \sin \omega t \tag{28}$$

and the pickup is an accelerometer in this range.

When $n^2 = \dfrac{1}{2} - \dfrac{1}{4}\dfrac{\omega^2}{p^2}$,

$$\sqrt{4n^2 \frac{\omega^2}{p^2} + \left(1 - \frac{\omega^2}{p^2}\right)^2} = 1 \tag{29}$$

When $n^2 = \dfrac{1}{2} - \dfrac{1}{5.6}\dfrac{\omega_1^2}{p^2}$,

$$\frac{\partial}{\partial n} \int_0^{\frac{\omega_1}{p}} \left[1 - \sqrt{4n^2 \frac{\omega^2}{p^2} + \left(1 - \frac{\omega^2}{p^2}\right)^2}\right]^2 d\left(\frac{\omega}{p}\right) = 0 \tag{30}$$

gives a minimum value over the range of frequency ratios from 0 to ω_1/p. Both equations 29 and 30 indicate that $n = 0.65$ will make the pickup an accurate accelerometer up to $\dfrac{\omega_1}{p} = 0.7$.

Any seismic pickup is either a displacement meter or an accelerometer, depending on the frequency range in which it is used. In the resonance range $0.7 < \omega/p < 4$, the pickup is neither a displacement meter nor an accelerometer. It can be used in this range if the records are corrected for dynamic magnification and phase shift.

Displacement meters (seismographs, pallographs, vibrographs) are built with p as small as possible, and only unavoidable naturally occurring damping is used.

Accelerometers are made with p as large as possible, and artificial viscous or eddy-current damping is provided to make n = 0.65. Equation 28 shows that the sensitivity of the pickup is inversely proportional to p^2. The larger p is made, the more accurate the accelerometer. But the larger p is made, the less sensitive the pickup becomes.

If an ideal seismic pickup were run through the resonance range of frequencies on a calibrating table it would have its maximum response x_0 when

$$\frac{\omega^2}{p^2} = \frac{1}{1 - 2n^2} \tag{31}$$

and the ratio x_0/y_0 at that frequency would be

$$\frac{x_0}{y_0} = \eta = \frac{1}{2n\sqrt{1 - n^2}} \tag{32}$$

When the frequency ω of maximum response and η have been determined on the calibrator, both p and n can be determined.

$$p^2 = \omega^2 \sqrt{\frac{\eta^2 - 1}{\eta^2}} \tag{33}$$

$$n^2 = \frac{1}{2}\left[1 - \sqrt{\frac{\eta^2 - 1}{\eta^2}} \right] \tag{34}$$

Equations 33 and 34 hold when $n \leq 0.707$.

With many very high-frequency pickups such as accelerometers it is often impossible to operate a calibrator up to the resonance frequency. In such cases if the mass of the seismic pickup is displaced relative to the case by a distance x_0 by giving the pickup case a bump, the subsequent motion is

$$x = x_0 e^{-npt} \sqrt{\frac{1}{1 - n^2}} \cos\left(p\sqrt{1 - n^2}\, t - \tan^{-1}\frac{n}{\sqrt{1 - n^2}} \right) \tag{35}$$

The period of the damped oscillation will be

$$T = \frac{2\pi}{p \sqrt{1 - n^2}} \tag{36}$$

and the successive damped amplitudes will have the following relationship,

$$\frac{x_t}{x_{t+T}} = e^{2\pi \frac{n}{\sqrt{1-n^2}}} = e^{\delta} \tag{37}$$

where δ is the logarithmic decrement,

$$\delta = \log_e \frac{x_t}{x_{t+T}} = 2\pi \frac{n}{\sqrt{1 - n^2}} \tag{38}$$

If δ and T are measured on the record,

$$p^2 = \frac{4\pi^2 + \delta^2}{T^2} \tag{39}$$

and

$$n^2 = \frac{\delta^2}{4\pi^2 + \delta^2} \tag{40}$$

The value of n can be determined approximately by counting the number of cycles m for the amplitude ratio, $\dfrac{X_{t+mT}}{X_t}$ to reach $1/e = 0.37$.   Then,

$$n^2 = \frac{1}{(2\pi m)^2 + 1} \tag{41}$$

If $m > 2$,

$$n \approx \frac{1}{2\pi m} \tag{42}$$

This method has no meaning below $m = 1$, at which value $n = 0.158$.   A pickup damped to $n = 0.65$ would show clearly only the first half-cycle of motion in the record.   For records from highly damped pickups which show only the first half-cycle of motion, an approximate value of n can be gotten from

$$n^2 = \frac{\log_e{}^2 \left| \dfrac{x_t}{x_{t+T/2}} \right|}{\pi^2 + \log_e{}^2 \left| \dfrac{x_t}{x_{t+T/2}} \right|} \tag{43}$$

22. Amplitude Calibration of Seismic Instruments.   The amplitude setting of a calibrating table does not always guarantee a constant amplitude over the whole range of frequencies tested.[20]   An independent check on the amplitude can be made by measuring the width of a band of light swept out by a thin illuminated line carried on the calibrating table by means of a microscope firmly attached to the rigid foundation of the calibrator.[21]   This is the simplest and most fundamental method of checking amplitudes.   Figure 8-30 shows a schematic representation of an amplitude-checking setup. Other nonseismic, independent checks on the amplitude of the calibrating table are:

1. A coil attached to the table moving in the field of a magnet attached to the fixed surroundings.   This will give a voltage proportional to the velocity of the table.   For simple-harmonic motion this can be translated to amplitude very easily.

2. A cantilever beam attached to the fixed surroundings with the free end on the moving table will have its strains in phase with and proportional to

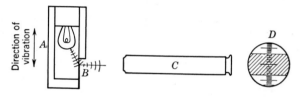

FIG. 8-30.   Schematic Representation of a System for Measuring Directly the Amplitudes of a Vibrating Body

The bakelite housing A, 1 in. long and $\frac{1}{4}$ in. square enclosing a small lamp, is attached to the vibrating body.   A small opening limited by the edge of a razor blade B allows a thin line of light to be seen at right angles to the length of the housing.   The cross-hatched section of the field D, as seen through a microscope C, represents the double amplitude of vibration.   If the edge of the razor blade is properly honed, the width of the line of light can be reduced to less than 0.00025 in.

the amplitude of motion of the table.   The lowest natural bending frequency of the cantilever beam must be higher than the highest frequency used on the calibrating table.   A metalectric strain gage attached to the bending beam will give records proportional to the amplitude of the table motion.

3. The change of distance between the plates of a capacitor—one attached to the fixed surrounding, the other attached to the moving table—will change its capacitance.   In an appropriate circuit the change of current will be proportional to the motion.

23. Frequency Calibration of Seismic Instruments.   Most calibrators are driven by rotating motors.   The frequency of the calibrating simple-harmonic motion is the same as the revolutions per second of the driving motor. This speed is best measured by a counting tachometer and an accurate stop watch.   If an electromagnetic calibrator built on the principle of the loud-speaker coil motor is used, its frequency can be measured electrically and checked against a standard 60-cycle wave.   On most electric networks this frequency is maintained constant within a small fraction of a cycle per second. The frequency can be checked readily if a record of the calibration run is made which contains time signals from clock signals of known frequency.

A Strobotac, calibrated against power-line frequency, may be used to check the frequency of the calibrating table. Tuning forks previously calibrated can be used as frequency standards. All frequency checking depends ultimately on a comparison of cycles per second against an accurate timing device.

24. Phase Calibration of Seismic Instruments. When a vibration meter is used to measure periodic motions which contain a harmonic, the frequency of which is in or near the resonant range of the instrument, the record is distorted in amplitude and shape. The record can only be corrected by determining the harmonic components of the record by Fourier Analysis. Each harmonic must be corrected in phase and amplitude. The corrected harmonics resynthesized will give a more accurate representation of the measured motion than the original distorted record.

For this reason the phase relationship between the calibrator motion and the record motion should be measured as part of any complete calibration procedure. For mechanical instruments, an electric contact closed by the calibrating table at its position of maximum amplitude and driving a recording mechanism which puts a dot on the record can be used. The recording mechanism, paper-piercing spark, or solenoid-driven clapper must have a quick response compared to the highest frequency recorded.

All the nonseismic methods of checking amplitude mentioned previously will also be good checks on the phase angle between the record and the calibrator-table movement.

25. Types of Calibrators. There are two general types of calibration systems in use for producing simple-harmonic motions of known and controllable amplitude and frequency:

1. Direct-drive or positive-displacement types.
2. Reaction types.

Direct-drive calibrators convert the rotary motion of a driving motor to linear motion by means of cams, eccentrics, connecting rods, or Scotch yokes. For torsional motion, constant rotation is transformed into simple-harmonic oscillations superimposed on an average rotational velocity by means of universal joints (Hooke's joints). Large loudspeaker coils attached directly to the table of a calibrator give linear vibratory motions directly without any mechanical transmission. The same principle can be used for torsional motion. Any single-phase motor produces simple-harmonic torques when driven by simple-harmonic single-phase current. Any d-c motor fed by alternating current will produce torsional oscillations without rotation.

Reaction-type calibrators consist of spring-mounted mechanical- or electromagnetic-vibration generators driven at frequencies above the natural frequency of spring-mass system of which they are a part.

A direct-drive calibrator produces large inertia-reaction forces since its center of gravity is continually oscillating. Therefore, it must be mounted on a very rigid foundation. It cannot give controllable amplitudes if mounted on a flexible floor. It should be mounted on thick concrete or solid rock in the basement and should be rigidly attached to the rigid foundation with a base construction such as shown in Fig. 8-31.

A motionless rigid foundation is necessary as a base for amplitude checks with a fixed microscope. The frame and table of the calibrator must both be rigid enough to have their local natural frequencies well above the highest frequency produced. There must be very close fits in all moving parts of the calibrator. And finally, the calibrated instrument must be clamped to the vibrating table as rigidly as possible.

The calibrating tables must not be loaded too heavily (with larger and heavier instruments than contemplated in the design). Even far below reso-

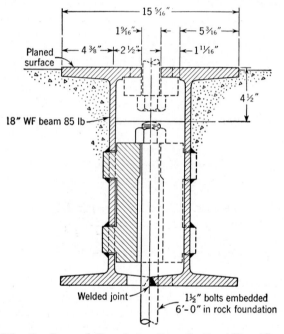

FIG. 8-31. Vibration Research Foundation Cross-Sectional View (Courtesy Equipment Information Booklet, Navy Department, David W. Taylor Model Basin)

This foundation provides a fixed plane to which vibration-calibration devices can be securely attached. In localities where a bedrock foundation is not accessible, solid-concrete foundations must suffice

nance dynamic distortions exist which are proportional to the weights carried, and, the larger the load carried, the closer the calibrator parts approach their lowest resonant frequency. Variation from preset amplitudes as high as 30 per cent have been observed on well-designed but overloaded calibrators. If the table is driven by a cam, the cam follower may lose contact with the cam if the table load produces larger inertia forces than the cam-loading spring is preset to hold.

Torsional calibrators produce inertia torque reactions and have the same need of rigid foundations, frames, and test shafts as linear calibrators. The calibration of instruments with larger moments of inertia than the design contemplated will cause dynamic distortion of the calibrating shaft.

26. Vibration Calibrators—Direct Drive. Commercial vibration tables for vertical and horizontal vibrations are available. The Johnson vibration testing machine[22] for horizontal motion is shown in Fig. 8-32. The Consolidated vibration calibrator[23] is shown in Fig. 8-33. This calibrator was built to operate both with vertical linear vibration and torsional vibration produced by an adjustable Hooke's joint. The Hooke's joint produces torsional

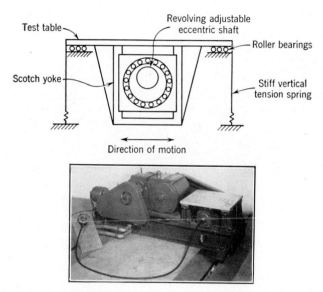

FIG. 8-32. Johnson Vibration-Testing Machine, Horizontal Motion

This is a mechanical direct-drive type of vibration machine which employs a scotch yoke and evolving eccentric shaft for approximate linear simple-harmonic motions. As shown in the schematic illustration, the table is guided by rollers and stiff vertical tension springs which are flexible in the direction of motion. The table is of aluminum construction. As shown in the photograph, the machine is bolted securely to steel rails embedded in bedrock. Circulating water-cooled oil lubrication is provided. Frequency control is obtained by a variable-speed transmission. This machine has a total motion of 0.062 in. at frequencies up to 3600 rpm. A maximum acceleration of 10 g is obtained with a table load of 100 lb. This machine is built in the Waugh Laboratories, New York

oscillations on the driven shaft, the amplitudes of which are functions of the angle between the driving and the driven shaft. Cormack[24] has expressed the relationship between the rotations of the driving and driven shafts of a Hooke's joint. If the angular velocity ω of the driving shaft is constant, and the angle between the driving and driven shafts is α then the rotation ϕ of the driven shaft is

$$\phi = \omega t + \sum_{n=1}^{n=\infty} \frac{1}{n} \tan^{2n} \frac{\alpha}{2} \sin 2n\omega t \qquad (44)$$

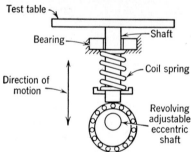

Fig. 8-33. Sperry–MIT Vibration Calibrator Made by Consolidated Engineering Corp

This machine was designed specifically for calibrating Sperry-MIT linear and torsional pickups. It is a direct-drive type of calibrator and employs a revolving eccentric shaft for driving a spring-loaded shaft in approximate simple-harmonic motion. This machine will produce a total motion of 0.100 in. at frequencies up to 5400 rpm. A maximum acceleration of 25 g is obtainable with a table load of 6 lb

Torsional vibrations are produced in the test shaft by a universal or Hooke's joint

For values of $\alpha < 30°$, only the first two terms of this expression are important:

$$\phi \approx \omega t + \tan^2 \frac{\alpha}{2} \sin 2\omega t \qquad (45)$$

For $\alpha = 30°$:

		Proportional Magnitudes
$\tan^2 \dfrac{\alpha}{2} = 0.071\ 77(4.112\ 12°)$		100.00
$\dfrac{1}{2} \tan^4 \dfrac{\alpha}{2} = 0.002\ 58(0.147\ 82°)$		3.60
$\dfrac{1}{3} \tan^6 \dfrac{\alpha}{2} = 0.000\ 13(0.007\ 45°)$		0.18

An independent check on the amplitude of torsional vibration is not easy to make on a Hooke's joint calibrator.

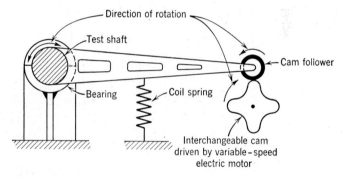

FIG. 8-34. Schematic Representation of a Torsional Calibrator with a Non-rotating Test Shaft

The rotating cam of this calibrator is designed so that the motion described by the follower is sinusoidal. Amplitude is varied by replacing cams

Mechanical-vibration calibrators are usually limited in frequency to 100 cps or less. The highest frequency attainable in mechanical vibrations is gotten by the air-jet self-excited calibrator. This can vibrate only at its own natural frequency. It consists of a heavy steel bar of uniform cross section mounted in pivot supports located at its free-free nodes. An adjustable air jet is placed under the center of the bar. The air gap between the center of the bar and the air jet is adjusted until the bar begins to vibrate, owing to the variation in pressure induced by the variation of the air gap with constant-volume flow and consequent variation of velocity. When the gap is small, the velocity of air flow increases, and the pressure falls. When the air gap is large, the velocity of air flow falls and the pressure rises. Calibrators of this type have produced accelerations as high as 400 g at 900 cps.

Figure 8-34 shows a direct-drive torsional-vibration calibrator which produces simple-harmonic motion, with no rotation.

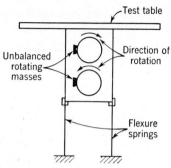

FIG. 8-35.   Schematic Illustration of a Mechanical Reaction-Type Calibrator

The rotating masses generate a force proportional to the square of the frequency of rotation, and the inertia reaction of the mass system also increases as the square of the frequency. This results in an approximately constant amplitude for a given table load if the unbalanced masses are driven above the resonance speed of the mass-spring system. An increase in table load decreases the amplitude obtainable with a given unbalance

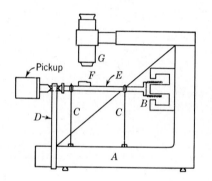

FIG. 8-36.   Electromagnetic Resonance-Type Calibrator (Allison Division, General Motors Corp)

A permanent-magnet loudspeaker unit B and a moving coil attached to the drive rod E are the driving elements of this calibrator. The pickup, drive rod and moving coil are supported by parallel flexure springs C. A tuning fork D is attached rigidly to base A and is clamped to the pickup drive rod E by knife-edges. A series of interchangeable tuning forks permits calibration of a 4 oz pickup up to 400 cps at 0.010 in. double amplitude with a maximum acceleration around 80 g. The unit is powered by a 50-watt booster amplifier. F and G comprise a magnified direct-reading system for checking the amplitude of vibration

As a simple reaction-type calibrator (without resonance) this machine can produce amplitudes of 0.020 in. at frequencies up to 50 cps with a 4-oz pickup attached

This type of calibrator does not disclose some of the diseases of rotating torsional-vibration pickups. Improper electrical shielding will produce first-order spurious records when an electric torsional pickup is rotated with uniform angular velocity. Mechanical unbalance will frequently produce first-order spurious records under the same condition. Uniform rotation sometimes causes a shift in the zero position of the inertia element which may lead to nonlinearity of the records if the shift plus the amplitude of motion add up to more than the allowable motion within existing magnetic fields. If nonrotating calibrators are used on torsional-vibration pickups, all these possibilities should be checked independently.

27. Vibration Calibrators—Reaction Type. Reaction-type calibrators that are entirely spring-mounted do not need extremely rigid foundations.[25] However, reaction-type calibrators that have rigid frames which are subjected to reaction forces must be as rigidly mounted as direct-drive calibrators.

Figure 8-35 shows a schematic outline of a mechanical reaction-type vibration calibrator for horizontal motion.

An inertia-torque reaction-type torsional-vibration calibrator developed by General Motors produces

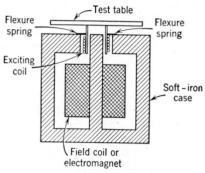

FIG. 8-37. Electromagnetic Reaction-Type Calibrator

The table amplitude produced by this calibrator is proportional to the current supplied to the exciting coil, and the frequency is varied by means of an electronic oscillator. This calibrator utilizes the electromagnetic loudspeaker principle for producing the driving force. The device is driven above its resonant frequency. In order to maintain constant amplitude over a range of frequencies, the current in the exciting coil must be kept proportional to the square of the frequency. The upper limit of the operating frequency depends on the current-carrying capacity of the exciting coil and the electric circuits connected to it

shaft speeds from 0 to 5000 rpm and torsional oscillations at frequencies from 0 to 300 cps, both controlled independently. Optical static calibration is provided.

Figures 8-36 and 8-37 show two electromagnetic loudspeaker reaction-type calibrators.

E. VIBRATION GENERATORS

28. General Considerations. Vibration generators are very useful devices for studying the dynamic (vibration) properties of structures under controlled conditions.[26] Vibration generators and vibration calibrators differ basically only in the following way. Vibration calibrators are vibration generators which are installed at fixed positions—they vibrate loads *which are attached to them,* the loads (vibration instruments) being small in size compared to the dimensions of the calibrator. Vibration generators are portable—*they are attached to structures* which usually are large compared with the vibration generator.

There are two general types of vibration generator—mechanical and electric.

29. Mechanical-Vibration Generators. Mechanical-vibration generators utilize the inertia reaction (centrifugal force) of unbalanced rotating weights

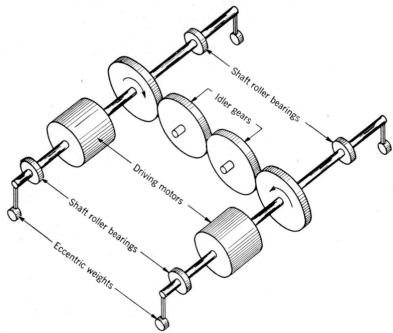

Fig. 8-38. Schematic Arrangement of Double-Shaft Mechanical-Vibration Generator

Two shafts driven by electric motors are geared together to rotate in opposite directions. Adjustable unbalanced rotating weights on the shaft ends create the desired periodic forces

to generate simple-harmonic forces. The amplitude of the simple-harmonic force is adjusted by varying the eccentricity of the unbalanced weights. The frequency of the simple-harmonic force is controlled by adjusting the speed of the d-c electric-drive motor. Where forces are wanted in a single fixed direction and couples are wanted in a single fixed plane, the eccentric weights are arranged in pairs which rotate in opposite directions. The vibration generator is attached rigidly to the structure being vibrated. Figure 8-38 shows a schematic arrangement of driving motors and eccentric weights in the common type of mechanical generator. Figure 8-39 indicates schematically the phasing of the eccentric weights to obtain unidirectional lines or planes of action of the simple-harmonic forces and torques.

Commercially made mechanical-vibration generators are available over a range of sizes, weights, and maximum produced forces. The smaller ones weigh about 100 lb and produce up to 400 lb, single amplitude, with a usable speed range between 800 to 3900 rpm.[27] The largest vibration generators weigh about 50,000 lb and produce up to 44,000 lb, single amplitude, with a

Starting Position	¼ Revolution from Starting Position	½ Revolution from Starting Position	¾ Revolution from Starting Position
Forces Normal to Base of Machine			
Resultant zero	Resultant up	Resultant zero	Resultant down
Tilting Moment About horizontal axis perpendicular to shaft axis			
Moment zero	Force near end up, far end down	Moment zero	Force near end down, far end up
Torsional Moment About vertical axis perpendicular to shaft axis			
Moment clockwise	Moment zero	Moment counterclockwise	Moment zero

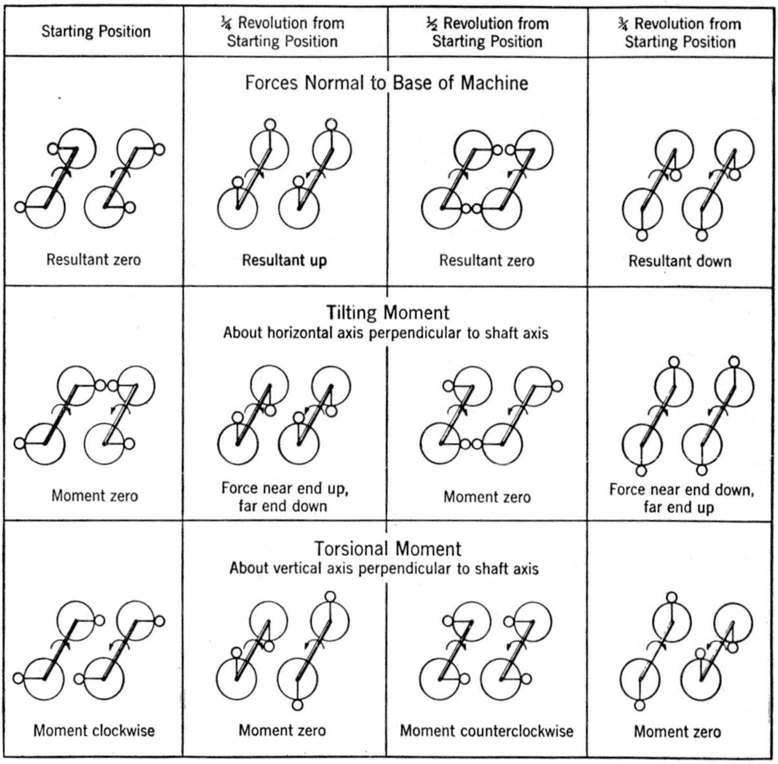

FIG. 8-39. Types of Cyclic or Periodic Forces and Moments Produced by Various Positions of Unbalanced Weights

Force normal to base of machine $4mr\omega^2 \sin \omega t$

Tilting moment $2mlr\omega^2 \sin \omega t$

Torsional moment $2mlr\omega^2 \sin \omega t$

ω = angular velocity of driving motor
m = mass of one eccentric weight
r = radius to center of gravity of one eccentric weight
l = distance between planes of eccentric weights

usable speed range between 55 and 480 rpm.[27] The force amplitude is proportional to the square of the angular velocity of the driving motor.

30. Electric-Vibration Generators. Most electromagnetic-vibration generators utilize the principle of the loudspeaker coil to generate linear simple-harmonic forces. The frequency and current in the coil winding are controlled to give the desired frequency and amplitude of the simple-harmonic force generated. A loudspeaker-type vibration generators can be used as both a reaction and a direct-drive generator. When it is used as a reaction vibration generator, a weight is attached to the coil, the frame of the generator is firmly attached to the vibrated structure, and the inertia reaction of the oscillating weight generates the simple-harmonic force. In direct-drive applications the frame of the generator is attached firmly to a rigid structure, and the coil is attached mechanically to the structure being vibrated. For vibrating structures which are lighter than the vibration generator, the frame of the generator is supported elastically, and the coil is attached mechanically to the structure being tested. Both the structure and the vibration-generator frame vibrate; but the larger amplitude of motion is in the tested structure. Figure 8-40 shows the Taylor Model Basin Electrodynamic vibration generator.

The loudspeaker type of vibration generator, when used as a reaction-type vibrator, is usually much heavier than a mechanical-vibration generator of the same rated maximum force. The electric controls, for frequency and current, are much more elaborate for loudspeaker-type vibration generators than for mechanical-vibration generators. The advantages offered by electric-vibration generators lie in the higher frequencies that are possible and the greater range in sizes of structures which can be tested. Used as a direct-drive unit, the loudspeaker vibration generator can be attached to structures with physical dimensions comparable to the dimensions of the loudspeaker coil itself.

Reaction-type vibration generators should be installed at antinodes of the structure being tested. Direct-drive vibration generators should be attached near to nodes of the structure being tested. All large structures must be vibrated by reaction-type generators since direct-drive generators need a fixed base of operation.

For generating torsional vibrations, single-phase electric motors are very useful since they generate simple-harmonic torques with amplitudes equal to the average torque produced. Any nonrotating electric motor fed with single-phase alternating current will generate simple-harmonic torsional vibration.

31. Applications of Vibration Generators. The chief use of vibration generators is to determine the dynamic properties of structures under controlled conditions.[28] These properties are the resonant frequencies of the structure (of which the lower ones are most important), the normal elastic curves of the structure at the resonant frequencies, and the damping properties of the structure. A comparison between the measured resonant frequencies and the known exciting frequencies gives information concerning the possibility of occurrence of critical speeds. The normal elastic curve locates the nodes and antinodes in the structure at resonance and permits a judgment on the location of maximum stresses in the structure when operation is at or near the critical speeds. In simple tension, compression, or twist, the maximum stresses are usually near the nodes (barring the effect of uneven design in the structure), and in bending the maximum stresses are near the antinodes.   The damping properties measured by the use of vibration generator indicates how violent the vibration may become under actual conditions of excitation and how sharply tuned the exciting force must be to be dangerous.

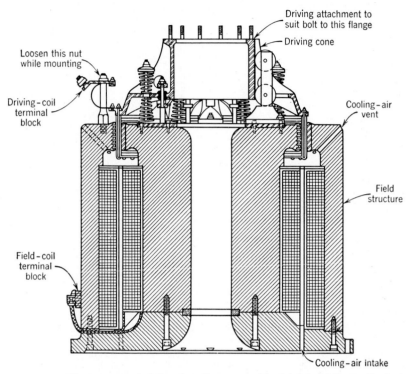

FIG. 8-40.   Electromagnetic-Vibration Generator (Taylor Model Basin Design)
    The base, consisting of the field structure, is rigidly attached to the structure to be vibrated.   Provision is made for attaching additional weights to the spring-supported driving cone, thereby increasing the driving force.   The loudspeaker cone can also be used as a direct-drive vibrator.   This generator has a frequency range from 20 to 2000 cps, the natural frequency of the driving system being 5 cps. The maximum available driving force is 150 lb.   The maximum double amplitude of the driving coil is $\frac{1}{2}$ in., and its maximum acceleration is 100 g.   The power required for the driving coil is 50 amperes at 30 volts, and the power required for the field coil is 2 ampere at 115 direct volts.   The generator weighs approximately 650 lb.   The driving cone is guided by rollers so that the generator may be mounted in any desired direction

    The vibration properties of turbine blades, turbine disks, airplane propellers, wings and fuselages, bridges, buildings (to determine the effect of earthquakes), and ships (hulls and superstructures) have all been studied by means of vibration generators.
    Vibration generators have been incorporated into the design of fatigue machines as the source of alternating load (augmented by resonance effects),

the test specimen being the spring member of the resonant mass–spring system. It is usually impossible to create destructive fatigue stresses in large structures by means of vibration generators, but these devices have been used to "shake down" complicated welded structures, disclosing points of high stress concentration or of high "locked up" stresses.[29]

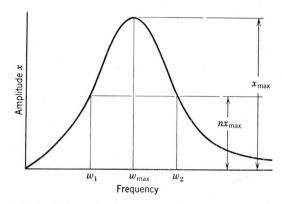

FIG. 8-41.   Method of Deducing Dynamic Constants of an Equivalent System of One Degree of Freedom

$$\frac{c}{c_c} \approx \frac{n}{4} \cdot \frac{\omega_2{}^2 - \omega_1{}^2}{\omega_{max}{}^2}$$

$$k \approx \frac{2}{n} \frac{\omega_{max}{}^2}{\omega_2{}^2 - \omega_1{}^2} \cdot \frac{rm_1\omega_{max}{}^2}{x_{max}}; \frac{lb}{in}$$

$$m \approx \frac{2}{n} \frac{1}{\omega_2{}^2 - \omega_1{}^2} \cdot \frac{rm_1\omega_{max}{}^2}{x_{max}}; \frac{lb\text{-}sec^2}{in}$$

$$c \approx \frac{1}{\omega_{max}} \cdot \frac{rm_1\omega_{max}{}^2}{x_{max}}; \frac{lb\text{-}sec}{in}$$

$$c_c \approx \frac{4}{n} \frac{\omega_{max}}{\omega_2{}^2 - \omega_1{}^2} \cdot \frac{rm_1\omega_{max}{}^2}{x_{max}}; \frac{lb\text{-}sec}{in}$$

Good for $\dfrac{c}{c_c} \leq 0.2$

$rm_1\omega_{max}{}^2$ = centrifugal force acting at ω_{max}

Finally, vibration generators have been used to calibrate vibration instruments.   They are used in the quick setting of concrete, the vibration bringing the excess water to the surface and creating a dense structure in the concrete when hardened.   Brick-making machinery uses the same technique in producing bricks of uniform dense structure.

32. Determination of Equivalent Local Systems.   A vibration generator located at a position in a structure (ship, building) can be used to determine an equivalent one-degree-of-freedom system at that position.   The complicated, multidegree of freedom properties of the actual structure can be replaced, for some purposes, by an equivalent mass, on an equivalent spring with an equivalent damping, all considered to be located at the generator position and moving in the direction of the generator force. If a machine which is expected to generate simple-harmonic exciting forces is mounted in the place of the vibration generator, the equivalent system calculated from the vibration-generator resonance curve need only be modified for the different masses in the mounted machine and the generator to predict whether vibrations with harmful amplitudes will occur. Figure 8-41 indicates the method of calculation for this equvalent single-degree-of-freedom system.

II. TRANSIENT MOTION

F. Stresses Due to Transient Motion

33. General Considerations. Transient motions are easier to describe negatively than positively. They are motions which are not steady-state motions. Transient motions are so variable in nature that an infinite number of mathematical equations with an unrestricted number of parameters would be necessary to describe them all. There are two general features of transient motions common to all transient motions.

1. A transient motion has measurable and variable aspects (displacement, velocity, acceleration) over a finite period of time τ, shorter than and included in the whole time of observation. To paraphrase Aristotle—"it has a beginning, a middle, and an end."

2. Transient motions are bounded at the beginning and at the end by steady-state motions.

If the time of observation is made short enough, it will be found that all motions would appear to be steady state. It is possible, in theory, to imagine transient motions in which $\tau = 0$ (unit-step acceleration); and in which $\tau = \infty$ (free vibration with viscous damping). However, in practice, the period τ is appropriately measured in microseconds or milliseconds for motions caused by impact of stiff bodies or detonating explosions; by seconds, for motions associated with vehicles (trains, automobiles, elevators, airplanes, ships); by minutes, for some "majestic" motions such as those of a launched ship; and by hours for the transient motions associated with the free vibration of large bodies with low natural periods.

The violence or intensity of a transient motion depends on the magnitude of the displacements, velocities, accelerations and their duration, and the physical and dynamical characteristics of the objects moved.

The effects of transient motions on physical structures and human beings have been the object of study and measurement for a long time. The seismologists have been measuring earthquakes for the past century. The transient motion of vehicles in starting and stopping, moving over bumps and in collisions, and the effects of impacts in the rolls of rolling mills have been measured by engineers many times in the last 50 years. During the recent war transient motions in diving airplanes, the effects of explosions and gunfire, and the motion of launched ships have been measured by numerous investigators.

Vibrations caused by transient motions usually have too few cycles even if the amplitudes are large enough to cause fatigue failure. Failures associated with transients are usually permanent deformations or complete fracture. The two aspects of transient motion which bear directly on these two types of failure are displacement and acceleration. Relative displacement between parts of a structure gives rise to stresses, and accelerations give rise to augmentation of the loads the parts must carry because of inertia reactions.

34. Measurement of Transient Motion. Transient motions *must* be recorded, and seismic-type pickups are used almost exclusively for measuring this type of motion. The theory and practice of measuring transient motions is in a rather sad state. The electrical engineer with the electromagnetic and cathode-ray oscillographs and the theories first developed by Heaviside has long been in a very favorable position with respect to the measurements of electrical transients. The mechanical engineer is just beginning to clarify his ideas on the measurement, instruments, and theories of transient motion of physical bodies.

35. Indicating Instruments. A few special devices for measuring a limited number of salient aspects of transient motions have been developed. These include the so-called peak accelerometers and the impulse spectrum meters. Peak accelerometers are instruments designed to measure the maximum acceleration which occurs during a transient motion. There are two general types of peak accelerometers, contact-peak accelerometers and "rupture"-peak accelerometers. They are of the "go" or "no–go" variety—each pickup being designed to indicate at or above a predetermined acceleration.

A contact-peak accelerometer consists of a mass on a spring which is attached to a body or plug which can be fastened firmly to the body whose motion is being studied. The mass is pushed down on the spring by a setscrew so that there is a definite spring load. The instrument is mounted in such a direction that, when the acceleration in that direction (in the sense opposite to d) reaches the magnitude $a = \dfrac{k}{m} d$, the contact between the mass and the setscrew is broken, and an electric circuit is opened. This operates an indicator which can be read at leisure. a is the acceleration at which the contact opens, k is the spring constant, m is the mass of the spring-suspended weight, and d is the preset deflection of the spring. The theory of these contact accelerometers has not been worked out in detail. In practice, they are very unreliable on large accelerations. Since the breaking of an electric circuit requires a minute but finite separation of the contact surfaces, these contact accelerometers always indicate accelerations lower than actually occur. If the period of the transient is very small, the contacts may never separate enough to indicate an open circuit. The electric circuits of a good contact accelerometer should carry very small currents, and perhaps the direction of development of these accelerometers should be toward circuits that indicate merely on changes of pressure between the contact surfaces. Figure 8-42 shows the NRL contact accelerometer.

"Rupture"-peak accelerometers have springs (rods) made of brittle material

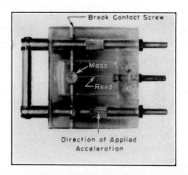

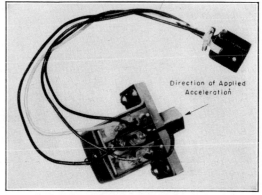

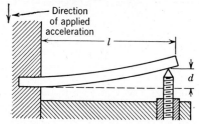

Schematic View of a Contact Accelerometer Reed
The acceleration in g's necessary to break contact is calculated as

$$a = \frac{8EId}{wl^3} \, g$$

where w is the weight of the reed, and I is its cross-sectional moment of inertia

FIG. 8-42. The NRL Contact Accelerometer

which are calibrated to break at a definite load w. When $a > w/m$, the rod breaks. These accelerometers never work with any reliability. No complete theory of them has been developed. Even during such simple transients as those described by a half sine wave the strain in the brittle springs depends completely on the ratio of the periods of the motion and the natural period of the accelerometer. For high-frequency transients the brittle rod is loaded at a high strain rate and becomes apparently stronger, so that the physical

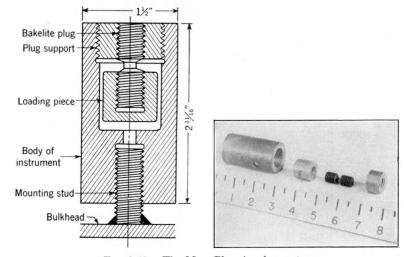

FIG. 8-43. The Mass-Plug Accelerometer

In the mass-plug accelerometer, a bakelite plug with a reduced section at midlength is the sensitive element. One end of the plug is attached to the instrument case by a threaded adapter, while the other end supports a loading piece of known weight. Ideally fracture of the plug is supposed to occur when the product of the mass of the loading piece and the acceleration normal to the base of the instrument exceeds the breaking strength of the plug. Practically, the mass-plug system vibrates when subjected to a shock, and when the amplitude of vibration exceeds a certain value, the plug fractures. The occurrence of this fracture, therefore, may or may not indicate the attainment of the acceleration which the instrument intends to indicate

characteristics of the accelerometer are themselves functions of the unknown motion which is supposed to break the spring (rod). Completely brittle rods being unobtainable, the rods go into the plastic range before they break. This is one of the reasons why no complete theory has been developed for this type of instrument. Figure 8-43 shows this type of accelerometer.

Figure 8-44 shows an impulse spectrum meter. In this instrument a number of seismographs of different natural period record simultaneously. If the maximum displacement x_{0n} of each spring–mass unit is multiplied by the natural circular frequency p_0 of the unit it gives a velocity v_0 which could be considered as the initial velocity of the unit if acted upon by an impulsive force of short duration. The theory of this instrument remains to be devel-

TABLE 8-8

Instrument	NRL Contact Accelerometer	Mass-Plug Accelerometer	TMB Multifrequency Impact Gage
Practical amplitude range, g's single	5–500	100–4500	5–20,000
Indicating method	Electric indication at make or break of contact at preloaded mass on cantilever	Fracture of bakelite plug	Total displacement at each of 10 reeds of different frequency is scribed on waxed paper
Natural frequency of element, cps		500–2600	25–2,000
Power required	100 alternating volts	None	None
Accessory equipment required	Neon light contact, make or break indicator	None	None
Method of damping	None	None	Friction of scriber on wax
Weight, lb	About 0.1	1¼	About 10
Over-all dimensions, in.	Cell about 2 × 2 × 2½; 7-cell holder 6 × 4½ × 4	1½D × 2¾	9½ × 8½ × 3
Method of mounting on vibrating structure	Clamped in holder which is bolted to structure	Screwed on to a ½ in. stud which is welded to structure.	Bolted to structure
Meaning of indication	Break contact presumed to indicate attainment of a given value of acceleration. Make contact is considered to indicate a certain impulsive velocity as well as acceleration.	Fracture of plug presumed to indicate that a definite value of acceleration has been attained.	Total displacement of reeds considered to indicate applied impulsive velocity. Frequency spectrum of shock is indicated.
General remarks	Use of a number of units permits bracketing of peak value of acceleration. Contact break may indicate accelerations of such high frequency or short duration that they have no practical effect.	Several plugs are used in an attempt to bracket the actual peak acceleration.	Good for comparison of similar shocks and for predicting behavior of simple systems to recorded shock
Figure	8-42	8-42	8-44

oped.   Until such a theory is developed the relationship between the various values of p_n and the motion being measured cannot be clearly understood or used.   However, the impulse spectrum meter does permit comparison of severity in shock of the same nature but different intensities.   It records the response of a given series of single-degree systems of different frequencies to the same shock which is a measure of the probable damage to be expected to occur to systems of similar dynamic characteristics.

Table 8-8 gives the characteristics of three indicating accelerometers.

36. Recording Instruments with Seismic Pickup.   All the recording seismic instruments in use for measuring steady-state vibrations can be used for measuring some transient motions.   The recording instruments in Tables 8-3 to 8-7 are suitable for measuring some transient motions.

FIG. 8-44. The Multifrequency Impact Gage

This gage for the recording of shock comprises 10 weighted cantilever reeds of different natural frequencies mounted on a common base.   The maximum relative displacement between each reed and the base of the instrument is recorded on waxed paper by a stylus at the end of the reed. The maximum displacement multiplied by the natural "circular frequency" of the reed is considered to indicate a quantity termed the "effective impulsive velocity" of the shock for that particular frequency.   A curve of the effective impulsive velocity plotted against natural frequency is called the "velocity-characteristic" curve of the shock.   This curve is useful for comparing shocks and for predicting the effect of the shock on instruments and equipment of known natural frequency

G. INTERPRETATION OF RECORDS OF TRANSIENT MOTION

37. General Considerations. The chief problem associated with transient-motion measurement (aside from the design of suitable instruments) is the interpretation of the transient-motion record itself.   The problem may be stated clearly as follows: What is the relationship between the stimulus or input (the motion being measured) and the response or output (the record) of a seismic instrument with all its transmitting, amplifying, and recording elements?[35]

38. Interpretation of Records of Transients Made by Accelerometers. For the ideal seismic pickup,

$$\ddot{x} + 2np\dot{x} + p^2x = -\ddot{y} \qquad (46)$$

where the symbols have the same meaning as in equation 24.

If an ideal linear transmission and magnification factor μ is assumed, the record X is

$$X = \mu x \tag{47}$$

and the relationship between the record X and the motion y is

$$\ddot{X} + 2np\dot{X} + p^2 X = -\mu\ddot{y} \tag{48}$$

The only things known about a measured transient acceleration are the record X and the dynamic characteristics p, n, and μ of the instrument.   The question posed is: What was the actual $\ddot{y}$ which caused the record?

Equation 48 indicates the operations which must be carried out on the record in order to correct for the distortion of the record.   Distortion may be defined as the difference between the form of the record X as a function of time and the form of the actual acceleration $\ddot{y}$ as a function of time.   The correction terms are:

(a) $\ddot{X}$—the record differentiated twice.

(b) $2np\dot{X}$—the first differentiation of the record multiplied by $2np$.

These terms, when added to the record X, multiplied by p^2, will equal the correct value at all times t of $-\mu\ddot{y}$.

To get accurate values of $\ddot{X}$ and $\dot{X}$ from a record is exceedingly difficult; therefore, a "good" accelerometer has a value of p^2 so large that the largest values of $\ddot{X} + 2np\dot{X}$ which appear in the record are negligible in comparison with $p^2 X$.   Then,

$$p^2 X \approx -\mu\ddot{y} \tag{49}$$

or

$$X \approx -\frac{\mu\ddot{y}}{p^2} \tag{50}$$

Equation 50 shows that a "good" accelerometer is relatively insensitive.

In order to estimate the errors in the approximation indicated in equation 50, equation 48 should be written

$$\frac{\ddot{X}}{p^2} + \frac{2n}{p}\dot{X} + X = -\frac{\mu\ddot{y}}{p^2} \tag{51}$$

The maximum error caused by $\dfrac{2n}{p}\dot{X}$ will occur at the point of steepest slope in the record.   If the record is replaced at this point by a straight line with the slope at the point, the magnitude of $\dfrac{2n}{p}\dfrac{\dot{X}}{X}$ can be estimated by the value of $\dfrac{n}{\pi}\dfrac{T}{\tau_1}\dfrac{X_1}{X}$.   In this expression T is the undamped natural period of the pickup, X_1 is the vertical side of the triangle formed on the straight line, τ_1 is the horizontal side of the triangle formed on the straight line translated to time units, and X is the ordinate of the record at the point of steepest slope.

The maximum error caused by $\ddot{X}/p^2$ will occur at the peak in the record with the smallest radius of curvature. If the record is replaced in the neighborhood of this point by a sine curve, $X = X_0 \sin 2\pi \dfrac{t}{\tau_2}$, which fits the record the magnitude of $\dfrac{1}{p^2} \dfrac{\ddot{X}}{X}$, can be estimated by the value of $\dfrac{T^2}{\tau_2{}^2} \dfrac{X_0}{X}$. In this expression T is the undamped natural period of the pickup, X_0 is half the height of the peak, τ_2 is twice the width of the peak in time units, and X is the ordinate of the record at the peak.

In records taken by accelerometers with n much less than 0.65, the most noticeable feature of the record will be large amplitude oscillations at the natural frequency of the pickup. A first approximate correction to these records is obtained by fairing a line through the midpoints of the vertical sides of the natural-frequency oscillations.

Accelerometers are the only instruments which can be used to measure motions of large magnitude. Displacement meters and velocity meters have such soft springs that they move through the entire clearance available and spoil the records of large motions. Such motions are the rolling and pitching of ships and oscillations of rolling stock.

When accelerometers are used to measure large slow motions, they can be mounted on rubber cushions to eliminate higher-frequency motions.

39. Interpretation of Records of Transients Made by Displacement Meters. If in a transient motion at the beginning of the transient when $t = 0$,

$$y = \dot{y} = X = \dot{X} = 0$$

the true relationship between the motion measured y and the record X is obtained by integrating equation 48 twice, term by term:

$$X + 2np\int X \, dt + p^2\int\int X \, dt \, dt = -\mu y \qquad (52)$$

The correction terms are

  (a) $2np\int X \, dt$

  (b) $p^2\int\int X \, dt \, dt$

These terms, when added to the record X, equal the correct value of μy.

The errors represented by the correction terms at a time τ after the start of the record are

$$\frac{2np}{X}\int_0^\tau X \, dt \approx 4\pi n \frac{\tau}{T} \frac{X_1}{X} \qquad (53)$$

and

$$\frac{p^2}{X}\int_0^\tau \int_0^\tau X \, dt \, dt \approx 4\pi^2 \frac{\tau^2}{T^2} \frac{X_1}{X} \qquad (54)$$

In equations 53 and 54 T is the undamped natural frequency of the pickup, X is the ordinate of the record at $t = \tau$, and X_1 is an average value of the record for the interval $0 < t < \tau$.

These corrections will be smaller, in general, if p is small or T is large. Equation 53 indicates that the damping n should be small in a displacement meter.

40. Interpretation of Records of Transients Made by Velocity Meters. A velocity pickup is a seismic instrument in which the relative velocity between the mass and case is the recorded quantity. The mass is a permanent magnet or an electromagnet. A coil fixed to the case generates a voltage when the magnet moves relative to it. The fundamental equation still holds

$$\ddot{x} + 2np\dot{x} + p^2x = -\ddot{y} \tag{55}$$

The generated voltage is

$$e = L\dot{x} \tag{56}$$

Therefore,

$$\dot{e} + 2npe + p^2 \!\int\! e\, dt = -L\ddot{y} \tag{57}$$

The correct velocity is obtained by integrating once term by term

$$e + 2np\!\int\! e\, dt + p^2 \!\int\!\!\int\! e\, dt\, dt = -L\dot{y} \tag{58}$$

The "open-circuit" voltage is proportional to the velocity $\dot{y}$ only if p is made small. For transients of very short duration, τ, compared to T, the undamped natural period of the pickup, the voltage measured by a high-impedance oscillograph attached to the terminals of the velocity pickup will be very closely proportional to the actual velocity.

A velocity pickup with a large value of p^2 is suitable for measuring the first derivative of the acceleration, $\dddot{y}$. $\dddot{y}$ has been called "Ruck" in Germany and "jerk" in the United States. It has been conjectured that human discomfort is correlated with $\dddot{y}$ rather than with $\ddot{y}$. If equation 57 is differentiated once, term by term, the relationship between voltage e and $\dddot{y}$ is

$$\ddot{e} + 2np\dot{e} + p^2e = -L\dddot{y} \tag{59}$$

When the velocity-meter coil is attached to a low-impedance recording instrument, current flows in the coil, and the relationship between the record and the motion becomes far more complicated than those shown in equations 57–59. The whole instrument from pickup to recording galvanometer becomes, under ideal conditions, a system of three degrees of freedom in which the mechanical characteristics of the pickup, the mechanical characteristics of the galvanometer, and the electrical characteristics of the entire electric circuit become important. Figure 8-45 shows a record of transient motions taken by a velocity pickup with low-impedance output.

The equation relating record to motion becomes for this case (in operational form):

$$(T_6{}^3D^6 + T_5{}^2D^5 + T_4{}^1D^4 + T_3{}^0D^3 + T_2{}^{-1}D^2 + T_1{}^{-2}D + T_0{}^{-3})X = -\dddot{y} \tag{60}$$

in which the constants T_n are characteristic times and depend on the values of n and p in the two mechanical systems and the electric circuit and $D^n = d^n/dt^n$. Integrating equation 60 once, twice, and three times, respectively, term by term, will give the acceleration, velocity, and displacement.

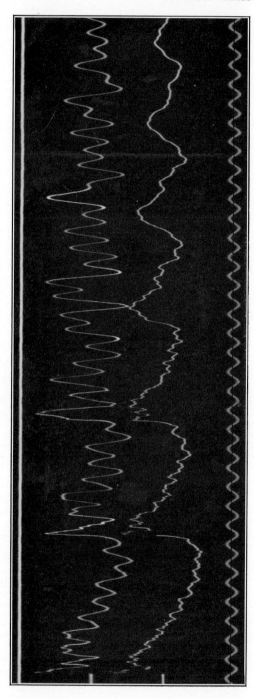

FIG. 8-45.　Records Taken by Velocity Meter with Low-Impedance Output

Top trace—Unused channel

Second trace—Sensitivity 5.07 ft/sec/in.

Third trace—Sensitivity 7.56 ft/sec/in.

Bottom trace—Timing wave, 100 cps

Natural frequency of pickup—3 cps

Natural circular frequency $p = 18.9$ rad/sec

Damping ratio $n = 0.03$

This record was taken by an instrument which consisted of these parts: the mechanical system of the pickup, the electric circuit and the mechanical system of the recording electromagnetic oscillograph. No amplifier was used so that the current flowing in the electric circuit was appreciable—in the order of 0.010 ampere maximum. Equation 60 shows that T_2^{-1} should be large compared with all the other coefficients in $Z(D)$ to make this record a highly accurate velocity record. The sensitivities given above are based on the assumption that this is true. But only a complete analysis of the mechanical and electric circuits can determine what the true errors are in these records. The assumption made in the sensitivity calibrations is that the detail of the motion being measured is all at frequencies far above the natural frequency of the pickup and far below the natural frequency of the galvanometer and the electric circuit.

41. General Relationship between Signal and Record.   In general, $S(t)$ is the signal being measured, and $X(t)$ is the record, that is, the output of the instrument.   Then, in operational form,

$$\left(\cdots + \frac{a-2}{D^2} + \frac{a-1}{D} + a_0 + a_1 D + a_2 D^2 + \cdots \right) X(t) = S(t) \quad (61)$$

in which

$$\frac{1}{D^n} = \int \cdots \int^n (\quad) \, dt^n$$

$$Z(D) \equiv \cdots + \frac{a_2}{D^2} + \frac{a_1}{D} + a_0 + a_1 D + a_2 D^2 + \cdots \qquad (62)$$

Thus,

$$Z(D)X(t) = S(t) \qquad (63)$$

and the corrected record $Z(D)X(t)$ is the signal $S(t)$.

H. Calibration of Seismic Instruments Used to Measure Transient Motions

42. General Considerations.   Very little can be said about the calibration of instruments used for measuring transient motions because very little has been done in this field.   Calibration can be carried out by subjecting the pickup to a known and controllable transient motion.   To obtain known and controllable transient motions is very difficult.

The free damped vibration of a calibrating table mounted on springs is the simplest known transient that can be used.

A calibrating table can be driven over carefully cut cams of desired shape. The design and construction of cam calibration systems is difficult and expensive.

Osborne and Carter[36] have used an underwater explosion wave to "calibrate" a tourmaline crystal hydrophone.   Underwater explosion waves can be "controlled" to some extent, but just how accurately "known" the characteristics of such waves are is open to question.

If $X(t)$ is the record or response of an instrument to a signal or input $S(t)$, the record and the signal are related as follows:

$$Z(D)X(t) = \left(\cdots + \frac{a_2}{D^2} + \frac{a_1}{D} + a_0 + a_1 D + a_2 D^2 + \cdots \right) X(t)$$

$$= S(t) \quad (64)$$

The object of calibration, in the most general sense, is to obtain the values of the coefficients a_n in Equation 64.   Calibration, as usually understood by engineers, leads only to the determination of the value of a_0.   A perfect instrument would give

$$a_0 X(t) = S(t) \qquad (65)$$

Equation 64 indicates that in the perfect instrument a_0 would be so large that $X(t)$ would be vanishingly small. Accuracy is always obtained at the expense of sensitivity.

43. Unit Step-Pulse Calibration. Osborne[37] has suggested a numerical method for determining the indicial admittance of a linear system when the response to a known transient is observed or the shape of the transient when the indicial admittance is known. The indicial admittance of an instrument is the response $X(t)$ of the system to a unit step-pulse signal $S(t)$. It is designated as $A(t)$. A unit step pulse is the simplest type of transient which is zero for all time before $t = 0$ and is one for all time after $t = 0$. The unit step pulse is designated mathematically as $\mathbf{1}$.

$$\mathbf{1} = 0 \quad \text{when} \quad -\infty < t < 0$$

$$\mathbf{1} = 1 \quad \text{when} \quad 0 < t < +\infty$$

One aspect of motion which can be obtained in a step pulse is acceleration. The indicial admittance of an ideal damped seismic pickup acted on by a step-pulse acceleration $-\ddot{y}_0 \cdot \mathbf{1}$ is

$$A(t) = \frac{X(t)}{\ddot{y}_0} = \frac{1}{p^2} \left\{ 1 - e^{-npt} \left(\frac{n}{\sqrt{1-n^2}} \sin p \sqrt{1-n^2}\, t \right. \right.$$
$$\left. \left. + \cos p \sqrt{1-n^2}\, t \right) \right\} \quad (66)$$

If the indicial admittance $A(t)$ of a more complicated instrument is obtained Carson's integral,

$$\frac{1}{Z(D)} = D \int_0^\infty e^{-Dt} A(t)\, dt \quad (67)$$

shows a general relationship between $Z(D)$ of Equation 64 and $A(t)$, provided the mechanical and electric network of the instrument is linear. In equation 67 the operator D is treated as an algebraic quantity and is not used as an operator.

If the indicial admittance, recorded by the instrument on a step-pulse acceleration calibrator, attains a limiting constant value θ, the constants a_n of the instrument can be obtained by integrations of the calibration record.

Suppose that

$$A(t) \quad \text{is known for} \quad 0 \le t \le T$$

and
$$A(t) = \theta \qquad \text{for} \qquad t \ge T$$

when
$$\theta \ne 0$$

$$Z(D) = a_0 + a_1 D + a_2 D^2 + \cdots \quad (68)$$

and the corrected record, that is, the signal is given by

$$S(t) = Z(D)X(t) = a_0 X(t) + a_1 \dot{X}(t) + a_2 \ddot{X}(t) + \cdots \quad (69)$$

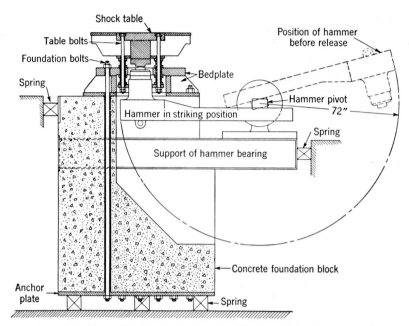

FIG. 8-46. The H-I Shock Machine for Medium-Weight Equipment

The machine is composed of four main parts, the foundation, the bedplate, the shock table, and the hammer, assembled as shown

The foundation is a massive block of concrete weighing about 100,000 lb, which is mounted on heavy springs to insulate the surrounding building from shock

The bedplate is a steel weldment weighing 7000 lb. It is secured on the foundation by 13 long bolts each 3 in. in diameter

The shock table is a steel structure weighing 4000 lb, consisting of a solid core with a horizontal plate on top of it, and 12 vertical stiffening webs extending radially out from the core to the extremities of the plate. Equipment to be tested is secured on the platform provided by the horizontal plate. The table can move 3 in. vertically, guided by 12 bolt assemblies which slide through holes in the bedplate. These assemblies consist essentially of 12 holding-down bolts, referred to as table bolts, extending from the platform down between the radial stiffeners and finally through hollow sleeves about each bolt; they serve mainly to arrest the vertical motion of the table after it has traversed the allowed clearance

The hammer consists of a 3000-lb steel weight on the end of a box-girder arm which is adjustable to a radius of either 5 or 6 ft. The hammer swings through a channel in the concrete block in the final portion of its arc

For this case the correction coefficients are

$$a_0 = \frac{1}{\theta}; \quad a_1 = \frac{E_0}{\theta^2}; \quad a_2 = \frac{E_0{}^2 + \theta E_1}{\theta^3}; \quad \cdots . \qquad (70)$$

where

$$E_0 = \int_0^T [\theta - A(t)]\, dt; \qquad E_1 = - \int_0^T t[\theta - A(t)]\, dt; \quad \cdots . \qquad (71)$$

When $\theta = 0$,

$$Z(D) = \frac{a_{-1}}{D} + a_0 + a_1 D + a_2 D^2 + \cdots. \tag{72}$$

and the corrected record is given by

$$S(t) = Z(D)X(t) = a_{-1}\int X(t)\, dt + a_0 X(t) + a_1 \dot{X}(t) + a_2 \ddot{X}(t) + \cdots. \tag{73}$$

For this case the correction coefficients are

$$a_{-1} = \frac{1}{A_0}; \quad a_0 = -\frac{A_1}{A_0{}^2}; \quad a_1 = \frac{A_1{}^2 - A_0 A_2}{A_0{}^3} \tag{74}$$

$$a_2 = -\frac{A_1{}^3 - 2A_0 A_1 A_2 + A_0{}^2 A_3}{A_0{}^4}; \cdots.$$

where

$$A_0 = \int_0^T A(t)\, dt; \quad A_1 = -\int_0^T t A(t)\, dt; \cdots. \tag{75}$$

$$A_n = \frac{(-1)^n}{n!} \int_0^T t^n A(t)\, dt$$

The correction operator so obtained will be the correction operator for any subsequent acceleration measured by the instrument.

The correction terms beyond a_2 can be obtained; but accurate practical methods for obtaining higher derivatives of records are nonexistent.

44. Shock Machines. In the field of transient motions the "shock machine" takes the place occupied by the vibration generator for steady state motions. Figure 8-46 shows a shock machine. These machines have recently been used extensively with good practical results. Whole assemblies and devices are mounted on the table of these machines and subjected to "shock." A "shock" may be defined as a transient motion resulting from an "impact" (large force of short duration). The motions of the parts during the transient can be recorded by high-speed photography, and those elements which break under the treatment can be redesigned.

III. INTEGRATION AND DIFFERENTIATION OF RECORD OF TRANSIENT MOTIONS

I. INTEGRATION AND DIFFERENTIATION

45. General Considerations. The interpretation and calibration of records taken by motion-measuring instruments with a seismic pickup call for successive integration and differentiation of the records. The integrating process can be carried out graphically, numerically, mechanically, or electrically with good accuracy. The differentiations present an extremely difficult practical problem, since even the first differential of a graphical record is hard to get with fair accuracy.

The integrating process assumes that a zero line, accurate in position and orientation, exists on the record or can be constructed on the record. The differentiation process requires a zero line accurately oriented and, at least, parallel to the true zero on the record. Both processes are best carried out on photographically enlarged copies of the original record. The trace of the record should be made as fine and distinct as possible so that the inner or outer edge of the trace can be used as the record for calculation purposes.

46. Scales. In any record the ordinate and abscissa are both in length units only. The ordinates are X in. long and the abscissa Z, although it represents time, is also in length units.

Suppose the actual units of the ordinates to be y. Then,

$$y = S_y X \tag{76}$$

and

$$t = S_t Z \tag{77}$$

where

$$S_y = \frac{\text{the number of units of } y}{\text{inch of the record ordinate}} \tag{78}$$

$$S_t = \frac{\text{number of seconds}}{\text{inch of the record abscissa}} \tag{79}$$

Then,

$$dy = S_y \, dX \tag{80}$$

$$dt = S_t \, dZ \tag{81}$$

and

$$\frac{dy}{dt} = \frac{S_y \, dX}{S_t \, dZ} \tag{82}$$

$$\frac{d^n y}{dt^n} = \frac{S_y \, d^n X}{S_t^n \, dZ^n} \tag{83}$$

When the velocity V of the recording surface is constant,

$$\frac{dZ}{dt} = \frac{1}{S_t} = V \tag{84}$$

For integration,

$$\int y \, dt = \int S_y X S_t \, dZ = S_y S_t \int X \, dZ \tag{85}$$

and

$$\int \cdots \int \int^n y \, dt^n = S_y S_t^n \int \cdots \int \int^n X \, dZ^n \tag{86}$$

If the record is enlarged, photographically m times, X becomes mX, and Z becomes mZ; then,

$$\frac{d(mX)}{d(mZ)} = \frac{m \, dX}{m \, dZ} = \frac{dX}{dZ} \tag{87}$$

and

$$\frac{d^n(mX)}{d(mZ)^n} = \frac{m}{m^n}\frac{d^nX}{dZ^n} = \frac{1}{m^{n-1}}\frac{d^nX}{dZ^n} \tag{88}$$

$$\int mXm\,dZ = m^2 \int X\,dZ \tag{89}$$

$$\int \cdots \int \int^n mX(m\,dZ)^n = m^{n+1} \int \cdots \int \int^n X\,dZ^n \tag{90}$$

In graphical integration when the curve being integrated is replaced by a series of rectangular steps and a pole length, H is chosen on the Z axis, the integral η has a scale

$$S\eta = HS_yS_t = \frac{\text{number of units of } \eta}{\text{inch of the integral curve ordinate}} \tag{91}$$

When η is the actual integral, X is the graphical ordinate of the integrand, Z is the graphical abscissa of the integrand, and H is the constant pole length along the Z axis in the same graphical length units as X and Z; then $X/H = d\eta/dZ$ at the particular value of Z where X is measured.

J. Integration

47. Mechanical Integration. The best method of integrating records is the mechanical method using an integraph.[53] The photographic enlargement of the record should be made as large as the integraph can handle.

48. Graphical Integration. For rough work graphical integration* can be used. Graphical integration of records is not recommended. It cannot compete in accuracy with numerical integration.

49. Numerical Integration. Accuracy of measurement does not warrant excessive refinement. Therefore, Simpson's parabolic rule is recommended.

The abscissa interval of the record in which the integral curve is desired is divided into $2q$ equal parts each Δ in. long. Δ is chosen small enough so that the curve in any interval 2Δ long has no inflection points. If there are inflection points in the curve to be integrated, the ordinates should be so spaced that the inflection point becomes one of the measured ordinates. Simpson's parabolic rule is based on the assumption that the curve is replaced locally by parts of parabolas which fit the curve.†

If ordinates of $f(Z)$ $(X_0, X_1, X_2, \cdots X_{2q})$ are erected at values of Z $(0, \Delta, 2\Delta, \cdots 2q\Delta)$, then,

$$\int_{Z_n}^{Z_{n+2}} f(Z)\,dZ = \frac{\Delta}{3}[X_n + 4X_{n+1} + X_{n+2}] \tag{92}$$

and

$$\int_{Z_0}^{Z_{2q}} f(Z)\,dZ = \frac{\Delta}{3}\left[X_0 + \sum_{1}^{2q-1} 4X_{n\text{ odd}} + \sum_{2}^{2q-2} 2X_{n\text{ even}} + X_{2q}\right] \tag{93}$$

* See reference 54, Ch 7, pp 102–113.
† See reference 15, p 280.

If the total integral is wanted at evenly spaced ordinates l inches apart then $\Delta = l/2$ in. The work can be arranged in tabular form. From the table it can be seen that the integral can be calculated systematically on a calculating machine.

TABLE 8-9

Z	X	$4X_{n\ odd}$	$X_{n\ even}$	Increments $\dfrac{3}{\Delta}\displaystyle\int_{Z_n}^{Z_{n+2}} f(Z)\, dZ$	$\dfrac{\Delta}{3}$ Increment	Total Integral
Z_0	X_0		X_0	0	0	0
Z_1	X_1	$4X_1$				
Z_2	X_2		X_2	$X_0 + 4X_1 + X_2$	$\displaystyle\int_{Z_0}^{Z_2} f(Z)\, dZ$	$\displaystyle\int_{Z_0}^{Z_2} f(Z)\, dZ$
Z_3	X_3	$4X_3$				
Z_4	X_4		X_4	$X_2 + 4X_3 + X_4$	$\displaystyle\int_{Z_2}^{Z_4} f(Z)\, dZ$	$\displaystyle\int_{Z_0}^{Z_4} f(Z)\, dZ$
Z_5	X_5	$4X_5$				
Z_6	X_6		X_6	$X_4 + 4X_5 + X_6$	$\displaystyle\int_{Z_4}^{Z_6} f(Z)\, dZ$	$\displaystyle\int_{Z_0}^{Z_6} f(Z)\, dZ$

If the probable error in measuring X_n is $\pm e$ in., the probable error of the integral in each interval 2Δ is

$$\text{Per cent error} = \frac{100\sqrt{18}\, e}{X_n + 4X_{n+1} + X_{n+2}}\ \% \tag{94}$$

Since the probable error of measurement e remains constant, the integral of a record magnified m times will only have $1/m$ times the probable error of the integral of the original record. Beside the error due to inexact measurements of X_n, there exists an error due to fitting the curve segments by parabolas. We have no means of evaluating this error, but this error is made smaller by taking Δ smaller.

50. Electrical Integration. In any pickup which has electric transmission an integrating circuit may be introduced to integrate the quantity measured before it is recorded. Clarke[55] has described some simple integrating circuits. For transient motions integrating circuits with capacitance in series should not be used since the currents generated by the instrument may be largely unidirectional.

A simple integrating circuit consists of a very large inductance L, in series with a very small resistance R. If an applied voltage E_{applied} is put across this series circuit, the voltage across the resistance R will be approximately proportional to the integral of E_{applied}. If the total resistance of the circuit is very small compared to the reactance of the coil at the lowest-frequency component of the applied voltage, $E_{\text{applied}} \approx L\dfrac{di}{dt}$ and $i = \dfrac{1}{L}\displaystyle\int E_{\text{applied}}\ dt$.   Then, $E_{\text{out}} =$

$Ri \approx \dfrac{R}{L}\displaystyle\int E_{\text{applied}}\ dt$.   A very accurate integrating circuit has a very small

R/L and, therefore, a small output.

Any amplifying circuit used to compensate for the low output of an accurate integrating circuit should be installed at a place which is not affected by the transient motions being measured since vacuum tubes are good accelerometers. The spacing between the filament, grids, and plates in the tube changes when the tube is accelerated, giving rise to "microphonic" distortion of the record.

K. Differentiation

51. Drafting-Machine Differentiation.   Differentiation of records is difficult to do with any high degree of accuracy.   Enlarged records, microscopic measurement, and smoothing of data may be necessary for derivatives higher than the first.   For quick approximate differentiation a drafting machine can be used, the straightedge of the drafting machine being aligned to the curve by eye.   This is good only for curves that are rather smooth.

52. Optical Differentiation.   Another method which is good on smooth curves is the reflection method.   A vertical mirror lined up along the true normal to the curve will give an image of the curve which is continuous and without a break if viewed along the curve toward the mirror image.   If the mirror is not lined up on the normal to the curve, the image shows a sharp break where the image and the curve meet.   If the mirror is mounted on the edge and forms a continuous part of the edge of a straightedge, a series of normals can be drawn along the straightedge which cross the curve.   Any perpendicular to a normal is parallel to the tangent to the curve at the point of intersection of the normal and the curve.[56-58]

53. Approximate Analytical Differentiations.   For estimating the order of magnitude of the first and higher derivatives of a record at points of special interest the parts of the record in the immediate neighborhood of these points may be replaced by analytical functions which fit the curve approximately. Parts of sine and cosine functions which fit the record can always be used to give rough estimates of derivatives.*   Power series can be laid out that fit ordinate measurements on either side of the point of interest.   At least the first derivative of these series will be fairly accurate.

54. Numerical Differentiation.   *Three-Ordinate Method.*   If successive positive ordinates X_1, X_2, X_3, $\cdots X_q$, spaced apart by equal distances Δ, are measured between an accurately located base line, parallel to the true zero line of the record, and the record trace, the first derivative of the record at the point where X_n terminates on the record trace is

$$\frac{dX_n}{dZ} = \frac{1}{2\Delta}\,(X_{n+1} - X_{n-1}) \tag{95}$$

* See article 4, p 305.

This simple formula is inherently inaccurate whenever X_n terminates on an inflection point in the record. At such places the absolute value of dX_n/dZ calculated from the formula is always less than the true absolute value of dX_n/dZ when the values of X_{n+1} and X_{n-1} are known correctly if the second derivative is negative at the inflection point, and it is always greater than the true value if the second derivative is positive at the inflection point.

Five-Ordinate Method. If X_n is the mid-ordinate in a successive series of five ordinates,

$$\frac{dX_n}{dZ} = \frac{1}{12\Delta} [8(X_{n+1} - X_{n-1}) - (X_{n+2} - X_{n-2})]* \tag{96}$$

Using this formula with absolutely correct values of the X's will give accurate values even when X_n terminates in an inflection point on the record trace.

If the probable error of measuring X_n is $\pm e$ in., the probable error for the three-ordinate method is

$$\text{Per cent error} = \frac{100 \sqrt{2}\, e}{X_{n+1} - X_{n-1}}\, \% \tag{97}$$

For the five-ordinate method it is

$$\text{Per cent error} = \frac{100 \sqrt{130}\, e}{8(X_{n+1} - X_{n-1}) - (X_{n+2} - X_{n-2})}\, \% \tag{98}$$

The probable errors in the numerical calculation of first derivatives of records can be very large.†

If the record is magnified m times with no distortion and the probable error of measuring the lengths of the ordinates is kept constant, the probable error of the first derivative found on the magnified record is $1/m$ times the probable error of the same derivative calculated from the original record.

No numerical formula for higher derivatives than the first are given or recommended, since they require accuracy of measurement beyond the powers of an ordinary reading microscope and beyond the help of usual photographic magnification of the record.

55. Electrical Differentiation. If an input voltage from an instrument is put across a circuit with a resistance R and an inductance L in series, the voltage across the inductance will be approximately proportional to the first derivative of the input voltage.[55] This will be more accurately true the larger the ratio R/L. If the resistance, R, is large compared to the reactance of the induction coil at the highest-frequency component of the impressed voltage, the voltage across the induction coil will be small, and the current will be nearly proportional to the applied voltage,

$$i \approx \frac{E_{\text{applied}}}{R}$$

* The five-ordinate method of differentiation was developed by Admiral David Watson Taylor, USN. No reference can be given here.
† See reference 15, p 280.

Then,

$$E_{\text{out}} = L \frac{di}{dt} = \frac{L}{R} \frac{d}{dt} (E_{\text{applied}})$$

For high fidelity in differentiation $L/R \to 0$, and the usual sacrifice of sensitivity to accuracy occurs.

High amplification of the low output of a highly accurate differentiation circuit may lead to troubles in the amplification circuits such as "microphonic" distortions if the vacuum tubes are moved and respond to accelerations.

Successive electrical differentiations of the signal, each recorded on a separate channel, along with the usual record, constitutes probably the only hope of getting fairly accurate derivatives. If these could be fed into a mixer circuit along with the record signal with proper phasing between the record signal and the signals from the differentiation circuits, an accurate record could be made. No one has succeeded in doing this to date; but it may be the most helpful possible development toward more accurate motion-measuring records. A basic difficulty which confronts any differentiating process is that a high-frequency component can have an arbitrarily small amplitude in the original record and an arbitrarily large amplitude in the differentiated record, if the frequency of the component is high enough.

BIBLIOGRAPHY

1. W. KNICEHAHN, "Messung mechanischer Schwingungen," *Verein deutscher Ingenieure Zeitschrift*, v 71, n 28, pp 997–99, July 9, 1927. Discusses optical methods of measuring vibrations.

2. ANONYMOUS, *The Development of Improved Means for Evaluating Effects of Torsional Vibration on Internal-Combusion Engine Installations*, War Engineering Board of the Society of Automotive Engineers, 1945, 578 pp. Pages 379 ff contain description and diagrams of this Chrysler optical torsiograph.

3. S. TIMOSHENKO, *Vibration Problems in Engineering*, 2d ed, D. Van Nostrand Co, New York, 1937. A general treatise on the theory of vibration of lumped and continuous physical systems.

4. H. STEUDING, *Messung mechanischer Schwingungen*, Berlin, 1928. A complete treatise on the instruments and methods of measuring varying quantities of mechanical interest.

5. J. ORMONDROYD, "The Use of Vibration Instruments on Electrical Machinery," *J AIEE*, v 45, 1926, pp 330–36. The theory of a few mechanical vibration measuring instruments.

6. H. M. JACKLIN and G. J. LIDDELL, "Riding Comfort Analysis," *Purdue Univ Eng Bull* 44, May 1933, pp 24–32. Investigation of effect of vibrations on human beings and measurement of vibratory accelerations in automobiles. The referenced pages describe an accelerometer with optical levers which was developed for the project.

7. C. A. HEILAND, *Geophysical Exploration*, Prentice-Hall, New York, 1940.

8. R. LEONHARDT, "Drei-komponenten Erschütterungsmesser," *Die Bautechnik A*, Heft 49, Berlin, Nov 13, 1931, p 704. Discussion of three component "shock-recording" instruments with optical magnification and photographic recording.

9. H. C. ROBERTS, *Mechanical Measurements by Electrical Methods*, Instruments Publishing Co, Pittsburgh, Pa, 1946. A comprehensive survey of principles,

circuits, and instruments used in detecting and recording mechanical strain, pressure, and vibration.

10. R. Whiddington, "The Ultra Micrometer, an Application of the Thermonic Valve to the Measurement of Very Small Distances," *Phil Mag*, series 6, v 40, 1920, pp 634–39. Discusses application of change of capacitance in measuring small distances.

11. E. C. Wente, "A Condenser Transmitter as a Uniformly Sensitive Instrument for Absolute Measurement of Sound Intensity," *Phys Rev*, v 10, 1917, pp 39–63.

12. A. V. De Forest, "Characteristics and Aircraft Application of Wire-Resistance Strain Gages," *Instruments*, v 15, 1942, pp 112–14 and 136–37.

13. R. O. Fehr, "Quartz Crystal Accelerometer," *G E Rev*, v 45, 1942, pp 269–72.

14. C. S. Draper, G. C. Bentley, and H. H. Willis, "The MIT–Sperry Apparatus for Measuring Vibration," *J Aeronautical Sciences*, v 4, 1936–37, p 695.

15. Whittaker and Robinson, *The Calculus of Observation*, 3d ed, Blackie & Son, London, 1940.

16. J. P. Den Hartog, *Mechanical Vibrations*, 3d ed, McGraw-Hill Book Co, New York, 1947. A general treatise on the vibrations of lumped and continuous physical systems.

17. C. A. Beevers and H. Lipson, *Proc Phys Soc (Lond.)*, v 48, 1936, pp 772–80; *Nature*, v 137, 1936, p 825.

18. M. A. S. Rose, "Numerical Fourier Analysis to Twenty-Nine Harmonics," *Nature*, v 152, 1943, pp 302–03.

19. H. K. Weiss, "Errors of the Dial Gauge as an Instrument for Measuring Amplitudes of Vibration," *Rev Sci Instr*, v 9, Nov 1938, pp 365–69.

20. I. Vigness and J. P. Walsh, "Some Considerations concerning Vibration Machines and Vibration Measurements," *Naval Research Lab Report* 0-2267. Effects of a flexibly mounted load on the vibration characteristics of reaction and direct-drive types of vibration machines.

21. J. M. Whitmore, "Calibrating Vibration-Measuring Instruments over a 30-to-1 Frequency Range," *Instruments*, v 14, n 10, p 280, Oct 1941. Describes two calibrating devices, one linear and one torsional, suitable for calibrating Sperry–MIT pickups at high frequency.

22. "Johnson Vibration Testing Machines," *Waugh Labs Bul* 3-5, Describes direct-drive vibration machines for producing horizontal, vertical, and rotary motions.

23. "Vibration Measuring Equipment, Sperry MIT," *Consolidated Eng Corp Publ* 23-103, Mar 1941. Describes Sperry–MIT instruments and calibrator.

24. P. Cormack "Harmonic Analysis of Motion Transmitted by Hooke's Joint," *Phil Mag*, series 6, v 44, July–Dec 1922, pp 156–60.

25. "Three Dimensional Vibration Table Cycles Automatically," *Prod Eng*, v 12, n 10, pp 664–65, Oct 1945. Describes recently developed reactions type vibration machine developed by L.A.B. Corp.

26. W. Spaeth, *Theorie und Praxis der Schwingungsprüfmaschinen*, Julius Springer, Berlin, 1934. Translated, by permission U. S. Alien Property Custodian, as *Theory and Practice of Vibration Testing Machines*. Discusses theory of mechanical vibration generators and their applications.

27. E. V. Berdahl, "Construction and Operation of the Losenhausen 440-pound Vibration Generator," report 539, David Taylor Model Basin, Navy Department, Washington, D. C., Apr 1945. Describes principles of operation and applications for this particular machine.

28. S. W. Herwald, R. W. Gemmel, and B. J. Lazan, "Mechanical Oscillators and their Electrical Synchronization," *Trans Am Soc Mech Engrs*, v 68, 1946, p 713.

29. R. T. McGoldrick and H. E. Saunders (Capt, USN), "Some Experiments in Stress Relieving Castings and Welded Structures by Vibration," *J ASNE*,

v 55, n 44, pp 589–609, Nov 1943. Discusses use of vibration generator to relieve stress.

30. M. F. BEHAR, *Fundamentals of Instrumentation*, Instruments Publishing Co, Pittsburgh, Pa, 1932.

31. C. S. DRAPER and O. P. BENTLEY, "Design Factors Controlling the Dynamic Performance of Instruments," *Trans ASME*, v 62, 1940, pp 421–32. Instruments with one degree of freedom discussed. Two parameters, a "characteristic time," and the "damping ratio" determine the dynamic errors. Examples of use in practical cases are given.

32. C. S. DRAPER and G. V. SCHLIESTETT, "General Principles of Instrument Analysis," *Instruments*, v 12, 1939, pp 137–42. Response of one degree of freedom instrument and a thermometer (no inertia) to signals of various types.

33. F. POSTLETHWAITE, "The Design of Vibration Pickup Units," *Engineering*, v 116, 1943, pp 362–64. Steady-state performance af R.A.E. vibrograph and Sperry pickup.

34. H. ZIEBOLTZ, "Analysis and Design of Translator Chains," Askania Regulator Co, Chicago, Ill.

35. KARL KLOTTER, *Messung mechanischer Schwingungen (Dynamik de Schwingungsmessgeräte)*, Springer-Verlag, Berlin, 1943. The last chapters give a quantitative discussion of distortions in records of transient motions.

36. M. F. M. OSBORNE and J. L. CARTER, "Transient Analysis of Linear Systems Using Underwater Explosion Waves," *J Applied Physics*, v 17, 1946, pp 871–73.

37. M. F. M. OSBORNE, "Transient Analysis of Linear Systems," *J Applied Physics*, v 14, 1943, pp 180–84. Finds indicial admittance from response to known transient and vice versa.

The use of high-speed photography was not mentioned in the chapter. It is, however, a widely used technique in the field of motion recording. Therefore, a few references, numbers 38–41, are given below.

38. H. J. SMITH, "Fastax, on Ultra High Speed Motion Picture Camera," *Bell Lab Rec*, v 22, Sept 1943.

39. J. L. BOON, "The Eastman High Speed Camera, Type III," *J Soc Motion Picture Engrs*, v 43, Nov 1944.

40. F. C. JOHANSEN, "High-speed Cinematography," *The Engineer*, v 177, n 4603, Mar 31, 1944.

41. H. E. EDGERTON and J. R. KILLIAN, *Flash*, Hall, Cushman, and Flint, Boston, 1939. Applications of stroboscopic light sources to high-speed photography.

42. "Sonntag 2000-Pound Universal Fatigue Testing Machine," *Baldwin Locomotive Works Bul* 207. Sonntag vibration generator as prime mover in a fatigue-testing machine.

43. "The Bernhard Mechanical Oscillator," *Waugh Labs Bul* 1.

44. B. V. LAZAN, "Some Mechanical Properties of Plastics and Metals under Sustained Vibrations," *Trans ASME*, v 65, n 2, Feb 1943. Describes a vibration generator used for fatigue tests and dynamic characteristics of materials.

45. R. O. FEHR, "Vibration Testing," *G E Rev*, v 45, n 12, pp 695–99, Dec 1942. Vibration meters for measuring oscillating stresses in apparatus. Mechanical- and electromagnetic-vibration generators are discussed.

46. M. GARDNER and J. BARNES, *Transients in Linear Systems*, John Wiley & Sons, London, 1942. La Place transform methods used on transients in electric circuits.

47. R. V. CHURCHILL, *Modern Operational Mathematics in Engineering*, McGraw-Hill Book Co, New York, 1944. General treatise on La Place transform methods for linear equations, ordinary and partial.

48. A. V. BEDFORD and G. L. FREDENHALL, "Analysis, Synthesis, and Evaluation of the Transient Response of Television Apparatus," *Proc Inst Radio Engrs*, v 30, 1942, pp 440–57. Gives charts which enable one to determine numer-

ically the steady-state phase and frequency characteristics from the indicial admittance and vice versa.

49. J. D. Trimmer, "Properties of Linear Systems Used in Vibration Measuring Instruments," *J Acoustical Soc America*, v 12, 1940, pp 127–30. The language is quite general. Actually, however, the author treats only single-degree-of-freedom systems.

50. R. G. Piety, "Interpretation of the Transient Behavior of the Reflection Seismograph," *Geophysics*, v 7, 1942, pp 123–132. Gives a graphical method of obtaining response to an arbitrary input from knowledge of response to impulsive input.

51. F. Rixmann, "Wirkung der Dämpfung bei Schwingungsentstörung und Schwingungsmessung," *Verein deutscher Ingenieure Zeitschrift*, v 85, 1941, pp 312–15. Influence of damping applied to vibration measuring instruments; basic difference in influence of damping on vibrating system and vibration-measuring apparatus. Differential equations and solution for absolute and relative damping. Phase difference between excited and recorded vibration. Bibliography.

52. M. Biot, "Theory of Elastic Systems Vibrating under Transient Impulse with an Application to Earthquake-Proof Building," *Proc Nat Acad Sciences*, v 19, 1933. Theory of continuous systems under transient loading.

53. Br. Abdank-Abakanowicz, "Les Integraphes," Gauthier-Villars, Imprimeur-Libraire, Paris, 1886, ch 3, pp 25–64. A general treatise on mechanical integration.

54. H. Von Sanden, *Practical Mathematical Analysis*, E. P. Dutton & Co, New York, pp 102–13. A general treatise on various methods of practical numerical computation.

55. J. G. Clarke, "Differentiating and Integrating Circuits," *Electronics*, Nov 1944, pp 138–42. Describes several circuits which can be used to differentiate and integrate electric signals.

56. M. Latshaw, "A Simple Tangentimeter," *J ACS*, v 47, pt 1, 1925, pp 793–94. Describes a mirror mounted perpendicularly to one leg of a steel square; the other leg is parallel to tangent when mirror image of curve shows no break.

57. O. W. Richards and P. M. Roope, "A Tangent Meter for Graphical Differentiation," *Science*, v 71, 1930, p 290. Describes a protractor with a prism mounted at the center of the rotating arm to be used for graphical differentiation. Error of less than 2 per cent claimed for slopes with tangent less than unity.

58. H. P. Simons, "An Improved Tangentimeter," *Indus and Eng Chem* (Analytical Edition), v 13, 1941, p 563.

59. A. Eagle, *Fourier's Theorem and Harmonic Analysis*, Longmans, Green & Co, London, 1925. Complete theoretical and practical treatise on Fourier analysis.

60. J. Lipka, *Graphical and Mechanical Computations*, John Wiley & Sons, New York, 1918. A standard treatise on practical computations.

61. A. G. Worthing and J. Geffner, *Treatment of Experimental Data*, John Wiley & Sons, New York, 1943. A comprehensive treatise on the reduction of experimental data to usable forms.

CHAPTER 9

STRAIN ROSETTES

By J. H. Meier

A. Introduction

1. Definition and Purpose of Strain Rosettes. A strain rosette consists of three or more straight surface lines which pass through or surround a point and represent the axes of strain gages employed to determine the state of plane stress at that point (Fig. 9-13).

Strain-rosette analysis is the art of arranging strain gages as rosettes at a number of points on the object to be investigated, taking the measurements, and computing the state of surface stress at these points.

Strain-rosette analysis is at present the most widely used experimental method of investigating biaxial stress fields. It serves two distinct purposes:

1. In a complicated structure it establishes the distribution of the surface stresses and thus relates the functioning of the various components.

2. At any individual surface point it furnishes the basis for judging the safety of the part by means of the theories of failure under combined stress.

2. Discussion of Basic Assumptions. Strain-rosette analysis is usually based on the assumptions of isotropic and homogeneous material and of strain gradients so small that the strains can be considered as substantially uniform over the area covered by the rosette gages.

A material is isotropic, if at any one point, its characteristics are the same in all directions. In strain-rosette analysis, the condition of isotropy involves only two characteristics: the modulus of elasticity, and Poisson's ratio. The strength of the material in various directions (with and across the grain, and so on) is not involved in the rosette calculation itself, but enters only in the interpretation of stresses. Within the elastic limit, all metal bodies except highly rolled thin sheets can be considered isotropic. If, however, the elastic properties change with direction, that is, if the material is not isotropic, the conventional rosette calculation holds only up to the point of establishing the principal strains. Convenient methods are available[28, 46] for correlating stresses and strains in orthotropic materials, such as wood and highly rolled thin sheets.

Similarly, for the purpose of strain-rosette analysis, engineering materials generally are sufficiently homogeneous to justify the assumption that modulus of elasticity and Poisson's ratio are constant all over the surface. This holds even for concrete; the only requirement is that the gage length employed be great enough to cover a representative portion.

Generally, strain gradients parallel to the surface are present in problems involving strain rosettes. Where they are appreciable, sensitivity has to be sacrificed for shorter gage length, as the rosette calculations neglect strain gradients. No fixed rule can be set, and the compromise depends primarily on engineering judgment. The introduction of a fourth gage line often is advisable in cases of considerable strain gradients, the redundant reading serving as an over-all check.

3. Use of the Terms "Plane Stress" and "Plane Strain." Strain-rosette analysis is based on strain-gage readings and, hence, on observations of strains along the surface. Usually there is no external pressure on the object in the gage area; thus, for a flat surface there exists a state of "plane stress" (also called two-dimensional or biaxial stress) and the strains parallel to the surface depend solely on the stresses parallel to the surface. By virtue of Poisson's ratio, there are also strains normal to the surface, that is, a three-dimensional state of strain exists. Strains normal to the surface do not enter into rosette calculations, however, and for the purpose of analogy the strain condition at the surface will be referred to as "plane strain" in this chapter. Obviously, where external pressure is applied to the surface over the rosette area, this condition must be considered when stresses are calculated from surface strains.

The stresses dealt with in strain-rosette analysis act on planes normal to the surface and in the immediate vicinity of the surface. "Stresses acting at a surface point" means the stresses on small portions of normal planes through the point. Normal planes are defined by surface lines and are usually identified by them.

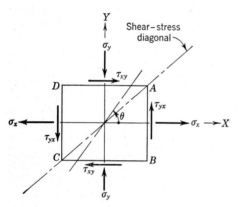

FIG. 9-1.   Elements of Stress

Although the surface may actually be curved, the curvature is generally neglected in the analysis of individual rosettes, and the local condition is still referred to as "plane stress" and "plane strain."

B. Stresses and Strains at a Point—Mohr's Circles

4. The State of Plane Stress.
Consider a rectangular surface element $ABCD$, with sides parallel to the X axis and the Y axis (Fig. 9-1). If it is assumed that no stresses act perpendicular to the surface, all stresses present are parallel to the surface. This is the general case of plane stress, and if the stress gradients within the element are neglected, the stress components are:

Normal stress σ_x on planes AB and CD.
Normal stress σ_y on planes BC and DA.
Shear stress τ_{yx} on planes AB and CD.
Shear stress τ_{xy} on planes BC and DA.

The condition of equilibrium requires that numerically

$$\tau_{xy} = \tau_{yx} \tag{1}$$

and that the arrows representing shear stresses meet at opposite corners of the element. The line going through these corners (A and C of Fig. 9-1) is called the shear-stress diagonal.[26]

The most frequently adopted sign convention takes normal stresses to be positive when they are tensile and negative when they are compressive. Shear stresses are usually called positive with respect to a system of coordinates when the shear-stress diagonal passes through the first and third quadrants.

The normal stress making an angle θ with the X axis is, by superposition,[12, 26]

$$\sigma_\theta = \frac{\sigma_x + \sigma_y}{2} + \frac{\sigma_x - \sigma_y}{2} \cos 2\theta + \tau_{xy} \sin 2\theta \tag{2}$$

The corresponding shear stress is

$$\tau_\theta = \frac{\sigma_y - \sigma_x}{2} \sin 2\theta + \tau_{xy} \cos 2\theta \tag{3}$$

In particular, τ_θ is zero, if

$$\tan 2\theta = \frac{2\tau_{xy}}{\sigma_x - \sigma_y} \tag{4}$$

Equation 4 defines two mutually perpendicular directions for which the shear stress is zero. These directions are called the "principal directions of stress," and the corresponding normal stresses are the "principal stresses." Since equation 3 is found to be one-half the first derivative of equation 2 with respect to θ, the principal stresses are the algebraically greatest and the algebraically smallest normal stresses at any one surface point. If they are called σ_{max} and σ_{min}, respectively, and coordinates coinciding with the principal axes of stress are used, the normal stress making an angle α with the direction of σ_{max} is

$$\sigma_\alpha = \frac{\sigma_{max} + \sigma_{min}}{2} + \frac{\sigma_{max} - \sigma_{min}}{2} \cos 2\alpha \tag{5}$$

The corresponding shear stress is

$$\tau_\alpha = \frac{\sigma_{min} - \sigma_{max}}{2} \sin 2\alpha \tag{6}$$

Thus, the condition of plane stress is completely defined and conveniently described by the principal stresses.

If we define

$$A'' = \frac{\sigma_{max} + \sigma_{min}}{2} \tag{7}$$

and

$$B'' = \frac{\sigma_{max} - \sigma_{min}}{2} \tag{8}$$

these quantities are calculated from the general stress components as[26]

$$A'' = \frac{\sigma_x + \sigma_y}{2} \tag{9}$$

and

$$B'' = +\tfrac{1}{2} \cdot \sqrt{(\sigma_x - \sigma_y)^2 + 4\tau_{xy}^2} \tag{10}$$

Introducing A'' and B'' into equations 5 and 6 yields the more convenient form,

$$\sigma_\alpha = A'' + B'' \cos 2\alpha \qquad (11)$$

and

$$\tau_\alpha = -B'' \sin 2\alpha \qquad (12)$$

Note that the angle between the direction of σ_{max} and the shear-stress diagonal of a square element is numerically 45° or less. The maximum shear stress τ_{max} occurs at 45° angles to the principal directions of stress and is numerically equal to B'', that is, one-half the difference between the principal stresses.

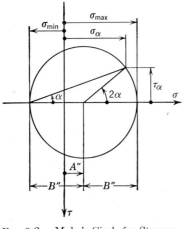

Equations 11 and 12 define a circle in a system of orthogonal coordinates σ and τ. The center lies on the normal stress axis, having A'' as abscissa, and the radius is B'' (Fig. 9-2). Any line passing through the point representing σ_{min} intersects the circle a second time at a point whose coordinates are the normal and the shear stress for the direction of the line. This circle is called Mohr's circle for stresses, for it was Otto Mohr who emphasized it in his publications. However, Mohr[3] attributes this circle to Culmann,[1] and there is a new trend to call it Culmann's circle (3d edition of reference 17, 61).

Fig. 9-2.   Mohr's Circle for Stresses

A number of relations of "plane stress" can be derived from Mohr's circle for stresses by purely geometrical considerations. For instance:

1. The sum of normal stresses for mutually perpendicular directions is constant.
2. The shear stresses for mutually perpendicular directions are numerically equal and opposite in sign.
3. The normal stresses are equal for the mutually perpendicular directions of maximum shear stress.

The state of plane stress is sometimes said[55] to consist of a uniform or hydrostatic component of stress (represented by the abscissa of the center of Mohr's circle, A'') and a shear component of stress (represented by the radius of Mohr's circle, B''). The directions of the principal stresses depend solely on the shear component of stress.

5. The State of Plane Strain.   Consider a surface point O as the origin of orthogonal coordinate axes X and Y (Fig. 9-3). In the unstrained condition, the coordinates of a nearby point P are x and y. As the surface undergoes deformation, P moves to P', thus changing its coordinates to $(x + u)$ and

$(y + v)$, respectively.   The strain components are defined by partial differentials[4, 27] as:

Normal strain parallel X axis: $\epsilon_x = \dfrac{\partial u}{\partial x}$ (13)

Normal strain parallel Y axis: $\epsilon_y = \dfrac{\partial v}{\partial y}$ (14)

Shear strain: $\gamma_{xy} = \gamma_x + \gamma_y = \dfrac{\partial v}{\partial x} + \dfrac{\partial u}{\partial y}$ (15)

Normal strains are positive when they are elongations.   Shear strains (that is, angular distortions) are positive when the shear-strain diagonal of an originally rectangular element with sides parallel to the coordinate axes and center

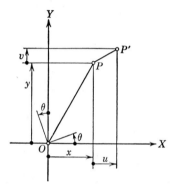

FIG. 9-3.   Elements of Strain   FIG. 9-4.   Distortion of Element by Shear

at the origin (Fig. 9-4) passes through the first and third quadrants.   The shear-strain diagonal is defined as the line passing through the acute corners of the distorted element.[26]

The normal strain along a line making an angle θ with the X axis is, by superposition,[4, 27]

$$\epsilon_\theta = \frac{\epsilon_x + \epsilon_y}{2} + \frac{\epsilon_x - \epsilon_y}{2} \cos 2\theta + \frac{1}{2} \gamma_{xy} \sin 2\theta \qquad (16)$$

Similarly, the shear strain referred to axes making angles θ with the X and Y axes is

$$\gamma_\theta = (\epsilon_y - \epsilon_x) \sin 2\theta + \gamma_{xy} \cos 2\theta \qquad (17)$$

γ_θ becomes zero, if

$$\tan 2\theta = \frac{\gamma_{xy}}{\epsilon_x - \epsilon_y} \qquad (18)$$

Equation 18 defines two mutually perpendicular directions for which the shear strain is zero.   These directions are called the "principal directions of strain," and the respective normal strains the "principal strains." Since equation 17 represents the first derivative of equation 16 with respect to θ, the principal strains are the algebraically greatest and the algebraically smallest normal strains at any one point. If we call them ϵ_{max} and ϵ_{min}, respectively, the normal strains along a line making an angle α with the direction of ϵ_{max} is

$$\epsilon_\alpha = \frac{\epsilon_{max} + \epsilon_{min}}{2} + \frac{\epsilon_{max} - \epsilon_{min}}{2} \cos 2\alpha \qquad (19)$$

The shear strain referred to axes making angles α with the principal axes of strain is

$$\gamma_\alpha = (\epsilon_{min} - \epsilon_{max}) \sin 2\alpha \qquad (20)$$

Thus, the state of plane strain is completely described by the principal strains. If we define

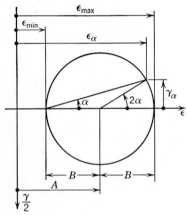

$$A = \frac{\epsilon_{max} + \epsilon_{min}}{2} \qquad (21)$$

and

$$B = \frac{\epsilon_{max} - \epsilon_{min}}{2} \qquad (22)$$

these quantities are calculated from the general strain components as[26]

$$A = \frac{\epsilon_x + \epsilon_y}{2} \qquad (23)$$

and

Fig. 9-5. Mohr's Circle for Strains

$$B = + \tfrac{1}{2} \sqrt{(\epsilon_x - \epsilon_y)^2 + \gamma_{xy}^2} \qquad (24)$$

Introducing A and B reduces equations 19 and 20 to

$$\epsilon_\alpha = A + B \cos 2\alpha \qquad (25)$$

and

$$\gamma_\alpha = -2B \sin 2\alpha \qquad (26)$$

Note that the angle between the direction of ϵ_{max} and the shear-strain diagonal of an originally square element is numerically 45° or less. The maximum shear strain γ_{max} occurs at 45° angles to the principal directions of strain and is numerically equal to $2B$, that is, the difference between the principal strains.

Equations 25 and 26 define a circle in a system of orthogonal coordinates ϵ and $\gamma/2$ (Fig. 9-5). The center lies on the normal strain axis, and its abscissa is A; the radius is B. Any line drawn through the point representing ϵ_{min} intersects the circle a second time at a point whose coordinates are the normal strain and the shear strain for the respective direction. This circle is called Mohr's circle for strains in analogy to Mohr's circle for stresses. It is a very convenient tool in strain-rosette analysis, as it translates trigonometric equations into relations of plane geometry. Analogous relations to those found for the state of plane stress from Mohr's circle for stresses can be deduced for the state of plane strain by purely geometrical considerations from Mohr's circle for strains.

6. Relations between Stresses and Strains. *Aeolotropic Materials.* The foregoing separate treatment of plane stress and plane strain holds for all materials, since no conditions as to elastic properties were introduced. However, the primary measurements of strain-rosette analysis being normal strains, the elastic behavior of the material must be known for calculating the stresses. For aeolotropic materials, the elastic properties change with direction, and the stress–strain relations become somewhat cumbersome.[5, 15] In particular, the principal axes of stress and strain generally do not coincide.

Orthotropic Materials. The three principal axes of elasticity for orthotropic materials are mutually perpendicular. If the principal axes of stress and elasticity coincide, the principal axes of strain also coincide with them. In general, the moduli of elasticity are different for the three axes, and Poisson's ratio for any one axis differs with respect to each of the other two axes. Highly rolled thin sheets are orthotropic, and recent literature considers wood as an orthotropic material.[15, 28, 46, 62] In both cases the direction of the grain represents one of the principal axes of elasticity. A surface element with sides parallel and perpendicular to the direction of the grain does not undergo any angular distortions when subjected to only normal stresses.

Direct analytical methods for relating surface stresses and strains for orthotropic materials are complicated.[15, 62] However, the problem can be solved conveniently in steps.[28, 46] For instance, if the principal stresses are known, the stresses for the directions parallel and normal to the grain are calculated (see equations 11 and 12). For these directions, the elastic constants (two moduli of elasticity, two values of Poisson's ratio, and the modulus of rigidity) are known, and the strains can be figured by superposition. Then, the components of strain lead to the principal strains in the usual way (see equations 18, 23, 24, 57, and 58). Obviously, the principal axes of surface stress and strain coincide only if one of the principal axes of strain is parallel to the direction of the grain.

Isotropic Materials. For isotropic materials, that is, for materials whose elastic properties are the same in all directions, the principal directions of stress and strain are coincident.[26, 63] Proof: According to the theory of elasticity, mutually perpendicular directions free from shear stress are also free from shear strain. The shear stress referred to the principal directions of stress is zero; hence, the shear strain for these directions is zero, and they are also the principal directions of strain.

Superposition of the fundamental equations of elastic deformation leads to the relations between the magnitudes of principal stresses and strains:

$$\epsilon_{max} = \frac{\sigma_{max} - \mu\sigma_{min}}{E} \qquad (27)$$

and

$$\epsilon_{\min} = \frac{\sigma_{\min} - \mu\sigma_{\max}}{E} \qquad (28)$$

where E is the modulus of elasticity and μ Poisson's ratio. Conversely,

$$\sigma_{\max} = \frac{E}{1 - \mu^2} \, (\epsilon_{\max} + \mu\epsilon_{\min}) \qquad (29)$$

and

$$\sigma_{\min} = \frac{E}{1 - \mu^2} \, (\epsilon_{\min} + \mu\epsilon_{\max}) \qquad (30)$$

When the abscissas and radii of Mohr's circles for stresses and strains are introduced (equations 7, 8, 21, and 22), these relations yield

$$A'' = A \, \frac{E}{1 - \mu} \qquad (31)$$

and

$$B'' = B \, \frac{E}{1 + \mu} \qquad (32)$$

Thus, a normal strain making an angle α with the direction of $\epsilon_{\max}$,

$$\epsilon_\alpha = A + B \cos 2\alpha \qquad (25)$$

corresponds to a normal stress (equation 11) of

$$\sigma_\alpha = A'' + B'' \cos 2\alpha = \frac{E}{1 - \mu} A + \frac{E}{1 + \mu} B \cos 2\alpha \qquad (33)$$

or

$$\sigma_\alpha = \frac{E}{1 - \mu} \left(A + \frac{1 - \mu}{1 + \mu} B \cos 2\alpha \right) \qquad (34)$$

Similarly, the shear strain of an element whose sides make an angle α with the principal axes,

$$\gamma_\alpha = -2B \sin 2\alpha \qquad (26)$$

corresponds to a shear stress of (equation 12)

$$\tau_\alpha = -B'' \sin 2\alpha = - \frac{E}{1 + \mu} B \sin 2\alpha \qquad (35)$$

Combining equations 26 and 35 leads to the definition of the modulus of elasticity in shear (also called modulus of rigidity):

$$G = \frac{\tau_\alpha}{\gamma_\alpha} = \frac{E}{2(1 + \mu)} \qquad (36)$$

7. Conversion of Strains to Stresses—Isotropic Materials.   Equations 27, 28, 29, and 30 form the basis for converting principal strains to principal stresses and vice versa; they are frequently used directly.   Analytical computation of the principal stresses from rosette data is facilitated by equations 31, 32, 59, and 60, because the step of calculating the principal strains is eliminated.   When the number of rosettes is great, one of the following methods of converting strains to stresses may be more expedient:

Equation 34 shows that, if the coordinate axes of Mohr's circles for stresses and strains are superimposed, and the normal stress scale is $E/(1 - \mu)$ times

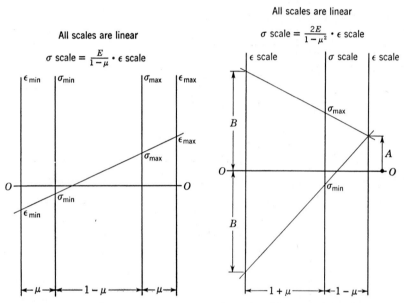

FIG. 9-6.   Nomograph for Converting Principal Strains to Principal Stresses

FIG. 9-7.   Nomograph for Converting Abscissa of Center and Radius of Mohr's Circle for Strains to Principal Stresses

the normal strain scale, Mohr's circles for stresses and strains are concentric. The radius of the stress circle then is $(1 - \mu)/(1 + \mu)$ times the radius of the strain circle.   Thus, where graphical solutions for Mohr's circle for strains are used (particularly on prepared forms), the most expedient method for finding the principal stresses is to add the proper stress scale on the normal strain axis and to draw Mohr's circle for stresses concentric to Mohr's circle for strains (Fig. 9-20).

Figure 9-6 shows a nomograph for converting principal stresses to principal strains.

Figure 9-7 shows a nomograph for finding the principal stresses from the abscissa of the center A and the radius B of Mohr's circle for true strains. By adjusting the position of the stress-scale axis, the simplified correction method for transverse gage sensitivity can be incorporated in this nomograph (see equation 56). The manufacturer's correction method can also be taken care of by the nomograph by changing the stress scale and the position of its axis.

Conversion charts for principal strains and stresses[32, 45] that do not require any lines to be drawn are based on the fact that when the coordinate axes represent the principal strains the curves for constant principal stresses are straight lines (see equations 29 and 30).

C. Strain-Rosette Measurements

8. Various Forms of Strain Rosettes and Mathematical Considerations of Their Merits. (See Table 9-2 for gage-line arrangements.) The equiangular strain rosette with its evenly distributed gage-line directions is best suited in cases where the direction of the principal strains cannot be established approximately before test.[23] When placed most unfavorably, the equiangular strain rosette covers three quarters of the range between the principal strains. Hence, extrapolation required is not serious, and reasonably reliable results can be expected (see also articles 31 and 32). The analytical and graphical solutions for the equiangular rosette require somewhat more labor than those for the rectangular rosette.

The rectangular strain rosette is particularly suited when the directions of the principal strains are approximately known in advance. The two outside gages are then placed in the expected directions of the principal strains, and their magnitude is obtained with very good accuracy. (Notice on Mohr's circle diagram that normal strains do not change rapidly as their directions deviate from the direction of the principal strains.) When the strain field is entirely unknown, however, the rectangular rosette is not so well suited as the equiangular rosette. When placed most unfavorably, the rectangular strain rosette covers only one-half of the range between the principal strains. Considerable extrapolation is thus required, bringing about decreased accuracy (see also article 32). The analytical and graphical solutions for the rectangular rosette are the most convenient.

The four-gage 45° rosette combines all the advantages enumerated previously for the equiangular and the rectangular rosettes. In addition, it furnishes a redundant reading that serves as a check. The convenient analytical solution is in agreement with the theory of least squares of errors. The compatibility of the gage readings can be checked readily by the theoretical relation, $\epsilon_1 + \epsilon_3 = \epsilon_2 + \epsilon_4$.

The T–delta rosette is not particularly attractive from a mathematical standpoint. The distribution of gage-line directions is less favorable than that of the four-gage 45° rosette, and the solutions are more cumbersome. The most commonly used formulas are not in agreement with the theory of least squares of errors, and the check obtained by the redundant reading is not so readily interpreted. The compatibility of observations can be checked before a complete analysis is made by the theoretical relation, $(\epsilon_1 + \epsilon_2 + \epsilon_3)/3 = (\epsilon_3 + \epsilon_4)/2$.

9. Review of Mechanical and Optical Strain Gages Adapted for Rosette Measurements. The Huggenberger mechanical extensometer has been used to a considerable extent for rosette work.[18, 19] Special jig plates are available (Fig. 9-8) to facilitate positioning of the gages.

Whittemore strain gages with 10 in. gage length (Fig. 9-9) were used for the rosette measurements on the Calderwood Dam.[13] Stainless-steel plugs were inserted into the concrete at the time of pouring by means of a template. After setting of the concrete, the template was removed, leaving a recessed strain rosette.

Unique strain rosettes of 10 ft gage length were used for measurements on the upstream face of the Calderwood Dam[13] under heads of up to 200 ft of

Fig. 9-8. Huggenberger Extensometer and Template for Laying Out Rosette Gage Axes (Courtesy Dr. A. U. Huggenberger, Zürich, Switzerland)

water. Invar reference wires between inserted plugs acted on levers whose motion was transmitted to the surface by means of steel wires that were kept under constant tension.

Special mechanical rosette strain gages were built for studies on the large rubber model of the Calderwood Dam.[13] On the downstream side, wire spurs were used, and the relative change of the positions of the points was observed by a microscope. On the upstream face, lever type three-element gages were employed (Fig. 9-10), and the scales were observed through a glass bottom tube while the gages were submerged.

"Hand-held" Olsen–DeShazer dial-type gages of approximately 1 in. gage length were used successfully for rosette analysis of railroad-car wheels.[27] Punch marks made with the aid of a template served as gage points.

An indicating and recording mechanical strain gage that can be swung

around into new positions without being removed from the mounting stud
was employed successfully for studies of the stresses in ship structures.[9]

Optical gages arranged in rosette fashion generally necessitate a considerable area covered by the rosette.[10] The rosette adaptor for the Tuckerman
strain gage[36] greatly reduces the actual gage area, but the mounting of the
unit requires appreciable extra space.

FIG. 9-9.   10-in. Whittemore Strain Gage Used for Rosette Measurements on
Concrete Dam, with Mercury Thermometer Shown in Place (Courtesy Aluminum
Co. of America)

The Tensor gage[25] is a very compact triple-element optical strain gage particularly built for rosette measurements (Fig. 9-11a). It is readily attached
to the object under study by means of a single centrally located suction cup.
The three readings obtained are linear functions of the strains along the gage
lines of an equiangular strain rosette, and lend themselves readily for the
calculation of the principal strains.

A special rosette gage was developed to observe large strains for investigating the behavior of materials in the post-yield range.[64] This triple-element

optical gage is fashioned after the rectangular rosette (Fig. 9-11*b*). The self-contained extensometer arms have one gage point in common. At the other gage point of each arm, a knife-edge fulcrum translates the elongation into the rotation of a mirror. A long optical path provides the necessary sensitivity. Scales, read with a telescope, are arranged on circles to maintain proper focusing. The knife-edge fulcrums can be reset readily when the effective ranges of the scales are covered, so that very large strains can be observed. A floating bridge for the attachment clamp allows severe straining of the specimen without disturbing the gage.

10. SR-4 Gages Used as Rosettes. The introduction of SR-4 bonded metalectric strain gages has greatly facilitated strain-rosette analysis and made possible its numerous applications. The general advantages of SR-4 gages over other types of strain gages is particularly appreciated in rosette work. SR-4 strain gages were, therefore, promptly followed by the SR-4 strain-gage rosettes. The main factors in favor of SR-4 rosettes are: negligible weight; small area; easy application to flat surfaces as well as to cylindrical and conical surfaces of considerable curvature; remote reading, permitting the observation of all three or four rosette gages by a single instrument; and good accuracy. These features not only are particularly attractive to the aircraft and the shipbuilding in-

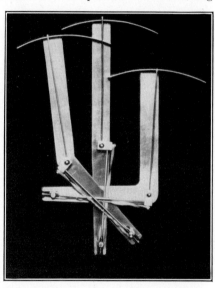

Fig. 9-10. Three-Component Templin Strain Gage for Use on Low Modulus Materials

Readings were taken by means of glass bottom tube while gage was submerged in water (Courtesy Aluminum Co of America)

dustries, but will outweigh certain advantages of other types of gages in the great majority of applications.

Although rosettes can be made up of individual gages applied to the structure (Fig. 9-12), prefabricated rosettes (Fig. 9-13) are generally preferable, because work and time are saved, and the gages of a rosette are brought into correct relative position by an accurate jig during manufacture.

11. Considerations for Choosing SR-4 Rosettes. Equiangular rosettes (types AR-4 and CR-4) are of the delta type (Fig. 9-13*a*). They have no elements crossing each other, but for a given gage length they cover a relatively large area. Their use is indicated, therefore, where the strain gradient perpendicular to the surface is relatively high and the strain gradient parallel to the surface relatively low.

Rectangular rosettes (types AR-1, AR-2, and CR-1) are of the star type (Fig. 9-13b), with elements crossing each other in three layers. For a given gage length they cover a minimum area. Thus, they are suited particularly where the strain gradient perpendicular to the surface is relatively low and the strain gradient parallel to the surface relatively high. These rosettes have the advantage that the two outside gages can be connected into circuits

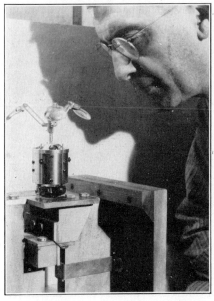

(a) The Tensor Gage, a Compact Triple-Element Strain Gage
Centrally located suction cup is used for mounting (Courtesy Douglas Aircraft Co)

(b) Large Strain Rosette Extensometer, Especially Developed for Investigation of Postyield Strain Relations
Floating bridge under attachment clamp prevents disturbance of gage by large strains (Courtesy J Sci Inst London)

FIG. 9-11.   Optical Rosette Gages

that yield signals proportional to the normal stresses along their gage lines or to the shear stress along the center gage line.[38]

The T–delta rosette (type AR-3) has two elements crossing each other and two entirely free (Fig. 9-13c). It covers the same area as the corresponding equiangular rosette (type AR-4). The fourth gage is thus introduced without increase in area or undue piling up of elements. This factor contributed most to the relative popularity of the T–delta rosette.

Special three-gage rosettes with wrap-around gages, such as star and Y rosettes falling within a ½ in. diameter circle without any elements crossing each other, were built by the Baldwin Southwark Division to meet extraordinary conditions. An assortment of special two-gage "rosettes" with gages at 90° to each other was developed for cases where the principal direc-

FIG. 9-12. Investigation of Shear Panel with Stringers by Equiangular Rosette Made up from Ordinary Resistance Wire Gages (Courtesy Douglas Aircraft Co)

tions of strain are known in advance and only their magnitude or the maximum shear strain is to be measured.[58]

12. Circuit and Wiring Problems of SR-4 Rosettes. The use of SR-4 rosettes involves the same problems throughout as the use of individual SR-4 strain gages. This holds for installation and wiring as well as for instrumenta-

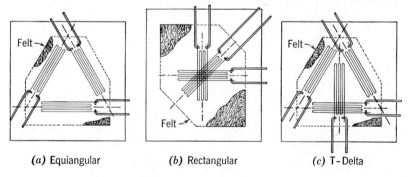

(a) Equiangular   (b) Rectangular   (c) T-Delta

FIG. 9-13. Prefabricated SR-4 Rosettes (Courtesy Baldwin Southwark Division, Baldwin Locomotive Works)

tion. Therefore, in most cases equipment available for single gages is used for rosette work and in exactly the same fashion. Since the number of gages is usually high in rosette work, scanning equipment is advantageous.

In cases where the number of rosettes is not very great and scanning equipment is not available, the chevron-type bridge of Fig. 9-14 is suggested. It requires twice the supply current of an ordinary Wheatstone bridge, but, where this is no obstacle, the following advantages are gained (if it is assumed that the impedance of the measuring device is reasonably high): The bridge circuits are closed near the point of measurement; hence, the resistance of the leads carrying the bridge supply and the signals is not critical. An ordinary three-pole rotary switch can be used near the measuring instrument for changing from one gage signal to another. A six-conductor cable with plug connections may be employed for rapid change from one rosette to another. A similar circuit is possible for four-gage rosettes.

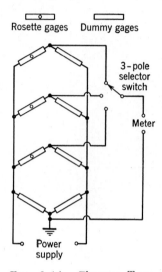

Rosette gages   Dummy gages

3-pole selector switch

Meter

Power supply

FIG. 9-14. Chevron-Type Bridge for Three-Gage Rosettes

Portable mercury-pool connectors (Fig. 9-15) making contact directly with the strain-gage lead wires are very convenient.[54] They can be moved from gage to gage in a short time and provide good contact without soldering. The lead wires are gradually weakened by amalgamation but can be expected to last for at least 15 readings.

When rosette measurements are made on thin sheets, and bending or buckling stresses are to be eliminated,[48] rosettes should be placed on both sides of the sheet (this again is a practice frequently used with single gages). The corresponding gages are connected in series, in parallel, or in opposite arms of a Wheatstone bridge to obtain the averaging effect automatically and thus keep the number

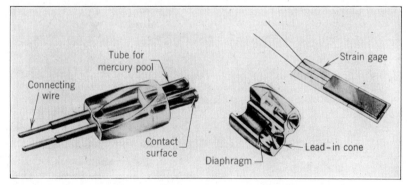

FIG. 9-15. Portable Mercury-Pool Connector for SR-4 Gages (Courtesy Bethlehem Steel Co., Shipbuilding Division)

of readings down. Where available equipment does not lend itself for averaging by the electric circuits, individual gage readings are taken and then averaged.

In certain aircraft problems, it is sufficient to establish the shear along a given line.[38]   The rectangular SR-4 strain rosette is particularly well suited for this purpose.   It is placed so that the axis of the middle gage coincides with the line along which the shear is to be measured.   As is readily seen from equations 25 and 26, the shear strain along the middle gage is equal to the difference in normal strain along the outside gages.   Either this difference can be calculated after individual readings are taken, or the difference can be obtained electrically by connecting the outside gages into adjacent arms of a Wheatstone bridge.   The middle gage is not used in this particular case, and special two-gage "rosettes" may be employed.

D. The Effect of Transverse Sensitivity of SR-4 Gages Used as Rosettes

13. Analysis of Grid Structures.   SR-4 gages are usually made up as grids (Fig. 9-13), in order to obtain a greater signal from a given gage length. Thus, they have some strain sensitivity in the direction perpendicular to the gage axis, which is commonly referred to as "cross sensitivity" or "transverse sensitivity."   Sample gages are calibrated under precisely known strain conditions to establish the effect of the grid structure.   The axial- and the transverse-strain sensitivities can be calculated readily for single-layer gages. Analytical and experimental values agree well.[43]   Difficulties are encountered, however, in the theoretical treatment of "wrap-around" gages, where the filament lies in two layers, and purely experimental determination of gage factors is indicated.   But even in this case satisfactory results are obtained from the most obvious approach of assuming that the gage response is a linear function of the strains along and perpendicular to its axis.[43]   If we introduce R as the gage resistance, ΔR as the resistance change due to strain, ϵ_a as the strain parallel to the gage axis, ϵ_n as the strain normal to the gage axis, F_a as the axial-strain sensitivity factor, and F_n as the transverse-strain sensitivity factor of the gage, we may express the gage response as

$$\frac{\Delta R}{R} = \epsilon_a F_a + \epsilon_n F_n \tag{37}$$

Very simple formulas for F_a and F_n of a single-layer grid-type gage are obtained by assuming sharp corners and wire portions arranged only parallel and normal to the gage axis.[35]   If we call the strain sensitivity of the wire F, the total filament length L, and the grid width W, we have

$$F_a = \frac{L - W}{L} F \tag{38}$$

and

$$F_n = \frac{W}{L} F \tag{39}$$

Formula 38 generally yields a somewhat low value for F_a and formula 39 a high value for F_n, because the actual grid has circular ends or is in sawtooth form.

Accurate analysis of the grid[37, 43] is based on subdividing the grid into V elements with axes parallel to the gage axis (Fig. 9-16a). The two branches of the V must not necessarily be adjacent in the gage configuration. Any configuration consisting of symmetrical portions with respect to parallel axes can be subdivided into V elements; hence, this analysis holds for all commonly used single-layer grids. For an individual V element with angle β between the two legs of the V, the axial-strain sensitivity is[43]

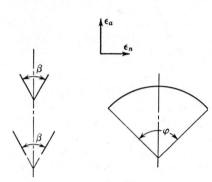

$$f_a = \frac{1 + \cos \beta}{2} F \qquad (40)$$

(a) V Elements   *(b)* Circular Arc

Fig. 9-16. Components of Grid Configuration

and the transverse-strain sensitivity

$$f_n = \frac{1 - \cos \beta}{2} F \qquad (41)$$

If a circular arc φ (Fig. 9-16b) is considered as made up of V elements with axes coinciding with the axis of symmetry of the arc, integration leads to

$$f_a = \frac{1}{2} \left(1 - \frac{\sin \varphi}{\varphi} \right) F \qquad (42)$$

and

$$f_n = \frac{1}{2} \left(1 + \frac{\sin \varphi}{\varphi} \right) F \qquad (43)$$

In particular, for a semicircle,

$$f_a = f_n = \tfrac{1}{2} F \qquad (44)$$

which, incidentally, holds for an arbitrarily orientated axis.

For all gages that can be subdivided into V elements, the gage factors are found as weighted averages:

$$F_a = \frac{\Sigma f_a \, \Delta L}{\Sigma \, \Delta L} \qquad (45)$$

and

$$F_n = \frac{\Sigma f_n \, \Delta L}{\Sigma \, \Delta L} \qquad (46)$$

where ΔL is the length of the two branches of individual V elements.

Since, for any V element, $\qquad f_a + f_n = F$ $\qquad\qquad$ (47)

it follows that $\qquad\qquad\qquad F_a + F_n = F$ $\qquad\qquad$ (48)

that is, the sum of the axial and the transverse sensitivity of a single-layer grid gage is equal to the strain sensitivity of the wire.

14. Correction for Transverse Gage Sensitivity. Gage factors for apparent strains and formulas for computing the true strains along the gage axes[43] are supplied with all SR-4 rosette gages. The true strains ϵ along individual gage lines are calculated as linear functions of apparent strains ϵ' along two or three gage lines. Formulas combining the calculation of true strains along the gage lines and the calculation of the principal strains from these true strains were also derived by the manufacturer.[43] Correction factors are applied (see Table 9-1) to the abscissa of the center and to the radius of Mohr's circle for apparent strains as calculated from the manufacturer's axial-strain sensitivity factor. The two factors render the formulas somewhat cumbersome, particularly for graphical solutions and rosette computers.

The procedure can be simplified by the elimination of one correction factor.[35, 40] For this purpose, the strain sensitivity of the filament F is used for calculating the apparent strain ϵ' from the gage response:

$$\epsilon' = \frac{\Delta R}{R}\frac{1}{F} = \epsilon_a \frac{F_a}{F} + \epsilon_n \frac{F_n}{F} \qquad\qquad (49)$$

If we observe that the true strain along the gage axis is

$$\epsilon_a = \epsilon_\alpha = A + B \cos 2\alpha \qquad\qquad (50)$$

and the normal strain perpendicular to the gage axis

$$\epsilon_n = \epsilon_{(\alpha+90°)} = A - B \cos 2\alpha \qquad\qquad (51)$$

and introduce the specific transverse gage sensitivity

$$k = \frac{F_n}{F_a} \qquad\qquad (52)$$

the apparent strain is recognized (see also equation 48) as

$$\epsilon_\alpha' = A + \frac{1-k}{1+k} B \cos 2\alpha = A' + B' \cos 2\alpha \qquad\qquad (53)$$

where A' is the abscissa of the center and B' the radius of Mohr's circle for apparent strains.

Hence, the relations between apparent strains are analogous to the relations between true strains. Any method for representing true strains may be employed for apparent strains. Furthermore, any convenient rosette solution may be applied directly to the apparent strains by treating them as if they were true strains. A', B', and α are then obtained immediately from the observed ϵ' values, and one simply has to observe that

$$A = A' \qquad\qquad (54)$$

and

$$B = B' \frac{1 + k}{1 - k} \tag{55}$$

Thus, when the simplified correction method for transverse gage sensitivity is used, Mohr's circles for apparent strains and true strains are concentric; the correction involves the radius only. Since proper choice of scale ratio leads to concentricity of Mohr's circles for true strains and stresses (article 7), all three Mohr's circles can be drawn concentrically.[37, 40] If the true strains are not of particular interest, the radius of Mohr's circle for stresses is directly obtained from B' as (see also Fig. 9-20)

$$\underbrace{\frac{1 - \mu}{E}}_{\text{Scale ratio}} B'' = \frac{1 - \mu}{1 + \mu} B = \frac{1 + k}{1 - k} \frac{1 - \mu}{1 + \mu} B' \tag{56}$$

The rosette gage factors supplied by the manufacturer are related to the factors of the simplified correction method as shown in Table 9-1. These relations hold also for special rosettes consisting of wrap-around gages, providing the manufacturer's correction formulas are the same as those for the corresponding rosettes of Table 9-1. For such gages the value calculated for F is no longer the strain sensitivity of the wire.

15. The Stress Gage. Assume a gage whose specific transverse sensitivity k is equal to Poisson's ratio μ of the material to which it is applied. Comparison of equations 34 and 53 shows that the apparent strain indicated by such a gage is proportional to the stress along its axis and is not affected by the stress perpendicular to its axis. (Note also from equation 56 that in this case Mohr's circles for apparent strains and stresses coincide, providing the scale ratio is chosen properly.) Gages of this type are called stress gages or dyadic gages.[37] Although individual stress gages are commercially available, they have not been built into rosettes. The main reasons for this are the appreciable sacrifice in axial sensitivity and the considerable gage width necessary to obtain sufficient specific transverse sensitivity.

E. STRAIN-ROSETTE COMPUTATIONS

16. The Problem. The magnitude and the orientation of the principal stresses are to be computed from the observed strains. There being three unknowns, normal strains in at least three directions are required. If we introduce the angles α_1, α_2, α_3 $\cdots$ between the direction of $\epsilon_{\max}$ and gage lines 1, 2, 3 $\cdots$, respectively, we can set up simultaneous equations of the form of equation 25 (whereby the differences $\alpha_2 - \alpha_1$, $\alpha_3 - \alpha_1$ $\cdots$ are known from the gage configuration). These simultaneous equations must be solved for A, B, and α_1. Then, the principal strains are found from A and B (equations 21 and 22) as

$$\epsilon_{\max} = A + B \tag{57}$$

TABLE 9-1

RELATIONS BETWEEN FACTORS FOR MANUFACTURER'S AND SIMPLIFIED
CORRECTION METHOD FOR TRANSVERSE GAGE SENSITIVITY

SR-4 rosettes, Configuration and Type Number	Manufacturer's Rosette Gage Factors a = axial-strain-sensitivity factor b = auxiliary sensitivity factor Manufacturer assumes apparent strains calculated on basis of gage sensitivity a		Relations between Manufacturer's Factors a and b and Factors F and k of Simplified Correction Method
	Correction Factor for Abscissa of Mohr's Circle for Apparent Strains	Correction Factor for Radius of Mohr's Circle for Apparent Strains	
Rectangular rosettes, Types AR-1, AR-2, CR-1 T–delta rosettes, Type AR-3	$1 - \dfrac{1}{b}$	$1 + \dfrac{1}{b}$	$a = F(1 - k)$ $b = \dfrac{1}{k}$ $F = \dfrac{ab}{b-1}$ $k = \dfrac{1}{b}$
Equiangular rosettes (or 60° rosettes), Types AR-4, CR-4	$1 - \dfrac{2}{b}$	$1 + \dfrac{1}{b}$	$a = \dfrac{3F(1-k)}{3+k}$ $b = \dfrac{3+k}{2k}$ $F = \dfrac{ab}{b-2}$ $k = \dfrac{3}{2b-1}$

and

$$\epsilon_{\min} = A - B \tag{58}$$

After converting A and B to A'' and B'', respectively (equations 31 and 32), the principal stresses are found (equations 7 and 8) as

$$\sigma_{\max} = A'' + B'' \tag{59}$$

and

$$\sigma_{\min} = A'' - B'' \tag{60}$$

The correction for transverse sensitivity of grid-type wire gages and the conversion from strains to stresses having already been discussed, the only remaining step of strain-rosette computations is the solution for A, B, and α_1.

The choice of the method for solving the problems is governed by:

1. The accuracy required.

TABLE 9-2

ANALYTICAL SOLUTIONS FOR MOST COMMONLY USED STRAIN ROSETTES

Names	Equiangular, 60° Delta	Rectangular, Three-Gage 45°, Star	Four-Gage 45°, Fan	T–Delta
Configuration				
$\alpha_1 - \alpha_2$	60°	45°	45°	60°
$\alpha_1 - \alpha_3$	120°	90°	90°	120°
$\alpha_1 - \alpha_4$			135°	30°
A	$\frac{1}{3}(\epsilon_1 + \epsilon_2 + \epsilon_3)$	$\frac{1}{2}(\epsilon_1 + \epsilon_3)$	$\frac{1}{4}(\epsilon_1 + \epsilon_2 + \epsilon_3 + \epsilon_4)$ or $\frac{1}{2}(\epsilon_1 + \epsilon_3)$ or $\frac{1}{2}(\epsilon_2 + \epsilon_4)$	$\frac{1}{2}(\epsilon_2 + \epsilon_4)$ or $\frac{1}{3}(\epsilon_1 + \epsilon_2 + \epsilon_3)$
B	$\frac{\sqrt{2}}{3}\sqrt{(\epsilon_1 - \epsilon_2)^2 + (\epsilon_2 - \epsilon_3)^2 + (\epsilon_1 - \epsilon_3)^2}$ or $\sqrt{(\epsilon_1 - A)^2 + \frac{1}{3}(\epsilon_2 - \epsilon_3)^2}$	$\frac{\sqrt{2}}{2}\sqrt{(\epsilon_1 - \epsilon_2)^2 + (\epsilon_2 - \epsilon_3)^2}$ or $\sqrt{(\epsilon_1 - A)^2 + (\epsilon_2 - A)^2}$	$\frac{1}{2}\sqrt{(\epsilon_1 - \epsilon_3)^2 + (\epsilon_2 - \epsilon_4)^2}$ or $\sqrt{(\epsilon_1 - A)^2 + (\epsilon_2 - A)^2}$ or $\sqrt{(\epsilon_3 - A)^2 + (\epsilon_4 - A)^2}$	$\frac{\sqrt{2}}{3}\sqrt{(\epsilon_1 - \epsilon_2)^2 + (\epsilon_2 - \epsilon_3)^2 + (\epsilon_1 - \epsilon_3)^2}$ or $\sqrt{\frac{1}{3}(\epsilon_1 - \epsilon_2)^2 + \frac{1}{4}(\epsilon_3 - \epsilon_4)^2}$
$\tan 2\alpha_1$	$\frac{\sqrt{3}(\epsilon_2 - \epsilon_3)}{2\epsilon_1 - \epsilon_2 - \epsilon_3}$ or $\frac{\sqrt{3}(\epsilon_2 - \epsilon_3)}{3(\epsilon_1 - A)}$	$\frac{2\epsilon_2 - \epsilon_1 - \epsilon_3}{\epsilon_1 - \epsilon_3}$ or $\frac{\epsilon_2 - A}{\epsilon_1 - A}$	$\frac{\epsilon_2 - \epsilon_4}{\epsilon_1 - \epsilon_3}$ or $\frac{\epsilon_2 - A}{\epsilon_1 - A} \quad \frac{A - \epsilon_4}{A - \epsilon_3}$	$\frac{\sqrt{3}(\epsilon_2 - \epsilon_3)}{2\epsilon_1 - \epsilon_2 - \epsilon_3}$
References	20, 26, 31, 43	26, 31, 43, 44	14, 18, 22, 27	22, 35, 42, 43

2. The amount of rosette analysis contemplated.

3. The speed of analysis required.

4. Requirements as to permanent records for future checks on calculation.

5. The preference and aptitude of the individual.

A selection of the great many methods advanced is presented in the following.

17. Analytical Solutions. Analytical solutions require somewhat more work and time than the analogous graphical solutions. They are indicated where greatest possible accuracy is required. Analytical solutions lend themselves readily for checking the compatibility of the redundant reading when four-gage rosettes are used. Furthermore, the formulas for four-gage rosettes can be made to conform with the theory of least squares of errors.[22, 23] Means for determining the probable error of the results are available;[22, 23] they were developed primarily for readings from mechanical gages and were rendered less important by the introduction of the more accurate SR-4 gages.

Table 9-2 shows the analytical solutions for the most commonly used rosettes. The identification of gage axes is that used by the manufacturer of SR-4 gages. In the case of the four-gage 45° rosette, the formulas containing all four gage readings are recommended, as they conform with the theory of least squares of errors. The solution for the T–delta rosette based on this theory is (see Table 9-2 for identification of gage lines):

$$A = \tfrac{1}{18}(4\epsilon_1 + 4\epsilon_2 + 7\epsilon_3 + 3\epsilon_4) \tag{61}$$

$$B = \tfrac{1}{9}\sqrt{27(\epsilon_1 - \epsilon_2)^2 + (5\epsilon_3 - \epsilon_1 - \epsilon_2 - 3\epsilon_4)^2} \tag{62}$$

or

$$\left. \begin{aligned} \tan 2\alpha_3 = \tan 2(\alpha_1 - 120°) &= 3\sqrt{3}\,\frac{\epsilon_1 - \epsilon_2}{5\epsilon_3 - \epsilon_1 - \epsilon_2 - 3\epsilon_4} \\ \tan 2\alpha_1 &= \sqrt{3}\,\frac{3\epsilon_4 - 5\epsilon_3 + 4\epsilon_2 - 2\epsilon_1}{3\epsilon_1 - 5\epsilon_3 - 8\epsilon_2 + 10\epsilon_1} \end{aligned} \right\} \tag{63}$$

Tabular forms for making the calculations[18, 27] are most convenient and reduce the possibility of errors.

In Table 9-2 and formula 63 note that α_1 is measured from the direction of ϵ_{max} to the direction of gage line 1, and is positive counterclockwise. This convention was adopted by the National Bureau of Standards.[11, 14, 16, 21] The angle α_1 is not completely defined by the sign of the tangent. If the correct value is not evident from inspection, it can be determined by the sign of the numerator and the denominator in the formulas for $\tan 2\alpha_1$, as shown in Table 9-3.

TABLE 9-3

Signs of Numerical Values
in Formulas for $2\alpha_1$

Numerator	Denominator	Range of $2\alpha_1$
+	+	$0° < 2\alpha_1 < 90°$
+	−	$90° < 2\alpha_1 < 180°$
−	−	$180° < 2\alpha_1 < 270°$
−	+	$270° < 2\alpha_1 < 360°$

Numerical Example. Given data:

Steel, $E = 30,000,000$ psi; $\mu = 0.286$

Equiangular SR-4 rosette, 120 ohms per gage

Manufacturer's axial-strain sensitivity factor: $a = 2.08$

Manufacturer's auxiliary sensitivity coefficient: $b = 75$

Strain-gage factors for simplified correction method for transverse-gage sensitivity (see Table 9-1):

$$F = \frac{ab}{b-2} = \frac{2.08 \times 75}{75-2} = \frac{156.0}{73} = 2.136$$

$$k = \frac{3}{2b-1} = \frac{3}{2 \times 75 - 1} = \frac{3}{149} = 0.020$$

Apparent strains: If "strain indicator" is available, set knob for gage sensitivity of 2.136, and read apparent strains directly in microinches per inch. If a similarly convenient instrument is not available, calculate apparent strains from observed resistance changes ΔR, using the factor F:

Gage	ΔR, Ohm	R, Ohm	$\Delta R/R$, Ohm/Ohm	$\epsilon' = \dfrac{\Delta R}{RF}$
1	+0.1286	120	0.001 068	+0.000 500 in./in.
2	+0.0974	120	0.000 812	+0.000 380 in./in.
3	+0.0512	120	0.000 427	+0.000 200 in./in.

Solution of rosette: See Table 9-2. If we choose the first formulas and remember that observed strain values are apparent strains, we have

$$A = A' = \tfrac{1}{3}(\epsilon_1' + \epsilon_2' + \epsilon_3') = \tfrac{1}{3}(0.000\ 500 + 0.000\ 380 + 0.000\ 200)$$

$$A = 0.000\ 360 \text{ in./in.}$$

$$B' = \frac{\sqrt{2}}{3}\sqrt{(\epsilon_1' - \epsilon_2')^2 + (\epsilon_2' - \epsilon_3')^2 + (\epsilon_1' - \epsilon_3')^2}$$

$$(\epsilon_1' - \epsilon_2') = 0.000\ 500 - 0.000\ 380 = 0.000\ 120 \text{ in./in.}$$

$$(\epsilon_2' - \epsilon_3') = 0.000\ 380 - 0.000\ 200 = 0.000\ 180 \text{ in./in.}$$

$$(\epsilon_1' - \epsilon_3') = 0.000\ 500 - 0.000\ 200 = 0.000\ 300 \text{ in./in.}$$

$$B' = 0.4713\sqrt{(0.000\ 120)^2 + (0.000\ 180)^2 + (0.000\ 300)^2}$$

$$B' = 0.4713 \times 0.000\ 3699 = 0.000\ 1743 \text{ in./in.}$$

Correction for transverse gage sensitivity: From equation 55,

$$B = B'\frac{1+k}{1-k} = 0.000\ 1743\,\frac{1+0.02}{1-0.02} = 0.000\ 1813 \text{ in./in.}$$

Orientation of rosette:

$$\tan 2\alpha_1 = \frac{\sqrt{3}\,(\epsilon_2' - \epsilon_3')}{2\epsilon_1' - \epsilon_2' - \epsilon_3'} = \frac{1.7321 \times 0.000\ 180}{2 \times 0.000\ 500 - 0.000\ 380 - 0.000\ 200}$$

$$\tan 2\alpha_1 = \frac{1.7321 \times 0.000\ 180}{0.000\ 420} = 0.7423$$

Numerator $+$; Denominator $+$; $0° < 2\alpha_1 < 90°$ (from Table 9-3)

$$2\alpha_1 = 36° 35'; \qquad \alpha_1 = 18° 18'$$

Principal strains and maximum shear strain:

Equation 57: $\epsilon_{max} = A + B = 0.000\ 360 + 0.000\ 181 = 0.000\ 541$ in./in.
Equation 58: $\epsilon_{min} = A - B = 0.000\ 360 - 0.000\ 181 = 0.000\ 179$ in./in.
Equation 26: Maximum shear strain $\gamma_{max} = 2B = 0.000\ 363$ in./in.

Conversion to stresses:

Equation 31, $A'' = A \dfrac{E}{1 - \mu} = A \dfrac{30,000,000}{1 - 0.286}$

$$A'' = 0.000\ 360 \times 42,017,000 = 15,130 \text{ psi}$$

Equation 32, $B'' = B \dfrac{E}{1 + \mu} = B \dfrac{30,000,000}{1 + 0.286}$

$$B'' = 0.000\ 1813 \times 23,328,000 = 4230 \text{ psi}$$

Principal stresses and maximum shear stress: Equations 59, 60, and 12,

$$\sigma_{max} = A'' + B'' = 15,130 + 4230 = 19,360 \text{ psi}$$

$$\sigma_{min} = A'' - B'' = 15,130 - 4230 = 10,900 \text{ psi}$$

Maximum shear stress: $\tau_{max} = B'' = 4230$ psi

True strains and stresses along gage lines: Equations 25 and 11,

Gage	2α	$\cos 2\alpha$	$B \cos 2\alpha$	$B'' \cos 2\alpha$	ϵ, in./in.	σ, psi
1	$36° 35'$	$0.802\ 99$	$0.000\ 145$	3400	$0.000\ 505$	$18,530$
2	$-83° 25'$	$0.114\ 64$	$0.000\ 021$	480	$0.000\ 381$	$15,610$
3	$-203° 25'$	$-0.917\ 64$	$-0.000\ 166$	-3880	$0.000\ 194$	$11,250$

18. Semigraphical Solution. The solution[24] consists of superimposing a master cosine curve over a plot (rectangular coordinates) of proportionately reduced strain readings versus the angle between the gage lines. The peaks of the master curve then indicate the directions of the principal strains and their reduced magnitudes. The true principal strains are obtained by multiplying the indicated values by the reduction factor. The reduction factor is chosen so that the radius of Mohr's circle is unity; that is, equation 25 becomes

$$\frac{\epsilon_\alpha}{B} = \frac{A}{B} + \cos 2\alpha \tag{64}$$

B must be calculated analytically, and the amount of numerical calculation is comparable to that of analytical solutions.

In order to overcome the necessity of calculating B and reducing the observed data, it was suggested[59] that a cosine wave, projected on the screen of a cathode-ray tube, be used as a master curve with variable amplitude. The plot is then held against the screen, and the amplitude and position of the cosine curve is adjusted until it passes through the plotted points. The results are read off directly on the transparent graph paper of the plot. The

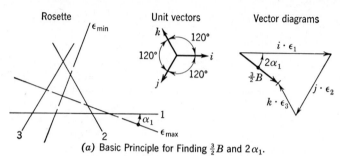

(a) Basic Principle for Finding $\frac{3}{2}B$ and $2\alpha_1$.

Scales for picking off observed strains by dividers

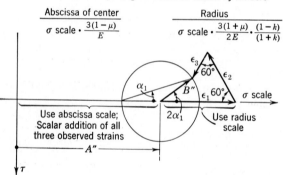

(b) Direct Construction of Mohr's Circle for Stresses

Fig. 9-17. Vector Solution for Equiangular Rosette

degree of accuracy obtainable is sufficient for many purposes. For four-gage rosettes, the compatibility of readings is readily checked, and an appropriate compromise can be found.

19. Graphical Solutions for Arbitrary Angles between Gage Lines. Graphical solutions for three-gage rosettes with arbitrary angles between gage lines are relatively convenient, whereas the corresponding analytical solutions are cumbersome. This general case is rarely encountered, however, and the graphical methods developed for it are useful primarily as a basis for the more simple solutions applying to the commonly used rosettes.

Vector diagrams for finding Mohr's circle[37] or Land's circle[6, 11] have been developed. A displacement diagram[52] was proposed for determining the principal strains.   Mohr's circle can also be obtained by geometrical locus.[33, 51] For given angles between gage lines, the respective points on Mohr's circle form similar triangles.   The problem thus reduces to finding a triangle of given angles whose vertices correspond to the respective strain readings, that is, lie on three parallel lines.   The triangle is obtained by the commonly known locus method, and its circumscribing circle is Mohr's circle.

20. Vector Solution for 45° Rosettes and the Equiangular Rosette.   Vector solutions[49, 55] use a scalar function of the gage readings for determining A and vector diagrams for B and the angle $2\alpha_1$.   The formulas of Table 9-2 suggest simple vector solutions for 45° rosettes.   There are only two terms under the square root for quantity B; hence, the corresponding vectors are at right angles to each other, and the resulting vector determines $2\alpha_1$.[49]

Figure 9-17a shows the basic principle of the vector solution for the equiangular rosette.   In order to bring Mohr's circle diagram in the conventional position, the mirror image of the vector diagram is used (Fig. 9-17b), and $2\alpha_1$ is measured counterclockwise from the ϵ_1 vector to the resulting vector. Auxiliary scales may be used so that the scalar addition of ϵ_1, ϵ_2, and ϵ_3, by means of dividers, leads directly to A'' and the vector addition to B''.   Mohr's circle for stresses is thus obtained directly.   The correction for transverse sensitivity of grid-type wire gages can be taken care of by adjusting the ratio for the radius scale.

Numerical Example.   Given data: Same as in example for analytical solution of equiangular rosette.   The calculation of the factors F and k and of the apparent strains is identical.   For the sake of comparison, the entire vector solution will be followed analytically step by step.

Scales:

Stress scale—Assume 1 in. represents 5000 psi.
Scale of observed (apparent) strains for finding abscissa of center of Mohr's circle for stresses—1 in. represents $5000 \dfrac{3(1 - \mu)}{E} = 5000 \times \dfrac{3(1 - 0.286)}{30,000,000} = 5000 \times 0.000\ 000\ 0714 = 0.000\ 357$ in./in., or 0.0280 in. represent 0.000 010 in./in.
Scale of observed (apparent) strains for finding radius of Mohr's circle for stresses—1 in. represents $5000 \dfrac{3(1 + \mu)}{2E} \dfrac{1 - k}{1 + k} = 5000 \dfrac{3(1 + 0.286)}{2 \times 30,000,000} \dfrac{1 - 0.02}{1 + 0.02} = 5000 \times 0.000\ 000\ 0643 \times 0.960 = 0.000\ 309$ in./in., or 0.0324 in. represent 0.000 010 in./in.

Abscissa of center of Mohr's circle for stresses: With dividers, pick off the apparent strain values on the abscissa scale determined previously, and perform scalar addition on normal stress axis of diagram.

$\epsilon_1' = 0.000\ 500$ in./in. is represented by 1.40 in.
$\epsilon_2' = 0.000\ 380$ in./in. is represented by 1.06 in.
$\epsilon_3' = 0.000\ 200$ in./in. is represented by 0.56 in.

The scalar sum is represented by   3.02 in.

Radius of Mohr's circle for stresses: With dividers, pick off the apparent strain values on the radius scale determined previously, and construct the vector diagram as shown in Fig. 9-17b.

$\epsilon_1' = 0.000\ 500$ in./in. is represented by 1.62 in.
$\epsilon_2' = 0.000\ 380$ in./in. is represented by 1.23 in.
$\epsilon_3' = 0.000\ 200$ in./in. is represented by 0.65 in.

The length of the resulting vector is 0.85 in.
Draw Mohr's circle for stresses with resulting vector as radius. The radius corresponds on the stress scale to $5000 \times 0.85 = 4250$ psi; this is the maximum shear stress.

Principal stresses: Read off directly on normal stress axis, at intersection with Mohr's circle,

$$\sigma_{max} = 19{,}350 \text{ psi (resulting from } 15{,}100 + 4250)$$

$$\sigma_{min} = 10{,}850 \text{ psi (resulting from } 15{,}100 - 4250)$$

Orientation of Rosette: Draw line representing direction of gage line 1 on Mohr's circle diagram. It passes through the point representing σ_{min} and

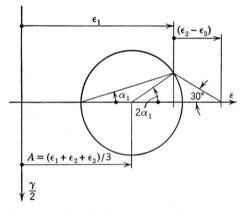

the end point of the resulting vector. Read off the angle this line makes with the normal stress axis: 18°, counterclockwise from the normal stress axis. Thus, to find the direction of σ_{max} at the point of the object investigated, go 18° clockwise from the direction of gage line 1.

21. Graphical Solutions for Equiangular Rosette. The construction of Mohr's circle[20, 26] of Fig. 9-18 is based on the second solution of Table 9-2. Quantities A and $(\epsilon_2 - \epsilon_3)$ are calculated nu-

FIG. 9-18. Graphical Solution for Equiangular Rosette

merically. The arrows in Fig. 9-18 indicate that the respective values are plotted in the direction shown when positive, in opposite direction when negative.

The solution of Fig. 9-19 requires no numerical calculations, as it is derived from a geometrical locus.[32, 52] Three parallel strain lines, ϵ_1, ϵ_2, and ϵ_3, are plotted to represent the gage readings. Through an arbitrary point N of ϵ_1 draw two lines making 60° angles with ϵ_1. Intersect one of them with ϵ_2, the other with ϵ_3. The two points so obtained define one side of an equiangular triangle, the third vertex of which lies on ϵ_1. The circumscribing circle of this triangle is Mohr's circle. The direction of the algebraically greater principal strain falls between the direction of the gage lines with the algebraically greater strains and makes the smallest angle with the algebraically greatest of the observed strains.

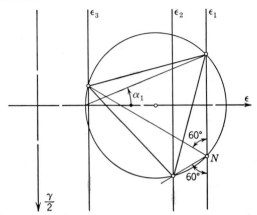

FIG. 9-19. Solution for Equiangular Rosette by Geometrical Locus

For still other graphical solutions for the equiangular rosette, see references 33, 48, and 52.

22. Graphical Solutions for the T–Delta Rosettes. The graphical solutions for the T–delta rosettes usually employ the gages at right angles for determining A and the three gages forming the delta for B. However, the three gages forming the delta may be treated as an equiangular rosette for the entire solution, the fourth gage serving simply as a check.

23. Graphical Solution for 45° Rosettes. The simplest and most commonly used graphical solution for the rectangular rosette[26] is based on the second solution of Table 9-2. It is very similar to the prepared form solution for 45° rosettes, the only difference being that A is found either by some other convenient geometrical means or analytically. This same solution can be applied to the four-gage 45° rosette; a check is obtained graphically from the theoretical relation $\epsilon_1 + \epsilon_3 = \epsilon_2 + \epsilon_4$.

For other graphical solutions for the rectangular rosette, see reference 52.

24. Prepared-Form Solution for 45° Rosettes. The prepared form[34] for the rectangular rosette consists of three parallel and equidistant lines provided with ϵ scales (Fig. 9-20). ϵ_1 is marked off on the top line, ϵ_2 on the center line, and ϵ_3 on the bottom line. The line connecting the ϵ_1 and ϵ_3 points intersects the center line at the center of Mohr's circle. The quantities $(\epsilon_1 - A)$ and $(\epsilon_2 - A)$ appearing in the second solutions of Table 9-2 are directly available from the graph. The point on Mohr's circle representing gage 1 is found on the perpendicular to the equidistant lines through the ϵ_1 point by plotting $(\epsilon_2 - A)$, upwards from the center line if positive, downwards if negative. When the form is used for the four-gage 45° rosette, both alternative terms for A of Table 9-2 are employed, and a check is obtained. Interpolation between the individual solutions leads to the most probable value.

The form is readily adapted to yield the true principal strains and the principal stresses: A stress scale (equal to $E/(1 - \mu)$ times the strain scale) is added to the center line. Considering the distance between the center and the bottom lines as unity, add parallel lines l and m at distances $(1 - \mu)/(1 + \mu)$ and $(1 - k)/(1 + k)$, respectively, from the center line. Draw a perpendicular line to the equidistant lines, and intersect it with the center line at K, with l at L, with m at M, and with the bottom line at N. These additions being incorporated in the prepared form, plot the radius of Mohr's circle for apparent strains as $\overline{MM'}$ on m and draw line KM'. This line intersects the bottom line at N' and l at L'. $\overline{NN'}$ is the radius of Mohr's circle for true

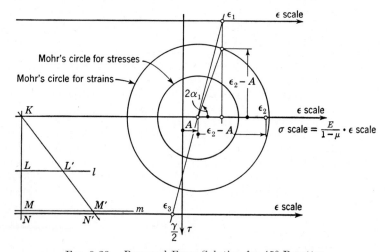

FIG. 9-20.   Prepared Form Solution for 45° Rosettes

strains, and $\overline{LL'}$ is the radius of Mohr's circle for stresses (see equations 34 and 53 for proof).

25. Solutions by Nomographs, Charts, and Slide Rules.   The nomograph solution for the rectangular rosette[57] of Fig. 9-21 is a combination of the vector method for finding quantity B and the nomograph of Fig. 9-7.   The strain quantities $(\epsilon_1 + \epsilon_3)$, $(\epsilon_1 - \epsilon_2)$, and $(\epsilon_2 - \epsilon_3)$ are obtained numerically or by dividers on the strain scales.   Scale ratios are so that the nomograph yields the principal stresses and the maximum shear stress directly from the strain quantities.   The angle α_1 is found from auxiliary curves relating it to $(\epsilon_1 - \epsilon_2)$ and $(\epsilon_2 - \epsilon_3)$.   These curves are based on the relation $\tan 2\alpha_1 = 1 - 2(\epsilon_1 - \epsilon_2)$ $/\{(\epsilon_1 - \epsilon_2) + (\epsilon_2 - \epsilon_3)\}$, which can be derived from the respective formulas of Table 9-2.

See references 16, 56, and 57 for further nomograph solutions leading directly to the principal stresses.

Charts for the rectangular rosette lead to a rapid solution for the principal strains or stresses and the maximum shear strain or stress, particularly if the strain quantities are combined by the electric circuits of the measuring instrument.[44] For such rather involved charts a compromise must be made between accuracy and convenience in reading.

"Rosette slide rules" were designed for the analysis of four-gage 45° rosettes.[27]

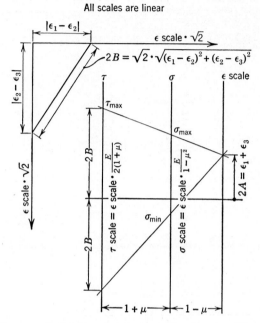

Fig. 9-21. Nomograph Solution for Rectangular Rosette (Courtesy Republic Aviation Corp)

26. Geometrical Computers. A mechanical computer for 45° rosettes,[44] using two sliding hairlines and a pivoted hairline with an index rider, was devised for use with simplified charts. It works on the vector principle, and some numerical calculations are necessary unless the strain quantities are electrically combined by the measuring circuits.

The geometrical computer (Fig. 9-22) for rectangular rosettes[54] is based on the principle of the prepared-form solution (Fig. 9-20). Individual strain observations are used directly, the average of ϵ_1 and ϵ_3 being established by a slidable parallelogram linkage moving over a strain scale. The radius of Mohr's circle for strains and the angle $2\alpha_1$ are obtained by a hairline properly pivoted on the linkage. Proportional dividers are used for finding the radius of Mohr's circle for stresses and for establishing the principal stresses on the stress scale.

27. Continuous-Computing Machines. Differential analyzers and continuous-computing machines developed for other purposes may be adapted[42] to strain-rosette problems. However, the particular characteristics of rosette equations suggest a more direct mechanical approach.

The original computing machine for strain rosettes[31] employed racks and pinions for scalar additions and mutually perpendicular slots, carrying a common pin, for vector additions. Its operation was rendered somewhat difficult by friction.

FIG. 9-22. Geometrical Computer for Rectangular Rosette (Courtesy Bethlehem Steel Co, Shipbuilding Division)

FIG. 9-23. Squaring Mechanism for Rosette Computer (Courtesy Prof W. M. Murray, Massachusetts Institute of Technology)

A new machine was built[47, 50] embodying differential gearing for scalar additions. Squares and square roots are handled by two fine cables winding from a grooved cone to a cylinder (Fig. 9-23) and vice versa. An ingenious differential-gearing system compensates for the finite diameter of the cone at the position where the respective quantity becomes zero. A servomotor is necessary for the square-root operation. The angle $2\alpha_1$ is determined by the vector method. This machine has remarkable accuracy with relatively low input torques. It may, therefore, be used in connection with three or four self-balancing bridge units, thereby operating fully automatically from electrical strain gages.

28. Selsyn Computer. The electromechanical vector computer[30, 39] employs three single-phase two-pole rotary transformers, called Selsyns or sinometers. The rotors are coupled together, their relative position corresponding to twice the angles between the gage lines. When the fields of the

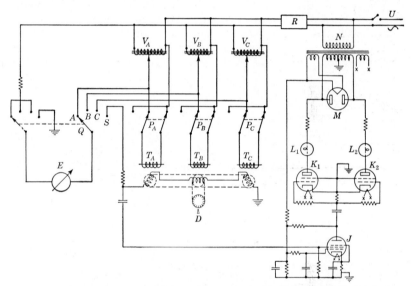

FIG. 9-24.   Circuit Diagram of Selsyn Computer for Radius of Mohr's Cricle from Equiangular Rosettes (Courtesy Douglas Aircraft Co)

transformers are excited by inphase voltages representing the observed strains (Fig. 9-24), the output of the series-connected rotors is proportional to the shear strain of the direction corresponding to the rotor position. The input autotransformers are operated manually, and the rotors are manually brought into the position yielding maximum output. This output is a measure of the maximum shear strain, and the rotor position indicates $(\alpha_1 + 45°)$. Accuracy in determining α_1 is increased by establishing the rotor position for zero output. The principal strains or stresses can be obtained from addition and subtraction circuits which also take care of the reduction from B to B''.

29. Resistance–Capacitance Network Computer for Rectangular Rosettes. The voltages representing the observed strains are fed manually into the computer[41, 45] by potentiometers. A resistance network adds the voltages ϵ_1 and ϵ_3. A resistance–capacitance phase-shift network is employed for the vector addition of $(\epsilon_1 - \epsilon_2)$ and $(\epsilon_2 - \epsilon_3)$, yielding directly a voltage propor-

tional to the maximum shear strain. The voltages so established are rectified, and the proper numerical factors are applied in the addition and
subtraction circuit furnishing the principal strains. The angle $2\alpha_1$ is indicated
by the straight-line pattern on the screen of a cathode-ray tube; the inphase
voltages applied to the deflection plates are $(\epsilon_2 - \epsilon_3)$ and $(\epsilon_1 - \epsilon_3)$.

30. Automatic Computers for SR-4 Rosettes. The electronic computing
apparatus for rectangular and equi-
angular rosettes[40] works directly from
SR-4 gages that are connected into a
chevron-type a-c bridge (similar to
that in Fig. 9-14) to maintain proper
phase relation. The bridge signals are
amplified individually, and the strains
along the three gage lines are shown
simultaneously on three meters. Part
of the amplifier output is fed into a
resistor network which yields A and
the differences between individual gage
readings and A. The proper differences are then added vectorially by off-
setting them electrically by 90° and
connecting them to grids of tubes with
coupled plates. The tube output represents B, and B'' is obtained from a
potentiometer circuit. Following rectification, the principal strains or
stresses are derived from summation
and difference networks for A and B or
A'' and B'', respectively, or by connecting the corresponding quantities to
the coils of dual-circuit meters. The
angle $2\alpha_1$ is obtained from the straight-
line pattern on a cathode-ray screen,
inphase voltages $(\epsilon_2 - A)$ and $(\epsilon_1 - A)$
being connected to the deflection
plates. The instrument shows the
principal strains or stresses as they
occur on the structure, the speed of response being limited only by the meters.

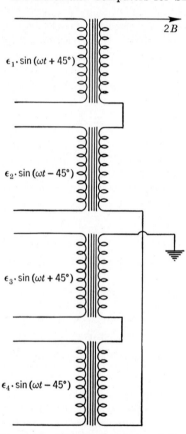

FIG. 9-25. Transformer Network for
Radius of Mohr's Circle from Four-
Gage 45° Rosette

The several buffer stages of the original apparatus caused some difficulties
in maintaining linearity. To overcome these, a transformer network was
suggested.[53] It is interposed before the last stage of the amplifiers that would
normally be employed for measuring individual strains. Figure 9-25 shows
the transformer network for B in the case of the four-gage 45° rosette. It is
based on the first formula of Table 9-2. The network for A is similar, but all
voltages are in phase, and all secondary windings are connected in the same

direction. The transformer network is suitable for all commonly used rosettes, as B can always be expressed as the square root of the sum of two squares. Numerical coefficients are taken care of by the number of turns in the respective secondary windings.

The electrodynamometer computer for principal strains[65] was developed for use in conjunction with rectangular, equiangular, and T-delta SR-4 rosettes. Switching and balancing equipment facilitates the scanning of 48 rosettes. The strain-signal outputs of a-c bridges are first combined in a manner that corrects for transverse gage sensitivity. Quantity A is then established in a summation network. The vector addition leading to quantity B is achieved by four electrodynamometer elements mounted on a common shaft. The input to three of the elements is derived from the strain signals, whereas the input to the fourth is the quantity needed to maintain electrodynamic balance. The system is kept in balance by an electronic servomechanism; the current required for balance represents quantity B. Addition and subtraction networks for quantities A and B furnish the principal strains, which are shown on meters calibrated in strain units. The angle $2\alpha_1$ is shown on a cathode-ray tube. The computer follows changes in strain rapidly and continually; the speed of operation is limited only by the servomechanism and the meters.

F. Effect of Errors in Observing Individual Strains and of Misalignment of Individual Gage Axes in Strain Rosettes

31. Errors in Strain Readings. Analysis of the effect of errors in individual gage readings[22, 23] shows that the absolute error in the magnitude of the computed principal strains is of the same order as the absolute errors in individual readings.

The influence of errors in individual gage readings on the direction of the computed principal strains is relatively small when the difference between the principal strains is great, but this influence becomes very great when the principal strains are nearly equal. However, in the case of nearly equal principal strains, that is, if Mohr's circle is very small, the directions of the principal strains are generally of little interest, and accurate determination is not essential.

Random errors in individual gage readings have the smallest influence on the computed magnitude and direction of the principal strains in the case of the equiangular strain rosette.[23]

32. Misalignment of Individual Gage Lines. When an accurately built-up rosette is misaligned as a unit, the magnitude of the computed principal strains is not affected, whereas the computed directions of the principal strains are in error by the amount of the rosette misalignment.

Misalignment of individual gages within a rosette is generally hard to determine, because gages are applied with considerable care, and the accuracy of application is about the same as the accuracy of determining the actual position of rosette gage lines when the rosette is in place. Therefore, formulas for calculating the effect of misalignment of individual rosette gage lines on the computed principal strains[23, 61] are of primary value in making a general estimate. The following conclusions were drawn from such formulas:

The error in the computed magnitudes and directions of the principal strains depends on the misalignment of the individual gages in the rosette and also on the orientation of the rosette relative to the principal directions.

Misalignment of a gage has the greatest effect on the gage reading when the gage axis makes an angle of approximately 45° with the principal directions (see equation 25). If a rosette with one misaligned gage is placed so that the misaligned gage axis assumes this unfavorable direction, at least one of the other gage axes makes a favorable angle with one of the principal directions. Therefore, the effect of misalignment on the computed magnitudes of the principal strains is smaller than the error in the reading of the misaligned gage. The error in the computed principal directions due to misalignment of a single gage may reach the amount of misalignment but will not exceed it, even if the gage is placed most unfavorably.

If several gages are misaligned, the error in the computed magnitude of the principal strains is, under the most unfavorable conditions, of the same order as the error in alignment of individual rosette gages. Misalignment of individual gage lines of 1° to 2° will not affect the accuracy of the results by more than plus or minus 2 per cent.

For a given misalignment of individual rosette gages and a given orientation of the rosette relative to the principal directions, the error in the magnitude of the computed principal strains caused by this misalignment is proportional to the difference between the principal strains.

The probable error in the computed directions of the principal strains is of the same order as the probable error in alignment of individual rosette gages.

No disproportionate errors are caused, therefore, by misalignment of gage lines that may occur when standard experimental techniques are employed.

When the principal strains are to be determined to greatest possible accuracy, the investigation should consist of two steps: (1) Determine the principal directions approximately, without taking into account the misalignment of individual gage lines that may possibly exist within the rosette, (2) use a rectangular rosette so placed that two gage lines are as nearly as possible in the principal directions.

From a theoretical standpoint, the average effect of misalignment of individual gage lines on the computed principal strains is less for the equiangular rosette than for the rectangular rosette. The inherent advantages of the equiangular rosette are not very great, however. Considering the many random factors involved, the use of the rectangular rosette is well justified from a practical standpoint.

G. Graphical Representation of Stresses and Strains at a Point

33. Mohr's Circle—Analogy between Stress and Strain Diagrams.
Mohr's circle is the most commonly used method of representing stresses and strains at a point. Since the stress or strain quantities appear as rectangular coordinates, Mohr's circle is particularly well suited when graph paper is

used. In this respect it is more convenient than any other method of representing the state of plane stress or plane strain.

From the analogy between the stress and strain equations and the respective Mohr's circles shown in section B, it is evident that any graphical method of representing stresses at a point can also be used for representing strains.

34. Land's Dyadic Circle. Land's circle (Fig. 9-26) is widely used in connection with strain-rosette analysis,[11, 19, 29] and serves a purpose similar to Mohr's circle. The diagram was originally published by Land,[2] but it owes its widespread application to Professor Westergaard[6] who is said to have

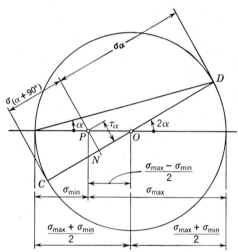

FIG. 9-26. Land's Circle (or Dyadic Circle) for Stresses

called it "dyadic circle."[11] The state of stress is described by a circle with center at O and

$$\text{Radius} = \tfrac{1}{2}(\sigma_{\max} + \sigma_{\min}) \tag{65}$$

and a point P so that the

$$\text{Distance } \overline{OP} = \tfrac{1}{2}(\sigma_{\max} - \sigma_{\min}) \tag{66}$$

Thus, P lies within the circle for principal stresses of equal sign and outside the circle for principal stresses of opposite sign. The diameter through P corresponds to the direction of the principal stresses. To obtain the stresses for a line making an angle α with the direction of $\sigma_{\max}$, draw the diameter CD making an angle 2α with PO, and the normal PN to this diameter.
Then,

$$\overline{ND} = \sigma_\alpha, \quad \overline{NC} = \sigma_{(\alpha+90°)}, \quad \text{and} \quad \overline{PN} = \tau_\alpha$$

Normal stresses represented by a distance lying partially or totally within the circle are of the sign indicated for the radius by equation 65.

35. Polar Diagrams. Polar diagrams[8, 22, 48] are obtained by plotting stresses or strains as radius vectors of their respective directions. They are the most instructive method of representing plane stress and plane strain, but are relatively cumbersome to draw. Figure 9-27a shows the polar diagram for normal stresses and normal strains for an element subjected to uniaxial tension. Figure 9-27b shows the corresponding polar diagram for shear stresses and strains.

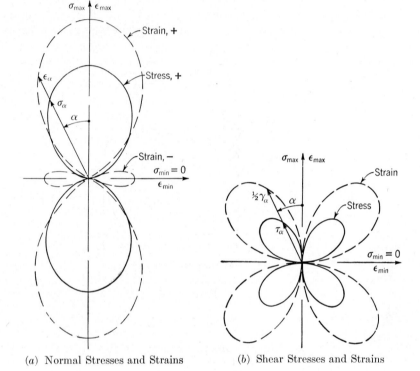

(a) Normal Stresses and Strains   (b) Shear Stresses and Strains

Fig. 9-27. Polar Diagrams for the Case of Uniaxial Stress

36. Ellipse of Stress. The resultant stress σ_{res} is defined as the vector sum of σ_α and τ_α (Fig. 9-28a). Consider a normal plane N rotated around a fixed point of a stress field and the resultant stress vectors drawn. These vectors define an ellipse, called ellipse of stress,[26] which can be constructed by the method of Fig. 9-28b. Although one of the earliest methods of representing plane stress,[1, 3] the ellipse of stress has not been widely used, mainly because of its inconvenience.

37. Displacement Diagrams. Displacement diagrams somewhat similar to Williot's diagram for trusses have been proposed for representing the state of plane strain.[52] They can be constructed directly from the normal strains in three arbitrary directions. These strains are represented as distances in their true directions, and no numerical calculations are required. However, the diagrams are not very convenient.

38. Arrows. Arrows indicating the directions and magnitudes of the principal stresses at a point are extremely convenient, particularly for representing stress fields (Fig. 9-29). They do not give, however, direct information as to the stresses in arbitrary directions.

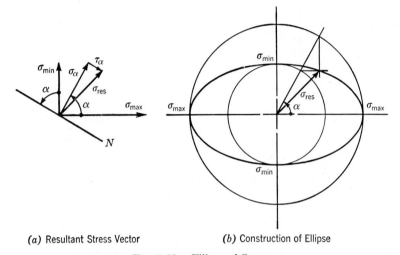

(a) Resultant Stress Vector   *(b)* Construction of Ellipse

FIG. 9-28.   Ellipse of Stress

H. GRAPHICAL REPRESENTATION OF STRESS FIELDS

39. General Remarks. If the principal stresses are determined for only a few points of a structure, tabular arrangement of the results is indicated. However, when the number of rosette measurements becomes great, graphical representation of the stress field can be surveyed more readily and generally leads to better understanding. In such cases it is extremely desirable to obtain at least an approximate picture of the stress field at the time that or promptly after the rosette readings are taken. This locates highly stressed areas or rosettes with dubious results in time to modify test procedure or to repeat certain readings.

40. Arrows. The most expedient method of representing a stress field is to indicate by arrows the principal stresses at all points of observation (Fig. 9-29). This intermittent representation gives a fair picture of the orientation of the stress field and of the magnitude of the stresses. It is ideal for preliminary checks of the results and in many cases satisfactory for final presentation. In order to avoid interference between arrows where the points of observation are close together, it is recommended[22] that only two arrows be drawn instead of the "cross" (see Figs. 9-16 and 9-28).

41. Stress Trajectories. Stress trajectories as such show only the orientation of the principal stresses, and, although stress concentrations may be

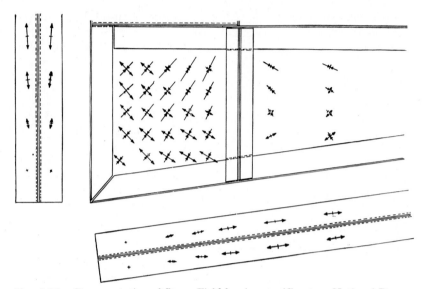

FIG. 9-29.   Representation of Stress Field by Arrows (Courtesy National Bureau
of Standards)

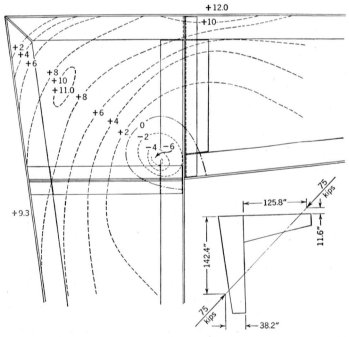

FIG. 9-30.   Representation of Stress Field by Curves Connecting Points of Equal
Algebraically Greater Principal Stress (Courtesy National Bureau of Standards)

expected at points where the curves of both families run closer together, definite numerical conclusions cannot be drawn. Auxiliary curves[22] may be used to show the magnitude of the principal stresses along the trajectories, but they tend to confuse the picture, particularly in the most interesting areas of stress concentration.

42. Curves Connecting Points of Equal Stresses. Three kinds of curves are of interest,[21] namely those connecting points of

1. Equal algebraically greater principal stress.
2. Equal algebraically smaller principal stress.
3. Equal shear stress.

Any one family of such curves (Fig. 9-30) by itself does not permit any conclusions as to the other, nor to the direction of the principal stresses. Thus, the method is suited to show the regions in which any one kind of stress is of interest, but it does not yield an easily understood general picture of the stress field.

43. Stresses at Important Sections. In some problems, particularly bending of beams with complex web shape,[21] and investigations of stress concentration,[22] the results are advantageously presented by showing the normal stress distribution along the most important sections. Similarly, the shear stresses are plotted for a number of sections when they are of primary interest, as, for instance, in aircraft-wing studies.

ACKNOWLEDGMENTS

The author wishes to express his sincere gratitude to all who have contributed information and illustrations to this chapter.

The helpful services in connection with references rendered by Professor W. M. Murray of the Massachusetts Institute of Technology and Professor Ed. Amstutz of the Swiss Federal Institute of Technology are greatly appreciated.

BIBLIOGRAPHY

1. C. CULMANN, *Die Graphische Statik*, 1st ed, Zürich, 1866. On page 226, first appearance of diagram representing state of plane stress, later called Mohr's circle; also 2d ed, v 1, Zürich, 1875, 4th sec, "Elements of the Theory of Elasticity," ch 1, "Forces which are Proportional to Lines and Areas," pp 513–62. Formulas for forces acting on arbitrary sections through a point and graphic representation by circular diagrams and ellipse of stress.
2. ROBERT LAND, "Der Spannungskreis bei Vollwandigen Traegern," *Vereins deutscher Ingenieure, Zeitschrift*, v 39, Dec 28, 1895, pp 1551–554. Using the example of the web of a built-up girder, the equilibrium of two-dimensional stresses at a point is shown. Their relations are graphically represented in a diagram that became known as "Land's circle" or "dyadic circle."
3. OTTO MOHR, "Welche Umstaende bedingen die Elastizitaetsgrenzen und den Bruch eines Materials?" *Abhandlungen auf dem Gebiet der Technischen Mechanik*, Abhandlung 5, Berlin, 1906, pp 189–219. Detailed study of two- and three-dimensional stress and strain conditions at a point, with particular reference to yielding and failure of materials. Graphical representation of relations by Mohr's circles for two- and three-dimensional cases. References to early publications on the state of plane stress.

4. C. E. FULLER and W. A. JOHNSTON, *Applied Mechanics*, v 2, John Wiley & Sons, 1st ed, New York, 1919, pp 64–76. The state of plane strain is treated analytically without introducing the condition of isotropy.

5. A. E. H. LOVE, *A Treatise on the Mathematical Theory of Elasticity*, University Press, 3rd ed, Cambridge, 1920, pp 32–109. A comprehensive study of stress and strain and their relations for aeolotropic and isotropic materials.

6. H. M. WESTERGAARD, *Anwendung der Statik auf die Ausgleichsrechnung*, Hubert and Co, Goettingen, 1925, pp 29–38. Mohr's circles for three-dimensional stress and Land's circle for plane stress are derived from the analogy between stress equations and the equations pertaining to the vectorial errors in the location of a point when the given coordinates are afflicted with errors. Construction of Land's circle from normal stresses in three arbitrary directions.

7. L. B. TUCKERMAN, G. H. KEULEGAN, and H. N. EATON, "A Fabric Tension Meter for Use on Aircraft," *U. S. Bur Standards Technologic* Paper 320, U. S. Govt Printing Office, July 24, 1926, pp 581–96. Description of a gage applying hydrostatic suction to a small elliptic portion of a stressed fabric and determination of the principal stresses from the resulting radii of curvature.

8. WILLIAM HOOVGAARD, "Determination of Stresses in Plating from Strain Measurements," *Trans Soc Naval Architects and Mar Engrs*, v 39, 1931, pp 25–33. Analytical solution for three- and four-gage 45° rosettes. Polar diagrams for representing the condition of plane stress. A similar paper by the same author, "Analysis of Strain Measurements and Polar Diagrams for Plane Stress," appeared in Stephen Timoshenko *60th Anniversary Volume*, Macmillan Co, New York, 1938, pp 81–8.

9. HENRY HUGHES, "Recording Strain Meter for Ships' Structures," *Engineering (British)*, v 132, n 3418, p 87, July 1931. Indicating and recording mechanical strain gage that can be swung around into a new position without removing it from the mounting stud. The dual records permit distinction between uniform normal stresses and bending stresses of plates.

10. "COMITÉ TECHNIQUE DE MÉCANIQUE, "Sur la Détermination expérimentale des tensions principales agissant dans les matériaux à la surface des ouvrages," *Recherches et Inventions (French)*, 14th yr, n 221, pp 33–47, Feb 1933. Optical strain gages applied to rosette problems. Ellipse of stress and solution for equiangular rosette.

11. WM. R. OSGOOD and R. G. STURM, "The Determination of Stresses from Strains on Three Intersecting Gage Lines and its Application to Actual Tests," *U. S. Bur Standards, J Research* Paper 559; v 10, May 1933, pp 685–92. Construction of Land's circle from normal strains in three arbitrary directions. Description of three-element mechanical rosette gages used on model of Calderwood Dam (ref 13), and application of commercial mechanical gages to structural research.

12. S. TIMOSHENKO, *Theory of Elasticity*, McGraw-Hill Book Co, New York and London, 1934, pp 1–26. Definitions of and relations between stress, strain, and elastic constants. Equilibrium of stresses at a point and representation of equations by Mohr's circle.

13. A. V. KARPOV and R. L. TEMPLIN, "Model of Calderwood Arch Dam," *Trans ASCE*, paper 1895, v 100, pp 185–262, 1935. Description of special mechanical strain gages used on Calderwood Dam and model thereof. Whittemore strain gages for downstream face of dam, wire operated lever gages with 10-ft gage length on upstream face. Model was made of rubber and litharge. Radial spurs fastened to pins arranged on a circle were observed by a microscope on the downstream side. On the upstream side, special three-element mechanical gages were installed and observed while submerged through a glass-bottom tube. The model tests were described by the same authors in "Building and Testing an Arch Dam Model," *Civil Eng*, v 2, n 1, pp 11–16, Jan 1932. Test equipment and procedure for dam and model were reviewed by H. N. HILL in "Some Experiences in Experimental Stress Determination at the

Aluminum Research Laboratories," *Experimental Stress Analysis*, v 2, n 1, Addison–Wesley Press, Cambridge, 1944, pp 18–21.

14. W. R. Osgood, "Determination of Principal Stresses from Strains on Four Intersecting Gage Lines 45° Apart," *U. S. Bur Standards J Research* Paper 851, v 15, Dec 1935, pp 579–81. Analytical solution for the four-gage 45° rosette that is in agreement with theory of least squares of errors.

15. F. Kollmann, *Technologie des Holzes*, Julius Springer, Berlin, 1936, pp 144–54. Reprinted in German by Edwards Brothers, Ann Arbor, Michigan, through permission of Alien Property Custodian. Elastic constants and general relations between stress and strain for anisotropic materials. Consideration of wood as rhombic system (in analogy to theory of crystals) and corresponding equations for elastic properties in arbitrary directions. Polar diagrams of elastic properties.

16. H. Stang and Martin Greenspan, "Graphical Computation of Stresses from Strain Data," *U. S. Bur Standards J Research* Paper 1034, v 19, Oct 1937, pp 437–41. Simplified analytical solution of four-gage, 45° rosette is based on Poisson's ratio of 1/3. Rapid graphical solution by charts and nomographs.

17. A. S. Niles and J. S. Newell, *Airplane Structures*, v 1, John Wiley & Sons, 2d ed, 1938, pp 195–201. Discussion of principal stresses and maximum shear stress. Construction of Mohr's circle from uniaxial bending stress and simultaneous shear stress. Third edition, 1943, p 196, refers to Mohr's circle as Culmann's circle.

18. G. E. Beggs and E. K. Timby, "Interpreting Data from Strain Rosettes," *Eng News-Rec*, v 120, n 10, pp 366–70, Mar 10, 1938. Adaptation of Huggenberger extensometer for rosette measurements, using pattern for positioning. Formulas and tabular solution for the four-gage 45° rosette. Continuation entitled "Strain Rosette Technique," v 120, n 11, pp 404–06, Mar 17, 1938. Calibration of Huggenberger extensometers and mounting of these gages for rosette work. Jig plate for drawing rosette pattern on surface.

19. F. L. Everett and Arthur McCutchan, "Investigation of Stress Conditions in a Full-Size Welded Branch Connection," *Trans ASME*, v 60, 1938, pp 339–410. Special mounting device for Huggenberger extensometer permits rapid positioning of gage. Graphic solution of four-gage 45° rosette by Land's circle. Superposition of two stress conditions and representation of resulting stresses by Mohr's circle. Stress field on surface of manifold represented by arrows.

20. R. D. Mindlin, "The Equiangular Strain Rosette," *Civil Eng*, v 8, n 8, Aug 1938, pp 546–47. State of plane strain derived from arbitrarily orientated element. Various arrangements, analytical and graphical solutions of equiangular rosette.

21. A. H. Stang, Martin Greenspan, and William R. Osgood, "Strength of a Rigid Steel Riveted Frame having Straight Flanges," *U. S. Bur Standards J Research Paper* 1130, v 21, Sept 1938, pp 269–314. Application of Whittemore strain gages to rosette problems on structural steel. Analytical solutions for equiangular and four-gage 45° rosettes. Representation of stress fields by arrows, contour curves, and stresses along important sections.

22. F. Roetscher and R. Jaschke, *Dehnungsmessungen und ihre Auswertung*, Julius Springer, Berlin, 1939. Reprinted in German by Edwards Brothers, Ann Arbor, Michigan, through permission of Alien Property Custodian. A very comprehensive treatise on strain-rosette analysis. Two- and three-dimensional conditions of stress and strain. Various mechanical strain gages suitable for rosette analysis. Formulas for symmetrical three- and four-gage rosettes. Treatment of redundant reading by theory of least squares of errors. Calculation and distribution of errors. Representation of stresses at a point by Mohr's circle and elliptical and polar diagrams. Various methods for representing stress fields.

23. R. Jaschke, "Fehlerfortpflanzung bei Dehnungsmessungen und Ausgleich

dieser Messungen nach der Methode der kleinsten Fehlerquadrate," *Ingenieur-Archiv*, v 10, 1939, pp 312–26.   Study of the influence of errors in individual measurements on orientation and magnitude of the principal strains.   The effect of errors in the direction of the gage lines and in the magnitude of the observed strains is demonstrated by many curves.   Proof that the equiangular rosette is the most favorable three-gage rosette for unknown stress fields. Treatment of four-gage 45° rosette and T–delta rosette, employing theory of least squares of errors.

24. H. N. HILL, "A Semi-Graphical Method for Analyzing Strains Measured on Three or Four Gage Lines Intersecting at 45°," *Nat Advisory Commit for Aeronautics*, May 1939, *Tech Note* 709.   The solution is based on reducing the observed strains and plotting them versus the angle between the gage lines. A master cosine curve on transparent paper is laid over the plot so that it passes through the points; its peaks indicate the directions and reduced values of the principal strains.   On the same subject: H. W. SIBERT, "Principal Stresses from Three Strains at 45°," *J Aeronautical Sciences*, v 7, n 1, pp 26–7, Nov 1939.

25. W. B. KLEMPERER, "The Tensor Gage," *J Aeronautical Sciences*, v 7, n 9, pp 403–04, July 1940.   Small triple-element optical strain gage is attached to surface by means of central suction cup.   Readings are linear functions of strains along all three gage lines; calculation of principal stresses.

26. M. M. FROCHT, *Photoelasticity*, v 1, John Wiley & Sons, 1st ed, New York, 1941, pp 1–41.   Comprehensive study of plane stress and plane strain.   Mohr's circles, ellipse of stress, analytical and graphical solutions for rectangular and equiangular rosettes.

27. R. L. KENYON and HARRY TOBIN, "Measurement of Stresses in Car Wheels," *Ry Mech Engr*, v 115, n 12, pp 516–23, Dec 1941, and v 116, n 1, pp 6–19, Jan 1942.   Study of plane strain is based on partial differentials and does not introduce condition of isotropy.   Rosette technique with Olsen–DeShazer gages.   Analytical solution of four-gage 45° rosette in tabular form and by special rosette slide rule.

28. C. B. NORRIS, *Technique of Plywood*, I. F. Laucks, Seattle, Washington, 1942, pp 71–111.   Wood considered as orthotropic material.   Method for finding principal strains in wood and plywood from principal stresses in arbitrary directions with respect to the grain.   The same author on the same subject: "The Application of Mohr's Stress and Mohr's Strain Circles to Wood and Plywood," *U. S. Dept Agric, Forests Products Lab Mimeograph* 1317, Madison, Wis, Feb 1943.

29. E. W. SUPPIGER and R. L. JORDAN, "The Determination of Stresses from Strains Measured on Three Intersecting Gage Lines," *Army Air Forces Tech Report* 4822, Oct 1942.   Representation of plane stress and plane strain by Land's circles.   Graphical and analytical solutions for rectangular and equiangular rosettes; several numerical examples.

30. W. B. KLEMPERER, "A Rosette Strain Computer," *Nat Advisory Commit for Aeronautics, Tech Note* 875, Dec 1942.   Manually operated electromechanical vector computer using coupled Selsyn devices.   Selsyn rotors are brought into position yielding greatest meter deflection.   This meter reading corresponds to maximum shear strain or stress, rotor position to orientation of rosette.

31. W. M. MURRAY, "An Adjunct to the Strain Rosette," *Experimental Stress Analysis*, v 1, n 1, Addison–Wesley Press, Cambridge, 1943, pp 128–33. Analytical solutions for the equiangular and 45° rosettes, and their interpretation by continuous mechanical computer.   Computer employs racks and pinions for scalar additions and mutually perpendicular slots carrying common pin for vector addition.

32. J. H. MEIER, Discussion following ref 31, pp 134–37.   Graphical solution of equiangular rosette that does not require any numerical calculations.   Conversion chart for principal strains to principal stresses.

33. H. M. HANSEN, Discussion following ref 31, pp 138–44.   State of plane strain represented by Mohr's circle and by elliptical diagram.   Graphical solution for rosette with arbitrary angles between gage lines by locus method, and modification of this general solution for rectangular and equiangular rosettes.

34. R. BAUMBERGER, Discussion following ref 31, pp 145–146.   Prepared form for rapid solution of rectangular rosette.

35. NORRIS F. Dow, "The Analysis of Strains Indicated by Multiple-Strand Resistance-Type Wire Strain Gages Used as Rosettes," *Nat Advisory Commit for Aeronautics, Advance Restricted Report* (now unclassified), Jan 1943.   Simple analysis of grid is based on assumption that portions of the strain-sensitive wire are arranged only parallel or perpendicular to gage axis.   Analytical solutions for rectangular, equiangular, and T–delta rosettes and correction for transverse gage sensitivity by adjusting radius of Mohr's circle.   Correction adapted to the semigraphical solution (ref 24).   Comparison of measurements obtained by Tuckerman gages and SR-4 rosettes.

36. A. E. McPHERSON, "Adaptor for Measuring Principal Strains with Tuckerman Strain Gages," *Nat Advisory Commit for Aeronautics, Tech Note* 898, June 1943.   Analytical solution of equiangular rosette is modified for use with adaptor that holds three Tuckerman strain gages at 120° angles.   Description of adaptor, details of construction, assembly, and calibration curves.

37. S. B. WILLIAMS, "The Dyadic Gage," *Experimental Stress Analysis*, v 1, n 2, Addison–Wesley Press, Cambridge, 1944, pp 43–55.   State of plane stress and representation by Land's circle.   Construction of Mohr's circle from three normal strains in arbitrary directions by vector diagram.   Analysis of wire grid and correction for transverse gage sensitivity.   Design of "stress gage."

38. A. H. FLAX and M. C. WARDLE, "Application of Electric Strain Gages to Aircraft Design Problems," *Experimental Stress Analysis*, v 2, n 1, Addison–Wesley Press, Cambridge, 1944, pp 50–66.   Relations between stresses and strains and apparent strains indicated by gages with transverse sensitivity.   Wheatstone bridge with two or four active arms and instrument calibrated directly for normal stresses along outside gage lines and shear stress along center gage line of rectangular rosette.

39. E. E. HOSKINS and R. C. OLESEN, "An Electrical Computer for the Evaluation of Strain Rosette Data," *Experimental Stress Analysis*, v 2, n 1, Addison–Wesley Press, Cambridge, 1944, pp 67–77.   Addition and subtraction circuits are added to the Selsyn computer of ref 30, so that the principal strains or stresses are obtained directly as meter readings.

40. J. H. MEIER and W. R. MEHAFFEY, "Electronic Computing Apparatus for Rectangular and Equiangular Strain Rosettes," *Experimental Stress Analysis*, v 2, n 1, Addison–Wesley Press, Cambridge, 1944, pp 78–101.   Instrument is directly connected to SR-4 rosettes and shows the principal strains or stresses automatically as they occur.   A resistance network is employed for scalar additions and a resistance–capacitance phase-shift network precedes the vector addition by triodes with coupled plates.   Compensation for transverse sensitivity of grid-type gages by potentiometer circuit.   The orientation of the rosette is indicated by the straight-line pattern on the screen of a cathode-ray tube.

41. S. S. MANSON, Discussion following ref 40, pp 102–05.   The manually operated analyzer of ref 45 is described and generally compared with the electronic computing apparatus.

42. W. M. MURRAY, "Machine Solution of Strain Rosette Equations," *Experimental Stress Analysis*, v 2, n 1, Addison–Wesley Press, Cambridge, 1944, pp 106–12.   Analytical solutions for 45° rosettes, the equiangular and the T–delta rosette and application of differential analyzer for solving rosette equations.

43. R. BAUMBERGER and F. HINES, "Practical Reduction Formulas for Use on Bonded Wire Strain Gages in Two-Dimensional Stress Fields," *Experimental*

Stress Analysis, v 2, n 1, Addison–Wesley Press, Cambridge, 1944, pp 113–47. Method for calculating transverse sensitivity of single-layer grid-type gages and comparison with experimental data. Manufacturer's formulas for the true strains along the gage lines and the true principal strains.

44. S. S. MANSON, "Charts for Rapid Analysis of 45° Strain Rosette Data," *Nat Advisory Commit for Aeronautics*, *Tech Note* 940, May 1944. Circuits for combining strains indicated by two gages of a rosette and charts for direct determination of the principal strains or stresses from the combined strain values. Mechanical vector computer for use with simplified charts.

45. S. S. MANSON, "An Automatic Electrical Analyzer for 45° Strain Rosette Data," *Nat Advisory Commit for Aeronautics*, *Tech Note* 941, May 1944. Manually operated computer employs resistance networks for scalar additions and resistance–capacitance networks for vector addition. Orientation of rosette is indicated by straight-line pattern on a cathode-ray screen. Amplifiers are used only in cathode-ray circuits.

46. Design of Wood Aircraft Structures, *ANC Bul* 18, Army–Navy–Civil Committee on Aircraft Design Criteria, U S Govt Printing Office, June 1944, pp 45–74. Elastic properties of wood parallel and perpendicular to the grain. Relations between Mohr's circle for stresses and Mohr's circle for strains in the case of wood.

47. T. A. HEWSON, "Rosette Strain Calculator," *Tech Eng News*, v 26, n 2, Mass Inst of Tech, pp 38, 39, 54, and 56, Oct 1944. Discussion of merits of continuous mechanical-rosette computer. Analytical solution for 45° rosettes and basic principles of computer.

48. Given Brewer, "Determination of Principal Stresses by Use of the Equilateral Strain Rosette," *Aero Digest*, Jan 1, 1945, pp 90–7, and 217. Formulas for equiangular rosette and graphical solution by means of superimposing transparency with observed strain data plotted on prepared form. Polar diagram of stresses.

49. ROBERTO CONTINI, "A Graphic Solution for Strains and Stresses from Strain Rosette Data," *J Aeronautical Sciences*, v, 12, n 1, pp 47–50, Jan 1945. Solution of equiangular rosette and 45° rosettes by means of vector diagrams. Prepared form for partial solution of equiangular rosette by vector method and completion of solution in tabular form.

50. T. A. HEWSON, "Strain Rosette Analyzer," Bachelor's Thesis in Mechanical Engineering, Mass Inst of Tech, June 25, 1945. Derivation of equations for all commonly used rosettes. Review of original mechanical computer, ref 31, and design of new computer with differential gearing and square and square-root mechanisms using cable winding from a cylinder to a grooved cone. Investigation of accuracy.

51. GLENN MURPHY, "A Graphical Method for the Evaluation of Principal Strains from Normal Strains," *J Applied Mechanics*, v 12, n 4, pp A–209–10, Dec 1945. Mohr's circle from normal strains in three arbitrary directions by locus method.

52. N. J. HOFF, "A Graphic Resolution of Strain," *J Applied Mechanics*, v 12, n 4, pp A–211–16, Dec 1945. Displacement diagrams for describing the state of plane strain from normal strains in three arbitrary directions (similar to Williot's diagram for trusses). Graphical solution for equiangular rosette on prepared form adapted for rapid construction of displacement diagrams. Mohr's circle from rectangular and equiangular rosettes by locus method.

53. J. H. MEIER, "Improvements in Rosette Computer," *Experimental Stress Analysis*, v 3, n 2, Addison–Wesley Press, Cambridge, 1946, pp 1–3. Transformer networks for solving rosette equations applicable to all commonly used rosettes. In the case of four-gage rosettes, the solutions obtained conform with the theory of least squares of errors.

54. W. V. BASSETT, H. CROMWELL, and W. E. WOOSTER, "Improved Techniques

and Devices for Stress Analysis with Resistance Wire Gages," *Experimental Stress Analysis*, v 3, n 2, Addison–Wesley Press, Cambridge, 1946, pp 76–80. Portable mercury-pool connector for rapid change from one gage to another. Geometrical computer for rectangular rosettes, employing a slidable parallelogram linkage moving over a strain scale, and proportional dividers for direct determination of the principal stresses. On the same subject: W. V. Bassett, "Practical Electric Resistance Strain Gage Procedure for Structural Tests on Ships," *ASTM Bul* 134, May 1945, pp 9–16.

55. K. J. Bossart and Given Brewer, "A Graphical Method of Rosette Analysis," *Experimental Stress Analysis*, v 4, n 1, Addison–Wesley Press, Cambridge, 1946, pp 1 to 8. Vector solution for the equiangular rosette. Analysis of resistance-wire grids with circular end loops and correction for transverse gage sensitivity.

56. T. A. Hewson, "A Nomograph Solution to the Strain Rosette Equations," *Experimental Stress Analysis*, v 4, n 1, Addison–Wesley Press, Cambridge, 1946, pp 9–26. Nomographs for rapid solution of all commonly used rosettes.

57. Norman Grossman, "A Nomographic Rosette Computer," *Experimental Stress Analysis*, v 4, n 1, Addison–Wesley Press, Cambridge, 1946, pp 27–35. Nomographs for rapid solution of rectangular and equiangular rosette.

58. C. H. Gibbons, communication from, Baldwin Locomotive Works, 1945.

59. H. N. Hill, communication from, Aluminum Company of America, 1945.

60. J. Charles Rathbun, "Circles of Stress and Strain Compared," *Eng News-Rec*, v 137, n 12, pp 376–79, Sept 19, 1946. Biaxial stress–strain relations; representation of analytical expressions by ellipse and circles of Culmann (Mohr) and Land. Analogy between circles of strain and inertia.

61. S. S. Manson, and W. C. Morgan, "Effect of Misalignment of Strain-Gage Components of Strain Rosettes, *Nat Advisory Commit for Aeronautics, Tech Note* 1133, Sept, 1946. Equations expressing the effect of misalignment of individual gages on computed principal strains for equiangular and rectangular rosettes. Error in calculated principal strains is proportional to maximum shear strain at gage point. Proof that readings of individual gages may be seriously affected by relatively small misalignment, but influence upon computed principal strains is of same order of magnitude as error in alignment. Experimental verification of analysis.

62. Fritz Stuessi, "Ueber die Grundlagen des Ingenieurholzbaues," *Schweizerische Bauzeitung*, v 65, n 24, pp 313–18, June 1947. Strength and elastic properties of wood in various directions. Equations relating strains to stresses in orthotropic materials and application to wood for planes parallel to the direction of the grain. Analysis and explanation of the elastic behavior of wood when stressed in planes perpendicular to the direction of the grain, in which case wood no longer acts as orthotropic material. Experimental verification.

63. A. N. Rankin, "Orientation of Strain Gages in Stress Analysis," *GE Rev*, v 50, n 9, pp 14–21, Sept 1947. Discussion of plane stress and plane strain, illustrated by Mohr's circles. Relations between principal stresses and strains. Analytical solution of rectangular rosette. Examples.

64. K. H. Swainger and J. Twyman, "An Optical Rectangular Rosette Extensometer for Large Strains," *J Sci Instr* (Lond.), v 25, n 6, pp 187–89, June 1948. Mirror-type triple-element extensometer for observing large strains in test specimens. Special development for observing strains in the post-yield region.

65. C. M. Hathaway, communication from, Hathaway Instrument Company, 1949.

CHAPTER 10

WORKING STRESSES

By C. Richard Soderberg

A. Introduction

The design of an engineering structure is fully rationalized when the designer is able to predict the performance and to establish beforehand the circumstances of operation under which failures will occur. The degree to which this rationalization can be carried depends on many circumstances, but it represents an ideal towards which the engineering profession is always striving. Nearly complete rationalization can be achieved only when the limitations of weight, space, cost, and other factors permit designs which are safe without extensive preliminary trials on experimental units. This condition is now approached in many fields of mechanical engineering, of which large power machinery is perhaps the most important. Here it is necessary to predict the performance and risk of failure with precision in the design stage. The aircraft engine is an example of a different extreme, in which the requirement of reliability is even greater, but here the incentives of weight reduction and improvement in performance are so great that extensive experimentation through a succession of experimental models is justified. Similar situations exist to a varying degree in the mass-production fields, where the ultimate unit cost of experimental constructions becomes small. It is no longer necessary to argue for the maximum of design rationalization in all cases, and our generation has seen a remarkable development in this respect. Problems which only a few years ago were considered too complicated for direct analytical approach are now taken in the stride of young and relatively inexperienced men.

The problem of mechanical strength occupies a central position in this urge towards rationalization. The term "working stress" is a concept which usually implies oversimplification of an exceedingly complex problem. The object of this chapter is to discourage this oversimplification and still leave a rational framework for the interpretation of accumulated experiences.

It cannot be too strongly emphasized that experience is the ultimate basis for the prediction of failures in engineering structures. The experience may be in the nature of statistical records of a large number of units in operation, or it may be obtained from more detailed stress measurements of individual units, or parts, but in all except a few simple and trivial cases the prediction must be related to experience. In a new and untried device the prediction of failure thus depends on how closely the predicted circumstances are paralleled by pertinent experience. In most cases the prediction is reasonably reliable for those circumstances which are foreseen; the great majority of important failures are due to circumstances which the designer failed to take into account.

B. The Phenomenon of Failure

It is usually assumed that there is a direct causal relationship between an imposed state of stress and a certain phenomenon of failure. In a popular sense the concept of failure is associated with *fracture*, but in most cases fracture is preceded by plastic *yielding*, and in many instances a certain amount of yielding is equivalent to failure. The relationship between stresses and failure is far from direct, however, as attested by the vast array of mechanical and metallurgical properties which are necessary to specify the essential strength properties of any one material. One important reason for the manifold aspects of the behavior of materials under stress lies in the imperfect means at our disposal for defining stress, even under the simplest of loading conditions.

The state of stress is almost always defined on the basis of isotropic materials. For polycrystalline metals, which cover practically all of the important elements of strength, this is equivalent to defining the stress components for a volume of the material, which contains a large number of individual grains or crystals. When we refer to a state of stress, therefore, we invariably consider the *average stress* over a large number of grains. It is now fairly well established that elastic deformations and the phenomena of yielding in ductile metals are governed wholly by this average stress, and for this reason our knowledge of yielding of polycrystalline metals is relatively complete. The fracture phenomenon, on the other hand, has its origin in extremely localized sections of the structure, and, hence, it is related not only to the average stress but also to the microscopic aspects of the stress.

The macroscopic stress, related to the ideal conditions of a fine-grain structure, is a definite entity which depends only on the forces or displacements. The microscopic aspect of the stress is an elusive concept, which also depends on the grain structure and which changes constantly with the plastic deformations. At the present time we do not even possess the mathematical tools for its description. We are thus forced to relate the fracture phenomena, as well as the yielding phenomena, to the macroscopic state of stress. As a result of this situation, it has become necessary to include a very large number of quantities in the specification of the mechanical-strength properties of any one material. Only a few of these appear in the direct evaluation of the risk of failure, the remainder having to do with qualitative aspects of the behavior under stress. Section C gives a summary of those properties which enter directly into the stress-analysis problem.

C. Strength Properties of Materials

1. Materials at Normal Temperature.   (a) *Steady Stress.*

Ductile materials: Yield strength.
                      Stress–strain curve relating stress and plastic strain.
Brittle materials: Ultimate strength. Usually different for tension and compression.

(b) *Alternating Stress.*

Ductile and   Endurance limit, or fatigue strength for a stated number of
brittle materials: reversals.

2. Materials at Elevated Temperatures.   (a) *Steady Stress.*

Ductile materials: Creep strength, giving a stated amount or rate of plastic deformation in a stated time.
                      Stress–strain rate curve, relating stress and creep rate.
Ductile and
brittle materials: Creep-to-rupture strength for a stated length of time.

(b) *Variable Stress.*

Ductile and   Fatigue strength for a stated number of reversals in a
brittle materials: stated time.

D. Yielding of Ductile Metals

The object of this section is to present the procedure by which the results of tests in tension or other uniaxial stress are extended to more general forms of stress applications in three dimensions. For yielding, this procedure actually rests on a firmer foundation than the interpretation of the tension test itself. Although the underlying reasoning is the same, it is desirable to treat separately the cases of normal and elevated temperatures.

3. Normal Temperatures. The region of normal temperatures is in itself very vaguely defined, but, in general, we may consider it as extending from room temperature to approximately one third of the absolute melting temperature. In this region the effect of strain rate is secondary, except for extreme ranges of strain rate, and the tension test gives a reasonably unique relation between tension stress s and plastic strain e, the stress–strain curve (Fig. 10-1). However, the stress–strain relation has a unique meaning only as long as the stress acts in one direction. In many important cases it merely specifies a limiting stress s_y at which yielding will start.*

* The attempt to define a region of "normal temperature" and a pattern of

Assume next that a three-dimensional state of stress, with principal stresses σ_1, σ_2, and σ_3 (Fig. 10-2), is applied to the same material. What will be the distribution of the corresponding plastic strains ϵ_1, ϵ_2, and ϵ_3? If there is a yield strength in tension, what are the corresponding values of the principal stresses at which yielding will start?

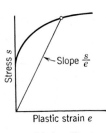

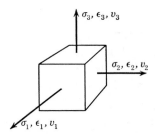

IG. 10-1. Stress–
Strain Curve

FIG. 10-2. Three-Dimen-
sional State of Stress and
Plastic Strain

The conditions which govern the plastic flow for small changes of shape are expressed through the three rules of yielding:[1]

1. The direction of the principal extensions coincide with those of the principal stresses.

2. The volume remains essentially constant. This gives

$$\epsilon_1 + \epsilon_2 + \epsilon_3 = 0 \qquad (1)$$

"normal behavior" is an example of pragmatic simplification of a very complicated phenomenon. The pattern of reasoning in the field of strength of materials grew out of experiences which were confined to the region of normal temperatures. The problems associated with elevated temperatures were encountered at a relatively recent stage and are still classified as examples of "abnormal" behavior. More complete knowledge than is now available might justify a more mature treatment for the entire field.

The specific questions involved may be listed as follows:

1. The existence of an elastic limit below which plastic deformations are imperceptible.

2. The existence of a unique stress–strain curve independent (without limits) of the strain rate.

3. The existence of a mechanical equation of state giving a relation among stress, strain, strain rate, and temperature.

In the region of normal temperatures all three of these questions are answered in the affirmative. At elevated temperatures they are probably all answered in the negative, but no sharp boundary between the two regions can be expected.

This important subject has been under study in recent years by Fisher, Mac-Gregor, Holloman, and others.[11-13] Among other results it has been shown that the combined effect of strain rate and temperature can be expressed through a "velocity-modified temperature" of the form $T_m = T\{1 - k \log (v/v_0)\}$ where T is the temperature, v the strain rate, and v_0 and k constants for each material. The correlation appears to be particularly good for very low temperatures.

3. The Mohr's circles for strain remain geometrically similar with the Mohr's circles for stress. This may be expressed by the three equations:

$$\frac{\epsilon_1 - \epsilon_2}{\sigma_1 - \sigma_2} = \frac{\epsilon_2 - \epsilon_3}{\sigma_2 - \sigma_3} = \frac{\epsilon_3 - \epsilon_1}{\sigma_3 - \sigma_1} = c \qquad (2)$$

Rules 1 and 3 are evidently equivalent to the assumption of isotropy. The quantity c is not independent of stress or strain, but for a fixed state of stress it remains a constant for each point.

To these three rules is added the Mises–Hencky criterion of yielding, which so far has been found to agree most consistently with experiments. In accordance with this criterion, we introduce the two quantities:

$$s = \frac{1}{\sqrt{2}} \sqrt{(\sigma_1 - \sigma_2)^2 + (\sigma_2 - \sigma_3)^2 + (\sigma_3 - \sigma_1)^2}$$

$$e = \frac{\sqrt{2}}{3} \sqrt{(\epsilon_1 - \epsilon_2)^2 + (\epsilon_2 - \epsilon_3)^2 + (\epsilon_3 - \epsilon_1)^2} \qquad (3)$$

These quantities have been given the names of *intensity of stress* and *intensity of strain*, respectively.[2] The former is a measure of the state of stress with respect to its propensity for causing yielding; the latter is a measure of the magnitude of the yielding or change of shape. These quantities have been chosen in such a manner that they are measured directly by the tension test. This is also the reason why they have been given the same symbols as the quantities measured in the tension test. If the tension test be made so that $\sigma_2 = \sigma_3 = 0$, the first of equations 3 gives $s = \sigma_1$. The measured plastic strain in the tension test is ϵ_1, but owing to the volume remaining constant the other strains have the values $\epsilon_2 = \epsilon_3 = -\frac{1}{2}\epsilon_1$, and the second of equations 3 gives $e = s_1$.

Rule 3 may also be expressed by three other equations by combining each pair of the equations 2. Subtracting the last from the first gives

$$\epsilon_1 - \epsilon_2 - (\epsilon_3 - \epsilon_1) = c[\sigma_1 - \sigma_2 - (\sigma_3 - \sigma_1)]$$

By application of rule 2 this becomes

$$\epsilon_1 = \tfrac{2}{3}c[\sigma_1 - \tfrac{1}{2}(\sigma_2 + \sigma_3)] \qquad (4)$$

and similar expressions may be obtained for ϵ_2 and ϵ_3.

Introducing rule 3 into equation 3 we also obtain

$$\frac{2}{3}c = \frac{e}{s} \qquad (5)$$

In this manner we obtain, for the principal plastic strains,

$$\epsilon_1 = \frac{e}{s}\left[\sigma_1 - \frac{1}{2}(\sigma_2 + \sigma_3)\right]$$

$$\epsilon_2 = \frac{e}{s}\left[\sigma_2 - \frac{1}{2}(\sigma_3 + \sigma_1)\right]$$

$$\epsilon_3 = \frac{e}{s}\left[\sigma_3 - \frac{1}{2}(\sigma_1 + \sigma_2)\right] \tag{6}$$

This result presents a close analogy with the usual form of Hooke's law for the elastic case. The modulus of elasticity E is replaced by s/e and Poisson's ratio μ by $\frac{1}{2}$.

For the case of *plane stress* ($\sigma_3 = 0$):

$$\epsilon_1 = \frac{e}{s}\left[\sigma_1 - \frac{1}{2}\sigma_2\right]$$

$$s = \sqrt{\sigma_1{}^2 + \sigma_2{}^2 - \sigma_1\sigma_2} \qquad \epsilon_2 = \frac{e}{s}\left[\sigma_2 - \frac{1}{2}\sigma_1\right]$$

$$\epsilon_3 = -\frac{e}{s}\frac{\sigma_1 + \sigma_2}{2} \tag{7}$$

For the case of *plane strain* ($\epsilon_3 = 0$):

$$\epsilon_1 = \frac{3}{4}\frac{e}{s}(\sigma_1 - \sigma_2) = \frac{\sqrt{3}}{2}e$$

$$s = \frac{\sqrt{3}}{2}(\sigma_1 - \sigma_2) \qquad \epsilon_2 = -\frac{3}{4}\frac{e}{s}(\sigma_1 - \sigma_2) = -\frac{\sqrt{3}}{2}e \tag{8}$$

For the case of *compression* $\sigma_1 = -\sigma$, $\sigma_2 = \sigma_3 = 0$; hence, $s = \sigma$, and

$$\epsilon_1 = -e; \quad \epsilon_2 = +\frac{e}{2}; \quad \epsilon_3 = +\frac{e}{2}$$

showing that the theory provides for symmetry of tension and compression.

For the case of *pure shear* $\sigma_1 = \tau$, $\sigma_2 = -\tau$, $\sigma_3 = 0$; hence, $s = \sqrt{3}\,\tau$, and

$$\epsilon_1 = \frac{\sqrt{3}}{2}e$$

$$\epsilon_2 = -\frac{\sqrt{3}}{2}e \qquad \gamma = \epsilon_1 - \epsilon_2 = \sqrt{3}\,e \tag{9}$$

$$\epsilon_3 = 0$$

showing that the intensity of stress is $\sqrt{3}\,\tau$; the shearing strain is $\sqrt{3}$ times the normal strain at this intensity of stress.

A better physical picture of the yielding process is obtained by considering the state of stress σ_1, σ_2, and σ_3 divided into its hydrostatic tension,

$$p = \frac{\sigma_1 + \sigma_2 + \sigma_3}{3} \tag{10}$$

and the remaining state of stress,

$$\left.\begin{aligned}
s_1 &= \sigma_1 - p = \tfrac{2}{3}[\sigma_1 - \tfrac{1}{2}(\sigma_2 + \sigma_3)] \\
s_2 &= \sigma_2 - p = \tfrac{2}{3}[\sigma_2 - \tfrac{1}{2}(\sigma_3 + \sigma_1)] \\
s_3 &= \sigma_3 - p = \tfrac{2}{3}[\sigma_3 - \tfrac{1}{2}(\sigma_1 + \sigma_2)]
\end{aligned}\right\} \tag{11}$$

The hydrostatic tension is a measure of the tendency to change the volume; the remaining stress components in equation 11 actually measure the tendency to change the shape. By equation 4 it is evident that the plastic strains distribute themselves in proportion to s_1, s_2, and s_3.

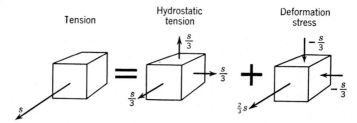

Fig. 10-3.   Resolution of Tension Stress

The tension test itself may be considered as consisting of the components (Fig. 10-3)

$$p = \frac{s}{3} \quad \text{and} \quad \left.\begin{aligned} s_1 &= \frac{2}{3}\,s \\ s_2 &= -\frac{1}{3}\,s \\ s_3 &= -\frac{1}{3}\,s \end{aligned}\right\} \tag{12}$$

The phenomenon of yielding is unaffected by the hydrostatic tension. This is not necessarily true for fracture phenomena.

4. Elevated Temperatures.   It is assumed that there is available a series of creep tests at constant stress at the temperature in question. The primary form of these test results give the plastic deformation e as a function of the time t (Fig. 10-4). For a limited region of stress these creep curves usually approach straight lines; in the steady state represented by this condition each constant stress s is associated by a constant *creep rate* $v = de/dt$. The stress–strain curve is now replaced by a stress versus strain-rate curve (Fig. 10-5).

This usually approaches a straight line in the log–log plot, at least for limited regions.

It is evident that the experimental material is now valid only for the case of constant stress. The basic conditions of plastic flow remain the same as for the case at normal temperature. For creep under the three principal stresses,

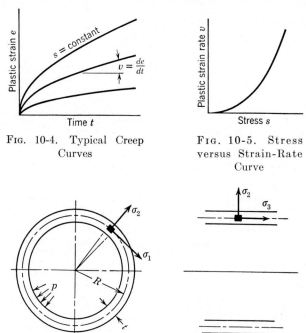

FIG. 10-4. Typical Creep Curves

FIG. 10-5. Stress versus Strain-Rate Curve

FIG. 10-6. Creep in Thin Cylinder

σ_1, σ_2, and σ_3, we obtain the principal creep rates, v_1, v_2, and v_3, which by equation 6 are determined by

$$v_1 = \frac{v}{s}\left[\sigma_1 - \frac{1}{2}(\sigma_2 + \sigma_3)\right]$$

$$v_2 = \frac{v}{s}\left[\sigma_2 - \frac{1}{2}(\sigma_3 + \sigma_1)\right]$$

$$v_3 = \frac{v}{s}\left[\sigma_3 - \frac{1}{2}(\sigma_1 + \sigma_2)\right] \tag{13}$$

where $v_1 = d\epsilon_1/dt$, etc., s is the intensity of stress as defined previously, and v is the quantity de/dt. Both s and v are measured directly in the tension–creep test.

As an example, consider the case of a thin closed tube under internal pressure (Fig. 10-6). The stresses at the center line of the tube are statically determinate and are found to be, when t is small compared with R,

$$\sigma_1 = \frac{pR}{t} - \frac{p}{2}; \quad \sigma_2 = -\frac{p}{2}; \quad \sigma_3 = \frac{pR}{2t} - \frac{p}{2} \tag{14}$$

which gives for the intensity of stress on the mean radius,

$$s_m = \frac{\sqrt{3}}{2} \frac{pR}{t} \tag{15}$$

If the tension creep rate corresponding to s_m is denoted by v_m, we obtain, for the creep rates at the mean radius,

$$v_1 = \frac{\sqrt{3}}{2} v_m; \quad v_2 = -\frac{\sqrt{3}}{2} v_m; \quad v_3 = 0 \tag{16}$$

A series of careful tests conducted by F. H. Norton at the Massachusetts Institute of Technology has confirmed these results within the experimental errors.[3]

It may be concluded that, as long as the assumption of isotropy is fulfilled, it is a relatively simple matter to extend the results of creep tests in tension to other cases of two- and three-dimensional states of stress. However, the premises also demand that the stresses remain constant in time, because the entire experimental procedure is built on this assumption. Cases in which the stresses vary with the time present much greater difficulties, and here it is usually necessary to obtain direct experimental results for each case. In many cases, such as disks and thick tubes, there is a steady state of stress which will be reached after a long time. This limiting state of stress may be determined for plane problems when the stress creep–rate relation can be written in explicit form. The case of boiler tubes and turbine disks have been solved in this manner.[4, 5]

One of the important applications of high-temperature materials is that of bolting. The basic problem involved is the *relaxation* of the tension stress in a bar which is held at constant length. In this case the stress varies sharply with the time, and the basic premises of the creep tests at constant stress are no longer valid. The solution of this problem is related to the question of whether or not there exists a mechanical equation of state, and no fully satisfactory formulation has as yet been made. There are available, nevertheless, approximate methods[6] which give predictions in reasonable agreement with experiments. Direct experimental data give the safest basis for design.

E. FRACTURE

5. Stress Concentration. As emphasized already, the principal weakness in the correlation of experimental data for the fracture phenomenon is due to the necessity of relating the phenomena to the macroscopic state of stress, in spite of the fact that the unknown microscopic stress is equally important.

The concept of average stress is always related to volumes including a large number of grains, but, depending on the method of the stress analysis, it is still possible to specify the stress with varying degrees of precision. A simple example is a bar of rectangular section in uniform tension (Fig. 10-7). If a small hole is drilled in the bar, the stress remains essentially the same at appreciable distances from the hole, but in its immediate neighborhood the state of stress is completely altered. The tangential stress at the edge of the hole is increased to something of the order of three times the average value without the hole. If, in particular, we are concerned with the problem of failure across the section $m-m$, the question arises whether attention should be focused on the maximum stress or on the average stress. The maximum stress is usually expressed in terms of the average stress by the *factor of stress concentration k*. Fracture experiments with ductile materials indicate that for steady stress the failure is practically unaffected by this stress concentration. If the material is brittle, however, the fracture will be promoted by the stress concentration; the same is true for ductile materials as well if the stress is alternating.

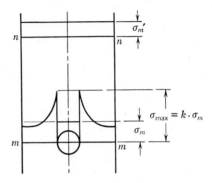

FIG. 10-7. To Illustrate Stress Concentration

The factor of stress concentration has a unique meaning only for plane problems, and even here its uniqueness depends on the basis adopted for the definition of the average stress. It is generally defined so as to specify an ideal maximum stress in the elastic state and is obtained by either direct analysis of the elastic problem or photoelastic measurements. By this idealization it is referred to the macroscopic stress in a material with a very fine grain structure.

For coarser grain structures it is to be expected that the failure is only indirectly related to this maximum of the macroscopic stress. This effect has been given considerable attention in connection with the fatigue problem, and, as might be expected, it has been found that coarse grain structures promote localized yielding and lessen the actual factor of stress concentration.

This effect is expressed through the *sensitivity index q*, defined by

$$q = \frac{k_f - 1}{k - 1} \quad \text{or} \quad k_f = 1 + q(k - 1) \tag{17}$$

k is the factor of stress concentration as defined previously, k_f is the factor which determines the value of the maximum stress at which fatigue fractures will occur. If the material without stress concentration has an endurance limit s_e, it will have an endurance limit of s_e/k_f when the stress-concentration factor is k.

Peterson[7] has related the sensitivity index q to the number of grains within 5 per cent of the peak stress for several materials. His results indicate that

$q = 1$ when the number of grains defined in this manner is of the order of 100,000 and decreases to about 0.4 when the number is 1. The data are too scattered to give any reliable clue as to the nature of the function involved, but the result is significant as one of the first attempts to correlate the effects of macroscopic and microscopic stress states.

The number of grains involved is more practically expressed through the gradient of stress expressed in terms of the grain diameter. This permits the introduction of a dimensionless quantity,

$$\delta = \frac{d\sigma}{dr} \frac{\lambda}{s_e} \tag{18}$$

when $d\sigma/dr$ is the maximum stress gradient, λ the grain diameter, and s_e the endurance limit. The correlation of the sensitivity index q with δ gives results of a similar nature as the other method. A dimensionless gradient of about 0.003 gives $q = 1$; $q = 0.5$ is reached at about $\delta = 0.2$.

These attempts to correlate the sensitivity index with relative grain size and stress gradient suggest the first stumbling steps towards full understanding of the effect of the microscopic aspects of the state of stress. Another approach has given much promise in recent years. This is the concept of *probability of failure* in a certain region as a function of stress and other variables. Weibull[8] was one of the first to formulate this approach which has yielded much useful insight into associated phenomena, such as the size effect in fatigue. A more fundamental application of statistical reasoning in exploring the behavior of the basic structure of materials[9] promises to carry this method of reasoning very far along the road towards a better understanding of the entire concept of mechanical strength.

6. Brittle Fractures under Steady Stress. The distinction between ductile and brittle materials has always been vague, but it used to be sufficient to segregate the materials by type. At normal temperatures mild steel has usually been considered as the prototype of ductile materials, whereas ordinary cast iron served as the prototype for brittle materials. A limit of approximately 5 per cent elongation has been advanced as the dividing boundary.

Cast iron at normal temperature also has a property which appears to be common to materials which exhibit brittle fractures under steady stress. There is very considerable difference between its ultimate strength in tension and in compression. This is true for concrete as well. Whether this phenomenon is universal for all brittle failures under steady stress is yet to be determined, but it is not unlikely that this is the case. As already pointed out, we may consider the state of stress in a tension test as consisting of a state of hydrostatic tension $s/3$, $s/3$, $s/3$ and the stress system $\frac{2}{3}s$, $-s/3$, $-s/3$ (Fig. 10-3). In the idealized compression test we may likewise consider the stress system as composed of the hydrostatic compression $-s/3$, $-s/3$, $-s/3$ and the stress system $-\frac{2}{3}s$, $s/3$, $s/3$.

The yielding phenomena have been found to proceed entirely independently of the hydrostatic tension or compression, and the cause of yielding is uniquely measured by the intensity of stress s. It is very unlikely, however, that the fracture phenomena proceed independently of the hydrostatic component of the stress. It is reasonable to expect fracture to be promoted by hydrostatic tension and delayed by hydrostatic compression. This is undoubtedly one of the reasons for the difference in ultimate strength in compression and tension. Although it has so far been clearly formulated only for materials of the type of cast iron and concrete, it is probably a phenomenon which accompanies brittle fractures in all materials under steady stress.[10]

With the use of high-strength materials at elevated temperatures, the old distinction between ductile and brittle materials is no longer tenable, and it is now known that, under prolonged application of stress and temperature, brittle fractures will usually occur even in materials which at normal temperatures would unquestionably be defined as ductile. One of the most important tests of high-temperature materials is the *creep-to-rupture test* in which a series of specimens are tested to fracture under constant load and constant temperature. The relation between rupture stress and the logarithm of the time required for rupture is usually a straight line. Specimens tested at high stress, which fail after a short time, usually fail with appreciable elongation and reduction of area. Specimens with lower stress, in which fracture occurs after a longer time, often fail without appreciable reduction of area, even though the total elongation may be quite large. This has made it necessary for the

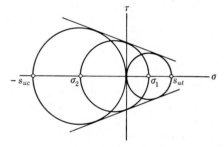

FIG. 10-8.   Failure of Brittle Materials

designer to consider brittle fractures for all materials under steady stress. Whether the rupture strength is different for tension and compression in these cases is still to be determined, and the effect of stress concentration is likewise practically unknown. Rationalized design procedures for high-temperature machinery urgently call for systematic investigation of this nature in connection with the creep-to-rupture test. Until this additional information is available, the design of such machinery will have to remain on an empirical basis.

Certain ductile materials under steady stress occasionally give evidence of brittle failures owing to progressive alterations in the grain structure. These may be caused by the combined influence of stress and corrosive action (intercrystalline deterioration) or by the combined influence of stress and temperature (carbon spherodization). This class of fracture phenomena, although extremely important, must be classed as evidences of faulty material for the application in question.

If it is assumed that the ultimate strengths in tension and compression, s_{ut} and s_{uc}, are known, the designer is still called on to find a rational basis for the extension of these results to cases of two- or three-dimensional stress. This problem is as yet very poorly understood, and the only rational method is that proposed by Mohr many years ago, which is a modification of the maximum shear theory. In Mohr's stress plane (Fig. 10-8) draw the circles for the tension and the compression test. Any other stress state for which the largest Mohr circle has a common tangent with the test circles is assumed to cause failure. If the two stresses are σ_1 and σ_2, it is easily shown that they are connected by the relation,

$$\sigma_1 s_{uc} - \sigma_2 s_{ut} = s_{uc} s_{ut}$$

or

$$\frac{\sigma_1}{s_{ut}} - \frac{\sigma_2}{s_{uc}} = 1 \qquad (19)$$

The values of σ_1 and σ_2 must be inserted in this equation with the proper sign and augmented by the appropriate factor of stress concentration. Figure 10-9 shows the relation between σ_1 and σ_2 which is obtained from the Mohr stress plane, or from equation 19.*

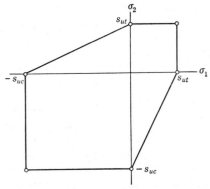

This procedure should be considered as no more than a rough approximation of an extremely complicated problem. This method degenerates into the maximum shear theory when the ultimate strengths in tension and compression are equal. If the tension and compression properties have been

FIG. 10-9. Failure of Brittle Materials

demonstrated to be the same, it is probably more accurate to relate the failure phenomenon to the Mises–Hencky theory in which the failure criterion becomes

$$s_u = \sqrt{\sigma_1{}^2 + \sigma_2{}^2 - \sigma_1 \sigma_2} \qquad (20)$$

when s_u is now the ultimate strength.

7. Fracture of Materials under Variable Stress. Fatigue. Brittle fractures may be precipitated in all materials under all conditions of service if the stresses are cyclic. This is the most common source of failure in engineering structures, and the subject of fatigue failures may well be given first place in the entire problem of mechanical strength. This important part of the problem of mechanical strength is also the most empirical in nature, and it will continue to remain so for a long time.[11,12]

The most important of the ductile materials used in machine design, par-

---

* In equation 19, σ_1 and σ_2 refer to the particular pair of the principal stresses which form the greatest shearing stress. When σ_1 and σ_2 are both either positive or negative, the plane of maximum shear stress shifts, and the equation applies to the numerically largest of σ_1 or σ_2 and the third principal stress σ_3, which is assumed to be zero.

ticularly carbon steels and the alloy steels with moderate amounts of alloying materials, give the most consistent picture with respect to fatigue strength. When tested in air under alternating stress, with specimens of standard size, form, and finish, they give evidence of the existence of an *endurance limit* s_e below which failures will not be precipitated for a very large number of cycles. In the absence of stress concentration this endurance limit is usually about one-half the ultimate tensile strength. Unlike quantities like yield strength and ultimate tensile strength, however, this quantity is in practically all materials subject to wide fluctuations from external causes, such as apparently trivial changes of corrosive conditions, size and finish of the specimens. When the temperature is raised beyond the normal range, the results become increasingly complex, and in many instances these effects are apparent only after a number of cycles greatly in excess of the standard duration of 10^7 cycles. As the field has been extended with respect to variations of material and operating conditions, it has become necessary to throw doubt on the existence of the endurance limit as a unique property of the material. In the majority of applications it is necessary to portray the fatigue properties of any one material and a specific set of operating conditions by an empirical relation, the *S–N* curve, which gives the relation between stress amplitude and the number of cycles for fracture.

The effect of stress concentration is known with a certain degree of precision only for those materials and conditions where the endurance limit is a unique property. The sensitivity index q, already referred to, is probably the most useful measure of the effect of stress concentration. It is influenced primarily by the gradient of stress as related to the grain structure, so that the effect of a certain theoretical concentration of stress is most severe in fine-grained heat-treated steels but relatively slight in coarse-grained annealed steels. Although heat treatment may improve the endurance limit of a standard fatigue specimen compared with that of a softer material, the difference may be largely lost in the presence of stress concentration. There has been progress in recent years towards a better understanding of this particular problem, but much remains to be done before the designer can apply the data to conditions which differ appreciably from the conditions of the test.

A considerable amount of investigation has also been made on the subject of fatigue failures under combined stress. Consistent results on this problem are available only in those cases where the endurance limit is a unique property, and here the Mises–Hencky criterion of failure appears to fit the test results most closely.[11] Since fatigue failures generally occur at or near free surfaces, the experimental material applies only to plane-stress problems. If the endurance limit is s_e, therefore, failure will occur under the principal stresses σ_1 and σ_2 when

$$s_e = \sqrt{\sigma_1{}^2 + \sigma_2{}^2 - \sigma_1\sigma_2} \qquad (21)$$

Hence, the endurance limit for the shear stress τ_e is $s_e/\sqrt{3}$.

The apparent validity of the Mises–Hencky theory of failure suggests that the hydrostatic component of the stress is without influence on fatigue failures.

This may well be true for the case of alternating stress, where all components of the stress vary around a mean value of zero, but it is unlikely to remain true for cases of pulsating stress.

In the great majority of strength problems, the major components of stress are static with less accurately known alternating stresses superimposed. The principal causes of failure originate in combinations of this type. The blading of turbines and compressors and aircraft propellers represent typical examples of this problem, but the conditions in various details of reciprocating engines are similar, although here the alternating stresses are usually known with greater precision.

This type of failure problem, which in fact embodies the vast majority of important cases, presents great logical difficulties because of the fundamentally different mechanism of failure in the two sources of stress. The Goodman diagram, giving the upper and lower limits of the stress cycle, represents the

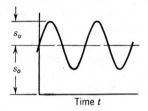

Fig. 10-10.   Steady   and   Fig. 10-11.   Failure under Steady and
Variable Stress   Variable Stress

first attempt at a rationalization of this problem. The same data may equally well be plotted as a relation between a steady component of stress s_0 and a variable component of amplitude s_v (Figs. 10-10 and 10-11) which will cause failure. In Fig. 10-11 the failure under steady stress will occur at the yield strength s_y if by failure is meant initial yielding. Fracture will not occur until the stress has reached the ultimate strength s_u, but by this time the material has been greatly modified by strain hardening. Under alternating stress, fracture will occur at the stress amplitude s_e. Owing to the effect of strain hardening, the material will sustain an alternating stress even when the steady stress has reached the yield strength. In ductile materials, the effect of the steady stress is not appreciably influenced by stress concentration, whereas the effects of the alternating stress are augmented. It is evident that strict logic is defeated by the complexity of this problem, and for practical purposes it seems reasonable to consider the two failures as occurring at s_e and s_y, respectively, and to assume that the failure relation is a straight line connecting these points. The equation of this line is

$$\frac{s_y}{s_e} + \frac{s_0}{s_y} = 1 \qquad (22)$$

This case is parallel to the case of failure of brittle materials under steady stress.

It is worth remembering, however, that there are many cases where the effect of the steady component of the stress is much smaller than suggested by equation 22. This is particularly the case in high-temperature applications.

F. WORKING STRESSES

It is evident from the preceding discussion that the problem of mechanical strength is too complex to permit the establishment of rigid rules for the determination of working stresses. However, the designer is forced to make decisions on many aspects of this problem, even when the available information is insufficient for a strictly logical procedure. Such decisions must be based on experience, and it is important that this experience is interpreted as logically as possible in the light of the state of knowledge at any one time. Rules for working stresses must be sufficiently flexible, therefore, so that they may be adjusted to new information.

From the early days of rational engineering the term *factor of safety*, denoting the ratio of the limiting stress to the actual stress has been used to express the margin between failure and success. The author has previously proposed that this be replaced by a *factor of utilization u*, which is the inverse of the factor of safety. This is a somewhat more logical concept, which has gained ground in recent years. Thus, if failure is precipitated by a value P_i of a load, an actual load P is equivalent to a factor of utilization:

$$u = \frac{P}{P_i} \qquad (23)$$

Similarly, if a series of forces $P_1, P_2, \cdots$ produce stresses in a certain member which are proportional to these forces, each force will represent a utilization of the strength, $u_1 = P_1/P_i$, $u_2 = P_2/P_i$, etc. The total utilization is then

$$u = u_1 + u_2 + \cdots \qquad (24)$$

A factor of utilization of 1 expresses the condition of failure.

The principal purpose of a set of rules for working stresses is to give as logical a definition of the factor of utilization as permitted by the state of knowledge. The advance in knowledge usually results in a more precise evaluation of the limiting strength but will occasionally result in a revision of the interpretation of the mechanism of failure and the resulting definition of the factor of utilization.

The following summary of the various cases of importance gives a definition of the factor of utilization which is consistent with the state of knowledge at the present time. A similar proposal[13] was made by the author several years ago, which at that time represented the practice of one of the large manufacturing companies. At that time the gas turbine and its attendant problems of failure at high temperatures had not yet appeared, nor had the steam turbine been developed to the point where creep and fracture at high temperatures were of paramount importance. The maximum shear theory was selected as the basic failure theory, although it was known even then that it failed to account for certain tests on yielding.

The following summary is somewhat more condensed, and the Mises–Hencky theory has been made the basis of most failure phenomena. This has been necessitated not only by the improvement in the state of knowledge since that time, but also as a matter of logical necessity. The phenomena of creep and yielding actually become more complicated and less satisfactory from a logical point of view if an attempt is made to describe them on the basis of the maximum shear theory. From the purely practical point of view the difference in the values of the factor of utilization is not of great importance.

The actual values of the factor of utilization (or factor of safety) which are to be used in each case constitute a matter which must remain the responsibility of the designer. The values chosen depend on whether the condition of operation is continuous or of short duration, such as in overspeed tests. They also depend on the experience available from similar undertakings and must always be lower for cases where the failure phenomenon is obscure than for simpler cases. Very few applications of ductile materials under steady stress should require a lower factor of utilization than 0.5 (factor of safety of 2). If experience indicates that a lower value is necessary, this should be regarded as an incentive for a more rational formulation of the particular problem in question.

G. Proposed Rules for Working Stresses

8. Ductile Materials at Normal Temperatures. (a) *Steady Stress.*

Mode of failure: Yielding.
Limiting stress: Yield strength in tension s_y.
Stress concentration: No effect on failure.

When material is subjected to the principal stresses σ_1, σ_2, and σ_3, determine the intensity of stress:

$$s = \frac{1}{\sqrt{2}} \sqrt{(\sigma_1 - \sigma_2)^2 + (\sigma_2 - \sigma_3)^2 + (\sigma_3 - \sigma_1)^2}$$

For plane stress, $\sigma_3 = 0$

$$s = \sqrt{\sigma_1^2 + \sigma_2^2 - \sigma_1\sigma_2}$$

Factor of utilization:

$$u = \frac{s}{s_y}$$

(b) *Alternating Stress.*

Mode of failure: Fracture.
Limiting stress: Endurance limit or fatigue limit for stated number of reversals, s_e
Stress concentration: Theoretical factor k, sensitivity index q, actual factor

$$k_f = 1 + q(k - 1).$$

The available information is by inference applicable only to plane stress. When material is subjected to two principal stresses with amplitudes σ_{1v} and σ_{2v}, respectively, determine the intensity of stress amplitude.

$$s_v = \sqrt{(k_{1f}\sigma_{1v})^2 + (k_{2f}\sigma_{2v})^2 - k_{1f}\sigma_{1v}k_{2f}\sigma_{2v}}$$

Factor of utilization:

$$u = \frac{s_v}{s_e}$$

(c) *Alternating and Steady Stress.*

Mode of failure: Fracture for alternating stress acting alone, yielding for steady stress acting alone, fracture for both acting together.

Limiting stress: s_e for alternating stress, s_y for steady stress.

Stress concentration: k_f applied to alternating stress, ignored for steady stress.

The available information is by inference applicable only to plane stress. When material is subjected to two principal stresses, each having steady components σ_{10} and σ_{20} and variable components σ_{1v} and σ_{2v}, determine the two components of the intensity of stress.

$$s_o = \sqrt{\sigma_{10}^2 + \sigma_{20}^2 - \sigma_{10}\sigma_{20}}$$

$$s_v = \sqrt{(k_{1f}\sigma_{1v})^2 + (k_{2f}\sigma_{2v})^2 - k_{1f}\sigma_{1v}k_{2f}\sigma_{2v}}$$

Factor of utilization:

$$u = \frac{s_o}{s_y} + \frac{s_v}{s_e}$$

9. Brittle Materials at Normal Temperatures.   (a) *Steady Stress.*

Mode of failure: Fracture.

Limiting stress: Ultimate strengths, tension s_{ut}, compression s_{uc}.

Stress concentration: Theoretical factor k, sensitivity index q, actual factor

$$k_f = 1 + q(k - 1)$$

Of the three principal stresses σ_1, σ_2, and σ_3, select the pair which gives the greatest shearing stress. Assume that this is σ_1 and σ_2, of which σ_1 is either the largest tension stress or the smallest compression stress.

Factor of utilization:

$$u = \frac{k_{f1}\sigma_1}{s_{ut}} - \frac{k_{f2}\sigma_2}{s_{uc}}$$

Insert σ_1 and σ_2 with their proper signs ($+$ for tension, $-$ for compression).

(b) *Alternating Stress.*   Proceed as in article 8b.

(c) *Alternating and Steady Stresses.*   Insufficient information available for rational procedure.   Proceed as in article 10c.

10. Ductile Materials at Elevated Temperatures. *(a) Creep under Steady Stress.*

Mode of failure: Yielding.

Limiting stress: Determined by stated limit on maximum creep rate. Information available on the relation between stress s and creep rate v in tension test.

Stress concentration: No effect on over-all yielding.

When material is subjected to principal stresses σ_1, σ_2, and σ_3, the principal creep rates are

$$v_1 = \frac{v}{s} \left[\sigma_1 - \frac{1}{2}(\sigma_2 + \sigma_3) \right]$$

$$v_2 = \frac{v}{s} \left[\sigma_2 - \frac{1}{2}(\sigma_3 + \sigma_1) \right]$$

$$v_3 = \frac{v}{s} \left[\sigma_3 - \frac{1}{2}(\sigma_1 + \sigma_2) \right]$$

where

$$s = \frac{1}{\sqrt{2}} \sqrt{(\sigma_1 - \sigma_2)^2 + (\sigma_2 - \sigma_3)^2 + (\sigma_3 - \sigma_1)^2}$$

Factor of utilization: Not clearly definable. May be taken as the ratio of s actually existing to the value of s corresponding to the maximum permissible creep rate.

(b) Fracture under Steady Stress.

Mode of failure: Fracture.

Limiting stress: Creep-to-rupture strength s_u for a stated length of time.

Stress concentration: Effect unknown, but it is recommended that a value of k_f be used as in other brittle failures.

No information available on effect of combined stress. Until experimental results are available, it is probable that cases of plane stress σ_1 and σ_2 can be treated by the Mises–Hencky theory. Hence,

$$s = \sqrt{(k_{f1}\sigma_1)^2 + (k_{f2}\sigma_2)^2 - k_{f1}\sigma_1 k_{f2}\sigma_2}$$

Factor of utilization:

$$u = \frac{s}{s_u}$$

(c) Alternating Stress. Proceed as in article 8*b*.

(d) Alternating and Steady Stresses. Insufficient information available so far, but on the basis that there exists a rupture strength s_u which is the same for tension and compression the following procedure would be suggested.

Mode of failure: Fracture in all cases.

Limiting stress: s_e for alternating stress, s_u for steady stress.

Stress concentration: k_f applied to all stresses.

When material is subjected to two principal stresses, σ_1 and σ_2, each having steady components σ_{10} and σ_{20} and variable components σ_{1v} and σ_{2v}, determine the components of the intensity of stress

$$s_o = \sqrt{(k_{f1}\sigma_{1o})^2 + (k_{f2}\sigma_{2o})^2 - k_{f1}\sigma_{1o}k_{f2}\sigma_{2o}}$$

$$s_v = \sqrt{(k_{f1}\sigma_{1v})^2 + (k_{f2}\sigma_{2v})^2 - k_{f1}\sigma_{1v}k_{f2}\sigma_{2v}}$$

Factor of utilization:

$$u = \frac{s_o}{s_u} + \frac{s_v}{s_e}$$

11. Brittle Materials at Elevated Temperatures.   The distinction between ductile and brittle materials is largely obliterated at elevated temperatures since brittle failures are equally possible in both.   The brittle materials would belong to a class where creep is small.   Proceed as in articles 10b, c, or d.

BIBLIOGRAPHY

1. A. NÁDAI and A. M. WAHL, *Plasticity*, McGraw-Hill, 1931, ch 13 and 14.
2. H. HENCKY: "The New Theory of Plasticity, Strain Hardening and Creep and the Testing of Inelastic Behavior of Metals," *Trans ASME*, v 55, 1933, pp 151–55.   Hencky applied the name "intensity of stress" to a quantity which differs only by a numerical factor from s.   The "intensity of strain" as defined by Hencky applies also to cases where there is a change of volume. When the volume change is zero it differs from e by a numerical factor.
3. C. R. SODERBERG, "Interpretation of Creep Tests on Tubes," *Trans ASME* v 62, n 3, pp 738–48.   A series of carefully conducted creep tests on tubes under internal pressure, conducted by F. H. Norton, are analyzed in the light of the theory of yielding.
4. R. W. BAILEY, "The Utilization of Creep Test Data in Engineering Design," *Proc Inst Mech Engrs (Lond.)*, v 131, Nov, 1935.   This paper has been of great importance on this subject, and it gives the solution of many problems. The approach is somewhat more complicated than that presented here, but the methods are clearly outlined.
5. C. R. SODERBERG, "The Interpretation of Creep Tests for Machine Design," *Trans ASME*, Nov 1936, p 733; "Plastic Flow and Creep in Polycrystalline Metals," *Proc 5th Int Congress Applied Mechanics*, 1938; "Plasticity and Creep in Machine Design," *Stephen Timoshenko 60th Anniversary Volume*, Macmillan Co, New York, 1938, pp 107–10.   These papers discuss various phases of the general problem of predicting deformation of machine structures from creep tests.
6. E. P. POPOV, "Correlation of Tension Creep Tests with Relaxation Tests," paper 47-APM-8 presented before the national meeting of the Applied Mechanics Division of the American Society of Mechanical Engineers, 1947. This paper re-examines experimental relaxation data obtained by Davis with methods proposed in ref 5.   The correlation appears satisfactory.
7. R. E. PETERSON, "Methods of Correlating Data from Fatigue Tests of Stress Concentration Specimens," *Stephen Timoshenko 60th Anniversary Volume*, Macmillan Co, New York, 1938, pp 179–83.

8. W. WEIBULL, "A Statistical Theory of the Strength of Materials," *Ingeniörs Vetenskapsakademiens Handlingar* 151, 1939.

9. JOHN C. FISHER, "A Mechanism for the Plastic Flow of Certain Simple Alloys," Sc.D. Thesis submitted 1947 to Mech Eng Dept, Mass Inst of Tech.

10. W. SEIGFRIED, "Failure from Creep as Influenced by the State of Stress," *Sulzer Tech Rev (Switz.)*, n 1, 1943; "Brittleness and Toughness of Metals at High Temperature, *Sulzer Tech Rev Switz.* n 1, 1945. These papers are significant as an attempt to relate brittle failures to the influence of the state of stress by studying creep tests on notched specimens.

11. *Prevention of the Failure of Metals under Repeated Stress*, handbook prepared for the Bureau of Aeronautics by the staff of the Batelle Memorial Institute. The literature in fatigue of metals is very extensive. This volume, with its wealth of data and bibliography, can serve as a single reference.

12. R. E. PETERSON, "Relation between Life Testing and Conventional Tests of Materials," *ASTM Bul* 133, March 1945. Empirical testing of machine structures has become perhaps the most important means of solution of problems where the direct rationalized method is not yet applicable. This paper gives many examples of this method.

13. C. R. SODERBERG, "Factor of Safety and Working Stresses," *Trans ASME*, v 52, pt 1, 1930, APM 52–2.

CHAPTER 11

RESIDUAL STRESSES

By Oscar J. Horger

459

A. Introduction

Residual stresses must be utilized if we expect to realize the potential strength characteristics inherent in materials. Their presence in the proper manner will greatly improve the design criterion of strength-to-weight ratio and reduce ultimate cost. Therefore, residual stress is fast becoming as important a factor as the usual mechanical and metallurgical properties in the consideration of the fatigue-strength characteristics of design members. Many properties such as tensile, hardness, impact, fatigue, microstructure, and hardenability are obtained by simple and standardized forms of tests and evaluated in a conventional manner. Our consideration of residual stresses is not subject to such routine analysis; it presents complications and is surrounded by inadequate theoretical knowledge along with the customary resistance to applying new findings to production practices.

Residual stresses in machine parts have been accepted until relatively recently as being generally undesirable from a standpoint of shop processing difficulties and premature service failures. Residual stresses were often associated with warping and distortion after heat treatment or machining, cracks produced in quenching or grinding, stress corrosion and season cracking, cracking due to excessive reduction in cold drawing, and early service failures of tools, dies, machine parts, and welded members. This negative attitude has prevailed for many years, even though in 1888 built-up guns[1] employing residual stresses were first manufactured in United States. Timoshenko[2] presents a review of the early literature and theoretical treatment of manufactured parts such as guns, turbine rotors,[3] and other cases where these internal stresses may be advantageously utilized. It was 1929, however, before it was first recognized (by Föppl[4] in Germany) that fatigue resistance could be increased through residual stresses obtained in cold-working operations.

Just as ordnance requirements initiated the useful application of residual stresses, so have the new requirements of the recent war greatly extended their application. Favorable internal-stress systems were so utilized that, in many cases, they actually represented the only factor of safety against failure as well as accelerating production output. These new and recent experiences will give encouragement and information to engineers on how similar benefits can be obtained in a peace industry.

Residual stresses may be obtained by (1) cold work, or by heating to produce (2) thermal and (3) transformation stresses or by a combination of (2) and (3). Cold working results from shot blasting, and this practice has been extensively reviewed by Almen,[5] Moore,[6] Frye,[7] and others;[8, 9] also cold rolling increases fatigue resistance as outlined for many practical applications in an earlier résumé. Other methods of cold working are discussed later, but the references already cited leave little question as to the merits of using some form of cold working. As yet, thermal and transformation stresses have been little employed to improve fatigue resistance. This subject deserves much greater attention and will occupy a substantial part of this chapter.

When the presence of residual stress is accompanied by a change in fatigue resistance, then this change is often attributed to the influence of these internal stresses alone. This contention as well as the manner in which the residual stresses function is very controversial. Residual stresses have rarely been isolated and are always accompanied by some kind of structural or phase changes in the material. Superposition of internal stresses on the stresses arising from the load is not understood in its application to fatigue problems. It should be understood, however, that no question exists as to the favorable effect of the proper residual stresses on fatigue resistance. This problem is presented later.

There is no simple method of determining the magnitude and distribution of residual stresses. Many investigations have been made using various procedures. Only a very brief review of the important methods is given here, as the complete solutions have been published.

B. MEASUREMENT OF RESIDUAL STRESSES

Residual stresses are usually measured by either mechanical or X-ray methods, although other procedures have been employed. Mechanical methods are destructive in that the part must be machined and the relaxation or change in shape must be accurately measured. Both elastic and plastic strains are determined over a relatively large area, and these stresses are macroscopic in nature; magnitude and distribution of stresses over the entire cross section can be calculated from these strains. X-ray analysis offers a nondestructive test but detects elastic stresses only. Stresses are only determined in the surface layer measured in terms of thousandths of an inch, or less where a biaxial stress condition exists. Since fatigue failure generally occurs at the surface, it becomes important to know the state of surface residual stresses. At the present stage of development the X-ray method is limited to materials which have a hardness below 35 to 40 Rockwell C and which yield reasonably clear diffraction lines. Although microscopic stresses have been examined, this chapter discusses only macroscopic stresses. Our science of metallurgy is very deficient in knowledge of microstresses existing between grains, even though such stresses are responsible for grain size, geometry, and physical characteristics.

Barrett,[11] Sachs and Van Horn,[12] and Sachs and Espey[13] published outstanding reviews of the literature on measuring residual stresses by mechanical methods. The theory and practice of measuring internal stresses by X-ray analysis was extensively treated by Barrett[11, 14] and others.[15] Residual stresses measured in welds was summarized by several investigators.[16–18] These references may be consulted for details, but several of the mechanical methods often employed are briefly reviewed here.

1. Stresses in Three Dimensions in Cylinders. Various methods had been developed for measuring residual stresses in either one or two planes, but the so-called boring-out method published by Sachs[19] in 1927 was the first to give the internal stresses in all three principal directions. This process is adaptable only to members having rotational symmetry in shape and stress distribution;

a solid or hollow cylinder is bored out or turned down in successive steps, and the accompanying changes in length and diameter are measured. Even though this method is mathematically desirable,* few investigators have employed it, except in Germany, because of the precision micrometer measurements and time required in machining. Wire strain gages[20] are now available, however, which practically eliminate the major difficulty of measuring diameter and length changes to an accuracy of 0.0001 in. or better.

Presented here are some laboratory techniques and refinements acquired in the use of Sachs's method which were found to improve its utility, especially when steep stress gradients prevail at the surface. Mathematics of this and

FIG. 11-1.   Control Box for Measuring SR-4 Strain-Gage Changes on Diameter and Length of Cylinders Due to Boring out

other methods are not repeated here because these developments can be found elsewhere.[12, 13, 19]

Various stages of boring-out operations† are shown in Fig. 11-1 for solid and tubular cylinders having wire strain gages of the SR-4 type cemented to the

---

* Barrett[11] states that the assumptions made by Sachs in his derivation are few: (1) the assumption of the equations for stresses in tubes under external and internal pressures which are deduced from elastic theory, and other well-known elastic-theory equations; (2) the assumption that the removal of a layer produces an equal change of longitudinal stress at all points on the cross section of the tube wall (a legitimate assumption when the tube diameter is small compared with its length); (3) the assumptions of symmetry of form and of stress distribution about the axis of the specimen and of constancy of stress along its length.

† The per cent bored out at each step is determined by the rate of change of the length and diameter dimensions, and these values must be plotted as boring proceeds. The best procedure is to start boring out with no more than 5 per cent stops in order to establish the end point (determined from the slope of the deformation curve) more accurately and then to increase to 10 per cent. If steep-stress gradient such as may occur at a surface is expected or indicated from the curve, then use much less than 5 per cent.

outer surface,* in a spacing of 90° in both longitudinal and transverse planes. These gages permit determining length and diameter changes after each boring-out operation by a greatly simplified method of electrical-resistance measurements. Cylinders may be bored out until about 98 per cent of the cross section is machined away by holding and clamping it in a special manner in the lathe (Fig. 11-2). Previous practice was to use Huggenberger strain gages, micrometers, or an optimeter[21] for measuring length and diameter changes.

FIG. 11-2. Boring out 9½-in.-diameter Cylinders for Determining Residual Stresses by Sachs's Method

Length of cylinders should be two to three times the diameter in order to minimize end effects, but in this respect the use of wire strain gages permits the use of a shorter cylinder. One of the cylinders shown in Fig. 11-1 has a ratio of a little over unity; it was cut from full-size heat-treated and finish-machined shafts, away from the ends, at a section which had only a diameter and length portion in the shaft of the size shown. Where the necessity arises of using such short lengths, it would be more accurate to apply the gages before the sections are cut away from the full-length piece in order to determine the influence, if any, of the protruding portions. Short solid or hollow cylinders,

* If a very steep surface-stress gradient is expected on a solid cylinder, then accuracy of residual-stress measurement is improved by first boring out with wire gages on the outside diameter. Next apply wire gages to the bore, and start turning off successive layers from the outside diameter, using light cuts. Finally, superimpose strain readings from the outside and inside diameters. If the cylinder is initially hollow, then the first step of boring the inside diameter can be eliminated.

particularly after various heat-treating operations, would introduce complications because of the end effects of quenching; the ends may be curved instead of flat, or an element of the outer or inner surface would be curved instead of straight. Obviously, such shape changes would give erroneous measurements of residual stresses.

Static checks should be made of the resulting longitudinal, tangential, and radial stress-distribution curves obtained by the boring-out method to confirm that equilibrium stress conditions are expressed. This is done with respect to forces acting as follows:*

1. The sum of all longitudinal stresses distributed over the cross section of the cylinder must equal zero. This check is most easily made by plotting the longitudinal stress against the area bored out; the area under tensile stresses must equal the area under compressive stresses.

2. The sum of circumferential stresses distributed over diametrical section of the cylinder must equal zero. To accomplish this, plot the circumferential stress against cylinder radius; again the area under tensile stress must equal the area under compressive stress.

3. The force exerted by the radial stresses acting on the inner surface of the tube at any assumed radius should be equal to the force represented by the area under the circumferential-stress curve between the assumed radius and the outer surface. This check may be carried out from the plots of radial stress against cylinder radius and circumferential stress against cylinder radius.

Equilibrium checks are most easily made at radius values when the circumferential stress is equal to zero. The radial and circumferential stresses are equal at the center of a solid cylinder.

Sachs's boring-out method extrapolates the diameter and length changes from the last boring-out step to the surface. This leads to difficulty where the stress gradient is steep and especially when its direction is reversed in the outermost layers. By slitting and cutting tongues in the finally bored-out cylinder, as shown in Fig. 11-3, it is possible to establish these surface stresses with greater accuracy.†

Inasmuch as Sachs's method of determining residual stresses is the most accurate mechanical procedure known, this review gives an extensive summary of findings based on this procedure. Other mechanical methods are discussed and must be used under certain conditions, but the quantitative value of the stresses is too often questionable.

2. Tangential Stress in Cylinders. Several methods for measuring tangential stress have been developed by various investigators. In all cases the longitudinal stresses as well as the radial ones are neglected, and, therefore, the results are only an approximation where multiaxial stresses exist.

---

* From correspondence with S. Timoshenko.

† Even here the stress must be assumed as being linearly distributed through the tongue thickness. Actual distribution could be approached by etching or machining one surface of the tongue and circumferential section in successive steps, according to reference 31.

Kalakoutzky,[22] Klein,[23] Macrae,[24] and Oding[25] turned thin rings from cylinders. These rings had a circle scribed on one face, and the diameter of such circles was measured before and after cutting out; a ring increasing in diameter indicates the presence of compressive tangential stresses whereas a decrease in diameter indicates tensile stresses.

Siebel[26] and Greene[27] cut transverse slices from bars and bored out or turned in successive steps, noting change in diameter from which the stress distribution was calculated.

FIG. 11-3.   Final Slitting and Tongues cut in 9½-in.-diameter Cylinders after Successive Boring out from Solid Sections

Thin-wall tubes were investigated by slitting longitudinally[28, 29] or cutting a circumferential tongue,[30] as shown in Fig. 11-4a and b. Such methods apply only when the residual-stress distribution is linear through the section, and this is often not the actual case. Slitting of both thin- and thick-wall slices is sometimes used to obtain an indication of residual stresses, that is, closing in means compression, and opening up means tensile stresses on the surface. It is then inferred that no change after slitting means absence of stress, but this is not necessarily true. For example, tension could exist on both surfaces and compression in the core so as to leave zero bending moment after slitting. A method for thin-wall tubes used by Sachs and Espey[31] is more general in that any type of stress distribution can be ascertained by combining the slitting and tongue methods with etching* or by machining away of

* Any etching procedure requires uniform removal of stock and also knowledge as to whether or not acid attack weakens the underlying grain boundaries.

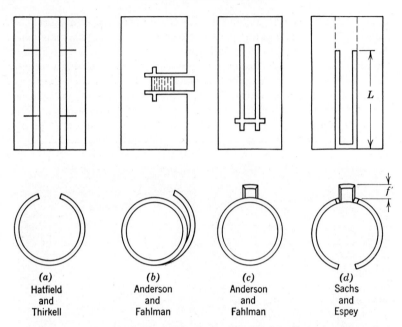

FIG. 11-4. Tongue and Slitting Methods Used by Various Investigators to Determine Longitudinal and Tangential Residual Stresses (Sachs and Espey)

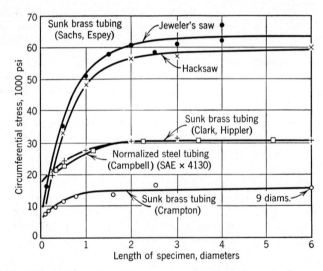

FIG. 11-5. Effect of Length of Specimen on Residual Stress in Brass and Steel
Tubing (Sachs and Espey)

successive layers.   The length of the cylinder should be at least twice the
diameter because of its influence on the tangential stresses measured, as shown
in Fig. 11-5.

   3. Longitudinal Stress in Cylinders.   Howard[32] in 1893 was second only to
Kalakoutzky[22] in measuring residual stresses.   He reported longitudinal
compressive stresses on the basis of an increase in length after boring out but
considered these stresses uniformly distributed over the cross section.   Heyn
and Bauer[33] were able to determine high residual stresses in drawn brass and
steel tubes and rods by turning them down layer by layer and measuring the
changes of length.   This method is still employed for solid cylinders where
the material is too hard to machine, as required by Sachs's boring-out method,
so that the outer layers are
ground off.   Longitudinal
stresses determined in this
manner are calculated too low
and at best are an approximation, because the influence of
the tangential and radial
stresses is neglected.   Nevertheless, many early investigations contributing to our
realization of residual stresses
were made by this method by
Mercia and Woodward,[34]
Porteven,[35] Jasper,[36] Masing,[37] Hoyt,[38] and Greene.[27]

   Kreitz[39] and Buchholtz and
Bühler[40] machined strips of
rectangular cross section from

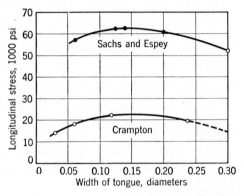

FIG. 11-6.   Effect of Tongue Width on Residual
Longitudinal Stress in Sunk Brass   Tubing,
Determined by Slitting Tongue (Sachs and
Espey)

the lengthwise direction of solid cylinders.   The curvature of these strips
was measured, as were changes in curvature by planing off one side
of these strips facing the core.   Stresses calculated from such measurements
were compared with those obtained by Sachs's boring-out method.   For
90,000 psi by Sachs' procedure only 28 per cent as much was found by the strip
method; for 17,000 to 38,000 psi only 36 per cent; for lower stresses 70 to
90 per cent.

   Thin-walled tubes were investigated by longitudinal tongues,[29, 30] as shown
in Fig. 11-4b and c.   Application of these tongue methods assumes that the
longitudinal-stress distribution is linear through the section.   This assumption
makes this procedure objectionable, and the method by Sachs and Espey[31]
should be applied so as to determine the actual distribution.   Here the width
of the tongue influences the stresses obtained according to Fig. 11-6 where
the tongue width should be preferably between 0.1 and 0.2 of the diameter.

   A comparison of stresses determined by Sachs's and Heyn's method was
reported for a brass tube 1.18 in. OD × 0.20 in. wall.   Maximum longitudinal stresses by Sachs's method were almost 40 per cent higher than

those obtained by Heyn procedure and also showed a somewhat different distribution.

4. Stresses in Plates. Heyn's method[33] has been applied to plates where there is a symmetrical stress distribution. Lazlo[41] and Staeblein[42] planed or etched off layers from one side and measured the deformation so that stresses could be calculated for the case of variable stress through the plate thickness.

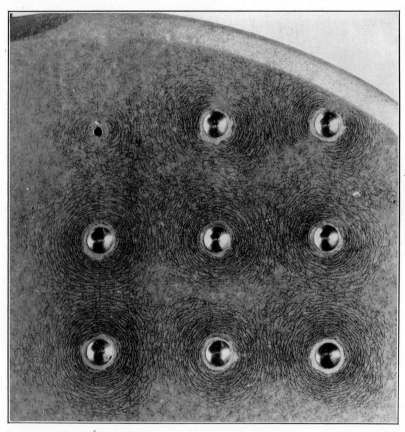

Fig. 11-7. Piston Head Stresscoated and Drilled to Show Presence of Compressive Residual Stress (Anderson)

Spraragen et al.,[16-18] Buchholtz,[43] and others[44] reported on residual stresses in welded plates where the stresses were considered uniform through the plate thickness. They cut the plate into small pieces after locating a series of gage points and rosettes on the surface from which deformations were measured. Reeve[45] reviewed methods and results of measuring residual stresses in welds. Also triaxial stresses were measured by X-ray method.[46]

Mathar[47] presented a novel method in which a hole was drilled and the deformations measured between gage points were located close to the edge of the hole. Welding stresses were also determined by this method.[48]   Also Anderson[49] stress-coated a flat surface on a forged and heat-treated engine piston and drilled a hole with a ⅛-in. sharp drill to about ⅛ in. depth.   Figure 11-7 illustrates cracks in the coating concentric to the drilled holes indicating that a state of compressive residual stresses prevailed at the surface.   If the cracks had radiated from the drilled hole, a state of residual tensile stress would be indicated.   This hole method is reviewed by Sachs and Espey[31] and Gadd.[49]

C. Formation of Thermal Stresses

Thermal stresses are developed when steel is heated and then suddenly cooled.   If the heating temperature is below the lower critical A_1 point, then pure thermal stresses are produced as no structural changes with resulting

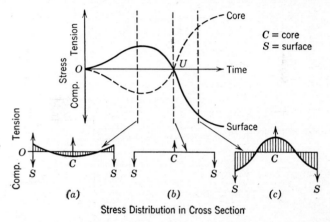

Fig. 11-8.   Transient Change of Stress Distribution in Rapidly Cooled Cylinders (Buchholtz and Bühler)

transformation stresses occur.   Usual quenching operations, however, involve cooling from a higher temperature, above the upper critical A_3, where both thermal and transformation stresses result.

Before residual thermal stresses can be produced, it is necessary that nonuniform plastic deformations occur in different zones of the body.   These are produced as a result of differential temperature with accompanying volume changes arising during the cooling cycle.   If the deformations arising during the cooling period are within the elastic strength of the steel, then no stresses remain after temperature equilibrium is reached.   Both the method of cooling and the strength properties of the steel at elevated temperatures influence the magnitude and distribution of the thermal stresses.

A qualitative representation of thermal-stress formation developed when solid-steel cylinders are suddenly quenched is illustrated in Fig. 11-8 by Buchholtz and Bühler.[50]   Here the entire cooling cycle is divided into three stress-forming phases in a, b, and c.   In the first phase and during the first few seconds after sudden cooling there arise increasing differences of temperature and volume between the surface layers and core. The surface is hindered from contracting by the higher-temperature core and causes tensile stresses in the surface and compression in the core as at a. At all times the longitudinal and tangential stresses through the cross section must be in equilibrium, and, depending on time, temperature, and material strength, the magnitude of these stresses may be as high as the shearing-deformation limit. With further cooling the decrease in temperature of the core is greater than at the surface, and the temperature differential between the surface and core becomes less as well as the internal stresses. Contraction of the core is greater than the surface layers can follow; tensile stresses in the surface change to

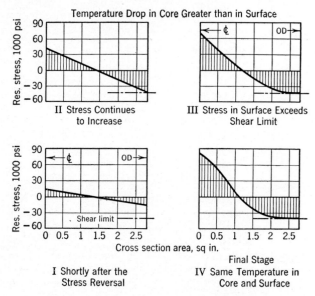

FIG. 11-9. Illustrating Stress Increase after Stress Reversal Due to Accelerated Cooling of a Steel Cylinder (Buchholtz and Bühler)

compressive stresses, and the compression stresses in the core become tensile stresses. The second phase b is then reached at relatively low temperature, point U, where the stress pattern begins to reverse itself. This stress-reversal point is located at a higher temperature for soft steels than for harder steels if cooling conditions are assumed the same. In the third phase c the stresses continue to increase during the continued course of the cooling process until the core reaches its final temperature so as to leave compressive stresses finally in the surface and tensile stresses in the core.

The phenomena which takes place after the stress reversal at point U in Fig. 11-8 corresponds approximately to the schematic arrangement in Fig. 11-9. Here four conditions are represented illustrating the state of the longitudinal stresses in the cross section of a solid cylinder suddenly cooled. Condition I exists temporarily immediately after the stress reversal or point U.

With further contraction of the core the stresses continue to grow as in II. Here the surface stresses are assumed to have reached the shearing-deformation limit, as may be the case for low-strength steels or high stressing.   If the material has a relatively high shearing-deformation limit so that high stresses can be supported elastically, then this straight-line stress distribution prevails until temperature equilibrium is reached.   Now, if the core still continues to contract, then the surface layers further deform and result in the stress distribution outlined in III.   Here the surface layers have exceeded the shearing-deformation limit but not in the core.   Possibility of plastic deformation is greater at the surface than in the core because the stress is biaxial rather than triaxial.   With further contraction of the core, yielding also takes place in the core as well as further plastic deformation of the surface layers to a greater depth, as shown in IV.

In all these examples the forces across any section must be in equilibrium, as previously discussed.   It is important to observe for conditions III and IV that (a) the neutral zone is shifted towards the center line of the cylinder, and (b) the magnitude of the tensile stresses in the core exceed those in the surface.

D. Method of Combining Transformation and Thermal Stresses

When steels are heated to the austenitic condition (above the upper critical temperature, A_3 point) and then suddenly cooled, there are three influences[51] acting to produce residual stresses:

1. First thermal shrinkage occurring before transformation.
2. Volume expansion as a result of transformation.
3. Second thermal shrinkage occurring after transformation.

For solid cylinders condition 2 results in tensile stresses in the surface and compression in the core; both conditions 1 and 3 finally produce a stress pattern opposite that due to transformation in 2 by causing compressive stresses at the surface and tension in the core (Fig. 11-9).   The exact manner by which these thermal and transformation stresses combine has never been established as a rigid set of rules.   Some valuable experimental data are introduced here regarding the knowledge available on this subject.

The results of an investigation having some bearing on both thermal and transformation stresses are shown in Fig. 11-10.   Quantitative measurements were made of the temperature differences arising in steel bars (1.9 in. diameter) of various carbon contents heated to austenitizing temperature and water-quenched.[52, 53]   These curves indicate the temperature differences between the surface and core and how the rate of temperature decrease becomes less with increasing carbon content.   These relationships involve the influence of increasing heat of transformation and decreasing heat conductivity with increasing carbon content.[54]   Curves of this type (Fig. 11-10) form a tentative basis for hardenability and its relationship with residual stresses; more research should be directed toward such fundamentals.

At about 300°F in Fig. 11-10 the rate of temperature decrease for the core becomes greater than that for the surface.   This temperature represents an internal approaching the stress-reversal point U in the internal thermal-stress system, according to the analysis in Fig. 11-8. The investigators[52] assumed from the curves (Fig. 11-10) that the stress-reversal point is located at about 210°F, but it would appear that this temperature would be related and would vary with the kind of transformation products or structure formed through the cross section. So these curves in Fig. 11-10 supplement those in Fig. 11-8; they indicate the mechanism by which a reversal in thermal-stress system becomes compression on the surface and tension in the core. This thermal-stress-change point is of much practical importance because (1) above this temperature the tensile stresses in the surface promote hardening cracks, and (2) its location is significant with respect to the temperatures at which transformation products are formed.

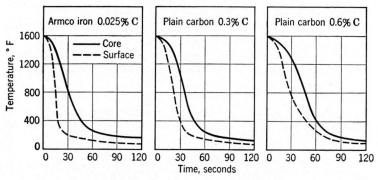

FIG. 11-10. Temperature Differential for Water-Quenched Cylinders of Various Carbon Contents (1.97 in. diameter) (Bühler *et al.*)

Constructional steels investigated will have passed through the temperature range of martensite formation,[55] during which time tensile transformation stresses form in the surface and compression in the core, before the thermal-stress reversal takes place. As is shown later, this condition leads to combined thermal and transformation stresses of compression in the surface and tension in the core for all constructional steels investigated which included many plain carbon and a few alloy steels. In high-carbon steel and very highly alloyed materials, however, the low-temperature range of martensite formation often results in transformation taking place after the thermal-stress reversal; then the transformation stresses will more easily overweigh the small thermal stresses so that high tensile stresses arise at the surface. This latter case of surface tensile residual stresses, according to Scott,[56] is explained by a negative coefficient of expansion. This means that the steel expands as a result of transformation products completed during the final cooling period. These steels with surface tensile stresses are therefore surface-sensitive so that frequently grinding or corrosion will readily lead to crack formation.

In order to clarify and substantiate the previous statements, regarding the superposition of thermal and transformation stresses, an investigation[51, 57] was made of the residual stresses developed in 11 different water-quenched low-carbon steels* with 0 to 27 per cent nickel content. These steels were chosen rather than quenched constructional steels because they could be machined as is required in Sachs's boring-out method used for determining residual

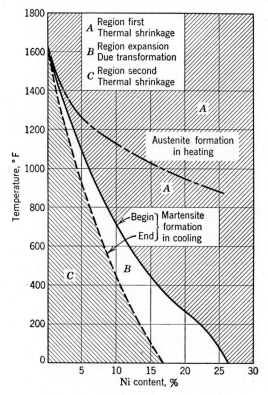

Fig. 11-11.   Division of Iron–Nickel Diagram into Three Regions Determining Residual Stresses Produced in Quenching (Bühler and Scheil)

stresses; also the temperature range of austenite transformation† can be varied over a wide range by changing nickel content as indicated in Fig. 11-11.

* Steels investigated were forged to 2.09 in. diameter, machined to 1.97 in. diameter, heat-treated, and then finally light-turned and ground to diameter before boring-out tests. The length of cylinders was 13.78 in. Carbon content varied from 0.025 to 0.06 per cent, silicon 0.01 to 0.18 per cent, manganese 0.29 to 0.53 per cent except in nickel-free steel which had only a trace of manganese.

† Transformation points were measured by slow cooling in the dilatometer. Rapid cooling would probably shift these temperatures to lower values for steels up to about 10 % Ni, but with higher nickel content little or no change would be expected. The fact that length changes obtained by dilatometer measurements are not necessarily proportional to volume changes was neglected. Also residual compressive stresses may lower the temperature range of transformation, and tensile stresses may raise it, but quantitative data are lacking. E. Scheil (Z Amorg Allg Chem, **207**, 1932, pp 21–40) states that martensite needles have a preference

The results of these residual-stress measurements through the cross section are summarized by the contour-line diagrams in Fig. 11-12. Here it is disclosed that the surface stresses are compression for steels in the approximate range of 0 to 15% Ni and in the region above 25% Ni content; between 15 to 25% Ni the surface stresses are tension. Increasing the nickel content affects the residual stresses by depressing the transformation temperature. It is important whether or not the transformation is completed when room temperature is reached and whether it takes place before or after the reversal of thermal stresses. Resultant actions of the thermal and transformation

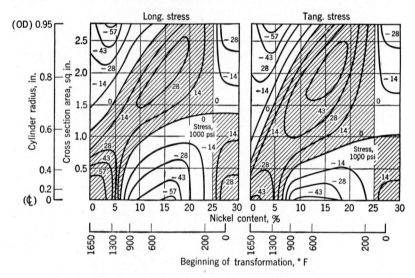

FIG. 11-12. Influence of Nickel Content on Residual-Stress Distribution in Steel Cylinders (1.9 in. ϕ × 13.8 in.) Quenched in Ice Water from 1650°F (Bühler and Scheil)

stresses can annul one another. This condition arises for both thermal and transformation stresses of about 15 and 25% Ni steels where the surface is practically in a stress-free condition.*

Although the action of certain laws is expressed in Fig. 11-12, it becomes necessary to separate and clarify the three individual processes of residual-stress formations outlined in items *a*, *b*, and *c*. This was accomplished by investigating the influence of different cooling conditions on these same nickel steels by Bühler and Scheil.[51]

---

for forming in definite crystal directions of the austenite in the plane of greatest shear-stress component.

* Although the surface stresses are practically zero, stresses of considerable magnitude exist below the surface. Methods of measuring residual stress based on surface determinations, such as X ray or the drilled-hole method of Mathar, would indicate the cylinder of these particular nickel contents as being practically free of stress. Such methods do not disclose the residual-stress condition below the surface.

Residual-stress measurements* in Fig. 11-13 were made on 11.7% Ni steel which was quenched in ice water at four different temperatures. Cylinders were heated to 1650°F, and then some were quenched from 1650°F; others were allowed to furnace-cool to 1290°, 930°, and 680°F and then were quenched from these temperatures. The last temperature is just above the upper limit of the transformation region for this steel which is 625° to 390°F.

From a consideration of Fig. 11-13 it is apparent how each of the three stress-forming influences disappears one after the other. As the quenching temperature decreases, the importance of surface thermal compressive stresses is reduced so that tensile transformation stresses predominate. This trend

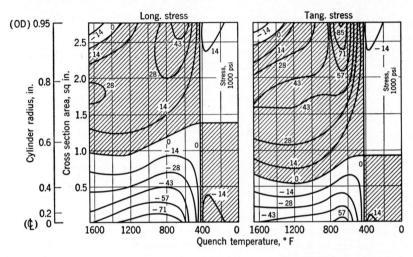

FIG. 11-13.   Influence of Quench-Bath Temperature on Residual-Stress Distribution for 11.7% Ni Steel Cylinders (1.9 in. ϕ × 13.8 in.) Quenched in Ice Water (Bühler and Scheil)

continues until at 680°F quench the effect of the first thermal shrinkage in a is eliminated, and almost pure transformation stresses remain,† leaving dangerous tensile stresses in the surface; in fact, deep longitudinal cracks were produced by this treatment. Decreasing the quench temperature below the end of martensite formation leaves only thermal stresses from second shrinkage in c; stresses are reversed from condition b with compression on the surface instead of tensile stresses but are of small magnitude.

Still further proof of these three stress-forming influences was obtained by again eliminating each factor by means of varying the temperature‡ of the

* Data shown in Fig. 11-16 below 680°F were supplemented on the basis of theoretical considerations.

† Thermal stresses due to second thermal shrinkage in c were not eliminated in this treatment, but the decrease of volume caused thereby is estimated as only one sixth of the volume increase owing to transformation.

‡ Unfortunately, it was not possible to keep cooling conditions comparable, since ice water, warm oil, and a salt bath of potassium nitrate and sodium nitrate

quenching bath in which 11.7% Ni steel was quenched.   Figure 11-14 quotes
the residual-stress measurements obtained after quenching in bath temperatures of 30°, 210°, 390°, 570°, and 750°F.   Similar tests were made on 16.9%
Ni steel producing results in Fig. 11-15.   Both Figs. 11-14 and 11-15 indicate
how one or more of these stress-forming factors may be eliminated so as to

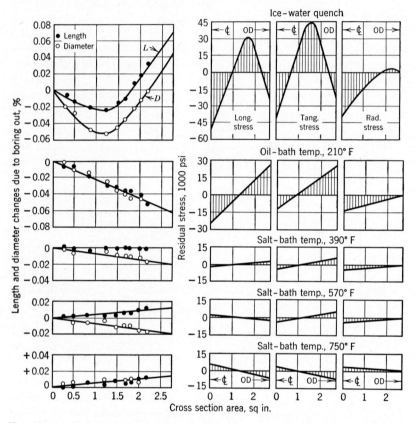

FIG. 11-14.   Influence of Quench-Bath Temperature on Residual-Stress Distribution for 11.7% Ni Steel Cylinders (1.9 in. φ × 13.8 in.) Quenched from 1650°F,
                     Then Air-Cooled (Bühler and Scheil)

leave compressive, tensile, or zero stresses on the surface by means of varying
bath temperature.*   This conclusion is confirmed[51] in Table 11-1 where

---

were used.   Water and oil form a vapour skin, whereas the salt bath does not.
Therefore, these stress comparisons include to some extent the influence of other
factors.

  * Specimens were cooled in air from the quench bath.   Although very low
transformation stresses are usually considered to develop as a result of this slow
cooling rate, Figs. 11-14 and 11-15 indicate that these stresses are of appreciable
value.

quenching in 390°F salt bath leaves zero surface stress contrasted with high surface stresses obtained by ice-water quenching.

Additional observations regarding the influence of bath temperature on residual stresses were made on SAE 52100 steel. Results[51] obtained in Fig. 11-16 indicate that the cooling speed in the region of martensite formation for this steel is also important in its influence on residual stresses.* In fact,

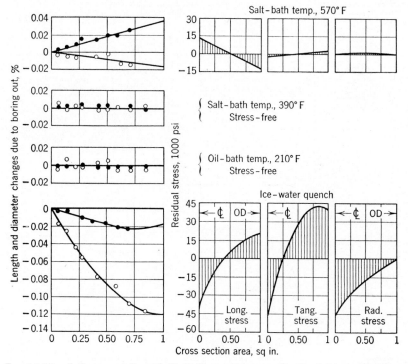

FIG. 11-15.   Influence of Quench-Bath Temperature on Residual-Stress Distribution for 16.9% Ni Steel Cylinders (1.2 in. $\phi \times$ 9.8 in.) Quenched from 1650°F, Then Air-Cooled (Bühler and Scheil)

the stress distribution in Fig. 11-16 is very similar to that for the 11.7% Ni steel in Fig. 11-13, both of which were ice-water-quenched.

The previous data offer some explanation for use of an interrupted quench. By this treatment parts are first prequenched in a drastic medium such as oil or water and then finish-cooled in a slower-cooling medium. Two opposing effects exist because in order to obtain deep hardening it is necessary to cool rapidly through the pearlitic stage,† but to minimize residual stresses slow

* After all these quench treatments the structure showed only martensite and undissolved cementite residues of spherical shape. Sachs's boring-out method could not be employed because of high hardness; so Heyn and Bauer's method[33] was applied which may give stress values 30 per cent low.

† Difficulty with deep hardening is usually experienced with unalloyed steels when cooling velocity is decreased because of increased bath temperature.

cooling is required through the martensite range. Alloy tool steels are often finish-quenched in a salt bath of about 400°F to suppress the formation of martensite until temperature equalization is obtained.

The application of these findings on low-carbon nickel steels to constructional steels is very difficult from a practical standpoint and requires some further interpretations. The austenite of constructional steels has a higher strength at elevated temperature than does the carbon-free austenite of the nickel steels of the type used to obtain the results in Fig. 11-12. Therefore,

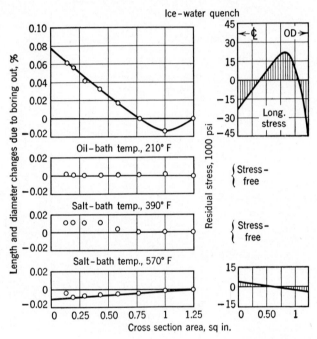

FIG. 11-16. Influence of Quench-Bath Temperature on Residual-Stress Distribution for SAE 52100 Steel (0.4 in. ϕ) Always Quenched from 1510°F (Bühler and Scheil)

the plastic deformations due to thermal stresses will be smaller for the constructional steels than for the nickel steels. Also the transformation products obtained with the low-carbon nickel steel are generally different from those obtained with constructional steels. This alone will lead to residual-stress systems differing from those shown, depending largely on the hardenability characteristics. The foregoing presentation of the superposition of the two types of stresses is best illustrated in its application to constructional steels by reference to typical examples.

The combination of transformation and thermal stresses was determined* by Bühler et al.[52] for solid cylinders of various constructional steels and

* Stresses were determined by Sachs's boring-out method.

Armco Iron.   Stress patterns obtained may all be characterized by the three types of distribution appearing in Fig. 11-17.

Example A presents a linear increase in the length and diameter on boring out.   Therefore, the longitudinal-stress distribution is also linear across the section, and the tensile stresses in the core have the same magnitude as at the

TABLE 11-1

RESIDUAL STRESSES IN NICKEL STEELS

Bühler and Scheil

Steel Chemical Analysis, %	Heat Treatment	Stress Component*	Stress at, psi		Max. Stress, psi	
			Center	Surface	Tension	Comp.
	Ice-water-quenched	L	−71,100	25,600	37,000	71,100
0.05 C	1650°F	T	−41,200	32,700	48,400	41,200
0.13 Si		R	−41,200	0	0	41,200
0.35 Mn	Quenched 1650°F in	L	0	0	0	0
16.90 Ni†	salt bath of 390°F,	T	0	0	0	0
	then air-cooled	R	0	0	0	0
	Ice-water-quenched	L	−65,400	−51,200	25,600	65,400
0.06 C	1650°F	T	−49,800	−59,700	35,600	59,700
0.11 Si		R	−49,800	0	5,700	49,800
0.42 Mn	Quenched 1650°F in	L	0	0	0	0
9.42 Ni‡	salt bath of 390°F,	T	0	0	0	0
	then air-cooled	R	0	0	0	0
	Ice-water-quenched	L	−37,000	19,900	19,900	37,000
0.05 C	1650°F	T	−45,500	39,800	42,700	45,500
0.13 Si		R	−45,500	0	......	45,500
0.35 Mn	Quenched 1650°F in	L	0	0	0	0
16.90 Ni‡	salt bath of 390°F,	T	0	0	0	0
	then air-cooled	R	0	0	0	0
	Ice-water-quenched	L	−15,600	15,600	15,600	15,600
0.05 C	1650°F	T	−11,400	22,800	22,800	11,400
0.18 Si		R	−11,400	0	0	11,400
0.44 Mn	Quenched 1650°F in	L	0	0	0	0
23.02 Ni‡	salt bath of 390°F,	T	0	0	0	0
	then air-cooled	R	0	0	0	0

* L = longitudinal; T = tangential; R = radial.

† Specimen diameter 1.97 in.

‡ Specimen diameter 1.18 in.

surface.   If the steel has a high elastic limit and tensile strength, then comparatively high residual stresses may be carried elastically.   Through-hardening steels often fall in this group.   This distribution is also found for thermal stresses arising in steels of about 0.30% C content which are water-quenched from the tempering temperature.

Example B exhibits a pronounced curved shape for the length and diameter changes.   This corresponds to a curved internal-stress distribution, and often the stress in the core exceeds that at the surface.   This condition is typical of a steel which has uniform structure through the cross section but has a low elastic limit compared to the residual stresses.   This distribution is also distinctive for the case of pure thermal stresses occurring in transformation-free bodies or for steel quenched below A_1.

Example C represents a steel which is not through-hardened because of either too large a diameter or lack of hardening capacity. A saddle formation of the stress in the core results, and the surface stress exceeds that in the core.

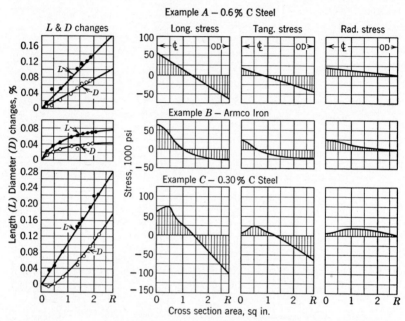

FIG. 11-17. Residual-Stress Distribution in 1.97-in.-diameter Bars Water-Quenched from 1560°F (Bühler *et al.*)

This is explained by the ineffective hardening of the core so that its shearing deformation is easily exceeded by the tensile residual stresses.

E. SOLID CYLINDERS AS QUENCHED

Data bearing on theoretical considerations regarding the superposition of transformation and thermal residual stresses have already been discussed. Here are presented various examples of residual-stress distribution found experimentally in solid cylinders in the as-quenched condition for Armco iron and constructional steels under the influence of different factors.[58]

5. Velocity of Cooling. Thermal stresses increase as the cooling velocity increases and then combine with transformation stresses. Figure 11-18 gives the residual compressive stress found in the surface* when it is cooled from

---

* Similar height diagrams and curves of a like nature given in this paper were published by Bühler to show the maximum residual stress; this maximum stress may be located anywhere in the cross section. In view of the importance of surface stresses, the reviewer has modified the original diagrams to show here only the stress at the surface which is compression in all cases. Therefore, the maximum

above A_3 at different quenching velocities as obtained by using water, oil, air, and furnace methods of cooling. It may be noted that the residual stress is about the same for Armco iron and 0.18% C steel whether oil- or water-quenched. There is also little difference in stresses between the water- and oil-quenched 0.59% C steel and spring steel, despite differences in quenching velocity. Between 0.24 and 0.49% C content range, however, the stress is definitely influenced by the velocity of quench.

Individual stress-distribution curves through the cross section for each condition in Fig. 11-18 can be described as being linear for all cases of air and furnace cooling, according to example A in Fig. 11-17; the magnitude of the longitudinal and tangential stresses is about the same at the surface as in the

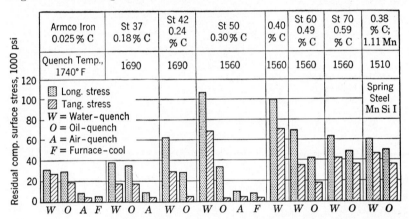

FIG. 11-18. Influence of Cooling Velocity after Heating above A_3 on Residual Surface Stress for 1.97-in.-diameter Bars (Bühler)

center or core of the cross section. The water- and oil-quenched Armco iron gave curves like example B in Fig. 11-17. All four steels with 0.18, 0.24, 0.30, and 0.40% C steels which were water- and oil-quenched exhibited curves similar to example C. All 0.49 and 0.59% C and spring steels water-quenched gave linear stress-distribution curves whereas, when they were oil-quenched, the curves were like example C.*

6. Quenching Temperature. Hardening stresses are also influenced by the temperature at which the steel is quenched. Figure 11-19 illustrates the surface compressive stresses found by quenching four different steels in water from various temperatures. The Armco iron and 0.18% C steel have about the same surface residual stresses, regardless of quenching temperature, except at the low value of 600°F. It is of practical importance to observe that the surface stresses are considerably influenced by quenching in the range

---

stress occurring may be greater than that shown, especially if the stress distribution is similar to example B in Fig. 11-17.

* Hereafter each figure will have the letters A, B, and C marked thereon to indicate the type of stress distribution across the section with reference to Fig. 11-17.

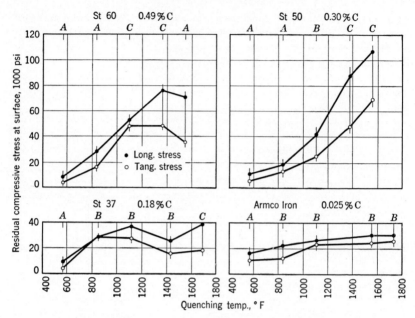

FIG. 11-19.   Relation between Surface Stress and Temperature of Quenching in
Water for 1.97-in.-diameter Bars (Bühler)

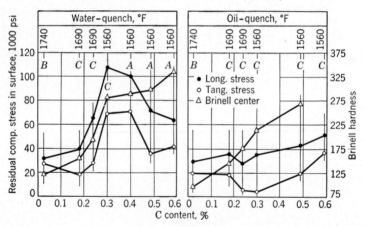

FIG. 11-20.   Relation between Surface Residual Stresses and Carbon Content for
1.97-in.-diameter Bars Quenched above A_3 (Bühler)

from just below A_3 to below A_1 for the 0.30 and 0.49% C steels.   It is well
known that the hardness and tensile properties are not changed by quenching
below A_1, even though considerable residual stress is present.

7. Carbon Content.   Relationship between the surface residual stresses
and carbon content is plotted in Fig. 11-20 for 1.97-in.-diameter bars quenched

from above A_3. It may be noted that water quenching produces maximum surface stresses at about 0.30% C content. Oil quenching results in surface stresses which are lower and little affected by carbon content in comparison with the water quench.

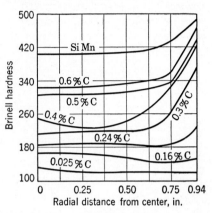

FIG. 11-21.   Hardness Survey on 1.97-in.-diameter Bars Water-Quenched above A_3 (Bühler *et al.*)

8. Hardenability. A hardness survey made across transverse sections of 1.97-in.-diameter bars is shown in Fig. 11-21 for various steels water-quenched from above A_3. The shallow-hardening steels of 0.30 to 0.40% C content show the greatest difference in hardness between the surface and center, and it is these same steels which also produce the greatest surface stresses (Fig. 11-20). Structurally these steels showed on the surface a thick martensitic shell and little or no hardening of the core or center section.

It is believed that hardenability curves correlated with metallurgical structure, temperature-gradient curves (Fig. 11-10), and strength properties at elevated temperatures (Table 11-3) would lead to a rapid means of determining residual stresses. Extensive research is needed in this direction and should include the influence of tempering treatments.

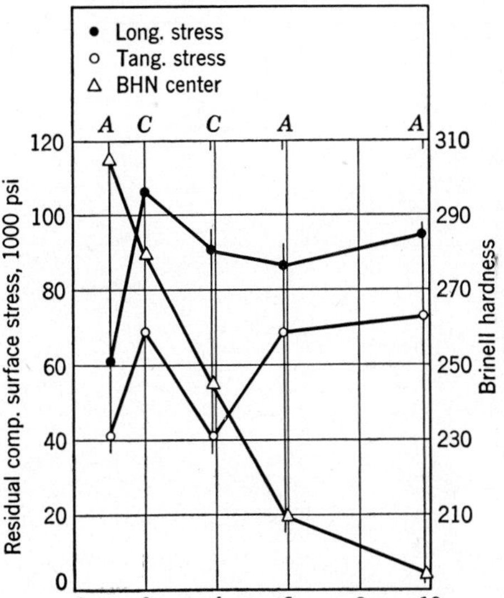

9. Specimen Diameter. The influence of specimen diameter on the surface residual stresses is given in Fig. 11-22 for 0.30% C steel water-quenched from 1560°F. Under through-hardening conditions obtained with the 1-in.-diameter specimen the residual stresses are relatively low compared to the maximum reached with the 1.97-in. cylinders. The surface stresses again decrease above 1.97 in. in diameter and then finally increase. This latter increase is explained by the greater thermal stresses produced in

FIG. 11-22.   Influence of Specimen Diameter on Residual Surface Stresses of 0.3% C Steel, Water-Quenched from 1560°F (Bühler)

large-diameter bars, as shown in Fig. 11-39.   Residual stresses are definitely
related to hardenability, but little research has been conducted toward
studying this correlation.   This field of research offers an opportunity for the
formulation of general laws concerning the production of residual-stress
systems by means of heat treatment.

F. Solid Cylinders Normalized or Quenched and Tempered

The practical condition under which most constructional steels are used
incorporates some type of normalize or quench and temper treatment.   Various types of heat treatments are discussed here from the standpoint of residual

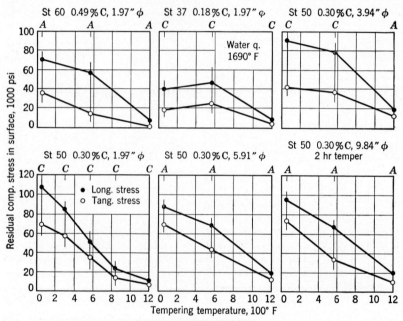

Fig. 11-23.   Influence of 1½-hr Temper on Residual Surface Stresses for Steels
Water-Quenched from 1560°F (Exceptions Noted) (Bühler)

stresses finally present in the surface of solid cylinders of different steels
(Table 11-2).   In some cases these cylinders were (a) oil- or water-quenched
from above A_3 and then tempered or (b) quenched from usually the tempering
temperature.   A combination of both transformation and thermal stresses is
produced in the treatment in a and principally thermal stresses in b.   This
process of quenching from the tempering temperature is of particular interest
from the standpoint of temper brittleness and utilization of favorable surface
stresses to improve fatigue resistance without changing the hardness and
tensile properties often specified for constructional steels.   All residual-stress
studies presented were obtained by Sachs's boring-out method.   In all cases
the longitudinal and tangential stresses on the surface were found to be in
compression and not in tension.

10. Plain Carbon Steels—Transformation plus Thermal Stresses. Three plain carbon steels (1.97-in.-diameter solid cylinders) of 0.18, 0.30, and 0.49% C content (Table 11-2) were water-quenched from 1560°F and then tempered for $1\frac{1}{2}$ hr at various temperatures. The surface stresses shown in Fig. 11-23 for all these conditions were in compression and are reduced in almost a linear manner with tempering temperature except for 0.18% C steel. Four different diameters were investigated from 1.97 through 9.84 in. for the 0.30% C steel. As would be expected, greater surface residual stresses remain behind in the larger than in the smaller sections at 570°F temper.

TABLE 11-2

CHEMICAL ANALYSIS, PER CENT

	C	Si	Mn	P	S	Cu	Cr
Armco iron	0.025	0.01	....	0.005	0.016	0.04	....
St 37	0.16	0.01	0.47	0.043	0.034	....	....
St 42	0.26	0.31	0.56	0.030	0.028	0.12	0.06
St 50 (1.9″)	0.30	0.20	0.75	0.051	0.030	....	....
St 50 (5.9 & 9.8″)	0.36	0.33	0.64	0.024	0.023	0.23	....
St 60	0.50	0.30	0.78	0.026	0.026	....	....
MnSi 50	0.24	0.28	0.83	0.048	0.034	0.21	....
MnSi I or 70	0.38	0.43	1.11	0.068	0.028	0.18	....
MnSi II	0.46	0.42	1.12	0.033	0.032	....	....
St 52	0.18	0.01	0.75	0.037	0.035	0.87	0.42

Length of tempering time influences the surface residual stresses for 0.30% C steel solid bars 1.97 in. in diameter, water-quenched from 1560°F. Up to $1\frac{1}{2}$ hr time at 570°F the stresses drop quickly to about one-half the value in the as-quenched state; between $1\frac{1}{2}$ and 8 hr no change appears. After 10 hr a small decrease in residual stress occurs, but it is still about 40 per cent of its initial magnitude. Yield and tensile-strength properties remain almost constant, regardless of large changes in surface stresses.

11. Plain Carbon Steels—Thermal Stresses. The magnitude and distribution of residual stresses presented in Figs. 11-24 through 11-27 were obtained on round bars of six different steels (Table 11-2). These cylinders were (a) normalized at 1560°F and water-quenched from the tempering temperature, (b) water-quenched from 1560°F and again quenched from the tempering temperature, or (c) heated below A_1 and water-quenched. In view of the relatively high tempering temperature after treating above A_3 in a and b, it would be expected that the thermal type of stresses would predominate.

In these tests, curves were obtained of the temperature of the surface and core similar to those in Fig. 11-10. The temperature difference between surface and core, as well as the course of the curves, was the same for steels 37, 50, and MnSi I. Therefore, the conditions governing pure thermal-stress formation were practically the same with the exception of strength properties. Steel 60 cooled somewhat more slowly, owing to its lower heat conductivity and MnSi II gave a larger temperature differential between the surface and core than the other steels.

The cooling rate from the tempering temperature influences residual stresses, as evidenced from Fig. 11-24. A 0.30% plain C steel (St 50) was water-quenched from 1560°F and then tempered at 1200°F but cooled from the temper in four different mediums of water, oil, air, and the furnace. Water quenching from the temper produced surface stresses over five times as great as the slower velocity of the air- and furnace-cooling methods; oil quenching gave stresses about $2\frac{1}{3}$ times as large. Also a comparison can be made of water quenching from 1200 instead of 1560°F (above A_3) which resulted in surface stresses about 40 per cent as great (Fig. 11-23).

Water quenching 0.30% plain C steel (St 50) from 1110°F after normalizing from 1560°F produces about 40,000 psi longitudinal and 25,000 psi tangential stresses in the surface. These longitudinal stresses are about 80 per cent

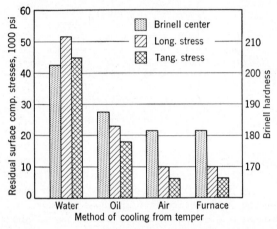

FIG. 11-24. Influence of Method of Cooling from Tempering Temperature of 1200°F on Residual Surface Stresses in 0.30% C Steel (1.97 in. ϕ, St 50) Water-Quenched from 1560°F (Bühler)

and the tangential 55 per cent as great as those obtained in Fig. 11-24 where the cylinders were water-quenched from 1560°F followed by another water quench from 1200°F. Tempering at 570°F for $1\frac{1}{2}$ hr reduces the surface stresses to about one-half the value obtained with no temper.

Residual-longitudinal-stress-distribution curves were obtained for four different steels in Fig. 11-25 (Table 11-2). Two of these steels were of the plain carbon type having 0.16 and 0.49% C content while two were MnSi spring steels. All these steels were water-quenched from a tempering temperature of 1110°F. Stress-distribution curves which are straight lines indicate that the shear-deformation limit was not exceeded after the stress reversal; the curved distribution shows that the shearing limit was locally exceeded during the cooling process.

Large-diameter cylinders (5.9 in.) of 0.36% plain C steel were first normalized and then water-quenched from 1110°F. The manner in which these residual stresses change with time of tempering at 840°F is illustrated in Fig. 11-26.

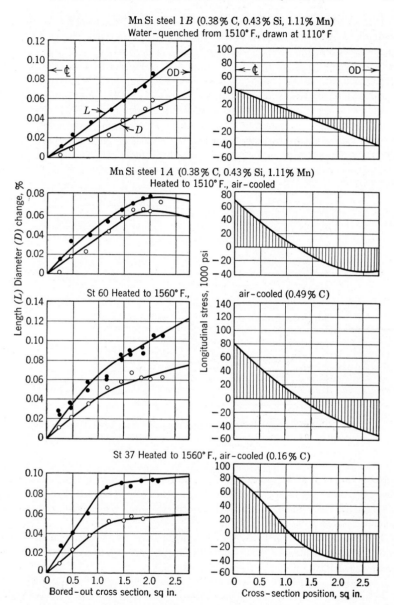

FIG. 11-25. Distribution of Longitudinal Stress through the Cross Section of 1.9-in. φ Steel Cylinders Water-Quenched from 1110°F after Prior Heat Treatment Indicated (Buchholtz and Bühler)

It is apparent that there is only a small change in tensile properties compared to the large variations in residual stresses.

The relationship between longitudinal-surface thermal stresses and the carbon content and yield strength is shown in Fig. 11-27 from the data in Fig. 11-25 and other results by the same author. Here straight lines are arbitrarily drawn between some points,* even though the conditions governing stress formation are not all comparable, as previously mentioned. The lower yield point used here was that obtained from the ordinary tensile test representing uniaxial stress at room temperature. Actually the residual stresses at the surface are biaxial and triaxial below the surface; also the residual stress may be related to yield strength at some elevated temperature. For these

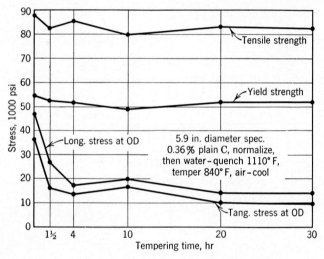

Fig. 11-26. Influence of Tempering Time on Thermal Stresses and Strength Properties (Buchholtz and Bühler)

reasons some question arises as to the applicability of the relationships in Fig. 11-27, but the following observations are made:

1. Higher thermal stresses are developed, as would be expected, at 1110°F quench than at 840°.

2. Both steels MnSi I and MnSi II quenched at 1110°F show that higher residual surface stresses are supported elastically than plastically if the shearing strength of the steel is sufficiently high.

3. A comparison of St 50 and MnSi I quenched at 840°F shows that the residual-stress distribution is linear in both cases. Table 11-3 reveals that, even though the tensile properties at elevated temperatures are much higher for MnSi I than for St 50, the surface stress is only about one half as much for the former as for St 50. At 1110°F quench, however, the surface stresses

* Each point is identified by letter *A* or *B* and type of steel. Letters *A* and *B* refer to the type of stress-distribution curve across the section, according to examples *A* and *B* in Fig. 11-17, and the kind of steel is as indicated in Table 11-2.

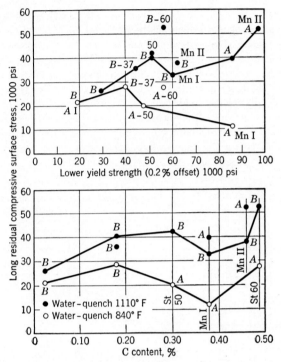

Fig. 11-27. Relationship of Carbon Content and Yield Strength to Surface Stresses in Water-Quenched Solid Cylinders 1.9 in. in Diameter (Data from Buchholtz and Bühler)

TABLE 11-3

STRENGTH PROPERTIES AT ELEVATED TEMPERATURES*

Test Temp., °F	Yield Strength, psi, for Offset		Tensile Strength, psi	Elong., %	Reduction of Area, %
	0.03 %	0.2 %			
St 50—0.30 % C, 0.20 % Si, 0.75 % Mn					
68	51,500	50,600	81,500	23.7	64
302	49,200	49,200	88,000	13.7	68
572	25,900	32,600	86,500	21.0	50
842	21,000	28,700	59,600	32.5	66
932	12,800	20,000	41,200	42.0	75
MnSi I—0.38 % C, 0.43 % Si, 1.11 % Mn					
68	83,900	87,000	115,100	19.0	62
302	77,900	77,900	103,800	11.4	59
572	48,800	60,700	105,400	12.3	42
842	36,000	55,200	85,300	18.7	67
932	16,900	31,000	50,100	41.3	90

* On basis of 30-sec loading period.

are about the same for both steels, even though plastic flow has developed in the outer layers of St 50 but remains linear for MnSi I.

12. Alloy Steels—Transformation and/or Thermal Stresses. Comparatively few residual-stress data have been published on alloy constructional steels, but Fig. 11-28 presents available information on Ni and CrNi steels. One important finding was that the surface stresses were always in compression and not in tension for the conditions investigated.

These steels were all oil-quenched from 1540°F and then air-cooled or water-quenched from the tempering temperature with subsequent retemper in some cases. It is apparent from Fig. 11-28 that water quenching VCN 25

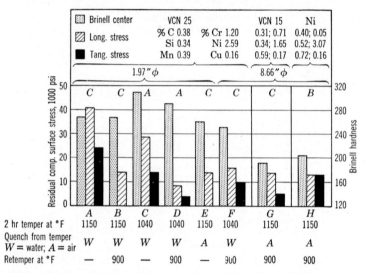

FIG. 11-28.   Surface Residual Stresses in Some Alloy Steels Oil-Quenched from 1540°F and Further Treated as Shown (Bühler)

steel from the temper in A produces 41,000 psi longitudinal surface stress or about three times as great as the air cool in E. Tests made on water-quenched cylinders retempered at 900°F for 2 hr, B, resulted in the same stress as the normalized condition E; no change in surface stress or hardness was found in B even after 10 hr temper. Condition E was also investigated with 900°F retemper for 2 and 10 hr, but no change was noted. Some indication of the influence of diameter on residual stresses is also found in the comparison of D and F. Here the longitudinal surface stress is 16,000 psi for 8.66 in. diameter and about one half as much for the 1.97 in. size.

G. TUBES AS QUENCHED

The importance of hollow shafts as machine elements makes it desirable for one to have a knowledge of the factors influencing residual stresses produced by various heat treatments. An extensive investigation was made by Fuchs[59] covering Armco iron and five different constructional steels (Table 11-2) of

1.97- through 9.84-in. diameters and various bores.* All residual stresses were determined by Sachs's boring-out method.

One finding of fundamental and practical interest was made regarding the difference in residual-stress distributions for tubes quenched from the bore only, from the outside only, and from both inner and outer surfaces (Fig. 11-29). These tubes (1.97 in. OD × 0.95 in. bore)† were of plain 0.30% C steel (St 50) water-quenched above A_3 at 1560°F. Quenching from the

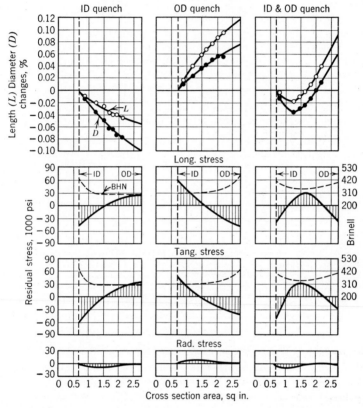

FIG. 11-29. Residual-Stress Distribution in 0.30% C Tubes Water-Quenched at 1590°F from Various Surfaces (1.97 in. ϕ × 0.94 in. ID, St 50) (Fuchs)

outside only gives stresses similar to those found in solid cylinders. Inside quench produces a reversed-stress distribution, that is, compression in the

* The 1.97-in.-diameter specimens were 15.75 in. long; the 5.91-in.-diameter specimens 17.72 or 25.6 in. long; the 9.06- and 9.84-in.-diameter specimens 25.6 in. long. In most cases the maximum bore studied was such that the area was 0.25 that of a solid section, except for St 42 where the maximum bore ratio was 0.4, and St 50 where it was 0.5.

† The ratio of the cross-sectional area of the bore to that of the outside diameter was 0.25.

bore and tension on the outer surface. When the tube is quenched simultaneously from inner and outer surfaces, then the two actions are superimposed; compressive stresses occur at both surfaces which are suddenly cooled and tensile stresses in the slowly cooled intermediate zone.

Many further findings by Fuchs are presented in the following discussion. All data apply to quenching from both surfaces.

H. Tubes—Thermal Stresses

Thermal stresses were investigated for plain 0.30% C steel (St 50) and Armco iron of 1.9 in. diameter with two different hole sizes, as shown in Fig. 11-30. Both were water-quenched, the former from below A_1 at 1110°F and the latter from below A_3 at 1560°F. The 0.59-in. bore (0.1 area ratio) in 0.30% C steel gives little change in stress distribution over the solid cylinder;

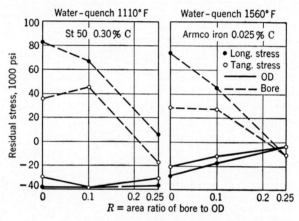

Fig. 11-30. Influence of Bore Ratio on Residual Thermal Stresses (1.97 in. ϕ) (Fuchs)

the larger bore of 0.94 in. (0.25 area ratio) shows the increasing influence of cooling from the bore by the tendency to form residual compressive stresses on that surface. Stress-distribution curves for the Armco iron displayed the same shape as for the 0.30% C steel, but their magnitude was some different (Fig. 11-30). Even here compressive stresses did not appear in the bore until the larger bore was reached. No change of section hardness occurred.

In summary, it can be said from these tests and others that residual thermal stresses decrease considerably with increasing bore.

I. Tubes—Transformation and Thermal Stresses

13. 0.26% Carbon Steel. *Water Quenching.* A 0.25% plain C steel (St 42) was quenched in water from 1560°F, and the residual stresses were determined in the as-quenched condition. Surface residual stresses were determined for 1.9-in.-diameter cylinders with no bore and with 0.4-, 0.8-, and 1.8-in. bores. The 0.4-in. bore ($R = 0.04$) gave about the same stresses on the outer surface as were obtained with the solid cylinder; also the bore stresses were tension (about 80,000 psi longitudinal and 40,000 psi tangential). This stress condition indicates that the action of the coolant on the small bore surface was not very effective. Outer-surface hardening of shallow depth was found with the structure below this skin surrounded by a ferrite network. Effect of bore diameter on residual stresses was first evidenced with an 0.8-in. bore ($R =$ 0.17). Here the outer surfaces stresses were two thirds of the values obtained with the solid bar; also the principal stresses in the bore changed from tension into about 15,000 psi compression. Pronounced bore effect was obtained with a 1.2-in. hole where the bore stresses were 0–7000 psi compression and the 0.1 stresses were 20,000–25,000 psi compression. It is important to associate these low stresses with the almost through hardening present which the investigator reported was accompanied by a structure of martensite with some islands of troostite.

Residual stresses after 570°F temper, of the quenched cylinders, were considerably reduced with the exception of the 1.2-in. bore where little change took place.

14. 0.30–0.36% Carbon Steel. * (*a*) *Water Quenching.* The influence of increased hardenability on residual stresses is apparent in Fig. 11-31 for 1.9-in.-diameter cylinders (both solid and hollow) St 50 having 0.30% C and higher manganese content compared with the afore-mentioned 0.26% C steel. Already the 0.6-in. bore ($R = 0.1$) is effective from a quenching standpoint in tending to produce bore stresses of about zero value and considerable reduction of outside-diameter stresses compared with solid cylinder. Hardening of both surfaces occurred with a soft core. Through hardening is approached with a 0.9-in. bore, and the entire cross section was reported as showing a martensitic structure.

(*b*) *Oil Quenching.* Oil-quenching (Fig. 11-31) instead of water-quenching the 0.30% C steel, as would be expected, considerably reduces the residual stresses for the as-quenched condition. As the bore increases, the residual stresses on the outside diameter change little compared to the large decrease at the inside diameter. Tangential stresses remain practically the same at both surfaces, regardless of bore ratio. Carbon content and quenching velocity here are such that no increase in hardness was obtained for the tubes over the solid cylinders; the structure showed a pronounced ferrite network for even the thin-wall tube.

(*c*) *Tempering Temperature.* The influence of the tempering temperature on residual stresses is expressed in Fig. 11-31 for water- and oil-quenched members of 1.9 in. diameter. Generally, the stress decrease for the tubes is similar to that for solid cylinders in a region of tempering temperature of 600°F and above. Between 300° and 800°F tempering temperature, the stresses decrease very fast in an almost linear manner; between 800° to 1200°F, the stress change is much less. Tempering water-quenched tubes at 300°F presents a marked increase in residual stress as well as a large decrease

* St 50 had 0.30 % C content in 1.9 in. diameter and 0.36 % C in 5.9 and 9.8 in. diameter, as evidenced in Table 11-2.

in hardness over the as-quenched condition. This was chiefly attributed to the decrease of volume as a result of diminished martensite at the inner and outer surfaces of the tubes which were not through-hardened. These should be compared with the water-quenched tubes which were through-hardened where the stress was decreased at 300°F temper (Fig. 11-31 for $R = 0.5$); stress was also linear between the outer and inner surfaces.

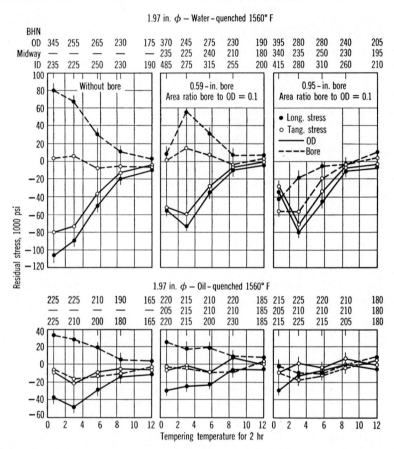

FIG. 11-31.   Influence of Tempering Temperature on Residual Stresses for 0.30% C Steel (ST 50) (Fuchs)

Segregation influences residual stresses, as found from tests on tubes (1.9 OD × 0.6 in. ID) having 2° of segregation which were tempered at 300°F for 10 hr after water-quenching from 1560°F. One tube with little segregation produced weak hardening in the bore and showed a smaller dip in the deformation curves than is indicated in Fig. 11-29; the hardening on the outer surface was preponderant. Another tube possessing greater segregation resulted in relatively greater surface hardening on the bore than at the outer surface;

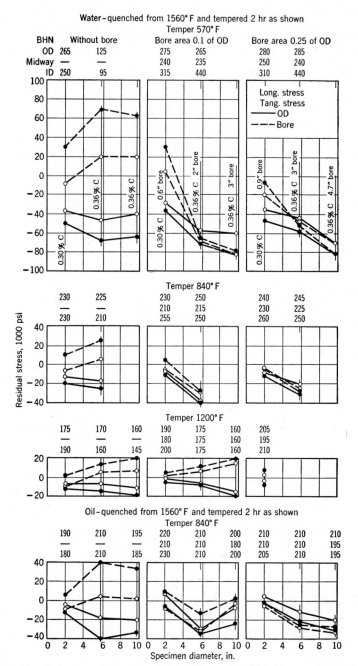

FIG. 11-32. Influence of Specimen Diameter on Residual Stresses for 0.30 and
0.36% C Steel (St 50) (Fuchs)

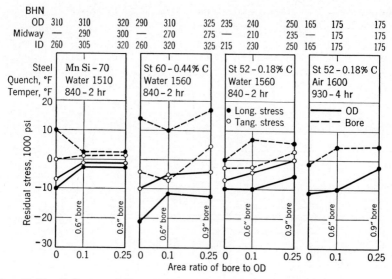

Fig. 11-33. Influence of Bore Ratio on Residual Stresses (1.97 in. ϕ) (Fuchs)

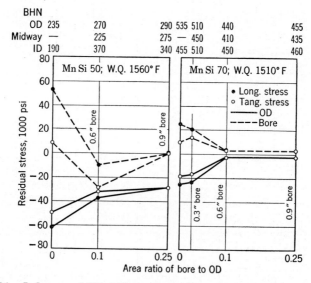

Fig. 11-34. Influence of Bore Ratio on Residual Stresses (1.97 in. ϕ MnSi)
Tempered 2 hr at 570°F (Fuchs)

compressive stresses in the bore, therefore, exceeded those at the outer surface, which is the case represented in Fig. 11-29.

When oil-quenched, the solid cylinder after 300°F tempering temperature (Fig. 11-31) showed an increase in stresses, and this finding was also confirmed by Sachs.[60]   Stresses for oil quenching are much less than for water quenching and generally decrease almost linearly with increase in tempering temperature.

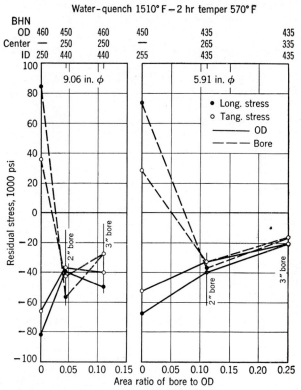

FIG. 11-35.   Influence of Bore Ratio on Residual Stresses for 0.38% C, 0.43% Si, 1.11% Mn Steel (MnSi 70) (Fuchs)

(d) *Specimen Size.*   Surface residual stresses and hardness values for 1.9- through 9.8-in.-diameter solid and tubular sections are presented in Fig. 11-32. Here the influence of size is given for cylinders subjected to several different heat treatments.

Figure 11-32 gives the residual stresses for 5.9-in.-diameter cylinders after water quenching and a 2-hr temper at 840°F.   Results for a 10-hr temper showed that the outer surface stresses would be decreased by 14,000 psi and the bore stresses by about 7000 psi.

At 840°F temper there is little difference in Fig. 11-32 between the stresses for tubes water- and oil-quenched, except for bore longitudinal and outside-diameter tangential stresses.

15. 0.44% Carbon Steel.   A plain 0.44% C steel of 1.9 in. diameter in solid
and tubular sections was water-quenched at 1560°F and tempered at 840°F
for 2 hr.   For these conditions the residual-surface stresses are shown in
Fig. 11-33.   Increased hardenability of this steel over the 0.30% C is evidenced by the greater hardness values, but the remaining residual stresses in
both steels are low because of the 840°F draw temperature.

16. MnSi Steels.   The two steels MnSi 50 and MnSi 70 (Table 11-2)
produced surface residual stresses, as shown in Fig. 11-34, when water-
quenched at 1560°F and tempered at 570°F in 1.9 in. diameter.   Increased

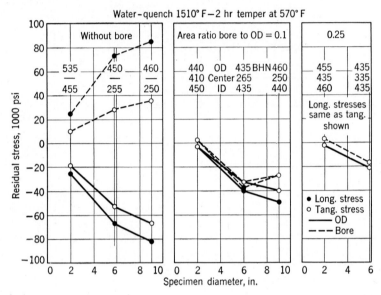

Fig. 11-36.   Influence of Specimen Diameter on Residual Stresses for 0.38% C,
0.43% Si, 1.11% Mn Steel (MnSi 70) (Fuchs)

hardenability of MnSi 70 over MnSi 50 resulted in lower stresses and pronounced martensite formation, for the former steel MnSi 50 (0.24% C) shows
higher stresses than the 0.30% C steel (Fig. 11-31) on the basis of solid
cylinders tempered at 570°F; as the bore increased, through hardening was
approached with the deeper-hardening MnSi 50 steel leaving lower stresses
than in the 0.30% C steel.   Tempering MnSi 70 tubes at 840° (Fig. 11-33)
instead of 570°F does not change the residual stresses because they are already
very small.

Whereas MnSi 70 in 1.9-in.-diameter tubular sections left very low residual
stresses (Fig. 11-34) because of through hardening, this same steel in 5.9- and
9.1-in.-diameter tubes exhibited much higher stresses (Fig. 11-35), because
of relative surface-hardening effect.   The shallow-hardening 0.36% C steel
(Fig. 11-32) water-quenched in the same tubular sections and with the same
drawing temperature produced much higher stresses than MnSi 70 of greater

hardenability (Fig. 11-35). Solid cylinders 9.1 in. in diameter of MnSi 70, except at the surface layer, exhibited a ferrite network which grew stronger toward the interior; even the 2-in. hole already diminished the ferrite residue with consequent reduction in residual stress (Fig. 11-35).

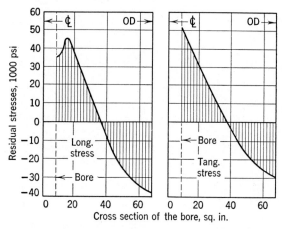

FIG. 11-37.   Residual Stresses in Piston Rod Bored after Quenching and Tempering (Sachs)

Surface stresses plotted versus specimen diameter for MnSi 70 steel tempered at 570°F in Fig. 11-36 may be compared with the 0.30–0.36% C steel in Fig. 11-32.   For tubular sections the deeper-hardening MnSi 70 steel leaves lower stresses than the shallow-hardening plain carbon steel. In the latter steel the stresses for the large-size tubular members approach that for the solid section, but in MnSi 70 the stresses for the tubular shape are much less than for the solid.

17. Precipitation-Hardening Steel.   A precipitation-hardening steel (St 52, Table 11-2) with chrome–copper alloy and 0.18% C content was investigated for residual stresses shown in Fig. 11-33. When water-quenched and tempered, this steel gives low surface stresses about the same as the lower-hardenability

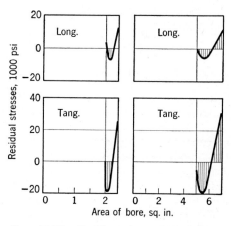

FIG. 11-38.   Residual Stresses in Normalized SAE 4130 Tubing (Sachs)

0.30% C steel (Fig. 11-31). Air cooling from 1600°F and tempering at 930°F also left very low stresses with the tangential and radial practically zero.

18. 0.70% Carbon Steel. Sachs[61] investigated heat-treated Diesel-engine piston rods 10 in. in diameter with $3\frac{1}{8}$-in. bore and found residual stresses up to 54,000 psi or 55 per cent of the tensile strength. These rods were forged from a 0.70% C steel (0.3% Si, 0.6% Mn) quenched as a solid bar in oil from 1560°F and tempered at 1240°F ($^{208}\!/_{222}$ Brinell) followed by probably quenching again from the drawing temperature. These bars were then bored out to form the tubular-rod design; residual stresses determined are reported in Fig. 11-37.

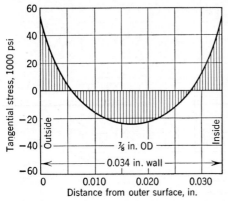

FIG. 11-39. Tangential Stress in SAE 4130 Oil-Quenched from 1550°F (Sachs)

19. SAE 4130 Steel. Sachs[31] reported residual stresses in aircraft tubing of thin wall section. Two different tube sizes of normalized SAE 4130 steel were investigated as shown in Fig. 11-38. Results for oil-quenched tubing are given in Fig. 11-39.

J. RESIDUAL STRESS VERSUS GRAIN SIZE

An observation often made in heat-treating operations is that the coarse-grained steels have a greater tendency to warp and crack than fine-grained steels. These practical findings are usually explained by a difference in hardenability, but Kontorovich and Livshits[62] related this problem to one of residual stresses. They air-hardened some Cr–Ni and Cr–Ni–W steels of various austenitic grain sizes (Table 11-4) and measured residual stresses.

Cr–Ni steel was processed from two different heats of substantially the same analysis where grain size was controlled by ladle additions; bars 2.17 in. in diameter and presumably hollow were annealed and then heat-treated in billet lengths by air cooling from 1650°F followed by a 3-hr draw in oil at 355°F. Tubular specimens were machined from these heat-treated members to dimensions of 1.97 in. OD × 1.18 in. ID × 0.39 in. length. Investigation of Cr–Ni–W steel was made from actual production parts processed from three different heats to the same chemistry specification but different grain size; these production parts were presumably solid and heat-treated according to Table 11-5. Tubular specimens were machined from the cylindrical portion of these parts to 3.54 in. OD × 2.36 in. ID × 0.39 in. length; the boring-out method was followed to measure tangential residual stresses.*

A comparison of residual stresses found in coarse- and fine-grained Cr–Ni steels is quoted in Fig. 11-40 and in the Cr–Ni–W steels in Fig. 11-41. It is apparent that the residual stresses are considerably greater for the coarse-

---

* The manner in which these specimens were prepared and their short length may leave some question regarding the validity of the stress values obtained. The results, however, do show comparative effect of grain size.

than for the fine-grained steels. Stress distribution for the Cr–Ni steels is of the kind typical of thick-walled cylinders cooled from both inner and outer surfaces; the progress of the stress in the Cr–Ni–W differs from that in the Cr–Ni because the tubular specimens have been machined from a solid heat-treated production part. It should be noted that part 1 (Fig. 11-41) shows a reverse-stress distribution and one of greater intensity than part 4 of the same grain size; the only difference is that two additional air-cooling treatments were given part 4 (Table 11-5). The inference is that this multiple treatment is detrimental because of the greater danger of surface cracking and distortion due to the presence of this severe stress system. With the exception of part 4 the stress curves (Figs. 11-40 and 11-41) indicate the predominating influence of thermal over transformation stresses, whereas for part 4 this is reversed.

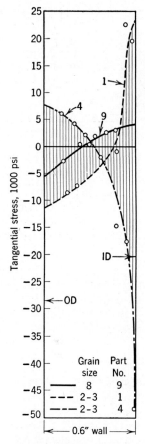

The three parts made from Cr–Ni–W steels

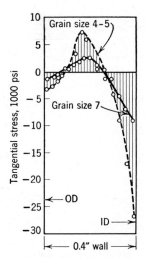

FIG. 11-40. Residual Stress Influenced by Grain Size for Cr–Ni Steel (Kontorovich et al.)

FIG. 11-41. Residual Stress Influenced by Grain Size for Cr–Ni–W Steel (Kontorovich et al.)

exhibited about the same tensile properties (Table 11-5), although a lower impact resistance was obtained for the fine- than for the coarse-grained steel; at the same time the internal stress was much different. An endurance limit was obtained of 66,900–69,700 psi for the coarse- and 71,100–75,400 psi for the fine-grained steels. These values were presumably based on small fatigue specimens machined out of production parts; if this was the case, then the difference in fatigue-strength values reflects the influence of grain size since the residual stresses would be small, if any.

TABLE 11-4

CHEMICAL ANALYSIS AND GRAIN SIZE

Chemical Analysis, %

Heat or Part No.	C	Si	Mn	Cr	Ni	W	McQuaid–Ehn Grain Size	Hardness, RC
4864	0.17	0.23	0.57	1.53	4.78	....	7	44–45
5338	0.17	0.34	0.35	1.43	4.29	....	4–5	42–43
9	0.16	0.23	0.43	1.27	4.27	0.86	8	38
1	0.16	0.36	0.45	1.49	4.30	1.09	2–3	37
4	0.15	0.20	0.41	1.51	4.28	0.96	2–3	38

TABLE 11-5

HEAT TREATMENT AND MECHANICAL PROPERTIES OF CR–NI–W STEEL

Part No.	Heat Treatment	Ult., psi	Elong., %	RA, %	Impact, ft-lb/in.^{2}	Hardness, RC
9	(a) Air-Cooled 1740°F (b) Air-Cooled 1560°F (c) Oil Temp. 340°F	175,000	14.2	52	638	38
1	Same as a, b, & c	176,400	15.4	56	820	37
4	Same as a & b, then temp. 356°F					
	Cool from 1560°F, temp. 356°F	160,000	15.2	58	909	34
	Cool from 1560°F, temp. 356°F	182,000	14.0	64	918	38

Variation in residual-stress intensity according to grain size was attributed to the fine-grained steel being more isotropic and permitting the internal stress to become better equalized through the section. The greater amount of grain-boundary matrix in fine- over coarse-grained steels makes it more favorable for plastic deformation, and this leads to a decrease in the residual stress.

K. INTERRUPTED QUENCH

Residual stress, distortion, and danger of cracking are reduced by using some type of interrupted quench, as represented by the three right-hand charts[63] in Fig. 11-42. This involves quenching from the austenitic temperature into some kind of hot bath maintained above the Ms temperature so that cooling is interrupted. After equalizing at the temperature of the quenching medium the parts are cooled slowly so that the austenite–martensite transformation occurs at a uniform rate throughout the section. In this manner the usual tensile transformation stresses are practically eliminated or much reduced in intensity.

Customary quench and temper procedure (left-hand diagram in Fig. 11-42) is more conducive to cracking or distortion from high internal stresses than when the interrupted quench is applied, particularly with higher-carbon steels. Cracking may occur during martensite formation owing to volume increases and accompanying tensile stresses because of nonuniform transformation through the cross section. Rawdon and Epstein[64] first proved the existence of such cracks which was later confirmed by Lucas[65] and Davenport,

Roff, and Bain.[66] Davenport[67] found tensile, impact, and fatigue properties considerably lower for 0.93% C steel specimens quenched and tempered to the same hardness of RC 50–51 as those austempered. Reduced mechanical properties may partly be explained by the minute cracks and/or unfavorable residual stresses.

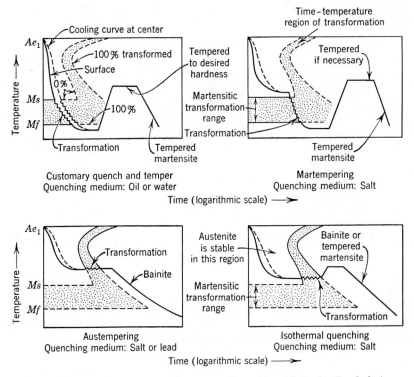

FIG. 11-42. Effects of Four Important Quenching Methods (Seasholtz)

L. CENTRIFUGAL CAST-STEEL TUBES

Residual stresses are produced in centrifugal cast-steel tubes[68] as shown in Fig. 11-43 for two different heat treatments. High compressive stresses develop in the bore and tension in the outer surface. This prestressing is of practical importance because it can be employed to increase the resistance of the tube to service loading from internal pressure, as for example, in a gun. Under bending or torsional type of loading, however, the residual tension stresses on the surface would not be expected to be favorable to optimum fatigue resistance.

These residual stresses are due principally to segregation occurring in the tube wall as produced by centrifugal forces in the casting process. Tubes investigated in Fig. 11-43 were of 0.3% C, 1.07 Cr, and 0.3% Mo and had 2.76 in. inner by 7.09 in. outer diameters. Segregation was found through the wall section of carbon, chromium, and molybdenum, but that for the carbon was most pronounced.   Carbon varied in the outer surface from about 0.24 per cent to a gradually increasing amount through the wall section and reached a final value of 0.56 per cent at the bore.

In the cooling of such an as-cast or heat-treated tube, transformation occurs at different temperature levels throughout the wall as a result of this segregation.   Pearlitic transformation occurs first in the outer layers while martensite

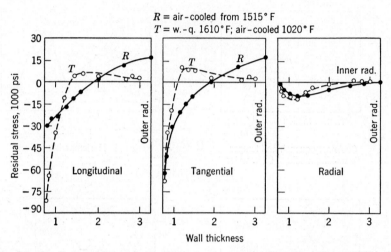

FIG. 11-43.   Internal Stress in the Wall of a Centrifugal Cast-Steel Tube (Caillaud)

products are last formed at the inner layers.   Accompanying volume changes arising at different time intervals form the origin for the final state of residual stresses.   Importance of mold speed on cracking has also been studied.[69]

M. FLAKING

Hairline or shatter cracks, termed flaking, can occur during the cooling of large sections like blooms, billets, and forgings of alloy steels.   It is generally conceded that these flakes are a result of the combined action of both hydrogen embrittlement and superimposed internal stress.   Tensile stresses arising from volume increases during transformation, particularly in segregated areas, are more detrimental than stresses of thermal origin.   An example of a fatigue fracture initiating from flaking is given in Fig. 11-44 for a 12-in.-diameter forging hammer rod.

It is frequently stated that hydrogen alone has never been found definitely to cause cracks, but it is reflected in low ductility; also stresses alone appear unable to produce flaking in the absence of hydrogen.   These two statements represent the views of many authorities, but there still exists some difference of opinion on the relative importance of these two factors.   Although the subject of hydrogen embrittlement is beyond the scope of this chapter, various investigators have reported practical means for minimizing its effect.   Detrimental tensile stresses caused in cooling can be eliminated by the proper kind of controlled cooling or annealing cycles.

Studies of flake formation and prevention have been made by many investigators. The subject was reviewed in the literature of several countries by Johnson, Poole, and Rosa;[70] the hairline-crack subcommittee of the Iron & Steel Institute,[71] Zappfe;[72] Cramer and Bast;[73] and Houdremont and Schra-

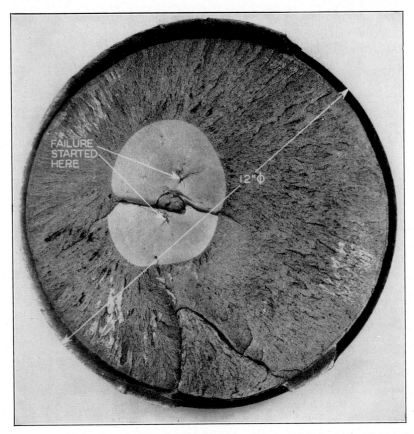

Fig. 11-44. 35,000-lb Hammer Rod Fatigue Failure Initiating from Internal Flakes

der.[74] Shatter cracks leading to fissures in railroad rails have been extensively reported by H. F. Moore.[75] Many additional literature sources may be found in the bibliographies of these references.

Although hairline cracks and so-called snowflakes are more obvious in steels, they also occur in weld deposits. Snowflakes in weld deposits do not necessarily develop from hairline cracks but may form during a tension test to give little change in tensile strength but large decreases in ductility. Lefevre[76] reviews means of overcoming these defects and concludes that they are caused by tensile stresses arising under conditions similar to those discussed for steel.

N. Residual Stresses Due to Cold Drawing

The occurrence of many cases of particularly longitudinal cracking after cold-drawing operations is responsible for the great amount of research spent in determining the residual-stress system produced in bars and tubes undergoing such mill operations. An example of tubes cracked after the second cold-draw pass is shown in Fig. 11-45 for a carbon-free allow steel of considerable strain-hardening capacity.

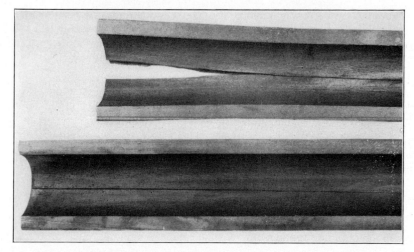

Fig. 11-45. Residual Stresses Causing Longitudinal Cracks Originating from Inner-Tube Wall

Cracking is a process involving the relief of stresses, and, therefore, it would be logical to investigate the tangential stresses. Factors of a metallurgical and mechanical nature may also govern the intensity of these stresses and the resistance of the material to cracking. Very often such cracking occurs only on a few pieces of a lot being processed; in such cases it may be that the high residual stresses in combination with isolated factors of a metallurgical and mechanical nature cause cracking. Although residual stresses in drawn brass products[77, 78] were the first to be studied because of their importance in the use of shells, the later investigations have been made on steel bars and tubes. It is this work which is briefly reviewed.

Fahrenhorst and Sachs[79] subjected 40 hot-rolled bars of 0.06% C steel* to 10 to 24 per cent reduction in one pass of cold drawing to obtain a final diameter of 1.57 in. These bars were selected from ingots which were bottom-

* Basic Bessemer steel: 0.06% C, 0.41% Mn; 0.045 and 0.06% P. Before drawing, residual stresses were less than 3000 psi. Two years elapsed after drawing before this residual-stress study was made.

and top-poured, killed, and rimmed and were from the top and bottom of the ingot. Five bars or 12 per cent cracked during drawing at 17 to 24 per cent reduction. Ingot-pouring practice, location in the ingot, microstructure, notched-bar impact strength, or hardness showed no relationship to the cracking. On bars cold drawn to 7.5 to 9.1 per cent reduction, the residual stresses measured by the boring-out method were about 40,000 psi tension in longitudinal and tangential directions on the outside diameter, whereas the inside-diameter stress was compression of 65,000–85,000 and 37,000–55,000, respectively. Straightening on a Medart-type machine had a marked

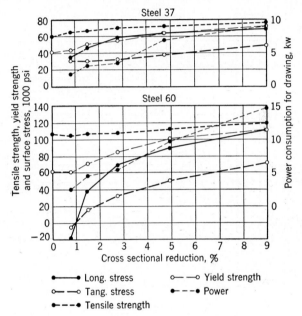

Fig. 11-46. Influence of the per cent Reduction by Cold Drawing of Steels 37 and 60 on Surface Stresses, Physical Properties, and Power (Bühler and Buchholtz)

influence in that outside-diameter tensile stresses produced in drawing were reversed to compressive stresses of 30,000–40,000 psi and accompanied by a redistribution through the cross section; the inside-diameter stress became compression values of zero to 60,000 psi with tension in the core. Similar reversal was previously found for brass.[80]

Bühler and Buchholtz[81] determined the residual stresses for three different steels (Table 11-6) with cold-draw reductions of 0.8 to 9 per cent. Hot-rolled bars of 0.10 and 0.50% C steels were first normalized and then lathe-turned to proper diameter to give desired reduction.* Residual stresses measured are given in Fig. 11-46 along with physical properties. The influence of tensile strength on residual stresses for hot-rolled bar stock from three steels (Table 11-6) with 9 per cent reduction is reported in Fig. 11-47.

* The cold-drawing die had a 1.89-in. hole and a single throat radius of 1.18 in.

TABLE 11-6

CHEMICAL ANALYSIS, PER CENT

Steel	C	Si	Mn	P	S	Cu	Cr
St 37	0.10	0.01	0.44	0.035	0.033	0.13	0.07
St 52	0.19	0.45	0.93	0.041	0.026	0.68	0.43
St 60	0.50	0.38	0.75	0.020	0.024	0.20	Trace

From Fig. 11-46 it may be noted that below 0.6 per cent reduction on 0.10% C steel the surface stresses are in compression; for the 0.50% C steel this point is at 0.8 per cent reduction. For larger values of reduction the surface stresses turn into tension. A second stress reversal was mentioned[82]

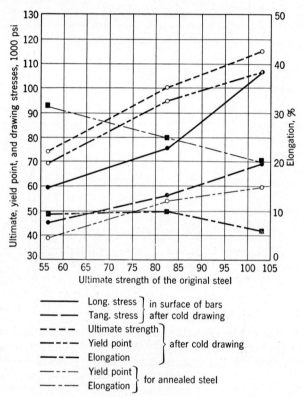

FIG. 11-47. Strength Properties before and after Cold Drawing and Dependence of Drawing Stresses on the Ultimate Strength of the Original Steel (Bühler and Buchholtz) (Specimen drawn from 1.968 to 1.890 in. diameter)

as occurring around 55–65 per cent reduction where tensile stresses develop in the core to form internal troughlike cracks. Surface stresses show a pronounced increase with increasing tensile strength of the steel before drawing as revealed in Fig. 11-47.

O. Cracking Due to Rapid Heating and Cooling

A slow rate of cooling or heating through the critical range is necessary if residual stresses leading to cracks are to be avoided in certain steels. Ingots crack longitudinally, as shown in Fig. 11-48, when the rate of heating is too rapid. Detrimental internal stresses arise from too high a temperature

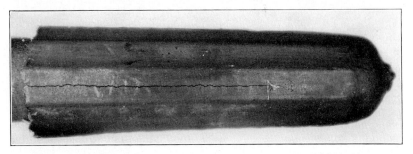

Fig. 11-48.   Ingot Cracked as Result of Too Rapid Heating (SAE 3245 Steel)

gradient occurring during nonuniform heating through the cross section. Undoubtedly the cast-ingot structure and a combination of other factors left the ingot in a vulnerable condition to be influenced by internal stresses.

When large sizes of alloy steel already containing high internal stresses are heated rapidly to a high temperature, this heat shock can result in cracking. Such a case is shown in Fig. 11-49 for 8-in. rounds of SAE 52100 steel.   Faulty

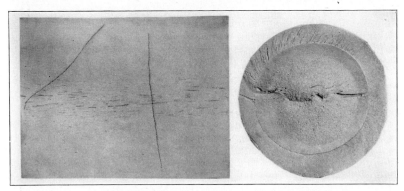

(a) Longitudinal section   (b) Transverse section

Fig. 11-49.   Internal Stress Develops Cracks in 8-in. Rounds of SAE 52100 Steel

cooling or heating operations in processing to 8-in. rounds produced large residual stresses; when these cold rounds were placed in a rotary furnace for reheating, the rapid heating superimposed additional internal stresses and caused these cracks to develop. General surface cracking developed in Fig. 11-50 owing to rolling blooms being too cold (25% Cr, 20% Ni). Considerable resistance to deformation is characteristic of such high-alloy steel, and

Fig. 11-50. Surface Cracking of Bloom Rolled Too Cold—(25% Cr, 20% Ni
Steel)

tensile stresses causing rupture are produced in the surface when the steel is
rolled at too low a temperature.

P. Ingot-Mold Cracking

Thermal stresses produced in ingot molds during the casting of ingots is
often responsible for mold failure typical of that shown in Fig. 11-51.   Failures
often develop near the open end where the axial stresses are reduced and the
tensile hoop stresses increased about 25 per cent over that at other sections

Fig. 11-51.   Thermal Cracks in Ingot Mold

away from the end.[83, 84] For this reason molds are often reinforced around the open end by a rib. Data on such failures were published in two reports.[85]

The cracking of ingot molds, caused by thermal stresses set up during the casting of ingots, was studied by Land.[86] His work is based on certain assumptions concerning the influence of temperature and stress on the plastic deformation and physical properties of ingot-mold iron. Under these assumptions the thermal stresses are shown to be about one-half the ultimate strength of the iron. Mold shape and end effects are discussed. Residual stresses are formed as the mold cools slowly after each ingot is cast; any such residual stresses would be superimposed on the thermal stresses produced during pouring and might have a dangerous cumulative effect.

Q. Piercing Rods on Tube Mills

Piercing rods $7\frac{1}{2}$ in. in diameter used on a Pilger mill in the manufacture of hot-rolled seamless-steel tubing were developing premature fatigue failure.[50] These rods were failing near the piercing end. The material was an air-hardening steel having a tensile strength of 128,000 psi. The residual-surface stress was determined in the region of fracture to be 60,000 psi tension. This combined with the action of bending and torsional stresses from external loading would lead to early fatigue failure.

The end of the rod opposite which failure occurred was found practically free of internal stresses. The presence of these tensile residual stresses in the region of failure was explained by heavy forces imposed on the heated working surface of the piercing rod. A flow condition undoubtedly followed similar to that found in drawing through a die. Also the temperature differential between the surface and core may have some small influence on these failures. It was recommended that these failures be averted by tempering the rods at regular intervals at about 1025° to 1100°F.

R. Residual Stresses in Rails

Railroad rails may contain residual stresses as a result of processing or operating loads and even through placing the rail in the track structure. Little information exists on this general subject, but much of that available pertains to processing. Here the residual stresses result from rolling, cooling, and straightening. It is considered that the rolling stresses are practically zero because of the customary high rolling temperatures.[87] Calculations[88, 89] have been made regarding cooling stresses which account for cracking by assuming a certain temperature differential between the surface and core of rail sections.

Meier[90] determined longitudinal stresses in rails by cutting longitudinal strips of 0.3×0.3 in. cross section from 1-ft-long sections taken from the centers of rail lengths. His findings for unstraightened and straightened rails are shown in Fig. 11-52. Meier recognized that such mechanical methods of stress measurement represented average values over the strips and noted that some strips bent when cut out, indicating the presence of residual stresses in other planes. In order to answer the question whether residual stresses persist after the rail is subjected to operating loads, Meier made fatigue tests on rail sections; rail with known residual stresses was subjected to alternating stresses of +2800 to +28,400 psi for about two million cycles, and no change in the residual-stress system was noticeable.

It is apparent from Fig. 11-52 that the stresses from straightening are generally greater than the cooling stresses. Straightening rails vertically is the basis for the preceding data, and 98-ft rails so straightened may shorten as much as 1½ in. Meier reported differences in maximum residual stress

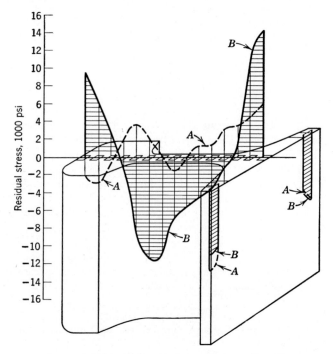

A = unstraightened rail; residual stress due to cooling only

B = same as A except rail straightened vertically

Fig. 11-52.   Residual Stress in Straightened and Unstraightened Rail (Meier)

after straightening of 10,000 to 28,000 psi because of various roll diameters and arrangements used in the several types of straightening machines. Horizontal straightening has less influence on the residual stresses.

X rays were used by Regler,[91] Iweronowa,[92] and Terminassow,[93] to determine residual stresses in rails, but Schönrock[87] appears to be the first to have used the Glocker[94] method which forms the present basis for stress analysis by X rays. Figure 11-53 gives the results of Schönrock[1] for unstraightened and straightened rails having a tensile strength of 100,000 psi and for straightened rails of 128,000 psi tensile strength.

Residual stresses developed by traffic were explored by Magee and Cress.[95]

Internal strains developed at the gage corner of new and used rail were measured in order to provide information on the cause of shelling. Wire-resistance-type strain gages of ¼-in. gage length were cemented to the leaving end of one rail so that they were in the joint gap between two rail ends, and additional gages were located in the upper web fillet away from the rail end. Residual strains were measured after various amounts of traffic over a 2-day

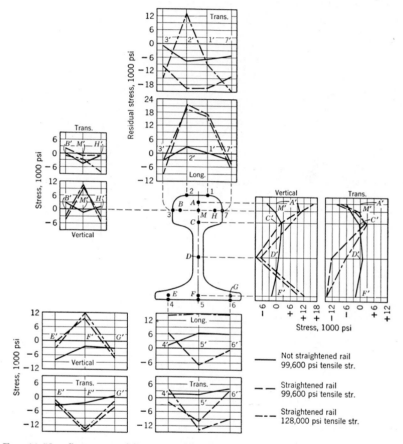

FIG. 11-53. Summary of Results of Residual Stresses in Three Different Rails
(Schönrock)

period. Some tensile strains equivalent to as much as 85,000 psi and compressive strains much above the ordinary yield point were obtained. Insufficient tests were made to permit general conclusions, but the following facts were discovered, as quoted from their report:

1. High residual stresses are developed within the rail head at points where the actual dynamic stresses during wheel passage are well below the yield point of the steel. Presumably residual stresses at these points are "balancing

stresses" caused by the yield point being exceeded elsewhere, as, for example, near the bearing surface.

2. The repetition or reversal of dynamic stresses accompanying wheel passage in the area where shelling develops was not found to be sufficiently high in these measurements to indicate fatigue failure. Computed dynamic shearing stresses from the measured direct stresses were also well below the fatigue strength.

3. Accumulated residual strains were found to be quite high in the area where shelling develops.

4. These measured stresses suggest the possibility that shelling may be the result of exhausted ductility due to excessive plastic flow and high residual strains rather than fatigue of the metal from repeated or reversed stresses.

The exact manner in which residual stresses influence various types of rail failures has never been investigated to a conclusion. Meier[96] stated that their effect is apparent and that high tensile stresses in the rail base are particularly detrimental. Any residual stresses must be considered in combination with those due to temperature and constraining forces to give the final prestressed condition; then this stress system is further modified by traffic loading. Ros[97] also measured residual stresses in rails which are summarized in Table 11-7. Ros concluded that, if production methods are closely controlled, then these residual rail stresses are of no practical importance on the fracture or fatigue strength of rails.

S. INJURY IN GROUND SURFACES

Residual stresses are generated in the grinding process and are responsible for several kinds of injury in ground surfaces. To determine the influence of various heat-treating and grinding practices on fatigue resistance, Staudinger[98] made fatigue tests in reversed bending of case-carburized, nitrided, and quenched and tempered steel-plate specimens (Fig. 11-54). Two carburizing steels (Table 11-8, 1407 and 1207) were case-carburized by four different

TABLE 11-7

RESIDUAL STRESS IN VARIOUS TYPE RAILS, PSI

	Heat-Treated	Two-Material	One-Material	Normal
Head { Surface	−36,100	+10,100	+10,700	−8000
Head { Max.	−37,300	+11,500	+11,800	−7800
Web, max.	+36,300	−23,500	+ 9,200	−5800
Rail Base, surface	−12,500	+ 5,100	+ 7,000	−4100

TABLE 11-8

CHEMICAL ANALYSIS OF STEELS TESTED BY STAUDINGER, PER CENT

Type Steel	C	Mn	Si	Cr	Mo	V
ECMo 80 Flw. 1407	0.17	0.92	0.35	1.35	0.25	....
EC 80 Flw. 1207	0.18	1.34	0.35	1.06	....	....
Flw. 1470	0.25	0.62	0.35	2.60	0.23	0.19
Flw. 1473	0.29	0.64	0.18	2.61	....	0.26
Flw. 1620	0.29	0.64	0.18	2.61	...	0.26

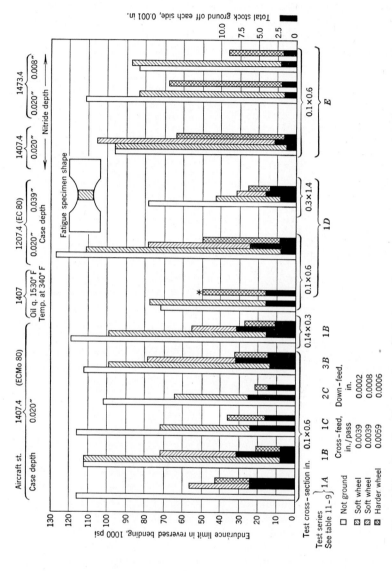

FIG. 11-54.   Bending Fatigue Strength Influenced by Heat Treatment and Grinding (Staudinger)

methods (Table 11-9) in three different carburizing compounds (Table 11-9); hardness of the case surface varied from RC 60 to 64 with a core strength between 171,000 and 228,000 psi, depending on the type of heat treatment

TABLE 11-9

VARIOUS HEAT TREATMENTS USED IN TEST SPECIMENS

Case-Hardening Methods, °F

Heat Treatment	A	B	C	D
Rate of temp. increase in carburizing	Normal	Rapid	Normal	Normal
Carburizing temp.	1620	1620	1650	1620
Intermediate hardening Temp.	1580	....	1580	....
Intermediate anneal in charcoal for 2 hr	1200	1200	1200	1200
Hardening in oil	1530	1530	1530	1470
Stress Relief, 1 hr	340	430	....	360

Case-Hardening Compounds Used on Test Specimens
1 = CMD 12 case-hardening powder
2 = EL 453 case-hardening powder
3 = C 5 carburizing salt bath

Example. Test Series identified as 2C in Figure 11-54 means that EL 453 powder was used for carburizing and method C case hardening was applied.

Also specimens of two nitriding steels (1470 and 1473) were nitrided on all sides to give a Vickers surface hardness of 880 to 900 with a core strength of 156,000 psi. For comparison with performance of a nitriding steel, another steel (1620) having the same analysis as one of the nitriding steels (1473) was quenched and tempered to about 156,000 psi tensile strength. Further, a carburizing steel (1407) was hardened without carburizing and then tempered.

These plate specimens were ground on a reciprocating-type surface grinder having a cross-feed. Two Norton grinding wheels of the following markings* were used:

A soft wheel: 38A60-J8 VBE
A harder wheel: 38A46-K

All wheels were 7.87 in. in diameter by 0.7 in. wide. Wheel speed was always 6120 ft/min, and the transverse speed of the table 33 ft/min. Grinding was done dry and without a coolant.

Results of fatigue tests are given in Fig. 11-54. The lowest bending fatigue values were obtained with certain test series of case-carburized specimens using the harder wheel for which Staudinger gave the following reasons:

Series 1C—Stress relieving after final hardening was omitted.
Series 2C—Case-carburizing compound EL 453 had too intense action.
Series 1B—Too rapid rate of temperature increase in carburization (it would seem that this factor is hardly of any importance).

* These markings correspond to the System given in *Grinding Wheel Information and Selection*, Norton Company, Worcester, Mass.

The low values for these series are explained by either grinding cracks or cementite-network formation in case-carburizing. The choice of carburizing medium (Table 11-9) had no influence on the grinding sensivity. Grinding cracks in the case-hardening steels (1407 and 1207) decreased the fatigue strength to one-third the value of the perfectly ground specimens; whereas poor grinding and grinding away too much of the case layer might decrease the alternating bending strength by 50 per cent. Nitrided steels were found less sensitive to grinding cracks and decreased the fatigue resistance about 35 per cent.

It was furthermore shown that, even for perfect grinding with the soft wheel, the alternating strength was usually decreased. Two reasons for this loss in fatigue resistance are:

1. A decrease in surface hardness may arise, which may be greater for a down-feed of 0.0008 in. than for 0.0002.

2. Surface layers of case-hardened and nitrided parts have high compressive stresses. Each grinding pass removed a portion of the external zone containing these residual stresses which are favorable to high fatigue strength.[99]

The larger-size case-carburized specimens (1207) having 0.039-in.-deep cases showed a decrease in fatigue strength of about 50 per cent, if grinding cracks existed. Regardless of specimen size or shape, grinding cracks had a detrimental influence on alternating strength. Quenched and tempered steel (1620 not shown in Fig. 11-54) showed a loss in fatigue resistance of 20 per cent when grinding with too hard a wheel. Too large a down-feed caused damage up to 5 per cent.

It is important to note from Fig. 11-54 that the alternating strength of the unground surface generally compares favorably with that of the ground one, and this was also confirmed by Wiegand.[100] In such cases the unground surfaces must be smooth and free of cracks, and satisfactory heat treatment must be obtained without surface decarburization or even grain-boundary cementite precipitation. The influence of retained austenite is very controversial. Some investigators believe that the least percentage possible is desirable to minimize danger of grinding cracks. On the other hand, the percentage of retained austenite present in many production parts is sufficient to cause some concern if this contention were true, because little grinding difficulty has been reported for such parts owing to this factor.

Aircraft gears which developed early fatigue failure, initiating in the root radius, were found to have surface cracks or damage due to grinding after case carburizing. The danger of grinding cracks developing was eliminated by grinding or machining and polishing the root radius after carburizing and before hardening.[18, 101] Almen[5] also discussed premature failure of gear teeth due to grinding injury or cracks.

A burned surface developed in grinding may be detected by shot blasting[102] after rough grinding and before finish grinding. The softer or burnt areas will be more readily attached and darkened by the impact of the shot. Stock removal is not so uniform in the roughing operation as it is in the finish grind, and surface injury is more likely to develop in the roughing operation. This damage occurs as a result of material and/or grinding conditions which lead to low fatigue resistance. Important findings and an excellent review of the literature have been presented by Tarasov[103] relative to the detection, causes, and prevention of injury in ground surfaces. Injury here is defined as cracks, burns, and high tensile stresses in ground surfaces. Although no fatigue data are given, Tarasov confirms the findings of Staudinger[98] and Brophy[104] that the metallurgical state of the steel can easily account for injury, as has already been discussed.

Residual stresses due to bone-dry grinding* were discussed by Tarasov. He gave curves showing how the practical factors of (1) wheel grade, (2) wheel speed, and (3) down-feed greatly influenced surface injury. Tempering up to about 300°F after grinding reduces the tendency to crack. Tarasov employed a controlled method of etch cracking previously utilized by Brophy,[104] to measure the degree of injury and residual stresses† in the ground surface. Although etching did not permit a quantitative measure of the residual stresses, difference of degrees could be detected. Here an increase in the length of etch cracks under constant etching conditions corresponds to more severe surface stresses.

Mickel and Sommer[105] reported that grinding cracks on case-carburized piston pins decreased the compressive fatigue resistance by 25 per cent when one steel‡ was used. This decrease was only 6 per cent for another steel.§

They reported these values on the basis of only a few tests but remarked that the decrease could be much greater, depending on the extent of the crack and its relative location to the highly stressed region.

Almen[5] took a 0.002-in. deep grinding pass across a $\frac{1}{16}$-in.-thick strip of annealed spring steel and found 270,000 psi tension on the surface.

Low-carbon normalized steel bars were ground to a depth of 0.022 in., and residual stresses were measured.[106] A maximum tensile surface stress of 25,000 psi was found, and the stressed zone had a depth of about 0.036 in. Layers were etched off, and the change in deflection of the bars was used to calculate the stresses by equations derived by Davidenkov.

An unusual experience of hardening the surface by grinding was reported by Holloway.[107] He ground a 0.35% C and 1.2% Mn steel quenched and

* The Norton wheel used 38A46-J8 VBE; 7 to 8 in. diameter $\frac{1}{2}$ in. wide; wheel speed 6000 ft/min; cross-feed 0.050 in. per pass; down-feed 0.002 in.; total down-feed 0.020 in.; transverse speed 40 ft/min.

† Surface stresses, when they are above a threshold level, can be developed into etch cracks by etching with hydrochloric or sulphuric acid, either hot or cold. Increasing the etching time or the etchant temperature makes it possible to develop lower stresses into etch cracks. The depth of surface cracks, occurring during or after grinding, is generally around 0.010 to 0.020 in., but the depth of the stressed layer from which such cracks originate appears to be of the order of 0.0005 in. According to Tarasov, the length of the crack is a more satisfactory criterion for determining the degree of residual stresses present than the number of cracks.

‡ EC60; 0.12–0.18% C, 0.25–0.35% Si, 0.45–0.55% Mn, 0.55–0.65% Cr; 0.20% Cu; core tensile strength 97,000–117,000 psi; surface RC 56–59.

§ EC80; 0.14–0.19% C, 0.20–0.35% Si, 1.07–1.30% Mn, 0.75–0.95% Cr, 0.1% V; 0.25% Cu; core tensile strength 139,000–154,000 psi; surface RC 58–62.

tempered to 286–293 VPN. After grinding, a partially martensitic layer 0.003 in. deep was present, having a hardness of 500–600 VPN.

Monma[108] ground quenched carbon steels. He reported that grinding cracks were caused by shrinkage due to $\alpha \rightarrow \beta$ martensite transformation in the surface layer caused by heat of grinding. Little difference in number of cracks resulted between wet and dry methods of grinding. Tempering at 300°F before grinding prevented cracks developing, because at this temperature $\alpha \rightarrow \beta$ transformation had taken place uniformly through the section before grinding.

Wulff[109] made electron-diffraction studies of the metallurgical state of surfaces prepared by grinding and other finishing methods using stainless steel. He concluded that flash temperatures in the surface layer of atoms could exceed 1300°F and in a subsurface layer above 400°F; this was also suggested by Bowden.[110]

No data have been found on the comparative grinding-damage susceptibility of steels of the through-hardening and surface-treated types where surface hardness is about RC 60 or above. It would appear that the surface-treated types would be less apt to damage from grinding; for example, the initial compressive stresses usually present with such surface treatments as case carburizing or nitriding must first be offset by tensile stresses from grinding before residual stresses become dangerous. In through-hardened steels there is no such protective layer of high surface-compressive stresses. On the other hand, stresses alone may not be the only detrimental factor as structural damage must also be considered.

T. GEARS

Benson[111] reported the premature fatigue failure of traction-gear rims because of unfavorable residual thermal stresses produced in water quenching from the tempering temperature of 1110°F. Calculated service stresses were moderate, and ample evidence existed that gears of the same design but without the unfavorable internal stresses were adequate. These gears were made from an oil-quenched Ni–Cr steel* and were machined all over, following the quench from the temper. Failure occurred by teeth breaking out and by radial cracks through the rim.

Such tooth failures in gears are not unusual and result from repeated overloading in service. In this case, however, the initiation point of failure had definite characteristics which eliminated such a simple explanation. The primary fatigue cracks did not originate at the top of the root radius F in Fig. 11-55a, where the maximum bending stress due to tooth loading exists and fatigue cracks due to overloading are normally found; instead, the cracks started at the bottom of the root radius (X, Y, and Z). Also cracks tended to grow in a radial direction through the rim, starting about 10° from a radial line, instead of about 45°, as is usual with simple tooth overloading. Cracks X and Y later progressed to break out a tooth, but crack Z severed the rim.

* Chemical analysis: 0.34 % C, 3.23 % Ni, 0.12 % Cr, nil Mo; physical properties: yield point 130,000 psi, ult. 141,000 psi; 19 % elong.; 49 % red area; Izod 40.

Further, these cracks did not start close to the end of the tooth, as would be expected from an overhung pinion; instead they initiated at a distance of $\frac{1}{2}$ to $\frac{3}{4}$ in. from the motor end of the teeth.

Residual thermal tensile stresses of considerable magnitude were found to exist, as shown in Fig. 11-55c and d. Failure was attributed to these unfavorable residual tensile stresses plus the tensile shrinkage stresses of about 17,000 psi obtained in mounting on the rim, all of which were super-imposed on the service stresses. To measure these residual circumferential thermal stresses, rings were machined from the gear rim (Fig. 11-55b), and differences in ring diameter were measured before and after cutting from the

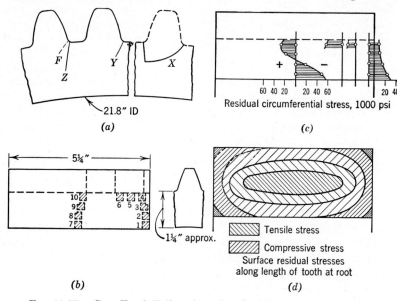

(a)

(c)

(b)

(d)

Fig. 11-55. Gear-Tooth Failure from Residual Tensile Stress (Benson)

gear. The computed stresses from diameter changes are given in the middle column of Table 11-10. These rings were also split, which permitted calculations of the stress gradient through the ring section to be made, as given in the last column of Table 11-10. Here the term "opening" means tensile stresses in the outer surface of the ring, and "closed" means compression. In view of the three-dimensional nature of the residual-stress system present, this method for determining only circumferential stresses would be expected to give stresses lower than those actually present.

Benson also complained of distortion in machining due to the release of these residual stresses which necessitated elaborate sequences of machining. He severely criticized the frequently used British practice of quenching from the tempering temperature which is required in order to obtain high-impact-strength values and expressed the thought that in most cases the increased impact resistance obtained was not necessary.

Gear-tooth performance as affected by residual stresses is discussed further under sections presenting various surface-treating processes.

Form versus generate grinding of case-carburized gears was investigated by Greaves, Kirstowsky and Lipson [111] Both fatigue tests and residual-stress measurements indicated that form grinding was less desirable than generate grinding. Original compressive stresses in the surface due to case carburizing were apparently offset by opposing tensile stresses due to grinding. Less tension stress was produced in generate than in form grinding.

TABLE 11-10

Ring No.	Average Residual Stress in Ring, psi	Stress Difference between ID and OD of Ring, psi
1	−35,800	5600 (opened)
2	−24,600	2240 (opened)
3	−22,400	Nil
4	−17,900	2240 (closed)
5	+11,200	6700 (closed)
6	+29,100	15700 (closed)
7	−47,000	24600 (opened)
8	−13,400	35800 (opened)
9	+26,200	15700 (opened)
10	+26,900	20200 (closed)

U. RIVETS

Residual stresses influence the clamping force of rivets as found by Schulz and Buchholtz.[112] They found that 1-in.-diameter rivets of 0.16% C steel

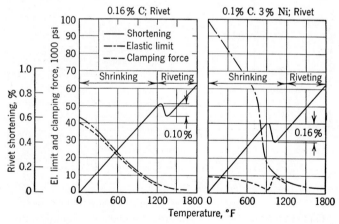

FIG. 11-56. Shrinking and Clamping Force of Carbon- and Nickel-Steel Rivets, 1 in. in Diameter (Schulz and Buchholtz)

having 38,400 psi yield strength produced a clamping force of 42,700 psi. This compares with a clamping force of 8500 psi for an alloy steel of 0.1% C and 3% Ni of 99,600 psi yield strength.

The explanation for the clamping force of the alloy-steel rivet being only one-fifth that of the carbon-steel rivet is given in Fig. 11-56. The shrinkage of the rivet, with decreasing temperature, is interrupted by the gamma–alpha transformation at which time an elongation of the rivet occurs.   In the case of the plain carbon-steel rivet this transformation and accompanying elongation occur during the riveting operation at about 1300°F; the nickel-steel rivet has a greater elongation than the carbon-steel rivet at the time of transformation, and, what is most important, this elongation occurs after completion of the riveting process at a lower temperature of about 1000°F. After completion of the riveting, a shortening of the carbon-steel rivet of 0.7 per cent takes place after transformation which compares with about 0.5 per cent for the nickel-steel rivet.

Alloy-steel-rivet applications have presented some difficulties.   An extensive review of this subject has been published,[112] and the practices and service experiences on railroads have been discussed for many years before engineering meetings of the American railroads.

V. CRANKSHAFTS

Machining operations on crankshafts partially relieve any residual stresses which may be present.   Stress relief in such an intricate-shaped part often results in distortion or warpage which is usually corrected by cold straightening.   This straightening operation of only several thousandths of an inch

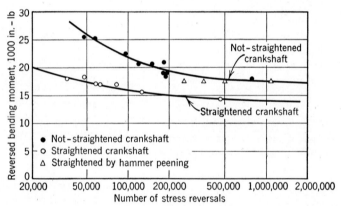

FIG. 11-57.   Effect of Straightening Crankshafts on the Fatigue Life (Schmidt)

leads to unfavorable residual tensile stresses being produced in the crank-journal fillet with consequent premature fatigue failure initiating in these fillets.   This subject was extensively investigated by Schmidt[113] for double-throw aircraft-engine crankshafts having three main journals.

Schmidt made fatigue tests in reversed bending on full-size crankshafts* having 3.07-in.-diameter journals which were (1) not straightened, (2) straightened at room temperature by plastically deforming the shaft with force vertical to the center main journal, and (3) straightened by peening

* The material was a low-nickel steel (aircraft steel 1460.5) heat-treated to 16,300–18,500 psi tensile strength.

the proper side of the crank cheeks with the ball head of a hand or air hammer. Fatigue results are given in Fig. 11-57.

Straightening according to method 2 gave an endurance limit 20 per cent lower than that of the unstraightened crankshafts; this loss of fatigue strength was even greater for a limited life, being 35 per cent at 50,000 cycles and 27 per cent at 100,000 cycles. One shaft straightened at 355°F instead of at room temperature resulted in no improvement over cold straightening. These straightened shafts all developed premature fatigue failure initiating at the two crank-journal fillets toward the center line of the shaft and adjacent to the center main journal. Here high tensile stresses remained from straightening, whereas unstraightened shafts fractured at all crank-journal fillets. Four shafts straightened by peening exhibited a fatigue resistance similar to those unstraightened.

Some explanation was sought for this 20 per cent decrease in fatigue strength. Residual longitudinal tensile stresses produced in crank-journal fillets from straightening by method 2 were determined by X ray* to vary between 85,000 to 100,000 psi. When the modified Goodman diagram (Fig. 11-58) is consulted for the steel used in these shafts, it is apparent that at a prestress of $R_1 = 100,000$ psi the range of fatigue strength is only 60 per cent of that when $R_1 = $ zero. This calculated reduction of 40 per cent compares with only 20 per cent found in the fatigue tests. This difference suggested further study to determine if it were due to gradual relief of residual stress by the effect of cyclic loading. Therefore, a shaft was straightened resulting in a residual longitudinal stress in the fillets of about 100,000 psi; then this shaft was subjected to 500,000 cycles of reversed bending slightly below the endurance limit. X-Ray measurements indicated that this residual stress was reduced to 48,000 psi. With reference again to Fig. 11-58, with a prestress

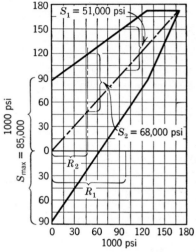

S_{max} = stress range without residual stress
S_1 = stress range with residual stress
S_2 = stress range with residual stress
R_1 = 100,000 psi (before fatigue test)
R_2 = 48,000 psi (after 500,000 cycles)

Stresses plotted are peak values in fillet

$$\frac{S_1}{S_{max}} = \frac{51,000}{85,000} = 0.6$$

$$\frac{S_2}{S_{max}} = \frac{68,000}{85,000} = 0.8$$

FIG. 11-58. Explanation for Reduced Fatigue Resistance of Straightened Crankshaft (Schmidt)

* Cranks were tempered to 142,000–156,000 psi in order to obtain an accuracy of plus or minus 7000 psi residual stresses. As a comment, this temper treatment would remove some of the residual stresses, but Schmidt did not discuss this point.

of $R_2 = 48,000$ psi it is shown that the range of fatigue strength is 80 per cent as great as when $R_2 = $ zero. This calculated 20 per cent reduction then agrees with that found in the fatigue test.

The foregoing explanation has considerable practical significance; it offers a method[114] for superimposing the residual stress on that due to the external load in order to determine its influence on the endurance limit. These stresses cannot be added mathematically as is often done by many investigators; instead it becomes more important to know the equilibrium value of the residual stress after cyclic stressing than it is to know its initial value. Then it may be possible to use the usual stress-range diagram,* as was done in Fig. 11-58. Application should be made of this analysis to other problems involving residual stresses as a means of verifying whether it can be safely used for design purposes.

W. Thermal Residual Stresses versus Fatigue Strength

Bühler and Buchholtz[115] presented convincing data that thermal residual surface-compressive stresses would increase the bending endurance limit, whereas initial tensile stresses would decrease it. Their laboratory tests were made in rotating bending on plain specimens 1.07 in. in diameter with various degrees of thermal residual stress but with no transformation stresses. The complete stress distribution was determined by the boring-out method and correlated with the fatigue resistance. Ten different steels in Table 11-11 were investigated under different heat treatments to produce physical properties, residual stresses, and endurance values in Table 11-12.

All constructional steels, furnace-cooled from 1110°F, showed zero stress at the outer surface (Table 11-12). On the other hand, all steels quenched from below A_1 at 1110°F, whether in oil, water, or salt water, always showed compressive stresses on the surface and compensating tensile stresses in the core. The more drastic the quench, the greater the surface stress and endurance limit, and yet the tensile properties were practically not affected. The endurance limit is increased in a progressive manner with increasing initial compressive stresses on the surface, according to Table 11-12. It would be expected that the percentage increase in endurance limit obtained in Table 11-12 would be much greater if notched instead of plain specimens of carbon steel had been tested.

Since surface residual compressive stresses were found to increase the fatigue resistance, it was believed that a decrease would be obtained if these initial stresses were in tension instead of compression. The contention was substantiated by the tests on Ni 12 and Ni 16 steels which is apparent from a consideration of the findings in Table 11-12. Again, if notched instead of plain specimens of this high-nickel steel had been tested, then the percentage decrease in endurance limit would be expected to be greater than the 12 to 16 per cent shown. Bühler used these nickel steels to obtain the initial tensile stress on the surface and still be able to machine the specimens in the

---

* The biaxial state of stress is neglected here, but in many problems its influence may not be too great.

TABLE 11-11

CHEMICAL ANALYSIS, PER CENT

Steel*	C	Mn	Si	P	S	Ni
C 10	0.10	0.45	0.25	0.030	0.030	.....
C 29	0.29	0.60	0.30	0.026	0.030	.....
C 33	0.33	0.62	0.29	0.022	0.026	.....
C 34	0.34	0.69	0.27	0.031	0.023	.....
C 36	0.36	0.74	0.40	0.031	0.032	.....
C 57	0.57	0.50	0.28	0.017	0.017	.....
C 98	0.98	0.27	0.18	0.012	0.025	.....
Mn–Si	0.35	1.28	0.37	0.033	0.031	.....
Ni 12	0.04	0.52	0.15	....	....	12.17
Ni 16	0.05	0.39	0.12	....	....	15.63

* Plain fatigue specimens for Mn–Si steel were 0.17 in. in diameter while for all other steel specimens were made 1.07 in. in diameter.

TABLE 11-12

FATIGUE STRENGTH VERSUS RESIDUAL STRESSES AND MECHANICAL PROPERTIES
Bühler and Buchholtz

Steel	Heat Treatment	0.2 Yield Strength, psi	Tensile Strength, psi	Red. Area, %	Endurance Limit		Residual Surface Stress, psi	
					psi	%	Long.	Tang.
C33	Furnace-cool from 1110°F	55,800	84,800	53	35,600	100	0	0
	Ice-water-quench from 1110°F	54,800	89,300	51	39,800	112	−32,700	−39,800
C34	Furnace-cool from 1110°F	49,600	91,500	54	39,800	100	0	0
	Oil (175°F)-quench from 1110°F	54,900	94,700	54	42,700	107	−29,200	−29,200
	Ice-water-quench from 1110°F	51,800	96,700	54	46,900	118	−45,500	−45,500
	Salt-water (−5)-quench from 1110°F	50,200	93,400	55	48,400	122	−48,400	−45,500
C36	Furnace-cool from 1110°F	52,200	99,000	..	42,700	100	0	0
	Ice-water-quench from 1110°F	52,800	98,100	..	49,800	117	−45,500	−39,800
C57	Furnace-cool from 1110°F	45,500	90,900	35	37,000	100	0	0
	Oil-quench from 1110°F	44,100	92,600	35	41,200	111	−34,100	−28,400
	Ice-water-quench from 1110°F	44,100	95,700	32	42,700	115	−48,400	−42,700
	Water-quench 1560°F; Air-cool 1110°F	86,900	115,800	60	45,500	100	0	0
	Water-quench 1560°F; Ice-water-quench 1110°F	86,900	118,100	60	51,200	112	−52,600	−45,500
Mn–Si	Furnace-cool from 1110°F	62,200	99,700	58	49,800	100	0	0
	Water-quench from 1110°F	61,400	101,100	58	52,600	106	−24,200	....
Ni 12	Air-cool from 1650°F	115,400	149,300	49	58,300	100	0	0
	Furnace-cool from 1650°F to 680°F; then ice-water-quench	113,800	152,500	41	51,200	88	+52,600	+102,400
Ni 16	Air-cool from 1650°F	121,600	167,100	40	62,600	100	0	0
	Ice-water-quench from 1650°F	127,700	166,000	44	52,600	84	+18,500	+42,700

boring-out operation; tensile stresses could be obtained with other types of steels, but their high hardness would make machining very difficult.

To investigate residual tensile stresses further some 0.34% C steel (Table 11-11) specimens were prepared having an outside diameter of 1.07 in. and a bore of 0.31 in. These specimens were water-quenched at 1110°F from the

TABLE 11-13
Tensile and Endurance for Stress-Free Steel

%C, See Table 11-11	Heat Treatment	0.2 Yield Point, psi	Tensile Strength, psi	Elong., %	Red Area, %	End. Limit, psi	Bending Stress, psi	No. Stress Reversals, millions	Residual Compressive Stress in Surface, psi	
									Long	Tang.
0.10	1 hr 1740°F, air-cool	36,700	59,100	29.5	72	35,600	34,100	1.9	14,200	7,000
0.29	1 hr 1580°F, air-cool	47,100	80,400	24.0	58	35,600	32,700	8.7	24,200	11,000
0.34	Air-cool from 1110°F	49,600	91,500	....	54	39,800	41,200	5.5	17,100	6,000
0.98	1 hr 1435°F, air-cool	54,300	121,000	12.0	19.0	42,700	42,700	5.4	35,600	17,000
0.98	Air-cool from 1240–1290°F	42,700	92,700	13.5	48	38,400	38,400	4.8	25,600	10,000
0.98		42,700	92,700	13.5	48	38,400	32,700	4.9	31,500	17,100

bore only so that tensile stresses were produced (15,600 longitudinal and 25,600 psi tangential) in the outer surface. This effect was explained by the low magnitude of the surface residual stresses which fade away, as is discussed later.

X. Residual Stresses Produced by Repeated Stressing

Longitudinal-surface-compressive residual stresses of 14,000 to 35,000 psi are produced if stress-free steel is subjected to rotating bending in a fatigue test at stresses in the neighborhood of the endurance limit.[115, 116] Four groups of normalized- or annealed-steel specimens of 0.10 to 0.98% C content and 1.07 in. diameter were subjected to 2 to 9 million stress reversals; the residual stress system was determined by the boring-out method before and after fatigue test. Residual surface-compressive stresses found at the end of the fatigue test are given in Table 11-13 along with other data. These findings as to residual compressive stresses in the boundary were true not only for mild steels, where the endurance limit is in the vicinity of the yield strength, but also for steels of high-carbon contents, for which the endurance limit is far below the yield strength. Contrary to usual conception, this indicates that small plastic deformations occur in the surface layer, considerably below the yield point, to produce such residual stresses.

It has been known for some time that certain procedures of understressing or overstressing could increase the endurance limit of many materials by as much as 25 to 35 per cent; the afore-mentioned findings of favorable compressive stresses may explain this augment. This improved endurance with repeated stressing was previously associated with the surface layers showing (a) an increase in hardness, (b) increased tensile strength, (c) compacting of grain structure, (d) aging effect, and/or (e) healing effect of minute inherent flaws which all material may be considered to contain. The question naturally arises that, if residual stresses, hardening, and other beneficial factors result after repeated stressing, then why not begin the life of fatigue specimens or design members with some of these desired characteristics.

This question was investigated by surface-rolling before fatigue-testing some 0.3-in. and larger-diameter rotating-beam plain fatigue specimens of normalized and tempered 0.48% C steel.[117] A maximum endurance limit was obtained which was 32 per cent higher than that of the unrolled specimens. About the same 32 per cent increase was obtained, however, by not rolling but by the process of first stressing just below the endurance limit and then increasing the bending stress in very small increments after each 10 to 50 million cycles. This procedure is called coaxing by Gough[118] and *trainieren* by German investigators. It would, therefore, appear that initial surface cold working may lead to the same endurance limit as coaxing. Residual stresses alone, as obtained by thermal treatment in Table 11-12, produced much smaller increase in endurance limit compared with the maximum of 32 per cent by surface rolling. The inference is that surface rolling is more beneficial because of strain hardening and other effects not produced in the thermal treatment. Residual stresses obtained by rolling are believed to be much greater than those obtained by the thermal treatment, but it is difficult to understand how this factor in itself could account for the difference in increased fatigue resistance obtained by surface working over thermal stresses.

Earlier research thoroughly supports the beneficial effects of coaxing on the endurance limit. Gough[118] obtained an increase of 28 per cent for 0.13% C steel in rotating bending, whereas Moore and Jasper[119] found as much as 25 per cent in their tests of a number of steels and wrought iron. Kommers[120] reported increases as large as 31 per cent for cast-iron plain and notched specimens and 23 per cent for Armco iron. French,[121] Bennett,[122] and Kommers[119] found beneficial effects by proper degrees of overstressing, and the so-called damage line is influenced by this phenomenon as established by Russell and Welcker[123] for 16 widely varying materials.

Y. FADING OF RESIDUAL STRESSES

Substantial proof exists that residual stresses originally present before test will change and generally level off or fade as a result of repeated stressing. The crankshaft previously discussed is one example, although in this case both thermal and transformation stresses were superimposed on stresses due to straightening. Also the 1.07-in.-diameter rotating-beam fatigue specimens reported by Bühler and Buchholtz[115] in Table 11-12 were investigated for residual thermal stresses by the boring-out method before and after fatigue testing. The changes in the longitudinal and tangential stresses found through the cross section are given in Fig. 11-59 for some of the steels investigated.

The 0.36% C steel showed an initial compressive stress of 45,500 psi longitudinally on the surface, and this was reduced to 5700 psi, a decrease of 87 per cent, after 0.97 million reversals at 48,400 psi bending stress. This latter stress was slightly below the endurance limit of 49,800 psi and below the yield strength of 52,800 psi. Surface tangential stress is also very much reduced. and the entire stress distribution through the cross section is leveled off, Similar statements can also be made regarding the 0.57% C-content steel.

Even in the presence of surface residual tensile stresses for the 12% Ni steels there was a 40 per cent reduction in the tangential stress after 1.35

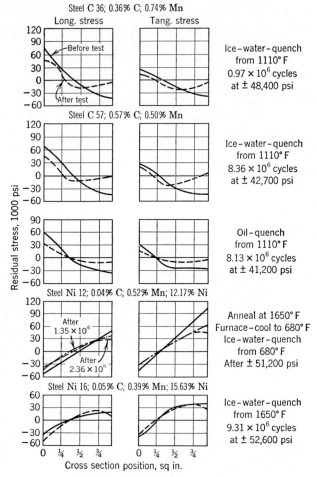

FIG. 11-59. Fading of Residual Stresses Due to Repeated Stressing (Bühler and (Buchholtz)

million reversals at a bending stress equal to the endurance limit. After 2.36 million reversals, this reduction was 55 per cent. The 16% Ni steel only showed a decrease of 30 per cent.

These statements refer to the fading of residual thermal stress in solid specimens, but 0.34% C-steel tubular specimens having tensile stresses in the surface were also investigated. The results in Fig. 11-60 are particularly interesting, because the initial surface tensile stresses actually changed into compression after various degrees of bending stress and a number of stress reversals were applied.

Section W discussed how the endurance limit was not decreased by these residual tensile stresses. The fact that these tensile stresses go into compression should offer an explanation. Therefore, it would appear that residual tensile stresses of the order of 15,600 psi (longitudinal) are not detrimental in reversed bending because of fading. Some materials may be influenced by

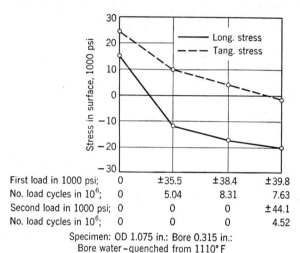

First load in 1000 psi;	0	±35.5	±38.4	±39.8
No. load cycles in 10^6;	0	5.04	8.31	7.63
Second load in 1000 psi;	0	0	0	±44.1
No. load cycles in 10^6;	0	0	0	4.52

Specimen: OD 1.075 in.: Bore 0.315 in.:
Bore water-quenched from 1110° F

FIG. 11-60. Influence of Repeated Stresses on the Residual Surface Stress on Hollow Cylinder Quenched from Bore (Steel C34, 0.34% C, 0.69% Mn) (Bühler and Buchholtz)

this degree of initial stress unless they have sufficient damping capacity to level off the stress peaks.

Fading of residual stresses was also established by means of X-ray measurements made by Gisen and Glocker[115] which were reviewed by Barrett.[14] Decrease in residual stresses after fatigue testing of shot-peened parts was reported by H. F. Moore.[163]

Z. FRACTURE PLANE AFFECTED BY RESIDUAL STRESS

Biaxial state of surface residual stress superimposed on the stresses due to the external load can alter the plane of fatigue fracture, as shown in Fig. 11-61 by Bühler and Buchholtz.[115] Fatigue specimens 1.07 in. in diameter of Ni 12 steel were tested in rotating bending, as previously reported in Table 11-12. When the surface residual stress was zero, then the fracture plane was perpendicular to the specimen length (Fig. 11-61); the same steel with a surface biaxial residual tensile-stress system of considerable magnitude exhibited a diagonal fracture (Fig. 11-61a) typical of a torsion failure although a bending load was applied.

This torsional type of fracture is explained by the large surface-tangential residual tensile stress (102,400 psi) compared with the lower longitudinal stress (52,700 psi). The path of fracture would, therefore, be influenced by the tangential component and be inclined to the length axis. When transformation stresses predominate over the thermal type, it is characteristic to

(a) Residual tensile surface stress = 52,700 long. and 102,400 psi tang.

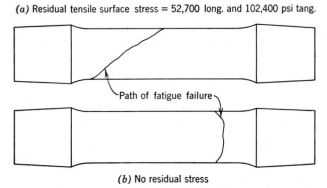

(b) No residual stress

FIG. 11-61.   Bending-Fatigue Fracture Influenced by Residual Stresses (Bühler and Buchholtz)

find the tangential exceeding the longitudinal stresses; whereas in constructional steels the thermal stresses invariably predominate, and the longitudinal stresses exceed the tangential.[57]

AA. FLAME HEATING

Thum and Erker[124] demonstrated how thermal residual stresses could be applied either to decrease or to increase fatigue resistance. Residual stresses were produced in specimens by local heating to a red heat below the critical temperature by means of a torch. Commercial-steel bar stock of $2\frac{5}{32}$ in. by $2\frac{3}{8}$ in. cross section of low-carbon content with as-rolled surface was the material tested under repeated tensile loading in a 50-ton pulsator.

Residual thermal stresses were produced across the test section by locally applying heat to the center area of the $2\frac{3}{8}$-in. width and then allowing the specimens to cool. Fatigue failure started in the middle of this heated region containing high tensile stresses rather than from the edge of the specimen, as was the case for the not-heated specimens. Despite these unfavorable residual tensile stresses the upper allowable fatigue-strength value was only 2 per cent less than that of the specimens having no initial stress from heating. Explanations for this small loss of fatigue strength are: (1) The upper tensile endurance value is above the yield strength of the steel, (2) residual stresses are not nearly so effective without as with stress concentration, and (3) the applied stress is uniform across the section. In (1) plastic deformations are produced in loading the specimen which reduce the residual stresses to a small remaining value[125] of little influence on the fatigue resistance.

Notched specimens were also prepared with residual thermal stresses and submitted to fatigue test in a manner similar to the plain specimens. The results are presented in Fig. 11-62. Residual tensile stresses produced at the outer edge of the specimen and compression around the hole as in (b) result in a 27 per cent increase in the upper fatigue limit over the case of (a) with no residual stress. When the residual-stress system in (b) is reversed as in (c) so as to produce initial tensile stresses around the hole, then a lost in fatigue resistance of 12 per cent occurs over that for case (a) with no residual stresses.

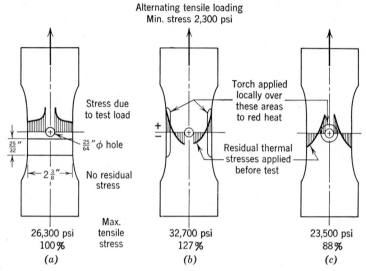

FIG. 11-62. Influence of Thermal Stresses on Fatigue Resistance of Notched Specimens (Thum and Erker)

It is important to note that favorable residual compressive stresses in (b) give a fatigue resistance 40 per cent greater than the unfavorable initial tensile stresses in (c). Mention should be made that all endurance values for the notched specimens were below the yield strength of the steel. When a specimen in (c) was stretched beyond the elastic limit prior to fatigue test, then a portion of residual stresses were lost while the remaining stresses still caused a slight increase in fatigue strength over that in (a).

Bühler and Lohmann[126] used the boring-out method to determine residual stresses in a mild-steel disk 3.8-in. in diameter by 0.79-in. thick. This disk was torch-heated to 1740°F in the center over 2-to-2¾-in.-diameter area and air-cooled. Tangential stress in the edge of 17,000 psi compression was reported; balancing stresses in the center were tension of 40,000 psi for each the radial and tangential components.

Bollenrath[127] measured residual stresses by the Mathar method of drilling holes in a 24-in.-square plate, 0.59 in. thick, of mild steel. This plate was torch-heated until the surface melted over a center band 3 to 4 in. wide across the plate. Maximum residual tensile stress of 71,000 psi was found in the heated zone which was above the tensile strength (53,000 psi) of the plate.

Siebel and Pfender[128] measured residual stresses by cutting strips from an 18-in.-square plate, 1.18 in. thick, of steel having 36,000 psi yield point. This plate was torch-heated in the middle to 750°F and air-cooled. Stresses found are plotted in Fig. 11-63.

Residual stresses in flame-cut plates have been reviewed[16] and reported by several investigators to vary from small tensile values to 55,000 psi tension. Only approximate methods of stress measurement were used. No cracking was encountered in steel less than 0.35% C. Large pieces of steel over 0.35% C cracked when not preheated.

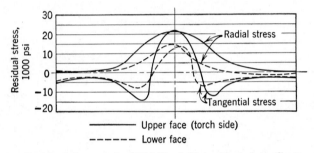

FIG. 11-63.　Residual Stresses in Mild-Steel Plate Heated in Center to about 750°F by Torch and Air-Cooled (Siebel and Pfender)

The influence of residual stresses on fatigue resistance as produced by flame heating 0.25% C plates was also reported from a limited number of tests by Bruchner and Munse.[128]

BB. Internal-Stress Peak Effect Due to Residual Stresses

Parts which are surface-hardened by such means as case carburizing, nitriding, and induction or flame hardening exhibit reduced fatigue resistance in the heat-affected or transition zone between the hardened and unhardened regions. This weakness may occur in a (1) subsurface area or (2) surface zone between the hardened and unhardened area; it is usually attributed to the physical and structural properties of the steel in the transition region being inferior to that in the hardened layer. Another explanation for this weakness discussed here is that the favorable residual compressive stresses in the hardened layer are balanced by opposing unfavorable tensile stresses in the transition zone. It is these residual tensile stresses which lead to an internal-stress peak;[129] premature fatigue failure initiates through this region of high tensile stresses.

The nucleus of fracture located below the surface may not necessarily occur at the depth of the hardened layer. Wiegand[99] explained this in Fig. 11-64 where the initiation point of fracture F is located in the region of high tensile stresses causing an internal notch. Maximum tensile stress occurs below the surface at F because of the combined effect of the internal stress from surface hardening superimposed on the stress due to external loading. Even though this internal-stress peak exists, it is well known that the actual fatigue resistance is greater for a surface-hardened condition than when the entire piece is quenched and tempered to the same tensile strength as the core; an example of this is given for a case-carburized condition in Table 11-14, series 1 and 2.

Evidence of an internal-stress peak in the surface layer occurs in the runout zone as a result of case carburizing,[99] as presented in Table 11-14. Fatigue strength of plain specimens with and without such an internal-stress peak is compared (series 1, 2, and 6). The tapered case structure on smooth cylindrical specimens (series 6) gives a lower fatigue strength than even those quenched

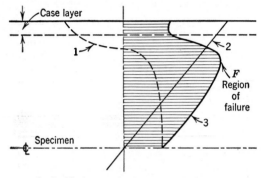

1 — Residual stress due to case carburizing
2 — Bending stress due to external loading
3 — Resultant stress from 1 and 2

FIG. 11-64.   Stress Distribution through Tension Side of Bending Specimen Case-Carburized (Wiegand)

and tempered (series 1) to the same tensile strength as the core of the case. Failure initiates at the surface and in the transition zone containing residual tensile stresses. Johnson[130] discussed a similar internal-stress peak arising from the end effect in induction-hardening a journal on a shaft.

If, in addition, this transition region happens to be located in an area containing an external-notch, which produces an external-stress peak, such as a fillet or oil hole, then still further weakening may occur. Almen[131] mentioned the decreased fatigue resistance of gear teeth from hardening the flank only; an internal-stress peak results in the runout zone which is located in the root radius of case-carburized gears, or filleted shafts[132] are improperly processed to the extent of too much of the case layer in the radius being ground away; premature fatigue failure occurs through the transition area containing an internal- and an external-stress peak.

Internal and external stress peaks exist simultaneously when the journal portion of a crankshaft is induction-hardened too close to the journal fillet; this condition results in low fatigue resistance as found by Williams and Brown[133] in Fig. 11-65. A similar example is cited by Johnson[130, 134] in the induction hardening of crankshaft journals where improvement results from keeping the heat-affected zone some distance away from the fillets. Improved fatigue resistance results in such examples if the soft transition area can be rolled, shot-peened, or surface-work-hardened as a means of introducing compressive stresses to offset the detrimental tensile stresses from induction hardening.

TABLE 11-14

NOTCH EFFECT IN TRANSITION REGION OF CASE-HARDENED SPECIMENS
Wiegand and Scheinost

Type Specimen, 0.55 in. Diameter	Series	Type Treatment	Fatigue Strength for 10^7 Cycles	
			Rotating Bending, psi	Reversed Torsion, psi
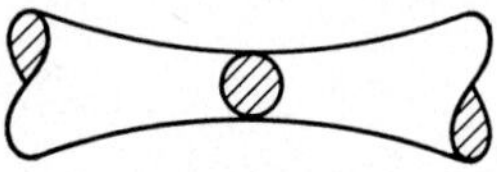	1	Quenched and tempered	88,300	35,600
	2	Case-hardened to depth 0.008 in. after grinding	99,600	44,800
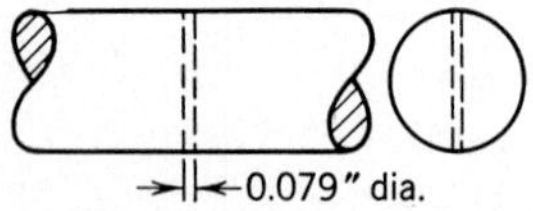	3	Quenched and tempered	48,400	17,100
	4	Hole drilled after case hardening	29,900	14,200
	5	Hole drilled before case hardening	62,600	41,200
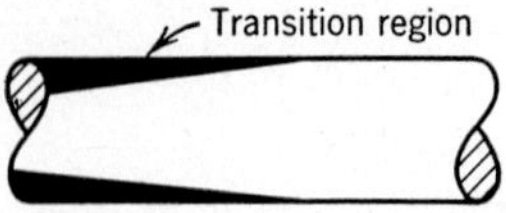	6	Case-hardened layer conical shaped to give transition	81,100	. . . . . .

→ ‖ ← 0.079″ dia.

Transition region

Cr–Ni–Mo Steel: 0.13 % C; 1.92 % Cr; 0.22 % Mo; 2.15 % Ni.
182,000 tensile strength for both quenching and tempering and core of case.
Hardness of case surface 60–62 RC.

Fatigue data[99] on case-carburized parts are presented in Table 11-14 (compare series 3, 4, and 5) to substantiate further these contentions regarding the presence of both internal and external stress peaks. In the example of the transverse hole (series 4) applied after carburizing, the fatigue failure initiated below the rim of the hole in the transition region F in Fig. 11-64; fatigue resistance is only 62 per cent of that for similar quenched and tempered specimens (series 3). Failure is expected to initiate below the surface of such surface-hardened parts but not to give a lower fatigue resistance than the quenched and tempered specimen which has the same tensile strength as the core structure below the case layer. This lower fatigue value is explained by the unfavorable residual tensile stresses occurring at an external notch. This effect is eliminated by drilling the hole before carburizing (series 5).

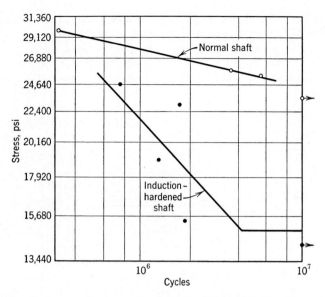

FIG. 11-65.   Endurance Tests on Crankshafts; "Normal" Was Carburized and
Quenched (Williams and Brown)

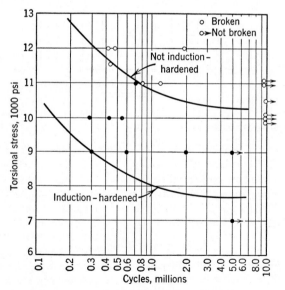

FIG. 11-66.   The Effect of Induction Hardening on the Endurance Limit of a
Cylindrical Specimen with an Oil Hole (Johnson)

Johnson[130, 134] found that crankshaft journals exhibited similar weakness at oil holes after induction hardening. Figure 11-66 illustrates his findings, and Fig. 11-67 shows how improvement was obtained by shot peening. German investigations[132, 135, 136] of flame-hardened crankshafts revealed that (1) it was necessary to flame-harden the journal fillet, and (2) journals that failed through the oil hole were little improved in torsional-fatigue resistance and may even be weakened by flame hardening. Zimmerman[187] tested $\frac{7}{16}$-in.-diameter specimens in rotating bending which had sharp- or square-cornered fillets. He found an endurance limit of 54,000 psi when the external notch was flame-hardened which was even higher than for an unnotched part

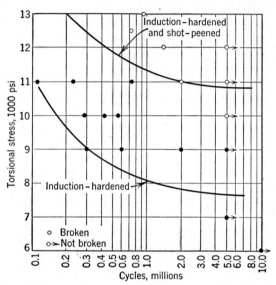

Fig. 11-67. The Effect of Shot Peening on the Endurance Limit of an Induction-Hardened Cylindrical Specimen with an Oil Hole (Johnson)

that had not been flame-hardened. These findings form a basis for production crankshafts[138] of one large automobile producer which are flame-hardened in the fillets as well as the journal portion.

It is, therefore, imperative that both the designer and the metallurgist evaluate the influence of this internal-stress peak effect before releasing parts for production.

CC. INDUCTION HARDENING

Residual stresses are obtained by induction hardening. These stresses are usually considered to be in compression in the surface layers and for this reason are favorable toward fatigue resistance.[139] Rapidly heating the outer surface of a cylinder by induction heating causes the outer layer to expand. Yielding occurs in this outer zone because of its reduced strength, and it is upset in compression on a cold core. Quenching this upset surface then produces residual stresses due to transformation (tension stresses) and thermal (compression stresses) changes in the outermost layer heated above the critical temperature. An intermediate layer just below the surface which was not heated above the critical would give only thermal or compressive stresses. It should be mentioned that this upset layer, if allowed to cool without hardening, would leave tensile stresses on the surface. Therefore, the final residual compressive stress on the surface of induction-hardened parts would not be expected to be nearly so great as that obtained by quenching a cylinder heated throughout above A_3.

Johnson[134] found 10,000 psi tensile in one member and in another 10,000 psi compressive stresses in the surface of induction-hardened parts $2\frac{5}{8}$ in. in diameter, as determined by the boring-out method. Other investigators report high compressive stresses on the surface, but such divergence in the findings may be due to the method employed to measure the residual stress or factors in the induction-hardening method and particularly the case depth and rate of heating. Details of stress measurement are seldom given by investigators, but it is customary to extrapolate the residual-stress curve through the hardened layer after machining away the softer core; if this is done, the gradient obtained could be in serious error as illustrated in Fig. 11-72.

Almen[131] found 40,000 psi compressive stress in the surface of a 6-in.-long crankshaft journal induction-hardened. Comparative fatigue results have been reported[140] on furnace- and induction-treated testpieces from three different steels. Another investigation[141] determined the residual stresses in cylinders (2.6 in. OD $\times$ 1.93 in. ID $\times$ 1.14 in. long) of four steels (Table 11-15) as affected by case depth and rate of cooling. These stresses were obtained by the Anderson and Fahlman method of cutting rings 0.39 in. thick and slitting; for this reason the stress gradient measured near the surface, especially if steep, may be in considerable error. Nevertheless, these results[141] have comparison value and are briefly quoted. The depth of the induction-hardened layer influences the surface residual stresses, as shown in Fig. 11-68; the stress gradient through the hardened region is given in Fig. 11-69. Surface stresses as influenced by different quenching mediums of water, 10 per cent soda solution, and still air are reported in Table 11-16. Tempering temperature and time reduce the surface residual stresses, as indicated in Fig. 11-70.

TABLE 11-15

The Influence of the Case Depth on Internal Stresses by Induction Hardening

Kontorovich & Livshitz

Steel Grade	Curve No. Fig.	Internal Stresses, psi, in the case after hardening to the indicated depths				
		0.039	0.079	0.118	0.157	0.197
1045	1	28,400	55,500	74,000	56,900	....
XHB	2	11,400	38,400	68,300	88,200	45,500
XHM	3	28,400	21,300	52,600	96,700	102,400
XMM	4	......	28,400	72,500	103,800	88,200

Steam hammer piston rods often develop fatigue failure in the tapered portion which fits into the ram, and this section has been induction-hardened.[142] Some forge shops report a substantial increase in service life through induction

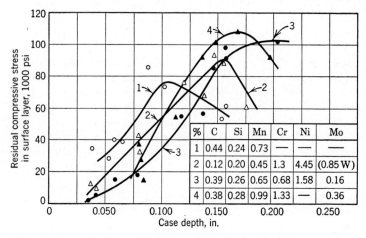

FIG. 11-68.   Influence of Case Depth on Residual Stress by Induction Hardening
(Kontorovich *et al.*)

hardening whereas others report little or no improvement.   Life variation may be due to the method of induction hardening, but probably other factors such as fitting of rod in ram and type of forging work being produced have an important bearing on this problem.

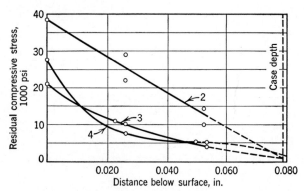

FIG. 11-69.   Distribution of Residual Stress through Case by Induction Hardening
(Kontorovich *et al.*)

Highly stressed gear teeth have been induction-hardened along the tooth profile and root radius.   Such gears have been reported[143] to run 3000 hr without failure in an accelerated fatigue test whereas oil-quenched and tempered gears were pitted after 100 hr.   Almen[131] and Martin and Gehr[144] discussed gear-tooth hardening. They stated that the fatigue resistance was unfavorably influenced by (a) induction hardening through the tooth section or (b) hardening flank only and not the root radius. Danger of surface

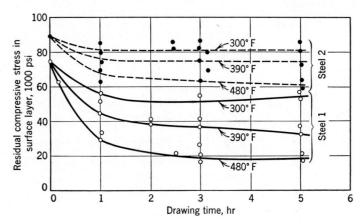

F<small>IG</small>. 11-70.   Influence of Drawing Temperature and Time on Residual Stress Due to Induction Hardening (Kontorovich *et al.*)

tensile stresses causing quenching cracks after induction heating can be prevented by decreasing the temperature gradient; use of an interrupted or oil quench or a steel less susceptible to cracking offers means for overcoming this difficulty.[144]

TABLE 11-16

T<small>HE</small> E<small>FFECT OF</small> C<small>OOLING</small> R<small>ATE ON THE</small> "S<small>TRUCTURE</small>," P<small>ROPERTIES, AND</small> I<small>NTERNAL</small>
S<small>TRESSES BY</small> I<small>NDUCTION</small> H<small>ARDENING</small>
Kontorovich & Livshitz

Steel Grade	Quenching Medium	RC	Structure of Hardened Case	Depth of Case, in.		Surface Residual Compressive Stress, psi
				Hardened Zone	Inter-mediate Zone	
XHB	Water	50–51	Highly dispersed martensite	0.161	0.008	90,000
	Soda solution	48–50	Larger grained martensite	0.189	0.016	97,000
	Air	44–46	Still larger grained mart.	0.185	Through	4,000
XHM	Water	61–62	Highly dispersed martensite	0.197	0.008	88,000
	Soda solution	59–60	Mart. & islets of troostite	0.213	0.012	74,000–94,000
	Air	35–42	Sorbite	Through		18,000
XMM	Water	62–63	Highly dispersed martensite	0.161	0.008	97,000
	Soda solution	60–61	Martensite	0.189		83,000
	Air	50–51	Troostite	0.157	Through	32,000

Distortion resulting from residual stresses and means for minimizing it in induction-hardened machined parts were presented by Lauderdale.[145] Stress concentration which may result from certain induction-hardening procedures was discussed in section BB under internal-notch effects.

DD. FLAME HARDENING

Favorable residual compressive stresses shown in Fig. 11-71 have been found on the surface of $7\frac{9}{16}$-in.-diameter tubular axles[146] (0.50% C, 0.25%

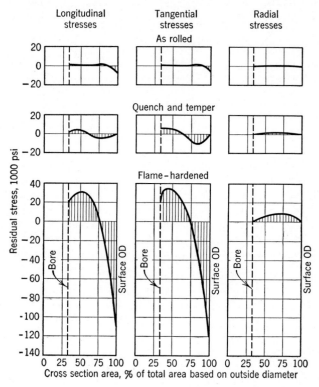

FIG. 11-71.   Comparison of Residual Stress in Tubular Railroad Axles by Different
Treatments

Ni, 0.13% Cr); tubes were flame-hardened by the spinning method where the flame head was equal to the length of the hardened area.   Internal stresses were determined by the boring-out method for the flame-hardened condition in comparison with tubes which were (a) quenched and tempered and (b) air-cooled from the hot-rolled condition off the mill.   Fatigue tests were made on these full-size tubes in rotating bending as a cantilever beam under conditions of high-stress concentration obtained by press-fitting a head over the tube in the region which was flame-hardened.   A correlation between the tensile and endurance values with the surface residual stresses is given in

Table 11-17 (series 1, 2 and 3). Flame-hardened tubes exhibited at least 83 per cent greater fatigue resistance than those not surface-treated, and this was attributed largely to the favorable high residual surface-compressive stresses. To judge by the tensile properties, the quenched and tempered tubes would be expected to have a higher endurance limit than the hot-rolled tubes, but this was not the case.

TABLE 11-17

INFLUENCE OF RESIDUAL STRESSES ON FATIGUE STRENGTH OF PRESS-FITTED ASSEMBLIES

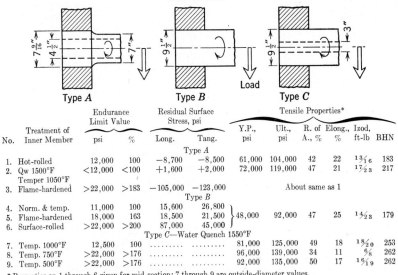

No.	Treatment of Inner Member	Endurance Limit Value		Residual Surface Stress, psi		Tensile Properties*					
		psi	%	Long.	Tang.	Y.P., psi	Ult., psi	R. of A., %	Elong., %	Izod, ft-lb	BHN
				Type A							
1.	Hot-rolled	12,000	100	−8,700	−8,500	61,000	104,000	42	22	$13\frac{7}{16}$	183
2.	Qw 1500°F Temper 1050°F	<12,000	<100	+1,600	+2,000	72,000	119,000	47	21	$17\frac{7}{23}$	217
3.	Flame-hardened	>22,000	>183	−105,000	−123,000	About same as 1					
				Type B							
4.	Norm. & temp.	11,000	100	15,600	26,800						
5.	Flame-hardened	18,000	163	18,500	21,500	48,000	92,000	47	25	$14\frac{7}{23}$	179
6.	Surface-rolled	>22,000	>200	87,000	45,000						
				Type C—Water Quench 1550°F							
7.	Temp. 1000°F	12,500	100	....	....	81,000	125,000	49	18	$18\frac{7}{20}$	253
8.	Temp. 750°F	>22,000	>176	....	....	96,000	139,000	34	11	$9\frac{6}{8}$	262
9.	Temp. 500°F	>22,000	>176	....	....	92,000	135,000	50	17	$16\frac{7}{19}$	262

* Properties on 1 through 6 given for mid-section; 7 through 9 are outside-diameter values.

Fatigue tests[147] were made on larger press-fitted assemblies, similar to those on the afore-mentioned tubes, $9\frac{1}{2}$-in.-diameter solid shafts (0.52% C) being used. Normalized and tempered shafts were progressively flame-hardened ($3\frac{1}{8}$-in. flame-head speed) locally under the portion where the wheel was pressed on; for comparison purposes others were tested without flame hardening. Fatigue results in Table 11-17 (series 4 and 5) indicate the superiority of flame hardening. Some difficulty was experienced with circumferential thermal cracks developing during flame hardening; even in the presence of such defects the endurance limit was increased by at least 63 per cent.

Residual-stress distribution through the entire section was determined by the boring-out method for different rates of travel of the flame head; for clarity these stresses are shown here only through the surface layer 0.3 in. thick, in Fig. 11-72. It may be noted that the residual stress both changes in direction and has a low magnitude near the surface, which was not found in the case of the tubes (Fig. 11-71). In fact, the residual stresses for the non-flame-hardened condition (Fig. 11-72) are not much different at the immediate surface than for the flame-hardened condition, but below the surface the stress

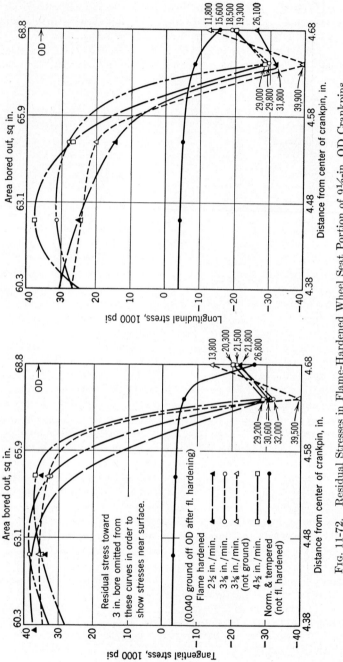

FIG. 11-72. Residual Stresses in Flame-Hardened Wheel Seat Portion of 9½-in. OD Crankpins

decreases abruptly. The effective depth of the residual compressive stresses by flame hardening (Fig. 11-72) is evidently essential in this case to produce the increased fatigue strength. The method of residual-stress analysis used to obtain Figs. 11-71 and 11-72 may have some bearing on these differences. The boring-out operations were continued further for the $9\frac{1}{2}$ in. so as to give a thinner wall of D/d ratio than for the tubular axles; also after final boring of the $9\frac{1}{2}$-in. cylinders they were slit and the tongues cut (Fig. 11-3), whereas this was not done for the tubular axles.* These operations are very important for surface-hardened specimens in order to detect any stress reversal or steep-stress gradient in the immediate surface layers. Such findings as in Fig. 11-72 raise the question of the validity of published data on residual stresses reported for particularly surface-hardened parts, unless the surface layer were machined or etched sufficiently thin to minimize errors due to extropolation.

Similar rotating bending-fatigue tests were made on press-fitted 2-in. shaft assemblies,[148] and the endurance limit was about three times as great for those flame-hardened as for those not surface-treated. The spin-hardening method was used, but no residual stresses were measured. In all the press-fit tests mentioned in this paper the endurance limit is given as the stress above which the axle will break off just inside the fitted portion after 85 million stress reversals; the axle may have shallow fatigue cracks, however, in the fitted portion, as detected after the wheel is pressed off following the completion of the test. The stress level at which these cracks initiate in the presence of fretting corrosion apparently is not much different for the flame-hardened than for the non-surface-treated condition; the propagation of these incipient fatigue cracks is greatly retarded by the layer of residual compressive stresses present on the flame-hardened member. Shafts not flame-hardened have no such protective layer of residual stress, and, once fatigue cracks initiate, they can propogate fast to dangerous depths and finally result in a broken shaft.

Kallen and Nienhaus[149] used the boring method to determine the residual stresses in a flame-hardened 4-in. shaft of medium-manganese steel. Compressive stresses were found in the surface, 185,000 psi longitudinally and 170,000 psi tangentially; these were balanced by tensile stresses in the center, 57,000 psi (radial and tangential) and 128,000 psi (longitudinal). Surface hardness was RC 50 and dropped off to 30 at $\frac{3}{8}$-in. depth and to 20 in the core.

Increased fatigue resistance by flame hardening is often attributed to the higher tensile strength with accompanying increased fatigue resistance of the hardened layer. Voss[150] reported a core tensile strength of 122,300 psi and surface zone of 291,600 psi for $1\frac{3}{4}$-in. crankshaft journals which were flame-hardened.

Earlier discussion in section BB included additional considerations regarding residual stresses accompanying flame hardening.

* Other variables were (a) the $9\frac{1}{2}$ in. members were flame-hardened by the progressive method and the tubular axles by the spinning method, and (b) an optimeter (Fig. 11-4) was used for making measurements of diameter and length changes during boring out in the case of tubular axles and SR-4 strain gages (Fig. 11-5) in the residual-stress study of the $9\frac{1}{2}$ in. members.

EE. Residual Stresses by Surface Rolling

Surface rolling to be effective in increasing fatigue resistance must plastically deform the surface layers. The core metal is strained elastically under

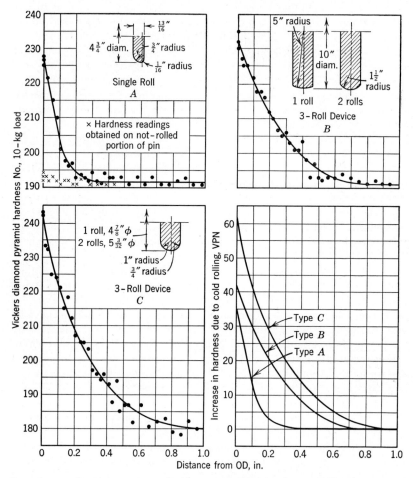

Fig. 11-73. Surface-Hardness Gradient on 913/16-in.-diameter Members Rolled with Different-Type Rollers

relatively low-tension stress while the surface layer is under high compressive stress. A number of 9½-in.-diameter solid shafts of plain carbon steel (0.52% C), normalized and tempered, were rolled. A three-roller device having type-B rollers, in Fig. 11-73, was employed, utilizing three different pressures of 12,000, 21,000 and 32,000 lb maximum load per roller. The boring-out method, supplemented by slitting and cutting tongues (Fig. 11-3) was followed to determine the large residual stresses given in Fig. 11-74. It should be noted that the stress in the surface layer also changes direction, similar to that discussed in Fig. 11-72, but to a lesser extent.

Effectiveness of these high residual stresses on fatigue strength[10, 147] is shown in Table 11-17 (series 4 and 6). Rotating bending tests made on press-fitted assemblies gave over 22,000 psi endurance limit for pins rolled at 21,000-lb roller pressure; this compares with only 11,000 psi for similar pins not rolled. Rolling, therefore, more than doubles the factor of safety against the pins breaking off just inside the edge of the press fit, as shown in Fig. 11-75.

Such rolling is effective in compressing the steel to a considerable depth.[10] Hardness surveys in Fig. 11-73 made on transverse sections cut from shafts under various rolling conditions show that it is not difficult to influence the hardness of the surface layer ½ in. and more deep. Tensile and fatigue properties of this layer are naturally increased by this work hardening over the unrolled condition. Part of the increased fatigue resistance in Table 11-17 is, therefore, due to the strain hardening and part due to residual stresses.[9] Additional hardness curves on 0.3-through 2-in.-diameter surface-rolled shafts have been measured and correlated with increased fatigue resistance.[0, 117] Roller shape, size, pressure, and yield strength of the shaft material determine depth of hardness penetration. This depth can be calculated.[151]

Similar internal-stress investigations were made earlier by Bühler[152] on bars of a smaller diameter rolled under several conditions. His results are given in Fig. 11-76 for two different bar diameters and two kinds of low-carbon annealed steel.

Favorable residual surface stresses

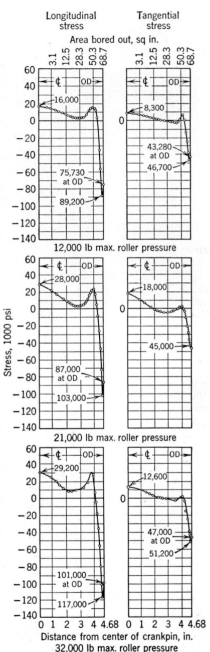

FIG. 11-74.   Residual Stresses in Rolled Wheel-Fit Portion of 9.5-in. ϕ Crankpins

obtained by surface cold working are not to be confused with the type obtained by usual mill operations in production of cold-rolled or drawn bar stock. Starting at less than 1 per cent reduction of area in mill operations

Fig. 11-75. Typical Fatigue Fracture of Crankpin Initiating Just inside the Press-Fitted Wheel

with some steels it was found that the surface stresses begin changing from favorable compression to unfavorable tension.[81] Reduction of area by surface rolling depends considerably on surface finish and is expressed in thousandths of 1 per cent reduction on large design members.

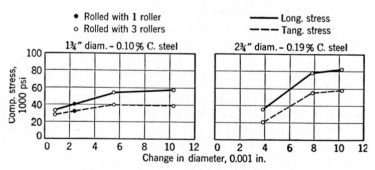

Fig. 11-76. Influence of Change in Diameter by Rolling on Surface Residual Stresses

Surface rolling has been applied to many production parts to improve fatigue resistance greatly, but usually residual stresses are not measured. This subject has been reviewed.[10] Richards[161] also applied rolling to rectangular bars of Al–Zn–Mg alloy and measured stresses.

FF. Nitriding

High residual compressive stresses are produced in the surface of nitrided parts which have been traced to the increase in volume of the nitrided layer as determined by measuring specific weight. About 71,000 psi residual compressive stress in the longitudinal direction was calculated from contraction of various-diameter bars which were ground off in two successive steps.[153] Initial surface stresses as high as 160,000 psi were reported by Almen[5] in Fig. 11-77 for strip stock, but Gentner[154] found only 27,000 psi on 1-in.-thick bars. In all cases only approximate methods were used to determine the magnitude of the residual stresses. The effect of the transverse stresses which were also compressive was disregarded.

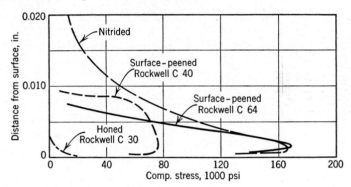

Fig. 11-77. Magnitude and Depth of Stress Imposed by Various Surface Treatments (Almen)

Increased fatigue resistance of nitrided plain specimens (0.3 in. in diameter), as determined by many investigators, is summarized in Fig. 11-78 by Mailänder[153] for different core tensile values and depth of case layer. Endurance of the nitrided members was 25 per cent greater than for those not nitrided when the case depth was 0.030 in.; it was 35 per cent greater for a case depth of 0.037 in. Also residual surface stress changes little with specimen diameter, as shown in Fig. 11-79. Mailänder concluded that this improved fatigue strength was not due to residual stresses but attributed it to the high alternating strength of the nitrided layer itself. Two reasons were given for this contention. First, it was found that fatigue fracture had its origin below the surface a distance of about the thickness of the nitrided layer. Ratio of the diameter of the bar over the nitrided layer to the diameter over the core was 1.25 and 1.35, which corresponded very closely to the increased fatigue resistance reported previously. This would indicate that the core layer adjacent to the case determines the fatigue strength, and it is no stronger than if it were a surface layer without the case protection.

As additional proof of his contention regarding residual stresses influencing fatigue resistance, Mailänder nitrided plain fatigue specimens of two different steels and then stretched them beyond the yield strength of the core so as to give a permanent set. Fatigue resistance was found to be practically the same for stretched as for the nonstretched; also, the depth of the origin of fracture below the surface did not change as a result of stretching. It was

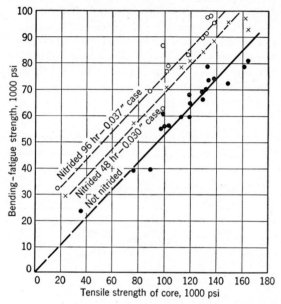

Fig. 11-78. Bending Fatigue Strength of Nitrided and Nonnitrided Specimens 0.295 in. Diameter (Mailänder)

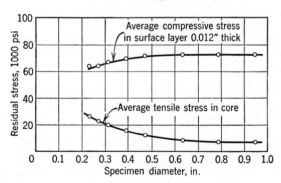

Fig. 11-79. Influence of Specimen Diameter on Residual Stress Due to Nitriding (Mailänder)

reasoned that, if residual stresses had an influence on fatigue values, then stretching would diminish the surface residual stresses and also change the depth at which failure occurred.

Wiegand[132] attributed the higher fatigue resistance of nitrided members to residual stresses and supported his contention with tensile strength and modulus values in Table 11-18. Since the tensile strength of the almost through-nitrided specimens exhibited no greater values than the core material, a quenched and tempered structure, he reasoned that the fatigue resistance would also be no different. This does not necessarily follow, and further evidence bearing on this question is discussed under case carburizing.

TABLE 11-18

STRENGTH AND ELASTICITY OF NITRIDED LAYERS

Wiegand

Testpiece*	Heat Treatment	Tensile Strength, psi, to Produce		Modulus of Elasticity, psi
		Incipient Tearing	Fracture	
Flat bar 0.079″ × 0.472″ section	{ Quench & temp.	....	156,500	30,500,000
	{ Nitrided 0.0315″ deep	133,700	133,700	....
Round bar 0.098″ diam.	Nitrided almost through 0.0433″ deep	130,900	130,900	30,360,000
Round bar 0.394″ diam. nitrided	{ 0.008″ deep	145,100	166,400	....
	{ 0.0118″ deep	139,400	157,900	....
	{ 0.0177 deep	135,100	....	....

* Cr–Mo–V Steel: 0.3% C, 2.5% Cr, 0.3% Mo, 0.25% V.

Landau[155] discussed the fatigue results of several investigators. He believes that residual stresses by nitriding are effective in increasing fatigue resistance but supports his contention largely on the basis of diagrammatic stress-distribution systems rather than by quantitative data. At the same time he emphasized the high hardness of the nitrided layer and calculated high tensile strength as being responsible for increased fatigue resistance.

Nitrided surfaces appear sensitive to high overloads such as are represented by the upper-slope portion of an $S–N$ curve. In this region plain specimens nitrided started failure from the outer surface.[153] Tensile strength of the core in these tests was 136,500 psi, and fatigue failure still started below the surface at 138,000 psi after 35,000 cycles. At 156,000 psi failure occurred at the surface. Wiegand[156] reported similar phenomena for notched specimens nitrided where the core had a tensile strength of 145,000–158,000 psi. The fatigue strength above 1,000,000 reversals was much in favor of the nitrided specimens, but below this number of loadings the superiority decreased until the $S–N$ curves crossed at 1000 cycles. At these high-load stresses the core material is above the yield point and does not offer proper support to the case so that cracking of the case layer occurs. A redistribution of residual stresses also develops.

Sutton[157] found that nitrided plain fatigue specimens under reversed-bending stresses gave 47 per cent increased endurance-limit value over nonnitrided pieces; under reversed axial loading nitriding led to only 3 per cent improvement. The nucleus of failure in bending was below the surface but under tension originated at the surface. This may suggest that residual stresses are not the principal contributing factor in obtaining increased fatigue strength. This finding as regards the small improvement is characteristic of surface-treated members without stress concentration. In the practical case stress concentration is generally present so that surface treatment would be expected to be beneficial under axial loading, as shown by Wiegand[132] for nitrided screw threads.

GG. Case Carburizing

Carburizing and hardening lead to compressive residual surface stresses, which Almen[5] found to be about 75,000 psi at the immediate surface. No

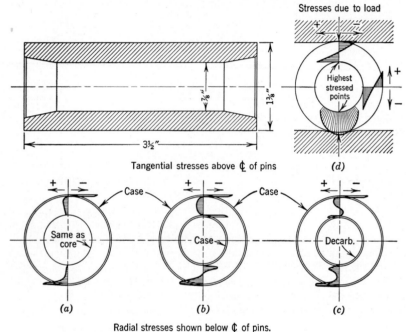

Radial stresses shown below ¢ of pins.
Tangential stresses shown above ¢ of pins.

Fig. 11-80.   Residual Stresses in Piston Pins (Mickel and Sommer)

complete quantitative data appear to have been published regarding the magnitude of such internal residual stresses, and this may be explained by the difficulty of handling such hard materials by relaxation or X-ray methods of stress analysis. Absorption of carbon in the case-hardened layer, however, is associated with an increase in volume and, therefore, residual compressive stresses. On the other hand, a decarburized surface represents a decrease of carbon corresponding to a decrease of volume; from this it is reasoned that a decarburized surface contains tensile residual stresses. Dickie[158] submitted an equation for calculating the tensile stress in a decarburized layer and made measurements to confirm the presence of such stresses.

An investigation of the fatigue resistance of piston pins for internal-combustion engines by Mickel and Sommer[105] involved a consideration of residual stresses.   Tubular piston-pin fractures usually occur from the bore, and some reasons given are: (1) any inclusions or metallurgical defects which have a natural preference for that location, (2) surface finish which is not so good on the inside as on the outside, (3) inspection difficulties which occur in examining the bore and locating any defects, (4) crushing stress due to exterior loading in the bore, (5) unfavorable residual stresses with some heat treatments.

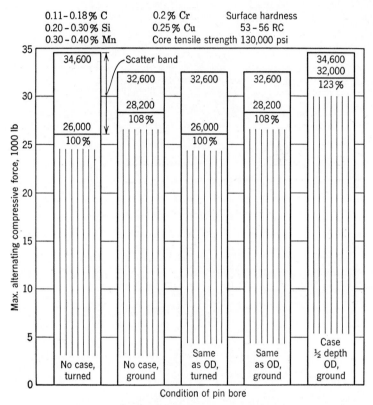

Fɪɢ. 11-81.   Fatigue Resistance of Piston Pins (1⅜ in. OD × ⅞ in. ID × 3½ in.) (Mickel and Sommer)

A severe internal-stress distribution is produced in case-hardened pins as shown in a, b, and c of Fig. 11-80 for three different conditions of the bore. When the outside diameter only is carburized as in a, the tangential stress is a maximum compression value in the outer layers unless the surface is damaged in grinding.   At the immediate outside surface the residual radial stress is zero but increases quickly to a maximum tension value a small distance below the surface.   If the hardness gradation is not uniform at the junction of the core with the bottom of the case layer, then abrupt internal-stress changes occur which act as an internal notch.   This condition leads to a "paving-block" type of fracture wherein the surface layer breaks loose, resulting in reduced fatigue resistance.[105]   The same type of failure results when the case layer is too shallow; the residual radial tensile stress combines with initial tangential compressive stress to give a high shearing stress leading to failure.   Such failures can be prevented by proper thickness of case layer and by a smooth and not too abrupt hardness transition between the core and case.

Figure 11-80*b* indicates the stress condition for case carburizing both outside diameter and inside diameter, whereas a decarburized surface on the bore produces tensile stresses as shown in *c*.   Mickel and Sommer[105] tested

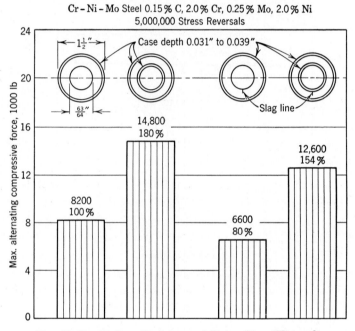

FIG. 11-82.   Fatigue Resistance of Piston Pins (Wiegand)

a number of piston pins under alternating compressive loading imposing stresses in the pin according to *d*.   The compressive loading varied from a small initial compressive force to a maximum as a means of determining the endurance-limit values.

Fatigue resistance of pins from 0.11–0.18% C steel with 0.2% Cr is shown in Fig. 11-81 where different conditions of the bore were investigated.   Although the magnitude of residual stresses was not determined, there is little variation in fatigue strength, regardless of bore condition, except when the case depth on the bore is one-half that on the outside diameter.   It is inferred from results that the methods of processing and/or this type of steel did not respond to residual stresses in the bore; or it may be in this instance that residual stresses were not a controlling factor in the strength of these pins.

A greater response to residual-stress formation in the pin bore was found by Wiegand[132] in similar fatigue tests of a different-type alloy steel as presented in Fig. 11-82. Fatigue resistance was increased 80 per cent by case-carburizing the bore with the outside diameter when no defects were present in the bore; this increase was 90 per cent when longitudinal defects such as slag lines existed in the bore.

Wiegand submitted evidence to show that the increased fatigue resistance in Fig. 11-82 was due to favorable residual stresses. He anticipated objection to this conclusion because this increase is often explained by the case layer having a higher hardness and corresponding higher static strength and fatigue strength than the core. He countered this objection on the basis that tensile-strength values obtained on bars case-carburized about all the way through the section were nearly always below or just above those for pseudocarburized material. The modulus-of-elasticity values were also comparable.

Contrary to Wiegand, the results of Woodvine[159] showed that the tensile strength of the case layer was about 50 per cent greater than that of the core. Peterson and Lessells[160] presented an excellent analysis of why surface strengthening increases fatigue resistance. Their explanation indicates that residual stresses could have little or no influence and that hardness, physical properties, and microchanges in themselves would account for increased fatigue resistance found for surface-strengthened members. This contention by earlier investigators was reviewed elsewheren [9, 10] in considerable detail.

A definite lack of data exists regarding residual stresses in surface-hardened layers obtained by different methods reviewed here and elsewhere in this chapter. Explanations are generally oversimplified. The complex nature of the problem requires further intensive research.

HH. Shot Peening

Almen[5] reported residual compressive stress in the outer layers of shot-peened steel specimens of over 100,000 psi (Fig. 11-77). Richards[161] shot-peened Al–Zn–Mg bars $\frac{1}{4}$ in. thick and found residual compressive stress in the surface layer of 30,000 to 70,000 psi, depending on shot size used. Depth of compressive stress varied from 0.020 to 0.030 in. Normalized bar stock of SAE 1045 steel cylinders 3 in. in diameter were shot-peened by Greaves[111] and found to have longitudinal and tangential compressive stresses of 37,000 and 50,000 psi, respectively.

Large increases in fatigue resistance due to shot peening have been reported in production parts by Almen.[162] A general review of the literature has also been published by H. F. Moore[163] and others.[9] Richards[161] demonstrated the improved corrosion fatigue strength of aluminum alloys of X76S-T for propeller blades and 25S-T specimens. Also H. F. Moore[164] measured the reduction of residual stresses in shot-peened parts by cycles of repeated stress.[163]

An engineering expression of the value of shot peening used by the spring industry is shown by the modified Goodman diagrams[9] in Figs. 11-83 and 11-84.

II. Axle Straightening

Horger and Lipson[165] found that the endurance limit in rotating bending of full-size automobile rear axles was 13,000 to 16,000 psi when the shafts were straightened in production. Similar unstraightened axles had an endurance limit of 20,000 psi or at least 25 per cent greater fatigue resistance than the straightened shafts. The detrimental effect of unfavorable tensile stresses

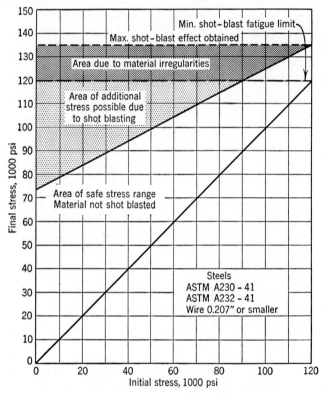

Fig. 11-83. Diagram Showing Greater Allowable Stresses Permitted on Shot-Peened Springs of Pretempered Wire (Gibson Co)

produced in straightening, which measured as high as 120,000 psi, was overcome by shot peening after straightening to give at least 43,000 psi endurance value.

JJ. Springs

Scragging or presetting of springs[166, 167] has been practiced for many years as a means of improving fatigue resistance. Becker and Phillips[2] reported an increase of 32 per cent in safe range of stress by scragging low-chromium steel leaf springs. If, in addition to scragging, the springs were also water-quenched from the tempering temperature, then about 45 per cent increased fatigue strength resulted.   Both the scragging and quenching treatment used induce favorable compressive stresses in the surface layers of the spring. Estimated maximum residual compressive stress in the surface zone was found to be as high as 83,000 psi by quenching from 1290°F.

Torsion-bar springs are prestressed[168, 169] by first shot peening and then twisting the bar through an angle of as much as 90°.   This twisting is repeated

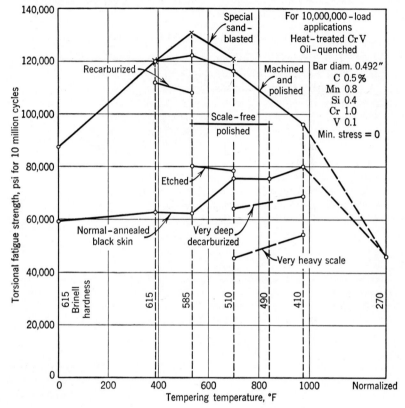

F<small>IG</small>. 11-84.   Influence of Surface Conditions and Tempering Temperature on Torsional Fatigue Resistance for 10,000,000 Load Applications (Manteuffel)

through a smaller angle so as to leave a permanent set of ¼°.   Residual surface-compressive stresses of 35,000 psi produced in this manner are depended on to give the high fatigue strength required in applications where torsion springs are used.[170]

KK. C<small>ABLE</small>

Wire and cable used in aircraft and bridge construction have developed failure in the looped ends at anchorage shoes or grommets as reviewed by Brewer.[171]   Heat-treated wire made into preformed loops has developed fatigue failure at the inside of the loop where Brewer showed that high residual tension stresses existed. Bridge cable from cold-drawn wire has not developed such failures. Also heat-treated wire has low-ductility characteristics in this zone of the bend with little ability for plastic flow under stress concentration, whereas cold-drawn wire is better in this respect.

Looped ends of aircraft bracing wires have been cured by using an air hammer to peen the wire down against the grommet after it was installed.[172] The explanation for this was that the residual stresses in the loop were ironed out and reduced to a very low figure.

LL. Prestress Applied Mechanically

Seeger[173] investigated the fatigue resistance of hollow shafts which were preloaded axially so as to produce compressive prestress below yield-strength value of the steel. Prestressing was obtained by tightening a bolt running axially through the hollow shafts. Several steels, a cast iron, and an aluminum alloy were the materials used. Some of these shafts had (a) no stress concentration (b) notch, and (c) press fit. These shafts were subjected to fatigue stressing in rotating bending, with and without corrosion, and also in reversed torsion.

Results of these bending tests are reported in Fig. 11-85. Plain specimens of the quenched and tempered steel in curve A showed a decrease of fatigue strength due to compressive prestress, but an increase was obtained in the presence of a notch as in curve D. Cast iron exhibits a marked strength increase due to prestress shown in curve B, compared to the decrease in A for steel. Even the corrosion-fatigue resistance of steels is greatly improved by prestress as reported in G and H.

Results of torsion tests in Fig. 11-86 shows a large gain in endurance values due to prestress.

Fatigue behavior in Figs. 11-85 and 11-86 was explained by (1) the relationship for the material of the separation resistance, causing brittle-type fracture, to the slip resistance, leading to ductile-type fracture, and (2) the resultant maximum shearing stress determined by separate shearing stresses produced by compressive prestress and applied load. Here is a good example of the influence of residual stresses alone on fatigue resistance without other factors being introduced. Most other cases are complicated by several factors influencing fatigue strength.

Various other examples of the beneficial application of prestress obtained by mechanical means are of value to the designer.

Bolts represent a simple illustration of the value of the proper initial tightening stresses on bolt fatigue resistance. Fatigue strength was increased as much as 150 per cent by proper preloading, and this factor is of equal importance to or greater than manufacturing practices and material selection. A rolled thread will maintain the prestress with less change than a cut thread because of better thread engagement owing to improved surface finish. Almen[174] has presented data on this subject of prestress, but extensive investigations of value to designers were reported by Thum and Würges[175] and Martinaglia.[176]

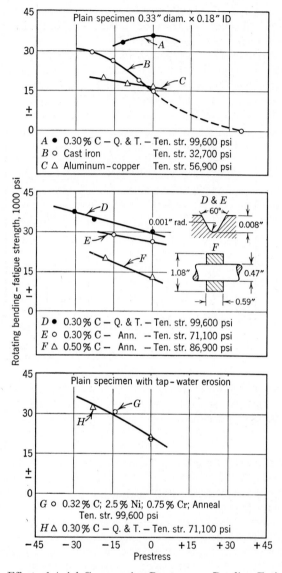

FIG. 11-85.   Effect of Axial Compressive Prestress on Bending Fatigue Strength
(Seeger)

Prestressing has been obtained in guns[1] by shrinking several tubular members over one another, by wrapping wire under tension on a central tube, and after World War I by autofrettage.   In this last method a single cylinder is subjected to high hydraulic pressure so as to enlarge the bore permanently about 6 per cent and the outside diameter by about 1 per cent for the average wall ratio used. In this way the elastic-strength pressure of a gun can be nearly doubled through the combined effect of the increased elastic limit and the residual compression stress near the bore.

Cast-steel driving-wheel centers for steam locomotives are prestressed in the axle bore previous to pressing the wheel on the axle. This operation consists of pressing an oversize tapered plug through the bore[10] so as plastically to deform the surface layers. In this manner the holding ability of press-fitted members is increased, and they may be pressed on and off a number of times

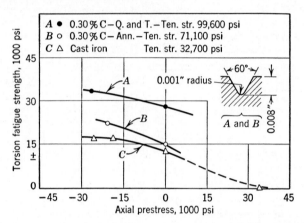

FIG. 11-86. Effect of Axial Compressive Prestress on Torsion Fatigue Strength (Seeger)

without loosing their fit. Compressor and turbine rotors are also improved by being subjected to overspeed operation as a means of obtaining centrifugal stresses above the yield point.[177]

MM. BEAMS

Precast and prestressed concrete beams have been used for the deck of a railway bridge in England in 1946.[178, 179] Concrete beams of conventional design would have been 51 in. deep, but the prestressed beams were only 41 in. because of the initial compressive stresses incorporated in the bottom flange.

To produce the initial compressive stress a special casting technique was followed. A load is applied to the reinforcing rods in the lower flange before the concrete is poured so as to cause the rods to extend. This load is maintained until the concrete has set and, when released, applies compressive stress to the concrete in which it is imbedded. This initial compressive stress is sufficiently high so that tensile stress due to maximum bridge loading will never exceed the prestress. In this manner the low tensile properties of concrete are overcome. The prestressing rods are made from 0.2-in.-diameter hard-drawn wire having a tensile strength of 224,000 psi. Secondary reinforcements are of mild steel.

NN. Columns

A convenient method of strengthening bridges is to increase the section of members by welding longitudinal steel plates or shapes to the members while they remain in place on the bridge. This welding operation leaves residual tension stresses in some regions of the member and compressive stresses in other locations. These stresses can be as high as the yield-point strength of structural steel which is about 36,000 psi; generally, these stresses are about 5000 to 15,000 psi. Square-ended columns having an l/r ratio of about 65 which are strengthened in this manner and which are straight after welding have the same unit load-carrying strength as the original column.[180]

Influence of prestretching and precompression on the buckling strength of Al–Cu–Mg alloy tubes was investigated by Bungardt.[186] Precompression of 0.2 to 1.0 per cent increased the buckling strength 25 to 30 per cent with increasing slenderness ratio. On the other hand, prestretching up to 1 per cent decreased the buckling strength at most by 10 per cent.

OO. Embrittlement

Cold-bent reinforcing bars tend to develop surface cracking at the inside region of the bend if the compression of the metal in this zone is above about 40 per cent, based on original bar dimensions. Such cracking is encountered especially in mild steels as was reported by Körber et al.[182] for six different steels including cast steel.

Internal tensile stresses are retained in the compressed zone of the bar, and embrittlement which occurs in this region is attributed to these unfavorable stresses. Opposing compressive stresses are produced in the stretched or outside portion of the bend. Apart from the reduced ductility and structural changes taking place in the steel on bending, it has been found that steel-quality factors enhance embrittlement; this occurs because inclusions and so on assume preferred orientation at right angles to the tension stress.

Similar difficulty was cited by Brewer from residual stresses in spring loops made from oil-tempered SAE 1065 steel having a tensile strength of 225,000 psi. Cold-drawn wire of the same steel and tensile strength did not exhibit cracking when acid-pickled.[183]

PP. Thermal Fatigue of Bearing Alloys

Small steel-backed bearings of tin-base alloy exhibit marked cracking through the alloy and finally disruption when repeatedly heated and cooled through 85–300°F. This phenomenon termed "thermal fatigue" has been investigated by Boas and Honeycombe.[184, 185] They found that noncubic metals like tin, cadmium, and zinc alloys (99 per cent purity) which were even unattached to a backing strip behaved in a similar manner. Rates of heating and cooling were found to be of little significance. The cause of stresses leading to failure is explained on the basis that these metals possess marked anisotropy of thermal expansion,[186] and repeated temperature changes produce plastic deformation; cubic metal lead exhibits no deformation or failure of this type. Stresses of this type have been calculated by Laszlo.[187]

These investigators expressed the thought that metals which possess a high degree of anistropy of thermal expansion cannot be obtained in a strain-free condition at room temperature by casting or annealing. Their findings may have some practical implications as regards service failures of bearings.

QQ. ALUMINUM ALLOYS

With the introduction of heat-treated aluminum alloys the problem of quenching stresses became important. These stresses may be unfavorable in that low-fatigue resistance, distortion, warping, or even tearing may result, especially in machining of solution-heat-treated materials. On the other hand, the cooling stresses may be favorable so as to increase fatigue resistance. It is, therefore, essential to have a knowledge of means of producing and controlling these residual stresses.

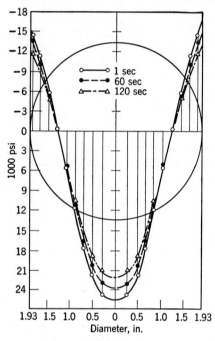

Wasserman[188] made X-ray determinations of quenching stresses. He found pure aluminum in 0.040-in.-diameter testpieces almost free of stresses; with increasing diameter the stresses reached a maximum of 7000–8500 psi at about 0.24 in. in diameter. Duraluminum (4.27% Cu, 0.53% Mg, 0.28% Mn) quenched from 930°F in ice water produced surface compressive stresses of about 6600 psi for 0.04-in.-diameter specimens; with increasing diameter the stresses rose first rapidly and then slowly to about 48,000 psi at 0.79 in. in diameter.

FIG. 11-87. Longitudinal Residual Stresses in Avional D Extruded Bar 1.97 in. in Diameter, Water- (68°F) Quenched from Anneal (970°F); Age 24 hr at 120°F with Different Cooling Periods before Quenching (Zeerleder)

Zeerleder[189] found that the alloy Avional D (4% Cu, 0.2% Si, 0.6 Mg, 0.5% Mn) in 1.9-in.-diameter bars gave quenching stresses of about the same magnitude as Wasserman[188] obtained for smaller sizes. Zeerleder used the Heyn and Bauer method to determine longitudinal stresses; this unidirectional consideration of strain gives stresses too low. His results showed that increasing time of cooling prior to quenching decreases stresses as in Fig. 11-87. Increasing temperature of the quenching bath reduces stresses, as exhibited in Fig. 11-88. Mechanical treatment such as stretching or upsetting of quenched pieces greatly modifies the internal stress, as illustrated in Fig. 11-89.

Quenching stresses were shown by Forrest to have a considerable influence on fatigue resistance.[190] Rotating-cantilever fatigue tests were made on two wrought- and one cast-aluminum alloy, plain and notched specimens prepared with varying degrees of internal stresses being used. Figure 11-90 indicates that the endurance values of plain specimens from wrought alloys are not influenced by residual stress,* but the cast material gave a 20 per cent increase with the presence of surface-compressive stresses from quenching. Findings regarding notched specimens were of greater practical importance from the standpoint of actual design members. The results in Fig. 11-90 present increases in fatigue strength of 40–80 per cent, when wrought specimens with annular notches contain the usual surface-compressive stress. Forrest made the interesting observation that some notched specimens having surface-compressive stresses from quenching ran many millions of cycles with visible cracks but without complete failure. This resistance of a crack in propagating through the surface layer containing residual compressive stresses has also been reported for steel.[147]

Heavy sinking passes applied in producing ⅝-in.-OD × ⅜-in.-ID tubing lead to high tensile stresses in the surface and reduced fatigue resistance,[190] according to Fig. 11-91. Rotating cantilever specimens having an annular notch were investigated. It was found that the fatigue-strength values varied in the ratio 1 to 1.8, with the higher values corresponding to specimens having compressive surface stress and the lower values to those having tensile stress in the outer layers of the tube wall.

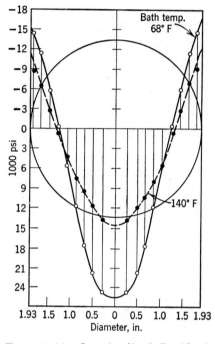

FIG. 11-88. Longitudinal Residual Stresses in Avional D Extruded Bar 1.97 in. in Diameter, Water-Quenched from 970°F; Age 24 hr at 120°F with 1-sec Cooling Period before Quenching (Zeerleder)

* In Fig. 11-90 the heat-treatments producing the residual stresses were as follows: Treatment A—for 150 alloy quench in nearly boiling water from 925°F and aged room temperature; same for L45 alloy but from 995°F and aged 330°F; same for alloy 298 but from 995°F and not aged. Treatments B and C were similar to A except quenched in water at room temperature after which alloy 150 was aged at room temperature, alloy L45 aged 330°F, and alloy 298 not aged.

Fischer[191] suggested obtaining favorable residual compressive stresses by stretching notched testpieces in tension and then determining the fatigue resistance. Forrest[190] made such tests in rotating bending on specimens machined from stress-free aluminum.* Notched pieces were statically prestressed in tension to 56,000 psi nominal stress through the base of the notch, which compares with a yield strength of 40,000 psi and ultimate of

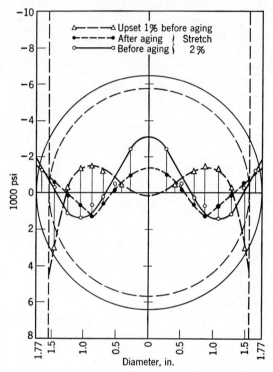

FIG. 11-89. Longitudinal Residual Stresses in Avional D Extruded Bar 1.97 in. in Diameter, Water- (68°F) Quenched from 950°F; Age 5 days at 68°F with 1-sec Cooling Period before Quenching (Zeerleder)

69,000 psi for the material used. Such prestressed specimens had twice the endurance limit of similar stress-free pieces, as shown in Fig. 11-92.

Sutton discussed the results of Forrest[190] and cited his experience with prestressing of heat-treated and straightened bars of a Duralumin alloy. Prestressing to about 89 per cent of the ultimate caused a considerable reduction in fatigue strength of plain and notched specimens, possibly 30 per cent. On this basis Sutton suggested close scrutiny of cold treatments which are expected to improve fatigue performance.

This principle of preloading was applied as a means of improving the fatigue

* Specimen BSS 6L1 was about the same as BSS 5T4 in Fig. 11-91, treatment A, except that elongation was about 16 per cent.

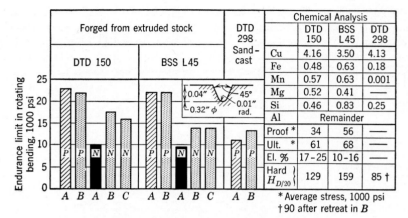

FIG. 11-90.   Effect of Residual Stress on Fatigue Properties of Aluminum Alloys
(Forrest)

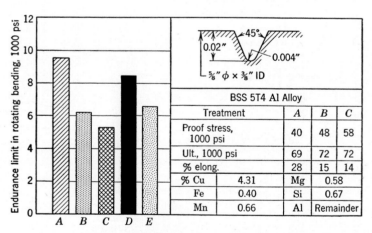

FIG. 11-91.   Effect of Residual Stresses on Fatigue Strength of Notched Aluminum-
Alloy Tubing (Forrest)

strength of spot-welded joints, as shown in Fig. 11-93 by Forrest.[190]   A simple
lap joint consisting of 0.7-in.-wide pieces of 20-gage (0.036 in.) Alclad sheet
was made having a single spot weld.   These spot-welded assemblies were
overloaded in tension before fatigue testing by application of a load equal
to two-thirds the average static stress to failure.   This preloading gave a
50 per cent increase in allowable mean stress when these pieces were tested
under fluctuating tension loading.   Also Field and associates[192] made fatigue

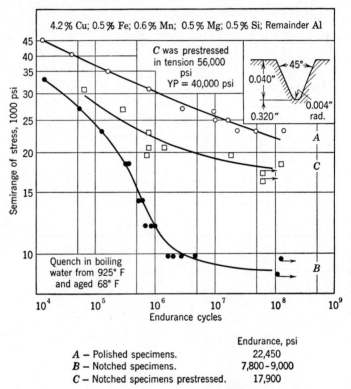

	Endurance, psi
A – Polished specimens.	22,450
B – Notched specimens.	7,800-9,000
C – Notched specimens prestressed.	17,900

FIG. 11-92.   Effect of Preloading on Fatigue Strength of Notched Specimens of
Stress-Free Aluminum (Forrest)

tests on spot-welded assemblies and obtained appreciable increase after cold
rolling with a 2.7 per cent reduction.   A greater reduction resulted in no
improvement over the unrolled material.   In these spot-weld tests the
increased fatigue resistance was believed to result from a redistribution of an
unfavorable internal stress to a favorable one rather than to cold working.

Means for reducing detrimental residual stresses likely to cause rupture in
quenching or machining as developed in quenched aluminum-alloy parts after
solution treatment were summarized by Benson[193] in Fig. 11-94.   He investigated internal stresses in wrought metal to DTD 410 (1.8–2.5% Cu, 0.6–1.4%
Ni, 0.65–1.2% Mg, 0.6–1.2% Fe, 0.55–1.25% Si, 0.05–0.15% Ti) quenched

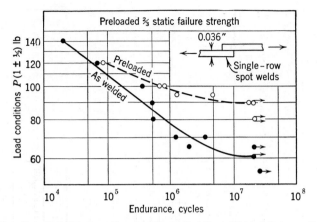

FIG. 11-93. Results of Fatigue Tests on Preloaded Spot Welds Made on Aluminum Sheet (Forrest)

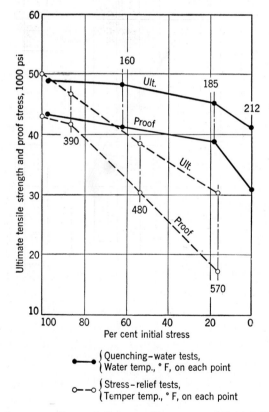

FIG. 11-94. Remanent Internal Stress as Percentage of Initial Stress (Benson)

TABLE 11-19

SURVEY OF MAGNITUDE OF COMPRESSIVE SURFACE-LAYER STRESSES INDUCED BY VARIOUS MACHINING OPERATIONS AND BY SHOT BLASTING

(Frommer & Lloyd)

All data refer to specimens which were fully heat-treated before the operation quoted.

When several similarly machined specimens were examined, the highest stress values obtained are quoted in the table.

The stress values quoted refer to the immediate surface when measurable X-ray patterns were obtainable from that surface; otherwise they refer to that stratum beneath the surface (exposed by etching) where first measurable patterns could be obtained.

The "thickness-of-compressive-stress layer" quoted indicates the depth of etching necessary to obtain practically "stress-free" patterns.

Type of Operation	Description	Cutting Speed, rpm	Feed, in./rev.	Depth of Cut, in.	Measurement Obtained at	Stress Sum (Compressive), tons/in².	Approximate Thickness of Compressive Stress Layer, in.	Alloy
Turning	Flat surface faced off with fine finishing cut	....	~0.0015	~0.0005	Actual surface (unetched)	3.3	~0.002	RR 56
	Cylindrical surface turned with rough cut	375	~0.012	~0.050	0.006 in. beneath original surface	7.2	~0.015	Y alloy
	Surface faced off under conditions producing chatter marks	....	....	....	0.005 in. beneath original surface	20.7	~0.024	RR 56
Recessing	Recess made with flat-bottom drill (½ in. diameter)	290	~0.005	....	Actual surface of base of recess (unetched)	6.9	>0.004 <0.015	RR 56
Surface milling (cutter not enclosed by material of job)	Flat surface side-milled with end mill (2 in. long, ⅜ in. diam)	220	~0.010	~0.125	Actual surface (unetched)	Nil	Nil	RR 56
	Flat surface milled with straddling mill (6 in. diam, ⅞ in. wide)	220	~0.010	~0.125	Actual surface (unetched)	Nil	Nil	RR 56
Milling of slots and grooves (cutter enclosed by material of job)	Tapered groove (⅞ in. deep, 5¼ in. long) made with 7° angle cutter ($\frac{7}{16}$ in. diam)	220	~0.010	~$\frac{7}{32}$	Actual surface of sidewall	14.7	~0.006	RR 56
	Arc-shaped groove sunk with formed, spiral-fluted milling cutter (tapered 4°, max. cutting diam 0.455 in.)	1700	Rough cut 0.05 Fine cut 0.01	0.010–0.020	Actual surface of sidewall	16.5	~0.011	Y alloy
Shot blasting	Flat surface faced off on lathe (fine finishing cut) and then shot-blasted	Diameter of steel shot = 0.040 in. Air pressure in mains ~30 psi Throttle at "half pressure"			0.006 in. beneath original surface	22.5	~0.025	RR 56

in water from about 985°F. In one series of tests the quenching water was at room temperature, and stress-relief temperature was varied; another series incorporated different temperature values for the quenching water. If the data in Fig. 11-94 are compared, it is apparent that minimizing internal stresses by increasing the quenching-water temperature involves less sacrifice of strength properties than final stress-relief operations. Benson points out that increasing the precipitation-hardening temperature is the procedure most convenient in practice but increasing quenching-water temperature is preferable for general engineering applications.

Frommer and Lloyd[194] made X-ray studies of residual stresses in aluminum alloys. A description is given of the apparatus and experimental technique that have been found most suitable, and a selection of some applications to some important practical problems is summarized. Their results showed how stresses could be greatly reduced in quenching by use of shrouds around thin sections of forgings having both heavy and light sections. Surface-layer stresses of a highly localized nature produced by various machining and shot-blasting operations are quoted from their findings in Table 11-19. Internal-stress distribution through thick-walled extruded tubes representing various methods of manufacture were also presented.

Many other investigators have measured residual stresses in aluminum alloys, but no correlation was reported with fatigue-strength properties. Some of these studies were reported by Grogan and Clayton,[195] Kempf, Hopkins and Ivanso,[196] Phillips and Brick,[197] Kempf and Van Horn,[198] and a book[12] was published discussing this subject.

BIBLIOGRAPHY

1. THOMAS J. HAYES, *Elements of Ordnance*, John Wiley & Sons, New York, 1938.
2. S. TIMOSHENKO, *Strength of Materials*, pt 2, D. Van Nostrand Co, New York, 1941.
3. H. DOBKIN, "Prestressing Rotating Disks," *Steel*, v 118, June 3, 1946, pp 104–06 and 150.
4. O. FÖPPL, "Das Drücken der Oberfläche von Bauteilen aus Stahl," *Stahl und Eisen* v 49, 1929, pp 575–77. Presents early findings regarding favorable influence on fatigue resistance of surface-compressive stresses obtained by hammer peening.
5. J. O. ALMEN, "Improving Fatigue Strength of Machine Parts," *Iron Age*, June 10, 1943, pp 65–9, 125–31. Also "Peened Surfaces Improve Endurance of Machine Parts," and related subjects in *Metal Progress*, Feb 1943, pp 209–15, 270; May 1943, pp 737–40; Aug 1943, pp 254–61; Sept 1943, pp 435–40, and "Shot Blasting to Increase Fatigue Resistance," *J Soc Automotive Engrs (Trans)*, v 51, n 7, July 1943, pp 249–68. Also see J. O. ALMEN, R. L. MATTSON, and H. E. FONDA, "Effect of Shot Blasting on the Mechanical Properties of Steel," pt 1, 2, and 3, *Office Sci Research and Develop* Reports 3274, 4825, and 6647.
6. H. F. MOORE, *Shot Peening*, American Wheelabrator and Equipment Corp, Mishawaka, Ind, 1946.
7. J. H. FRYE, "Shot Peening Applied to Ordnance Parts," *Am Soc Metals Symposium on Shot Peening*, Oct 1944.
8. A. E. PROCTOR, "Shot Peening and Some of Its Applications," presented before naval gun factory personnel, Washington, D. C., Oct 18, 1946.

9. O. J. HORGER, "Mechanical and Metallurgical Advantages of Shot Peening," *Iron Age*, Mar 29 and Apr 5, 1945.

10. O. J. HORGER, "Stressing Axles and Other Railroad Equipment by Cold Rolling," *Surface Stressing of Metals, Am Soc Metals*, Feb 1946.

11. CHARLES S. BARRETT, "Internal Stresses—A Review," *Metals and Alloys*, v 5, pp 131, 154, 170, 196, and 224, 1934. A later review in *Proc Soc Experimental Stress Analysis*, v 2, n 1, 1944.

12. G. SACHS AND KENT R. VAN HORN, *Practical Metallurgy*, American Society for Metals, Cleveland, 1940.

13. G. SACHS AND G. ESPEY, "The Measurement of Residual Stresses in Metal," *Iron Age*, v 148, Sept 18 and 25, 1941, pp 63–71 and 36–42.

14. CHARLES S. BARRETT, Structure of Metals, McGraw Hill Book Co, New York, 1943.

15. G. SACHS, C. S. SMITH, J. D. LUBAHN, G. E. DAVIS AND L. J. EBERT, "Nondestructive Measurement of Residual and Enforced Stresses by means of X-ray Diffraction," *Am Welding Soc Research Sup* v 11, July 1946, pp 400–12s and H. R. ISENBURGER, "Bibliography of Stress Analysis by Means of X-Ray Back Reflection Method," Nov 1944, pp 571–72s. Also see W. A. WOOD, "Study of Internal Stresses in a Metal by X-Ray Diffraction," *Proc Inst Mech Eng*, v 152, n 2, 1945, pp 232–54; J. T. NORTON, "X-ray Methods in the Field of Residual Stresses," *Proc Soc Experimental Stress Analysis* v 2, n 1, 1944, pp 157–160 and v 1, n 2, 1943, pp 73–81.

16. W. SPRARAGEN AND G. E. CLAUSSEN, "Shrinkage Stresses in Welding—A Review of the Literature of January 1937," *Am Welding Soc Research Sup*, Nov 1937, pp 2–62; "Review of the Literature on Fatigue of Welded Joints," v 16, Jan 1937, pp 1–42s.

17. W. SPRARAGEN AND M. A. CORDOVI, "Shrinkage Stresses in Welding—A Review of the Literature from January 1937 to September 1943," *Am Welding Soc Research Sup*, v 9, May 1941, pp 209–46s.

18. W. SPRARAGEN AND D. ROSENTHAL, "Review of the Literature on Fatigue Strength of Welded Joints," *Am. Welding Soc., Research Suppl.*, v 21, July 1942, pp 297–348s.

19. G. SACHS, "Der Nachweiss Innerer Spannungen in Stangen und Rohren," The Determination of Residual Stresses in Rods and Tubes, *Zeitschrift für Metallkunde*, v 19, 1927, pp 352–7; *Trans. ASME*, 1939, p. 821.

20. O. J. HORGER, H. R. NEIFERT AND R. R. REGEN, "Residual Stresses and Fatigue Studies," *Proc. Soc. Exp. Stress Analysis*, v 1, n 1, 1943, pp 10–18.

21. O. J. HORGER AND H. R. NEIFERT, "Correlation of Residual Stress in the Fatigue Strength of Axles," *J. Applied Mechanics, Trans. ASME*, v 64, June 1942, pp A-85–90.

22. N. KALAKOUTZKY, *The Study of Internal Stresses in Cast Iron and Steel*, St. Petersburg, 1887 (Russian) also in London, 1888.

23. H. KLEIN, "Untersuchungen an kaltgereckten, dickwandigen Rohren und besonderer Berücksichtigung der Veränderungen der Werkstoffeigenschaften," Turned Thin rings from thick walled tubing to measure residual tangential stresses resulting from cold working, *Mitt. Kaiser-Wilhelm Inst. Eisenforsch.*, v 11, 1929, pp 331–52.

24. A. E. MACRAE, *Overstrain in Metals and Its Application to the Autofrettage Process*, H. M. Stationery Office, London, 1930.

25. J. A. ODING, *J. Electrotechn*, (Russian) 1930, pp 414–22.

26. E. SIEBEL, "Die Wirkung des Einwalzens von Rohren auf die Werkstoffeigenschaften und die Spannungsverhältnisse der Rohrplatte," Transverse Slices Cut From Rolled Tubing and Slices bores Out to Determine Residual Tangential Stresses, *Mitt. Kaiser-Wilhelm Inst. Eisenforsch.*, v 11, 1929, pp 279–85.

27. O. V. GREENE, "Estimation of Internal Stresses in Quenched Hollow Cylin-

ders of Carbon Tool Steel," *Trans Am Soc Steel Treating*, v 18, 1930, pp 369–403.

28. W. H. HATFIELD AND G. L. THIRKELL, "Season Cracking," *J. Inst Metals* (*Lond.*), v 22, 1919, pp 67–126; W. JUNG–KOENIG, W. LINICUS, AND G. SACHS, *Metallwirtschaft*, v 11, 1932, pp 395–401.

29. A. PINKERTON AND W. H. TAIT, "Season Cracking in Arsenical Copper Tubes," *J. Inst. Metals*, v 36, 1926, pp 233–41. D. K. CRAMPTON, "Internal Stress and Season Cracking in Brass Tubes," *Trans. AIME*, Inst Metals Division, 1930, pp 233–48, 248–55. A. KRECEK, "Innenspannungen in Messingrohren," *Zeitschrift für Metallkunde*, v 23, n 6, June 1931, pp 178–85.

30. R. J. ANDERSON AND E. G. FAHLMAN, "A Method for Measuring Internal Stresses in Brass Tubes," *J Inst Metals* (*Lond.*), v 32, 1924, pp 367–83; v 34, 1925, pp 271–300.

31. G. SACHS AND G. ESPEY, "A New Method for Determination of Stress Distribution in Thin Walled Tubing," *Am Inst Mining and Met Engrs Metals Technology Tech Pub* 1384, Oct 1941. This method suggested by J. FOX, *Engineering*, v 129, 1930, pp 65–7; v 136, 1933; pp 375–76; and complete but complicated formulas proposed by N. DAVIDENKOW, *Zeitschrift für Metallkunde*, v 24, 1932; pp 25–9 were greatly simplified by Sachs and Espey.

32. J. E. HOWARD, "Internal Strains in Section of Harveyized Steel Bar," *Report 5992 of Tests of Metals*, Watertown Arsenal, 1893, pp 285 and 532.

33. E. HEYN AND O. BAUER, "Ueber Spannungen in Kesselblechen" (Stresses in Boiler Plate), *Stahl und Eisen*, v 31, 1911, pp 760–65; *Internationale Zeitschrift für Metallographie*, v 1, 1911, pp 16–50; E. HEYN, *J Inst Metals* (*Lond.*), v 12, 1914, pp 3–37; "Untersuchung der gerissenen Stirnwand eines Schiffskesseis" (Cracking of Front Head on Ship Boilers), *Stahl und Eisen*, v 32, 1912, pp 1169–674; *Materialienkunde Machinenbau*, v 2, 1912; *Mitteilungen aus dem Königlichen Materialprüfungsamt*, v 35, 1917, pp 1–25; "Einige weitere Mitteilungen über Eigenspannungen und damit zussammenhängende Fragen" (Further Discussion of Residual Stresses and Associated Problems), *Stahl und Eisen*, v 37, 1917, pp 442–48, pp 474–79, and pp 497–500; *Naturwissenschaften*, v 9, 1921, pp 321–25; *Physl Metallography*, translated by M. A. GROSSMAN, John Wiley & Sons, 1925.

34. P. D. MERCIA AND R. W. WOODWARD, "Failure of Brass—Microstructure and Initial Stresses in Wrought Brasses of the Type 60 per cent Copper and 40 per cent Zinc," *U. S. Bur Standards Technological Paper* 82, 1917, 72 pp.

35. M. PORTEVIN, "Efforts internes developpés dan les métaux et les alliages par l'effet d'un refroidissement rapid" (Internal Stresses Developed in Metals and Alloys By Means of Rapid Cooling). *Compte Rendu*, v 167, 1918, pp 531–33; "Étude de l'influence des divers facteurs sur la création des efforts internes longitudinaux lors du refroidissement rapid des cylindres d'acier" (Study of the Influence of Various Factors Causing Longitudinal Residual Stresses by Rapid Cooling of Steel Cylinders), v 169, 1919, pp 955–57; "La Réduction et la disparation des efforts internes dans les aciers, par rechauffage suivi du refroidissement lent" (The Reduction and Distribution of Residual Stresses in Steel after Reheating Following a Slow Cool), v 175, 1922, pp 959–61; "Sur la Détermination des efforts internes dans les cylindres circulaires métalliques" (Determination of Residual Stresses in Metal Cylinders), v 186, 1928, pp 939–41; "Influence des divers facteurs sur les tensions internes d'étirage" (Influence of Various Factors on the Residual Stresses in Wire Drawing), pp 1463–465.

36. T. MCLEAN JASPER, "The Calculation of Quenching Stresses in Steel by Using Direct Measurements," *Engineering* (*Lond.*), Sept 5, 1924, pp 343–44.

37. G. MASING, "Über die Entwicklung von Eigenspannungen beim Kaltwalzen von Messing" (Development of Residual Stresses in Cold-Worked Brass), *Zeitschrift für Metallkunde*, v 17, 1925, pp 183–86.

38. S. L. Hoyt, "Stresses in Quenched and Tempered Steel," *Trans Am Soc Steel Treating*, v 11, 1927, pp 509–30, 658.
39. K. Kreitz, *Stahl und Eisen*, v 50, 1931, pp 667–68, discussion of paper by R. Mailänder, "Die Verminderung von Eigenspannungen durch Anlassen," (Decrease of Residual Stresses by Tempering), pp 662–67.
40. H. Buchholtz and H. Bühler, "Vergleich der Verfahren zur Bestimmung von Eigenspannungen in Vollzylindern" (Comparison of Methods for Determining Residual Stresses in Solid Cylinders), *Stahl und Eisen*, v 52, 1932, pp 490–92.
41. F. Laszlo, "Ein neues Verfahren zur Messung innerer Spannungen in Messingrohren" (A New Method of Measuring Residual Stresses in Brass Tubes), *Stahl und Eisen*, v 45, 1925, pp 1609–610.
42. F. Staeblein, "Spannungsmessungen an Einseitig Abgelöschten Knüppeln" Stress Measurements on Billets Quenched From One Side), *Kruppsche Monatshefte*, v 12, May 1931, pp 93–9.
43. H. Buchholtz, "Residual Stresses in Structural Members," *Welding Industry*, v 3, 1935, pp 267–71, 337–39.
44. E. P. DeGarmo, J. L. Meriam, and Finn Jonassen, "Residual Stresses in Intersecting Butt Welds," *Am Welding Soc Research Sup*, Aug 1946, pp 451–63s.
45. L. Reeve, Internal Stresses in Welding and Their Determination, *Welding Industry*, v 4, 1936, pp 344–55.
46. D. Rosenthal and J. T. Norton, "A Method for Measuring Triaxial Residual Stress in Plates," *Am Welding Soc Research Sup*, May 1945, pp 295s–307s.
47. J. Mathar, "Determination of Initial Stresses by Measuring the Deformations Around Drilled Holes," *Trans. ASME*, v 56, 1934, pp 249–54; *Archiv für das Eisenhüttenwesen*, v 9, 1935–36, pp 205–07.
48. J. L. Meriam, E. Paul DeGarmo, and Finn Jonassen, "A Method for the Measurement of Residual Welding Stresses," *Am Welding Soc, Research Supp*, v 11, June 1946, pp 340–343s.
49. R. G. Anderson, "Improving Engine Parts by Direct Measurement of Strain," *Trans Soc Automotive Engrs J*, v 54, n 9, pp 466–75, 501–02. Also see C. W. Gadd, "Residual Stress Indications in Brittle Lacquer," *Proc Soc Experimental Stress Analysis*, v 4, n 1, 1946, pp 74–7.
50. H. Buchholtz and H. Bühler, "Zusammenkang zwischen Wärmespannungen und Festigkeitseigenschaften von Stahl" (Relation between Thermal Stresses and Strength Properties of Steel), *Archiv für das Eisenhüttenwesen*, v 8, Feb 1933, pp 335–40.
51. H. Bühler and E. Scheil, "Einfluss der Abschreckbedingungen auf die Eigenspannungen von Stählen" (Effect of Quenching Conditions upon the Residual Stresses in Steels), *Archiv für das Eisenhüttenwesen*, v 7, n 6, Dec 1933–34, pp 359–63.
52. H. Bühler, H. Buchholtz and E. H. Schulz, "Eigenspannungen bei der Wärmebehandlung von Stahl" (Residual Stresses in the Heat Treatment of Steel), *Archiv für das Eisenhüttenwesen*, v 5, Feb 1942, pp 413–18.
53. See E. Mauer for Method of obtaining these curves: "Wärmespannungen beim Abkühlen grosser Güsse bzw. beim Vergüten grosser Schmiedestücke in Form von Vollzylinder" (Thermal Stresses in Cooling Large Castings and in the Heat Treatment of Large Forgings of Solid Cylinders), *Stahl und Eisen*, v 47, 1927, pp 1123–27; similar discussion for tubular members in v 48, 1928, pp 225–28.
54. See Fig. 34 in recent data and references regarding these factors by E. Griffith, *Physical Properties of a Series of Steels" pt 2*, Iron and Steel Inst advance copy dated Sept 1946; S. M. Shelton and W. H. Swanger, "Thermal Conductivity of Irons and Steels and Some Other Metals in the Tem-

perature Range 0° to 600°C" *Trans Am Soc Steel Treating*, v 21, 1933, p 1061.

55. R. A. GRANGE AND H. M. STEWART, "The Temperature Range of Martensite Formation," *Am Inst Mining and Met Engrs Tec Publ* 1996, 1946. Twelve constructional steels of carbon and low alloy type were investigated and it was found that martensite formation began and ended in the range of about 700° to 300°F.

56. H. SCOTT, "Origin of Quenching Cracks," *U. S. Bur Standards Sci Paper* 513, 1925, pp 299–344.

57. H. BÜHLER AND E. SCHEIL, "Zusammenwirken von Wärme—und Unwandlungsspannungen in Abgeschreckten Stählen" (Combined Effect of Thermal and Transformation Stresses in Quenched Steels), *Archiv für das Eisenhüttenwesen*, v 6, Jan 1933, pp 283–88.

58. H. BÜHLER, "Beitrag zur Frage der Eigenspannungen in Stahl durch Wärmebehandlung" (Contribution on the Question of Residual Stresses in Steel Due to Heat Treatment), Vereinigte Stahlwerke Dortmund, *Mitteilungen Forschungs-Institut*, v 2, 1930–32, pp 149–92. These data were further abstracted in ref 52. All residual stresses determined by boring-out method.

59. S. FUCHS, "Über den Einfluss von Langsbohrungen auf die Eigenspannungen Wärmebehandelter Stahlzylinder" (Effect of Longitudinal Bores on the Residual Stresses of Heat-Treated Steel Cylinders), Vereinigte Stahlwerke Dortmund, *Mitteilungen Forschungs-Institut*, v 3, 1933, pp 199–234. Also summarized by H. BUCHHOLTZ AND H. BÜHLER, "Residual Stresses in Heat Treated Hollow Cylinders," *Archiv für das Eisenhüttenwesen*, v 7, 1933–34, pp 315–17.

60. G. SACHS, "Röntenographische Untersuchungen an Schweissnähten" (X-Ray Investigation of Welded Joints), *Mitteilungen des deutschen Materialprüfungsanstalten*, Sonderheft 10, 1930, p. 145.

61. G. SACHS, "Internal Stresses in Piston Rods of a Large Diesel Engine Ocean Liner," *Trans. Am Soc Metals*, v 27, 1939, pp 821–36.

62. I. KONTOROVICH AND L. LIVSHITS, "Dependence of Residual Stresses in Steel upon Austenitic Grain Size," *Stahl*, v 1, n 4, May 1941, p 58–60.

63. A. P. SEASHOLTZ, "Modern Heat Treating Practice," *Steel*, Apr 29, 1946, p 30.

64. H. S. RAWDON AND S. EPSTEIN, "Structure of Martensitic Carbon Steels and Changes in Microstructure Which Occur upon Tempering," *U. S. Bur Standards Sci. Papers*, v 18, 1925, pp 373–409.

65. F. F. LUCAS, "On the Art of Metallography," *Trans AIME*, v 95, 1931, pp 11–44.

66. E. S. DAVENPORT, "Microscopic Cracks in Hardened Steel, Their Effects and Elimination," E. S. ROFF, E. C. BAIN, *Trans Am Soc Metals*, 1934, v 22, pp 289–310.

67. E. S. DAVENPORT, "Austempering," *Heat Treating and Forging*, v 23, 1937, pp 170–73, 177.

68. J. CAILLAUD, "Internal Stresses in Centrifugal Cast Steel Tubes," *Le gènie civil*, v 123, Jan 1946, p 12; abstracted in *Engrs Digest* (British), v 7, n 6, June 1946, p 162; Am ed, v 3, n 6, June 1946, p 302.

69. L. NORTHCOTT AND D. MCLEAN, "Centrifugally Cast Steel," *Steel*, April 29, 1946, pp 94–104.

70. E. R. JOHNSON, S. W. POOLE AND J. A. ROSA, "Flaking in Alloy Steels," *Open Hearth Proc AIME*, v 27, 1944, p 358–77.

71. J. H. ANDREW, A. K. BOSE, G. A. GEACH, AND H. LEE, "The Formation of Hair-line Cracks" part 1, *J. Iron and Steel Inst (Lond.)*, v 146, n 2, 1942, pp 193–202; part 2, p 203–43; further correspondence, v 147, n 1, 1943, p 453–57; also paper 22, 1946, *J. Iron and Steel Inst*, "The Removal of Hydrogen From Steel." See *Engineering*, Dec 6, 1946, pp 509–10, for discussion.

72. C. Zappfe, "Fish-Eyes in Steel Welds Caused by Hydrogen," *Metal Progress*, v 42, Aug 1942, pp 201–06; C. A. Zappfe and C. E. Sims, "Hydrogen in Steel and Cast Iron," *Metals and Alloys*, v 13, 1941, pp 737–42; "Hydrogen Embrittlement, Internal Stress and Defects in Steel," *Trans AIME*, v 145, 1941, pp 225–71.

73. R. E. Cramer and E. C. Bast, "The Production of Flakes by Treating Molten Steel with Hydrogen and the Time of Cooling Necessary to Prevent Their Formation," *Trans Am Soc Metals*, v 27, 1939, pp 433–57; v 25, 1937, pp 923–34.

74. E. Houdremont and H. Schrader, "Combined Action of Hydrogen and Stresses in the Formation of Flakes," *Stahl und Eisen*, v 61, 1941, pp 649–53.

75 H. F. Moore, "Annual Progress Reports of the Joint Investigation of Fissures in Railroad Rails," *Univ Ill Eng Exp* 1935–45.

76. M. Lefevre, "Snowflakes and Hair-line Cracks in Weld Metal," *Revue de la soudure*, v 1, n 2, 1945, pp 39–49; *Arcos*, v 23, n 102, July 1946, pp 2411–429; abstracted in *Engrs Digest*, v 4, n 3, Mar 1947, pp 131–35.

77. G. Sachs, "Der Nachweis innerer Spannungen in Stangen und Rohren" (Determination of Internal Stresses in Bars and Tubes), *Zeitschrift für Metallkunde*, v 19, 1927, pp 352–57.

78. H. Bühler and E. H. Schulz, *Zeitschrift für Metallkunde*, v 26, 1934, pp 199–203.

79. W. Fahrenhorst and G. Sachs, "Über das Aufreiben von kaltgezogenem Rundeisen" (The Cracking of Cold-Drawn Steel Bars), *Metallwirtschaft*, v 10, n 41, 1931, pp 783–88 and 880–81.

80. G. Sachs, "Innere Spannungen in Metallen" (Internal Stresses in Metals), *Zeitschrift*, v 71, 1927, pp 1511–516.

81. H. Bühler and H. Buchholtz, "Einfluss der Querschnittsverminderung beim Kaltziehen auf die Spannungen in Rundstangen" (Influence of Cold-Draw Reduction upon the stresses in Round Bars), *Arch für das Eisenhüttenwesen*, v 7, n 7, 1934, pp 427–30.

82. W. Linicus and G. Sachs, "Untersuchung eines gebrochenen Drahtseils" (Investigation of Broken Wire Cable) *Mitteilungen Forschungs-Institut*, Dortmund, v 2, 1931, pp 17–32.

83. S. Timoshenko, *Theory of Elasticity*, McGraw-Hill Book Co, New York, 1934.

84. C. H. Kent, "Thermal Stresses in Thin Walled Cylinders," *J Applied Mechanics, Trans ASME*, 1931, v 53, pp 167–180.

85. "Seventh report on the Heterogeniety of Steel Ingots," *First Report of the Ingot Moulds Subcommittee*, Iron and Steel Inst, 1937, p 143; *Second Report* 25, Special Report 16, 1939, p 265.

86. T. Land, "Thermal Stresses in Ingot Moulds," *J Iron and Steel Inst*, v 147, n 1, 1943, pp 75–93.

87. K. Schönrock, "Amount of Internal Stresses in Rails Treated in Various Manners," *Proceedings 4th Int Rail Assembly*, Düsseldorf, 1938, pp 14–25.

88. P. Bardenheuer, "Eigenspannungen in Walzstäben unter besonderer Berücksichtigung der Schienen" (Residual Stresses in Rolled Parts with Special Regard to Rails), *Stahl und Eisen*, v 45, 1925, pp 1098–101.

89. J. R. Freeman and G. W. Quick, "Secondary Brittleness in Rail Steel" *Iron Age*, v 125, 1930, p 714; "Tensile Properties of Rail and Other Steels at Elevated Temperatures," *Trans AIME*, v 90, 1930, pp 225–79.

90. H. Meier, "Eigenspannungen in Eisenbahnschienen" (Residual Stresses in Railroad Rails), *Organ für die Fortschritte des Eisenbahnwesens*, v 91, 1936, p 320.

91. F. Regler, *Proc 2d Int. Rail Assembly*, Zürich, 1932, pp 188–201.

92. W. J. Iweronowa and W. Akinow, *J Tech Physics (Leningrad)*, v 7, 1937, pp 917–25.

93. J. Terminassov and L. Charsson, *J Tech Physics (Leningrad)*, v 7, 1937, p 1363.

94. R. Glocker, Materialprüfung mit Röntgenstrahlen (*Material Testing with X-Rays*), 2d ed., Julius Springer, Berlin, 1936, p 304.

95. G. M. Magee and E. E. Cress, "Strains Produced on End of Outer Rail Head of 6 Degree Curve," *Bul Am Ry Eng Assn.*, v 47, n 458, pp 438–43, Feb 1946.

96. H. Meier, "Eigenspannungen in Eisenbahnschienen" (Residual Stresses in Railroad Rails), *Vereines deutscher Ingenieure Zeitschrift*, v 81, n 12, pp 362–63, Mar 20, 1937.

97. M. Ros, "Laboratory Tests and Experiences with Ordinary, Compound, and Heat Treated Steel Rails," *Proc 4th Int Rail Assembly*, Düsseldorf, 1938, pp 97–105.

98. H. Staudinger, "Biegewechselfestigkeit einsatzgehärteter und nitrierter Stähle mit Schleifrissen" (Alternating Bending Strength of Case-Hardened and Nitrided Steels with Grinding Cracks), *Verein deutscher Ingenieure Zeitschrift*, v 88, Dec 23, 1944, pp 681–86. This is abstract of dissertation by author at Tech Hochschule, Berlin.

99. H. Wiegand and R. Scheinost, "Einfluss der Einsatzhärtung auf die Biege— und Verdrehwechselfestigkeit von glatten und quergebohrten Probestäben" (Influence of Case Carburizing upon the Alternating Bending and Torsional Strength of Smooth and Transversely Bored Test Specimens), *Archiv für des Eisenhüttenwesen*, v 12, 1938–39, pp 445–48.

100. H. Wiegand, "Oberfläche und Dauerfestigkeit" (Surface and Fatigue Strength), dissertation, Tech Hochschule, Darmstadt, 1940. Reviewed in ref 132.

101. M. Ulrich, "Increasing the Fatigue Strength of Gear Wheels by Special Shaping, Hardening, and Machining of the Root Radius," *Luftwissen*, v 9, n 11, pp 311–12, Nov 1942, see *J. Iron and Steel Inst*, translation 198.

102. E. G. Herbert, "The Work-Hardening of Steel by Abrasion," *J Iron and Steel Inst*, n 2, 1927, pp 265–82.

103. L. P. Tarasov, "Detection, Causes, and Prevention of Injury in Ground Surfaces," *Trans Am Soc. Metals*, v 36, 1946.

104. G. R. Brophy, "Stresses and Cracks in Hardened and Ground Steel," *Trans Am Soc Steel Treating*, v 18, July–Dec 1930, pp 423–39.

105. E. Mickel and P. Sommer, "Einfluss des Stahles auf die Haltbarkeit von Kolbenbolzen" (Influence of the Kind of Steel on the Endurance of Piston Pins), *Arch Eisenh*, v 17, n 9–10, Mar–Apr 1944, pp 227–34.

106. L. A. Glikman and V. A. Stepanov, "Residual Stresses Caused by Grinding," *J Tech Physics (Leningrad)*, v 16, n 7, p 791–802, 1946; *Engrs Digest*, v 4, n 8, pp 378–79, Aug 1947.

107. A. Holloway, "Hardening by Grinding," *Machinery (British)*, Mar 7, 1946, pp 305–06.

108. Kaizo Monma, "Grinding Cracks in Quenched Steels," *Iron Age*, Feb 29, 1940, pp 44–45.

109. John Wulff, "Surface Finish and Structure," AIME, *Metal Tech Paper* 1318, June 1941, pp 295–300.

110. F. P. Bowden and L. Leben, "The Nature of Sliding and the Analysis of Friction," *Proc Royal Soc (Lond.)*, v 169, 1939, pp 371–91.

111. L. E. Benson, "The Quenching of Steel After Tempering and the Impact Test," *Engineering*, Aug 14, 1942, pp 134–35; Grinding of Gear Teeth discussed by R. Greaves, E. Kirtowsky and C. Lipson, "Residual Stress Study," *Proc Soc Experimental Stress Analysis*, v 2, n 2, pp 44–58, 1945.

112. E. H. Schulz and H. Buchholtz, "Dauerfestigkeit von Verbindungen aus Baustahl St. 52" (Fatigue Strength of Connections Consisting of Constructional Steel St. 52), *Stahl and Eisen*, v 53, n 21, pp 545–53, May 25, 1933.

"Application of Iron, Steel, and Alloy Rivets," *Ry Mech Eng*, Nov 1940, pp 463–48; Mar 1942, pp 101–04; Feb 1943, pp 77–9; W. M. WILSON, W. H. BRUCKNER, AND T. H. McCRACKIN, "Tests of Riveted and Welded Joints in Low Alloy Structural Steels," *Univ Ill Eng Exp Sta Bul* 337, 1942, 76 pp; A. E. R. DE JONGE, *Bibliography on Riveted Joints*, American Society of Mechanical Engineers, 1945, 250 pp.

113. R. SCHMIDT, "The Bending Fatigue Strength of Machined Crankshafts after Straightening, with Notes on the Stress Distribution Obtained by Extensometer and X-Ray Diffraction Measurements," *Luftwissen*, v 9, Sept 1942, pp 263–67; see *J Iron and Steel Inst*, translation 157.

114. J. T. NORTON AND D. ROSENTHAL, "An Investigation of the Behavior of Residual Stresses under External Load and Their Effect on Safety," *J Am Welding Soc, Research Supp*, v 8, Feb 1943, pp 63–78.

115. H. BÜHLER AND H. BUCHHOLTZ, "Über die Wirkung von Eigenspannungen auf die Schwingungsfestigkeit" (The Effect of Residual Stress on the Dynamic Bending Strength), *Mitteilungen Forschungs-Institut*, Dortmund, v 3, n 8, Sept 1933, pp 235–48; "Die Wirkung von Eigenspannungen auf die Biegeschwingungsfestigkeit," *Stahl and Eisen*, v 53, Dec 1933, pp 1330–1332. X-Ray study of change in residual stresses due to alternating bending was made by F. GIESEN AND R. GLOCKER, "Röntgenographische Bestimungen der zeitlichen Änderung des Eigenspannungszustandes bei Biegewechselbeanspruchung," *Zeitschrift für Metallkunde*, v 30, 1938, pp 297–98.

116. E. H. SCHULZ AND H. BUCHHOLTZ, "Über die Entwicklung der Dauerprüfung in Deutschland" (The Effect of Residual Stresses on the Bending Fatigue Strength, Development of Fatigue Testing in Germany), *Internationaler Verband für Materialprüfung Kongressbuch*, Zürich, 1932 1, pp 278–303.

117. O. J. HORGER, "Effect of Surface Rolling on the Fatigue Strength of Steel," *J Applied Mechanics, Trans ASME*, v 57, Dec 1935, pp 128–36 PA.

118. H. J. GOUGH AND H. J. TAPSELL, *Aeronautical Research Comm, Reports and Memoranda*, n 1012, April 1926.

119. H. F. MOORE AND T. M. JASPER, "Investigation of the Fatigue of Metals," Univ Ill Eng Exp Sta Bul 142, 1924, 86 pp.

120. J. B. KOMMERS, "Understressing and Notch Sensitivity in Fatigue," *Eng News-Rec*, v 109, Sept 22, 1932, pp 353–55; *Proc ASTM*, v 30, 1930, p 368; *Proc ASTM*, v 43, 1943, p 749.

121. H. J. FRENCH, "Fatigue and the Hardening of Steels," *Trans Am Soc Steel Treating*, v 21, Oct 1933, pp 899–946.

122. J. A. BENNETT, "Study of the Damaging Effect of Fatigue Stressing on SAE X4130 Steel," *U S Bur Standards Research Paper* RP1733, v 37, Aug 1946, pp 123–39.

123. H. W. RUSSELL AND W. A. WELCKER, "Damage and Overstress in the Fatigue of Ferrous Metals," *Proc ASTM*, v 36, pt 2, 1936, pp 118–38.

124. A. THUM AND A. ERKER, "Einfluss von Wärme-Eigenspannungen auf die Dauerfestigkeit" (Effect of Thermal Residual Stress on the Fatigue Strength), *Verein deutscher Ingenieure Zeitschrift*, v 81, Feb 27, 1937, pp 276–78.

125. F. BOLLENRATH, *Abh Aerodyn Inst Techn Hochsch Aachen*, v 14, Berlin, 1934.

126. H. BÜHLER AND W. LOHMANN, "Beitrag zur Frage der Schweissspannungen" (Welding stresses) *Elektroschweissung*, v 5, 1934, pp 141–5, 165–70.

127. F. BOLLENRATH, "Behinderte Formänderung in Schweissnähten" (Residual Stress in Welded Joints), *Stahl and Eisen*, v 54, 1934, pp 630–34, 873–78.

128. E. SIEBEL AND M. PFENDER, "Formänderungen und Eigenspannungen von Schweissverbindungen" (Residual Strain and Stress in Welded Connections), *Archiv für das Eisenhüttenwesen*, v 7, 1933–34, pp 407–15. Also W. H. BRUCHNER AND W. H. MUNSE, "The Effect of Metallurgical Changes Due to Heat Treatment upon the Fatigue Strength of Carbon Steel Plates," *Welding J*, Oct 1944, pp 499s–510s.

129. H. WIEGAND, "Innere Kerbwirkung und Dauerfestigkeit," ("Internal Notch Effect and Fatigue Strength"), *Metallwirtschaft*, v 18, 1937, pp 83–5.

130. W. G. JOHNSON, "Practical Applications of the Motor Generator Type of Induction Heating, (Frequencies up to 10,000 Cycles)," Article appeared in the book *Induction Heating*. A series of Five Lectures, Am. Soc. for Metals, Cleveland, Ohio, 1946.

131. J. O. ALMEN, "Some Needed Precautions When Induction and Flame Hardening," *Metal Progress*, v 46, Dec 1944, pp 1263–267.

132. H. WIEGAND, "Oberfläche und Dauerfestigkeit" (Effect of Surface Treatment on Fatigue Strength), BMW Flugmotorenbau, 1940, *Verein deutscher Ingenieure Zeitschrift*, v 84, 1940, p 505. See *J Iron and Steel Inst*, transactions 155, Oct 1943.

133. C. G. WILLIAMS AND J. S. BROWN, "Fatigue Strength of Crankshafts," *Engineering*, v 154, pp 58–9, 78–80.

134. W. G. JOHNSON, "Residual Stresses in Crankshafts," *Proc Soc Experimental Stress Analysis*, v 2, n 1, pp 214–25, 1944.

135. A. THUM, "Der Werkstoff in der konstruktiven Berechnung" (Materials in the Calculation of Design), *Stahl and Eisen*, v 59, 1939, pp 252–63.

136. H. CORNELIUS AND BOLLENRATH, "Dauerhaltbarkeit von hohlen Kurbelwellenzapfen mit Innenverstärkung an der Ölbohrung" (Endurance of Hollow Crankshaft Pins with Internal Reinforcement at the Oil Hole), *Verein deutscher Ingenieure Zeitschrift*, v 82, 1938, pp 885–89.

137. J. H. ZIMMERMAN, "Flame Testing," *Welding J*, Feb 1940.

138. "Crankshaft Hardening," *Steel*, Apr 29, 1940, pp 51, 52, and 78.

139. D. L. MARTIN AND F. E. WILEY, *Induction Hardening of Plain Carbon Steels*, *Trans* American Society for Metals, v 34, 1945, pp 351–406.

140. E. V. SHLEYER AND I. A. ODING, "The Influence of High Frequency Surface Hardening on the Mechanical Properties of Structural Steels," *Vestnik Metallopromyshlennosti*, n 7, 1940, pp 7–17.

141. I. E. KONTOROVICH AND L. C. LIVSHITS, "Residual Internal Stresses in Steels Hardened by the High Frequency Surface Hardening Process," *Metallurg (Russian)*, n 8, 1940, pp 30–7.

142. "Induction Hardening Ram-Tapered Areas of Steam Hammer Piston Rods," *Industrial Heating*, v 13, April 1946, pp 628, 630, 632; Also see *Metal Progress*, v 49, n 4, April 1946, p 753; J. M. LESSELS, "The Measurement of Stresses in Steam Hammer Rods," *Proc Soc Experimental Stress Analysis*, v 2, n 1, pp 34–40, 1944.

143. G. C. RIEGEL, "Case Hardening Large Gears with High Frequency Current," *Metal Progress*, July 1943, pp 78–83.

144. D. L. MARTIN AND R. A. GEHR, "Induction Hardening of Steel," *Steel*, v 120, Feb 3, 1947, pp 100–01, 148–56.

145. R. H. LAUDERDALE, "Basic Requirements of Materials for Induction Hardening," *Product Eng*, v 18, May 1947, pp 110–15.

146. O. J. HORGER AND T. V. BUCKWALTER, "Fatigue Strength Improved by Flame Treatment," *Iron Age*, Dec 18, 1941, pp 47–53; *J. Applied Mechanics, Trans ASME*, v 64, June 1942, pp A-85–90; *Proc ASTM*, v 41, 1941, pp 682–95.

147. O. J. HORGER AND W. I. CANTLEY, "Design of Crank Pins for Locomotives," *J. Applied Mechanics, Trans ASME*, Mar 1946, pp A-17–33

148. O. J. HORGER AND T. V. BUCKWALTER, "Fatigue Strength of 2–in Diameter Axles with Surfaces Metal Coated and Flame Hardened," Proc ASTM, 40, 1940, pp 733–45

149. H. KALLEN AND H. NIENHAUS, "Anwendung der Oberflächenhärtung bei Achsen und Wellen von Schienenfahrzeugen" (Investigation of Railroad Axles Which Were Flame-Hardened), *Glasers Annalen*, v 121, July 15, 1937, pp 45–8.

150. H. Voss, "Örtliche Oberflächenhärtung von Kurbelwellen" (Local Surface Hardening of Crankshafts), *Verein deutscher Ingenieure Zeitschrift*, v 79, 1935, pp 743–49.

151. See discussion of ref 7 by S. Way, *J. Applied Mechanics, Trans ASME*, v 47, June 1935, p A-69–71. Also discussion of ref 8 by R. E. Peterson and A. M. Wahl, v 58, June 1936, pp A-74–75.

152. Hans Bühler, "Eigenspannungen in Prägepolierten Stahlstangen" (Residual Stresses in Surface-Rolled Steel Bars), *Archiv für das Eisenhuttenwesen*, v 11, May 1935, pp 515–16.

153. R. Mailänder, "Eigenspannungen und Biegewechselfestigkeit verstickter Stahlproben" (Residual Stresses and the Alternating Bending Strength of Nitrided Steel Specimens), *Archiv für das Eisenhüttenwesen*, n 6, Dec 1936, pp 257–61.

154. F. Gentner, "Günstige Druckeigenspannungen in Nitrierschichten" (Favorable Residual Stresses in Nitrided Layers), *Technische Mitteilungen Krupp*, n 1, Feb 1937, pp 19–21.

155. D. Landau, *Fatigue of Metals*, Nitralloy Corp, New York, 1942.

156. H. Wiegand, "Verhalten harter Oberflächenschichten bei Betriebsbeanspruchung" (Behavior of Surface Layers in the Presence of Operating Loads), *Verein deutscher Ingenieure Zeitschrift*, v 87, Mar 6, 1943, pp 137–38.

157. H. Sutton, "Fatigue Properties of Nitrided Steel," *Metal Treatment*, v 2, 1936, pp 89–92.

158. Discussion by H. A. Dickie, (p 440), of paper by G. A. Hankins and M. L. Becker, "Effect of Surface Conditions Produced by Heat Treatment on the Fatigue Resistance of Spring Steels," *J Iron and Steel Inst*, v 124, n 2, pp 387–460, 1931.

159. J. C. R. Woodvine, "The Behavior of Case Hardened Parts Under Fatigue Stresses," *Carnegie Scholarship Memoirs Iron and Steel Inst*, 1924, pp 197–237.

160. R. E. Peterson and J. M. Lessells, "Effect of Surface Strengthening on Shafts Having a Fillet or a Transverse Hole," *Proc Soc Experimental Stress Analysis*, v 2, n 1, pp 191–99.

161. D. G. Richards, "A Study of Certain Mechanically Induced Residual Stresses," *Proc Soc Experimental Stress Analysis*, v 3, n 1, 1945, pp 40–61.

162. J. O. Almen, R. L. Mattson, and H. E. Fonda, "Effect of Shot Blasting on the Mechanical Properties of Steel," pt 1, 2, and 3, *Office Sci Research and Develop Reports* 3274, 4825, and 6647.

163. H. F. Moore, "Shot Peening," American Foundry and Equipment Co, Mishawaka, Ind.

164. H. F. Moore, "A Study of Residual Stress and Size Effect," *Proc Soc Experimental Stress Analysis*, v 2, n 1, pp 171–77.

165. O. J. Horger and C. H. Lipson, "Automotive Rear Axles and Means of Improving Their Fatigue Resistance," *ASTM Tech Publ* 72, 1946.

166. A. M. Wahl, *Mechanical Springs*, Penton Publishing Co, 1930.

167. M. L. Becker and C. E. Phillips, "Internal Stresses and Their Effect on the Fatigue Resistance of Spring Steels," *J Iron and Steel Inst*, v 133, 1936, pp 427–53.

168. C. O. Herb, "Making Torsion Bar Springs," *Machinery*, v 51, Aug 1945, pp 141–49.

169. "Torsion Bar Springs," *Metal Progress*, May 1947, pp 771–74.

170. H. O. Fuchs and R. L. Mattson, "Measurement of Residual Stresses in Torsion Bar Springs," *Proc Soc Experimental Stress Analysis*, v 4, n 1, pp 64–71, 1946.

171. G. Brewer, "Residual Stresses in Wire Loops at Anchorage Shoes or Grommets," *Metal Progress*, v 44, Sept 1943, pp 441–47.

172. K. Arnstein and E. L. Shaw, "Fatigue Problems in the Aircraft Industry," *Metals and Alloys*, 1939, pp 203–09.

173. G. SEEGER, "Dauerfestigkeit unter Druckvorspannung" (Fatigue Strength in the Presence of Compressive Prestress), *Verein deutscher Ingenieure Zeitschrift*, v 80, May 30, 1936, pp 698–99.

174. J. O. ALMEN, "On the Strength of Highly Stressed, Dynamically Loaded Bolts and Studs," *J Soc Automotive Engrs*, v 52, Apr 1944, pp 151–58.

175. A. THUM AND M. WÜRGES, "Die zweckmässige Vorspannung in Schrauben-verbindungen" (The Suitable Prestress in Screw Connections), *Deutsche Kraftfahrtforschung*, Verein Deutscher Ingenieure, Berlin, n 43, 1940.

176. L. MARTINAGLIA, "Schraubenverbindungen—Stand der Technik" (Screw Connections—Present State of Technique), *Schweizerische* Bauzeitung, v 119, Mar 7, 1942, pp 107–12; Mar 14, 1942, pp 122–26.

177. H. DOBKIN, "Prestressing Rotating Disks," *Steel*, v 118, June 3, 1946, pp 104–06, 150.

178. "Precast Prestressed Railway Bridge," *Engineering*, v 164, Sept 12, 1947, p 263.

179. R. L. M'ITMOYLE, "Prestressed Concrete Bridge Beams Being Tested in England," *Ry Age*, v 123, Sept 20, 1947, pp 47–82.

180. W. WILSON AND R. BROWN, "Effect of Residual Longitudinal Stresses Upon the Load Carrying Capacity of Steel Columns," *Univ Ill Exp Sta Bul* 280, 1935, 26 pp.

180. K. BUNGARDT, "Influence of Degree of Prestretching and Precompression on the Buckling Strength of Light Metal," *U. S. Dept Commerce Report* PB37652.

182. F. KÖRBER, A. EICHINGER, AND H. MÖLLER, "The Behavior Under Tensile Stress of Metals Deformed by Compression," *Mitteillungen Kaiser-Wilhelm Institut für Eisenforschung* v 23, n 9, 1941, pp 123–33; see *J Iron and Steel Inst*, translation 258, Jan 1946.

183. G. BREWER, "Failure of Spring Loops by Stress Corrosion," *Metal Progress*, v 47, Apr 1945, pp 707–12.

184. W. BOAS AND R. W. K. HONEYCOMBE, "Thermal Fatigue of Metals," *Nature*, v 153, Apr 22, 1944, pp 494–95.

185. R. W. HONEYCOMBE, "Conditions Leading to Fatigue Failure in Sleeve Bearings," *Univ Melbourne Symposium on Failure of Metals by Fatigue*, paper 21, Dec 1946.

186. E. SCHMIDT AND W. BOAS, *Kristallplastizität*, Berlin, J. Springer, 1935. p 202.

187. F. LASZLO, "Tesselated Stresses," *J Iron and Steel Inst*, pt 1, v 147, no. 1, pp 173–99, 1943; pt 2, v 148, n 2, pp 137–159, 1943; pt 3, v 150, n 2, pp 183–209, 1944; pt 4, v 152, n 2, pp 207–28, 1945; "Graphitisation of Steel Influenced by Tessellated Stresses," v 147, n 1, p 201–04, 1943.

188. G. WASSERMAN, "Über Abschreckspannungen" (Quenching Stresses), *Mitteillungen Kaiser-Wilhelm-Institut für Eisenforschung*, v 17, 1935, pp 167–74.

189. A. VON ZEERLEDER, "Quenching Stresses in Aluminum Alloys," *J Inst Metals*, v 67, 1941, pp 87–99.

190. G. FORREST, "Some Experiments on the Effects of Residual Stresses on the Fatigue of Aluminum Alloys," *J Inst Metals (Lond.)*, v 72, 1946, pp 498–527.

191. G. FISCHER, "Über die Kerbwirkung bei Dauerwechselbeanspruchung und den Einfluss der Kaltverformung auf die Dauerhaltbarkeit" (Notch Effect with Alternating Stress and the Influence of Cold Working on the Fatigue Strength), *Luftfahrtforschung*, v 1, 1938, p. 517.

192. G. H. FIELD, H. SUTTON AND H. E. DIXON, *Trans Inst Welding*, v 6, 1943, p 49.

193. L. E. BENSON, "Control of Internal Stresses in Heat Treated Aluminum Alloy Parts," *J Inst Metals (Lond.)*, v 72, 1946, pp 501–10.

194. L. FROMMER AND E. H. LLOYD, "The Measurements of Residual Stresses in

Metals by the X-Ray Back Reflection Method, With Special Reference to Industrial Components in Aluminum Alloys," *J Inst Metals (Lond.)*, v 70, 1944, pp 91–124.

195. GROGAN AND CLAYTON, "Dimensional Stability of Heat Treated Aluminum Alloys," *J Inst Metals (Lond.)*, v 45, 1931, p 157.

196. L. W. KEMPF, H. L. HOPKINS, AND E. V. IVANSO, "Internal Stresses in Quenched Aluminum and Some Aluminum Alloys," *AIME, Metals Tech Publ* 535, Feb, 1934, pp 1–23.

197. A. PHILLIPS AND R. M. BRICK, "Effect of Quenching Strains on Lattice Parameter and Hardness Values of High Purity Aluminum—Copper Alloys," *AIME Metals Tech Publ* 563, Sept 1934, 19 pp; *Tech Publ* 650, Sept 1935, 16 pp.

198. L. W. KEMPF AND K. R. VAN HORN, "Relief of Residual Stress in Some Aluminum Alloys," *AIME Metals Tech Publ* 1334, June 1941, 15 pp.

Above three references are from the Series: *Metals Technology*, Am. Inst. Mining & Met. Engrs, Tech Publications, n 535, n 650, n 1334.

CHAPTER 12

METHODS OF CRACK DETECTION

By Charles Lipson

A. INTRODUCTION

Cracks generally are produced by any of the following conditions:

1. Machining and grinding operations.
2. Working operation.
3. Service loading.

Machining, if done at excessive speeds or excessive feed, may result in tearing of metal and the resultant crack formation. The cracks are surface cracks, and their direction corresponds to the direction of feed. Grinding will produce cracks as a result of localized heating when the speed of grinding is excessive. Severe grinding produces residual tensile stresses which exceed the tensile strength of the material and exhibit themselves in the form of grinding checks and cracks. These are always located at the surface, and their direction and distribution corresponds to the direction of grinding. A region particularly susceptible to the formation of grinding cracks is the transition zone between a straight and a filleted section, since at this point two different grinding operations form a junction resulting in a notch or an actual crack.

Cracks may also result from improper forging, casting, rolling, and heating operations or during uneven cooling from the finishing temperature. These cracks will occur at any depth, and their orientation may be definite, dependent on the direction determined by working, (such as rolling marks), or they may occur at random as in the case of quenching cracks. For example, cracks produced in rolling or drawing rods, tubes, or wires are usually parallel to the axis.

Service loading results in cracks at the surface, or in the case of surface-treated parts they may occur at the junction of the case and the core. They frequently occur at a discontinuity in section where the effect of stress concentration is particularly pronounced. The direction of the cracks usually corresponds to the direction or plane of the applied load.

The mere existence of a crack does not necessarily indicate a dangerous condition, and many cases are on record where the cracked part behaved satisfactorily in service. Whether a crack will or will not lead to failure depends on several conditions, the principal of which are: shape of the crack, location of the crack, type of material, and the conditions of loading.

The shape of the crack is related to the direction of the applied stress, and the crack is particularly significant if its principal dimension is at right angle to the direction of the tensile stress. Location of the crack is also significant, and in a piece subjected to a bending or torsional load a crack found at the neutral axis is not dangerous. The same crack would be dangerous if a pure axial load was applied, a rare case in most industrial applications. Since the maximum stress in bending and in torsion occurs at or near the surface, surface cracks must be regarded as real danger points.

The type of material is also important in deciding whether a given crack might result in failure. Some materials, such as heat-treated steels of high hardness, are "notch sensitive," whereas annealed steels are less susceptible to notches. Cast iron is particularly not sensitive to notches. A crack, therefore, that in cast iron will not result in failure, in hardened steel would be particularly dangerous.

As to the condition of loading, cracks may lead to failure only when the part is subjected to fatigue loading. Under static loading the existence of a crack is not deleterious to the strength of the part.

It is thus obvious that, although the experimental methods of crack detection, particularly as set up in inspection processes, are simple, the matter of interpretation of these cracks is a matter of judgment and calls for knowledge of stress analysis, metallurgy, and service operations.

The methods for crack detection described in this chapter are only the representative or typical methods, or those that offer promise for future development. Presumably any number of test methods can be developed from any set of physical conditions, but only those that have the obvious feature of simplicity and reliability or that furnish a particularly effective solution to a representative group of problems are considered here. None of these methods represents a solution to all the problems because of the great diversity of manufactured parts and conditions.

Present discussion does not include the radiographic methods of crack detection (X rays, gamma rays), and a separate chapter in the handbook is devoted to this topic.

B. General Methods

In spite of the significant progress made in the field of crack detection, many methods which have been in use in the past still find wide application at the present time. These methods are based on simple mechanical or optical principles, and they are characterized by a simplicity of operation.

1. Visual Inspection. This is undoubtedly the oldest method used in crack detection, and it can be considered as indispensable in all engineering inspection problems. It is used both aided and unaided by some additional device such as a magnifying glass or photographic camera. When used by trained personnel, it represents an effective means for detecting surface cracks, blowholes, shrinkage cracks in castings and forgings, and the like.

2. Acoustic Methods. The simplest and probably the oldest method of testing by acoustic means, and one that is still extensively used in practice, involves hammering or tapping the part and listening to the sound produced. The assumption is that a part free from cracks will vibrate at its natural frequency. Conversely, absence of a "pure" note should be an indication of the existence of a crack.

This method of testing is not always reliable. It is reported, for example, that, when wheels, in which very large cracks were artificially produced by drastic quenching, were struck by a hammer, they rang as well as sound wheels. The difficulty is that longitudinal waves of medium frequency spread around the cracks instead of being stopped by them. In addition, the note emitted by the struck body depends on the degree of restraint imposed on the body by the method of support. Besides, the natural frequency of the struck body may be so high as to be inaudible to the human ear.

For these reasons the acoustic method, though simple in operation and very effective in many cases, cannot be considered as totally reliable. The degree of its advantage, however, is attested by its widespread use in industry. It is particularly used in the railroad industry to test the soundness of wheels; and in the shipping industry to test steel castings for ship hulls and anchors, on pipes, forgings, welds, and the like.

A refinement of the acoustic method involves the use of the stethoscope, and successful results are reported by the Union Carbide and Carbon Company in the examination of welded tanks, pipes, and so on. Tests conducted, however, at the National Physical Laboratory on welded structures are not particularly encouraging.

The acoustic method may be combined with a magnetic method to produce satisfactory results. The article under test is magnetized so that a magnetic flux passes through the weld. Defects in the weld cause a disturbance in the flux lines, distorting the field in the vicinity of the defect. The "tester" comprises a searching device connected up, through an amplifier, to earphones. The searching device consists of an electromagnetic vibrator which produces a characteristic "hum." The intensity and pitch of the "hum" undergo a change which can be detected in the earphones whenever the searching device approaches the distorted magnetic flux in a defective weld.

3. Damping Method. Detection of cracks by means of damping is relatively new, and it is not yet widely applied in industry. The method involves striking the body with a hammer and measuring consecutive amplitudes of free vibration, from which damping capacity is determined. When an object

is set into free vibration, the amplitudes of these vibrations decrease expo-
nentially.   This is due to internal friction of the object and is known as the
damping property of vibration.   The specific damping capacity may be determined by measuring the logarithmic decrement of vibration.   This can be
obtained by vibrating the object first at its natural frequency and then at
frequencies on each side of the peak frequency and noting the amplitudes.

Since damping capacity is characteristic of the material, the assumption is
that a material having cracks should have a higher damping capacity.   Figure
12-1 shows the directional effect of damping in a material free from defects
compared with a material with inter-
nal cracks.   The sound material shows
a symmetrical distribution of damping
whereas the cracked material shows an
anisotropic damping.

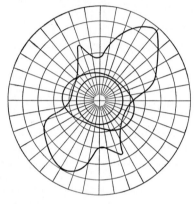

4. Leakage Test.   This form of test
is used for the detection of cracks in
connection with proof-testing pressure
vessels, containers, castings, and so on.
The usual procedure is to paint the
joints and seams with whitewash and
then to fill the container with oil.   The
existence of a crack is revealed by the
leakage of oil with consequent staining
of the whitewash.

Fig. 12-1.   The Directional Effect of
Damping in a Material Free from
Defects and Stressing, Compared
with That in a Stressed Material
with Internal Cracks

The unstressed material shows the
same value for the damping in all
directions, whereas the stressed or
defective material distinctly shows
anisotropic damping

For the detection of cracks in aluminum, anodic oxidation may be used.
If cracks are present, they will appear
as stains on the film of aluminum oxide.

The specific procedure used in leakage tests varies, of course, with each
type of application.   In some cases hot
oil is used; in others steam, air, soapsuds, and so on.   Air is used with the
part under investigation immersed in water and cracks being detected through
the appearance of air bubbles.   In some cases soapsuds are placed inside the
vessel, soap bubbles indicating leakage.

5. Drilling Tests.   Drilling tests accompanied by visual inspection are
extensively used for the detection of cracks in large forgings and castings.   At
particularly suspicious sections a hole is drilled, and the internal walls are
examined for cracks.   The holes are then plugged and welded.

A modification of this method, particularly used for the detection of cracks
in welds, involves milling out a small portion of the weld after which a visual
inspection is made.   This is often facilitated by etching the surface to make the
crack more visible.

6. Oil-Whiting Method.   This method involves the use of oil which would
penetrate a crack.   The oil is then wiped off the surface, and the surface is

coated with whiting. The part is then struck or moved to allow the oil to come out of the cracks and to discolor the whiting.

It is reported that this method is used with some success in the examination of springs for possible cracks. Instead of whiting being used, the springs are sand-blasted, and cracks exhibit themselves as dark streaks on an otherwise smooth surface.

The Zyglo method developed by the Magnaflux Corporation represents another modification of the oil–whiting method. The part is coated with a fluorescent penetrant, which is subsequently wiped off the surface. A developer is then applied to draw the penetrant from the crack, and when viewed under ultraviolet light it locates the position of the crack.

7. Etching Tests. Etchants are extensively used for the detection of cracks; a typical etchant is a 50 per cent solution of hydrochloric acid at approximately 160°F. Special precaution should be taken with hard steels, for if not sufficiently tempered they will develop cracks from the etchant itself. Internal and surface cracks produced by grinding, forging, rolling, quenching, and so on are easily revealed by the etching method.

C. Magnetic Methods

The development of the magnetic methods of crack detection can be traced to the end of the last century when a patent was applied for by A. Herring for detecting cracks in metals by means of a compass needle. This was followed by the work of W. Medcalf, C. W. Burrows, and others. The first practical application of the ideas can be attributed to W. E. Hoke who developed in 1921 an actual magnetic detector which utilized iron particles suspended in oil. This work was extended by A. V. de Forest and his associates who made a major contribution in developing an equipment for the use of industrial plants. Simultaneously,

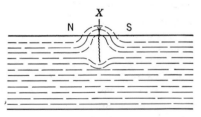

Fig. 12-2. Diversions of Flux by Crack

work was done by Kinsley in developing the magnetic inductive methods for crack detection.

The magnetic method of crack detection is based on the fact that the magnetic permeability of the material is markedly affected by the presence of a crack, permeability being lower for a faulty material than for a sound one. The magnetic lines of force in a magnetized piece will be diverted in those regions where there is a change in permeability, and, since the permeability is less near the crack than in the uncracked area, the lines of force will go through the air over the crack.

This is illustrated in Figs. 12-2 and 12-3. Figure 12-2 shows a magnetized piece, with the magnetic lines of force shown by dotted lines. X is the crack, and it causes the lines of force to pass through the air and set up N and S poles as shown. These poles will attract magnetic particles sprayed or blown on the piece and in this manner will indicate the location of a crack. The same phenomenon is shown in Fig. 12-3 for a bar magnetized by a current flowing longitudinally.

The magnetic method offers many obvious advantages to the technique of crack detection, but it also has two serious limitations. It is not applicable to nonferrous materials, and, in addition, insignificant variations in mechanical properties frequently produce large variations in the magnetic field which in turn may give a false indication of the presence of a crack.

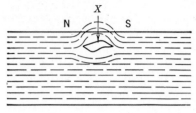

FIG. 12-3. Diversions of Flux by Internal Cavity

8. Methods of Magnetization and Detection. The remanent magnetism in a piece is usually not sufficient to reveal the existence of cracks, and for this reason it is necessary to magnetize the piece by means of an external field. The method of magnetization will depend on several factors, such as the form and size of the part to be inspected, probable location of the crack, and matter of convenience. In cracks at right angle to the axis of the piece, longitudinal magnetization is required which can be affected by a current passing through a conductor wrapped around the piece. On the other hand, if the cracks are parallel to the axis, as in rolling or drawing rods, tubes, and wires, circular magnetization is necessary. This is obtained by passing a current through the piece. If the crack position is random, as in quenching cracks, the field of excitation is combined. By means of a d-c electromagnet, a longitudinal field is applied in order to detect cracks which are at right angle to the field, while at the same time a circular field is applied by an alternating current for the detection of cracks in the longitudinal direction.

Continuous flux is obtained through a d-c magnetization while alternating flux is obtained by means of an alternating current. In general, the advantage of a d-c magnetization lies in the fact that a uniform magnetic field is obtained and a greater degree of penetration is achieved. It is reported, for instance, that cracks 3 in. below the surface have been thus detected. The disadvantage is that the demagnetization process is more involved with direct than with alternating current. If the part is magnetized by an alternating current, demagnetization simply involves stepping down continuously the maximum current applied. In d-c magnetization, however, a special auxiliary demagnetization equipment is needed, or demagnetization must be carried out immediately after the part is magnetized and the current stepped down continuously with frequent changes of the direction of the field.

Detection of cracks involves locating the magnetic poles which appear near the crack across which a magnetic flux was produced. The simplest though very inadequate method utilizes a small pivoted bar magnet which is moved relative to the piece and in this manner discerns a variation in the magnetic field produced by the crack. Another method (the magnetic-inductive method) involves the use of search coils in which a current is induced by the magnetic flux in the specimen. The existence of the crack is detected by the changes in the coil current produced by the changes in the magnetic flux. Still another method involves the use of magnetic particles, dry or in a liquid

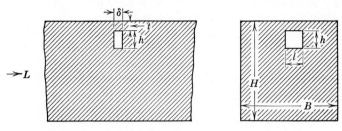

FIG. 12-4. Description of the Parameter in Fig. 12-5

form, to delineate the form of the crack. This method is known as the magnetic-powder method, and it is extensively used in industrial applications.

9. The Magnetic-Powder Method. As has been pointed out before, the magnetic-powder method involves the use of iron particles which affect the magnetic resistance of the crack. The gain in energy achieved by the presence of the iron filings is the force with which the filings are retained in the neighborhood of the crack. When this force is greater than the force which must be exerted to blow away or to wash away the cracks, the crack can be detected.

There are several factors which affect the detection of the crack, and the relation between pertinent variables is shown in Fig. 12-5. Figure 12-5 gives the least detectable width of a crack as a function of the field strength. It may be noted that the field strength should be at least 30 ampere turns per centimeter and that no advantage is derived by using strengths above 90 ampere turns per centimeter. Figure 12-6 shows that the magnetic-powder method is not very

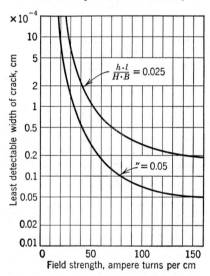

FIG. 12-5. The Maximum Width of a Flaw That Can Be Indicated in Relation to the Field Strength

Effect of a flaw 2.5 to 5 per cent of the cross section; crack situated at the surface; length of filings 5×10^{-4} cm

effective in detecting subsurface cracks, an increase in the field strength above 60 ampere turns per centimeter not producing any greater depth effect.

The magnetizing methods, as has been pointed out before, depend on the type of application. As to the detection of cracks, fine iron filings are used. These filings are usually prepared from low-carbon steels so that they will not have an appreciable residual magnetism and are ground fine to prevent clogging. Cracks are detected by either the dry or the wet method. The dry method has the advantage of being clean and more sensitive to subsurface cracks but has the disadvantage that iron filings cling to cracks and are difficult to remove. As a result, the wet method is used much more extensively. Magnetization and crack detection may be done simultaneously or separately, and the choice depends on the type of cracks suspected, type of material, and so on.

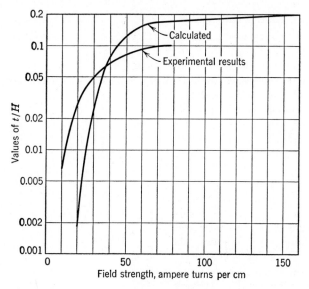

FIG. 12-6.　Depth Effect of the Magnetic-Powder Method in Relation to the Field Strength

Effect for 10^{-3} cm width of crack; 5 per cent weakening of cross section; 5×10^{-4} cm length of filings

For the detection of very small cracks, particularly if they are located in crevices, small fillets, bottoms of splines, and similar places, a fluorescent medium is used in which filings are suspended. The examination is made with the aid of ultraviolet light. This process is commercially known as Magnaglo.

The magnetic-powder method is widely used in the United States, commercial instruments being manufactured by the Magnaflux Corporation. Surface cracks in castings, forgings, rolled, machined, and ground parts are easily detected by this method, both in the laboratory and on the assembly lines. As a tool of inspection it contains a hazard, however, in that thousands of pieces may pass without any crack, and by the time a cracked piece appears the inspector may overlook it because of monotony and visual fatigue.

10. The Magnetic-Inductive Method. The magnetic-powder method is generally not sensitive to cracks located much below the surface, and the magnetic inductive method was developed for this range of applications. Different types of equipment have been built to suit different conditions, but they are all based on the principle that a change in a magnetic flux due to the presence of a crack induces a current in the search coil. The coils can be movable or stationary, depending on the type of application. In the movable-coil type of equipment a magnetic field is induced by a permanent magnet, and sudden changes in this field, caused by the presence of a crack, induce a current in a search coil which is passed over the piece. The signal is then amplified and recorded. This method has been successfully used in the examination of welds, steel cables, and so on.

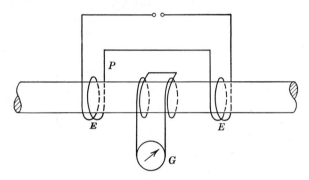

FIG. 12-7. Circuit of Cable Tester

E = excitation coils
P = testing coil, differentially connected
G = ballistic galvanometer

In the equipment with stationary coils either the piece is moved relative to the search coil, or an a-c field is used for magnetization. The form in which this method was used when applied to the testing of cables (Fig. 12-7) involved winding two excitation coils around the cable and using a search coil consisting of two single coils and situated between the excitation coils. The cable is moved at a uniform rate between the coils, and the electromotive force induced in the search coil is detected on a ballistic galvanometer.

In the United States three different instruments have been developed for the detection of metallurgical and manufacturing irregularities. Although their primary function is not the detection of cracks, they can be used for that purpose in spite of the reticence of the advertising claims. These instruments are the Cyclograph, the Magnetic Analysis Comparator, and the Ferrograph.

The Cyclograph, manufactured by the Allan Du Mont Company, contains a test coil which controls the frequency of an oscillator. The testpiece when inserted into the test coil produces core losses, and these in turn affect the output of the oscillator. The resultant signal is viewed on the screen of a cathode-ray tube. This instrument is not applicable to the detection of surface cracks but will detect internal defects. When operating in the frequency range of 2000 to 10,000 cycles the core losses are mainly governed by the magnetic properties of the material, and the Cyclograph acts as a magnetic-inductive instrument.

The Magnetic Analysis Comparator operates at a lower frequency than the Cyclograph. The instrument contains two coils, primary and secondary, and it is set up to produce a sine wave on the oscilloscope screen when a piece void of cracks is passed through the coils. When the testpiece is then inserted, the existence of a crack produces electromotive forces which manifest themselves in a distortion of the sine wave. This instrument is being used in the inspection of bars and tubes and will respond to the existence of a crack.

The Ferrograph is a hand-sorting instrument operating at a low frequency (26 cycles), and it utilizes the remanent magnetism. The testpiece is inserted in a transformer, and the existence of a flaw is evidenced by a voltage induced in the secondary winding.

D. Supersonic Methods

Supersonic methods represent a relatively recent development in the science of crack detection. In 1930 Muhlhauser applied for a patent in which he proposed to study flaws in metal with an ultrasonic receiver and transmitter. Sokoloff conducted experiments in the United States, and F. A. Firestone and others developed practical instruments for crack detection in the laboratory and in the shop.

Supersonic methods involve the use of sound waves of high frequency (up to 10 megacycles). Because of this feature, supersonic methods do not possess the limitations characteristic of audible sound waves. These, being of moderate frequency, have a low penetrating power, bend easily around corners, and, consequently, cannot locate cracks with sufficient sharpness. Supersonic waves, on the other hand, have a great penetrating power, are focused easily, and are easily deflected or reflected from defects in the material.

Several methods have been developed for the detection of cracks. In one of them the piece is set in vibration at its natural frequency (in the supersonic range), and the vibration is then picked up by electronic means. This usually comprises an oscillator which beats with the incoming frequency so that the frequency of the beats falls in the audible range.

Another method of crack detection is based on the damping capacity of the material. The principle is similar to that described in section B; the instrumentation depends on the type of application. The methods which offer a considerable promise are those in which the supersonic wave is actually passed through the piece and the reflected or absorbed wave is measured. These methods are incorporated in several instruments developed commercially.

11. The Reflection Method. The reflection method has been effectively developed by F. A. Firestone, and it is incorporated in a commercial instrument known as the Supersonic Reflectoscope. A quartz crystal is attached to the part being tested through a thin film of oil. The crystal is connected to a high-frequency oscillator which causes it to emit supersonic sound waves. The electric impulses are impressed on the supersonic waves and radiate discontinuously. A group of supersonic waves radiates from the crystal, is reflected from the end of the part being tested, and then returns back to the crystal. The crystal, thus subjected to oscillatory-wave pressure, generates voltage, which is picked up, amplified, and recorded on the screen. If a crack is present in the piece, the supersonic wave is reflected from it back to the crystal before the reflection from the end of the piece. The whole process is repeated 60 times a second so that a continuous wave form appears on the oscilloscope screen.

It is reported that cracks anywhere at the surface down to a depth of several feet can be detected by this method. The crack can be only a few thousands of an inch long. The method is applicable to various metals and plastics, fabricated as forgings or castings, with the limitation that the surface tested be smooth and homogeneous.

An interesting method involving the reflection of supersonic waves was developed by Sokoloff. A crystal is placed in a large flat vessel filled with oil in such a way as to send the sound vertically upwards. At the point where the beam meets the liquid surface an oblique ray of light is reflected on a screen. The testpiece is placed in the oil slightly below the surface. Changes in the light beam indicate the existence of a flaw in the piece.

12. The Absorption Method. This method is incorporated in a Brush analyzer. The analyzer consists of two crystals, one of which acts as a generator of supersonic waves, the other as a receiver. The piece is passed between the two, and a crack is detected by a change in the energy received. The instrument is effective in detecting the existence of a crack but not its shape or location. For this reason it is more effective as a means of inspection for cracks in large-scale production.

E. Electrical Methods

The electrical methods for crack detection are not so numerous nor so extensively developed as the magnetic methods. Since the use of the latter is restricted to ferrous materials, there appears a distinct need for a method which would be applicable to aluminum, magnesium, brass, and other non-ferrous metals.

13. The Drop-of-Potential Method. This method consists of applying a predetermined set of potentials to the testpiece and measuring the resultant current distribution. Presence of a crack will affect the distribution of the current, and this in turn will reveal the existence of the crack.

This method has been successfully applied to welded joints, and a good correlation is reported between the voltage reading across the welds and the weld quality.

It has also been used in testing turbine rotors. A 10,000-ampere current is passed through the rotor between copper contacts, so that the current flows longitudinally. Contact is made at a number of equally spaced points, and the potential differences between neighboring points are measured by a potentiometer.   If these readings are not uniform, the existence of a flaw is suspected.

Another application is found in the railroad-track inspection for defective rails.   After the crack is located by the Sperry apparatus built into a special self-propelled car, the car is stopped, and the extent of the crack is determined by the drop-of-potential method.   From the examination it is determined whether the crack is sufficiently serious to necessitate the removal of the rail.

14. The Eddy-Current Method.   The eddy-current method is based on the principle that a change in a magnetic field will produce an electromotive force in the testpiece exposed to the magnetic field.   This force produces local electric currents (eddy currents), and these in turn set up magnetic fields which can be detected by search coils.   Any factors, such as cracks, which affects the strength of the eddy currents, will affect the current in the search coil.

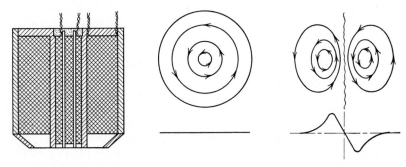

Fig. 12-8.   Pickup Unit and Systems of Eddy Currents It Induces in Homogeneous
Plate

The usual method of applying this method is to utilize two field coils in series, with the testpiece passing through them.   Inside each field coil is located a search coil.   The search coils are wound in such a manner that the current from the field coils is neutralized, and only the difference of the eddy current fields is measured.   This method is very well suited to nonmagnetic materials.   Ferrous materials must be magnetized to saturation by means of a direct current before the eddy-current method is applied.

A particularly successful effort to develop an eddy-current instrument is described in the *ASME Transactions*, v 63, 1941.   The instrument consists of an a-c electromagnet which is excited by a coil supplied with alternating current through the leads.   If the magnet is placed on a plate, then, because of its axial symmetry, the system of eddy currents induced will be circular, as shown in Fig. 12-8.   If the plate, on the other hand, has a crack in it, the current will not go through the crack and will be broken to give two current systems as shown.   A small pickup electromagnet moved across the plate with the crack will encounter an electromotive force which will be an indication of the crack.

This is one of many possible arrangements for detecting cracks by means of eddy currents, and it can be applied not only to flat plates but also to objects irregular in shape. It locates cracks in metals having high conductivity such as copper, aluminum, and Duralumin. If the conductivity is less, as in lead, or the crack is located well below the surface, vacuum-tube amplification is required.

In another instrument, developed for the detection of cracks in tubes and pipes, standard tube and test tube are inserted in a set of energizing coils carrying an alternating current and a set of test coils. When the test tube is void of cracks, the coils are in a balanced relation. The presence of a crack upsets the balance and is indicated on the indicating device. This method is applicable to nonferrous tubings. Steel tubings are first saturated magnetically with d-c windings or a direct current superimposed on a-c windings to make them nonmagnetic. This method is applicable to the detection of longitudinal cracks. For the detection of short flaws a suitable modification in test arrangement is used.

Another arrangement utilizing the principle of eddy current has a conductor passing through solenoid coils acting as the primary winding of a transformer connected to an a-c source. The testpiece acts as a secondary winding of a transformer, and eddy currents are induced in it by the solenoids. The existence of a crack in the testpiece changes the impedance of the solenoid which is measured by a suitable bridge arrangement.

The Cyclograph, previously described, is a magnetic-induction instrument when operating in the frequency range of 2000 to 10,000 cycles. At higher frequencies (the instrument operates up to 200,000 cycles) the Cyclograph represents an eddy-current arrangement.

BIBLIOGRAPHY

1. "The Non-Destructive Testing of Materials by Electrical and Magnetic Methods," *J Inst Elec Engrs (Lond.)*, v 84, n 509, May 1939. A symposium on nondestructive testing of materials by electrical, magnetic, radiographic, acoustic, and general methods, including both European and American practices. Extensively illustrated by photographs of equipment and parts tested. Considerable discussion of the papers presented is included.
2. H. BEVAN SWIFT, *Principles of Magnetic Crack Detection*, E. & F. N. Spon Ltd, London, 1944. A simple and effective treatise on the technique and application of magnetic methods to crack detection. The principles underlying the process and the methods of interpretation of markings are included.
3. G. B. YOUNG, *Magnetic Crack Detection; Notes on Working Principles and Use of Apparatus*, C. Griffin & Co, Ltd, London, 1942. In this book is presented an outline of the working principles of the magnetic method, together with practical information on the use of equipment and the interpretation of the magnetic markings.
4. ROSS GUNN, "An Eddy-Current Method of Flaw Detection in Nonmagnetic Metals," *Trans ASME*, v 63, 1941, p A-22. An equipment suitable for location of cracks in nonmagnetic materials is described. The principle involves the use of alternating magnetic fields which induce eddy currents. Sensitive pickup coils measure the departure of the eddy-current pattern from the pattern in a sample free from cracks.
5. H. C. KNERR, "Electrical Detection of Flaws in Metal," *Metal and Alloys*, Oct 1940, p 464. An electrical method for detection of cracks in ferrous and

nonferrous materials, particularly in welded and seamless tubing, is described. An electric current is caused to flow transversely to the direction of possible crack, and the resulting effect is measured in one of several ways.

6. W. SCHRIP, "Testing Non-Ferrous Metals by New Magneto-Inductive Method," *Engrs Digest*, v 2, n 5, p 238, May 1945. The principle, the apparatus, and the method of measurement are described. The method is based on the principle of a conductor passing through one or two solenoid coils connected to an a-c source of audible frequency. Eddy currents are induced by the solenoids in the material, and the deviation from the presence of a crack is detected.

7. L. BERGMANN, *Ultrasonics and Their Scientific and Technical Applications*, H. S. Hatfield, G. Bell & Sons, Ltd, London 1938. This book represents a general account of the science of ultrasonics, showing what has been done in this field up to the present. The approach to the subject is experimental, with only a sufficient theory presented for proper understanding of the subject. Application of ultrasonics to crack detection is treated briefly.

8. R. W. WOOD, *Supersonics, the Science of Inaudible Sound*, Brown Univ, 1939. A series of lectures delivered by the author at Brown University. The history and the physical and biological effects of supersonics are presented. No specific application to the science of crack detection is discussed. A comprehensive bibliography on the subject is given.

9. F. A. FIRESTONE, "Supersonic Reflectoscope for Interior Inspection," *Metal Progress*, Sept 1945, p 505. An instrument for detection of subsurface cracks in magnetic and nonmagnetic materials by means of supersonic sound waves is described. Supersonic waves are generated in a crystal which is in contact with the work. These waves are reflected by an internal flow in the material and the resultant interference with the incident wave is noted and measured on a cathode-ray oscilloscope screen.

CHAPTER 13

INTERPRETATION OF SERVICE FRACTURES

By R. E. Peterson

1. Introduction. In the service failure of a machine part a knowledge of the characteristic features of various kinds of fractured surfaces is often of considerable value in planning an experimental-stress-analysis program aimed at solving the problem. For example, the appearance of the fracture may show that it was caused by alternating torsion and thus eliminate all bending tests from the experimental-stress-analysis program. The details of the surface may also disclose whether the failure developed in a short or a long period of service—information which is of value in judging the percentage improvement (that is, decrease in peak stress) needed to prevent further failures. The material presented has been chosen on a basis of usefulness in this initial step of many stress-analysis investigations. It is not intended to cover other aspects of fracture involving strength or rupture theory, research with idealized specimens, and so on.

It should be pointed out that the subject is not a well-documented one, and experience shows that serious mistakes may easily be made in judging what appear to be relatively simple cases. For example, Fig. 13-1 shows[1] a fracture of a rotor which most engineers would judge at once to be due to fatigue. As a matter of fact, the rotor had not been run at all; cracks had been developed during heating and cooling of the forging.

It is proposed to discuss fatigue failures first since of all service failures these account for the largest single source, estimated by some authorities at as high as 80 per cent of all failures of machine parts. Furthermore, fatigue failures often occur with no warning and thus may result in a catastrophe with loss of life. Plastic deformations in the fracture section of fatigue failures are often so minute that the two broken pieces fit closely when held together.

A service failure displaying the characteristics of the conventional short-time tensile test is extremely unlikely, since such a failure would develop in the usual acceptance and overspeed tests of machinery. Long-time creep and creep–rupture effects are another matter and are discussed later, together with some brief remarks on impact fracture.

2. Bending-Fatigue Fractures. Fatigue failures due to bending are the most prevalent type encountered, with the torsion type next and the axial type seldom occurring in service. Although it can be said that service conditions usually involve combinations of variable and steady stresses and sometimes also both bending and torsion, usually a dominant type of failure is found; we shall try, therefore, to set up simple criteria for comparison purposes.

Fig. 13-1.   Fracture of Turborotor Due to a Flaw Has Appearance of Fatigue Failure, although Rotor Was Never in Service (Lasche)

Vibration and misalignment are the chief causes of bending failures, although in many cases, such as vehicle axles, the service conditions are so variable that occasional failures occur.

Practically all service fatigue failures occur at a region of stress concentration, such as the end of a keyway, the edge of a press-fitted member, a fillet at a shoulder of a shaft, the bottom of a thread, or the edge of an oil hole.   The conventional fatigue specimen is made with a very large contour radius at the critical section and, therefore, is essentially free from stress concentration. Any further remarks concerning the "no-stress-concentration" case will be solely for the purpose of clarifying the manner of failure, that is crack progress in a general way, and not for the purpose of illustration of a type of service failure.

Fatigue fractures in general show smooth and coarse areas as is evident from the illustrations of this section. The smooth area is due to crack development with the smoothness caused by repeated opening and closing of the crack, whereas the coarse area is due to final rupture and is usually quite rough and "crystalline-appearing." The garage mechanic will say that the metal has crystallized, but it is well known that the metal is crystalline to begin with and that recrystallization does not occur. The rough rupture area is similar in appearance to that of a broken tensile or impact testpiece.

Figures 13-2 and 13-3 illustrate fatigue fractures produced under laboratory conditions in rotating specimens subjected to bending in a fixed plane.[2] For an understanding of the characteristic features shown in Figs. 13-2 and 13-3, a few observations on the mechanism of crack development are necessary. We

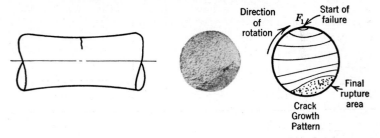

FIG. 13-2.   Typical Fracture—"No-Stress-Concentration" Case (Conventional Fatigue Specimen)

will not concern ourselves here with the initiation of a crack on a microscale, which has been shown to be due to shear stress[3] for ductile materials. Once started, and as far as appearance to the eye is concerned, a fatigue crack follows a general direction normal to the main tensile-stress field,* except as the crack becomes deep and rupture becomes imminent (Figs. 13-4, 13-26, 13-29). In the conventional bending-fatigue specimen (Fig. 13-2) the crack penetrates radially, that is, in a direction perpendicular to the axis. In the filleted shaft (Fig. 13-26), a consequence of the crack following a course dictated by the normal stress field is the characteristic "dished" fracture surface.

A plot of the strength of individual grains along a peripheral circle might look like Fig. 13-5. If the stress level is at S', just exceeding the endurance limit, failure will start at one place, corresponding to the weakest spot F_1. For the "no-stress-concentration" case (Fig. 13-2), the crack progresses across the section until rupture occurs with a segmental area bounded on one side by the shaft periphery. Note that the rupture area is not directly opposite F_1 but is displaced angularly in a direction related to the direction of rotation as

* An exception to this general relation concerning crack direction occurs when a second crack affects the stress field of the first. See text in connection with Fig. 13-30.

shown[4] in Fig. 13-2.   For the high-stress-concentration case of a shaft with a
deep groove or small fillet, there is a relatively higher peripheral stress (Fig.
13-6) which causes a more rapid spread of the crack at the surface, resulting

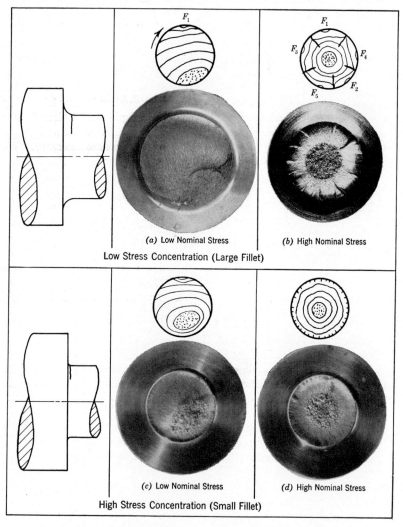

(a) Low Nominal Stress

(b) High Nominal Stress

Low Stress Concentration (Large Fillet)

(c) Low Nominal Stress

(d) High Nominal Stress

High Stress Concentration (Small Fillet)

FIG. 13-3.   Laboratory Fatigue Fractures—Stress-Concentration Case of Shaft
    with Fillet (Rotating Shaft Subjected to Bending in a Fixed Plane)

in an enclosed rupture area of approximately elliptical form (Fig. 13-3c).
The low-stress-concentration case Fig. 13-3a is intermediate, with an appearance more like Fig. 13-2, again if it is assumed that the stress is slightly above
the endurance strength.

If the stress level is raised to S'' failure begins at a number of additional places F_2, F_3, F_4, etc. In the "no-stress-concentration" case the weakest point, the next weakest, and so on will occur randomly on the surface, so that even at relatively high stress the fracture surface will usually, although not

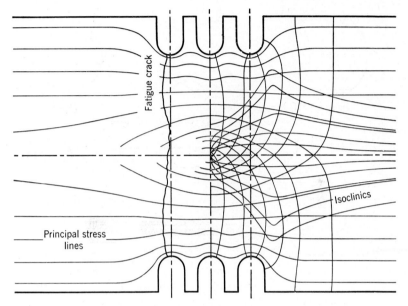

Fatigue crack

Isoclinics

Principal stress lines

FIG. 13-4.   Direction of Fatigue Crack in Relation to Stress Lines (Oschatz)

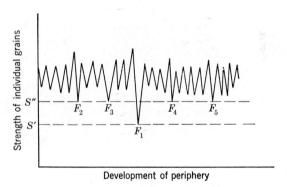

Strength of individual grains

S'' F_2 F_3 F_4 F_5

S' F_1

Development of periphery

FIG. 13-5.   Schematic Diagram of Sources of Failure

always, show only one "starting point" of failure. In the stress concentration case of a grooved or filleted shaft, however, a high stress plane perpendicular to the axis localizes the failure in the axial direction, so that at S'' a number of sources F_1, F_2, F_3, F_4, etc. can occur on a single peripheral circle (Fig. 13-3b, d), as the shaft rotates with the result that the crack tends to penetrate concentrically with a final rupture area which is centrally located and of approximately circular form.

We see, therefore, that the position of the rupture area in fractures of grooved or filleted shafts should depend on stress level. That this is the case

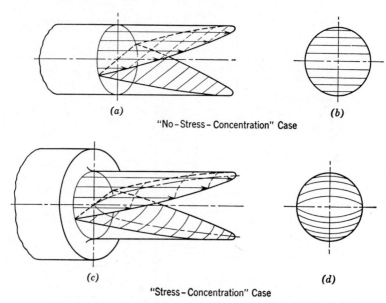

(a)   (b)

"No-Stress-Concentration" Case

(c)   (d)

"Stress-Concentration" Case

FIG. 13-6.   Stress Fields for Rotating-Beam Specimens

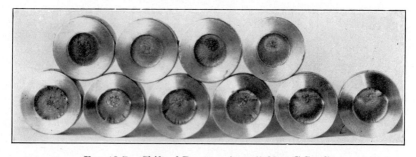

FIG. 13-7.   Shift of Rupture Area (0.20% C Steel)

(a) Upper row: Sharp-cornered specimens; stresses, respectively, 19,200, 15,200, 14,900, and 14,000 psi, reading from left

(b) Lower row: Fillet radius $\frac{1}{32}$ in.; stresses, respectively, 23,800, 17,100, 16,200, 15,100, and 14,900 psi, reading from left

is shown by Fig. 13-7.   Displacement measurements of these and other fractures of low-carbon steel are plotted in Fig. 13-8.

The type of relationship shown by Fig. 13-8 is of value in considering the degree of improvement in design needed to prevent further failures.   If the rupture area is centrally located, we see that an improvement of the order of 30–100 per cent may be needed. Incidentally, the centrally located rupture

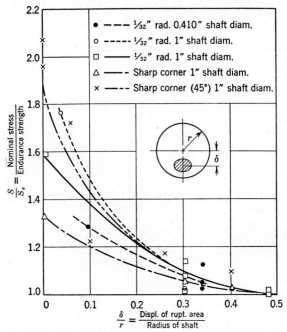

FIG. 13-8. Shift of Rupture Area as a Function of Stress Level (0.20% C Steel Specimens)

area also means that the number of stress cycles probably did not exceed 300,000 which information is often useful in "reconstructing" the conditions leading to failure. If, however, the rupture area is widely displaced as shown in Fig. 13-3a, c the stress was not much above the endurance strength, probably exceeding it by less than 10 per cent. This means that the shaft almost succeeded in doing its job, and a large improvement may not be needed to prevent further failures. Incidentally, the number of stress cycles indicated by this type of fracture is usually of the order of several million. Between the two extremes just described, there are, of course, all the intermediate cases.

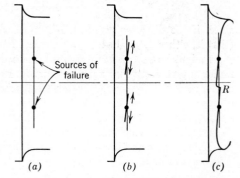

FIG. 13-9. Formation of Ratchet Marks

Knowledge of characteristic surface markings and an understanding of the mechanism of their development are of considerable value in trying to deduce the conditions involved in a service failure. A consequence of multiple-starting points of failure (Figs. 13-3b and 13-7b) is that radial lines are formed where the cracks starting from separate sources join each other.[2,4] One might wonder why such radial lines should form in view of the foregoing remark concerning axial localization. As illustrated in Fig. 13-9, fatigue cracks tend to travel in a slightly helical manner, and where the cracks "break over" as at R in Fig. 13-9c a radial "ratchet mark" is formed. The helical course of crack progress is apparently due to internal friction or torque,

FIG. 13-10. Helical-Crack Development and Ratchet Marks in Laboratory Test of Rotor Model

since, if the direction of rotation is reversed, the helix angle changes sign (that is, either "right-hand" or "left-hand" thread using screw notation).

As might be expected, ratchet marks become less pronounced as the fillet radius approaches a sharp corner. In Fig. 13-7, the specimens having a sharp corner (top row) do not show ratchet marks whereas the high-stress specimens of the $\frac{1}{32}$ in.-radius group (bottom row) show well-defined ratchet marks. A striking example is that of Fig. 13-10 which illustrates a laboratory failure of a rotor model[5] having three radial holes, 120° apart. Cracks started on both sides of each hole and progressed to form the three large ratchet marks shown.

Toolmarks or grinding scratches often influence the course of a crack, and in such cases "break-over" steps similar to ratchet marks are formed where approaching cracks are following different parallel toolmarks.[6]

The other main class of fracture surface markings of importance is illustrated by Fig. 13-11, and is known as "beach marks."* Further examples are to be

* Terminology for surface markings is not in a satisfactory condition. In

found in Figs. 13-18 and 13-27. Such markings are characteristic of service
failures and are very rarely found in the laboratory. The marks represent
successive positions of the crack bottom and are probably due either to varying
applied load or to periods of rest with slight plastic flow at the crack bottom
which is obviously a region of high-stress concentration. For our present
purpose, it should be noted that a very fine detailed pattern of beach marks
indicates a relatively long period of crack growth which suggests that the
degree of improvement needed is probably not large.

At a high-stress level a crack penetrates through a part rapidly, but it is
interesting to note that, as the stress level decreases toward the limiting
endurance value, the period of crack
development may be of relatively long
duration.[8, 9] In Fig. 13-12 data on
crack penetration[9] obtained by a
"heat tinting" method with a grooved
specimen show that at a stress level
of approximately 15 per cent above
the limiting value about $1\frac{1}{2}$ million
cycles were required to develop the
crack from a barely detectable condition to rupture of the specimen.

A few typical special cases of bending-fatigue failures will now be described. Bolt failures are often due to
excessive flexibility of the structure being bolted, resulting in bending failure.
Failure of a bolt originating at a position

FIG. 13-11.   Beach Marks on Service
Fracture of Automobile Rear Axle

corresponding to the first thread of the nut is shown in Fig. 13-13. Note
from Fig. 13-13 that a high-stress concentration exists at this position.[10]
Failures sometimes occur under the head of a bolt in the fillet. It has been
estimated[11] that the distribution of bolt failure is about as follows: 65 per cent
at the first thread of the nut; 20 per cent at the end of the threaded portion
of the bolt; 15 per cent under the head.

In Fig. 13-14 is shown a failure starting at the end of a profiled keyway in an
overhung pinion shaft of a streetcar drive. If the keyway is of sled-runner
type,[12] failure due to bending occurs up on the radius portion as shown in
Fig. 13-15.

A typical example of the cantilever-beam type of gear-tooth fatigue failure
is shown in Fig. 13-16. Note the similarity with the static fractures of Figs.
13-45 and 13-46; this is discussed further in connection with static fracture of
brittle materials.

reference **7** "ripple mark" is used to describe both types of marking mentioned in
the foregoing, whereas in reference 2 the writer has used the term "beach mark"
in an unfortunate way. It is believed that the use of the terms "ratchet mark"
(or the more inclusive "break-over mark") and "beach mark" as herein described
would form a satisfactory basis for descriptive purposes.

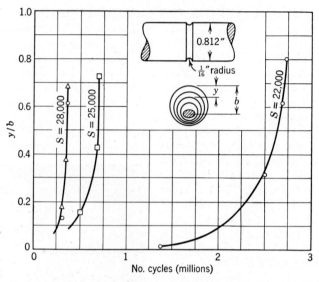

Fig. 13-12.   Penetration of Fatigue Crack in Grooved Specimen of Normalized
0.45% C Steel (Limiting Fatigue Strength—19,000 psi)

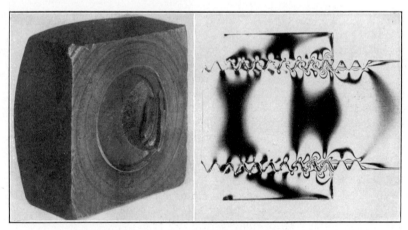

(a) Fatigue fracture

(b) Photoelastic pattern (M. Hetényi)
Slice of three-dimensional model in which
stresses were set up by the fixation method

Fig. 13-13.   Comparison of Fatigue Failure of a Bolt with the Photoelastic Stress
Pattern

(Note failure in bolt at first thread in nut, corresponding to high-stress concentration)

Fatigue failure of a turbine blade[13] (Fig. 13-17) is generally due to bending vibration associated with resonance phenomena.   Root failures usually occur at a fillet and shroud failures at the hole or notch used for fastening.

A crankshaft failure due to bending is apt to occur across the cheek as shown in Fig. 13-18.   A torsion failure is quite different as is shown later

FIG. 13-14.   Service Failure of Streetcar Drive Pinion at Keyway

(Fig. 13-27).   The crankshaft fracture characteristics may be different if the ratio of cheek width to shaft diameter is substantially different from that of the crankshaft illustrated.

A bending-fatigue fracture of a shaft with a transverse hole lies entirely in a transverse plane through the center of the hole.   It has been shown[14] that the

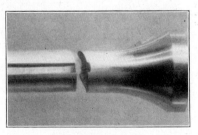

FIG. 13-15.   Fatigue Failure of Laboratory Test Shaft at Sled-Runner Keyway

maximum stress occurs not at the surface but at a short distance down the hole.   Certain fatigue fractures (Fig. 13-19) seem to offer confirmatory evidence.

Press- or shrink-fitted members are widely used in all kinds of machinery in the form of gears, pulleys, wheels, sheaves, couplings, and so on.   A high degree of stress concentration exists at the edge of the fit which coupled with

FIG. 13-16.   Service Failure of Gear Teeth Due to Fatigue

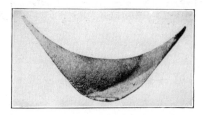

FIG. 13-17.   Fracture of Turbine Blade Due to Repeated Bending (Lasche)

fretting corrosion (a phenomenon discussed later) results in reducing the bending-fatigue strength of a shaft to 30–50 per cent of its full value. A typical failure is shown[15] in Fig. 13-20 and for comparison the failure of a solid piece of the same outline. Note that the start of failure of the press-fitted member is inside the edge; in a 2-in.-diameter shaft this distance was

FIG. 13-18.   Bending Type of Service Failure of Diesel-Engine Crankshaft

about $\frac{1}{16}$ in., but this dimension probably depends on such factors as stress level, shaft diameter, and press-fit pressure.[16]

3. Torsion-Fatigue Fractures.   In line with the remark in the preceding section that, apart from the micro-origin, a fatigue crack generally follows a path dictated by the normal stress field, one would expect alternating torsion cracks to follow a path 45° to the axis. It is almost a certainty that a crack of approximately 45° helix (Fig. 13-21) found in service is due mainly to alternating torsion. Although there are cases where torsion produces other results, to be described presently, it can be said that bending or axial stresses do not in practice produce the diagonal crack which is uniquely characteristic of torsion failure.

It has been found[17, 18, 19] that conventional specimens (without stress concentration) of certain ductile materials tested in alternating torsion start

FIG. 13-19.   Fatigue Fracture of Shaft with Transverse Hole
Failure appears to start below outer surface

to crack in either an axial or a circumferential direction* (Fig. 13-22), sometimes finally branching out diagonally. In harder materials cracks tend to follow the diagonal direction entirely unless influenced in ways to be discussed presently.

An interesting example of a torsion failure is shown in Fig. 13-23, the crack occurring on the journal of a bus drive. It is, of course, realized that most

* In discussion of his paper before the VII International Congress of Applied Mechanics (London, Sept. 1948), J. A. Sauer stated that in his torsion fatigue tests of 14S-T aluminum he had noted that relatively highly stressed specimens (short life) tended to crack axially and circumferentially, while specimens stressed at a lower level (long life) tended to crack in a helical manner.

shafting material comes in rolled bar form and consequently shows a directional effect.

If the bar contains pronounced "stringers" or nonmetallic inclusions, a "splitting" failure of the type shown[20] in Fig. 13-24 is produced by alternating torsion.

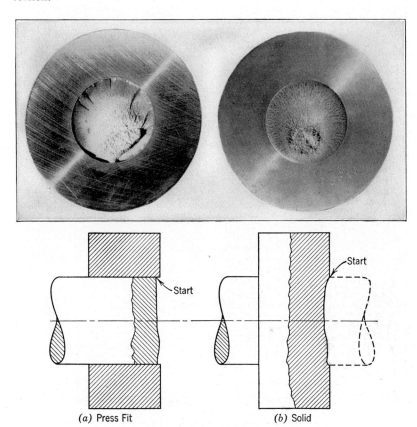

(a) Press Fit   (b) Solid

Fig. 13-20.   Mode of Failure for Press Fit and Corresponding Solid Shape

A mathematical analysis[17] has indicated that, with failure starting at a small localized stress concentration, a helical crack is to be expected as a result of alternating torsion. This is completely confirmed in all cases of torsion tests of a shaft with a transverse hole, regardless of material.

The fracture appearance depends on the degree of stress concentration; for example, as a fillet radius becomes smaller, the fracture tends to become localized in the fillet in the form of "saw-teeth" (Fig. 13-25).

Sometimes it is difficult to judge the type of stressing where a sharp corner or fillet is involved, since the saw-teeth become in effect a circumferential crack (Fig. 13-26).   The torsion failure of the crankshaft[22] shown in Fig. 13-27 is a similar example in which the original crack is circumferential; incidentally this is a case which could easily be misjudged. Other tests[18] have shown a tendency for the crack to stay in the fillet over a smaller part of the periphery and finally to break away in a helix. It was thought[22] that this phenomenon

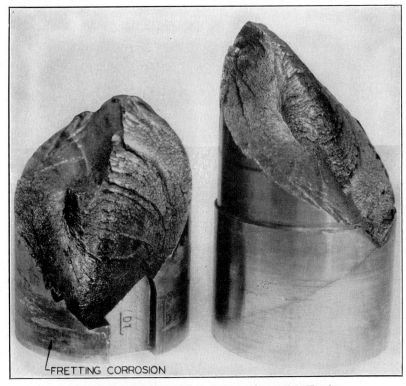

FRETTING CORROSION

FIG. 13-21. Service Failure Due to Alternating Torsion

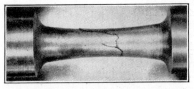

FIG. 13-22. Type of Cracks Developed in Ductile Steel by Alternating Torsion
(Dolan)

of the crack staying in the fillet might be determined by a critical ratio of r/d, (fillet radius/shaft diameter), but it is now evident that the answer is not a simple one. Stress level may be a factor in this connection. It is interesting to note that, even when initial cracking is entirely limited to the fillet (Fig. 13-26), a saw-tooth "ray" pattern[21] develops within, probably corresponding to a high-stress level.

Coming back to Fig. 13-27, one might question the statement that the failure was due to alternating torsion; this was settled by model tests[22] wherein typical bending and torsion fractures were obtained in crankshaft models. Recent papers on crankshaft stresses have thrown additional light on this problem.[23]

Fig. 13-23.   Torsion Failure in Journal of a Bus Drive

It is well known that compression of a helical spring results mainly in twisting the wire so that one might expect to find characteristic torsion failures. That such is the case is shown by Fig. 13-28.   Sometimes a spring will develop a split along the wire which, as mentioned in the foregoing, can happen in an alternating torsion test of a straight section where stringers or inclusions are present in the material.

A splined shaft subjected to alternating torsion fails along the bottom edges of the splines as shown in Fig. 13-29.   This is another example of where a highly localized stress field strongly influences crack development.

Fig. 13-24.   Splitting Fracture of Torsion Bar of Ductile Material (Seeger)

In Fig. 13-30 a comparison is made of the torsion-fatigue cracks and the corresponding stress field for a shaft with a keyway.   In the specimen at the left, one of the keyway corners is rounded in order to obtain a single crack; note that this crack progresses approximately normal to the original stress field.   In the specimen at the right, the two cracks no longer follow the

FIG. 13-25.　Service Failure of Diesel-Driven Shaft Showing Saw Teeth Due to
Alternating Torsion

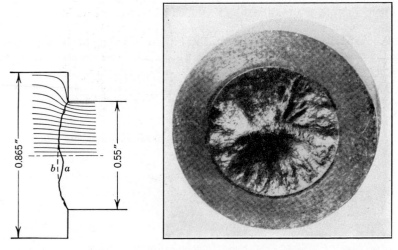

FIG. 13-26.　Comparison of Torsion-Fatigue Fracture and Corresponding Stress
Field for a Sharp-Shouldered Shaft (Oschatz)

In drawing, a denotes the fatigue crack, and b denotes a line perpendicular to
the main stress field

original stress field, a circumstance which Oschatz explains as due to "cross effect" of the cracks on the stress field.[21]

In a loose-fitted member, nearly all the alternating torque is transmitted through the key, resulting in failure starting at the bottom edge of the keyway of the shaft and producing a peeling type of fracture (Fig. 13-31a). Occa-

FIG. 13-27.   Torsion Type of Service Failure of Diesel-Engine Crankshaft

sionally the peeling process goes entirely around the shaft and results in a sharp-edged separated shell like that of Fig. 13-31b, c, which has much the appearance of a gadget for coring a grapefruit. In this case there was evidently some pressure originally between the shaft and the fitted member, or at least the fit was probably not so loose as the case illustrated by Fig. 13-31a.

4. Special Cases of Fatigue Failure.   A type of failure known as "pitting" occurs on the tooth surface of gears (Fig. 13-32), especially those having a relatively high-pressure angle such that beam failure does not result first as the loading is increased. Pitting can be reproduced in all its essential features in a pair of normally loaded rotating rollers,[24] wherein the well-known Hertz contact stresses are developed. Pitting does not develop on dry rollers; it has been shown that the presence of oil, or a liquid, is necessary to develop

FIG. 13-28.   Fatigue Fracture of a Helical Spring

the crack to a stage where a particle breaks out. The crack develops at a small angle with the surface in a direction such that the initial tip of the crack goes through the contact area first (Fig. 13-33). It is thought that original small cracks start in both directions but that crack growth depends on the afore-mentioned conditions which results in hydraulic pressure within the crack. This means, of course, that, if the direction of rotation is reversed, the pitting cracks should develop in the opposite direction; experiments have shown this to be true.

Pitting on gear teeth appears in the region of the pitch line, as shown in Fig. 13-32. The individual pits are quite small, and by the time a number

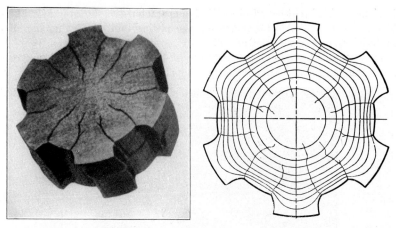

FIG. 13-29. Fatigue Cracks in Spline of Automobile-Drive Shaft (Oschatz)
Stress field obtained by means of soap-film analogy method

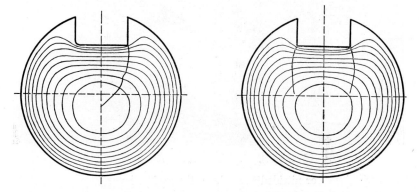

FIG. 13-30. Comparison of Torsion-Fatigue Crack and Corresponding Stress
Field for Shaft with Keyway (Oschatz)

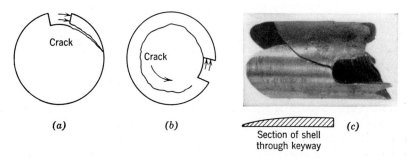

FIG. 13-31. Peeling Type of Fracture Starting at a Keyway

have merged it is not easy to identify the characteristics shown in Fig. 13-33. The methods available for increasing the pitting limit are higher hardness material, smoother surfaces, and higher viscosity of lubricant.

It is possible for fatigue failures to start internally, and we will now consider the conditions under which parts fail in service in this manner.   In

FIG. 13-32.   Pitting of Gear Teeth

case-carburized[25] or nitrided[26] members, the surface layer is so much harder and stronger than the core material that failure starts just under the hard layer when such members are subjected to alternating stress. The origin of such a failure has a characteristic "fish eye" as shown[26] in Fig. 13-34.

FIG. 13-33.   Pitting Failure

Most failures starting internally are due to defects, many of which, such as flakes and shatter cracks, have been shown[27] to be due to the action of hydrogen in the thermal processes of making the steel bar or forging. Rail failures of the "transverse-fissure" type have the appearance[28] of Fig. 13-35, the large bright spot in the railhead representing what was an "internal fissure" in the rail. The nucleus of the fissure is always a "shatter crack" (top of Fig. 13-35) produced in making the rail. Cooling procedures in rail manufacture have been worked out for avoiding shatter cracks.

Steam-hammer piston rods are subjected to axial-stress waves which sometimes cause failures of the kind shown[29] in Fig. 13-36.   This failure shows characteristics similar to the previous illustrations of rail failure.

Welded members tested in fatigue occasionally show sources of failure starting from internal nuclei, particularly where large masses of weld metal are deposited rapidly.

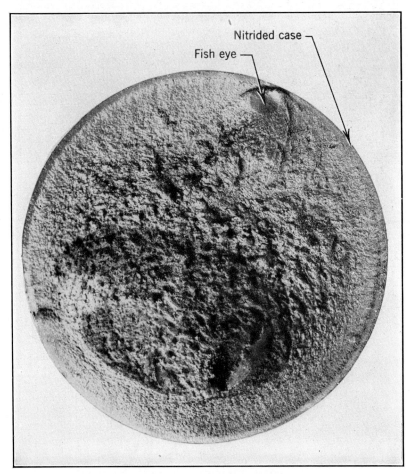

Fig. 13-34.   Fish eye under Nitrided Case of a Fatigue Test Specimen

In large cylindrical forgings it is possible for rather large internal ruptures to occur as a result of temperature gradient if proper heating and cooling schedules are not followed.[30]   Although this type of defect is a rare occurrence, it should be noted that such a defect is not detected by surface-inspection means and may, therefore, go unnoticed.   The boring of a center hole furnishes a means of detection.   Supersonic waves offer an effective inspection method.   In Fig. 13-37 a failure due to this kind of defect is shown, the two large internal areas of rough appearance having been produced thermally in making the forging and the thin outer band having been developed from the inside out by service cycling.   It is important to recognize the foregoing case

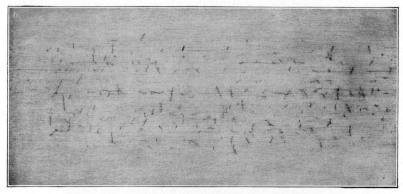

Shatter Cracks (Longitudinal Section through Railhead)

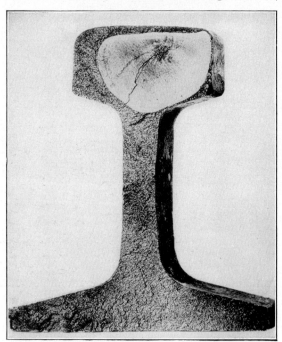

FIG. 13-35.   Transverse Fissure Type of Rail Failure (Seely)

clearly, since the usual conclusion would be that the rough central area represents the last area to fail instead of the first.

It is rather generally appreciated that simultaneous corrosion and repeated stressing of a steel specimen (that is, flooding the specimen with water during

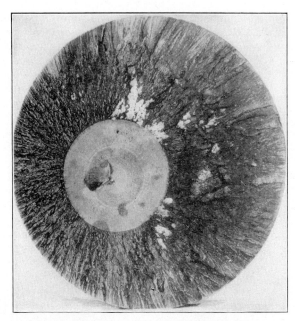

Fig. 13-36.   Steam-Hammer Piston-Rod Fracture Starting at a Flake (Lessells)

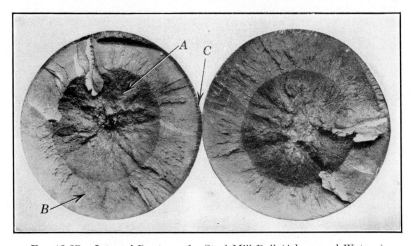

Fig. 13-37.   Internal Rupture of a Steel-Mill Roll (Adams and Watson)

testing) lowers the endurance limit drastically, whereas prior corrosion, or rusting, and subsequent testing have considerably less effect. An electrochemical theory has been suggested,[31] but for our purpose the important feature is the development of etched notches. The appearance of such notches on a nickel–steel specimen tested in bending and simultaneously corroded by water is shown[32] in Fig. 13-38. The effect of alternating torsion produces the interesting corrosion-fatigue appearance shown[33] in Fig. 13-39.

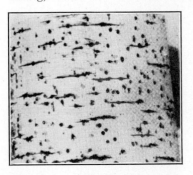

FIG. 13-38.   Corrosion Fatigue of a Nickel–Steel Shaft in Bending (McAdam)

Fretting corrosion was mentioned in connection with press-fitted members.[15] Wherever minute relative motion occurs between two parts,[34] particles are torn loose, and these oxidize, so that in

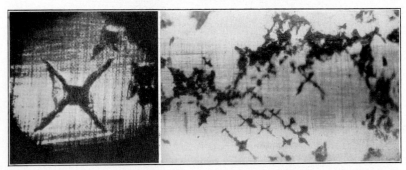

FIG. 13-39.   "X Marks" Characteristic of Alternating Torsion and Simultaneous Corrosion (Dusold, left; Dolan, right)

steel, a reddish brown powder, sometimes called "cocoa," is found at the edges. It should be emphasized that we are dealing not with gross rubbing in the usual sense but with very minute relative motions. If the shaft shown in Fig. 13-40 is bent back and forth by a moment $\pm M$, then the amount of slip will increase from zero at some point A to $\pm dl$ at the edge. Although a precise analysis of this problem is difficult, a rough calculation for a 2 in.-diameter shaft of axle steel at a value of stress corresponding to the

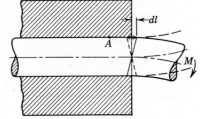

FIG. 13-40.   Sketch Showing Relative Motion of Shaft at Edge of Collar

limiting condition in fatigue shows that the order of magnitude of slip at the edge is a small fraction of one thousandth of an inch. Special tests have shown[34] that fretting can be produced by a relative motion having a total amplitude as small as 2.3 millionths of an inch. The shiny brown bands found on a shaft after removal of a gear or ball bearing which has been in service for some time are, therefore, accounted for by the small elastic deformations due to loading or vibration. An example of the appearance of such a surface is shown in Fig. 13-21. The effects of fretting corrosion on strength and methods of improvement are beyond the scope of this chapter. The characteristic feature of failure starting a slight distance inside the edge was mentioned in connection with press-fitted members. Apparently enough material is rubbed away to move the point of maximum stress inward. The other features of fractured surfaces for cases where fretting corrosion influ-

Fig. 13-41.   Laboratory Fatigue Failure of Automatic-Type Babbitt Bearing

ences the crack initiation are not unusual, and for press-fitted members one finds all the types of rupture areas[35] shown in Fig. 13-3.

The effect of temperature, either low or elevated, does not change the general characteristics of fatigue fractures. At elevated temperature, of course, oxidation occurs, and sometimes shading of oxide color is found corresponding to variable time of exposure. There is also a tendency for fractures at elevated temperature to be relatively coarser.

Fatigue failures can occur in quite soft metals. The crazing[36] sometimes found on babbitted engine bearings (Fig. 13-41) is due to fluctuations in load.

Nor are fatigue failures limited to metals, but sometimes occur in quite flexible materials. Figure 13-42 illustrates fatigue cracks in a rubber tire, the cracks developing simultaneously at the four quadrant positions at a sharp and apparently unnecessary corner. These cracks penetrated the casing as shown, causing a blowout. Fatigue cracks in other nonmetals, such as plastics, cement, glass, and porcelain, seem to follow the same general direction as for metals.

5. Static or Constant-Load Fractures.   Failures under gradually increasing load, so-called "static" failures, as in the usual "short-time" tensile test, are not given much space in this chapter, because such failures are almost unheard

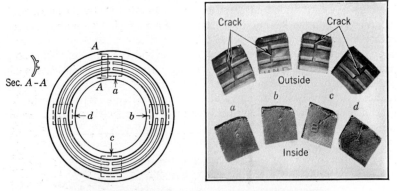

FIG. 13-42.   Fatigue Failure of an Automobile Tire

(Note cracks occurring at four places simultaneously at a sharp corner in the side decorative design.   Cracks penetrated casing as shown, causing a blowout)

FIG. 13-43.   Typical Tensile Fracture of Brittle and Ductile Materials

of in service.   As a matter of general interest, however, tensile fractures of specimens of ductile and brittle steels are shown in Fig. 13-43.   A ductile material fails first by slip resulting in a necking of the specimen.   This in turn creates a triaxial-stress condition inside the piece resulting in a transverse fracture at the middle of the piece[37] (Fig. 13-44).   Final failure shows shearing of the outer zone along an angle, resulting in the well-known "cup-and-cone" fracture.

Brittle materials tend to fracture along a path dictated by maximum normal stress unless disturbed by directional effects in the material. For example, a brittle member, tested in torsion, fails along a helical path. Figures 13-45 and 13-46 show a comparison of laboratory failures of hardened* steel gear teeth due to static loading and the corresponding Stresscoat and photoelastic pattern.[38] Note the similarity to the fatigue failure of Fig. 13-16. Static tests of models of brittle material such as plaster of Paris,[39, 40] have shown a similar geometrical appearance of fracture to that of a corresponding ductile-steel member broken by fatigue, and this suggests that brittle models may have some use for comparative purposes (see also Chap. 14).

At room temperature a steel member carrying a given static load can be expected

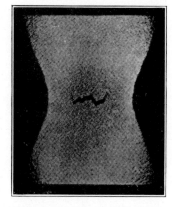

Fig. 13-44. Internal Crack in an Aluminum Testpiece Due to Triaxial-Stress Condition Occurring during Necking (Ludwik)

to do so indefinitely, barring corrosive effects. At elevated temperature, however, the member may, after a certain length of time and with

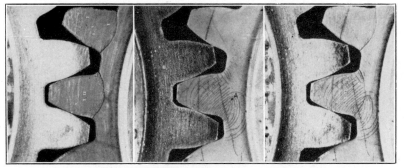

(a) Static fracture in a hardened steel gear   (b) Stresscoat pattern   (c) Superposition of a and b

Fig. 13-45.   Comparison of Laboratory Static Fracture in a Gear Tooth and the Corresponding Stresscoat Pattern (Boor and Stitz)

no increase in load, suddenly snap off. Fractures of tensile specimens at elevated temperature as a function of time are shown[42] in Fig. 13-47. The

* Case depth 0.050 in. has hardness Rockwell C 60 (approximately 625 Brinell); core hardness Rockwell C 26 (approximately 275 Brinell). Note that failure originates in a brittle material and propagates through a ductile material; a similar condition sometimes is found in chain failures.[41]

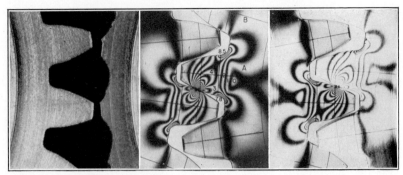

(a) Static fracture in a   (b) Photoelastic stress   (c) Superposition of a
    hardened steel gear   pattern   and b

FIG. 13-46. Comparison of Laboratory Static Fracture in a Gear Tooth and the
            Corresponding Photoelastic Stress Pattern (Boor and Stitz)

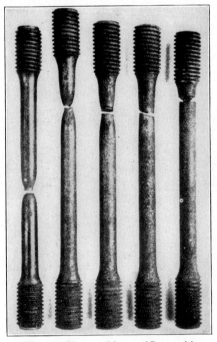

	(a)	(b)	(c)	(d)	(e)
Stress, psi/1000	86.1	71.1	64.0	56.9	49.8
Time to rupture	1 min	40 hr	259	3569	8477 hr
Elongation, %	9.17	16.8	6.8	6.2	2.2

FIG. 13-47. Fractures of Tensile Testpieces of Ni–Cr–Mo Steel at 932° F as a
            Function of Time (Thum and Richard)

FIG. 13-48.   Service Failure of Cr–Mo–V Bolts in Steam Plant, with Steam Temperature about 900° F (Thum and Richard)

Short-time test, room temp.	Short-time test, 1000°F	Long-time test, 1000°F, 60,000 psi, 18.4 hr	Short-time test, 1000°F after 18.4 hr at 1000°F without stress

FIG. 13-49.   Fractures of Cr–Mo–W Bolt Models (McVetty)

brittle type of failure shown by the specimen at the right of Fig. 13-47 is known as a "creep–rupture" failure. Such failures are generally intergranular and, consequently, have a coarse "crystalline" appearance. Being of a brittle nature, such failures are strongly influenced by stress concentration. Service failures of this kind in a steam plant are illustrated in Fig. 13-48. Tests with bolt models at 1000°F (Fig. 13-49) show that failure occurs in the minimum straight section in a short-time test, but in a long-time test failure occurs in the threaded portion which has a larger cross-section area but which

(a) 391 hr   (b) 300 hr

FIG. 13–50. Creep–Rupture of Cr–Mo–V Bolt Models—(1000°F, 58,000 psi)
(McVetty)

also involves stress concentration. Note that time and temperature alone do not produce this result. The remarkable degree to which fracture details are reproduced is shown in Fig. 13-50, both specimens being tested at the same load and temperature.

As shown in Fig. 13-51 micrographic examination is a useful method of distinguishing between "creep–rupture" failures and fatigue failures, since the former are intercrystalline and the latter are usually transcrystalline.

Specimens of lead, or lead alloy, exhibit at room temperature characteristics such as occur in steel only at high temperature. This is shown[43] in Fig. 13-52 illustrating a creep–rupture failure at room temperature. Failure of soldered joints has been known to occur in service owing to creep–rupture effect.

The addition of a lateral tension (biaxial-tension case) results in a reduction of elongation[44, 45] (Fig. 13-53); in other words, a more brittle type of fracture is produced. Triaxial tension, such as occurs in a specimen having a deep V groove, results in a completely brittle type of fracture. Owing to absence of flow phenomena, this test has been used to develop what has been called the "cohesion strength"[46] of the material.

Brittle-type fractures in ductile materials have occurred in welded ships under special conditions described in a report[47] of the Board of Investigation appointed by the U. S. Navy.

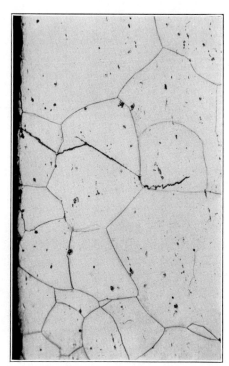

(a) Creep–rupture failure (inter-crystalline)

(b) Fatigue failure (transcrystalline)

FIG. 13-51.   Characteristic Cracks in Microstructure Due to Creep–Rupture and Fatigue Failures (Hull)

In steam boilers, hydrogen embrittlement sometime occurs, resulting in an extremely brittle fracture.[48] A corrosive condition plus residual stress causes brittle failures in cold-formed brass articles, such as cartridge cases (Fig. 13-54), the phenomenon being known as "season cracking."[49]

Glass is of special interest since it does not have a grain structure and can be made free of directional effects so that under certain conditions fractures are very regular. For example, certain glass plates fracturing during manu-facturing will break into precise rectangles while cylindrical glass castings

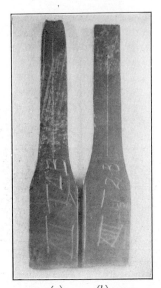

(a)   (b)
Stress, psi 3,000   2,000
Time to
  fracture 32 min   42 hr

FIG. 13-52 (left).   Influence of Time on Fracture of Lead-Alloy Specimens at Room Temperature (Dollins)

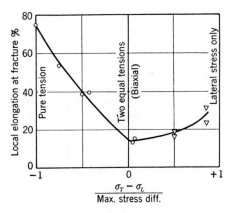

FIG. 13-53.   Deformation as Function of Biaxial Stress (Siebel and Maier)

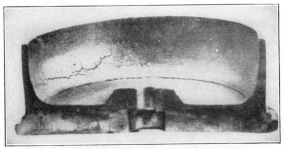

FIG. 13-54.   Season Cracking of Brass Cartridge Case (Moore, Beckinsale, and Mallinson)

have been known to split into exact halves with perfectly smooth surfaces.[50] It has also been shown that a perfect helical fracture can be obtained in glass tubing by heating and quenching in a certain way.[51]   A compression test of a glass plate carried out under carefully controlled conditions results in a complete shattering into minute pieces.[75]   These examples may seem surprising, since ordinarily broken glass is quite irregular.   In most cases impact is involved, accounting for the majority of the features seen; some of these features are discussed in the next section.

Internal ruptures of the "fish-eye" type, described in the preceding section on fatigue, sometimes occur in tensile tests, occasionally in weld metal (Fig. 13-55).

6. Impact Fractures.   Of the various types of failure, the impact type is the least understood, particularly the relationship between tests and service application.   The impact test does not furnish quantitative design data, as do many other tests.   However, some phenomena shown by the impact test are of interest and may be useful in a general way.

In connection with notched-bar-impact tests of steel, two types of fracture should be noted—ductile and brittle (Fig. 13-56).   These two types may be produced in the same material by varying the following test conditions: (1) geometry of test piece, (2) striking velocity, (3) ambient temperature.   If foot-pounds of energy is plotted as ordinate and one of the afore-mentioned variables as abscissa, then a typical S diagram is obtained[52] (Fig. 13-57) showing a transition zone between brittle and ductile fractures.

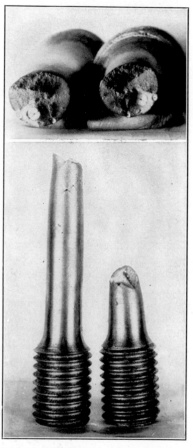

FIG. 13-55.   Fish eyes in Tensile Test Specimen Containing a Weld

Where temperature is the only variable, the transition zone sometimes occurs in the neighborhood of 0°F, which explains why railroads experience certain types of impact fractures in severely cold weather.   Incidentally, fatigue properties do not decrease in a similar way at low temperature.

Explosions usually result in brittle fractures, even though the material is quite ductile judged by the tensile tests.   An interesting characteristic observed in the case of an exploded tank[53] was that "herringbone" marks on the ruptured surfaces (Fig. 13-58) pointed toward the origin of failure.

Impact fractures of brittle materials such as tool steel, porcelain, and glass have certain characteristics in common. The most interesting work has been done with glass.[50, 54, 55] Two kinds of surface marks have been classified—"ribs" and "hackles." *Rib marks* are shown at *A* in Fig. 13-59. These are like the previously discussed fatigue "beach marks" in that they represent various stages of the crack front. The fracture direction approaches a rib mark on the concave side and leaves on the convex side. Although rib marks are found on glass fractures initiated by impact, they can also be produced by relatively slow tearing of

FIG. 13-56. Typical Brittle and Ductile Fractures of Charpy-Impact Specimens

glass.[54] Fracture travels more rapidly in a tension region resulting in a wider spacing of rib marks than in a compression region. In Fig. 13-59a the fracture passed from left to right, with tension on the top and compression on

the bottom. *Hackle marks* are shown at *B* in Fig. 13-59. These are perpendicular to the rib marks and represent regions where separately advancing cracks are continuously "breaking over" to form a major crack.* In these two respects, hackle marks resemble fatigue "ratchet marks," although the mechanism of their initiation is apparently different, since hackle marks start internally and ratchet marks start at the surface. Hackle marks are evidence of an explosive type of failure usually produced under severe forces or impact conditions. Hackle marks point toward the fail-

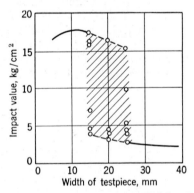

FIG. 13-57. Influence of Width of Testpiece on Impact Value (Greaves)

ure and, therefore, are especially valuable in identifying the origin of failure where the rib marks are too faint. The similarity of hackle marks to the "herringbone marks" (Fig. 13-58) associated with explosive failures of steel

---

* As a result of this behavior, a section perpendicular to the hackle marks shows a series of terraces.

FIG. 13-58.   Herringbone Marks Pointing toward Source of Failure in Fractured
Plate from Tank Explosion (Brown and Smith)

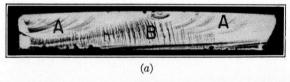

(a)

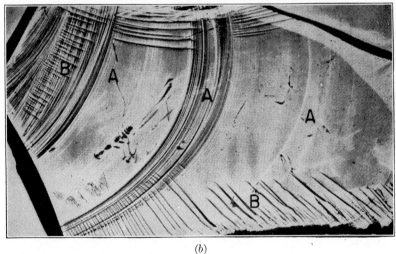

(b)

FIG. 13-59.   Fracture Details of Glass (Oughton)
A—Rib marks B—Hackle marks

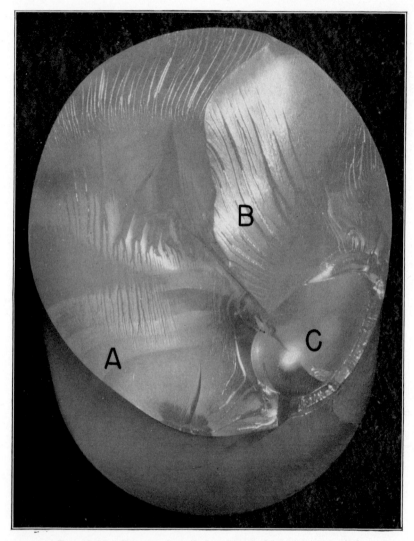

FIG. 13-60.   Fracture Details in a Plastic Material (Fosterite)
A—Rib marks B—Hackle marks C—Flaw

members should be noted.   It is apparently not necessary that a material
be as brittle as glass to show hackles and ribs, since these are also found in a
plastic material (Fig. 13-60).   Sometimes the source of failure in glass is
located at a round spot from which the hackles spread in raylike fashion[56]
(Fig. 13-61).   Note the similarity to Fig. 13-36 representing a failure in steel.
    In a paper before the Seventh International Congress of Applied Mechanics
in London, September 1948, Mrs. C. F. Tipper has thrown light on the forma-

tion of herringbone marks (Fig. 13-58). Incidentally such marks are not limited to the biaxial stress case of Fig. 13-58 (failure of pressure vessels), but also occur in the failure of ship plate.[47] In fact, Mrs. Tipper's results were obtained in a tension tests of notched plates (Fig. 13-62). Ahead of the crack is a plastic wedge; sections through this wedge at A–A, B–B and C–C (Fig. 13-62) are shown at the right. At A–A, a large ragged opening exists at the middle of the plate, connected by cracks to the plate surfaces; at B–B a small opening exists with no cracks extending to the surfaces; and at C–C only small holes exist. A development of these sections along a plane D–D results in a

Fig. 13-61.   Fracture   of   Glass   Rod
(Smekal)

crack front having roughly the shape of a V. Normals to this front, similar to the "hackle marks" just discussed, would have the shape of herringbone

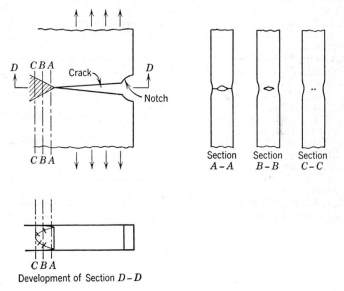

Fig. 13-62.   Mode of Failure of a Notched Plate in Tension (After Mrs C. F. Tipper)

marks and would also point in the direction of the origin of failure. Incidentally, Mrs. Tipper showed by means of micrographs that the "holes" at C–C were the result of cleavage of unfavorably oriented grains, while between such separations plastic deformation and tearing occurred in other grains. The coarse appearance of the fracture is a result of this manner of failure.

7. Conclusion. An endeavor has been made in the foregoing sections to develop types of fracture corresponding to known simple loading conditions. Complicated cases involving combinations of simple conditions are apt to be encountered, and, until further laboratory work has been done, it is necessary to use judgment based on considerations of stress analysis.

In examining fractured surfaces, be sure first to do a good cleaning job, using a solvent such as carbon tetrachloride, alcohol, or gasoline. It is not necessary to use a high-power microscope, but sometimes a lower-power glass (2 to 4×) is helpful. It is especially important for both visual inspection and photography to experiment with different angles of oblique lighting to bring out some of the fine detailed markings properly.

BIBLIOGRAPHY

The annotated listings refer to publications that constitute a bibliography on fracture.

A. References Quoted in Text

Many of these references contain only an illustration used in this chapter.

1. O. Lasche and W. Kieser, *Materials and Design in Turbo–Generator Plant*, Oliver & Boyd, London, 1927, p 127.
2. R. E. Peterson, "Stress Concentration Phenomena in Fatigue of Metals," *Trans ASME*, 1933, p 162. Part 2 of this paper deals with studies of fatigue fractures.
3. H. Gough, "Crystalline Structure in Relation to Failure of Metals—Especially by Fatigue," *Proc ASTM*, v 33, pt 2, 1933, p 3.
4. F. Bacon, "Cracking and Fracture in Rotary Bending Tests," *Engineering (British)*, v 134, 1932, p 372. A detailed study of considerable interest in connection with this chapter.
5. R. E. Peterson, "Fatigue Tests of Model Turbo–Generator Rotors," *Mech Eng*, v 53, 1931, p 211.
6. R. Mailänder, "Dauerbruche und Dauerfestigkeit," *Kruppsche Monatshefte*, v 13, 1932, p 65.
7. H. F. Moore and J. B. Kommers, *Fatigue of Metals*, McGraw-Hill Book Co, New York, 1927. Chapter 9, "Fatigue Failure under Service Conditions," is a valuable reference.
8. H. F. Moore, "A Study of Fatigue Cracks in Car Axles," *Univ Ill Eng Exp Sta Bul* 165, p 20.
9. R. E. Peterson, Discussion (p A-417) of paper (p A-23) by A. V. de Forest, "The Rate of Growth of Fatigue Cracks," *Trans ASME*, v 58, 1936.
10. M. Hetényi, "A Photoelastic Study of Bolt and Nut Fastenings," *Trans ASME*, v 65, 1943, p A-93.
11. W. Staedel, "Dauerfestigkeit von Schrauben," *Mitteilungen der Material-prüfungsanstalt Darmstadt*, v 14, 1933, p 22.
12. R. E. Peterson, "Fatigue of Shafts Having Keyways," *Proc ASTM*, v 32, 1932, p 413.
13. H. Krüger, *Dampfturbinenschaufeln*, Julius Springer, Berlin, 1930.
14. M. M. Frocht, "Studies in Three Dimensional Photoelasticity," *Trans ASME*, v 66, 1944, p A-10.
15. R. E. Peterson and A. M. Wahl, "Fatigue of Shafts at Fitted Members with a Related Photoelastic Analysis," *Trans ASME*, v 57, 1935, p A-1.

16. O. J. HORGER AND T. V. BUCKWALTER, "Fatigue Comparison of 7-inch Diameter Solid and Tubular Axles," *Proc ASTM*, v 41, 1941, p 682.

17. R. V. SOUTHWELL AND H. J GOUGH, "On the Concentration of Stress in the Neighborhood of a Small Spherical Flaw; and on the Propagation of Fatigue Fractures in Statistically Isotropic Materials," *Aeronautical Research Commit Report* 1003, Jan 1926, p 862.

18. T. J. DOLAN, "The Combined Effect of Corrosion and Stress Concentration at Holes and Fillets in Steel Specimens Subjected to Reversed Torsional Stresses," *Univ Ill Exp Sta Bul* 293, 1937.

19. J. O. SMITH, "The Effect of Range of Stress on the Torsional Fatigue Strength of Steel," *Univ Ill Exp Sta Bul* 316, 1939.

20. G. SEEGER, "Wirkung von Druckvorspannungen auf die Dauerfestigkeit," *Mitteilungen der Materialprüfungsanstalt Stuttgart*, 1935, p 46.

21. H. OSCHATZ, "Gesetzmässigkeiten des Dauerbruches," *Mitteilungen der Materialprüfungsanstalt Darmstadt*, v 2, 1933, p 19. This is an excellent reference in fracture studies. The work relates crack directions with stress fields. A number of the illustrations used in this chapter are from this source.

22. R. E. PETERSON, "Fatigue Problems in the Electrical Industry," *Metals and Alloys*, v 10, 1939, p 276. Contains many of the illustrations used in this chapter, and has some additional examples.

23. "Symposium on Crankshaft Stresses," *Proc Soc Experimental Stress Analysis*, v 2, n 2, 1944, p 118. Contains illustrations of failures produced under laboratory conditions.

24. S. WAY, "Pitting Due to Rolling Contact," *Trans ASME*, v 57, 1935, p A-49. An interesting fundamental study of this type of failure. Contains photographic examples.

25. J. G. R. WOODVINE, "Behavior of Case-Hardened Parts under Fatigue Stresses," *Iron and Steel Inst (Lond.) Carnegie Scholarship Memoirs*, v 13, 1924, p 197.

26. R. E. PETERSON AND J. M. LESSELLS, "Effect of Surface-Strengthening on Shafts Having a Fillet or a Transverse Hole," *Proc Soc Experimental Stress Analysis*, v 2, n 1, 1944, p 191.

27. C. A. ZAPFFE AND C. E. SIMS, "Hydrogen, Flakes, and Shatter Cracks," *Metals and Alloys*, v 11, 1940, p 145.

28. *Progress Reports of Rails Investigation*, Univ of Illinois Experiment Station. 1934–42.

29. J. M. LESSELLS AND G. S. CHERNIAK, "The Measurement of Stresses in Steam Hammer Piston Rods," *Proc Soc Experimental Stress Analysis*, v 2, n 1, 1944, p 34.

30. J. R. ADAMS AND H. L. WATSON, "Forged Steel Rolls," *Iron and Steel Engr*, v 15, 1938, p 48. Contains interesting examples of internal failures.

31. D. J. McADAM, "Fatigue and Corrosion Fatigue of Metals," *Proc Int Congress of Testing Matls (Amsterdam)*, v 1, 1927, p 305.

32. D. J. McADAM AND G. W. GEIL, "Pitting and its Effect on the Fatigue Limit of Steels Corroded under Various Conditions," *Proc ASTM*, v 41, 1941, p 696.

33. T. DUSOLD, "Der Einfluss der Korrosion auf die Drehschwingungsfestigkeit," *Mitteilungen des Wöhler Instituts*, v 14, 1933, p 48.

34. G. A. TOMLINSON, P. L. THORPE, AND H. GOUGH, "An Investigation of the Fretting Corrosion of Closely Fitting Surfaces," *Proc Inst Mech Engrs (Lond.)*, v 141, 1939, p 223.

35. A. THUM AND F. WUNDERLICH, "Dauerbiegefestigkeit von Konstruktionsteilen an Einspannungen, Nabensitzen und ähnlichen Kraftangriffstellen," *Mitteilungen der Materialprüfungsanstalt Darmstadt*, v 5, 1934. Describes a considerable number of practical examples.

36. A. B. WILLI, "Engine Bearings," *J Soc Automotive Engrs*, v 45, 1939, p 513.

37. P. LUDWIK, "Bestimmung der Reissfestigkeit," *Zeitschrift für Metallkunde*, v 9, 1926, p 269.
38. F. H. BOOR AND E. O. STITZ, "Stress Distribution in Gear Teeth," *Proc Soc Experimental Stress Analysis*, v 3, n 2, p 28, 1946.
39. R. E. PETERSON, "An Investigation of Stress Concentration by means of Plaster of Paris Specimens," *Mech Eng*, v 48, 1926, p 1449.
40. F. B. SEELY AND T. J. DOLAN, "Stress Concentration at Fillets, Holes, and Keyways as Found by the Plaster Model Method," *Univ Ill Exp Sta Bul 276*, 1935.
41. H. J. GOUGH AND A. J. MURPHY, "The Causes of Failure of Wrought-Iron Chain and Cable," *Proc Inst Mech Engrs (Lond.)*, v 92, pt 1, 1928, p 293.
42. A. THUM AND K. RICHARD, "Versprödung und Schädigung warmfester Stähle bei Dauerstandbeanspruchung," *Archiv für das Eisenhüttenwesen*, v 15, 1941, p 33.
43. C. W. DOLLINS, "Discussion of Symposium on Significance of the Tensile Test," *Proc ASTM*, v 40, 1940, p 585.
44. E. SIEBEL AND A. MAIER, "Der Einfluss mehrachsiger Spannungszustande auf das Formänderungsvermögen metallischer Werkstoffe," *Verein deutscher Ingenieure Zeitschrift*, v 77, 1933, p 1345.
45. E. A. DAVIS, "Yielding and Fracture of Medium Carbon Steel under Combined Stress," *Trans ASME*, v 67, 1945, p A-13.
46. W. KUNZE, "Kohäsionsfestigkeit," *Mitteilungen der deutschen Materialsprüfungsanstalten*, v 20, 1932, p 1.
47. Report of Board of Investigation "Design and Methods of Construction of Welded Steel Merchant Vessels," *Welding J*, v 23, 1944, p 794. Describes cases of ships broken into two separate parts.
48. C. A. ZAPFFE, "Boiler Embrittlement," *Trans ASME*, v 66, 1944, p 81.
49. H. MOORE, S. BECKINSALE, AND C. E. MALLINSON, "The Season Cracking of Brass and Other Copper Alloys," *J Inst Metals (Lond.)*, v 25, 1921, p 35.
50. F. W. PRESTON, "A Study of the Rupture of Glass," *J Soc Glass Technology*, v 10, 1926, p 234. A basic study in the brittle materials field.
51. J. J. HOPFIELD, "Spiral Cracks in Glass Tubes," *Nature*, v 158, 1946, p 582.
52. R. H. GREAVES, "Meaning of the Notched-Bar Impact Test," *Proc Int Assn Testing Matls*, Zürich, 1930, v A, p 225.
53. A. L. BROWN AND J. B. SMITH, "Failure of Spherical Hydrogen Storage Tank," *Mech Eng*, v 66, 1944, p 392.
54. J. B. MURGATROYD, "The Significance of Surface Marks on Fractured Glass," *J Soc Glass Technology*, v 26, 1942, p 156. A detailed study of ribs and hackles.
55. C. D. OUGHTON, "Analysis of Glass Fractures," *Glass Industry*, Feb 1945, p 72. Excellent pictures of fracture details.
56. A. SMEKAL, "Dauerbruch und spröder Bruch," *Metallwirtschaft,-wissenschaft, -technik*, v 16, 1937, p 189.

B. ADDITIONAL RECOMMENDED SOURCES OF INFORMATION ON FRACTURES

57. Battelle Memorial Institute, *Prevention of the Failure of Metals*, John Wiley & Sons, New York, 1941. Figures 1–71 show service failures. Descriptive notes are given.
58. E. SIEBEL, *Handbuch der Werkstoffprüfung*, v 2, Julius Springer, Berlin, 1939. Various types of failure are described throughout the book.
59. H. J. GOUGH, *The Fatigue of Metals*, Scott, Greenwood & Son, London, 1924. Some interesting examples of failure are described in Chapter 8.
60. *British Engine, Boiler, and Electrical Insurance Co Technical Reports*. This is perhaps the best single reference covering service failures.
61. O. GRAF, *Die Dauerfestigkeit der Werkstoffe und der Konstruktionselemente*, Julius Springer, Berlin, 1929. This book contains numerous examples of service failure.

62. H. F. Moore, "Stress, Strain, and Structural Damage," Marburg Lecture, *Proc ASTM*, v 39, 1939, p 549. An interesting survey of the relationship of various types of failure.

63. E. Seidl, "Bruch- und Fliess-Formen der Technische Mechanik," Zerreiss-Form, *Verein deutscher Ingenieure Verlag*, v 3, Berlin. Contains tensile test failure examples, as well as analysis of geological distortions and cracking.

64. R. Cazaud and L. Persoz, *La Fatigue des métaux*, Dunod, Paris, 1937. Chapter 2 describes service failures.

65. C. DeFreminville, "Reliability of Materials and Mechanisms of Failure," *Trans ASME*, v 41, 1919, p 907. The latter part contains examples of failure in brittle materials.

66. H. DeLeiris, *L'Analyse morphologique des cassures*, Association Technique Maritime et Aéronautique, 1945. Contains examples of herringbone fractures of the type encountered in ship plates.

67. C. A. Zapffe and M. Clogg, "Fractography—a New Tool for Metallurgical Research," *Trans Am Soc Metals*, v 34, 1945, p 71. Also "Cleavage Structures of Iron–Silicon Alloys," p 108. Deals with micrographic examination of untouched fractured surfaces. Many details of crystal structure can be disclosed by this method. Some of the gross features seem similar to those found in glass. See bibliography items 50, 54, and 55.

68. G. M. Enos, *Visual Examination of Steel*, American Society for Metals, Cleveland, Ohio, 1940. Contains much useful information, especially with regard to metallurgical factors influencing failure.

69. D. M. Davis, "Fatigue Failures of Aircraft Parts—Their Cause and Cure," *Aeronautical Eng Rev*, v 5, 1946, p 18. Examples of failure of aircraft parts are given in the second section of the article.

70. C. W. Newberry, "An Investigation into the Occurrence and Causes of Locomotive Type Failures," *Proc Inst Mech Engrs (Lond.)*, v 142, 1940, p 289. Contains interesting illustrations and discussions of fractures of locomotive wheel rims.

71. S. W. Poole and R. J. Johnson, "A Review of Some Mechanical Failures of Steel Plant Machine Equipment," *Proc Soc Experimental Stress Analysis*, v 3, n 2, p 61, 1946. States that of 76 failures in 18 months in Republic Steel plant equipment over half were due to fatigue, the remainder to welding or heat treating defects and overstressing. Six typical examples of failure are described and corrective measures stated.

72. "Panel Discussion of Fatigue Failure of Manufactured Parts," *Proc Soc Experimental Stress Analysis*, v 3, n 2, 1946, p 123. Contains presentation of eight representatives of industry; includes discussion.

73. S. A. Gordon, "Some Repeated Load Investigations of Aircraft Components," *Proc Soc Experimental Stress Analysis*, v 4, n 2, 1937, p 39. Describes failures of bolts and of drive brake spindle.

74. R. A. MacGregor, W. S. Burns, and F. Bacon, "Relation of Fatigue to Modern Engine Design," *Trans North East Coast Inst Engrs and Shipbuilders*, v 51, 1935, p 161. Contains interesting examples of service failures.

C. References Added Just Prior to Publication

75. E. F., Poncelet, "Fracture and Comminution of Brittle Solids," *Metals Technology*, v 11, 1944. Particular attention is called to Fig. 7 showing disintegration of a glass plate.

76. A. Thum and K. Federn, *Spannungszustand und Bruchausbildung*, 1939, Julius Springer (Berlin). Not generally available. Copy in Library of Congress, Washington, D. C.

77. E. Gassner, "Strength Investigations in Aircraft Construction under Repeated Application of Load," *Nat. Advisory Commit., Aeronautics Tech. Memo.* 1087 (1946). Translated from *Luftwissen*, Feb. 1939, p. 61.

CHAPTER 14

BRITTLE MODELS AND BRITTLE COATINGS

By M. Hetényi

A. BRITTLE MODELS

1. Characteristics of Brittle Fractures. Stress analysis by means of brittle models is based on the following properties of brittle materials: (*a*) that they fracture without appreciable deformation, and (*b*) that fracture occurs when the maximum tensile stress in the piece reaches a certain limiting value. If we make a model out of a brittle material which has, in addition to the aforementioned properties, a nearly linear stress–strain relationship up to the point of failure, we find that stress ratios in the piece will be about the same at the time of fracture as at any lower value of the load. It is evident, therefore, that if such a model is tested to destruction and the ultimate stress the material can withstand is known from calibration specimens, the magnitude of the maximum stress in the model for any value of the load can be simply established.

The failure of brittle materials has, however, a number of characteristic features which will considerably influence the results obtained by the aforementioned testing procedure. For instance, the ultimate strength seems to be defined in a rather accidental manner by the condition of the material at a certain critical point, which is usually limited to a very small volume compared to the bulk of the entire testpiece, and this circumstance almost invariably causes a considerable scattering of the test results. The probability of occurrence of such weak points within the most highly stressed parts of the model and the comparative magnitude of the maximum stress area in the model and in the calibration pieces will have to be taken into account in the interpretation of such text results, as is shown later.

The question of the ultimate cause of brittleness is, of course, of great importance in these investigations. It is known, for instance, that under triaxial compressive stresses of great intensity it is possible to produce large permanent deformations in the most brittle materials, whereas under triaxial tensile stress the majority of ductile materials fail in a brittle manner. It is also known that, by testing ductile materials at high velocities (impact) or under rapidly alternating loads (fatigue), rupture surfaces can be produced which have all the characteristics of brittle failures. On the basis of these observations it may be generally stated that the ultimate cause of brittleness is always mechanical in character and is the result of certain types of stress distribution. If the internal structure of the material is such that it inherently produces a stress distribution (most often through high local concentration of stresses) that precludes the possibility of plastic yielding, then the material will be generally regarded as "brittle" and will fail as such under the simplest uni- or biaxial conditions of stress. This theory, based on the assumption of "internal flaws" in the structure of brittle materials, was developed by Griffith[1] and Smekal[2] and is generally accepted at present as the most likely explanation of the puzzling phenomena observed in the fracture of brittle materials.

From a historical point of view it is of interest to note that the first systematic investigation in the strength of materials, carried out by Galileo[3] over 300 years ago, was apparently based on experiments with beams of stone or other brittle materials. Though Galileo correctly established the influence of the length and cross-sectional dimensions on the strength of beams, he made the faulty assumption that the entire cross section is in tension and that it tends to rotate around one edge on bending. It is easily seen how this assumption could be prompted by observing the occurrence of brittle fractures in bent beams.

The use of brittle materials in modern strength investigations was introduced by C. Bach[4] through his classical experiments with cast iron. In more recent years, model tests were also made with concrete,[5] glass,[6] and synthetic resins,[7] examples of which are shown in Fig. 14-1. Though these tests threw considerable light on the behavior of the respective materials under various conditions of stress, the materials themselves, with the possible exception of synthetic resins, were not found very suitable for the prediction of maximum stress through model tests. Also, the production of a large number of identical specimens of these materials, required in tests of this type, is rather difficult. For these reasons, most of the brittle models today were made of plaster of Paris or pottery plaster, which are closest to an ideal material for the purpose; the use of these is discussed later in more detail.

2. Plaster Models. As a result of experiments by a number of investigators,[8-13] the best way of preparing plaster models is fairly well established and may be described as follows.

For the material, commercial molding plaster, plaster of Paris, or a high-grade pottery plaster (as obtainable from the U. S. Gypsum Company) may be used. The chemical composition of all these materials is nearly the same, but the last one (pottery plaster) is preferable because it is somewhat slower in setting, thus permitting a longer time for working with the material. The ultimate strength and elastic modulus of the finished product is greatly dependent on the proportion of water in the mixture, the strength increasing, but, at the same time, the setting time decreasing, with a decreasing amount of water. The best proportion was found to be 70 lb of water to 100 lb of plaster, which mixture, on proper handling, gives a material with approximately 1,000,000 psi modulus of elasticity, about 1800 psi compressive, and 600 to 800 psi tensile strength.

The mixture is prepared by pouring the plaster slowly into pure (drinking) water at room temperature and then allowing it to stand and blend for 10 to 12 min. At the end of this period, a stirring operation should be started, the purpose of which is to liberate the entrapped air bubbles. Stirring can be effected by a small immersed propeller or by mechanical shaking of the mixing tub, and should be continued for 5 min. Violent stirring is to be avoided, as it would produce the opposite of the desired effect; that is, it would introduce

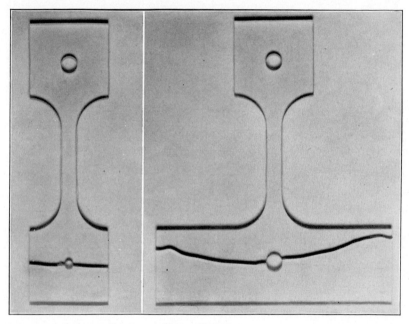

Fig. 14-1. Fracture Specimen of Methyl Methacrylate Resin (Plexiglas), Exhibiting the Sensitivity of the Material to Small Differences of Stress Concentration

more air into the mixture. After 5 min of stirring, a mixture is obtained that is smooth and uniform in appearance and is ready to be poured into finished molds, if the models are to be casted, or into blank molds, if the final models are to be shaped by machining. Molds may be made of clay, concrete, steel, or glass plates, the surfaces of which should be oiled in each case to facilitate the removal of the plaster. The plaster undergoes a small volume expansion on setting, which enables it to fill the molds completely. After 15 min of setting, the plaster warms up and sweats, forming a film of water between the casting and the oiled surface of the mold, which permits an easy removal of the mold from the already hardened material. The obtained specimens should be stored in a moist room for about 2 days and then dried for a minimum of 3 weeks at room temperature. It is not advisable to attempt drying at elevated temperature, because the plaster may be dehydrated at a too rapid rate ("burned"), when it becomes very weak and chalky.

With this procedure, the resulting specimens have a distinctly metallic ring when struck, their surface shows no cavities or discontinuities when examined under a low-power microscope, and they exhibit a practically straight-line stress–strain relationship up to the point of rupture. The material may be turned in an ordinary engine lathe or may be drilled or shaped in a milling machine. The speed of cutting may vary considerably, and the only precaution that needs to be taken is to keep the depth of cuts at moderate values.

At the same time when the models are made, a few calibration specimens, or control pieces, should be prepared from the same mixture and by the same casting and curing procedure. The purpose of these calibration pieces is to establish the value of the maximum stress at which the material will fail. For this reason the specimens are usually made of the simplest form, and loaded in such a manner that the magnitude of the maximum stress can be easily and accurately calculated. The maximum stress in the model is then derived by way of comparison between the fracture loads of the model and of the calibration pieces, respectively.

The plaster-model method was used in the investigation of stresses at holes, fillets, and keyways by R. E. Peterson,[8] Trinks and Hitchcock,[10] and Seely and Dolan.[12] Curved beams were tested by Seely and James,[9] a variety of structural models was investigated by Roark and Hartenberg,[11] and the stress distribution in bent plates was analyzed by Newmark and Lepper.[13] In most of these investigations the results of the plaster-model tests were compared with available results of the mathematical theory of elasticity, with photo-elasticity, and in some cases with fatigue-test data. Such a comparison is illustrated in Fig. 14-2. As a rule, the stress concentration factors derived from plaster-model tests are considerably below those obtained by calculation or by photoelasticity and are about the same and seldom above those derived from fatigue tests.

On the basis of the previously discussed experimental work, the following rules may be recommended in the use of the plaster-model method of stress analysis:

(a) The type of stress distribution and the relative volume of the most highly stressed material should be as closely as possible the same in the calibration pieces as in the model.

(b) Reliable quantitative values for the maximum stress in the model may be established only by testing a larger number of (not less than 6) identical specimens.

(c) For extremely high and very localized concentration of stress, the method is likely to give inconsistent results. A possible explanation for this is discussed in the following section.

3. The Statistical Theory of Strength. The particular features of the test results obtained in the fracture of brittle materials may be explained by the statistical theory of strength, which was originally proposed by Weibull,[14, 15] and to which further contributions were made by Frenkel and Kontorova[16] and others.[17−20]

This theory is based on the assumption that the ultimate strength of a testpiece is determined by its weakest point, which is a product of unfavorable coincidence between stress intensity and a defective state of the material. The likelihood of such coincidence may be calculated by the laws of probability, if the characteristic distribution of defects through the bulk of the material and the type of stress distribution in the specimen are known. The result of such calculation is not a precise value for the strength of the

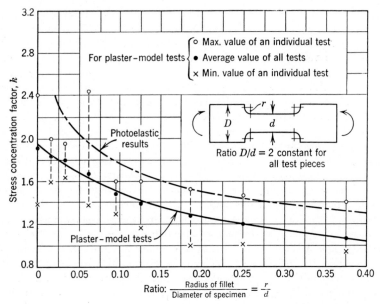

FIG. 14-2.   A Comparison between the Stress-Concentration Factors Derived from Plaster-Model Tests of Round Filleted Shafts in Bending and Those Obtained Photoelastically by E. E. Weibel with Flat Bakelite Specimens of Similar Proportions (F. B. Seely and T. J. Dolan[12])

testpiece but an indication of the degree of probability that fracture will occur at a certain value of the load.

For the distribution of faults in the material, Weibull assumes a power law with two arbitrary parameters that can be adjusted to fit any particular material.   Weibull's assumption is mathematically the simplest and provides the greatest versatility for the investigation of more complicated problems. There are, however, factors in favor of the normal Gaussian distribution used by Frenkel and Kontorova,[16] and further possibilities are open through a number of other distributions available in mathematical statistics.[20]

Through this statistical point of view it is easily seen that, for the same type of stress distribution, the probability of fracture will increase with the size of the specimen, larger testpieces exhibiting relatively lower strength and a greater dispersion of individual test results. This is all in agreement with the so called "size effect" observed not only in static fracture of brittle materials, but also in all impact and fatigue tests. Support of this theory may be found in the plaster-model tests of Peterson,[8] who observed that the presence of very small holes in tension specimens caused no noticeable reduction in the ultimate strength of the pieces. This may be explained by the fact that by the reduction of the size of the holes the localized stress peaks at the boundaries of the holes will cover such minute volumes of the material that the probability of their coinciding with defective spots becomes negligibly small.

Among the quantitative proofs of Weibull's theory we may mention that it made possible the calculation[14] of the difference in tensile, bending, and torsional strength observed much earlier by Kuntze in a series of tests with brittle models made of a mixture of plaster and stearic acid. Also the tests made by Davidenkov, Shevandin, and Wittman[19] with brittle-steel specimens at low temperatures gave quantitative confirmation of Weibull's theory.

The statistical theory of strength had also a number of applications beyond the field of brittle fractures. Among these we may quote the work of Daniels[17] who investigated the strength of bundles of threads and reached the interesting conclusion that a bundle containing n threads is likely to sustain a P load only if there are k threads in the set $(k \leq n)$ whose strength exceeds the value of P/k. The effect of the principal variables in fatigue tests was analyzed statistically by Freudenthal.[18]

4. Stress Crazing of Synthetic Resins. Indication of the maximum tensile stress in a model may be obtained by making the piece out of one of the synthetic materials which develops crazing under sustained static loads.

The crazing marks first appear as fine hairlines on the surface of the material, and, under prolonged loading, they gradually spread and deepen, though they never seem to enter areas where the stress is under a certain limiting value. The lines develop normally to the tensile stresses and show up the best when the piece is viewed at an angle under oblique lighting, when they appear in bright reflection as illustrated in Fig. 14-3.

Sensitivity for stress crazing was observed in Plexiglas, Lucite, Vinylite, and photoelastic Bakelite (BT-61-893). In each case, crazing is produced at a comparatively low value of stress that may be as small as one fifth of the ultimate tensile strength of the material. Klemperer[21] observed that crazing in Plexiglas first appears in about 4 days at a stress of 4000 psi, and it takes over 30 days to develop the lines at 3000 psi. The formation of the crazing can be greatly accelerated, however, by wetting the surface of the specimen while it is under load, with alcohol or carbon tetrachloride. This etching action brings out in less than a minute a full crazing pattern that would otherwise require weeks to develop. In spite of etching, however, Plexiglas appears to be indefinitely resistant to crazing at stress values under 2000 psi.

Though crazing lines are obviously sharp fissures wedging into the material, their presence seem to have an unexpectedly small effect on the ultimate strength of the piece. Completely crazed Plexiglas specimens were tested to fracture by Klemperer,[21] who found that the strength of such pieces was about 7300 psi, amounting only to a 27 per cent reduction in the strength of the material that is otherwise around 10,000 psi.

In attempting an explanation for the crazing phenomenon, one may be inclined to regard it as the first indication of incipient failure that is to lead eventually to a delayed fracture of the material. It is well established that glass[22] and also most of the synthetic resins fail under continued loading at one half to one third of the value of the stress that is required to produce fracture at an instantaneous application of the load. This behavior of certain

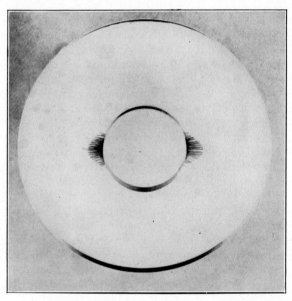

FIG. 14-3. Stress-Crazing Pattern Indicating Points of Maximum Tensile Stress in a Plexiglas Ring Compressed by Concentrated Forces at End Points of Horizontal Diameter

materials is frequently referred to as delayed fracture or "static fatigue," and it can be greatly accelerated by wetting or etching the surface of the specimens under load, which draws an obvious comparison with stress-crazing phenomena. In spite of this, however, the foregoing reasoning cannot furnish an acceptable explanation for the origin of all stress crazing, since we have such examples as Columbia Resin CR-39 (Allyl Diglycol Carbonate), with a marked sensitivity for delayed fracture, which shows no inclination for stress crazing even when stressed close to its ultimate strength and wetted, at the same time, by any of the usual etching agents (alcohol, carbon tetrachloride, or ether).

Further study, and an ultimate explanation of the cause of stress crazing will probably contribute greatly to our understanding of the structure and strength of glass and resinous materials. For the present, its only application is to furnish a striking indication of the most highly stressed regions in models of structural and machine parts, and it is being used for such instructive purposes in the design departments of some aircraft companies.

B. Brittle Coatings

5. Oxide Coatings. The use of brittle coatings as strain indicators is based on the observation that such coatings, through their rupture, can reveal the magnitude of strain in the underlying material of the testpiece. If the surface of a specimen is coated by an adhering brittle substance, on application of a load, the coating will evidently crack first at the point where the strain is the greatest. By observing the initial formation of the cracks and their subsequent spreading as the load is increased, the nature and approximate magnitude of the stresses in the most critical areas of the test piece may be established.

The first brittle coating used for strain detection was probably the mill scale, the thin iron-oxide layer which forms on the surface of hot-rolled steel stock. This scale, being comparatively inextensible, breaks at fairly low values of strain, emitting slight crackling sounds as the first evidence of fracture. It requires, however, strains of the order of 1 per cent or more to cause visual indication of the rupture, and for this reason mill scale can be used only as an indicator of yielding in mild steel specimens. At strains of such magnitude the edges of the cracks are sufficiently separated and the scale flaked off along the slip lines or Lüders' lines of maximum shearing strains, to show along these lines the metal beneath the oxide scale. For photographic recording it is very desirable, however, to increase the contrast between the slip lines and their background. Oiling the surface is helpful in this respect, but better results are obtained by painting the surface of the piece before testing with thin whitewash (lime and water) which forms a white coat on drying. This coat flakes off with the oxide scale along the slip lines, making these appear as dark pencil lines against a white background, as shown in Fig. 14-4. The surface of the testpiece should be cleaned of grease before the whitewash is applied with a soft brush, and in a very thin solution, the application being repeated if the first layer does not appear sufficiently white after evaporation of the water.

In place of whitewash, R. S. Johnston[24] used white Portland cement in water, obtaining excellent photographic records of the development of Lüders' lines in the web plates of large built-up columns. He found this method sensitive enough to show the otherwise invisible minute slip lines which occurred around the identification marks stamped into the cold-steel plates.

Strain-indicating oxide films can also be produced on the surface of any previously machined mild-steel specimen by heating. Such tests were made by W. Mason[25] who brought his testpieces up to a temperature of 1400°F in an electric oven in about 30 min and held them there for 15 min, when they were quickly removed and allowed to cool at room temperature. This treatment produced on the bright surface of the machined specimens a brittle oxide layer which was much more uniform in its consistency and better suited for the purpose than the ordinary mill scale.

On aluminum-alloy specimens brittle films may be produced by anodic coatings which adhere to the surface very well and give good indication of the progress of yielding in the underlying material.

6. Various Resinous Coatings. The first record of the use of a strain-indicating resinous coating was published by Sauerwald and Wieland[26] in 1925. They used a solution of shellac in alcohol which cracked only at large values of strain. It was employed to indicate regions of yield in notched-bar-impact tests with nonferrous metals.

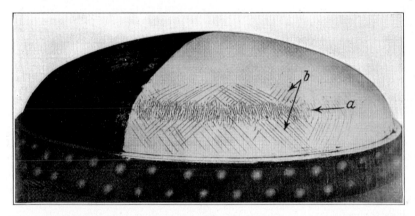

FIG. 14-4. Appearance of Slip Lines through Whitewash Coating on a Dished Boiler Head under Internal Pressure

Lines a were the first ones to appear owing to the maximum meridional bending stress in the knuckle. At increasing pressure these were joined by lines of the type b, which were caused by the rising difference between meridional and hoop stresses (E. Seibel and A. Pomp,[23])

The first brittle coating that cracked within the elastic limit of ordinary steels was described by Dietrich and Lehr[27] in 1932. It was the so-called "Maybach" lacquer, named after the manufacturing concern where it was developed, and its use was covered by Deutches Reichs-Patent 534,158. As it was disclosed in a later publication,[30] this lacquer consisted of a solution of colophony in benzol. It required baking to develop the necessary brittleness, and its cracking sensitivity could not be sufficiently controlled to give quantitative information concerning magnitudes of strain. Through the appearance of the first crack in the coating, it gave a reliable indication only of the point and direction of the maximum tensile stress in the piece. On the basis of this information, the rest of the test consisted in applying short-gage-length extensometers at the indicated points and perpendicularly to the tension cracks, to measure accurately the values of strain. In this manner, Dietrich and Lehr analyzed the stress distribution in crankshafts, connecting rods, and other machine parts.

From the subsequent publications[29, 30] which appeared on the use of this coating in the next 8 years, it is apparent that the lacquer was never developed to the stage where it would have been capable of giving quantitative results. Nevertheless, this was the first demonstration that a coating can be produced which can render valuable information without stressing the test object beyond its elastic limit and impairing thereby its further use. This "non-destructive" feature of tests with suitable coatings, against the other types which may only be regarded as "damage indicators," is perhaps the most important single factor that made the brittle-lacquer method of stress analysis practicable.

In 1934 Portevin and Cymboliste[31] published a set of very clear photographs of isostatics, obtained also by a lacquer which apparently cracked within the elastic limit of the metallic testpieces used. The authors listed a number of possibilities for such coatings, as natural and phenolic resins with a large variety of solvents, without disclosing, however, the specific combinations used in the tests. Tylecote[32] in 1942 investigated isostatic patterns in spot-welded aluminum-alloy plates by use of a resin-type varnish thinned in xylol. His best lacquer started to crack at a strain value of 0.0015 in./in., which was well within the elastic limit of the aluminum-alloy specimens. It was found necessary, however, to bake the coated pieces to produce such cracking sensitivity, and the process could not be controlled quantitatively.

A striking method of producing resin coatings on structural objects was developed in England by B. P. Haigh[33] and used later by J. S. Blair.[34] This consisted of heating up the testpieces to 140°C and then dusting on to the surface powdered resin which had a melting point slightly above 100°C. The resulting coating cracked sometimes at elastic-stress values, but its principal use was to facilitate the observation of Lüders' lines in yielding. Complex bridge-type structures up to 100-ft span were tested in this manner and also pressure vessels and tubes under internal pressure.

7. Stresscoat. The most suitable material at present for the preparation of a strain-indicating brittle coating is "Stresscoat," a product of the Magnaflux Corporation.* It is a coating which, when used with suitable precautions, can give quantitative indication of the maximum strain values within the elastic range of steel specimens. Its basic ingredients are limed wood rosin K and dibutyl phthalate, with carbon disulfide as solvent. These, with some other modifying components, are mixed in a variety of proportions to produce lacquers which will have the desired strain sensitivity at various levels of temperature and humidity.

Since the coating is markedly affected by small changes in temperature, the method can be used to its best advantage in the laboratory, though there are provisions for making tests out-of-doors under favorable conditions.

A Stresscoat test normally begins by measuring prevailing temperature and humidity with a sling psychrometer and then selecting a suitable coating material from the selection chart shown in Fig. 14-5. There are 12 lacquers

---

* Stresscoat methods, equipment and materials are covered by the following U. S. patents: 2,186,014; 2,294,897; 2,310,845 and 2,325,116.

(nos. 1200 to 1211) available for general test-room use. The lacquer of the number which appears in the selection chart at the intersection of the dry- and wet-bulb readings of the psychrometer will give a coating which will crack first at a strain value of 0.0007 to 0.0008 in./in. This threshold sensitivity of any particular lacquer can be more definitely established by use of the calibration bars which are supplied with each standard Stresscoat outfit. These bars are coated at the same time as the principal test object, are kept

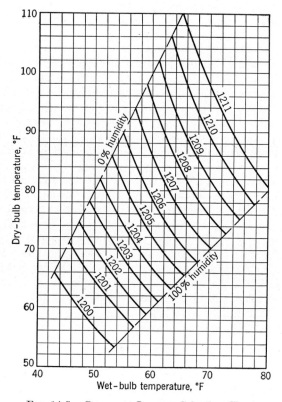

Fig. 14-5.   Stresscoat Lacquer Selection Chart

close to it during the entire drying period, and are tested in cantilever bending during the main test. The limit of crack propagation along each cantilever gives, in a suitable strain scale, the threshold sensitivity of the applied coating.

The best method of applying the lacquer is by spraying it with a spray gun on the surface of the testpiece which should be previously cleaned of grease and loose particles. The evenly distributed fine air bubbles which are thus introduced into the lacquer contribute appreciably to the consistency of crack formation in the coating. The bubbles appear to have two functions: (1) they facilitate an even drying of the lacquer, and (2) they intercept the spreading of the cracks into regions where the strain is below the normal threshold sensitivity of the coating. On account of the offensive carbon disulfide solvent in the lacquer, spraying should be done in a spray booth, or, if this is not possible, a gas mask should be worn by the operator. The thickness of the coating does not need to be completely uniform; between the limits of 0.004 to 0.008 in. it will have about the same cracking sensitivity. The correct thickness can be best judged from the color of the deposited layer. It takes considerable experience to produce a suitable coating on complex test-pieces, and practical details on this, as well as on later phases of the testing

FIG. 14-6. Initial and Full Crack Pattern on a Generator Bracket Tested in Cantilever Bending by the Brittle-Lacquer Method[43]

technique, may be found in the booklet on "Operating Instructions for Stress-coat," published by the Magnaflux Corporation.

After the testpiece and the calibration bars have been coated, they should be kept at a uniform temperature during the entire drying period (optimum 12 to 24 hr) and the subsequent test. If the temperature is kept within $\pm 2°F$, and there is not more than $\pm \frac{1}{2}°F$ difference at any time between the temperature of the testpiece and the calibration bars, the method is capable of furnishing values of the maximum strain in the testpiece with an accuracy of about ± 10 per cent. A temperature fluctuation of $\pm 5°F$ already prevents quantitative conclusions from the tests. Even in this case, however, the lacquer is still likely to indicate reliably the point and the direction of the maximum stress in the piece. On account of the difficulties involved in providing a suitable temperature control, many experimenters prefer to use Stresscoat only in such a qualitative manner and to measure the strain in subsequent stages of the test by means of extensometers, applied at the points and in the directions indicated by the crack pattern in the coating.

The first cracks which appear in the lacquer are rather inconspicuous, and they can be best detected by using a flashlight at a small angle of incidence to the surface of the testpiece.   If the surface was originally dull, the observa-

FIG. 14-7.   Stress Concentration in a Flanged Shaft Subjected to Torsion, as Shown by Stresscoat

tion of the cracks can be greatly facilitated by applying to the testpiece an undercoating, consisting of bright aluminum powder in suspension, before the piece is sprayed with the lacquer.   The first crack in the coating, having its origin at the point of maximum tensile stress and running perpendicularly to the direction of this stress, has the same appearance as the first fatigue crack if the testpiece is subjected to alternating loading.   It can thus be utilized in the prediction of fatigue failures.

On successive increase of the load, the cracks spread, and the limit of their propagation always marks the line along which the extensional strains have about the same magnitude. These lines are sometimes called isoentatic* lines, or lines of equal stretch, and they may be traced on the surface of the lacquer to denote the extent of the spread of the cracks at any particular value of the load.

Though Stresscoat lacquers become brittle on drying, they exhibit appreciable creep under sustained loads. If the duration of the load is more than

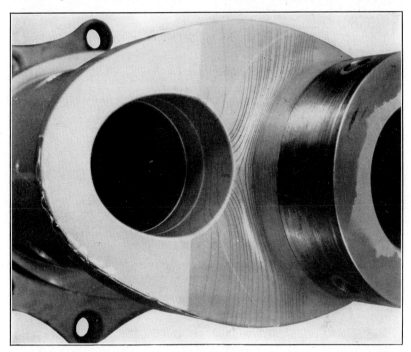

FIG. 14-8. Stresscoat Pattern on Crankshaft Loaded in Bending (W. T. Bean, Jr.[45])

10 sec, the effect of creep on the cracking sensitivity should be taken into account by means of the creep-correction chart available for the purpose.[35] This creep tendency of the lacquer can also be utilized in the determination of compressive stresses in a specimen. By loading the piece slowly and thus permitting relaxation of the lacquer, it is possible to bring the testpiece up to full load in about 1 hr without cracking the coating. If the piece is then kept under full load for another hour or more, the coating will become practically stress-free, and, when the applied load is suddenly released, a crack pattern will be formed which will indicate the distribution of the highest compressive strains in the testpiece under normal loading. The same result can be

* From the Greek iso (equal) and entasis (stretching).

obtained, of course, by applying the load before the piece is coated, but then the load has to be maintained during the entire drying period, that is, for 12 hr or more.

Ordinarily there is enough residual tension in the dried coating to creep the cracks open even after release of the load.   However, if a photographic record

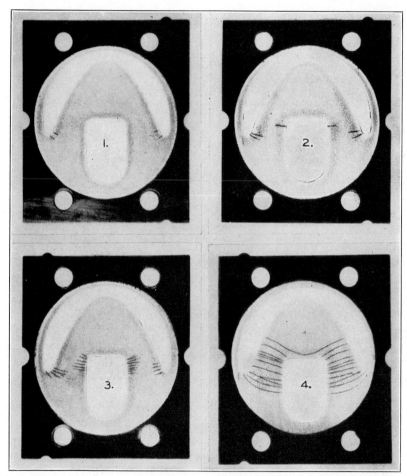

FIG. 14-9.   Stresscoat Patterns on a Flapper Valve at Various Stages in the Deflection of the Tongue[43]

of the pattern is required, the cracks may be intensified by a red-dye etchant which is supplied by the producers of the lacquer.   This dye solution is painted on the surface of the lacquer; it penetrates into the cracks and stays there after the surface is wiped clean with an etchant emulsifier.   All the photographs shown of Stresscoat patterns in this chapter were obtained of testpieces etched in this manner.   Once the lacquer coating is etched, it is

unsuitable for further tests.   For this reason, each of the pictures shown in
Fig. 14-9 of the successive stages of crack development in a refrigerator flapper
valve, were obtained from a separate test.   The red-dye etchant is also used
for increasing the cracking sensitivity of coatings.   The application of the
etchant on loaded specimens decreases the threshold value of the lacquer by
approximately 6 numbers, from 0.0008 to about 0.0002 in./in. strain for
instance.   Results obtained by sensitization remain chiefly qualitative,

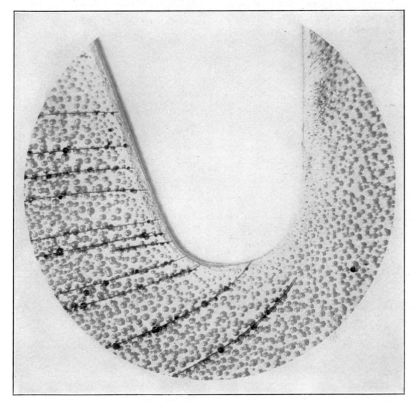

Fig. 14-10.   Bubble Structure in Stresscoat Lacquer at the Fillet of a Flapper
Valve[43]

however, their principal use being to indicate the direction of the principal
stresses in less highly stressed areas of the specimens.

As shown by the number of articles written on this method,[35–57] Stresscoat
is being used in the analysis of a large variety of stress problems.   Its principal
advantages are that it does not require the preparation of models, as it is
applied directly to the surface of the actual structural or machine part under
investigation, and that it is a nondestructive method of testing which does not
affect in any way the further use of the test object.   Though it often gives
only qualitative indication of the strain distribution, the fact alone that it can

disclose the point and the direction of the maximum stress in any complicated object, places this procedure in a unique position among the available methods of experimental stress analysis.

Stresscoat shows, with an exceptional precision, the principal stress trajectories (isostatics). Both sets of the orthogonal trajectories can be developed

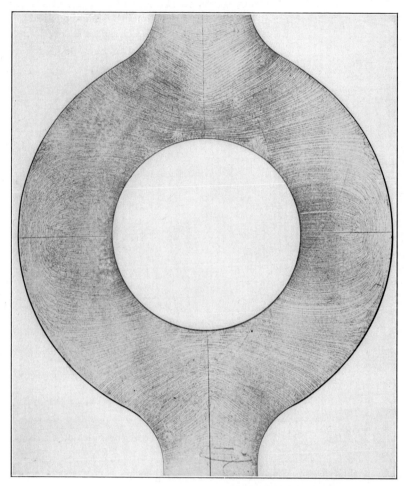

FIG. 14-11a.   Set of Isostatic Lines in an Eyebar in Tension, Obtained by Direct Loading (A. J. Durelli[49])

in this manner, one by direct loading, and the other by relaxation of the lacquer. Since the purpose of tests of this type is to obtain a fully developed pattern including the less highly stressed regions of the testpiece, the lacquer is usually sensitized by chilling its surface or by using the previously discussed red-dye etchant while the piece is under full load. From the formation of the isostatic pattern, by means of established theorems of the theory of elasticity, a number of characteristic features of the stress distribution may be directly derived. Another possible use of the isostatic lines was pointed out by H. Neuber,[48] who showed theoretically that in any plane-stress system, the

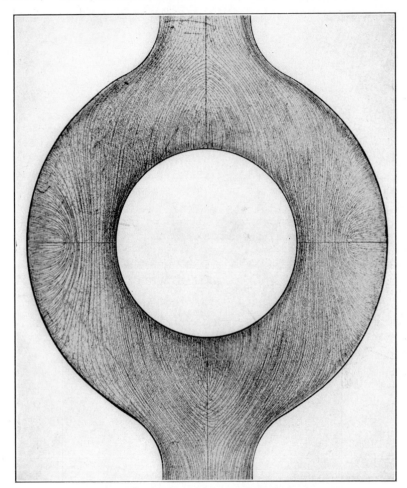

Fig. 14-11b. Complementary Set of Isostatic Lines in an Eyebar in Tension, Obtained by Relaxation (A. J. Durelli[49])

distance between an unloaded boundary and a neighbouring principal-stress trajectory is inversely proportional to the boundary stress values. Application of this method and also other Stresscoat studies of isostatic patterns may be found in the publications by Durelli.[49, 50]

Applications of Stresscoat to impact-stress problems are illustrated in Figs. 14-12 to 14-16. A comparison between the patterns produced in a

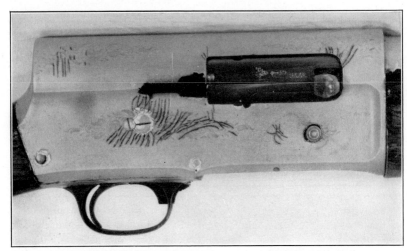

FIG. 14-12.   Impact Strain Patterns on Breech of a Shotgun (Greer Ellis and F. B. Stern, Jr.[51])

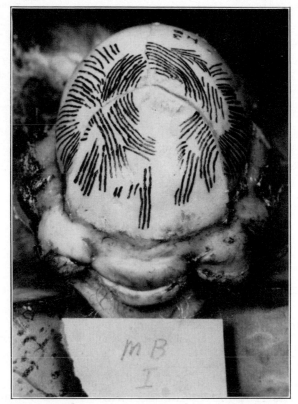

FIG. 14-13.   Deformation Pattern of the Skull of a Living Anesthetized Monkey (Macaque) Due to a Hammer Blow in the Top Mid-Line Region

Further tests of the dead animal with contents of the skull intact and tests of the empty dried skull indicated that the direction of strain paths were essentially the same in each case (H. R. Lissner and E. S. Gurdjian[52])

cantilever plate by static and impact loads, respectively (Figs. 14-15 and 14-16), shows that the stress distribution is fundamentally of a different character in these two cases. Tests thus far seem to indicate that the velocity of deformation has small influence on the cracking sensitivity of Stresscoat lacquers, and, on this basis, a static calibration of the loading appears to be satisfactory. There is need, however, for more quantitative information in this regard. Approximate values of the maximum impact strains may be established either by repeating the test with coatings of different cracking sensitivity or, if the testpiece has one or more axes of symmetry with respect to applied load, by using a different coating in each segment of the specimen.

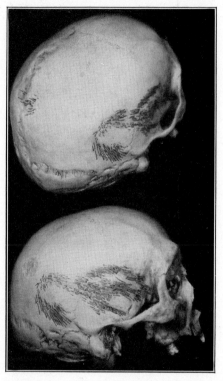

Stresscoat may also be used in the study of residual stresses.[54-56] For this purpose it is advisable to choose a coating which is several numbers below the one indicated by the selection chart for the prevailing temperature and humidity level. The sensitivity of this coating may be further increased by drying it at 10° to 20°F above room temperature and by using the red-dye etchant during the test. The test consists of drilling small holes, about $\frac{1}{8}$ in. in diameter and $\frac{1}{8}$ in. deep, into the surface of the coated testpiece and observing the formation of the crack pattern which is caused by the release of strain in the surface layer through the removal of the material from the hole. Examples of the en-

Fig. 14-14. Deformation Pattern of the External Surface of the Human Skull Due to a Blow on the Side of the Head Well toward the Back

The areas of maximum tensile deformation occur on the side of the head toward the temple and are at a considerable distance from the point of impact (E. S. Gurdjian and H. R. Lissner[53])

suing patterns are shown in Fig. 14-17. The extent of the spreading of the cracks from the boundary of the holes may be regarded as an approximate measure of the magnitude of the released stresses. Since the state of stress is essentially biaxial in these cases, correct interpretation of the results depends greatly on whether the cracks in the coating are produced by a limiting value of stress or strain. Tests made with torsional

Fig. 14-15.   Strain Figures in a Cantilever Plate (Clamped along the Bottom Edge) Due to a Concentrated Static Load Applied at the Center

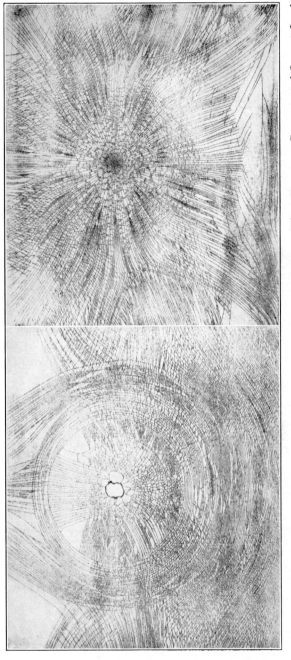

FIG. 14-16. Strain Figures in a Cantilever Plate (Clamped along the Bottom Edge) Due to a Concentrated Impact Load Applied at the Center

specimens,[43] indicate that, under biaxial stresses of equal magnitude but of opposite sign, the lacquer cracks at closely the same strain value as under uniaxial stresses in the calibration bars.   There is need, however, for more tests before this question may be answered in the general case.

For outdoor tests in the 20° to 60°F temperature range, there are some special lacquers available which are numbered several grades below the ones shown in the selection chart in Fig. 14-5.   These lacquers may also be used at

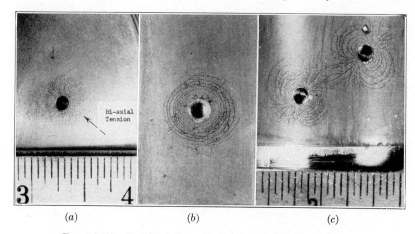

(a)   (b)   (c)

FIG. 14-17.   Residual-Stress Indications by Brittle Coatings
(a) Biaxial tension, set up by internal quenching in top surface of aluminum-piston crown
(b) Biaxial compression, produced by case hardening (63 Rockwell C)
(c) Shear pattern produced by presetting a torsional suspension bar (C. W. Gadd[55])

room-temperature tests if the purpose is to provide a coating which will crack only at large (plastic) values of strain.[57]

BIBLIOGRAPHY
Brittle Fractures in General

1. A. A. GRIFFITH, "The Phenomena of Rupture and Flow in Solids," *Phil Trans Royal Soc (Lond.)*, series A, v 221, 1921, pp 163–98.   The first exposition of the "internal-flaw" theory to account for the large difference between experimental and theoretical values of strength.   See also, by the same author, "The Theory of Rupture," *Proc 1st Int Congress Applied Mechanics*, Delft, 1924, v 1, p 55.
2. ADOLF SMEKAL, "Die Festigkeitseigenschaften spröder Körper," *Ergebnisse der exakten Naturwissenschaften*, v 15, Julius Springer, Berlin, 1936, pp 106–88. Comprehensive development of a physical theory of mechanical strength of brittle materials, in accordance with Griffith's assumptions.   Detailed bibliography on the subject is included.
3. GALILEO GALILEI, *Dialogues Concerning Two New Sciences*, translated by H. Crew and A. deSalvio, Northwestern Univ, 1946.   The two new sciences are dynamics and strength of materials, which includes the first systematic analysis of the strength of bent beams, with derivation of the contour line of a cantilever

of uniform strength. Illustrations show fracture of beams of apparently brittle materials.

4. C. BACH, *Elastizität und Festigkeit*, Julius Springer, 5th ed Berlin, 1905. A classical work on coordinated experimental and theoretical stress analysis. Most often-quoted source of data on the strength of cast iron.

5. R. J. ROARK, R. S. HARTENBERG, AND R. Z. WILLIAMS, "The Influence of Form and Scale on Strength," *Univ Wisc Eng Exp Sta Bul* 84, 1938, p 55. Analysis of the strength of notched, grooved, and filleted specimens subjected to static and impact bending, tension, and torsion. Test pieces made of cast iron, concrete, plaster, and a variety of aluminum alloys.

6. W. WEIBULL, "Investigation into Strength Properties of Brittle Materials," *Ingeniörs Vetenskaps Akademiens, Handlingar* 149, Stockholm, 1938, 27 pp. Investigation of the ultimate strength of glass plates subjected to ball pressure. The strength was found to be directly proportional to the ball radius and greatly dependent on the rate of application of the load.

7. M. M. FROCHT, "The Behavior of a Brittle Material at Failure," *J Applied Mechanics, Trans ASME*, v 58, 1936, pp A-99–103. Fracture tests with bakelite models show strength reduction that is about the same as the photoelastically determined stress-concentration factors.

Plaster Models

8. R. E. PETERSON, "An Investigation of Stress Concentration by Means of Plaster of Paris Specimens," *Mech Eng*, v 48, 1926, pp 1449–452. Tests of flat bars with holes in tension, round bars with fillets and threads in bending.

9. F. B. SEELY AND R. V. JAMES, "The Plaster-Model Method of Determining Stresses Applied to Curved Beams," Univ Ill *Eng Exp Sta Bul* 195, Aug 1929, p 33. Curved beams with U-shaped axes and circular, rectangular, trapezoidal, T- and H-shaped cross sections, tested in bending.

10. W. TRINKS AND J. H. HITCHCOCK, "Strength of Roll Necks," *Trans ASME*, v 55, 1933, RP 55-5, pp 67–74. Plaster models of rolling mill rolls tested in bending and torsion to determine maximum stress value occurring at the fillet in the roll neck.

11. R. J. ROARK AND R. S. HARTENBERG, "Predicting the Strength of Structures from Tests of Plaster Models." *Univ Wisc Eng Exp Sta Bul* 81, 1935, p 51. Reports of tests on models of disks, cylinder heads, column footings, notched beams, structural frames, and arches.

12. F. B. SEELY AND T. J. DOLAN, "Stress Concentration at Fillets, Holes, and Keyways as Found by the Plaster Model Method," *Univ Ill Eng Exp Sta Bul* 276, June 1935, 32 pp. Models of round shafts with fillets, holes, and keyways, tested in pure and cantilever bending and in torsion.

13. N. M. NEWMARK AND H. A. LEPPER, "Tests of Plaster-Model Slabs Subjected to Concentrated Loads." *Univ Ill Eng Exp Sta Bul* 313, June 1939, 53 pp. Stress analysis of circular and rectangular slabs under various conditions of support. The effect of biaxial flexure on the strength of plaster is also investigated.

Statistical Theory of Strength

14. W. WEIBULL, "A Statistical Theory of the Strength of Materials," *Ingeniörs Vetenskaps Akademiens, Handlingar* 151, Stockholm, 1939, 45 pp.

15. W. WEIBULL, "The Phenomenon of Rupture in Solids," *Ingeniörs Vetenskaps Akademiens, Handlingar* 153, Stockholm, 1939, 55 pp. An extension and supplementation of the theory proposed in the preceding publication, on the basis of more experimental evidence.

16. J. I. FRENKEL AND T. A. KONTOROVA, "A Statistical Theory of the Brittle Strength of Real Crystals," *J Physics (USSR)*, v 7, 1943, pp 108–14. On the

basis of normal distribution law, the influence of the volume on the most probable value of brittle strength of testpieces is derived, leading to results which are at variance with those of Weibull.

17. H. E. DANIELS, "The Statistical Theory of the Strength of Bundles of Threads," *Proc Royal Soc (Lond.)*, series A, v 183, 1945, pp 405–35.

18. A. M. FREUDENTHAL, "The Statistical Aspect of Fatigue of Materials," *Proc Royal Soc (Lond.)*, series A, v 187, 1946, pp 416–29. Shows that by application of the probability theory one may deduce the same relationships between the principal variables of fatigue tests as those observed experimentally.

19. N. DAVIDENKOV, E. SHEVANDIN, AND F. WITTMAN, "The Influence of Size on the Brittle Strength of Steel," *J Applied Mechanics, Trans ASME*, v 69, 1947, pp A-63–67.

20. B. EPSTEIN, "Statistical Aspects of Fracture Problems," *J Applied Physics*, v 19, 1948, pp 140–47. A critical review of the work done by Weibull and others, pointing out further possibilities of application of the statistical theory.

Stress Crazing of Synthetic Resins

21. W. B. KLEMPERER, "Stress Pattern Crazing," *Theodore von Kármán Anniversary Volume*, California Inst of Technology, 1941, pp 328–37.

22. T. C. BAKER AND F. W. PRESTON, "Fatigue of Glass under Static Loads," *J Applied Physics*, v 17, 1946, pp 170–78. The influence of the duration of loading on the strength of glass was already investigated by Smekal, see bibliography, item 2.

Oxide Coatings

23. E. SIEBEL AND A. POMP, "Der Zusammenhang zwischen der Spannungsverteilung und der Fliesslinienbildung an Kesselböden mit und ohne Mannloch bei der Beanspruchung durch inneren Druck," *Mitteilungen Kaiser-Wilhelm-Institut für Eisenforschung zu Düsseldorf*, v 8, Abhandlung 62, 1926, pp 63–77.

24. R. S. JOHNSTON, "Compressive Strength of Column Web Plates and Wide Web Columns," *U. S. Bur Standards Technologic Paper* 327, v 20, 1926, pp 733–82.

25. W. MASON, "The Lüders' Lines on Mild Steel." *Proc Phys Soc (Lond.)*, v 23, 1910–11, pp 305–33.

Various Resinous Coatings

26. F. SAUERWALD AND H. WIELAND, "Über die Kerbschlagprobe nach Schüle-Moser, etc," *Zeitschrift für Metallkunde*, v 17, 1925, pp 358–64, 392–99.

27. O. DIETRICH AND E. LEHR, "Das Dehnungslinienverfahren." *Verein deutsche Ingenieure Zeitschrift*, v 76, 1932, pp 973–82.

28. H. KAYSER AND A. HERZOG, "Die Untersuchung zweiachsig beanspruchter Konstruktionsglieder mit Hilfe der Reisslackverfahrens," *Die Bautechnik*, v 14, 1936, pp. 310–16. Determination of isostatic lines in structural parts, chiefly welded joints, with a lacquer of undisclosed composition which apparently cracked within the elastic limit of structural steels. The only conclusions drawn in the paper with regard to stress distribution are those which can be deduced from the observed formation of the isostatics.

29. O. DIETRICH, "Das Maybach-Dehnlinienverfahren in der Anwendung bei Metallen." *Metallwirtschaft*, v 19, 1940, pp 337–42. Use of the lacquer reported in reference 28, chiefly in the development of isostatic patterns in notched bars. On the basis of lacquer tests and of strain measurements made with short-gage-length extensometers, the unjustifiable claim is made that, in twisted bars of rectangular cross section, the maximum stress occurs at the corners.

30. E. SIEBEL, W. SEUFERT AND W. STEURER, "Anwendung des Dehnlinienverfahrens bei Zelluloid modellen," *Vereines deutsch Ingenieure Zeitschrift*, v

84, 1940, pp 889–90. With a solution of colophony in toluol, a coating is produced that dries to a brittle state at room temperature without the application of heat that was required in the process described in reference 27. This makes the coating applicable to celluloid models, by the use of which some clear isostatic patterns are developed. The authors suggest that the intensity of stress at various points may be estimated by observing the spacing of cracks. No attempt is made, however, to establish the cracking strain sensitivity of the coating by calibration.

31. A. PORTEVIN AND M. CYMBOLISTE, "Procédé d'étude de la distribution des efforts élastiques dans les pièces métalliques," *Revue de Métallurgie*, v 31, 1934, pp 147–58.

32. R. F. TYLECOTE, "Examination of Stress Distribution in Spot Welded Joints in Light Alloys by means of the Brittle Lacquer Process," *Quarterly Trans Inst Welding*, v 5, n 3, pp 120–32, July 1942.

33. B. P. HAIGH, "Electric Welding as an Integral Part of Structural Design." *Trans North East Coast Inst Engrs and Architects*, v 56, 1939–40, pp 43–82.

34. J. S. BLAIR, "The Resin Method of Indicating Yield." *The Engineer*, v 174, 1942, pp 455–56.

Stresscoat

35. *Operating Instructions for Stresscoat*, Magnaflux Corp.

36. A. V. DE FOREST, "A New Method of Measuring Strain Distribution—Brittle Coatings." *Instruments*, v 12, 1939, p 113.

37. A. V. DE FOREST AND GREER ELLIS, "Brittle Lacquers as an Aid to Stress Analysis," *J Aeronautical Sciences*, v 7, 1940, pp 205–08. General description of the method. Illustrations include unetched progressive patterns in a flat tension bar with hole and Lüders' lines around Brinell impression in mild steel.

38. A. V. DE FOREST, GREER ELLIS AND F. B. STERN, JR, "Brittle Coatings for Quantitative Strain Measurements," *J Applied Mechanics, Trans ASME*, v 64, Dec 1942, pp A-184–88. Description of the quantitative use of the method. The strain sensitivity and flaking sensitivity of the lacquers are shown in graphs as functions of temperature, humidity, and thickness of coating.

39. GREER ELLIS, "Practical Strain Analysis by Use of Brittle Coatings," *Proc Soc Exp Stress Analysis*, v 1, n 1, 1943, pp 46–53. Tabular summation of Stresscoat characteristics and techniques. Discussion of tests with aircraft-engine cylinder fastenings and propeller barrels.

40. R. G. ANDERSON, "Factors Involved in Improving Aircraft-Engine Piston Design," *Proc Soc Exp Stress Analysis*, v 1, n 1, 1943, pp 61–75.

41. R. G. ANDERSON, "Testing of Machine Parts by the Brittle Lacquer Method," *Prod Eng*, v 14, 1943, pp 611–14. Study of the effect of ribs in aircraft-engine crankcases on the stress distribution. Stresscoat patterns on piston and wristpin boss are shown.

42. M. HETÉNYI AND W. E. YOUNG, "How Brittle Lacquer Strain Analysis Aids Design," *Machine Design*, v 16, 1944, pp 147–51, 268.

43. M. HETÉNYI AND W. E. YOUNG, "Application of the Brittle Lacquer Method in the Stress Analysis of Machine Parts," *Proc Soc Exp Stress Analysis*, v 1, n 2, 1944, pp 116–29. Applications include gearmotor housings, gear teeth, generator brackets, refrigerator flapper valves, and a study of the strain sensitivity of the lacquer in the biaxial state of stress of a round bar in torsion.

44. W. J. CLENSHAW, "The Measurement of Strain in Components of Complicated Form by Brittle Lacquer Coatings," *Proc Inst Mech Engrs (Lond.)*, v 152, 1945, pp 221–23. Describes Stresscoat tests of dovetail joints under impact loads. A method of extrapolation proposed for the prediction of yielding at reentrant corner.

45. C. S. RICKER, "Engine Reliability Enhanced by Stresscoat Analysis," *Aviation*, v 45, n 1, pp 115–19; n 3, pp 86–8, 1946.   Shows Stresscoat applications by W. T. Bean of Continental Aviation and Engineering Corp.   Problems include aircraft-engine crankcases and hollow crankshafts with oil holes.

46. F. H. BOOR AND E. O. STITZ, "Stress Distribution in Spur Gear Teeth." *Proc Soc Exp Stress Analysis*, v 3, n 2, 1946, pp 28–39.   Correlation of photo-elastic and Stresscoat patterns with the paths of failure in gear teeth.

47. M. H. POLZIN, "Unveil Plane Wheel Service Stresses with Laboratory Stress-coat Analysis," *J Soc Automotive Engineers*, v 55, 1947, pp 26–8, 32.   Brittle coatings are used for finding direction of principal stresses in spokes of airplane wheels at various angular positions.   Magnitude of stresses is determined by subsequent application of strain gages.

48. H. NEUBER, "Der ebene Stromlinienspannungszustand mit lastfreiem Rand," *Ingenieur-Archiv*, v 6, 1935, pp 325–34.

49. A. J. DURELLI: "Determination of Stresses on Free Boundaries by Means of Isostatics," *Proc 15th Semiannual Eastern Photoelasticity Conf*, Boston, June 1942, pp 32–42.   A study of the practicability of the method proposed by Neuber (bibliography ref 48).

50. A. J. DURELLI, "Experimental Determination of Isostatic Lines," *J Applied Mechanics, Trans ASME* v 64, Dec 1942, pp A-155–60.   Detailed discussion of the use of Stresscoat in the determination of isostatics in plane photoelastic models.

51. GREER ELLIS AND F. B. STERN, JR., "Dynamic Stress Analysis with Brittle Coatings," *Proc Soc Exp Stress Analysis*, v 3, n 1, pp 102–11, 1945.   Describes method for the determination of the cracking sensitivity of Stresscoat lacquers at high rate of deformation.   Discusses firing tests on a shotgun and drop tests on an aircraft landing gear.

52. H. R. LISSNER AND E. S. GURDJIAN, "A Study of the Mechanical Behavior of the Skull and Its Contents When Subjected to Injuring Blows," *Proc Soc Exp Stress Analysis*, v 3, n 2, pp 40–6, 1946.   Stresscoat tests on skulls of animals, living and dead, and on human skulls, indicating the distribution of tensile strains due to blows on different parts of the skull.   Records of pressure waves through the brain are also obtained by means of pressure plugs.

53. E. S. GURDJIAN AND H. R. LISSNER, "Deformations of the Skull in Head Injury Studied by the Stresscoat Technique," *Surgery, Gynecology, and Obstetrics*, v 83, 1946, pp 219–33.

54. A. V. DE FOREST AND F. B. STERN, JR., "Stresscoat and Wire Strain-Gage Indications of Residual Stresses," *Proc Soc Exp Stress Analysis*, v 2, n 1, 1944, pp 161–69.

55. C. W. GADD, "Residual Stress Indications in Brittle Coatings," *Proc Soc Exp Stress Analysis*, v 4, n 1, pp 74–77, 1946.   Description of technique and illustration of patterns obtained for various types of residual-stress systems.

56. GREER ELLIS, "Stress Determination by Brittle Coatings," *Mech Eng*, v 69, 1947, pp 567–71.   Describes static tests on crankshafts, dynamic tests on a shotgun, and residual-stress measurements in welded plates, aluminum-alloy forgings, and phenolic resins.

57. J. MIKLOVITZ, "The Initiation and Propagation of the Plastic Zone in a Tension Bar of Mild Steel under Eccentric Loading," and "The Initiation and Propagation of the Plastic Zone in a Tension Bar of Mild Steel as Influenced by the Speed of Stretching and Rigidity of Testing Machine," *J Applied Mechanics, Trans ASME*, v 69, Mar 1947, pp A-21–30, and A-31–38.

A. INTRODUCTION

1. Application of Model Analysis. In the field of structural engineering, the use of models has steadily become more and more prevalent in the last 25 years. Today model analysis of structures not only is extremely important as a tool for research and development but also forms an important supplement to the mathematical methods used in the actual design of structures. Perhaps the most widely publicized use of models in this latter respect has been in connection with the design of most of the important and well-known suspension bridges erected during the last 20 years. Further evidence of the importance of model analysis in the field of structural design are the well-equipped laboratories which have been established by several Governmental agencies. There are also many academic institutions which have fine model-analysis laboratories established primarily for educational and research purposes.

Model analysis of structural problems encountered in either research or actual design may be used for one or more of three reasons: (1) because mathematical analysis of the problem concerned is virtually impossible; (2) because the analysis, though possible, is so complex and tedious that the model analysis offers an advantageous short-cut; and (3) because the importance of the problem is such that verification of the mathematical solution by model test is warranted. The stress distribution in an irregularly shaped member may be investigated by use of a model for the first reason; a model test may serve as the basis for the analysis of a complex building frame for the second reason; and a model study of the proposed design of a suspension bridge may come under the third classification.

The objective of tests of a structural model may generally be placed in one of the following four categories: stress analysis of the model, determination of stress distribution, determination of critical or buckling loads, or analysis of the characteristics of the normal modes of vibration. As used in this chapter, *stress analysis* means the determination of the total axial stress, the total shear stress, and the resisting moment acting on any cross section of the model, whereas *stress distribution* is the term used to designate the manner in which the stress intensities vary across any cross section of a member.

2. Standard Methods of Model Analysis. Certain methods are commonly used for the stress analysis of a model. Among them are the brass-wire model method, the Beggs method, the Eney deformeter, the Gottschalk Continostat, the moment indicator and the moment deformeter. All these methods are discussed in this chapter. The photoelastic method is also used to a limited extent in the stress analysis of structural models, but its principal application is, of course, in the solution of stress-distribution problems. The use of mechanical- or electric-strain gages to measure the various strain components of a structural model furnishes the basis for the other most common method of solving stress-distribution problems experimentally. Both these methods are discussed elsewhere in this handbook.

Experimental methods of determining buckling loads and vibrational characteristics are also discussed in this chapter.

3. Design of Models. Whenever a reduced-scale model is used to study an actual structure, it is necessary, of course, that the model be designed so that full-scale behavior of the prototype may be deduced from the observations of the behavior of the model. In order that this may be accomplished, it is necessary that the dimensions of the model and the characteristics of the material used in its construction bear certain definite relations to the dimensions and material of the prototype. The principles which govern the relationship between a model and its prototype are called the principles of similitude. Certain of these principles govern the design of the model, and others establish the means of extrapolating the results of the model tests to predict the performance of the prototype.

The determination of the principles of similitude are discussed briefly in this chapter and in more detail in part II of the appendix.

The choice of the proper material for the construction of models is of great importance. Not only must the material be such that its structural action is suitable to its use, but also the ease with which it can be fabricated for a small model must be borne in mind. For many models, the materials of the prototype may be used. Steel is often used, and reinforced concrete may be used if the model is sufficiently large.

It is often desirable to use a material which has a lower modulus of elasticity than the material of the prototype so that distortions which are large enough to be measured accurately may be obtained without the application of forces which are too great. The use of Duralumin or brass in place of steel is sometimes convenient for this reason. Brass has the additional advantage that it may be soldered easily, thereby facilitating the construction of the model.

Celluloid is one of the most widely used materials in the construction of the models used in conjunction with the more common model methods of stress analysis, and its properties are discussed in more detail in the next article.

The selection of the scale of a model depends on many factors: some of the more important are: the properties of the materials available for its construction; the capacity of the equipment to be used in loading the model, the dimensions of the instruments to be used in testing of the model, the limitations of machinery to be used in fabricating the model, and the funds and time available for the experimental program. As the scale of a model is reduced, it becomes increasingly difficult to maintain exact geometric similarity, and the duplication of all the details of the prototype is physically impossible. Some details of the design are obviously unimportant and may be omitted from the model. In other cases, the details of the structural connections have a great influence on the result, and a large enough scale must be used so that the structural action of the model is adequate.

4. Properties of Model Materials. The properties of model materials—such as steel, brass, Duralumin, wood, and concrete—are well known and need not be reviewed here. Celluloid is widely used for structural models and has, in common with certain other plastic materials, certain properties which are not well known and require further discussion.

Celluloid (or cellulose nitrate) has some very desirable properties as a model material, but it also has some that are very undesirable. It is very readily machined, has a low modulus of elasticity, is homogeneous, and may be readily welded by using acetone. On the other hand, its elastic properties change decidedly with age, temperature, and humidity. More serious still, celluloid creeps under a constant load; that is, if a load is applied, some 85 per cent of the deformation occurs within a few seconds, but the remaining 15 per cent takes place more slowly. It would be necessary to wait an appreciable period—about 15 min—before motion would be essentially complete. Even then small movements would still be occurring.

This creep phenomena may be more easily understood by referring to Fig. 15-1. Suppose a weight W is hung on the celluloid member shown. Almost instantaneously the member would undergo about 85 per cent of its total elongation, but the remaining 15 per cent would take place gradually, as shown in Fig. 15-1b. If the member were loaded instead with a weight of $2W$, the elongation would vary with time as is also shown in Fig. 15-1b. The elongation which had taken place up to certain times after loading— such as $t = 1, 2, 5, 10$, etc.—may be read off of the curves in Fig. 15-1b for various loads $W, 2W, 3W$, etc. If these elongations were plotted against the loads as shown in Fig. 15-1c, it would be found that all the elongations which were measured at 1 min after loading would lie along a straight line for all practical purposes. The same would be true for the elongations measured at times $t = 2, 5, 10$, etc. All of these straight lines would likewise pass through the origin. This latter plot discloses a very important characteristic of the creep of celluloid. At any particular instant after loading, the instantaneous elongation (or strain) is directly proportional to the load (or stress intensity); that is, at any instant the material is following Hooke's law and has an instan-

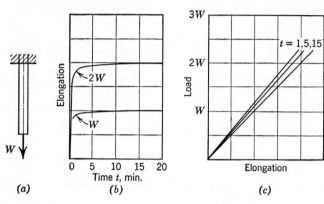

FIG. 15-1. Creep Properties of Celluloid

taneous modulus of elasticity E_t. The effect of creep is to lower this instantaneous value of the modulus with time.

It is extremely important that the creep of celluloid has this characteristic; otherwise, its usefulness as a material for structural models would be impaired. In view of the creep of celluloid, if a constant load W were applied to the end of a cantilever beam, the elastic curve would progressively assume different positions as the time after loading increased, as shown in Fig. 15-2a. Of course, after about 15 min, the rate of creep would have become so small that the beam may be considered to have come to rest. Suppose, however, a fixed deflection, Δ_b, were introduced at the end of the beam, as shown in Fig. 15-2b. The

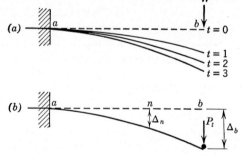

FIG. 15-2. Effect of Creep on Deflection of Celluloid Beam

force P_t that is applied to the beam by the pin which maintains the fixed deflection at b decreases with time owing to the creep and the resultant lowering of the instantaneous modulus E_t. Since E_t does not vary with the stress intensity and is, therefore, constant for the entire beam, the deflection at point b may be expressed as $\Delta_b = K_b \dfrac{P_t}{E_t}$, where K_b is a constant which depends only on the dimensions of the beam. Hence, $P_t/E_t = \Delta_b/K_b = C$, a constant which does not vary with time. The deflection at any point n may be expressed as $\Delta_n = K_n \dfrac{P_t}{E_t} = K_n C$, also constant and independent of time, since K_n is a constant depending only on the dimensions of the beam and the location of point n. It is apparent, therefore, that not only does the end of the cantilever remain fixed in position but also the entire elastic curve of the beam does likewise. It may, therefore, be concluded that the deflected position of a celluloid model will not change with time if a fixed deformation is applied to the model instead of a constant load.

5. Use of Spring Balance to Overcome Creep. It has been shown in the previous article that the deflected shape of a celluloid model does not change with time if a fixed deflection is introduced at one point on the model. Due to creep, however, the effective modulus of celluloid does change with time, and, therefore, the external forces and internal stresses of the model likewise change with time. Thus, it is difficult to interpret the strains and deflections, even though they do not change with time and, there-

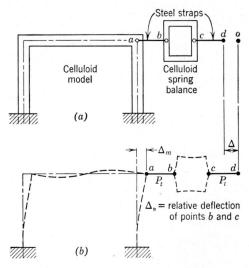

Fig. 15-3.   Celluloid Spring Balance

fore, may be measured without difficulty.   In other words, we cannot conclude simply from the measured strains that a certain load will produce certain stresses in the model—all we know is that some unknown load produces certain strains and deflections.

Through the use of a so-called celluloid spring balance, we may circumvent this difficulty, however, and interpret the measurements of the strains and deflections.   Such balances may be designed in a number of different forms and shapes, depending on the problem at hand.   Suppose, for example, that we wished to analyze the celluloid model of the rigid frame shown in Fig. 15-3 when it was acted on by a horizontal force H at the top of the right column.   To do this, the model could be connected to a balance as shown in Fig. 15-3a.   Then by pulling point d to the right, a horizontal deflection Δ could be applied to the combined system of model and balance.

If it is assumed that the steel straps ab and cd may be considered as being infinitely rigid in comparison to the celluloid model and spring balance, part of this total deflection Δ is introduced into the model and the remainder into the balance.   Thus,

$$\Delta = \Delta_m + \Delta_s \tag{1a}$$

If both the balance and model have been made out of the same piece of celluloid, it is legitimate to assume that the instantaneous modulus E_t is the same for both.   If it is recognized that the instantaneous value of the tension in both straps is the same and equal to P_t and, therefore, that the distorting force on both model and balance is also the same and equal to P_t, the deflections Δ_m and Δ_s may be expressed as follows:

$$\Delta_m = K_m \frac{P_t}{E_t} \tag{1b}$$

$$\Delta_s = K_s \frac{P_t}{E_t} \tag{1c}$$

where K_m and K_s are constants, the value of which depends only on the geometry and dimensions of the model and balance, respectively.

Substituting in equation 1a from equations 1b and 1c, we find that

$$\frac{P_t}{E_t} = \frac{\Delta}{K_m + K_s} \tag{1d}$$

and, therefore, conclude that the ratio of P_t to E_t remains constant and does not change with time.   In other words, although both P_t and E_t change with time, they always bear a constant relationship to each other.   Substituting now from equation 1a back into equations 1b and 1c, we find that

$$\Delta_m = \frac{K_m \Delta}{K_m + K_s} \tag{1e}$$

$$\Delta_s = \frac{K_s \Delta}{K_m + K_s} \tag{1f}$$

Since the right-hand sides of both these equations contain only constants which do not change with time, this means that both Δ_m and Δ_s remain constant and do not change with time.   In other words, by using a celluloid spring balance in this manner and introducing a fixed deflection Δ into the combined system of model and balance, we produce a distortion of both balance and model, which remains constant and does not change with time.

Suppose that the model had been distorted in this manner and that the resulting strains in it had been measured.   Suppose that we then wish to interpret these strains so as to obtain the stresses in the model due to a horizontal force H.   Although the stresses in the model vary with time, we may express the instantaneous value of the stress intensity σ_t in terms of E_t and its corresponding strain e.

Thus, $$\sigma_t = E_t e \tag{1g}$$

From equation 1c,
$$E_t = \frac{K_s}{\Delta_s} P_t \tag{1h}$$

Therefore,
$$\sigma_t = \frac{K_s}{\Delta_s} e P_t \tag{1j}$$

Assume that K_s, the constant of the spring balance, has been either computed or determined previously from a calibration test. The desired stress intensity σ_t has been expressed, therefore, in terms of the known constant K_s, the measured quantities e and Δ_s, and the unknown value of P_t. By assigning various values to P_t the corresponding stress intensities may be obtained. If $P_t = H$, the corresponding stress intensity σ_H is found to be

$$\sigma_H = \frac{K_s e}{\Delta_s} H \tag{1k}$$

In this manner, the strain measurements may be interpreted to give the stresses in terms of a horizontal force H.

The use of the spring balance is discussed in subsequent articles. The determination of the constant of the spring balance by calibration test is also discussed in detail. The purpose of this present discussion has been simply to introduce the idea of the balance and illustrate how it could be used to overcome the difficulties associated with the creep properties of celluloid.

B. Model Methods for Stress Analysis

6. General. One of the most frequent uses of structural models is to obtain the stress analysis of a model of a statically indeterminate structure. There are numerous methods and techniques which have been developed for this purpose. In using some of these methods, the required results may be obtained by loading the model in the same manner as the prototype. The elastic deformation of the model is then similar to that of the prototype, and strain measurements then lead to the required results. Such a method is said to be a direct method of model stress analysis. Suspension-bridge model studies are usually conducted in this manner; the moment indicator is also used in a direct manner.

Contrasted to direct methods of model analysis are those methods in which the model is loaded in a manner which bears no direct relation to the actual loading on the prototype. Such methods are called indirect methods. Usually such methods involve first finding influence lines for the model. These results may be extrapolated to the prototype, and the stresses in the prototype due to the given condition of loading may then be computed from these extrapolated influence lines. The methods of using the Beggs deformeter and the moment deformeter are examples of indirect methods of model analysis.

7. Theory of Certain Indirect Methods. Müller–Breslau's Principle. There are several methods of obtaining influence lines for structural models which are merely different experimental techniques of utilizing an idea which is known in structural-engineering literature as Müller–Breslau's principle. This principle may be stated as follows: *The ordinates of the influence line for any stress element (such as axial stress, shear, moment or reaction) of any structure are proportional to those of the deflection curve which is obtained by removing the restraint corresponding to that element from the structure and introducing in its place a deformation into the primary structure which remains.*

This principle is applicable to any type of structure, whether it be a beam, truss, or frame, or whether it be statically determinate or indeterminate. In the case of indeterminate structures, this principle is limited to structures

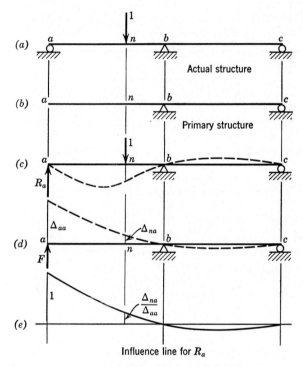

Fig. 15-4. Müller–Breslau's Principle

the material of which is elastic and follows Hooke's law. This limitation is not particularly important, however, since the vast majority of practical cases fall into this category. The spline method, the brass-wire model method, the Beggs deformeter, the Eney deformeter and the Gottschalk Continostat are all model methods which are experimental applications of Müller–Breslau's principle.

The validity of this principle may be demonstrated in the following manner. For this purpose, consider the two-span continuous beam shown in Fig. 15-4a. Suppose the influence line for the vertical reaction at a is required. This influence line could be plotted after this reaction had been computed for a unit vertical load applied successively at various points n along the structure. This reaction could be computed in the following manner for each of the positions of the unit load. Temporarily remove the roller support at a from the actual structure, leaving the primary structure shown in Fig. 15-4b. Suppose this primary structure were acted on by the unit load at a point n and a vertical upward force R_a at point a. If this force R_a had the same value as the vertical reaction at point a on the actual structure, then the stresses—and, hence, the distortion—of the primary structure would be exactly the same as those of the actual structure. The elastic curve of the primary structure under such conditions would, therefore, be as indicated in Fig. 15-4c with the vertical deflection at point a being zero.

Suppose we now consider the primary structure to be acted on by simply a vertical force F at point a. In this case, the primary structure would deflect as shown in Fig. 15-4d. Thus, we have considered the primary structure under the action of two separate and distinct force systems: (1) the forces shown in sketch c and (2) those shown in sketch d. Applying Betti's law* to this situation, we know that the virtual work done by the force system in sketch c during the distortion produced by the system in sketch d is equal to the virtual work done by the force system in sketch d during the distortion produced by the system in sketch c, or

$$(R_a)(\Delta_{aa}) - (1)(\Delta_{na}) = (F)(0)$$

(2)

and, therefore,
$$R_a = \frac{\Delta_{na}}{\Delta_{aa}}(1)$$

where Δ_{aa} = upward deflection of point a on the primary structure due to an upward force F at point a

Δ_{na} = upward deflection of point n on the primary structure due to an upward force F at point a

From this equation, it is apparent that the reaction R_a when the unit vertical load is applied at any particular position of point n is proportional to the deflection Δ_{na} at that point. The shape of the influence line for R_a is, therefore, the same as the shape of the elastic curve of the structure when it is acted on by an upward force F at point a. The magnitude of the influence-line ordinate at any point n may be obtained by dividing the deflection at that point on this elastic curve by the deflection at point a. In this manner, we have demonstrated that influence lines may be obtained in the manner outlined by Müller–Breslau's principle.

In a similar manner, the validity of this principle could be demonstrated for the influence line for any stress element of any structure. In the general case, equation 2 may be written as follows for any stress element X_a:

* Betti's law may be stated as follows: In any structure the material of which is elastic and follows Hooke's law and in which the supports are unyielding and the temperature constant, the external virtual work done by a system of forces P_m during the distortion caused by a system of forces P_n is equal to the external virtual work done by the P_n system during the distortion caused by the P_m system.

$$X_a = \frac{\Delta_{na}}{\Delta_{aa}} \, (1) \tag{3}$$

It is important to note the sign convention of this equation, namely: X_a is plus when in the same sense as the introduced deflection Δ_{aa}; and Δ_{na} is plus when in the opposite sense to the applied unit load the influence of which is given by the ordinates of the influence line. Note further that X_a may represent either a force or a couple. If X_a is a force, the corresponding Δ_{aa} is a linear deflection; but, if X_a is a couple, the corresponding Δ_{aa} is an angular rotation.

It is also important to note that the magnitude of any influence-line ordinate is independent of the magnitude of the force F which must be applied to introduce the deflection Δ_{aa} into the primary structure. All that is necessary, therefore, is to introduce some suitable deflection Δ_{aa} into the primary structure. Just what force must be applied to introduce this deflection makes no difference. Thus, influence lines may be determined in this manner from celluloid models without any difficulty being encountered due to creep.

8. Instruments for Measurement of Deflections. Practically all the model methods of stress analysis involve measuring linear deflections of the model. Such deflections are commonly measured by one of the following methods: steel scale or cross-section paper; dial gage; micrometer barrel; or filar-micrometer microscope.

If the deflections of a model are rather large, they do not have to be measured by precise methods. In such cases, a steel scale graduated in one-hundredths of an inch or ordinary cross-section paper may be mounted adjacent to a model and the deflection measured in this manner with the aid of a magnifying glass. Cross-section paper is quite useful for such purposes, because on inspection it will be found that the lines are not solid but actually are composed of a series of dots spaced about $\frac{1}{50}$ in. apart.

When the deflections are small, it is necessary to use one of the more precise methods of measurements. Dial gages graduated in thousandths or ten-thousandths of an inch may be used. Such gages have the disadvantage, however, that the spring which is attached to the plunger applies sufficient force to alter the deflections of a flexible model by an appreciable amount. Where a dial gage cannot be used for this reason, it will be necessary to use either a micrometer or a microscope.

The principal disadvantage involved in using a micrometer is that it is difficult to establish the exact point of contact between the model and the micrometer. This difficulty may be overcome by using some type of contact indicator. The simplest type of indicator is a battery-and-lamp system wherein the model and micrometer are part of the circuit and the micrometer acts as the switch which closes the circuit by making contact with the model. A much-improved contact indicator using a 6E5 "magic-eye" radio tube has been suggested.[2] The wiring diagram for this device is shown in Fig. 15-5. In this arrangement, the contacts on the model and micrometer are connected to the grid circuit of the tube, and their coming together causes the "magic-eye" cathode-ray target to become completely illuminated. This device is very sensitive and will establish the point of contact of polished steel contacts within three or four millionths of an inch.

The filar-micrometer microscope is perhaps the most useful instrument for measuring model deflections when all things are considered. The type of microscope which is supplied with the Beggs Deformeter apparatus is very convenient. The apparent field of view of this microscope is shown in Fig. 15-6. There are two orthogonal cross-hairs which may be moved across the field by turning the micrometer head. There is likewise an index which moves with the cross-hairs along a fixed scale which makes an angle of 45° with each of the cross-hairs. One complete turn of the micrometer head causes the index to move one full division along the fixed scale. By bringing the cross-hairs tangent to two successive positions of the target it is possible to obtain the movement of the target

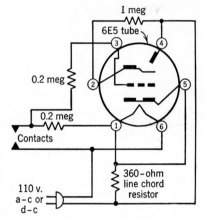

FIG. 15-5.   Contact Indicator

from the difference of the micrometer readings for the two settings. This arrangement of the cross-hairs and the fixed scale makes it possible to read both the horizontal and vertical movements of the target with one orientation of the microscope. The value of one of the micrometer divisions in

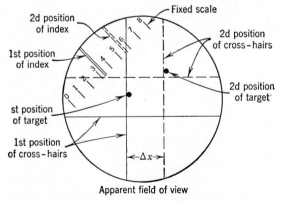

FIG. 15-6.   Field of Filar Micrometer Microscope

inches may be calibrated easily by observing with the microscope a known movement of a target placed on the plunger of a dial gage.

After a little practice, almost anyone may learn to use a micrometer microscope successfully. There are certain important rules which should be observed, however, namely:

1. Choose clear, well-defined, and readily identified targets.
2. Adjust the eyepiece carefully to eliminate parallax.
3. Focus the microscope on the target as sharply as possible.
4. Orient the cross-hairs accurately.
5. Do not touch unnecessarily the microscope or the table on which it is mounted.

If parallax is present, the image of the target will not lie in the plane of the cross-hairs, and this will lead to difficulty in reproducing readings. Poor focusing not only makes it difficult to bring the cross-hairs tangent to the target but also, in effect, changes the magnification of the microscope and, therefore, its calibration factor.

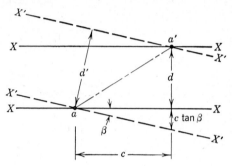

FIG. 15-7.   Error Caused by Poor Orientation

Poor orientation leads to errors of the type shown in Fig. 15-7. Suppose the target a moves to a'. To obtain the vertical component d of this movement, the cross-hair X–X should be oriented in a horizontal direction. The difference between the two solid-line positions of cross hair X–X would give the correct distance d. Suppose, however, that the cross-hair was oriented poorly and was set at an angle β to the horizontal as indicated by the dashed-line positions X'–X'. The difference between the two positions of X'–X' would indicate that the supposedly vertical movement was the distance d'. From the sketch,

$$d' = \cos \beta(d + c \tan \beta) = d \cos \beta + c \sin \beta \qquad (4)$$

This equation may now be used to study the effect of poor orientation:

If $c = 0$ and $\beta = 1°$, $d' = 0.9999d$, $\therefore 0.0\%$ error

If $c = 0.5d$ and $\beta = 1°$, $d' = 1.0086d$, $\therefore 0.9\%$ error

If $c = 5d$ and $\beta = 1°$, $d' = 1.0871d$, $\therefore 8.7\%$ error

This comparison shows that, if the resultant movement of a point is essentially in the same direction as the component which is being measured, then an error in orientation does not have much effect on the measurement. If, however, the resultant movement of a point is such that the component being measured is small in comparison to the component normal to this, then a small error in orientation makes an appreciable error in the measurement.

9. Simplified Indirect Methods. Perhaps the simplest method which utilizes Müller–Breslau's principle is the spline method of obtaining influence lines for the reactions of continuous beams. The procedure consists simply of selecting a long flexible spline of steel, brass, or wood and laying it down on a board on which a piece of cross-section paper has been mounted. The spline may be held in place between two nails driven into the board on each side of the spline at the support points. A vertical displacement may then be introduced at the reaction, the influence line of which is desired. The elastic curve of the spline in such a case may be marked on the paper and the influence-line ordinates obtained by reading the deflection ordinates on the cross-section paper and dividing each of them by the introduced displacement.

Very good accuracy may be obtained by using a ⅛-in.-square steel spline and introducing deflections of about one sixth of the span length either way from its mean position. Introducing equal displacements both ways from the undeflected position of a model and measuring the movement of a point between these two deflected positions constitute a technique used in many methods of model analysis. Such a technique not only has the advantage of producing larger deflections without the possibility of overstressing the model but also in some cases minimizes errors in the measurements due to changing the geometry of the model.

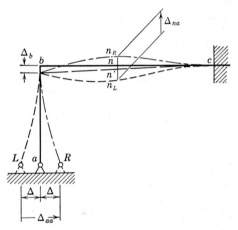

It happens that this technique does not affect the geometrical error encountered in the case of the reaction influence lines of a continuous beam. This technique is effective, however, in the case shown in Fig. 15-8. Here the influence line for the horizontal reaction at point a may be obtained by introduc-

FIG. 15-8.   Errors Caused by Change in Geometry

ing a horizontal displacement to either the right or the left at this point. In either instance, deflecting the column into a curve causes a small drop of the top of the column Δ_b, which is greatly exaggerated in the sketch. As a result, a point n would drop to the position of n' owing simply to the rotation of chord bc of the elastic curve of the girder. Thus, if the deflection of point n were measured from n to n_L, it would be too large by the amount nn'; or, if it were measured from n to n_R when the introduced displacement was to the right at point a, the deflection of n would be too small by the same amount nn'. Note, however, that if point a were displaced from L to R, and the resulting displacement of n were measured from n_L to n_R, the error nn' due to the change in geometry would have been eliminated from this measurement. The displacement from n_L to n_R would give, therefore, the correct value for the deflection Δ_{na} corresponding to an introduced displacement of a of Δ_{aa}. Introducing equal displacements both ways from the mean position, therefore, eliminates certain errors resulting from changing the geometry of the structure. This technique is not a "cure-all," however, and does not eliminate all errors due to changing the geometry of a structure.

The so-called brass-wire model method is simply a more or less generalized version of the spline method, wherein the models are fabricated out of brass wire. A rather large variety of two- and three-dimensional models can be built up in this manner. Even members with varying moment of inertia may be simulated by soldering end to end a number of small pieces of different-sized brass wires. Brass wires may normally be obtained in a wide range of gage sizes, and, of course, brass may be easily soldered to facilitate fabrication. Simple templates may be improvised to introduce the displacements, and the resulting deflections may be measured by using a magnifying glass in combination with cross-section paper or a steel scale, by a micrometer barrel or by some other simple device.

Both the spline and brass-wire model methods utilize simple models and simple means of introducing displacements and measuring the resulting deflections. To obtain suitable accuracy it is necessary to introduce rather large distortions so that the lack of precision in the measuring devices does not introduce too large an error in the results. As a result in certain cases, errors due to change in geometry may become significant and may be impossible to minimize. In such event, it may be necessary to use a method which utilizes more refined instruments and techniques.

10. Certain More Refined Indirect Methods. The Gottschalk Continostat[3] is simply an extension of the spline and brass-wire model methods. The Continostat itself consists of a long steel-base bar to which a number of adjustable arms are attached. These arms may be arranged to provide the supports of a model. They may likewise be adjusted so as to introduce displacements at the support points and thereby distort the model into the shape of the influence lines for the various reactions. Certain other attachments are provided which can be inserted at an internal cut in the model and thereby obtain the influence lines for thrust, shear, and moment at such a point. A set of thin steel splines is also supplied with the apparatus. These splines may be quickly clamped together to construct models of various beams and rigid frames. The model and Continostat are set up on top of a sheet of cross-section paper, and the distorted shape of the model is drawn directly on this sheet. Since the influence-line ordinates are scaled directly from the cross-section paper, rather large deformations must be introduced, and, therefore, this method is subject to the same criticism as the spline and brass-wire model methods, as far as errors due to change in geometry are concerned.

The Eney deformeter[4, 5] is a simplified modification of the Beggs deformeter. This instrument was designed so that the introduced deformations produce displacements which are sufficiently large to be measured accurately with either a steel scale or a micrometer. Either celluloid or cardboard models may be analyzed with this deformeter. This deformeter is designed to introduce rather small deformations in both a plus and minus direction, and, therefore, errors due to change in geometry are less than such errors in the case of the other methods discussed previously.

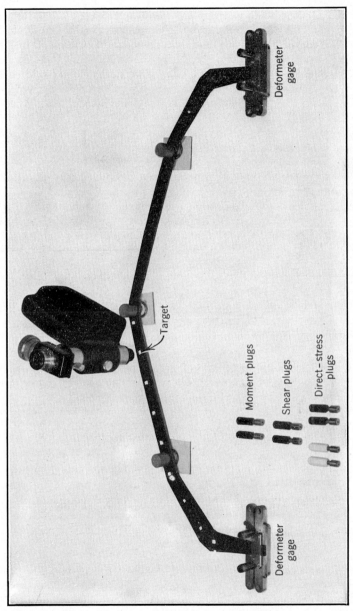

Fig. 15-9. A Typical Application of the Beggs Method

11. The Beggs Method. The Beggs method[6-8] is the most general and usually the most satisfactory experimental method which is based on Müller–Breslau's principle. This technique was developed by the late Professor George E. Beggs of Princeton University. The equipment consists of a set of deformeter gages and plugs for introducing the deformations and a micrometer microscope for measuring the resulting deflections. In order to obtain influence lines for reactions, the deformeter gage is used to replace the support of the model at that point, one-half the gage being attached to the model and the other half to the mounting surface. To obtain influence lines for internal moments, shears, and axial stresses, it is necessary to cut the model and connect one-half the deformeter gage to each side of the cut. By inserting different types of plugs between the two halves of the gage, an axial, shear, or angular deformation may be introduced into the model, thus distorting it into the shape of the corresponding influence line. A typical application of the Beggs method is shown in Fig. 15-9.

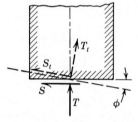

This method has the advantage that a more reliable and accurate means is used for introducing the deformations, and a more precise instrument is used for measuring the deflections which are produced. This enables one to introduce smaller distortions and thus reduce errors due to changing the geometry of the structure. The models used with the Beggs method are usually made from celluloid or a high-grade cardboard. Since the deformeter gages introduce constant distortions rather than applying constant loads to the structure, no trouble is encountered due to the creep characteristics of celluloid. The method can be used without modification for any planar structure, regardless of whether the members are straight or curved or are of constant or varying moment of inertia.

Fig. 15-10. Orientation of Beggs Deformeter Gage

The usual precautions must be observed in using the microscope in this method. Care must also be used when mounting the deformeter gages to be sure that the long axis of the gage is normal to the axis of the member. If the gage is not so mounted, the influence data obtained for the shear and axial stress will be in error. With reference to Fig. 15-10, if the gage is mounted in the direction indicated by the dashed line, the test data will give the values of the thrust T_t and shear S_t perpendicular and parallel to this direction. To obtain the true thrust and shear, T and S, it is necessary to measure the angle ϕ and convert the test data as indicated below:

$$T = T_t \cos \phi + S_t \sin \phi$$

$$S = S_t \cos \phi - T_t \sin \phi$$

It should be apparent that such an error in the orientation of the gage does not affect the data obtained for the moment at this point.

One should also be careful to attach the model to the gage so that the axis of the member lies at the center of the gage. If this is not done, the influence-line ordinates for the moment at this point will be in error, because the angular deformation introduced by the gage not only rotates the cross section of the model but also introduces an axial displacement of its centroid.

The Beggs plugs may be calibrated in the following manner. Attach a strip to one-half the gage, and fasten the other half to the mounting surface. Insert the various plugs into the gage and measure the resulting displacement of a target on the strip with the microscope. In this manner, the deformations introduced by the various plugs may be calibrated in microunits and thence converted to inch units, if desired, using the calibration constant of the microscope.

12. The Moment Deformeter. The moment deformeter[16] is an instrument which deforms a model so that it takes the shape of the influence line for the

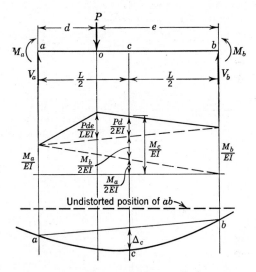

FIG. 15-11. Theory of Moment Deformeter

bending moment at the section located at the center of the instrument. This deformation is accomplished without cutting the model as is necessary when using the Beggs method.

The action of this instrument depends on a relationship which exists between bending moment and deflection. Consider a segment ab of a member, this segment being initially straight and having a constant EI. Suppose that a load P is applied at point o as shown in Fig. 15-11. The effect of the load P is to distort the structure and produce bending moments throughout. The bending moments thus produced at the ends of this segment are M_a and M_b, which are assumed to act as shown. The bending-moment diagram for this portion may then be drawn easily. Using the moment-area theorems, Δ_c, the deflection of point c on the elastic curve from the chord ab, may be computed and the resulting expression simplified to

$$\Delta_c = \frac{M_c L^2}{8EI} - \frac{P d^3}{12EI} \tag{5}$$

Thus the moment at c due to the load P acting at any point o in the segment ab is found to be

$$M_c = \frac{8EI}{L^2} \Delta_c + \frac{2}{3} \frac{P d^3}{L^2} \tag{6a}$$

where d is the distance from point o to either end, a or b, whichever is closer. If the load P is applied at a point outside the segment ab, the second term of equation 6a vanishes, and

$$M_c = \frac{8EI}{L^2} \Delta_c \tag{6b}$$

Thus, it is apparent that the bending moment at c could be easily computed if the deflection Δ_c could be measured easily on a model.

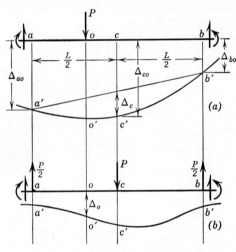

FIG. 15-12.   Development of Moment Deformeter

There is a convenient way of obtaining Δ_c which may be explained by the following considerations. First consider the structure to be acted on by the force P applied at point o. This would cause the structure to be distorted, and the deflected shape of the segment ab is shown in Fig. 15-12a. Next consider the structure to be acted on by the special force system shown in Fig. 15-12b. The deflected shape of the segment ab under such conditions is also shown in this sketch. Applying Betti's law to this situation, we know that the virtual work done by the external-force system in sketch a during the distortion produced by the external-force system shown in sketch b is equal to the virtual work done by the system in sketch b during the distortion produced by the system in sketch a; therefore,

$$(P)(\Delta_o) = -\left(\frac{P}{2}\right)(\Delta_{ao}) + (P)(\Delta_{co}) - \left(\frac{P}{2}\right)(\Delta_{bo}) \tag{7a}$$

or

$$\Delta_o = \Delta_{co} - \frac{(\Delta_{ao} + \Delta_{bo})}{2}$$

From the geometry of Fig. 15-12a, it is apparent that

$$\Delta_c = \Delta_{co} - \frac{(\Delta_{ao} + \Delta_{bo})}{2} \tag{7b}$$

and, therefore, from equations 7a and b, it may be concluded that

$$\Delta_o = \Delta_c \tag{8}$$

Thus, if a system of loads such as that shown in Fig. 15-12b is applied to a segment ab, the model distorts so that it takes the shape of the influence line for Δ_c.

In the development leading to equations 6a and b, M_c denotes the bending moment at c caused by a load P acting on the model. If m_c denotes the bending moment at c due to a unit value of P, then,

$$m_c = \frac{M_c}{P} \tag{9}$$

and from equation 6a the following relation is apparent:

$$m_c = \frac{8EI}{L^2}\frac{\Delta_c}{P} + \frac{2}{3}\frac{d^3}{L^2} \tag{10}$$

If the values of Δ_c are obtained using the loading condition shown in Fig. 15-12b, then, by equation 8,

$$m_c = \frac{8EI}{L^2}\frac{\Delta_o}{P} + \frac{2}{3}\frac{d^3}{L^2} \tag{11a}$$

As before when Δ_o is measured at a point o outside the segment ab, the second term in equation 11a vanishes, and

$$m_c = \frac{8EI}{L^2}\frac{\Delta_o}{P} \tag{11b}$$

Thus, for the portion of the model lying outside the segment ab, if the loading of Fig. 15-12b is applied, the deformed model takes the shape not only of the influence line for Δ_c but also of the influence line for m_c outside the limits of the segment ab. To obtain the actual ordinates for m_c at any point o outside the segment ab that value of Δ_o must be multiplied by $8EI/L^2P$, all quantities which concern the segment ab. If the value of Δ_o, at points within the segment, is known, the influence line ordinates for m_c may be computed using equation 11a.

To determine the values of the influence-line ordinates, one must know in addition to Δ_o the values of E, I, L, d, and P. With the exception of P and E, all of these are easily determined. When used with a celluloid model, it is necessary to apply a fixed distortion corresponding to the type of loading shown in Fig. 15-12b instead of constant loads P and $P/2$. A moment deformeter which embodies the principles shown diagrammatically in Fig. 15-13 may be shown to produce a distorted shape of both the model and balance beam which does not change with time and thus effectively eliminates creep. If a plug, which has a diameter larger by an amount Δ than the undistorted distance between the model and balance beam, is forced into place between the two pieces, a distorted shape of both balance and model will be produced which will not change with time. This assumes that both model and balance have been made out of the same piece of celluloid and, therefore, have the same creep characteristics. It also assumes that the frame of the instrument is made out of metal and is heavy enough to be assumed rigid, compared to the flexible celluloid members.

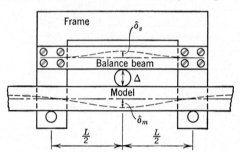

FIG. 15-13. Schematic Diagram of Moment Deformeter

The pressure P_t, applied by this plug to the model and balance will, of course, change with time, proportionally to the change in effective modulus E_t, but the elastic curve of both members will not change.

If, in addition to the deflections Δ_o at the various points o on the model, the deflection δ_s of the balance were also measured, then recalling the discussion in article 5, we recognize the following relationships:

$$\delta_s = K_s \frac{P_t}{E_t} \quad \text{or} \quad \frac{E_t}{P_t} = \frac{K_s}{\delta_s} \tag{12}$$

where K_s is a geometrical constant of the balance beam, which depends on its dimensions and the manner in which it is attached to the instrument frame. Thus, if K_s were computed and δ_s were measured, the ratio of E_t to P_t would be known not only for the balance beam but also for the model—providing that both balance beam and model are made from the same sheet of celluloid.

If we substitute from equation 12, equations 11a and b may be written in the following form for use on a celluloid model where δ_s has been measured on the balance beam of the instrument. The influence line ordinates for the bending moment at c are obtained from equation 13a for points o within the segment ab,

$$m_c = \frac{8IK_s}{L^2} \frac{\Delta_o}{\delta_s} + \frac{2}{3} \frac{d^3}{L^2} \tag{13a}$$

and from equation 13b for points o outside the segment ab,

$$m_c = \frac{8IK_s}{L^2} \frac{\Delta_o}{\delta_s} \tag{13b}$$

Targets
A

Distorting
plugs

FIG. 15-14.   A Typical Application of the Moment Deformeter

The value of K_s may be computed but the accuracy of the result may not be good because of the uncertain fixity conditions at the point of attachment of the balance beam. As a result, it is more satisfactory to obtain K_s by a calibration test run on a statically determinate cantilever beam, where the bending moments are known by statics.

The latest model of the moment deformeter is shown mounted on a celluloid model in Fig. 15-14. It may be noted that the principle of this instrument is essentially the same as that shown in simplified form in Fig. 15-13. The deflections δ_s and Δ_o are measured with the same type of micrometer microscope as used with the Beggs method.

This instrument provides an effective means of obtaining influence lines for bending moments at internal sections of a model without the necessity of cutting the model. The method does have the disadvantage that, in order to use the foregoing simple interpretation of the measurements, it is necessary to apply the instrument to a segment of the model which is initially straight and has a constant I.

13. The Moment Indicator. The moment indicator[9] is a convenient instrument which furnishes a direct method of obtaining bending moments in a model. The theory of this instrument is based on the Manderla–Winkler equations which are used primarily in the analysis of secondary stresses in trusses. These equations are applicable to a member or a portion thereof which is initially straight and has constant E and I, and to which no external loads are applied between the ends of the portion under consideration.

The Manderla–Winkler equations are simply expressions for the moments acting on the ends of a member in terms of the slopes of the elastic curve of these two ends of the member. Let M_{AB} be the moment acting on the A end of member AB, and M_{BA} be the moment on the B end—the end moments being positive when clockwise on the end of the member. Also, let τ_A and τ_B be the slope of the tangent to the elastic curve at points A and B, respectively. Such slopes are measured with reference to the chord AB of the elastic curve and are positive when the tangent rotates clockwise with reference to the chord. The Manderla–Winkler equations may be derived using the moment area theorems and may be stated as follows:

$$M_{AB} = \frac{2EI}{L} \left(2\tau_A + \tau_B\right)$$

$$M_{BA} = \frac{2EI}{L} \left(\tau_A + 2\tau_B\right)$$

(14)

Keeping these relationships in mind, we may now proceed to the development of the theory of the moment indicator.

Referring to Fig. 15-15, suppose two arms were attached at points A and B of a member. As the model was loaded and distorted by loads applied outside this segment, the two arms would rotate through the same angles as the tangents to the elastic curve at their point of attachment. If we recognize that the rotations are actually through small angles, the following relative movements of the targets a and a', and b and b' may be computed easily. Let Δ_a and Δ_b represent the relative movements of the targets, being positive when the targets move apart; then,

$$\Delta_a = \frac{2L}{3}\tau_A + \frac{L}{3}\tau_B = \frac{L}{3}(2\tau_A + \tau_B)$$

$$\Delta_b = \frac{L}{3}\tau_A + \frac{2L}{3}\tau_B = \frac{L}{3}(\tau_A + 2\tau_B)$$

(15)

If we substitute from equation 15 in equation 14, the following expressions are obtained for the end moments at points A and B:

$$M_{AB} = \frac{6EI}{L^2}\Delta_a$$

$$M_{BA} = \frac{6EI}{L^2}\Delta_b$$

(16)

in which a positive Δ (or a relative movement apart) indicates a positive end moment (or clockwise on the end of the segment). Hence, if Δ_a and Δ_b are measured with a microscope and if E were known, the moments could be determined at the points of attachment of the moment indicator.

Here again, if celluloid is used as the model material, the creep problem must be overcome. Of course, constant loads cannot be applied to a celluloid model because its deflection will change with time. If, however, a fixed deformation is applied to the model at the point and in the direction of the specified loading, the deflected position of the model will not change with time. The movements of the targets of the moment indicator may then be measured without difficulty with a microscope. How-ever, it would still be impossible to com-

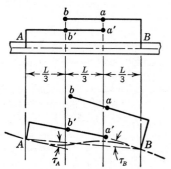

FIG. 15-15. Theory of Moment Indicator

pute the end moments from equation 16, because E is unknown and changing with time. Further, the corresponding load on the model is also unknown and is changing with time directly proportional to the change in E. In such a case, however, it is possible to obtain the relative value of the moments because they are proportional to the product of I and the moment-indicator deflections.

Quite often these relative values of the end moments may be converted into absolute values in terms of the load through the use of conditions of static equilibrium. Consider as an example the simple frame shown in Fig. 15-16. Suppose that the moment indicator has been mounted in turn on each column, and thereby relative values of the moments at two points on each column have been obtained for some fixed horizontal displacement imposed at the top of column 1–2. In this case, the relative value of the end moments in each column could be extrapolated from the relative values measured at the points of attachment of the indicator. Let these relative values at the ends of the columns be m_{12}, m_{21}, etc., and then the absolute values could be expressed as

$$M_{12} = Cm_{12} \qquad M_{34} = Cm_{34}$$

$$M_{21} = Cm_{21} \qquad M_{43} = Cm_{43}$$

Isolation of each column as a free body would enable us to compute the shear in each column in terms of the unknown constant C. If the girder were now

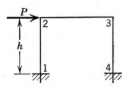

FIG. 15-16. Conversion of Relative into Absolute Values of End Moments

isolated as a free body cutting it from the columns just below the column tops, having the shears on the stub ends of the columns in terms of C, the statics equation $\Sigma H = 0$ applied to the isolated girder would enable us to find C in terms of P. Once we have C in terms of P, the absolute values of the end moments in terms of P may be obtained without difficulty.

The foregoing procedure of converting relative values into absolute values of moments may often be done very easily. There are cases, however, when either there are no suitable equations of statics available, or, if so, to solve them is too laborious. In such cases, the use of a celluloid spring balance in the loading system leads to a direct solution for the absolute values of the moments in the model.

The use of a spring balance to overcome creep was discussed in article 5. In Fig. 15-3 the balance is shown connected to the same type of model as depicted in Fig. 15-16. Suppose that a moment indicator were mounted on the model in Fig. 15-3 and that readings were taken on the targets of both the indicator and the spring balance. Referring to equation 1h in article 5, we may recall that, having measured Δ_s, we may then express E as

$$E = \frac{K_s}{\Delta_s} P \qquad (17)$$

Substituting from equation 17 in equation 16 gives

$$M_{AB} = \frac{6IK_s}{L^2} \frac{\Delta_a}{\Delta_s} P \qquad (18)$$

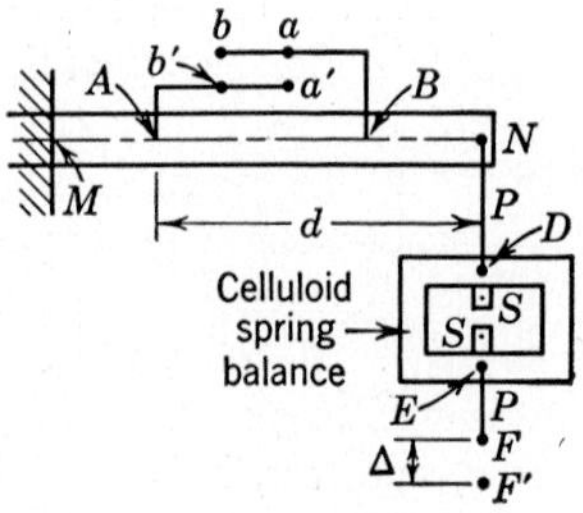

FIG. 15-17. Calibration of Spring Balance

If we use the celluloid spring balance in this manner, therefore, it is easy to obtain the absolute values of the moments in terms of the load P.

This presumes, of course, that the constant K_s of the balance is known.

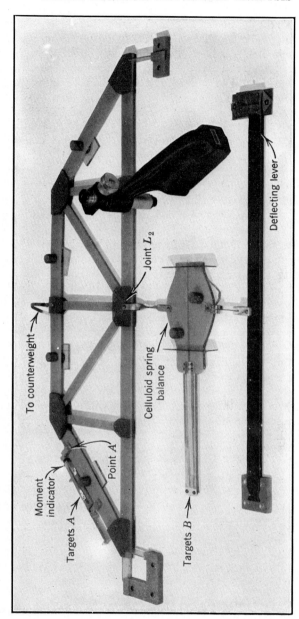

Fig. 15-18. A Typical Application of the Moment Indicator

The value of this constant could be computed, but it could be obtained more accurately from a calibration test on a statically determinate cantilever beam such as shown in Fig. 15-17. If the indicator is attached as shown, the deflections Δ_a and Δ_s may be measured with the microscope. If we know that the moment M_{AB} is equal to P times d, it would then be an easy matter to back-figure K_s by applying equation 18.

The moment indicator provides a very satisfactory model solution for many problems. A typical setup of the moment indicator in combination with a celluloid spring balance is shown in Fig. 15-18. It should be recalled that the theory of the moment indicator was based on the Manderla–Winkler equations. In order to use the previous simple interpretation of the measurement, it is necessary, therefore, to apply the indicator to a portion of a member which is initially straight and has a constant I. It would be possible to interpret the indicator readings in cases where I varied within the portion, but the computations would be very cumbersome.

14. The Photoelastic Method. Of course, the photoelastic method is used principally to study localized effects of stress distribution, but it may sometimes be used to advantage in the analysis of composite structures. In the latter case, it is desirable that the model be composed of members which have portions where the normal stresses on transverse cross sections are distributed linearly, or essentially so. The stress analysis of such models can be carried out simply from the photograph of the isochromatics. Once we have found the edge stresses at a given cross section from the isochromatics, it is then easy to compute the bending moment and axial stress at that cross section. If the bending moments have been determined in this manner at two cross sections in a member, it is easy to compute the shear on these cross sections simply by statics. Once the moment, shear, and axial stress have been determined at one cross section of each member, similar quantities may be computed easily at any other cross section of the model.

C. OTHER USES OF STRUCTURAL MODELS

15. Determination of Buckling Loads. Structural models may also be used advantageously to determine critical or buckling loads of columns, beams, and other structural elements. Such information may be obtained most readily by running tests under loads which are somewhat less than the buckling load and then interpreting the test data by Southwell's method or some adaptation thereof. In such tests, the load is applied in a series of increments, and certain deflections are measured after each increment of loading. If this information is plotted in a certain manner, the plotted points lie on a straight line the slope of which may be interpreted to give the critical buckling load. The chief advantage of this procedure is that the necessary data may be obtained from measurements taken at loads which are smaller than the buckling load, and as a result the model is not destroyed in conducting the test. The model may be retested, therefore, after any desired modifications in its design have been made.

In Southwell's original paper,[11] the theoretical proof of his method was

given only for the case of a simple strut.   He demonstrated that, if the ratio
of lateral deflection to the corresponding axial load was plotted as an ordinate
against the deflection itself as an abscissa, the plotted points would lie along
a straight line the inverse slope of which was equal to the critical load of the
strut.

Subsequently Lundquist[12] suggested a modification of Southwell's procedure.   Donnell[13] and other investigators have suggested and applied variations of Southwell's method for more complex types of buckling.   These
studies indicate that this procedure or some variation of it may be applied to
all cases in which buckling does not introduce appreciable second-order stresses.

**16. Determination of Frequencies and Shapes of Normal Modes of Vibra-
tion.**   The frequencies and shapes of the normal modes of vibration are of
interest in the analysis of structures which are subjected to dynamic-loading
conditions.   Such information may be obtained experimentally by using an
adaptation of the so-called "sonic method" which is used quite commonly
to determine the modulus of elasticity of concrete.   The testing equipment
includes an oscillator–amplifier unit, a vibrator, a pickup, and an oscilloscope.

The model is vibrated by the pulsating force supplied by the vibrator, the
frequency of which is controlled by the oscillator.   The frequency of the
vibrator is varied until a resonant condition is produced in the model.   Resonance is indicated by a peak response in the voltage output of the pickup
which is mounted adjacent to the vibrating model.   The voltage of the pickup
is amplified and measured by a cathode-ray oscilloscope.   After a resonant
condition has been produced in the model, the frequency is held constant, and
the pickup is moved to various points on the model, thereby obtaining readings
which are proportional to the amplitude of the displacement at these points.
In this way, it is possible to measure the frequency and shape of one of the
normal modes of vibration of the model.   By starting with the lowest frequency of the oscillator and traversing its entire range of frequencies, it is
possible to determine the various resonant frequencies and thereby identify
the various modes of vibration which lie within the range of the equipment.

This experimental technique is based on the following considerations.
When an impulsive load of the following type acts on a structure with an
intensity of

$$p(t,\ x) = f(t)q(x) \tag{19}$$

the resulting displacement at any time t, $z(t,\ x)$, may be expressed in terms of
the shapes and frequencies of the normal modes of vibration of the structure,
$u_n(x)$ and ω_n, respectively, by the following equation:

$$z(t,\ x) = \sum_{n=1}^{n=\infty} \frac{q_n}{\omega_n^2} F_n(t)u_n(x) \tag{20}$$

The shapes $u_n(x)$ have been normalized so that the shape functions have the
following properties:

$$\int u_n(x)u_m(x)\frac{c}{g}\,dx = \begin{cases} 0 \text{ if } n \neq m \\ 1 \text{ if } n = m \end{cases} \tag{21}$$

the integration being carried out over the entire structure. In this equation, c represents the weight per unit length along the members of the structure. In equation 20,

$$q_n = \int q(x)u_n(x)\,dx \tag{22}$$

and

$$F_n(t) = \omega_n \int_0^t f(t')\sin\omega_n(t-t')\,dt' \tag{23}$$

where $f(t)$ as used in equations 19 and 23 represents the *total* impulsive load applied to the entire structure at any time t. Thus, from equation 20 it is evident that the total displacement is the sum of an infinite number of terms —one term for each of the n normal modes of vibration of the structure.

The quantity q_n is a factor which determines the degree to which any particular mode n participates in the total displacement of a structure under static load. Hence, q_n could be called the participation factor for the nth mode. This factor depends both on the shape of the particular mode and the distribution of the applied load. As a result, an impulsive load may be distributed in such a manner that the participation factor is equal to zero for certain modes, and, therefore, such modes are not excited by this load and do not participate in the motion of the structure.

The quantity $F_n(t)$ is commonly referred to as the equivalent static load for the nth mode. This factor gives the value by which the static participation of the nth mode should be multiplied in order to obtain its dynamic contribution under an impulsive loading at any time t. From equation 23, it is evident that $F_n(t)$ depends both on the frequency ω_n of the nth mode and the manner in which the applied impulsive load varies with time. This variation of the impulsive loading with time is defined by the function $f(t)$ which gives the total applied load acting on the entire structure at any time t.

Suppose a structure were acted on by an impulsive load of the type in equation 19, which also varied harmonically with time or

$$p(t, x) = (f_1 \sin \beta t)q(x) \tag{24}$$

since

$$f(t) = f_1 \sin \beta t \tag{24a}$$

Suppose further that this load was a concentrated load acting at some known point on the structure. The participation factor q_n could then be computed without difficulty if the shapes of the normal modes were known. It would be found that any modes which had a node point at the point of application of the load would not participate in the resulting motion. Likewise, the equivalent static load for the nth mode could be found by substituting in equation 23 from equation 24a and integrating; or

$$F_n(t) = \omega_n \int_0^t f(t')\sin\omega_n(t-t')\,dt'$$

$$= \omega_n \int_0^t f_1 \sin\beta t' \sin\omega_n(t-t')\,dt'$$

which, after integration and substitution of the limits, reduces to

$$F_n(t) = \frac{f_1 \omega_n}{(\beta^2 - \omega_n{}^2)} \{\beta \sin \omega_n t - \omega_n \sin \beta t\} \quad \text{if } \beta \neq \omega_n \tag{25}$$

For the case where $\beta = \omega_n$, the right-hand side of equation 25 assumes the indeterminate form of $0/0$ and the limiting value of $F_n(t)$ may be found in the usual manner to be

$$F_{n_1}(t) = \frac{f_1}{2} (\sin \omega_{n_1} t - \omega_{n_1} t \cos \omega_{n_1} t) \quad \text{if } \beta = \omega_{n_1} \tag{26}$$

If a structure is acted on by an impulsive loading which varies harmonically with time with a frequency β, which does not coincide with any of the frequencies of the n normal modes ω_n, the resulting displacement at any time t may be computed from equation 20, using the equivalent static load for any particular mode as computed from equation 25. In such cases where $\beta \neq \omega_n$, $F_n(t)$ will always be a finite number at any time t. If, however, the frequency of the load β does coincide with ω_{n_1}, the frequency of one of the normal modes n_1, the value of $F_{n_1}(t)$ is given by equation 26 and is seen to increase steadily with time. The contribution of this mode n_1 in equation 20 becomes steadily more predominant in comparison with the terms for all the other modes. As a result, after a short time the displacement of the structure becomes very large and vibrates essentially with the shape and frequency of the n_1 mode.

This discussion suggests an experimental approach for determining the shapes and frequencies of the normal modes of vibration of a structure. If a structure were vibrated by an oscillator which applied a concentrated load which varied harmonically with time with a controlled frequency of β, and if the resultant displacement of the structure could be measured by some suitable pickup, the frequency β could be varied until a resonant condition was recorded by the pickup. Such resonant frequencies correspond to the frequencies of the normal modes of vibration. If the structure is kept vibrating in one of these resonant conditions, the amplitude of the vibration could be measured by the pickup at enough points to establish the shape of that mode of vibration.

In all this discussion, it has been assumed that the vibration is not damped by friction—in which case the displacement at a resonant frequency would, therefore, increase steadily with time. In the actual case, however, the motion is damped by internal friction. The first term inside the braces in both equations 25 and 26 represents a "free vibration" which has a frequency of ω_n; the second term represents a "forced vibration" which has the same frequency as the applied load. The friction gradually damps out the free-vibration portion of the motion and prevents the forced-vibration portion from steadily increasing without end and limits it to a steady finite value. The general technique suggested in the previous paragraph is not altered, however, by the presence of friction.

FIG. 15-19.   Determining Characteristics of the Normal Modes of Vibration of a
Flat Plate Supported at the Four Corners
Note vibrator hanging under the plate in the left foreground

A typical application of this experimental method is shown in Fig. 15-19. The basic piece of equipment is an oscillator–amplifier unit which drives the vibrator so as to apply an impulsive harmonic load to the model. The vibrator is a permanent-magnet speaker, the cone of which has been removed and the voice coil of which is attached to a plunger. This plunger is connected to the link by which the vibrator is suspended from the model. The major portion of the mass of the speaker is suspended from the plunger by "soft" springs so that the mass of the vibrator does not alter the mass of the model to any appreciable extent.

The most satisfactory type of pickup is that shown in Fig. 15-19. This type of pickup can be used only with steel models, however. It consists of a magnetized rod which is encircled by a coil. This coil is enclosed by the cylinder located near the lower end of the rod. The position of the pickup is adjusted so that the end of the rod is almost touching the model. As the model vibrates, the air gap between the model and the tip of the rod varies and thereby varies the magnetic flux. This variation of the flux develops an electromotive force in the coil, which may be amplified and measured with a cathode-ray oscilloscope. The maximum voltage produced at the terminals of the coil may be shown to be directly proportional to the amplitude of the vibration of the model.

D. PRINCIPLES OF SIMILITUDE

17. General. The principles of similitude governing the relationships between a model and its prototype may be determined by either of two approaches. The conditions of similarity may be expressed in mathematical form, using established laws of structural mechanics, and the principles of similitude rigorously deduced from them; or the principles may be deduced by using the methods of dimensional analysis. The first method is generally used for structural models since the mathematical laws which structures follow are usually well known. However, in cases where the mathematical laws are not known but the factors affecting the phenomena are known, the principles of similitude may be determined by the dimensional-analysis approach.

An application of the first approach is discussed in the next article. The reader is referred to part II of the appendix for a discussion of the second approach.

18. Derivation Using Established Laws of Structural Mechanics. To illustrate the derivation of the principle of similitude by this approach, consider the problem of extrapolating influence-line data from a model to its prototype. For this purpose, consider a beam which is statically indeterminate to the first degree, such as shown in Fig. 15-20.

Suppose we wished to obtain the influence lines for the vertical reaction at a, R_a, and the moment at b, M_b. In either case, we could apply Müller–Breslau's principle and thereby obtain the desired influence lines as indicated in Fig. 15-20. Of course, this procedure could be applied either to the prototype or to its model. If this procedure were applied to the prototype, the expressions for the ordinates of these two influence lines would be

$$R_a{}^P = \frac{\Delta_{na}{}^P}{\Delta_{aa}{}^P}\,(1) \tag{27}$$

and

$$M_b{}^P = \frac{\Delta_{nb}{}^P}{A_{bb}{}^P}\,(1) \tag{28}$$

where the index P indicates that these quantities refer to the prototype.

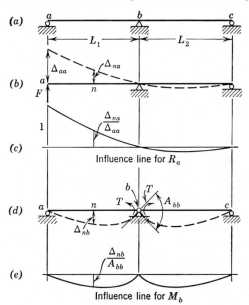

FIG. 15-20. Principles of Similitude

On the other hand, if Müller–Breslau's procedure were applied to the model, the ordinates for the two influence lines for the model would be

$$R_a{}^M = \frac{\Delta_{na}{}^M}{\Delta_{aa}{}^M}\,(1) \tag{29}$$

and

$$M_b{}^M = \frac{\Delta_{nb}{}^M}{A_{bb}{}^M}\,(1) \tag{30}$$

where the index M refers to the model. Of course, if the principles of similarity between model and prototype were known, the ordinates of these influence lines could be measured experimentally on a small-scale model, and then these results could be extrapolated to the prototype. In other words, to do this we need to know the relation between $R_a{}^M$ and $R_a{}^P$ and between $M_b{}^M$ and $M_b{}^P$.

From equations 27 to 30, it is apparent that these relationships between the reactions or moments on the model and those on the prototype depend on the relationship between deflections. The relationship between deflections of the model and the prototype may be investigated by considering the computations of such deflections by the method of virtual work. To compute beam deflections, the law of virtual work may be expressed as

$$\sum Q\delta = \int M_P M_Q \frac{dx}{EI} \tag{31}$$

If a force F^P acted at point a of the primary structure of the prototype, as shown in Fig. 15-20b, the vertical deflection of point n could be computed from

$$(1)\ (\Delta_{na}{}^P) = \int M_P{}^P M_Q{}^P \frac{dx^P}{E^P I^P} \tag{32}$$

In the same manner, equation 31 could be applied to compute a similar deflection on the model due to a force F^M at a, or

$$(1)\ (\Delta_{na}{}^M) = \int M_P{}^M M_Q{}^M \frac{dx^M}{E^M I^M} \tag{33}$$

Suppose that the model had been constructed so that the following relations existed between the model and prototype:

$$L^M = kL^P, \quad I^M = \alpha I^P, \quad E^M = \beta E^P, \quad F^M = \gamma F^P \tag{34}$$

In view of these relations, it is then apparent that the following additional relations are true for the statically determinate primary structure shown in Fig. 15-20b:

$$M_P{}^M = k\gamma M_P{}^P \qquad M_Q{}^M = kM_Q{}^P \tag{35}$$

Substituting in equation 33 from equations 34 and 35 and comparing with equation 32, we have

$$(1)\ (\Delta_{na}{}^M) = \frac{k^3\gamma}{\alpha\beta} \int M_P{}^P M_Q{}^P \frac{dx^P}{E^P I^P} = \frac{k^3\gamma}{\alpha\beta}\ (1)(\Delta_{na}{}^P)$$

Therefore,
$$\Delta_{na}{}^P = \frac{\alpha\beta}{k^3\gamma} \Delta_{na}{}^M \tag{36}$$

These relationships are true for any of the vertical deflections in Fig. 15-20b. Substituting, therefore, in equation 27 from equation 36 and comparing with equation 29 give

$$R_a{}^P = R_a{}^M \tag{37}$$

and, therefore, the corresponding influence-line ordinates for R_a are exactly the same for both model and prototype.

In a similar manner, the vertical deflection Δ_{nb} and the relative angular rotation A_{bb} of the primary structure shown in Fig. 15-20d may be investigated for model and prototype. In this case, of course, the deflections are caused by couples T^P on the prototype and couples T^M on the model. Proceeding as before with the exception that we will let

$$T^M = \gamma T^P$$

we will find that

$$\Delta_{nb}{}^P = \frac{\alpha\beta}{k^2\gamma}\, \Delta_{nb}{}^M \tag{38}$$

$$A_{bb}{}^P = \frac{\alpha\beta}{k\gamma}\, A_{bb}{}^M \tag{39}$$

Substituting in equation 28 from equations 38 and 39 and comparing with equation 30 yield

$$M_b{}^P = \frac{1}{k}\, M_b{}^M \tag{40}$$

and, therefore, the influence-line ordinates for M_b on the model should be multiplied by $1/k$ to obtain the corresponding ordinates on the prototype.

Of course, this discussion has been limited to a beam which is indeterminate to the first degree, but it could now be extended successively to include beams or frames which were indeterminate to the second, third, etc., or to any degree. Such considerations would lead to the following general conclusion for any indeterminate beam or frame, the stress analysis of which can be carried out satisfactorily by considering only the effect of bending distortion:

A model should be dimensioned so that the axial length of its members is k times those of the prototype; the moment of inertia of its cross sections is α times those of the prototype; and the modulus of elasticity of the model is β times that of the prototype. If this is done, then the ordinates of the influence line for any reactive force, shear, or axial stress on the prototype are equal to the corresponding ordinates on the model; but the ordinates of the influence line for any moment on the prototype are equal to $1/k$ times the corresponding ordinates on the model.

In this manner, the principles of similitude may be developed for models of trusses and other types of structures, providing the solution of the problem can be formulated in mathematical form.

E. GENERAL CONSIDERATIONS

19. Planning a Model Analysis. It is difficult, if not impossible, to write a complete list of instructions which will cover the planning of the model analysis of any and all problems which might be encountered. There are, however, certain factors which are more or less common to most such problems and, therefore, should be discussed.

The first factor which should be considered is the purpose of the proposed model study. If the model is being used to check the design of an actual structure, then the principles of similitude must be established for the given problem and observed as closely as is possible and practical when the model is designed and constructed. Contrasted to this type of model study is that in which the model is being used to develop or study the mathematical theory for a certain type of problem. In such instances the model may be considered actually a small-sized structure for which the mathematical results are computed and compared with the experimental results. In other words, model and prototype are synonymous, and similitude is not a factor. When models are used in this manner, a number of different models are selected so that the relative dimensions of the various elements are varied sufficiently to cover the entire range which might be encountered in large-sized structures of this type.

The next step in planning a model study is to select the most appropriate method of model analysis for the particular problem at hand. Quite often the choice of the method is limited by such factors as availability of equipment and suitable model material and experience of the laboratory personnel. If it is assumed that there are no such limitations, the method of analysis may be selected simply on the basis of the advantages and disadvantages of the various methods which are applicable to the problem at hand.

Once the method of analysis has been selected, the limiting dimensions of the model may be established. To illustrate how to do this, suppose that it has been decided to use the Beggs method for the stress analysis of a given problem. First of all, the width of the model at any point where the deformeter gage is to be attached should not exceed $\frac{3}{4}$ in. which is the normal capacity of the clamping device on the gage. On the other hand, the minimum width at any point in the model should preferably not be less than $\frac{1}{4}$ in. This is controlled by the working tolerances which should be permitted in constructing celluloid models. Such models can be finished quite easily to satisfy a tolerance of ± 0.002 in. If the width of a member is less than $\frac{1}{4}$ in., the tolerance in the width would cause a variation in the moment of inertia of more than ± 2 per cent, which is about the maximum that should be permitted. The length scale and the thickness of the members should be selected so that the model is neither too stiff nor too flexible. If the model is too stiff, the springs of the deformeter gage will not be strong enough to distort the model. If the model is too flexible, some of the compression members may buckle.

Similar factors are involved in establishing the limiting dimensions of any model. Careful consideration must be given to the limitations imposed by the proposed methods of measuring strains and deflections, or by the proposed technique of loading or distorting the model. Of course, the more experience one has, the easier it is to make such decisions.

When planning a model study, people often overlook the fact that some of the most informative model studies can be conducted with relatively simple models. Elaborate, complex, and expensive models may be impressive, but they do not necessarily produce the most valuable results. If it still seems necessary and desirable to make such a model, precede such a study with enough studies of simplified models to be sure that the proposed model and method of analysis will yield satisfactory results.

20. Interpreting Model Results. The first step in interpreting model results comes when the experimental data are actually being measured and recorded. One should continually be studying the data as they are accumulated, being sure that the data from duplicate tests are consistent, checking to see that the measurements from point to point vary in a reasonable and orderly manner, taking precautions to see that constant test conditions and techniques are being maintained, and so on.   In this way, if questionable or unexpected data are being obtained, the measurements may be checked and verified before the test setup is altered.   It is often helpful to make rough plots of data as they are being obtained in order to spot quickly any inconsistent measurements.

After the test data have been analyzed and the test results have been computed, the information should be plotted or tabulated in such a manner that its reasonableness may be estimated.   The best way of judging the results, of course, is to apply any physical checks which are available.   For example, in any static problem, the test results must satisfy the laws of static equilibrium $-\Sigma F_x = 0$, $\Sigma F_y = 0$, and $\Sigma M = 0$.   Of course, static checks may be applied to the entire model or any portion of it.   Such checks are extremely useful.

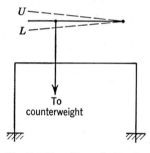

FIG. 15-21.   Error in Loading Model

There is perhaps no better way of judging the reliability of model results for a static problem.

It is oftentimes difficult to load a model exactly as specified.   For example, suppose the model shown in Fig. 15-21 has been analyzed for a vertical load using the moment indicator. To do this the distorting device would have been arranged as indicated.   Just how successful we were in applying the desired vertical load will be indicated by the model results. Suppose the joints were in equilibrium under the experimental end moments in the members.

Suppose, however, that the shears in the columns which were computed by statics from these end moments were not equal and opposite.   This would indicate that the load which was actually applied to the model had a horizontal as well as a vertical component.   To correct these results for this error in loading we could analyze the model for a horizontal load using the setup shown in Fig. 15-3.   Then, using this information we could adjust the values of the first test so as to remove the effect of the undesired horizontal component of the load.   In this manner, therefore, the laws of statics may often be used to assist us in correcting for the effect of errors in loading.

Whenever the results obtained from a model are to be extrapolated in order to predict the behavior of its prototype, the principles of similitude must be fulfilled when the model is designed, constructed, and tested.   The requirements of these principles can seldom be met exactly, and in almost all practical cases it will be found that the behavior of a model differs to some extent from that of its prototype.   Scale effect is defined as the degree to which a prediction made from a model test will not be fulfilled in the full-scale structure.   Scale effect may be caused by unavoidable inaccuracies in test conditions.   As the scale of a model is reduced, it becomes impossible to reproduce all the details of the prototype in a small model.   The elimination of such details may contribute to scale effect. The excellence of the workmanship in building the model must increase as the scale is reduced in order to minimize the resulting scale effect.

It is evident that scale effect may arise from a variety of sources, some of which are beyond control. Scale effect should always be suspected, and, if the purpose of the test is to provide an accurate indication of the behavior in full scale, similar models of different scales may be built and tested and the laws of behavior determined empirically from the results of the series of model tests.

BIBLIOGRAPHY

1. McCullough and Thayer, *Elastic Arch Bridges*, John Wiley & Sons, New York, 1931, Ch 7.
2. B. Mills, "A Sensitive Contact Indicator," *Rev Sci Instr*, v 12, n 2, p 105, Feb 1941.
3. Otto Gottschalk, "Mechanical Calculation of Elastic Systems," *J Franklin Inst*, v 202, n 1, pp 61–88, July 1926.
4. W. J. Eney, "New Deformeter Apparatus," *Eng News-Rec*, Feb 16, 1939, p 221.
5. W. J. Eney, "Model Analysis of Continuous Girders," *Civil Eng*, v 11, n 9, p 521, Sept 1941.
6. G. E. Beggs, "An Accurate Mechanical Solution of Statically Indeterminate Structures by Use of Paper Models and Special Gages," *Proc Am Concrete Inst*, v 18, 1922, pp 58–82.
7. G. E. Beggs, Discussion of "Design of a Multiple-Arch System," *Trans ASCE*, 1925, v 88, pp 1208–230.
8. G. E. Beggs, "The Use of Models in the Solution of Indeterminate Structures," *J Franklin Inst*, v 203, n 3, pp 375–86, Mar 1927.
9. A. C. Ruge and E. O. Schmidt, "Mechanical Structural Analysis by the Moment Indicator," *Proc ASCE*, Oct 1938.
10. C. H. Norris, "Model Analysis of Structures," *Proc Soc Stress Analysis*, v 1, n 2, July 1944.
11. R. V. Southwell, "On the Analysis of Experimental Observations in Problems of Elastic Stability," *Proc Royal Society (Lond.)*, v 135A, 1932, p 601. This method is also summarized in
    S. Timoshenko, *Theory of Elastic Stability*, McGraw-Hill Book Co, New York, 1936, p 177.
12. E. E. Lundquist, "Generalized Analysis of Experimental Observations in Problems of Elastic Stability," *Nat Advisory Commit for Aeronautics Tech Note* 658.
13. L. H. Donnell, *On the Application of Southwell's Method for the Analysis of Buckling Test*, contributions to the Mechanics of Solids dedicated to S. Timoshenko, Macmillan Co, New York, 1938, p 27.
14. R. D. Conrad, "Structural Models," part 1, "Theory," *U S Navy Dept Construction and Repair* 13, 1938.
15. G. E. Beggs, R. E. Davis, and H. E. Davis, *Tests on Structural Models of Proposed San Francisco-Oakland Suspension Bridge*," Univ of California Press, 1933.
16. J. B. Wilbur, "Structural Analysis Laboratory Research," *Mass Inst of Tech Dept of Civil and Sanitary Eng Publ* 65, Dec 1938; 68, Dec 1939; 73, Dec 1940; 80, Dec 1941.

CHAPTER 16

ANALOGIES

By Raymond D. Mindlin and Mario G. Salvadori

700

A. Introduction

It frequently occurs that the characteristics of two or more apparently different physical phenomena can be expressed in identical mathematical form. When this is so, the physical systems are said to be *analogous*. Although one may speculate on the possibilities of discovering a fundamental law of nature which might explain the existence of analogies,[1] such a law is not a prerequisite for either the discovery or the use of the analogies themselves. It is sufficient to consider an analogy as a chance coincidence of mathematical forms.

Many uses have been found for analogies:

1. If two systems are analogous, it is only necessary to study one of them in order to gain insight into both. An early example in mechanics is a theorem by Kirchhoff[2] according to which the equations of equilibrium of a thin rod, bent or twisted by couples at its ends, are identified with the equations of motion of a rigid body turning about a fixed point.

2. Improvements in the technique of solving problems in one field are automatically improvements in analogous fields. Modern methods of analyzing electric circuits are of inestimable value in the theory of mechanical vibrations.[3-5]

3. Specific solutions of boundary value problems are often directly applicable to several analogous physical systems. Thus, the solution of a problem of the slow motions of a viscous fluid in two dimensions is at once the solution of a problem of flexure of a plate and the solution of a problem in plane elasticity.[6] A similar relation exists between elastic and visco-elastic bodies.[7]

4. Not to be underestimated is the use of an analogy in obtaining a mental grasp of the essential features of a complicated system. It is much easier to visualize the shape of a soap film than to think about the shearing stress in a twisted bar.

5. From a practical point of view, the most useful aspect of an analogy is the possibility of its employment as a calculating device. Solutions of equations representing a physical system are often extraordinarily difficult to obtain, and numerical methods of solution are often very lengthy. Direct physical measurements on the system, or a scale model of it, may not be feasible. However, it is frequently the case that measurements on an analogue of the system are practicable. Thus, the analogous system may serve as a calculating machine[12] for solving the equations governing the original system. It is with this aspect of analogies that the present chapter is concerned.

Even with the restriction of a study of analogies to their use as calculating devices, the remaining possibilities are so numerous that further limitations are necessary if even a moderately thorough treatment is to be given in a reasonable amount of space. In applied mechanics alone there are scores of useful analogies.[1, 8] The numbers run high even in special branches of applied mechanics, such as elasticity and fluid mechanics.[9, 10] Accordingly, this chapter is confined to analogies, involving experimental procedures, which have proved to be useful or give promise of being useful in the quantitative determination of states of stress in elastic bodies. Some interesting analogies in the field of stress analysis which are thereby omitted are Nádai's sand heap and roof analogies[11] and the numerous analogies between stress and fluid flow.

In passing from the state of stress in an elastic solid to the measurement of a quantity in an analogous system, five main steps are to be noted:

1. Conversion of the original physical system to mathematical form.
2. Conversion of the analogous physical system to mathematical form.
3. Identification of the two mathematical expressions.
4. Physical realization of the analogous system.
5. Measurement of quantities in the analogous system.

In each of these steps, factors may be introduced which limit the range of applicability or the accuracy of the results. Only in the third step is it possible and, indeed, necessary to achieve complete mathematical rigor. The establishment of an analogy is dangerously unfinished and certainly not wholly understood without a complete identification of the corresponding equations, variables, coefficients, and boundary conditions in the mathematical expression of the physical system and its analogue. On the other hand, the accuracy of the physical realization of the "analogue machine" and the accuracy of the measurements need be pursued only to the extent warranted by the assumptions made in the conversion of both physical systems to mathematical form.

I. TORSION AND FLEXURE OF CYLINDRICAL BARS

The components of shearing stress in a cylindrical or prismatical bar, which is bent by a terminal load or twisted by terminal couples, may be expressed in terms of a function of the coordinates of points in the bar. This function is governed by special equations derived from the general equations of elasticity in accordance with the *Saint-Venant theory*. The special equations have exactly the same form as those governing the steady flow of electricity in a plate and the deflections of a constant-tension membrane stretched over an opening of the same shape as the cross section of the bar. Accordingly, measurements made on the membrane or the plate give complete information as to the state of shearing stress in the bar.

In applying the Saint-Venant theory of torsion and flexure to a physical bar, the transverse dimensions of the bar are considered to be small in comparison with its length, because the distribution of the stresses at the ends, which constitute the applied forces and couples, may not be identical with those contemplated by the theory. If the discrepancy is large, the theory will not apply to those portions of the bar within distances from the ends of approximately the maximum linear dimension of the cross section.

B. Essential Features of the Saint-Venant Theory

Consider a system of rectangular coordinates with the z axis coinciding with the line of centroids of the bar's cross section; the x and y axes parallel to the principal axes of the section; and the origin lying in one of the end faces (Fig. 16-1). At the other end face ($z = c$) a transverse load P_x is applied parallel to the x axis. In general, the terminal load may not act parallel to a principal axis of the section but it can always be resolved into two components, parallel to the principal axes, each of which may be considered separately.

1. Components of Stress. In accordance with the semi-inverse method of Saint-Venant, the state of stress in the bar is assumed to be

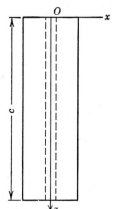

$$\sigma_x = \sigma_y = \tau_{xy} = 0 \tag{1}$$

$$\sigma_z = \frac{P_x(z - c)x}{I_y} \tag{2}$$

$$\tau_{yz} = -\frac{\partial \varphi}{\partial x} \tag{3}$$

$$\tau_{zx} = \frac{\partial \varphi}{\partial y} - \frac{P_x}{2I_y}\left(x^2 - \frac{\mu y^2}{1 + \mu}\right) \tag{4}$$

where μ is Poisson's ratio, I_y is the second moment of area of the cross section about the y axis:

$$I_y = \int\int_R x^2 \, dx \, dy \tag{5}$$

Fig. 16-1. Coordinate System for St.-Venant Torsion and Bending

(the integral being extended over the region R of the net section) and φ is a function of x and y only. If φ can be determined so as to satisfy all of the equations and conditions of the theory of elasticity, the uniqueness theorem* assures that the stresses (equations 1 to 4) are the true stresses in the bar. The requirements of the theory of elasticity are that the components of stress satisfy the equations of equilibrium and the boundary conditions and, in the present case, lead to single-valued components of displacement.

It may be verified, by direct substitution, that the system of stresses (equations 1 to 4) satisfies the equations of equilibrium, in the absence of body forces (see Appendix I, equations 28).

2. Boundary Conditions. On a cylindrical surface of the bar, the boundary conditions (Appendix I, equations 2) reduce, by virtue of equations 1 to 4, to

$$\tau_{zx}l + \tau_{yz}m = 0 \tag{6}$$

where (see Fig. 16-2)

$$l = \cos\,(x, \nu) = \frac{dy}{ds} \qquad m = \cos\,(y, \nu) = -\frac{dx}{ds} \tag{7}$$

Substituting equations 3, 4, and 7 in equation 6, we have the following condition to satisfy at each point of each boundary:

* See Appendix I, article 16.

$$\frac{\partial \varphi}{\partial y}\frac{dy}{ds} + \frac{\partial \varphi}{\partial x}\frac{dx}{ds} = \frac{\partial \varphi}{\partial s} = \frac{P_x}{2I_y}\left[x^2 - \frac{\mu y^2}{1 + \mu}\right]\frac{dy}{ds} \tag{8}$$

Suppose that there are n internal boundaries (that is, n cylindrical holes in the bar), in addition to the external boundary, and that the shapes of the boundaries as they appear in a right cross section are the $n + 1$ curves $C_i (i = 0, 1, 2, \cdots, n)$. Then the conditions (equation 8) may be written, after one integration, as

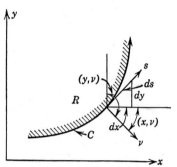

$$\varphi_{C_i} = \frac{P_x}{2I_y}\int_0^s x^2 l \, ds - \frac{\mu P_x y_{C_i}^3}{6(1 + \mu)I_y} + k_i$$

$$(i = 0, 1, 2, \cdots, n), \tag{9}$$

where φ_{C_i} is the value of φ at a point on the boundary C_i, and k_i is a constant, in general different for each boundary. It is customary to identify $i = 0$ with the external boundary.

FIG. 16-2. Normal and Tangential Coordinates at a Point on a Boundary

At the end $z = c$ of the bar, the resultant force in the x direction is

$$\int\int_R \tau_{zz}\, dx\, dy = \int\int_R \left[\frac{\partial \varphi}{\partial y} - \frac{P_x x^2}{2I_y} + \frac{\mu P_x y^2}{2(1 + \mu)I_y}\right] dx\, dy$$

$$= \int\int_R \left[-\frac{\partial}{\partial y}\left(x\frac{\partial \varphi}{\partial x}\right) + \frac{\partial}{\partial x}\left(x\frac{\partial \varphi}{\partial y}\right)\right.$$

$$\left. + \frac{\partial}{\partial x}\left(-\frac{P_x x^3}{6I_y} + \frac{\mu P_x xy^2}{2(1 + \mu)I_y}\right)\right] dx\, dy$$

$$= \int_C \left[x\frac{\partial \varphi}{\partial x}dx + x\frac{\partial \varphi}{\partial y}dy + \left(-\frac{P_x x^3}{6I_y} + \frac{\mu P_x xy^2}{2(1 + \mu)I_y}\right)dy\right]$$

the last step being accomplished by the use of Green's theorem,[13] the subscript C indicating that the line integral is extended in the positive s direction (see Fig. 16-2) over all $n + 1$ boundaries. Hence,

$$\int\int_R \tau_{zz}\, dx\, dy = \int_C \left[x\frac{\partial \varphi}{\partial s}ds + \left(-\frac{P_x x^3}{6I_y} + \frac{\mu P_x xy^2}{2(1 + \mu)I_y}\right)dy\right]$$

Then, using equation 8,

$$\int\int_R \tau_{zz}\, dx\, dy = \int_C \frac{P_x x^3}{3I_y}\, dy = \frac{P_x}{I_y}\int\int_R x^2\, dx\, dy = P_x, \tag{10}$$

where Green's theorem and equation 5 have been used. It is seen that the components of stress (equations 1 to 4), combined with the boundary conditions (equation 8), produce a terminal load P_x in the x direction at the end $z = c$.

The couple about the z axis is

$$M_z = \int \int_R (\tau_{yz}x - \tau_{zx}y) \, dx \, dy$$

$$= - \int \int_R \left(x \frac{\partial \varphi}{\partial x} + y \frac{\partial \varphi}{\partial y} - \frac{P_x x^2 y}{2I_y} + \frac{\mu P_x y^3}{2(1 + \mu)I_y} \right) dx \, dy \quad (11)$$

Similarly, it can be shown that all the remaining components of force and couple vanish at $z = c$. It should be observed that equation 11 implies the possibility of a nonvanishing M_z even if $P_x = 0$.

3. Single-Valuedness Conditions. A necessary condition for the components of displacement to be single-valued is that the equations of compatibility (Appendix I, equations 34) be satisfied. Using equations 1 to 4, we find the compatibility equations reduce to

$$\frac{\partial \nabla^2 \varphi}{\partial x} = 0 \qquad \frac{\partial \nabla^2 \varphi}{\partial y} = 0$$

and, hence,

$$\nabla^2 \varphi = B \tag{12}$$

where B is a constant, and

$$\nabla^2 = \frac{\partial^2}{\partial x^2} + \frac{\partial^2}{\partial y^2}$$

To establish sufficient conditions for single-valuedness, we must obtain, first, general expressions for the displacements. These are found by inserting equations 1 to 4 in the stress-displacement relations (Appendix I, equations following equations 30) and integrating, with the results:

$$u = -\theta yz + \frac{P_x}{2EI_y} \left[cz^2 - \frac{z^3}{3} + \mu(c - z)(x^2 - y^2) \right] \tag{13}$$

$$v = \theta xz + \frac{\mu P_x xy(c - z)}{EI_y} \tag{14}$$

$$\frac{\partial w}{\partial x} = \theta y + \frac{1}{G} \frac{\partial \varphi}{\partial y} - \frac{P_x}{2EI_y} [2cz - z^2 + (2 + \mu)x^2 - \mu y^2] \tag{15}$$

$$\frac{\partial w}{\partial y} = -\theta x - \frac{1}{G} \frac{\partial \varphi}{\partial x} + \frac{\mu P_x xy}{EI_y} \tag{16}$$

where G is the shear modulus and θ is the angle of twist, of the bar, per unit of length. In arriving at equations 13 to 16, the end conditions,

$$u = v = \frac{\partial u}{\partial z} = \frac{\partial v}{\partial z} = \frac{\partial v}{\partial x} = 0$$

at the origin, were used.

u and v are single-valued, but, in order to assure single-valuedness of w, it is necessary to have

$$\int_{C_r} dw = 0 \qquad (17)$$

where C_r is any closed curve in the region R of the section.

Now, in any plane $z = \text{const}$,

$$\int_{C_r} dw = \int_{C_r} \left(\frac{\partial w}{\partial x} dx + \frac{\partial w}{\partial y} dy \right) \qquad (18)$$

If C_r surrounds no holes, or if the section of the bar is solid, equation 18 becomes, if equations 15 and 16 and Green's theorem are used,

$$\int_{C_r} dw = -\frac{1}{G} \int \int_{R_r} (\nabla^2 \varphi + 2G\theta)\, dx\, dy$$

where R_r is the simply connected region enclosed in C_r. In order to satisfy equation 17, the constant B in equation 12 must be equal to $-2G\theta$. Hence, for a solid bar, the differential equation,

$$\nabla^2 \varphi = -2G\theta \qquad (19)$$

is a necessary and sufficient condition for single-valuedness of displacement.

For a bar containing n holes, there are n internal boundary curves $C_i (i = 1, 2, 3, \cdots, n)$. Substituting equations 15 and 16 in equation 18, applying Green's theorem, and using equations 17 and 19, we have

$$\frac{1}{G} \int_{C_i} \left(\frac{\partial \varphi}{\partial y} dx - \frac{\partial \varphi}{\partial x} dy \right) + \int_{C_i} \left\{ \theta y - \frac{P_x}{2EI_y} [2cz - z^2 + (2 + \mu)x^2 - \mu y^2] \right\} dx$$
$$+ \int_{C_i} \left(-\theta x + \frac{\mu P_x xy}{EI_y} \right) dy = 0 \qquad (i = 1, 2, 3, \cdots, n) \quad (20)$$

If equation 20 is satisfied on $i = 1, 2, 3, \cdots, n$, it will be satisfied identically on $i = 0$.

The first integral on the left-hand side of equation 20 is

$$-\int_{C_i} \frac{\partial \varphi}{\partial \nu} ds$$

while the second two integrals become, by Green's theorem,

$$\int \int_{A_i} 2\theta\, dx\, dy = 2\theta A_i$$

where A_i is the area enclosed in the i th boundary curve C_i. Hence, in order to satisfy equation 17 in a multiply connected bar, we must have

$$\int_{C_i} \frac{\partial \varphi}{\partial \nu} \, ds = 2G\theta A_i, \qquad (i = 1, 2, 3, \cdots, n) \tag{21}$$

The differential equation,

$$\nabla^2 \varphi = -2G\theta \tag{19}$$

the boundary conditions for each point of each boundary,

$$\varphi_{C_i} = \frac{P_x}{2I_y} \int_0^s x^2 l \, ds - \frac{\mu P_x y_{C_i}{}^3}{6(1 + \mu)I_y} + k_i \qquad (i = 0, 1, 2, \cdots, n) \tag{20}$$

and the single-valuedness condition for each *internal* boundary

$$\int_{C_i} \frac{\partial \varphi}{\partial \nu} \, ds = 2G\theta A_i \qquad (i = 1, 2, 3, \cdots, n) \tag{21}$$

determine the function φ for a bar bent by a terminal load P_x and twisted to an amount θ per unit of length.

In order to maintain the twist θ, the force P_x must be applied at a distance $\bar{y}$ from the x axis, where

$$\bar{y} = -\frac{M_z}{P_x} = \frac{1}{P_x} \int \int_R \left(x \frac{\partial \varphi}{\partial x} + y \frac{\partial \varphi}{\partial y} - \frac{P_x x^2 y}{2I_y} + \frac{\mu P_x y^3}{2(1 + \mu)I_y} \right) dx \, dy \tag{22}$$

If the cross section of the bar is simply connected (that is, contains no holes), the single-valuedness conditions (equation 21) are not required, and the constant k_i in equation 9 may be taken equal to zero since any constant may be added to φ without affecting the stress.

4. Flexureless Torsion. If we take $P_x = 0$, the bar is twisted but not bent. The conditions on φ become

$$\nabla^2 \varphi = -2G\theta \tag{23}$$

$$\varphi_{C_i} = k_i \qquad (i = 0, 1, 2, \cdots, n) \tag{24}$$

$$\int_{C_i} \frac{\partial \varphi}{\partial \nu} \, ds = 2G\theta A_i \qquad (i = 1, 2, 3, \cdots, n) \tag{25}$$

The torque producing the twist θ is, from equation 11,

$$M_z = -\int \int_R \left(x \frac{\partial \varphi}{\partial x} + y \frac{\partial \varphi}{\partial y} \right) dx \, dy$$

$$= \int \int_R \left[2\varphi - \frac{\partial}{\partial x} (x\varphi) - \frac{\partial}{\partial y} (y\varphi) \right] dx \, dy$$

$$= 2 \int \int_R \varphi \, dx \, dy + \int_{C_i} \varphi(y \, dx - x \, dy)$$

where Green's theorem has been used and the line integral is taken in the positive s direction (Fig. 16-3) along all $n+1$ boundaries. Then, using equation 24, we have

$$M_z = 2 \int\int_R \varphi \, dx \, dy$$

$$- 2k_oA_o + 2\sum_{i=1}^{n} k_iA_i \quad (26)$$

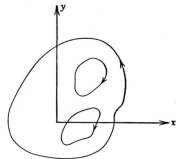

where A_o is the area of the gross section. It is seen that the torque is equal to twice the volume enclosed by the surface $\varphi = \varphi(x, y)$ and the portions of $n+1$ planes bounded by the $n+1$ curves C_i at levels $\varphi_{C_i} = k_i$.

FIG. 16-3. Positive Directions along Boundaries of a Multiply Connected Section

The torsional rigidity C of the bar is defined as the ratio of the torque to the angle of twist per unit of length:

$$C = \frac{M_z}{\theta} \quad (27)$$

The resultant shearing stress at any point acts along the tangent to the contour $\varphi = $ const through that point. This may be seen by calculating the

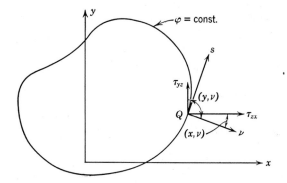

FIG. 16-4.   Components of Stress at a Point on a Contour of Constant Shear

value of the component of shearing stress along the normal ν (Fig. 16-4) to the contour:

$$\tau_{yz} \cos(y, \nu) + \tau_{zx} \cos(x, \nu) = \frac{\partial\varphi}{\partial x}\frac{dx}{ds} + \frac{\partial\varphi}{\partial y}\frac{dy}{ds} = \frac{\partial\varphi}{\partial s} = 0$$

The magnitude of the resultant shearing stress at any point Q is (Fig. 16-4)

$$\tau = \tau_{yz} \cos(x, \nu) - \tau_{zx} \cos(y, \nu) = -\frac{\partial \varphi}{\partial x}\frac{dx}{d\nu} - \frac{\partial \varphi}{\partial y}\frac{dy}{d\nu} = -\frac{\partial \varphi}{\partial \nu} \quad (28)$$

that is, it is equal to the maximum slope of the surface φ at Q.

5. Torsionless Flexure. If we set $\theta = 0$, the bar is bent but not twisted. The conditions on φ become

$$\nabla^2 \varphi = 0 \tag{29}$$

$$\varphi_{C_i} = \frac{P_x}{2I_y}\int_0^s x^2 l\, ds - \frac{\mu P_x y_{C_i}{}^3}{6(1+\mu)I_y} + k_i \qquad (i = 0, 1, 2, \cdots, n) \tag{30}$$

$$\int_{C_i}\frac{\partial \varphi}{\partial \nu}\, ds = 0 \qquad (i = 1, 2, 3, \cdots, n) \tag{31}$$

and the line of application of the force P_x, to maintain torsionless flexure, must be distant from the x axis by an amount (see equation 22):

$$\bar{y} = \frac{1}{P_x}\int\int_R \left[x\frac{\partial \varphi}{\partial x} + y\frac{\partial \varphi}{\partial y} - \frac{P_x x^2 y}{2I_y} + \frac{\mu P_x y^3}{2(1+\mu)I_y}\right] dx\, dy \tag{32}$$

The length $\bar{y}$ is the y coordinate of the *flexural center* with respect to the centroid ($x = y = 0$) of the section.

6. Alternative Expression of Flexureless Torsion. The shearing stress, in a bar which is twisted but not bent, may be expressed in terms of a function ψ which satisfies Laplace's equation $\nabla^2 \psi = 0$ (instead of equation 23) by letting

$$\varphi = \psi + F \tag{33}$$

where F is a function of x and y for which

$$\nabla^2 F = -2G\theta \tag{34}$$

Suitable functions F are

$$F = -\tfrac{1}{2}G\theta(x^2 + y^2) \tag{35}$$

$$F = -G\theta x^2 \tag{36}$$

$$F = -G\theta y^2 \tag{37}$$

Substituting equation 33 in equations 23 and 24, we find the differential equation and boundary conditions for ψ to be

$$\nabla^2 \psi = 0 \tag{38}$$

$$\psi_{C_i} = k_i - F_{C_i} \qquad (i = 0, 1, 2, \cdots, n) \tag{39}$$

where ψ_{C_i} and F_{C_i} are the values of ψ and F on the boundary C_i.

For the single-valuedness conditions, we note that

$$\int_{C_i}\frac{\partial \varphi}{\partial \nu}\, ds = \int_{C_i}\frac{\partial \psi}{\partial \nu}\, ds + \int_{C_i}\frac{\partial F}{\partial \nu}\, ds$$

But

$$\int_{C_i} \frac{\partial F}{\partial \nu}\, ds = -\int_{C_i} \left(\frac{\partial F}{\partial y} dx - \frac{\partial F}{\partial x}\, dy \right)$$

$$= -\int\int_{A_i} \nabla^2 F\, dx\, dy \quad \text{(by Green's theorem)}$$

$$= 2G\theta \int\int_{A_i} dx\, dy \quad \text{(by equation 34)}$$

$$= 2G\theta A_i$$

Hence equation 25 becomes

$$\int_{C_i} \frac{\partial \psi}{\partial \nu}\, ds = 0 \qquad (i = 1, 2, 3, \cdots, n) \tag{40}$$

The components of shearing stress are

$$\tau_{yz} = -\frac{\partial \psi}{\partial x} - \frac{\partial F}{\partial x} \qquad \tau_{zx} = \frac{\partial \psi}{\partial y} + \frac{\partial F}{\partial y} \tag{41}$$

and the torsional rigidity is

$$C = \frac{2}{\theta} \left[\int\int_R (\psi + F)\, dx\, dy - k_o A_o + \sum_{i=1}^{n} k_i A_i \right] \tag{42}$$

C. Differential Equation of a Membrane

Consider a homogeneous membrane under a uniform tension T per unit of length and subjected to a normal pressure p per unit of surface area. If the slope of the membrane relative to a plane (say, x_1, y_1) is everywhere small,[*] the ordinate (ζ) of the membrane surface, measured in the positive z_1 direction, is governed by the differential equation:[†]

$$\frac{\partial^2 \zeta}{\partial x_1^2} + \frac{\partial^2 \zeta}{\partial y_1^2} = -\frac{p}{T} \tag{43}$$

If there is no pressure exerted against the membrane, equation 43 reduces to

$$\frac{\partial^2 \zeta}{\partial x_1^2} + \frac{\partial^2 \zeta}{\partial y_1^2} = 0 \tag{44}$$

The similarity of equations 43 and 44 to the differential equations governing the functions φ and ψ is the point of departure for establishing a complete

[*] See article 10.
[†] See reference 10, p. 239.

analogy between the torsion and bending problems and the shape of a membrane surface. In order to accomplish this, the boundaries of the membrane must be of such shape and held in such manner that the properties of ζ will be similar to those required of φ or ψ by their boundary and single-valuedness conditions.

D. PRESSURE-MEMBRANE ANALOGY FOR FLEXURELESS TORSION

7. Conditions on ζ. The function φ for flexureless torsion (see article 4) is specified by

$$\frac{\partial^2 \varphi}{\partial x^2} + \frac{\partial^2 \varphi}{\partial y^2} = -2G\theta \tag{45}$$

$$\varphi_{c_i} = k_i \qquad (i = 0, 1, 2, \cdots, n) \tag{46}$$

$$\int_{C_i} \frac{\partial \varphi}{\partial \nu} \, ds = 2G\theta A_i \qquad (i = 1, 2, 3, \cdots, n) \tag{47}$$

Let the linear geometrical scale ratio of lengths parallel to the x, y plane of the prototype to lengths parallel to the x_1, y_1 plane of the model be λ. Then, setting $x = \lambda x_1$, $y = \lambda y_1$, and

$$\varphi = \frac{2G\theta\lambda^2 T}{p} \zeta \tag{48}$$

in equation 45, we find that the function ζ, thus defined, satisfies equation 43. Equation 48 gives the relation between the membrane ordinates and the function φ.

Referring to the boundary conditions (equations 46), we specify the shapes of the boundaries C_i' of the membrane to be geometrically similar to the boundaries C_i of the section of the bar, with scale ratio λ. Then, the analogue of equations 46 is

$$\zeta_{c_i'} = k_i' \qquad (i = 0, 1, 2, \cdots, n) \tag{49}$$

where

$$k_i' = \frac{p}{2G\theta\lambda^2 T} k_i \tag{50}$$

This requirement can be satisfied for $i = 0$ by stretching the membrane over an opening, of shape C_o', in a flat plate whose elevation above the x_1, y_1 plane is k_o'. For the internal boundaries, disks whose edges are the curves C_i' ($i = 1, 2, 3, \cdots, n$) are placed, in the proper positions over the opening, with their edges at elevations k_i' above the x_1, y_1 plane.

To determine the elevations k_i', the single-valuedness conditions (equations 47) are used. Substituting equations 48 in equations 47, we have the single-valuedness conditions in terms of ζ:

$$T \int_{C_i} \frac{\partial \zeta}{\partial \nu_1} \, ds_1 = pA_i', \qquad (i = 1, 2, 3, \cdots, n) \tag{51}$$

where

$$\nu_1 = \frac{\nu}{\lambda}, \quad s_1 = \frac{s}{\lambda}, \quad A_i' = \frac{A_i}{\lambda^2} \tag{52}$$

in which A_i' is the area of the ith disk.

Now, for small membrane slopes, $T\dfrac{\partial \zeta}{\partial \nu_1}$ is the component, in the z_1 direction, of the membrane tension. Hence, the quantity on the left side of equation 51 is the total force, in the z_1 direction, exerted by the membrane on the ith disk. The right side of equation 51 is the resultant of the pressure p on the ith disk. Thus, equation 51 states that each disk must be in equilibrium

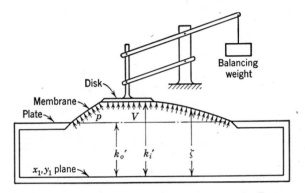

Fig. 16-5. Section of a Multiply Connected Membrane under Pressure, Analogue of St.-Venant Torsion

under these two forces alone. This may be done by balancing out the gravitational force on each disk, leaving it acted on only by the membrane tension and the applied pressure, and restricting its motion to pure displacement in the z_1 direction (see Fig. 16-5). If the external boundary is kept at an arbitrary level k_o', the n disks will then reach equilibrium levels k_i'. The value assigned to k_o' is immaterial since an arbitrary constant may be added to φ and, therefore, to ζ without affecting the stresses. The analogy is thus complete.

8. Resultant Shearing Stress and Torsional Rigidity. To determine the stresses, we note from equations 28, 48, and 52 that the resultant shearing stress at any point is given by

$$\tau = -\frac{2G\theta\lambda T}{p}\frac{\partial \zeta}{\partial \nu_1} \tag{53}$$

Hence, the resultant shearing stress at any point is obtained by measuring the maximum slope $(\partial \zeta/\partial \nu_1)$ of the membrane at that point and multiplying by the constant $-2G\theta\lambda T/p$.

The torsional rigidity of the bar is, from equations 27, 26, 48, 50, and 52,

$$C = \frac{4G\lambda^4 T}{p} \left[\int \int_{R_1} \zeta \, dx_1 \, dy_1 - k_o' A_o' + \sum_{i=1}^{n} k_i' A_i' \right]$$

$$= \frac{4G\lambda^4 T}{p} V \tag{54}$$

where V is the volume enclosed by the membrane, the n disks, and the plane of the hole in the plate. If the bar is solid, V is simply the volume bounded by the membrane and the plane of the plate over which it is stretched.

From equations 27, 53, and 54, the resultant shearing stress may be expressed as

$$\tau = -\frac{M_z}{2\lambda^3 V} \frac{\partial \zeta}{\partial \nu_1} \tag{55}$$

9. Alternatives to Measuring p/T. It may be observed from equation 54 that knowledge of the ratio p/T is required for determining the torsional rigidity. This ratio is usually difficult to measure, but its measurement may be avoided by performing an auxiliary membrane experiment for a simple torsion problem whose solution can be obtained mathematically. Similarly, to find the stress τ, either p/T must be known, or V must be measured, according to equations 53 and 55. If C is not required, both these measurements may also be avoided by the auxiliary experiment for which the mathematical solution is known.

The simplest of all torsion problems is that for a solid bar of circular cross section. It may be verified that, for this case,

$$\varphi = \frac{G\theta}{2} (a^2 - r^2) \tag{56}$$

where a is the radius of the section, $r^2 = x^2 + y^2$, and k_o has been taken equal to zero.

In the auxiliary membrane experiment, a membrane is stretched over a circular opening of radius a_1 and the same tension T and pressure p are used as in the main experiment. We now measure the ordinate $[\zeta]_{r_1=0}$ of the highest point of the membrane, reckoned from the plane of the edge of the membrane. Then, from equation 48,

$$[\varphi]_{r=0} = \frac{2G\theta\lambda^2 T}{p} [\zeta]_{r_1=0}$$

or, if we use equation 56 and remember that $a = \lambda a_1$,

$$\frac{p}{T} = \frac{4}{a_1^2} [\zeta]_{r_1=0} \tag{57}$$

Alternatively, if slopes rather than ordinates are measured, we measure the maximum slope $[\partial \zeta / \partial r_1]_{r_1=a_1}$ of the membrane and note that, from equation 48,

$$\left[\frac{\partial \varphi}{\partial r}\right]_{r=a} = \frac{2G\theta\lambda T}{p}\left[\frac{\partial \zeta}{\partial r_1}\right]_{r_1=a_1}$$

Hence, using equation 56 gives

$$\frac{p}{T} = -\frac{2}{a_1}\left[\frac{\partial \zeta}{\partial r_1}\right]_{r_1=a_1} \tag{58}$$

Again, if volumes are measured, we note that

$$\iint_R \varphi\, dx\, dy = \frac{2G\theta\lambda^4 T}{p}\iint_{R_1} \zeta\, dx_1\, dy_1$$

Hence,

$$\frac{p}{T} = \frac{8V_c}{\pi a_1{}^4} \tag{59}$$

where V_c is the volume enclosed between the membrane and the plane of the circular opening of radius a_1.

Depending on which type of measurement is made, p/T is obtained from equation 57, 58, or 59 and is then used in equations 53 and 54.

The foregoing procedure is based on the assumption that p/T is the same for the circular membrane as for the experimental membrane. It is easy to make p the same for both, but the duplication of T may at times be uncertain. A check on the value of p/T obtained with the circular membrane may be made by observing that, from equation 51,

$$\frac{p}{T} = \frac{1}{A_i}\int_{C_{i'}} \frac{\partial \zeta}{\partial \nu_1}\, ds_1$$

so that by taking a sufficient number of readings of $\partial \zeta / \partial \nu_1$ around any boundary, the value of p/T may be calculated without the use of the circular membrane at all.

10. Effect of Excessive Slopes of the Membrane Surface. The simple case of a membrane stretched over a circular opening may also be used to investigate the limitation on slopes in order for the approximate equation 43 to hold within a certain degree of accuracy. According to the approximate equation, the membrane has the shape of a paraboloid of revolution,

$$\zeta = \frac{p(a_1{}^2 - r_1{}^2)}{4T} \tag{60}$$

whereas the actual shape (if gravity is neglected) would be a spherical surface of radius

$$R_1 = \frac{2T}{p} \qquad (61)$$

as may be seen from considerations of symmetry and equilibrium under the tension T and pressure p (Fig. 16-6). Hence, the membrane does not repre-

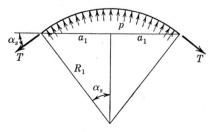

sent the surface φ exactly. The maximum error in slope of the membrane due to this discrepancy occurs at the boundary $r_1 = a_1$ where the slope is, from Fig. 16-6 and equation 61,

$$\tan \alpha_s = \left[\left(\frac{2T}{pa_1} \right)^2 - 1 \right]^{-\frac{1}{2}}$$

FIG. 16-6.   Equilibrium of a Membrane Stretched to a Spherical Surface

whereas the analogy contemplates that the slope is $-d\zeta/dr_1$ which, from equation 60, is found to be $pa_1/2T$ on the boundary. Hence, the percentage error in resultant shear stress is

$$E = 100 \left\{ \frac{\dfrac{pa_1}{2T} - \left[\left(\dfrac{2T}{pa_1} \right)^2 - 1 \right]^{-\frac{1}{2}}}{\dfrac{pa_1}{2T}} \right\}$$

The full line in Fig. 16-7 represents this quantity plotted against α_s, where α_s is the angle which the meridional tangent at $r_1 = a_1$ makes with the x_1, y_1

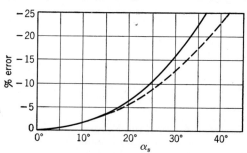

FIG. 16-7.   Error in Resultant Shear Stress Due to Excessive Membrane Slope

plane. Note that the percentage errors are negative; that is, the stress obtained from the spherical membrane will be too large. If the angle α_s is measured, rather than $\tan \alpha_s$, and if the stress is taken to be proportional to α_s rather than to $\tan \alpha_s$, the error will be slightly overcome since the angle is always less than its tangent. The corresponding errors are given by the dashed line in Fig. 16-7.

By comparing the volume under the spherical surface with the volume under the paraboloidal surface, it is found that the error, due to excessive slope, in determining torsional rigidity is considerably less than the error in stress.

11. Alternative Procedure for Multiply Connected Sections.   The differential equation and edge conditions governing the ordinates ζ, analogous to the function φ for flexureless torsion, were found to be

$$\nabla_1^2 \zeta = -\frac{p}{T} \tag{62}$$

$$\zeta_{c_i} = k_i' \qquad (i = 0, 1, 2, \cdots, n) \tag{63}$$

$$\int_{C_i'} \frac{\partial \zeta}{\partial \nu_1} ds_1 = \frac{pA_i'}{T} \qquad (i = 1, 2, 3, \cdots, n) \tag{64}$$

where

$$\nabla_1^2 = \frac{\partial^2}{\partial x_1^2} + \frac{\partial^2}{\partial y_1^2}$$

In order to satisfy the conditions of equations 64 for a single membrane, a delicate balancing device was found to be necessary for each internal boundary of a multiply connected section.   This device may be avoided by performing a series of $n + 1$ membrane experiments in each of which the boundaries are fixed.

Let the $n + 1$ membranes be specified by ζ^j, $j = 0, 1, 2, \cdots, n$, and let the required membrane surface ζ be expressed as

$$\zeta = \sum_{j=0}^{n} m_j \zeta^j \tag{65}$$

where the $n + 1$ constants m_j are to be determined so as to make ζ satisfy equations 62 to 64.

If each of the membranes ζ^j has a tension T and is subjected to a pressure p, the equations,

$$\nabla_1^2 \zeta^j = -\frac{p}{T} \qquad (j = 0, 1, 2, \cdots, n) \tag{66}$$

will be satisfied automatically.   Substituting equation 65 in equation 62 and using equation 66, we find that we must have

$$\sum_{j=0}^{n} m_j = 1 \tag{67}$$

in order to satisfy the differential equation 62.

To satisfy the boundary conditions of equations 63, we set

$$\zeta_{c_i}{}^j = e_{ij} \qquad (i = 0, 1, 2, \cdots, n, \quad j = 0, 1, 2, \cdots, n) \tag{68}$$

where the e_{ij} are arbitrary constants. It is convenient to take

$$e_{ij} = \begin{cases} e, & i = j \\ 0, & i \neq j \end{cases} \qquad (69)$$

that is, in each of the $n + 1$ membrane experiments, n boundaries are fixed at zero elevation while one boundary is raised to a level e. Thus, $n + 1$ membrane surfaces are obtained, each having a different boundary elevated by an amount e above the remaining boundaries.

The requirements imposed by the single-valuedness condition of equations 64 are found by substituting equation 65 in equations 64, with the result,

$$\sum_{j=0}^{n} m_j \int_{C_i'} \frac{\partial \zeta^j}{\partial \nu_1} ds_1 = \frac{pA_i'}{T} \qquad (i = 1, 2, 3, \cdots, n) \qquad (70)$$

Now,

$$\int_{C_i'} \frac{\partial \zeta^j}{\partial \nu_1} ds_1$$

is a constant, say q_{ij}, which may be determined, for each of the n internal boundaries (C_i') of each of the $n + 1$ membranes ζ^j, by measuring $\partial \zeta^j / \partial \nu_1$ at a number of points around each boundary and integrating either graphically or numerically. We then have n equations:

$$\sum_{j=0}^{n} m_j q_{ij} = \frac{pA_i'}{T} \qquad (i = 1, 2, 3, \cdots, n) \qquad (71)$$

in the $n + 1$ unknowns m_j. These, along with equation 67, completely determine the m_j. These m_j, combined with the measured ordinates ζ^j of the $n + 1$ membranes, give the required function ζ when substituted in equation 65.

It will also be noticed that substituting equation 65 in equations 63 gives

$$\sum_{j=0}^{n} m_j \zeta_{C_i'}{}^j = k_i'$$

Hence, using equations 68 and 69, we have

$$m_j e = k_i' \qquad (i = j = 0, 1, 2, \cdots, n) \qquad (72)$$

Thus, the $n + 1$ elevations, k_i', of the $n + 1$ boundaries of the function ζ are known, and the true membrane surface ζ may be produced physically if desired.

E. ZERO-PRESSURE MEMBRANE ANALOGY FOR FLEXURELESS TORSION

12. Conditions on ζ. The function ψ for flexureless torsion is specified by

$$\frac{\partial^2 \psi}{\partial x^2} + \frac{\partial^2 \psi}{\partial y^2} = 0 \tag{73}$$

$$\psi_{C_i} = k_i - F_{C_i} \qquad (i = 0, 1, 2, \cdots, n) \tag{74}$$

$$\int_{C_i} \frac{\partial \psi}{\partial \nu}\, ds = 0 \qquad (i = 1, 2, 3, \cdots, n) \tag{75}$$

We again let λ be the geometrical scale ratio of lengths parallel to the x, y plane of the prototype to lengths parallel to the x_1, y_1 plane of the membrane model. We set

$$\psi = \frac{2G\theta\lambda^2}{\Upsilon}\, \zeta \tag{76}$$

$$F = \frac{2G\theta\lambda^2}{\Upsilon}\, F' \tag{77}$$

$$k_i = \frac{2G\theta\lambda^2}{\Upsilon}\, k_i{}' \tag{78}$$

where Υ is a conversion factor which plays the same part as p/T in section D, except that it is assigned beforehand so as to make the slope of

$$F_{C_i}{}' = \frac{\Upsilon}{2G\theta\lambda^2} F_{C_i} \qquad (i = 0, 1, 2, \cdots, n) \tag{79}$$

small.

By substituting equations 76 to 78 into equations 73 to 75, we obtain

$$\frac{\partial^2 \zeta}{\partial x_1{}^2} + \frac{\partial^2 \zeta}{\partial y_1{}^2} = 0 \tag{80}$$

$$\zeta_{C_i} = k_i{}' - F_{C_i}{}' \qquad (i = 0, 1, 2, \cdots, n) \tag{81}$$

$$\int_{C_i{}'} \frac{\partial \zeta}{\partial \nu_1}\, ds_1 = 0 \qquad (i = 1, 2, 3, \cdots, n) \tag{82}$$

To satisfy equation 80, a constant-tension membrane is used without lateral pressure.

To satisfy equations 81, the projections $(C_i{}')$ of the membrane boundaries on the x_1, y_1 plane must be geometrically similar to the curves C_i, with scale ratio λ, and similarly placed. Also, the ordinates to the membrane boundaries must have the values $k_i{}' - F_{C_i}{}'$, where the constants $k_i{}'$ are as yet unknown. For the outer boundary this is accomplished by supporting the outer edge of the membrane on a wall whose height is everywhere proportional to the quantity $k_o' - F_{C_o'}$. For each inner boundary, if any, a plug is used, the boundary of whose cross section is the curve C_i', with provision for attaching the membrane so that its boundary ordinates on C_i' have the values $k_i' - F_{C_i'}$.[*]

Finally, equations 82 require the z_1 component of the resultant force of the membrane on each plug to vanish. This requires the weight of the plug to be balanced out and the motion of the plug to be restricted to pure translation in the z_1 direction (see Fig. 16-8). The levels k_i' ($i = 1, 2, 3, \cdots, n$) will then

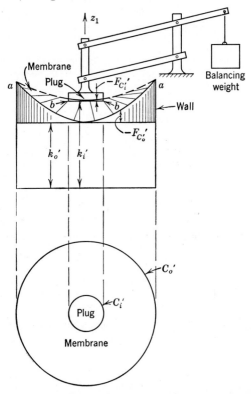

FIG. 16-8. Section of a Multiply Connected Zero-Pressure Membrane, Analogue of St.-Venant Bending

be reached automatically, while the level k_o' may be assigned arbitrarily since a constant may be added to ψ and F, and, therefore, to ζ and F', without affecting the stresses. This completes the analogy.

13. Components of Shearing Stress and Torsional Rigidity. From equations 41 and 76, the components of shearing stress are

$$\tau_{yz} = -\frac{2G\theta\lambda}{\Upsilon}\frac{\partial\zeta}{\partial x_1} - \frac{\partial F}{\partial x} \qquad \tau_{zx} = \frac{2G\theta\lambda}{\Upsilon}\frac{\partial\zeta}{\partial y_1} + \frac{\partial F}{\partial y} \tag{83}$$

---

[*] Note that, from equations 35 to 37, the function F is always negative (for positive θ) so that the ordinates $-F_{C_i'}$ are actually added to k_i' (see Fig. 16-8).

Hence, each component of shearing stress is composed of two parts. For example, τ_{yz} is made up of a part $(\partial\zeta/\partial x_1)$ involving the measured slope of the membrane in the x_1 direction and a part $(\partial F/\partial x)$ computed from the known function F.

From equations 42, 77, and 76, the torsional rigidity is

$$C = \frac{4G\lambda^4}{\Upsilon}\left[\int\int_{R_1}(\zeta + F')\,dx_1\,dy_1 - k_o'A_o' + \sum_{i=1}^{n}k_iA_i\right] \tag{84}$$

$$= \frac{4G\lambda^4 V}{\Upsilon} - GI \tag{85}$$

where V is the volume bounded by the membrane, the portions of the $n+1$ planes bounded by the curves C_i', at levels k_i', and the cylindrical surfaces (a–a and b–b in Fig. 16-8) connecting the boundaries of these planes with the corresponding edges of the membrane. I is the centroidal second moment of area of the section if F is given by equation 35. If F is given by equation 36, I is twice the second moment of area of the section about the y axis. If F is given by equation 37, I is twice the second moment of area of the section about the x axis.

14. Alternative Procedure for Multiply Connected Sections. As in the case of the pressure membrane, a zero-pressure membrane surface satisfying equations 80 to 82 may be found by performing $n+1$ membrane experiments and writing

$$\zeta = \sum_{j=0}^{n}m_j\zeta^j \tag{86}$$

Each of the membrane surfaces ζ^j is obtained from a zero-pressure membrane experiment, and, therefore,

$$\nabla_1^2\zeta^j = 0 \tag{87}$$

Hence, substituting equation 86 in equation 80 and using equation 87, we see that the differential equation governing ζ will be satisfied automatically.

For each boundary C_i' of each membrane ζ^j, we make

$$\zeta_{C_i'}{}^j = e_{ij} - F_{C_i'}' \tag{88}$$

where

$$e_{ij} = \begin{cases} e, & i = j \\ 0, & i \neq j \end{cases} \tag{89}$$

That is, the boundaries are constructed exactly as described in article 12, with the modification that, for each of the $n+1$ experiments, all the heights k_i' except one are made equal to zero. Thus, $n+1$ membrane surfaces ζ^j are obtained, each having a different boundary elevated by an amount e.

Then,

$$\zeta_{c_{i'}} = \sum_{j=0}^{n} m_j \zeta_{c_{i'}i} = \sum_{j=0}^{n} m_j(e_{ij} - F_{c_{i'}}') = m_i e - F_{c_{i'}}' \sum_{j=0}^{n} m_j$$

so that the boundary conditions (equation 81) become

$$m_i e - F_{c_{i'}}' \sum_{j=0}^{n} m_j = k_i' - F_{c_{i'}}' \qquad (i = 0, 1, 2, \cdots, n)$$

or

$$k_i' - m_i e = \left(1 - \sum_{j=0}^{n} m_j\right) F_{c_{i'}}' \qquad (i = 0, 1, 2, \cdots, n) \tag{90}$$

The left-hand side of equation 90 is a constant, as is the quantity in parentheses on the right, whereas the quantity $F_{c_{i'}}'$ is, in general, a variable. Hence, in order to satisfy equation 90, we must have

$$\sum_{j=0}^{n} m_j = 1 \tag{91}$$

$$k_i' = m_i e \qquad (i = 0, 1, 2, \cdots, n) \tag{92}$$

The single-valuedness conditions (equation 82) become, if equation 86 is used,

$$\sum_{j=0}^{n} m_j \int_{C_{i'}} \frac{\partial \zeta^i}{\partial \nu_1} ds_1 = 0 \qquad (i = 1, 2, 3, \cdots, n) \tag{93}$$

where the integrals are constants, determined as described in article 11.

The n equations 93, along with equation 91 are solved for the $n + 1$ constants m_j which are then inserted in equation 86 to yield the true shape of the membrane surface ζ. The membrane may be produced physically by setting the levels of the outer wall and plugs in accordance with equations 92.

15. Additional Function to Reduce Slopes. If the difference between the maximum and minimum ordinates of the membrane is made as small as possible, the slopes will be reduced, and errors due to excessive slope will be minimized. This may be effected by adding to the membrane surface ζ a function $-G'$ where

$$G' = a + bx_1 + cy_1 + fx_1y_1, \tag{94}$$

in which a, b, c, f are constants chosen so as to minimize the maximum ordinate difference. Then,

$$\zeta' = \zeta - G' \tag{95}$$

is a new membrane having the desired property.

The boundary conditions on ζ' become, from equations 95, 81 and 82,

$$\zeta_{C_i'}' = k_i' - F_{C_i'}' - G_{C_i'}' \qquad (i = 0, 1, 2, \cdots, n) \qquad (96)$$

$$\int_{C_i'} \frac{\partial \zeta'}{\partial \nu_1} ds_1 + \int_{C_i'} \frac{\partial G'}{\partial \nu_1} ds_1 = 0 \qquad (i = 1, 2, 3, \cdots, n) \qquad (97)$$

But

$$\int_{C_i'} \frac{\partial G'}{\partial \nu_1} ds_1 = \int\int_{A_i'} \nabla^2 G' \, dx_1 \, dy_1 = 0$$

since $\nabla^2 G' = 0$. Hence, equation 97 becomes

$$\int_{C_i'} \frac{\partial \zeta'}{\partial \nu_1} ds_1 = 0 \qquad (i = 1, 2, 3, \cdots, n) \qquad (98)$$

Hence, the only change in constructing the membrane is the addition of the boundary ordinates $-G_{C_i'}'$.

In terms of the new membrane ζ', the stresses (equation 83) and torsional rigidity (equation 85) become

$$\tau_{yz} = -\frac{2G\theta\lambda}{\Upsilon} \left(\frac{\partial \zeta'}{\partial x_1} + b + fy_1 \right) - \frac{\partial F}{\partial x} \qquad (99)$$

$$\tau_{zx} = \frac{2G\theta\lambda}{\Upsilon} \left(\frac{\partial \zeta'}{\partial y_1} + c + fx_1 \right) + \frac{\partial F}{\partial y} \qquad (100)$$

$$C = \frac{4G\lambda^4}{\Upsilon} \left[\int\int_{R_1} (\zeta' + F' + G') \, dx_1 \, dy_1 - k_o'A_o' + \sum_{i=1}^{n} k_i'A_i' \right] \qquad (101)$$

F. Membrane Analogy for Torsionless Flexure

16. Similarity to Membrane for Torsion. It may be observed that the conditions (equations 73 to 75) on the function ψ for flexureless torsion are almost identical with the conditions (equations 29 to 31) on the function φ for torsionless flexure. The only difference is that the function F_{C_i} is replaced by H_{C_i} where

$$H_{C_i} = -\frac{P_x}{2I_y} \int_0^s x^2 l \, ds + \frac{\mu P_x y_{C_i}^3}{6(1 + \mu)I_y} \qquad (102)$$

The boundary ordinates of the membrane are calculated according to the rule:

$$H_{C_i'} = \frac{\Upsilon_1 I_y}{P_x \lambda^3} H_{C_i} \qquad (103)$$

$$k_i' = \frac{\Upsilon_1 I_y}{P_x \lambda^3} k_i \qquad (104)$$

where Υ_1 is a conversion constant. Hence,

$$\zeta_{C_{i'}} = \frac{1}{2}\,\Upsilon_1\int_0^{s_1} x_1{}^2 l\,ds_1 - \frac{\Upsilon_1 \mu y_{1C_{i'}}{}^3}{6(1+\mu)} + k_i' \qquad (105)$$

$$= k_i' - H_{C_{i'}} \qquad (106)$$

so that

$$\varphi = \frac{P_x\lambda^3}{\Upsilon_1 I_y}\,\zeta \qquad (107)$$

From this point the construction of the zero-pressure membrane for torsionless flexure follows exactly the same procedure described in article 12 or 14.

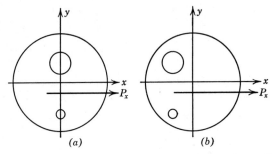

(a)   (b)

FIG. 16-9. If the Bar is Loaded as Shown in b, the Membrane Surface is Discontinuous

17. Components of Shearing Stress and Center of Flexure. From equations 107, 3, and 4, the shearing stress components are

$$\tau_{yz} = -\frac{P_x\lambda^2}{I_y\Upsilon_1}\frac{\partial\zeta}{\partial x_1} \qquad \tau_{zx} = \frac{P_x\lambda^2}{I_y\Upsilon_1}\frac{\partial\zeta}{\partial y_1} - \frac{P_x}{2I_y}\left(x^2 - \frac{\mu y^2}{1+\mu}\right) \qquad (108)$$

From equations 107 and 32 the y coordinate of the center of flexure is given by

$$I_y\bar{y} = \frac{\lambda^5}{\Upsilon_1}\int\int_{R_1}\left(x_1\frac{\partial\zeta}{\partial x_1} + y_1\frac{\partial\zeta}{\partial y_1}\right)dx_1\,dy_1$$

$$-\frac{1}{2}\int\int_R\left(x^2 y - \frac{\mu y^3}{1+\mu}\right)dx\,dy \qquad (109)$$

18. Failure of the Flexure Analogy. It should be observed that the boundary $\zeta_{C_{i'}}$ of equation 105 is a continuous curve only if

$$\int_{C_{i'}} x_1{}^2 l\,ds_1 = 0 \qquad (110)$$

where the integral is carried completely around the curve C_i'. This integral (by Green's theorem) is simply the moment of the area A_i', enclosed within C_i', about the principal y axis of the *whole* section. Hence equation 110 will be true for all boundaries only if the principal y axis passes through the centroid of *every* area A_i.   This is always true for a solid section and is also true for a hollow section such as is shown in Fig. 16-9 when loaded as shown in *a*.   If the section is shaped as shown in *b*, the integrals in equation 110 do not vanish.   When this is the case, the membrane has a discontinuity, and it is not apparent how such a membrane surface can be produced physically.

G. MEMBRANE-ANALOGY TECHNIQUES

The membranes used in the actual performance of torsion- or bending-analogy experiments are of three kinds:

Soap film.

Rubber membrane.

Meniscus of separation between two immiscible liquids.

Soap films have been used extensively in connection with both pressure and zero-pressure analogies, because their unit tension T (arising from surface tension) is automatically uniform throughout.

19. Pressure Soap Film.   (*a*) *Apparatus.*   The first membrane-analogy experiment was performed by Anthes, who used a pressure soap film to solve a variety of torsion problems in 1906.[15]   In the Anthes apparatus, the soap film is stretched over an opening in the vertical side of a rectangular box. The film is distended by introducing a measured amount of air displaced from a glass tube.   The quantity of air is controlled by elevating a flask of water joined to the tube by a flexible connection.

The apparatus developed by Griffith and Taylor[17] in 1917 has become widely used for soap-film experiments and is described in detail (Fig. 16-10).

The circular test hole and the experimental hole are cut from a flat aluminum plate 0.05 in. thick and beveled on the under side of the opening to an angle of 45°.   The aluminum plate is clamped between two parts of a square cast-iron box, the lower part of which is a $\frac{1}{4}$ in.-deep tray supported on leveling screws and the upper part of which is a square frame.   The inside of the tray is blackened, and the inside of the frame is enameled white.

The two parts are clamped together, and the joint is made tight by means of grease or thick oil that must be wiped out carefully in order to avoid contact with the films.

The lower part is connected with a flask of water or, better, of soap solution, by means of a rubber tube and a three-way cock; the upper part communicates with the outer air by means of a plain tube through the wall of the frame.

A glass plate, $\frac{1}{4}$ in. thick, slides freely on the edges of the upper frame and has fixed to it a depth micrometer, the lower end of which is made to touch the film.   A drawing board, pivoted on a horizontal axis, can be swung down so as to touch a pencil point on the upper end of the micrometer, thus recording the position, in the x_1, y_1 plane, of the point being measured.

The largest linear dimension of the experimental hole is of the order of 1 to 3 in. while the radius of the circular hole is chosen equal to twice the ratio of the area to the perimeter of the experimental hole, in order to make the average boundary slope of the experimental hole equal to the slope at the edge of the circle.

When the cross section to be studied has a line of symmetry or a line known beforehand to be practically perpendicular to the contours, the model hole can be stopped along such a line by a "septum" (that is, a vertical plate), and only a portion of the section need thus be studied.

Various soap solutions have been used, among which the following have given good results:

Englemann[25]—45 parts of water, 5 parts of sodium oleate (by weight). With addition of a little sugar, the membrane dries without breaking.

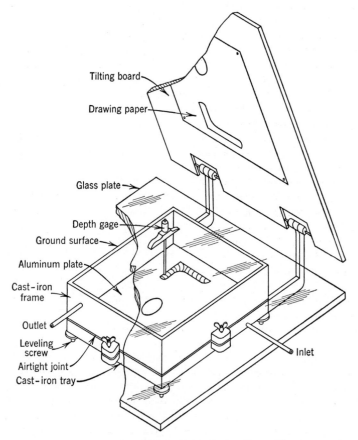

Tilting board

Drawing paper

Glass plate

Depth gage

Ground surface

Aluminum plate

Cast-iron frame

Outlet

Leveling screw

Airtight joint

Cast-iron tray

Inlet

FIG. 16-10. Sketch of the Griffith and Taylor Soap-Film Apparatus

Johnston[26]—Triethynolamine oleate 10%, glycerin 30%, water 60% (by weight). Films last 3 to 4 days.

Cushman[20]—2 grams of sodium oleate, 30 cc of glycerin, 1 liter of water. Films last up to 25 hr. Add more oleate or glycerin for large holes.

The soap solution must be stored in an airtight container and should not come in contact with grease or acids.

In performing the experiment, the aluminum plates are thoroughly cleaned and accurately leveled. The soap film is stretched over the holes by means of a smooth piece of celluloid or a wire, and surplus solution is drained off. In order to avoid accumulation of solution around the boundaries, it is well to blow the membrane up, collect the surplus solution, and then suck the membrane down so that the water will drain toward the center of the hole during the actual experiment.

The blowing of the membrane is performed by allowing soap solution to run from a buret into a sealed flask so as to displace air from the flask through a tube into the lower half of the cast-iron box. The readings of the buret can be estimated to 0.01 cc. Owing to the change in pressure, the change of volume of air below the film is not equal to the volume of displaced solution. A calibration curve for the correction of this error can be obtained by using sections of known torsional rigidity. Such a curve is given by Johnston.[26]

(b) *Measurement of Slope. The Anthes checkerboard.* In his original experiment, Anthes[15] set a vertical black and white checkerboard in front of the vertical film. The center of the board had a small hole at which the objective lens of a camera was placed. Photographs were taken of the undistorted and distorted reflections of the checkerboard in the flat and inflated films. The shifts of the corners of the checkerboard in the two photographs give, by means of a simple graphical construction, the values of the slopes at these points. The method allows a check of theoretically known results within 1 to 3 per cent but appears not to have been used in succeeding tests by others.

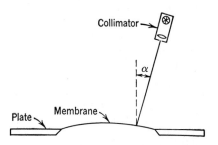

Fig. 16-11. Principle of the Griffith and Taylor Autocollimator for Measuring Slope of Soap Film

Griffith and Taylor autocollimator.[17a] In this instrument (Fig. 16-11), a collimated bundle of light rays from a small source is directed on the surface of the film. The collimation axis is rotated about a horizontal axis until the reflected ray coincides with the incident ray. The angle between the collimation axis and the vertical measures the slope of the film. The apparatus is carried on a pair of right-angle guides in order to locate the point at which the slope is measured. The accuracy obtained is about 2 to 4 per cent, the chief error arising from the fact that the film has a tendency to spread over the plate at the boundary. In order to avoid this source of error, a contour line very near the boundary may be taken as the true boundary of the section.

Quest collimator.[21] A more sensitive direct measure of the film slope is obtained by means of the Quest collimator (Fig. 16-12). In this apparatus the incident ray is vertical, and the reflected ray makes an angle 2α with the vertical. An arc of a circle, made of two steel angles and graduated in degrees, swings around the collimation axis of the apparatus until the ray reflected

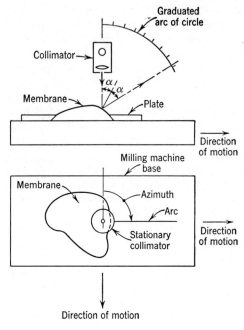

FIG. 16-12. Quest Collimator

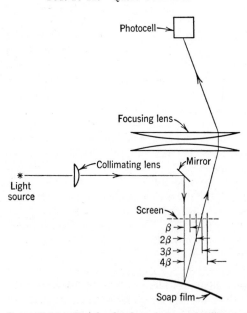

FIG. 16-13. Reichenbächer Automatic Slope
Recorder

from the film is intercepted. The azimuth of the arc being indicated on a horizontal graduation, both the maximum slope α and its direction are measured at the same time. The box carrying the soap films is mounted on a milling-machine base, while the collimator is stationary. In this way the coordinates of the point whose slope is being measured can be accurately fixed, and the slope can be evaluated point by point.

It is advisable to repeat the measurement of the boundary slope of the comparison circle frequently during the experiment to make sure that the pressure under the films has not changed.

Automatic slope recorder.[27] In the automatic slope recorder developed by Reichenbächer (Fig. 16-13), a horizontal ray of light is reflected vertically downward by a 45° mirror, strikes the film, and is reflected at an angle of 2α to the vertical. A horizontal screen of opaque material, with ten concentric annular openings equally spaced, is held above the film at a distance which is large compared with the elevations of the film. The reflected ray can pass through the screen only through one of the annular openings, that is, only if its inclination to the vertical is a multiple of the inclination β corresponding to the annulus of smallest diameter. Beyond the screen a system of lenses focuses the source on a photoelectric cell which operates the shutter of a camera. Whenever the slope α is a multiple of β, a source of light flashes into the camera and a dash is recorded on a photographic plate.

To record the lines of constant slope $\alpha = m\beta$, $(m = 1, 2, \cdots , 10)$ the box containing the soap films and the camera is kept stationary while the complete optical system moves across the film first in one direction and then in a direction at right angles to it. At points where $\alpha = m\beta$ a short dash is impressed on the photographic plate, and the intersection of the two dashes at right angles locates the point. After traversing the film with parallel lines spaced a few millimeters apart in both directions, the locus of the points of slope $\alpha = m\beta$ appears as a dark band on the photograph, constituting a contour line of the stress surface. The error on known sections is 3 to 4 per cent.

Photogrammetric method.[24] A. Thiel has developed a special photogrammetric camera by means of which photographs of the films can be obtained directly. In order to photograph transparent soap films, lycopodium powder is spread on them, and the photographs show the dots of powder resting on the films. The technique of spreading the powder is complicated and lengthy. The film solution must, therefore, be very pure to last the time necessary for the spreading. The mapping of the film surface from the photographs is performed by regular photogrammetric procedures, and the slopes can be determined from the map by graphical or numerical methods.

Contours.[17a] When the contour lines of the film surface are obtained as indicated under "Measurement of Volume," the slope at any point can be evaluated graphically or numerically by dividing the minimum distance between two contour lines into their difference in level. Inasmuch as the maximum slope is usually the only measurement of practical importance, the contour-line method is convenient, as it allows quick identification of the point where the maximum slope occurs, since in that region the contours are crowded together most closely.

With care, accuracy of the order of 2 per cent can be obtained.

(c) *Measurement of Volume.* *Contours.* The Griffith and Taylor vertical micrometer[17a] (spherometer) can be used to plot contour lines of the film surface; the micrometer is set at a given height, and the locus of points having this height is plotted. The lower point of the micrometer is wetted with soap solution, and contact with the film is indicated when the film seems to move up the point. The error in the elevation thus measured is within ± 0.001 in. With a contour map, the volume of the film can be computed by graphical or numerical methods as a sum of volumes of horizontal slices. The maximum error obtained by this method was 1.6 per cent.

The "black-spot" method. When a soap film (convex upward) stands for a long time, the solution gradually flows downward, under gravity, until the film thickness at the highest elevation becomes less than the wave length of the incident light. Since no light is reflected from a film of such thinness, a black spot appears at the highest elevation and gradually spreads over the film as the downward flow of solution continues. During this process, the boundary of the nonreflecting region is always a contour of the film surface.

Photographs of the black spot taken when its boundary reaches equally spaced elevations build up a record of the contours by means of which the volume may be computed as before.

The accuracy obtainable is not so good as that obtained by other methods.

Integration. When the slopes at the corners of a square grid have been measured, numerical or graphical integration allows the plotting of equally spaced sections of the membrane. Another numerical integration gives the volume of the film. The accuracy obtainable by this method depends on the accuracy of the slope measurements but is comparable with the accuracy obtained by other methods.

Direct measurement. The simplest way of measuring the volume of the film consists in measuring the amount of air used in blowing the bubble.

This can be done either by lifting the soap solution flask as described previously or by moving a piston of known diameter into a tight cylinder containing the soap solution and connected with the box by means of a tube.

Since in most cases the box contains both the experimental and the circular check holes, various methods have been devised for the measurement of the volume under each hole.

Griffith and Taylor[17a] blew the circular film first and measured its volume by means of the boundary slope, knowing that the film surface is a sphere. By carefully flattening the spherical bubble by means of a plate pushed on it, they then transferred the known volume of air to the experimental hole.

Johnston[26] measured (by the flask method) the amount of air used in blowing both films, measured the volume of the spherical film by determining the elevation of the top of the film, and obtained the volume of the experimental film by subtraction.

Reichenbächer[27] first blew the circular film to given volumes by pushing a calibrated rod into a tight cylinder containing the soap solution. To record the volumes, a linear scale was held above a horizontal glass plate protecting the film, and the images of the scale reflected by the glass plate and the blown film were compared. The apparent length of the image reflected by the film decreases when the film is blown down (sucked), and the experimental volumes chosen were those that made the ratio of the two reflected images of the scale equal to $\frac{3}{4}$, $\frac{1}{2}$, $\frac{1}{3}$, $\frac{1}{4}$. Then, both the circular and the experimental membranes were blown together to the same values of the afore-mentioned ratio in order to guarantee that the circular film had the same volume as before, and the total volume was measured again by means of the calibrated rod. A subtraction gave the volume of the experimental film. The ratios of the volumes of the experimental film to the volumes of the circular film were taken, and their average had an error of only $1\frac{1}{2}$ per cent on known sections.

(*d*) *Sources of Error.* Various causes of error are inherent in the pressure-film method:

1. Approximate instead of rigorous equation of the film surface. This cause can be minimized by keeping the maximum slope α small (see article 10).

2. Weight of film. This error can be reduced either by holding the film vertical or by performing two experiments, one blowing the film up, the other sucking the film down, and averaging results. This source of error limits the holes to a maximum dimension of approximately 3 in.

3. Vibrations of the film. To avoid film vibrations, the films must be covered with a glass plate, and the air in the room must be stationary. It is sometimes necessary to support the box on a vibration-absorbing cushion.

4. Change of volume due to temperature. The temperature in the room should not vary more than a few degrees during the experiment.

5. Change of pressure. This is mainly due to change in temperature and may be particularly critical when various films are tested in the course of a study of multiply connected sections.

6. False slope at the boundaries. The film must be well drained as explained previously.

7. Boundaries not perfectly flat. The edges of the holes in the plate should be machined flat within 0.001 in. and should be leveled carefully.

8. Systematic errors. These are the errors inherent in the measuring devices (collimator, micrometer, photogrammetric camera, and so on) and in the numerical and graphical methods.

Owing to all these sources of error, the total error to be expected from a pressure-film test is of the order of 5 per cent.

20. Zero-Pressure Soap Film. (*a*) *Apparatus.* The apparatus used in zero-pressure soap-film tests for torsion or bending is identical with the apparatus described under "Pressure Soap Film" (article 19*a*) except for the omission of the tube connecting the lower half of the box with the soap-solution flask or cylinder. The lower half of the box has a hole which allows the pressure below and above the film to be the same.

For a simply connected section, the film, instead of being stretched on a horizontal hole, is now stretched on a wall of variable height built on a given boundary shape in the horizontal plane.

The boundary ordinates, or "wall heights," can be obtained by either cutting and filing a wall made out of thin brass sheet,[20] or cutting, out of a sheet of celluloid or brass, a hole of suitable shape and supporting this sheet at the correct height on the boundary by means of nuts and washers on vertical studs.[17c]

The second method is in general more complicated since the shape of the hole to be cut out must be such that, when bent, its projection on a horizontal plane be a given shape.

(*b*) *Special Device.* When the film is used in a torsion test, a very simple procedure for building the boundary wall[30] is suggested by the use of the function $F = -G\theta x^2$ (see equation 36). The boundary ordinates lie on the surface of a parabolic cylinder $z_1 = kx_1^2$ (where k is a constant), and the shape of the actual hole to be cut from a flat plate can be obtained by computing the ordinates:

$$\bar{x} = \int_0^{x_1} \sqrt{1 + \left(\frac{dz_1}{dx_1}\right)^2}\, dx_1 = \int_0^{x_1} \sqrt{1 + 4k^2x_1^2}\, dx_1$$

$$= \frac{x_1}{2}\sqrt{1 + 4k^2x_1^2} + \frac{1}{4k}\log_e(2kx_1 + \sqrt{1 + 4k^2x_1^2})$$

where x_1 is the value of the x coordinate of the projection of the boundary on the horizontal plane, and $\bar{x}$ is the corresponding x coordinate on the developed surface. Thus, the shape of the hole to be cut out of a flat sheet is known. After the hole is cut out, the sheet is curved on the cylinder $z_1 = kx_1^2$, which can be built once and for all, and the edge of the curved plate gives the boundary ordinates.

(c) *Sources of Error and Advantages.* Although most of the sources of error mentioned under "Pressure Soap Films" (article 19d) still exist with no-pressure films, the following advantages often outweigh the lengthy construction of the boundary wall.

1. By using the auxiliary function G' (see article 15) the slopes of the membrane can be greatly reduced, with a corresponding reduction in errors due to excessive slope.

2. The apparatus is simplified as airtight joints are not required.

3. The laborious adjustment and maintenance of constant pressure is avoided. This is especially important with multiply connected sections, where the film may break during pressure manipulation.

The methods for measuring slopes are identical with the methods for pressure membranes.

21. Rubber Membranes. A rubber membrane, uniformly stretched, can supplant the soap film both in the pressure and zero-pressure experiments.

In order to obtain a constant tension T throughout the membrane, a rubber sheet is ruled with equally spaced lines in two perpendicular directions and is then stretched over a frame until the ruled network is, say, doubled in size.

The rubber pressure membrane can be blown by air, while the zero-pressure membrane is held down on the boundary wall by means of a mating template.[23]

The advantages of rubber membranes are the following:

1. The large allowable tension diminishes the sag due to weight.

2. The membrane lasts indefinitely.

3. The larger allowable dimensions of the membranes permit greater accuracy in the measurement of the ordinates and in the building of the boundary heights.

An ingenious use of the rubber membrane was devised by Kopf and Weber.[22] The membrane is stretched over holes in an aluminum plate which is the top of a jar containing a mixture of paraffin of specific weight equal to unity. When the jar is heated, the paraffin melts, and a small amount of water poured over the membrane distends the membrane into the paraffin. The jar is then cooled, and the shape of the deflected membrane is frozen in the paraffin block. To measure the slope and volume, the impression is blackened, and the block is sliced on a lathe, a photograph being taken of the resulting section at every cut. The edges of the blackened portions are the contours.

The main advantage of the method consists in the simplicity of the operations and the leisure with which the contours can be obtained from the frozen mold of the membrane's shape.

The accuracy obtained is of the order of 2 per cent.

22. Meniscus Surface. (a) *Apparatus.* Piccard and Baes[18] in 1926 were the first to use the separation surface of two immiscible liquids as a membrane for torsion-analogy experiments. Owing to capillarity, there is an equivalent constant tension on the surface, and the meniscus can be used both for pressure and zero-pressure experiments.

The apparatus of Piccard and Baes (Fig. 16-14) is used for pressure-membrane experiments and consists of a zinc jar filled with an electrolyte of density 1.08 and covered by a plate cut to the shape of the experimental hole. The zinc jar fits snugly into a glass jar, the upper part of which is filled with chlorotoluene, a liquid of density 1.08, that does not mix or react with the electrolyte. If small amounts of electrolyte are added or subtracted by means of a buret, the meniscus surface can be distended to the desired height. The glass jar is contained in a square glass jar filled with water to allow lateral observation of the meniscus.

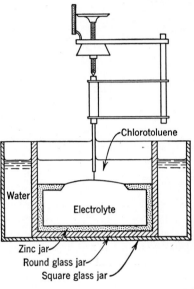

Fig. 16-14. Piccard and Baes Meniscus Apparatus and Depth Gage

The apparatus developed by Sunatani, Matuyama, and Hatamura[29] can be used for both pressure and zero-pressure experiments. In the first case (Fig. 16-15) a closed wall A of constant height, erected on a boundary similar to the shape of the experimental cross section, rests on the bottom of a large glass jar and communicates, by means of a small tube B, with a vertical tube C external to the glass jar. The closed wall is filled to its upper edge with an electrolyte. The glass jar is then filled with a mixture of nitrobenzene and toluene of the same density as the electrolyte. By adding small amounts of electrolyte through the vertical tube, the meniscus is distended to the desired height.

When zero-pressure experiments must be performed, (Fig. 16-16), the heights of the closed wall are made equal to the ordinates of the corresponding boundary function ζ_c. The volume inside of the wall communicates with a small vessel B, also resting on the bottom of the glass jar. The electrolyte is poured carefully into B until A is just filled. The jar is then filled with the nitrobenzene–toluene mixture.

(b) *Measurement of Slope. Contours.* In the Piccard and Baes[18] apparatus, the elevation of the meniscus is measured by means of a vertical micrometer carried by a milling machine base, on the principle of the Griffith and Taylor

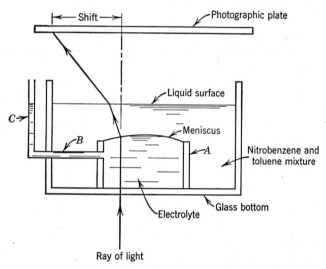

FIG. 16-15. Sunatani, Matuyama, and Hatamura Pressure Meniscus Apparatus

spherometer. The liquids chosen are such that the upper (chlorotoluene) is a nonconductor, while the electrolyte is a conductor. The needle of the micrometer is connected with an electric circuit including a buzzer which is actuated when the needle touches the electrolyte. Contours are easily mapped in this fashion and check the theoretical contours of known sections.

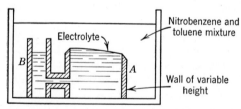

FIG. 16-16. Sunatani, Matuyama, and Hatamura Zero-Pressure Meniscus Apparatus

By means of the contour map, the slope can be computed at any point in the usual manner.

Lines of constant slope. Piccard and Baes[18] devised an optical apparatus which records lines of constant slope in the following manner. A camera is held above the meniscus with its axis perpendicular to the plane of the membrane's boundary. A collimator, inclined at a given angle 2α with the vertical, emits parallel rays that strike the meniscus and are reflected at various angles. Those rays striking the meniscus at points having slope α are reflected vertically and enter the aperture of the camera. The collimator is rotated around the axis of the camera, and the reflected ray entering the camera describes a line of constant slope α on the photographic plate.

By changing the slope 2α of the collimator and repeating a complete rotation for every inclination, the map of the constant slope line is completely photographed.

It is important to notice that the path followed by the incident and reflected rays must be free of refraction. This is achieved by immersing the collimator in the upper liquid. In order to avoid the use of large quantities of chlorotoluene, the upper liquid is plain water and the lower a mixture of chlorotoluene and toluene of density equal to 1. A long exposure time is necessary to avoid distortion of the pictures due to motion of the upper liquid.

Refraction. In the Sunatani, Matayama, Hatamura[29] apparatus, a source of light carried on a stand, movable in two directions at right angles, is placed directly below the glass jar, and a ray of light, after entering the jar vertically and passing through the electrolyte, is refracted at the meniscus surface and again at the free surface of the upper liquid, striking a photographic plate placed above the apparatus (Fig. 16-15). The horizontal shift

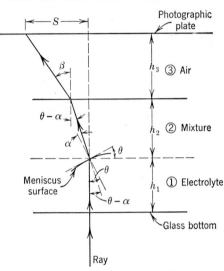

FIG. 16-17. Optical Path through Sunatani, Matuyama, and Hatamura Apparatus

of the image of the light source due to the two refractions is proportional to the slope of the meniscus and takes place in a direction perpendicular to the contours of the meniscus as is here shown.

Calling μ_{12} the index of refraction in passing from the electrolyte to the upper mixture, μ_{23} the index of refraction in passing from the mixture to air, h_2 the vertical distance between the meniscus and the free surface of the mixture, h_3 the distance between the photographic plate and the free level of the mixture, we have, with the symbols of Fig. 16-17 and assuming the angles of incidence and refraction to be small:

$$\frac{\theta}{\alpha} = \mu_{12} = \frac{1}{\mu_{21}} \qquad \frac{\theta - \alpha}{\beta} = \mu_{23} = \frac{1}{\mu_{32}}$$

$$\beta = \mu_{32}(\theta - \alpha) = \mu_{32}\theta - \mu_{32}\alpha = \mu_{32}(1 - \mu_{21})\theta$$

Then, the shift S is given by

$$S = h_2(\theta - \alpha) + h_3\beta = h_2(1 - \mu_{21})\theta + h_3(1 - \mu_{21})\mu_{32}\theta$$

$$= (1 - \mu_{21})(h_2 + \mu_{32}h_3)\theta$$

When the elevations of the meniscus over its boundary are small in comparison with the distance between the boundary and the free level of the mixture, h_2 is practically constant.   Letting

$$K = (1 - \mu_{21})(h_2 + \mu_{32}h_3)$$

we obtain

$$S = K\theta$$

The two liquids chosen have very different refractive indices in order to magnify the shift.   Also, the shifts can be enlarged to any desired size by varying the distance of the camera from the meniscus.

When pressure experiments are performed, light is first flashed at the corners of a square grid with a flat meniscus, so that the rays remain vertical for lack of refraction and have zero shifts.   The meniscus is then formed, and light is flashed again at the same points.   The photographic plate thus contains a direct record of the shifts at every corner of the grid.   On a circular membrane used for comparison, the error in the shifts was found to be only 0.2 per cent.

When zero-pressure experiments are performed, light is first flashed without liquids in the jar and then with liquids, obtaining as before a direct point by point photograph of the shifts, that is, of the meniscus slopes.

A technique was also developed for obtaining data for all points simultaneously by photographing a grid of lines ruled on a glass plate placed in the jar under the ordinate wall.

(c) *Measurement of Volume.*   The volume can be measured directly by draining the liquid from inside the wall into a burette until the meniscus is horizontal (this can be checked by means of the optical system since, with a horizontal meniscus, there is no shift due to slope).

(d) *Advantages of the Meniscus Method.*   1. The meniscus surface has no weight and, therefore, leads to an increased accuracy by avoiding the error due to membrane sag and by allowing the use of larger models.

2. The meniscus surface lasts indefinitely and maintains its shape unaltered, without large changes in volume due to temperature variations or vibrations due to air instability.

3. The shifts, measuring the slopes, can be magnified optically to any required degree, without increasing the actual slopes of the meniscus.

The meniscus method seems, therefore, to present very definite advantages in comparison with the soap-film method.

H. Electric Potential in a Thin Plate of Constant Thickness

The distribution of steady-state potential V in a thin plate of constant thickness is governed by the differential equation:

$$\frac{\partial^2 V}{\partial x^2} + \frac{\partial^2 V}{\partial y^2} = 0 \tag{111}$$

where the coordinate plane x, y is coincident with the plane of the plate.[32]

The similarity of equation 111 to equation 38 is the basis for the analogy between the torsion problem expressed in terms of the function ψ (article 6) and the static potential problem in the plate, while the similarity of equation 111 to equation 29 is the basis for the analogy between the bending problem expressed in terms of the function φ (article 5) and the static potential problem in the plate.

To complete the analogies, the boundaries of the plate must be of such shape and held at such voltages that the properties of V on the boundaries will be similar to those required of φ or ψ by their boundary and single-valuedness conditions.

Hence, what has been said of the membrane functions ζ can be repeated word for word for the V function, and the reader is referred to sections E and F of this chapter for a detailed discussion of the theory of these analogies.

I. The Technique of Measurement of Two-Dimensional Potential Fields

The necessity for measurement of a two-dimensional static potential distribution arises in many branches of physics, and the literature on the subject is extensive. Although in the past many experimenters have used metal

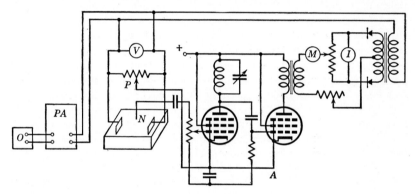

Fig. 16-18.   Electric Circuit of Philips Electrolytic Tank for the Solution of Laplace's Equation

plates, whose boundaries were kept at given potentials, it is now customary to use an electrolytic tank of constant depth.

A typical modern electrolytic tank[33] has dimensions of the order of several square feet and is filled with tap water (whose electric conductivity is ample). The bottom of the tank, and such portions of its boundaries as require it, are insulated with a coat of paraffin, whereas the boundary electrodes are made of copper, sand-blasted (whenever needed) to keep them clean in order to reduce contact resistance.

As shown in Fig. 16-18, the supply voltage is provided by a 400-cps oscillator O feeding into a power amplifier PA. Alternating current is used in order to avoid decomposition of the electrolyte. The voltage at a point in the tank relative to the lowest electrode voltage is measured by a needle probe N connected to the sliding contact of a potentiometer P.   The probe and the sliding contact are two opposite junctions of a Wheatstone bridge whose unbalance is amplified.   In this way a fairly precise measure of the probe voltage is obtained.   The potentiometer used can be read to four significant figures.   An output meter M on the amplifier A indicates a balance in the bridge circuit.

In practice, it is not possible to find a point of zero output, owing to a phase shift between the probe voltage and the potentiometer voltage.   This phase shift reduces the accuracy with which the point of minimum output can be located.   To avoid this difficulty and to improve the accuracy of the meter, a phase indicator I is added, whose pointer indicates zero when the phase difference between the supply voltage and the voltage to be measured passes through 90° and, thus, when the part of the probe potential which is in phase equals the potential of the potentiometer.

The phase indicator being very sensitive, the amplifier's output meter is first roughly adjusted, and the phase indicator is set to zero by a vernier adjustment of the potentiometer.

The probe electrode is supported on a frame, movable in two directions at right angles, by means of a mount which permits the rotation of the probe about a vertical axis and also permits a lateral displacement of 0.5 mm to either side of its central position.   By rotating the mount, the orientation of the needle can be found for which the small lateral displacement will produce no change in voltage.   This position locates the direction of the equipotential line through the point, while a rotation of 90° gives the orientation of the flow lines and allows the measurement of the maximum potential gradient. The recording of the point and the drawing of equipotential lines are performed by means of a pantograph which can be made to mark a sheet of paper. Motion of the frame carrying the probe in one direction can be obtained by means of an electric motor.   By moving the probe by hand in the other direction, while keeping the meter reading at zero, equipotential lines can be drawn directly.   An accuracy of 1 per cent in the measurement of the field can be obtained.

A detailed description of a simpler setup used in connection with a Manganin plate is given in reference 34.

II. ELECTRICAL ANALOGIES FOR THE TORSION OF BARS OF VARYING CIRCULAR SECTION

The components of shearing stress in a solid or hollow bar of varying circular section, twisted by terminal couples, may be expressed in terms of a function of the coordinates of points in the bar.   This function satisfies the same differential equation as that which governs the static electric potential in a thin homogeneous plate of varying thickness.   Measurements of electric potential in the plate give complete information on the state of stress in the bar.

Refer the bar to a system of cylindrical coordinates with the z axis coincident with the axis of the bar and r, θ measured in the radial and tangential directions, respectively (Fig. 16-19). Two equal and opposite couples M_z are applied to the end faces of the bar about the z axis.

In accordance with the semi-inverse method of Saint-Venant, the state of stress in the bar is assumed to be

$$\sigma_r = \sigma_\theta = \sigma_z = \tau_{rz} = 0 \tag{112}$$

$$\tau_{r\theta} = F_1(r, z) \tag{113}$$

$$\tau_{\theta z} = F_2(r, z) \tag{114}$$

If the functions F_1 and F_2 can be determined so that the components of stress (equations 112 to 114) satisfy the equations of equilibrium, the boundary conditions and the conditions of compatibility, these stresses will be the true stresses in the bar. In this case the sufficiency conditions for single-valuedness of displacements are identically satisfied if we exclude complete annular cavities. With equations 112 to 114, all but one of the equilibrium equations in cylindrical coordinates (reference 10, p 277) are found to be satisfied. The remaining equation reduces to

$$\frac{\partial}{\partial r} (r^2\tau_{r\theta}) + \frac{\partial}{\partial z} (r^2\tau_{\theta z}) = 0 \tag{115}$$

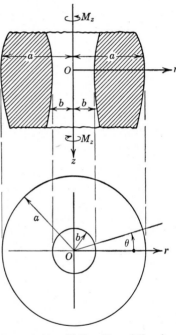

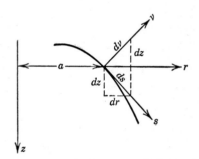

FIG. 16-19. Hollow Bar of Varying
Circular Section

FIG. 16-20. Coordinates at a Point on the
Boundary of a Meridional Section

By means of equations 112 to 114, the boundary conditions on the lateral surfaces of the bar (reference 10, p 278) reduce to

$$\tau_{r\theta}l + \tau_{\theta z}m = 0 \tag{116}$$

where (Fig. 16-20)

$$l = \cos (r, \nu) = \frac{dr}{d\nu} = \frac{dz}{ds} = \cos (z, s) \tag{117}$$

$$m = \cos (z, \nu) = \frac{dz}{d\nu} = -\frac{dr}{ds} = -\cos (r, s) \tag{118}$$

while the compatibility conditions in terms of stresses (Appendix I, equations 35) are also found to be all satisfied but one, which reduces to

$$\frac{\partial}{\partial r}\left(\frac{\tau_{\theta z}}{r}\right) - \frac{\partial}{\partial z}\left(\frac{\tau_{r\theta}}{r}\right) = 0 \tag{119}$$

J. MICHELL'S SOLUTION[41]

23. Components of Stress. By taking

$$\tau_{r\theta} = -\frac{1}{r^2}\frac{\partial\varphi}{\partial z} \tag{120}$$

$$\tau_{\theta z} = \frac{1}{r^2}\frac{\partial\varphi}{\partial r} \tag{121}$$

where φ is a function of r and z only, the equilibrium condition (equation 115) is satisfied identically.

24. Boundary Conditions. Substituting equations 120 and 121 in equation 116, the boundary condition reduces to

$$\frac{\partial\varphi}{\partial s} = 0 \text{ on each boundary} \tag{122}$$

If the external and internal radii of the cross section of the bar at a depth z are called $a(z)$ and $b(z)$, equation 122 is equivalent to

$$\varphi(a, z) = k_1 \tag{123}$$

$$\varphi(b, z) = k_2 \tag{124}$$

where k_1 and k_2 are constants. It can be verified that the resultant forces and couples on any cross section of the bar are identically zero except for a couple about the z axis, which is given by

$$M_z = \int_b^a 2\pi r^2 \tau_{\theta z}\, dr = 2\pi \int_b^a \frac{\partial\varphi}{\partial r}\, dr$$

$$= 2\pi[\varphi(a, z) - \varphi(b, z)] = 2\pi(k_1 - k_2) \tag{125}$$

25. Compatibility Condition. If we make use of equations 120 and 121, the compatibility condition (equation 119) becomes

$$\frac{\partial}{\partial r}\left(\frac{1}{r^3}\frac{\partial\varphi}{\partial r}\right) + \frac{\partial}{\partial z}\left(\frac{1}{r^3}\frac{\partial\varphi}{\partial z}\right) = 0 \tag{126a}$$

or

$$\frac{\partial^2\varphi}{\partial r^2} - \frac{3}{r}\frac{\partial\varphi}{\partial r} + \frac{\partial^2\varphi}{\partial z^2} = 0 \tag{126b}$$

The differential equation 126 and the boundary conditions for each point of the boundary (equation 122) determine the function φ for the bar.

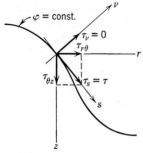

The resultant shearing stress τ at any point on a meridional section of the bar acts along the contour $\varphi = $ const through that point. This may be seen by calculating the value of the shearing stress along the normal ν to the contour (Fig. 16-21):

$$\tau_\nu = \tau_{r\theta} \cos (r, \nu) + \tau_{\theta z} \cos (z, \nu)$$

$$= - \frac{1}{r^2} \left(\frac{\partial \varphi}{\partial z} \frac{\partial z}{\partial s} + \frac{\partial \varphi}{\partial r} \frac{dr}{ds} \right)$$

$$= - \frac{1}{r^2} \frac{\partial \varphi}{\partial s} = 0 \qquad (127)$$

Fig. 16-21.   Components of Stress at a Point on a Shear-Stress Line

The magnitude of the resultant shearing stress is

$$\tau = \tau_s = \tau_{r\theta} \cos (r, s) + \tau_{\theta z} \cos (z, s)$$

$$= \frac{1}{r^2} \left(\frac{\partial \varphi}{\partial z} \frac{dz}{d\nu} + \frac{\partial \varphi}{\partial r} \frac{dr}{d\nu} \right)$$

$$= \frac{1}{r^2} \frac{\partial \varphi}{\partial \nu} \qquad (128)$$

The lines $\varphi = $ const are called *shear-stress lines*.

K. ALTERNATIVE SOLUTION OF MICHELL'S PROBLEM[42]

26. Components of Stress. The stresses in the twisted bar can also be expressed in terms of another function ψ, of r and z, by assuming

$$\tau_{r\theta} = Gr \frac{\partial \psi}{\partial r} \qquad (129)$$

$$\tau_{\theta z} = Gr \frac{\partial \psi}{\partial z} \qquad (130)$$

27. Equilibrium and Compatibility Conditions. When we substitute equations 129 and 130 in equation 115, the latter reduces to

$$\frac{\partial}{\partial r} \left(r^3 \frac{\partial \psi}{\partial r} \right) + \frac{\partial}{\partial z} \left(r^3 \frac{\partial \psi}{\partial z} \right) = 0 \qquad (131a)$$

or

$$\frac{\partial^2 \psi}{\partial r^2} + \frac{3}{r} \frac{\partial \psi}{\partial r} + \frac{\partial^2 \psi}{\partial z^2} = 0 \qquad (131b)$$

while by the same substitution it may be seen that the compatibility condition (equation 119) is satisfied identically.

28. Boundary Conditions. If we make use of equations 129, 130, 117, and 118, equation 116 becomes

$$Gr \left(\frac{\partial \psi}{\partial r} \frac{dr}{d\nu} + \frac{\partial \psi}{\partial z} \frac{dz}{d\nu} \right) = 0$$

or

$$Gr \frac{\partial \psi}{\partial \nu} = 0 \tag{132}$$

on each boundary. It can be verified that the resultant forces and couples on any cross section of the bar are identically zero except for a couple about the z axis, which is given by

$$M_z = \int_b^a 2\pi r^2 \tau_{\theta z} \, dr = 2\pi G \int_b^a r^3 \frac{\partial \psi}{\partial z} \, dr \tag{133}*$$

The differential equation 131 and the boundary condition (equation 132) determine the function ψ within a multiplying constant, which can be evaluated by means of equation 133.

The resultant shearing stress at any point in a meridional section of the bar acts at right angles to the contour ψ = const through that point. This may be seen by calculating the shearing stress $\tau_{s'}$, along the direction s' of this contour (Fig. 16-22):

* That M_z is independent of z may be verified by differentiating M_z with respect to z:

$$\frac{1}{2\pi G} \frac{dM_z}{dz} = \int_b^a r^3 \frac{\partial^2 \psi}{\partial z^2} \, dr + r^3 \frac{\partial \psi}{\partial z} \frac{dr}{dz} \Big]_{r=b}^{r=a}$$

$$= -\int_b^a r^3 \frac{\partial^2 \psi}{\partial r^2} \, dr - \int_b^a 3r^2 \frac{\partial \psi}{\partial r} \, dr + r^3 \frac{\partial \psi}{\partial z} \frac{dr}{dz} \Big]_{r=b}^{r=a} \quad \text{(by 131b)}$$

$$= -r^3 \frac{\partial \psi}{\partial r} \Big]_{r=b}^{r=a} + r^3 \frac{\partial \psi}{\partial z} \frac{dr}{dz} \Big]_{r=b}^{r=a} \quad \text{integrating by parts}$$

$$= r^3 \left(\frac{\partial \psi}{\partial z} \frac{dr}{dz} - \frac{\partial \psi}{\partial r} \right) \Big]_{r=b}^{r=a}$$

$$= r^3 \frac{ds}{dz} \left(\frac{\partial \psi}{\partial z} \frac{dr}{ds} - \frac{\partial \psi}{\partial r} \frac{dz}{ds} \right) \Big]_{r=b}^{r=a}$$

$$= -r^3 \frac{ds}{dz} \left(\frac{\partial \psi}{\partial z} \frac{dz}{d\nu} + \frac{\partial \psi}{\partial r} \frac{dr}{d\nu} \right) \Big]_{r=b}^{r=a} \quad \text{(by 117, 118)}$$

$$= -r^3 \frac{ds}{dz} \frac{\partial \psi}{\partial \nu} \Big]_{r=b}^{r=a} = 0 \quad \text{(by 132)}$$

along an equipotential boundary, and

$$\frac{\partial V}{\partial \nu} = 0 \tag{143}$$

along an insulated boundary.

M. Jacobsen's Analogy[43]

If the specific resistance R of the plate material is constant, and the thickness h of the plate is made proportional to x^3, equation 141 reduces to

$$\frac{\partial}{\partial x}\left(x^3 \frac{\partial V}{\partial x}\right) + \frac{\partial}{\partial y}\left(x^3 \frac{\partial V}{\partial y}\right) = 0 \tag{144}$$

The similarity of equations 144 and 131a is the basis for the analogy between the torsion problem expressed in terms of the equiangular function ψ and the steady-flow problem in the plate. To complete the analogy, the boundaries of the plate must have such shape and be held in such conditions that the properties of V will be similar to those required of ψ by the boundary conditions.

Let the linear-geometrical scale rates of lengths in the meridional section of the twisted bar to the corresponding lengths in the plate be λ and let the x, y plane coincide with the r, z plane.

The end boundaries of the plate (*assumed to coincide with the two equiangular lines bounding the ends of the meridional section of the bar**) are held at a constant-potential difference, while the lateral boundaries are insulated. The potential V in the plate will satisfy equation 144 and the boundary condition (equation 143) along the lateral boundaries of the plate. Hence, by equation 132, the value of the function ψ at a point r, z in the meridional section of the bar is proportional to the voltage V at the point $x = r/\lambda$, $y = z/\lambda$ of the plate:

$$\psi(r, z) = \Upsilon V(x, y) \tag{145}$$

The constant of proportionality Υ may be determined by means of equation 133:

$$M_z = 2\pi G \int_b^a r^3 \frac{\partial \psi}{\partial z} \, dr = \Upsilon \lambda^3 2\pi G \int_B^A x^3 \frac{\partial V}{\partial y} \, dx$$

where $A = a/\lambda$, $B = b/\lambda$, from which

$$\Upsilon = \frac{1}{2\pi G \lambda^3} \frac{M_z}{\displaystyle\int_B^A x^3 \frac{\partial V}{\partial y} \, dx} \tag{146}$$

* If the end sections are not shaped like the true equiangular lines, the results will be in error by an amount and to an extent which will depend on both the end shape and the shape of the meridional section (see article 31).

From equations 139 and 145, the resultant shear stress at a point is

$$\tau = \Upsilon G x \frac{\partial V}{\partial s_1} \tag{147}$$

where s_1 is the direction of the flow line at the point.

The ratio of the shear stresses at two points P_1, P_2 in the bar is given by

$$\frac{\tau_{P_1}}{\tau_{P_2}} = \frac{x \dfrac{\partial V}{\partial s_1}\Big]_{P_1}}{x \dfrac{\partial V}{\partial s_1}\Big]_{P_2}} \tag{148}$$

N. Thum and Bautz's Analogy[44]

If the specific resistance R of the plate material is constant and the thickness h is made inversely proportional to x^3 equation 141 reduces to

$$\frac{\partial}{\partial x}\left(\frac{1}{x^3}\frac{\partial V}{\partial x}\right) + \frac{\partial}{\partial y}\left(\frac{1}{x^3}\frac{\partial V}{\partial y}\right) = 0 \tag{149}$$

The similarity of equations 126a and 149 is the basis for a complete analogy in terms of the stress function φ.

Let the lateral boundaries of the plate be held at constant (but different) potentials, and let the end boundaries (assumed to coincide with two equiangular lines of the bar's meridional section)* be insulated. The potential V in the plate satisfies equation 149 and the boundary conditions

$$V(A,\, y) = V_1 \tag{150} \qquad\qquad V(B,\, y) = V_2 \tag{151}$$

where, as in section M, $A = a/\lambda$, $B = b/\lambda$. Comparison with equations 123 and 124 shows that the value of the function φ at a point (r, z) in the meridional section of the bar is proportional to the potential V at the point $x = r/\lambda$, $y = z/\lambda$ of the plate. Hence:

$$\varphi(r,\, z) = \Upsilon' V(x,\, y) \tag{152}$$

The constant Υ' may be determined by means of equation 125:

$$M_z = 2\pi[\varphi'(a,\, z) - \varphi(b,\, z)] = 2\pi \Upsilon'(V_1 - V_2)$$

from which

$$\Upsilon' = \frac{M_z}{2\pi(V_1 - V_2)} \tag{153}$$

From equations 128 and 152 the resultant shear stress at a point is

$$\tau = \frac{\Upsilon'}{\lambda^3}\frac{1}{x^2}\frac{\partial V}{\partial \nu_1} \tag{154}$$

* See end of article 31.

where ν_1 is the direction perpendicular to the equipotential line at that point. The ratio of the shear-stress resultant at two points P_1, P_2 in the bar is given by

$$\frac{\tau_{P_1}}{\tau_{P_2}} = \frac{x_{P_2}{}^2 \left[\dfrac{\partial V}{\partial \nu_1}\right]_{P_1}}{x_{P_1}{}^2 \left[\dfrac{\partial V}{\partial \nu_1}\right]_{P_2}} \tag{155}$$

O. ELECTRICAL-ANALOGY TECHNIQUES

30. Jacobsen's Analogy. The first electrical-analogy experiments on torsion of axially symmetrical shafts were performed in 1925 by Jacobsen[43] who used his analogy in determining the stress-concentration factor for circular shafts of two diameters connected by a circular fillet (Fig. 16-23).

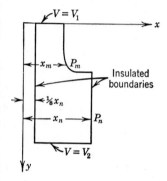

FIG. 16-23. Plan View of Jacobsen's Model

Jacobsen's model was made of a steel plate with one surface flat and the other curved to the cylindrical shape $h = cx^3$. Since it is impractical to make the side $x = 0$ of the model of zero thickness, the steel plate was cut at a distance from the x axis equal to one-eighth of the largest width of the model. The plate thus represents the meridional section of a hollow shaft. To the two ends of the model, straight and perpendicular to the sides, were soldered copper electrodes. These were kept at a constant potential difference. The potential gradient $\partial V/\partial s_1$ along the external side of the model, was measured by means of a sensitive galvanometer, whose terminals were connected to two needles kept 2 mm apart by embedding them in a block of hard rubber.

The ratio of the radius of the bar times the gradient, at the point (P_m) of maximum gradient, to the value of the same product at a point (P_n) distant from the fillet, is the stress-concentration factor as given by equation 148 (see Fig. 16-23).

Since the readings of the galvanometer are influenced by stray currents and thermoelectric effects, ten readings were taken for each point on each side of the model, and calibration readings were taken after each plate reading. A maximum discrepancy of 9 per cent was found between readings taken on two faces of the model at the same point. By taking the average of these two readings, the error in the stress-concentration factor, due to the thickness of the model, was estimated at 5 per cent. Additional errors due to faulty contact, current variation, and observation were estimated at 1.8 per cent.

The following causes of error were not estimated:

1. The shaft under consideration is solid, while the model represents a hollow shaft.

2. The galvanometer readings give the average gradient over a distance of 2 mm and do not measure the peak value of the gradient at the fillet.

3. The ends of the model are straight equipotential lines rather than curves following the equiangular lines of the prototype.

The ends of the model would be straight if the cylindrical portions of the model were infinitely long. This cause of error is important and is considered in article 31.

Jacobsen's results check reasonably with the graphical results of Willers[47] but differ from both the experimental results of Weigand and the theoretical work of Sonntag.

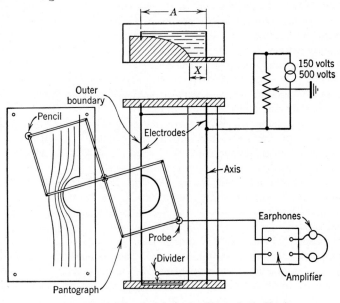

Fig. 16-24.   Thum and Bautz Electrolytic Tank

31. Thum and Bautz's Analogy. In their experiments on stress concentration in shafts of varying diameter, Thum and Bautz[44] used an electrolytic tank made of wood with a paraffin-coated bottom (Fig. 16-24). The sides of the tank were formed by two electrodes with insulated ends. One of the electrodes, representing the axis of the shaft, was straight, and the other curved according to the meridional section to be examined. A fixed potential difference from an a-c source was maintained between the electrodes. The bottom of the tank was curved according to the law $h = c/x^3$ up to a distance X from the side representing the axis of the shaft and was flat from $x = 0$ to $x = X$. Since it is impossible to build a tank of infinite depth, this approximation had to be made. Thum and Bautz assert that the influence of the approximation on the stress determination is negligible, provided X be of the order of one third of the maximum width A of the plate. The tank is filled with tap water.

The equipotential lines were plotted by exploring the field with a point electrode connected to one of the terminals of an earphone. The other terminal of the earphone was connected to a voltage divider and bridge as shown in Fig. 16-24.

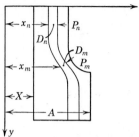

The absence of noise in the earphone indicated that the potential of the field was equal to the previously set unbalance of the bridge. The position of the exploring electrode was located on a piece of paper by means of a pantograph. Thus, by moving the electrode so as to keep the earphone noise at a minimum, a contour of constant potential was traced.

In order to determine the stress-concentration factor along the outer boundary of the shaft, the normal gradient $\partial V/\partial \nu_1$ must be measured at the point of maximum stress and at a point removed from it, according to equation 155.

FIG. 16-25. Measurements Required for Thum and Bautz Extrapolation Procedure for Determining Stress-Concentration Factor

To this end the normal distances D_m and D_n between two equipotential lines at their point of closest approach P_m and at a point P_n, where they are practically parallel to the sides of the model, are measured, as well as the radii x_m and x_n (see Fig. 16-25). The stress-concentration factor k is obtained by plotting the curve:

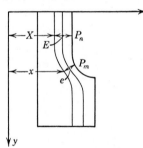

$$\alpha = \frac{x_n{}^2 D_m}{x_m{}^2 D_n} \qquad (156)$$

versus x_m and extrapolating to the boundary.

This method of computing k is affected by a rather large extrapolation error, which can be reduced by using the following procedure, due to K. M. Saul.[46] If e and E are called the distances from the lateral boundary, measured along the normal to the equipotential lines, of the same equipotential line in the stress-concentration region and away from it (Fig. 16-26), and it is remembered that the boundary is an equipotential line, the stress-concentration factor becomes

FIG. 16-26. Measurements Required for Saul Extrapolation Procedure for Determining Stress-Concentration Factor

$$k = \frac{x^2}{X^2} \lim_{e \to 0} \left(\frac{E}{e}\right) \qquad (157)$$

where x and X are the radial distances of the equipotential line from the axis.

In Fig. 16-27 the distances E are plotted versus the corresponding distances e for various equipotential lines. The limit appearing in equation 157 is the slope of the tangent to the curve E at the origin. This slope ($\tan \theta_0$) can be evaluated rather accurately and gives the stress-concentration factor,

$$k = \frac{x^2}{X^2} \tan \theta_0 \qquad (158)$$

which is more accurate than the factor obtained by extrapolating equation 156.

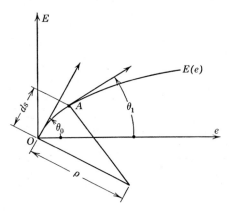

FIG. 16-27. Graphical Construction Used in Saul and Solet Extrapolation Procedures

G. Solet[46] showed that there is an error of about 5 per cent in locating the tangent to the E curve at the origin by Saul's extrapolation, mainly because the E curve is defined at the right of the origin only, and because meniscus effects change the depth of the tank in the neighborhood of the lateral boundary, where the depth is smallest.

The extrapolation can be improved as follows:

Consider (Fig. 16-27) a point A on the E curve, a short distance ds from the origin along the curve. Calling θ the angle between the tangent to E at A and the e axis, and ρ the radius of curvature of the arc ds we have

$$d\theta = \theta_0 - \theta_1 = \frac{ds}{\rho}$$

and

$$\tan \theta_0 - \tan \theta_1 \approx d \tan \theta$$
$$= (1 + \tan^2 \theta_1) \, d\theta$$

from which

$$\tan \theta_0 = \tan \theta_1 + (1 + \tan^2 \theta_1) \frac{ds}{\rho} \qquad (159)$$

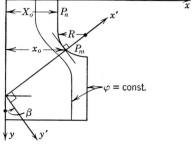

FIG. 16-28. Measurements Required in Solet Extrapolation Procedure

With the symbols of Fig. 16-28, it can be proved that

$$\frac{1}{\rho} = \left(\frac{1}{R} + \frac{3 \cos \beta}{x_0} \right) \sin \theta_0 \cos^2 \theta_0 - \frac{3}{X_0} \sin^2 \theta_0 \cos \theta_0 \qquad (160)$$

In order to determine k, a point A is chosen on the E curve, and the tangent to the curve at A is drawn, determining $\tan \theta_1$. This can be done very accurately because the curve E is defined at both the right and left of A. Then $\tan \theta_0$ is roughly evaluated from the same graph and $1/\rho$ is computed by equation 160. By measuring ds on the curve E, an improved value of tan θ_0 is then obtained by means of equation 159. The error in the determination of tan θ_0 is thus reduced to 2 to 3 per cent.

The advantages of the Thum and Bautz method over Jacobsen's are the following:

1. The Thum and Bautz method does not require a measure of the potential but only the drawing of equipotential lines.

2. The point of maximum stress can be easily located in the fillet region.

3. When Saul's extrapolation is used, an error in the thickness of the tank gives errors of the second order in k.

4. It is easier to change the shape of the model.

One of the main causes of error in both methods is due to the assumption, made in the theory but not satisfied in the experiments, that the shaft terminates with equiangular surfaces. In the experiments, the ends of the model are flat, corresponding to equiangular surfaces for a *cylindrical* shaft.

In order to investigate this source of error, Solet[46] determined the stress-concentration factors for a shaft with a semicircular notch (radius R) varying the ratio of the length L to the width W of the tank:

L/R	6	8	12	∞
L/W	$\frac{3}{4}$	1	1.5	∞
k	1.75	1.64	1.58	1.50

(The last result was obtained by measuring the distance between two equipotential lines in the model of a circular cylindrical shaft.) It is seen from the foregoing results that the influence of the ratio L/W on k is considerable and that large ratios must be used in the experiment to obtain correct values of the theoretical stress-concentration factor.

Solet compared his stress-concentration factors and those of Thum and Bautz with those obtained by direct experimental strain measurements. The results of Solet, derived by means of a long tank were 2 to 3 per cent off; those of Thum and Bautz were off by more than 15 per cent.

III. TWO-DIMENSIONAL STRESS AND STRAIN

Several types of two-dimensional stress distributions, which are difficult to investigate by direct strain measurement or model analysis, have analogues that can be handled easily experimentally. Most of these analogies become evident when the general formulation of the two-dimensional stress problem is studied, in terms of the Airy stress function.[48] This function takes its simplest form for the case of plane strain.

P. PLANE STRAIN

32. Strain-Displacement–Stress-Temperature Relations. The state of plane strain may be defined by setting the component w, of the displacement, equal to zero and restricting the components u and v of the displacement to be functions of the coordinates x and y only (see Appendix I, article 8). When this is done, the relations connecting components of strain, displace-

ment, and stress and temperature, in a homogeneous, isotropic elastic body,
become

$$\epsilon_x = \frac{\partial u}{\partial x} = \frac{1}{E}\left[(1 - \mu^2)\sigma_x - \mu(1 + \mu)\sigma_y\right] + (1 + \mu)\alpha\theta \qquad (161)$$

$$\epsilon_y = \frac{\partial v}{\partial y} = \frac{1}{E}\left[(1 - \mu^2)\sigma_y - \mu(1 + \mu)\sigma_x\right] + (1 + \mu)\alpha\theta \qquad (162)$$

$$\gamma_{xy} = \frac{\partial v}{\partial x} + \frac{\partial u}{\partial y} = \frac{2(1 + \mu)}{E}\tau_{xy} \qquad (163)$$

also

$$\tau_{yz} = \tau_{zx} = \gamma_{yz} = \gamma_{zx} = \epsilon_z = 0 \qquad (164)$$

$$\sigma_z = \mu(\sigma_x + \sigma_y) - E\alpha\theta \qquad (165)$$

where the symbols α and θ are, respectively, the coefficient of linear thermal
expansion and the temperature in excess of a uniform initial temperature.
These are the relations existing in what H. M. Westergaard[50] has called a
constrained slice, that is, a slice of a cylindrical body bounded by parallel planes
(normal to the axis of the cylinder) which are not free to warp. The loading
on the slice is everywhere parallel to the bounding planes and does not vary
through the thickness (or varies only symmetrically with respect to the middle
plane and to a moderate degree).

33. Airy's Function and the Equations of Equilibrium.   When the components of stress are expressed in terms of Airy's stress function φ and a body
force potential V by

$$\sigma_x = \frac{\partial^2\varphi}{\partial y^2} + V \qquad (166)$$

$$\sigma_y = \frac{\partial^2\varphi}{\partial x^2} + V \qquad (167)$$

$$\tau_{xy} = -\frac{\partial^2\varphi}{\partial x\,\partial y} \qquad (168)$$

the equations of equilibrium are satisfied identically (see Appendix I,
equations 20).

34. Conditions on φ at a Point on the Boundary.   If equation 164 is taken
into account, the boundary conditions at a point on a cylindrical surface of
the slice become

$$\bar{X} = \sigma_x l + \tau_{xy} m \qquad \bar{Y} = \tau_{xy} l + \sigma_y m \qquad (169)$$

where

$$l = \frac{dy}{ds} \qquad m = -\frac{dx}{ds} \qquad (170)$$

(see Fig. 16-2). Hence,

$$\bar{X} = \left(\frac{\partial^2 \varphi}{\partial y^2} + V\right)\frac{dy}{ds} + \frac{\partial^2 \varphi}{\partial x \, \partial y}\frac{dx}{ds} = \frac{\partial}{\partial s}\left(\frac{\partial \varphi}{\partial y}\right) + Vl \qquad (171)$$

$$\bar{Y} = -\left(\frac{\partial^2 \varphi}{\partial x^2} + V\right)\frac{dx}{ds} - \frac{\partial^2 \varphi}{\partial x \, \partial y}\frac{dy}{ds} = -\frac{\partial}{\partial s}\left(\frac{\partial \varphi}{\partial x}\right) + Vm \qquad (172)$$

Integrating along a boundary, we have

$$\frac{\partial \varphi}{\partial x} = -\int_0^s \bar{Y}\,ds + \int_0^s Vm\,ds + \alpha_i \qquad (173)$$

$$\frac{\partial \varphi}{\partial y} = \int_0^s \bar{X}\,ds - \int_0^s Vl\,ds + \beta_i \qquad (174)$$

where α_i and β_i are constants. If the slice is multiply connected, α_i and β_i will, in general, be different for each boundary C_i $(i = 0, 1, 2, \cdots, n)$. If the boundary and body-force loadings $(\bar{X}, \bar{Y}, V)$ are known, the functions of s,

$$A_i = -\int_0^s \bar{Y}\,ds + \int_0^s Vm\,ds \qquad (i = 0, 1, 2, \cdots, n) \qquad (175)$$

$$B_i = \int_0^s \bar{X}\,ds - \int_0^s Vl\,ds \qquad (i = 0, 1, 2, \cdots, n) \qquad (176)$$

are also known for each point of each boundary.

Multiplying equation 173 by dx/ds and equation 174 by dy/ds, and adding and integrating along the boundary, we have

$$\varphi_{C_i} = \int_0^s (B_i l - A_i m)\,ds + \alpha_i x + \beta_i y + \gamma_i \qquad (i = 0, 1, 2, \cdots, n) \quad (177)$$

Also, multiplying equation 173 by $dx/d\nu$ and equation 174 by $dy/d\nu$, and adding and noting (see Fig. 16-2) that

$$\frac{dx}{d\nu} = \frac{dy}{ds} = l \qquad \frac{dy}{d\nu} = -\frac{dx}{ds} = m \qquad (178)$$

we have

$$\left.\frac{\partial \varphi}{\partial \nu}\right]_{C_i} = A_i l + B_i m + \alpha_i l + \beta_i m \qquad (i = 0, 1, 2, \cdots, n) \qquad (179)$$

Thus, the boundary stress conditions require that the function φ and its normal derivative $\partial \varphi / \partial \nu$ be specified at each point of each boundary in accordance with equations 177 and 179.

If the slice is simply connected, the values of the constants α_o, β_o, γ_o on the single boundary C_o may be chosen arbitrarily since the addition of a function,

$$\varphi_o = -\alpha_o x - \beta_o y - \gamma_o$$

makes them disappear and does not affect the stresses. In an $(n + 1)$-connected slice, three additional conditions on φ are required for each of n boundaries C_i $(i = 1, 2, 3, \cdots, n)$ in order to determine the $3n$ constants $\alpha_i, \beta_i, \gamma_i$ $(i = 1, 2, 3, \cdots, n)$. These constants are known as Michell's boundary constants.[48]

35. Differential Equation Governing φ. Any function $\varphi(x, y)$ will yield components of stress which satisfy the equations of equilibrium if the components are calculated by equation 166 to 168. More than one set of components of stress, corresponding to different functions φ, can be found that will satisfy the equilibrium equations and a stated set of boundary conditions because the three components of stress $\sigma_x, \sigma_y, \tau_{xy}$ need satisfy only two equilibrium equations. Thus, the equations of statics are not sufficient to determine a unique state of stress; that is, the problem is "statically indeterminate." To find the additional conditions to be satisfied by φ we study the components of displacement.

Consider the line integrals,

$$\int_{C_r} du \qquad \int_{C_r} dv$$

where C_r is any closed curve in the slice. From the first integral, we have

$$\int_{C_r} du = \int_{C_r} \left(\frac{\partial u}{\partial x} dx + \frac{\partial u}{\partial y} dy \right)$$

$$= \int_{C_r} (\epsilon_x \, dx + \tfrac{1}{2}\gamma_{xy} \, dy) - \int_{C_r} \omega_z \, dy \qquad (180)$$

where, by equations 161 to 163,

$$\omega_z = \frac{1}{2}\left(\frac{\partial v}{\partial x} - \frac{\partial u}{\partial y} \right) = \frac{\partial v}{\partial x} - \frac{1}{2}\gamma_{xy} = \frac{1}{2}\gamma_{xy} - \frac{\partial u}{\partial y}$$

Now,

$$\int_{C_r} \omega_z \, dy = y_r \int_{C_r} d\omega_z - \int_{C_r} y \, d\omega_z \qquad (181)$$

where y_r is the y coordinate of the starting point of integration on C_r. But

$$\int_{C_r} d\omega_z = \int_{C_r} \left(\frac{\partial \omega_z}{\partial x} dx + \frac{\partial \omega_z}{\partial y} dy \right)$$

$$= \int_{C_r} \left(\frac{1}{2}\frac{\partial \gamma_{xy}}{\partial x} - \frac{\partial \epsilon_x}{\partial y} \right) dx + \int_{C_r} \left(\frac{\partial \epsilon_y}{\partial x} - \frac{1}{2}\frac{\partial \gamma_{xy}}{\partial y} \right) dy \qquad (182)$$

and, similarly,

$$\int_{C_r} y \, d\omega_z = \int_{C_r} y \left(\frac{1}{2}\frac{\partial \gamma_{xy}}{\partial x} - \frac{\partial \epsilon_x}{\partial y} \right) dx + \int_{C_r} y \left(\frac{\partial \epsilon_y}{\partial x} - \frac{1}{2}\frac{\partial \gamma_{xy}}{\partial y} \right) dy \qquad (183)$$

Hence equation 180 becomes

$$\int_{C_r} du = \int_{C_r} \left[\epsilon_x + (y - y_r) \left(\frac{1}{2} \frac{\partial \gamma_{xy}}{\partial x} - \frac{\partial \epsilon_x}{\partial y} \right) \right] dx$$
$$+ \int_{C_r} \left[\frac{1}{2} \gamma_{xy} + (y - y_r) \left(\frac{\partial \epsilon_y}{\partial x} - \frac{1}{2} \frac{\partial \gamma_{xy}}{\partial y} \right) \right] dy \quad (184)$$

Applying Green's theorem to the right-hand side of equation 184, we have

$$\int_{C_r} du = \int \int_{R_r} (y - y_r) \left(\frac{\partial^2 \epsilon_y}{\partial x^2} + \frac{\partial^2 \epsilon_x}{\partial y^2} - \frac{\partial^2 \gamma_{xy}}{\partial x \partial y} \right) dx\, dy - \sum_i \int_{C_i} du \quad (185)$$

where R_r is the portion of the solid enclosed in C_r, and the summation is taken over all internal boundaries C_i that may be enclosed in C_r (the integrations must be performed in the positive direction of s). Notice that the components of strain, together with their first and second derivatives, are assumed to be continuous.

If the region enclosed in C_r is simply connected, the line integrals on the right-hand side of equation 185 are not present. In that case we see that the condition

$$\frac{\partial^2 \epsilon_y}{\partial x^2} + \frac{\partial^2 \epsilon_x}{\partial y^2} = \frac{\partial^2 \gamma_{xy}}{\partial x\, \partial y} \quad (186)$$

is a necessary and sufficient condition for single-valuedness of the component of displacement u. The same conclusion is reached in considering the component v. Thus, the compatibility condition (equation 186) (see Appendix I, equation 22) is not only a necessary condition for single-valued displacements but, in a simply connected region, or in a simply connected subregion of a multiply connected region, also a sufficient condition.

Adopting the requirement of single-valued displacements in simply connected regions and replacing the components of strain in equation 186 by their expressions in terms of φ, through the use of equations 161 to 163 and 166 to 168, we find

$$\nabla^4 \varphi = - \frac{1 - 2\mu}{1 - \mu} \nabla^2 V - \frac{E}{1 - \mu} \alpha \nabla^2 \theta \quad (187)$$

where

$$\nabla^4 = \nabla^2 \nabla^2 = \left(\frac{\partial^2}{\partial x^2} + \frac{\partial^2}{\partial y^2} \right) \left(\frac{\partial^2}{\partial x^2} + \frac{\partial^2}{\partial y^2} \right)$$

Equation 187 and the boundary conditions,

$$\varphi_{C_o} = \int_0^s (B_o l - A_o m)\, ds$$

$$\left. \frac{\partial \varphi}{\partial \nu} \right]_{C_o} = A_o l + B_o m$$

where A_o and B_o are given by equations 175 and 176, constitute a complete statement of the boundary-value problem of plane strain in a simply connected slice.

36. Displacements in a Multiply Connected Slice.   Examination of equation 185 shows that equation 186 or equation 187 is only a necessary but not a sufficient condition for single-valuedness of u in a multiply connected region. The contributions of the line integrals around all the internal boundaries must be accounted for.   If u is to be single valued, each of

$$\int_{C_i} du \qquad (i = 1, 2, 3, \cdots, n)$$

must vanish separately, since C_r can be taken so as to include any number of the internal boundaries in any combination.   However, it is not necessary physically that u be single valued in a multiply connected slice if we admit the type of displacement known as a *dislocation* (see Fig. 16-29a).   Calling a_i the amplitude of the dislocation in u for the ith boundary, we have

$$a_i = \int_{C_i} du \qquad (i = 1, 2, 3, \cdots, n)$$

$$= \int_{C_i} \left(\frac{\partial u}{\partial x} dx + \frac{\partial u}{\partial y} dy \right)$$

$$= \int_{C_i} (\epsilon_x \, dx + \tfrac{1}{2} \gamma_{xy} \, dy) - \int_{C_i} \omega_z \, dy \qquad (188)$$

but

$$\int_{C_i} \omega_z \, dy = y_i \int_{C_i} d\omega_z - \int_{C_i} y \, d\omega_z \qquad (189)$$

where y_i is the y coordinate of the starting point of integration on the ith boundary.

In equation 189 we have the term,

$$\int_{C_i} d\omega_z$$

which represents a rotational dislocation of the type shown in Fig. 16-29c. Admitting this type of discontinuity, of magnitude c_i, in a multiply connected slice, we write

$$c_i = \int_{C_i} d\omega_z \qquad (i = 1, 2, 3, \cdots, n)$$

$$= \int_{C_i} \left(\frac{1}{2} \frac{\partial \gamma_{xy}}{\partial x} - \frac{\partial \epsilon_x}{\partial y} \right) dx + \int_{C_i} \left(\frac{\partial \epsilon_y}{\partial x} - \frac{1}{2} \frac{\partial \gamma_{xy}}{\partial y} \right) dy \qquad (190)$$

Noting that

$$\int_{C_i} y \, d\omega_z = \int_{C_i} y \left(\frac{\partial \omega_z}{\partial x} \, dx + \frac{\partial \omega_z}{\partial y} \, dy \right)$$

$$= \int_{C_i} y \left(\frac{1}{2} \frac{\partial \gamma_{xy}}{\partial x} - \frac{\partial \epsilon_x}{\partial y} \right) dx + \int_{C_i} y \left(\frac{\partial \epsilon_y}{\partial x} - \frac{1}{2} \frac{\partial \gamma_{xy}}{\partial y} \right) dy$$

we can write equation 188 as

$$a_i + y_i c_i = \int_{C_i} \left[\epsilon_x + y \left(\frac{1}{2} \frac{\partial \gamma_{xy}}{\partial x} - \frac{\partial \epsilon_x}{\partial y} \right) \right] dx$$

$$+ \int_{C_i} \left[\frac{1}{2} \gamma_{xy} + y \left(\frac{\partial \epsilon_y}{\partial x} - \frac{1}{2} \frac{\partial \gamma_{xy}}{\partial y} \right) \right] dy \qquad (i = 1, 2, 3, \cdots, n) \quad (191)$$

Similarly, considering the displacement component V, we find

$$b_i - x_i c_i = \int_{C_i} \left[\frac{1}{2} \gamma_{xy} - x \left(\frac{1}{2} \frac{\partial \gamma_{xy}}{\partial x} - \frac{\partial \epsilon_x}{\partial y} \right) \right] dx$$

$$+ \int_{C_i} \left[\epsilon_y - x \left(\frac{\partial \epsilon_y}{\partial x} - \frac{1}{2} \frac{\partial \gamma_{xy}}{\partial y} \right) \right] dy \qquad (i = 1, 2, 3, \cdots, n) \quad (192)$$

where x_i is the x coordinate of the starting point of integration on the ith boundary and b_i is the amplitude of a translational dislocation of the type shown in Fig. 16-29b.

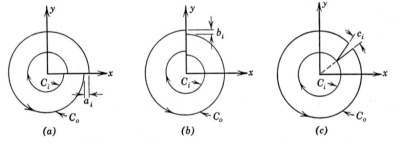

Fig. 16-29.   The Three Fundamental Two-Dimensional Dislocations Illustrated for the Case of a Circular Ring

Equations 190, 191 and 192 constitute $3n$ conditions on the components of strain and, hence, the same number of conditions on φ. These are just the number required to determine the $3n$ boundary constants α_i, β_i, γ_i, $(i = 1, 2, 3, \cdots, n)$. To express these conditions in terms of φ, we have only to replace the strains by their expressions in terms of φ.

37. Rotation Condition.   Replacing the components of strain in equation 190 by their expressions in terms of φ, through equations 161 to 163 and 166 to 168, we have

$$c_i = \frac{1 - \mu^2}{E} \int_{C_i} \left[\frac{\partial}{\partial x} (\nabla^2 \varphi)\, dy - \frac{\partial}{\partial y} (\nabla^2 \varphi)\, dx \right]$$

$$+ \frac{(1 - 2\mu)(1 + \mu)}{E} \int_{C_i} \left(\frac{\partial V}{\partial x}\, dy - \frac{\partial V}{\partial y}\, dx \right)$$

$$+ \alpha(1 + \mu) \int_{C_i} \left(\frac{\partial \theta}{\partial x}\, dy - \frac{\partial \theta}{\partial y}\, dx \right)$$

Hence,

$$\int_{C_i} \frac{\partial (\nabla^2 \varphi)}{\partial \nu}\, ds = \frac{E c_i}{1 - \mu^2} - \frac{1 - 2\mu}{1 - \mu} \int_{C_i} \frac{\partial V}{\partial \nu}\, ds - \frac{E \alpha}{1 - \mu} \int_{C_i} \frac{\partial \theta}{\partial \nu}\, ds$$

$$(i = 1, 2, 3, \cdots, n) \quad (193)$$

This is the first of Michell's three conditions on φ for each internal boundary of the slice.

38. Displacement Conditions. Referring to equation 191 we note that, integrating by parts,

$$\int_{C_i} \left(\epsilon_x\, dx + \frac{1}{2} \gamma_{xy}\, dy \right) = [x \epsilon_x]_0^0 + \frac{1}{2} [y \gamma_{xy}]_0^0 - \int_{C_i} \left(x \frac{\partial \epsilon_x}{\partial x}\, dx + \frac{1}{2} y \frac{\partial \gamma_{xy}}{\partial y}\, dy \right)$$

$$- \int_{C_i} \left(x \frac{\partial \epsilon_x}{\partial y}\, dy + \frac{1}{2} y \frac{\partial \gamma_{xy}}{\partial x}\, dx \right)$$

$$= - \int_{C_i} \left(x \frac{\partial \epsilon_x}{\partial x}\, dx + \frac{1}{2} y \frac{\partial \gamma_{xy}}{\partial y}\, dy \right)$$

$$- \int_{C_i} \left(x \frac{\partial \epsilon_x}{\partial y}\, dy + \frac{1}{2} y \frac{\partial \gamma_{xy}}{\partial x}\, dx \right)$$

the terms outside the integrals vanishing because of the assumption of continuous strains.

Equation 191 then becomes

$$a_i + y_i c_i = - \int_{C_i} \left(y \frac{\partial \epsilon_x}{\partial y} + x \frac{\partial \epsilon_x}{\partial x} \right) dx + \int_{C_i} y \left(\frac{\partial \epsilon_y}{\partial x} - \frac{\partial \gamma_{xy}}{\partial y} \right) dy$$

$$- \int_{C_i} x \frac{\partial \epsilon_x}{\partial y}\, dy \quad (194)$$

When the strain components in equation 194 are replaced by their expressions in terms of φ, we find

$$\frac{E(a_i + y_i c_i)}{1 + \mu} = (1 - \mu) \int_{C_i} y \left[\frac{\partial}{\partial x} (\nabla^2 \varphi)\, dy - \frac{\partial}{\partial y} (\nabla^2 \varphi)\, dx \right]$$

$$+ (1 - 2\mu) \int_{C_i} y \left(\frac{\partial V}{\partial x}\, dy - \frac{\partial V}{\partial y}\, dx \right) + E \alpha \int_{C_i} y \left(\frac{\partial \theta}{\partial x}\, dy - \frac{\partial \theta}{\partial y}\, dx \right)$$

$$- \int_{C_i} x \left[(1 - \mu) \frac{\partial (\nabla^2 \varphi)}{\partial x} + (1 - 2\mu) \frac{\partial V}{\partial x} + E \alpha \frac{\partial \theta}{\partial x} \right] dx$$

$$+ \int_{C_i} \left(x \frac{\partial^3 \varphi}{\partial x^3}\, dx + y \frac{\partial^3 \varphi}{\partial x\, \partial y^2}\, dy \right) + \int_{C_i} \left(x \frac{\partial^3 \varphi}{\partial x^2\, \partial y}\, dy + y \frac{\partial^3 \varphi}{\partial x^2\, \partial y}\, dx \right) \quad (195)$$

Now, integrating by parts, we get

$$\int_{C_i} \left(x\, \frac{\partial^3 \varphi}{\partial x^3}\, dx + y\, \frac{\partial^3 \varphi}{\partial x\, \partial y^2}\, dy \right) + \int_{C_i} \left(x\, \frac{\partial^3 \varphi}{\partial x^2\, \partial y}\, dy + y\, \frac{\partial^3 \varphi}{\partial x^2\, \partial y}\, dx \right)$$

$$= 2 \left[x\, \frac{\partial^2 \varphi}{\partial x^2} + y\, \frac{\partial^2 \varphi}{\partial x\, \partial y} \right]_0^0 - \int_{C_i} \left(\frac{\partial^2 \varphi}{\partial x^2}\, dx + \frac{\partial^2 \varphi}{\partial x\, \partial y}\, dy \right)$$

$$= - \int_{C_i} \frac{\partial}{\partial s} \left(\frac{\partial \varphi}{\partial x} \right) ds$$

the term outside the integral vanishing because the stresses are continuous. But, from equation 172

$$\frac{\partial}{\partial s} \left(\frac{\partial \varphi}{\partial x} \right) = Vm - \bar{Y}$$

Hence equation 195 may be written:

$$\int_{C_i} \left(y\, \frac{\partial(\nabla^2 \varphi)}{\partial \nu} - x\, \frac{\partial(\nabla^2 \varphi)}{\partial s} \right) ds = \frac{E(a_i + y_i c_i)}{1 - \mu^2}$$

$$- \frac{1 - 2\mu}{1 - \mu} \int_{C_i} \left(y\, \frac{\partial V}{\partial \nu} - x\, \frac{\partial V}{\partial s} \right) ds - \frac{E\alpha}{1 - \mu} \int_{C_i} \left(y\, \frac{\partial \theta}{\partial \nu} - x\, \frac{\partial \theta}{\partial s} \right) ds$$

$$- \frac{1}{1 - \mu} \int_{C_i} (\bar{Y} - Vm)\, ds \qquad (i = 1, 2, 3, \cdots, n) \quad (196)$$

This is Michell's second condition on φ for each internal boundary of the slice.

Similarly, from equation 192 we find

$$\int_{C_i} \left(y\, \frac{\partial(\nabla^2 \varphi)}{\partial s} + x\, \frac{\partial(\nabla^2 \varphi)}{\partial \nu} \right) ds = - \frac{E(b_i - x_i c_i)}{1 - \mu^2}$$

$$- \frac{1 - 2\mu}{1 - \mu} \int_{C_i} \left(y\, \frac{\partial V}{\partial s} + x\, \frac{\partial V}{\partial \nu} \right) ds - \frac{E\alpha}{1 - \mu} \int_{C_i} \left(y\, \frac{\partial \theta}{\partial s} + x\, \frac{\partial \theta}{\partial \nu} \right) ds$$

$$- \frac{1}{1 - \mu} \int_{C_i} (\bar{X} - Vl)\, ds \qquad (i = 1, 2, 3, \cdots, n) \quad (197)$$

which is the last of Michell's three conditions.

39. Recapitulation. The boundary-value problem of plane strain, expressed in terms of Airy's stress function φ, is

$$\nabla^4 \varphi = - \frac{1 - 2\mu}{1 - \mu}\, \nabla^2 V - \frac{E}{1 - \mu}\, \alpha \nabla^2 \theta \qquad (198)$$

$$\varphi_{C_i} = \int_0^s (B_i l - A_i m)\, ds + \alpha_i x + \beta_i y + \gamma_i$$

$$(i = 0, 1, 2, \cdots, n) \quad (199)$$

$$\frac{\partial \varphi}{\partial \nu} \Bigg]_{C_i} = A_i l + B_i m + \alpha_i l + \beta_i m \qquad (i = 0, 1, 2, \cdots, n) \tag{200}$$

$$\int_{C_i} \frac{\partial (\nabla^2 \varphi)}{\partial \nu} \, ds = \frac{E c_i}{1 - \mu^2} - \frac{1 - 2\mu}{1 - \mu} \int_{C_i} \frac{\partial V}{\partial \nu} \, ds - \frac{E\alpha}{1 - \mu} \int_{C_i} \frac{\partial \theta}{\partial \nu} \, ds$$
$$(i = 1, 2, 3, \cdots, n) \quad (201)$$

$$\int_{C_i} \left(y \frac{\partial (\nabla^2 \varphi)}{\partial \nu} - x \frac{\partial (\nabla^2 \varphi)}{\partial s} \right) ds = \frac{E(a_i + y_i c_i)}{1 - \mu^2}$$
$$- \frac{1 - 2\mu}{1 - \mu} \int_{C_i} \left(y \frac{\partial V}{\partial \nu} - x \frac{\partial V}{\partial s} \right) ds - \frac{E\alpha}{1 - \mu} \int_{C_i} \left(y \frac{\partial \theta}{\partial \nu} - x \frac{\partial \theta}{\partial s} \right) ds$$
$$- \frac{1}{1 - \mu} \int_{C_i} (\bar{Y} - Vm) \, ds \qquad (i = 1, 2, 3, \cdots, n) \quad (202)$$

$$\int_{C_i} \left(y \frac{\partial (\nabla^2 \varphi)}{\partial s} + x \frac{\partial (\nabla^2 \varphi)}{\partial \nu} \right) ds = -\frac{E(b_i - x_i c_i)}{1 - \mu^2}$$
$$- \frac{1 - 2\mu}{1 - \mu} \int_{C_i} \left(y \frac{\partial V}{\partial s} + x \frac{\partial V}{\partial \nu} \right) ds - \frac{E\alpha}{1 - \mu} \int_{C_i} \left(y \frac{\partial \theta}{\partial s} + x \frac{\partial \theta}{\partial \nu} \right) ds$$
$$- \frac{1}{1 - \mu} \int_{C_i} (\bar{X} - Vl) \, ds \qquad (i = 1, 2, 3, \cdots, n) \quad (203)$$

Q. Analogy between Free and Constrained Slices

It is possible to construct a *free-slice* analogue of a constrained slice.[50] The free slice has the same cylindrical boundaries as the constrained slice, but the thickness of the free slice should be small, in general, in comparison with its other dimensions.   In addition, the two parallel bounding planes of the free slice must be unstressed and free to warp, and the loading of the slice must be distributed symmetrically across its thickness so that the middle plane of the slice remains plane.   Under these conditions a state of stress is obtained in which, to a close approximation,

$$\sigma_z = \tau_{yz} = \tau_{zx} = 0 \tag{204}$$

where the x, y plane is the middle plane of the free slice.

In general the thinner the slice the better is equation 204 realized; but the necessity for thinness is not great, as good results are obtained even when the thickness exceeds neighboring dimensions at right angles.

The advantage of using a free rather than a constrained slice is that the former usually can be loaded and examined more easily.

40. Strain-Displacement–Stress-Temperature Relations in a Free Slice. If equation 204 is taken account of, the strain-displacement–stress-temperature relations for a free slice become

$$\epsilon_x = \frac{\partial u}{\partial x} = \frac{1}{E} (\sigma_x - \mu \sigma_y) + \alpha \theta \tag{205}$$

$$\epsilon_y = \frac{\partial v}{\partial y} = \frac{1}{E}(\sigma_y - \mu\sigma_x) + \alpha\theta \tag{206}$$

$$\epsilon_z = \frac{\partial w}{\partial z} = -\frac{\mu}{E}(\sigma_x + \sigma_y) + \alpha\theta \tag{207}$$

$$\gamma_{xy} = \frac{\partial v}{\partial x} + \frac{\partial u}{\partial y} = \frac{2(1 + \mu)}{E}\tau_{xy} \tag{208}$$

41. Airy's Stress Function for the Free Slice.   We again express the components of stress in terms of an Airy Stress function φ and a body-force potential V:

$$\sigma_x = \frac{\partial^2\varphi}{\partial y^2} + V \tag{209}$$

$$\sigma_y = \frac{\partial^2\varphi}{\partial x^2} + V \tag{210}$$

$$\tau_{xy} = -\frac{\partial^2\varphi}{\partial x\,\partial y} \tag{211}$$

With these expressions and equation 204, the equations of equilibrium are satisfied identically (see Appendix I, equations 28).

42. Conditions on φ.   In general,[52] all six of the compatibility conditions (Appendix I, equations 34) restrict the function φ under the conditions specified by equation 204, but, when the thickness of the free slice is small, the z dependence of φ is negligible, and only the condition

$$\frac{\partial^2\epsilon_x}{\partial y^2} + \frac{\partial^2\epsilon_y}{\partial x^2} - \frac{\partial^2\gamma_{xy}}{\partial x\,\partial y} = 0 \tag{212}$$

need be used.   Hence, if the relations of articles 40 and 41 are used in equation 212, the differential equation governing φ is found to be

$$\nabla^4\varphi = -(1 - \mu)\nabla^2 V - E\alpha\nabla^2\theta \tag{213}$$

Equation 213 for the free slice replaces equation 187 for the constrained slice as the necessary and sufficient condition for single-valuedness of displacements in simply connected regions and as a necessary condition in multiply connected regions.

In a multiply connected slice the two conditions on φ for each point of each boundary are found in exactly the same manner as in article 34 (for the constrained slice) and have the same form:

$$\varphi_{C_i} = \int_0^s (B_i l - A_i m)\,ds + \alpha_i x + \beta_i y + \gamma_i$$

$$(i = 0, 1, 2, \cdots, n) \tag{214}$$

$$\frac{\partial\varphi}{\partial\nu}\bigg]_{C_i} = A_i l + B_i m + \alpha_i l + \beta_i m \qquad (i = 0, 1, 2, \cdots, n) \tag{215}$$

where

$$A_i = - \int_0^s \bar{Y} \, ds + \int_0^s V m \, ds \qquad (i = 0, 1, 2, \cdots, n) \qquad (216)$$

$$B_i = \int_0^s \bar{X} \, ds - \int_0^s V l \, ds \qquad (i = 0, 1, 2, \cdots, n) \qquad (217)$$

$$\bar{X} = \sigma_x l + \tau_{xy} m \qquad \bar{Y} = \tau_{xy} l + \sigma_y m \qquad (218)$$

Similarly, the three conditions on φ for each internal boundary are

$$\int_{C_i} \frac{\partial(\nabla^2 \varphi)}{\partial \nu} \, ds = E c_i - (1 - \mu) \int_{C_i} \frac{\partial V}{\partial \nu} \, ds - E\alpha \int_{C_i} \frac{\partial \theta}{\partial \nu} \, ds$$
$$(i = 1, 2, 3, \cdots, n) \qquad (219)$$

$$\int_{C_i} \left[y \frac{\partial(\nabla^2 \varphi)}{\partial \nu} - x \frac{\partial(\nabla^2 \varphi)}{\partial s} \right] ds = E(a_i + y_i c_i)$$
$$- (1 - \mu) \int_{C_i} \left(y \frac{\partial V}{\partial \nu} - x \frac{\partial V}{\partial s} \right) ds - E\alpha \int_{C_i} \left(y \frac{\partial \theta}{\partial \nu} - x \frac{\partial \theta}{\partial s} \right) ds$$
$$- (1 + \mu) \int_{C_i} (\bar{Y} - V m) \, ds \qquad (i = 1, 2, 3, \cdots, n) \qquad (220)$$

$$\int_{C_i} \left[y \frac{\partial(\nabla^2 \varphi)}{\partial s} + x \frac{\partial(\nabla^2 \varphi)}{\partial \nu} \right] ds = -E(b_i - x_i c_i)$$
$$- (1 - \mu) \int_{C_i} \left(y \frac{\partial V}{\partial s} + x \frac{\partial V}{\partial \nu} \right) ds - E\alpha \int_{C_i} \left(y \frac{\partial \theta}{\partial s} + x \frac{\partial \theta}{\partial \nu} \right) ds$$
$$- (1 + \mu) \int_{C_i} (\bar{X} - V l) \, ds \qquad (i = 1, 2, 3, \cdots, n) \qquad (221)$$

43. The Analogy. If we compare equations 213 to 221 with the corresponding equations in section P, it may be seen that, if in all the formulas pertaining to the constrained slice, we replace E, μ, and α by $\bar{E}$, $\bar{\mu}$, and $\bar{\alpha}$, where

$$\bar{E} = \frac{E(1 + 2\mu)}{(1 + \mu)^2} \qquad (222)$$

$$\bar{\mu} = \frac{\mu}{1 + \mu} \qquad (223)$$

$$\bar{\alpha} = \frac{\alpha(1 + \mu)}{1 + 2\mu} \qquad (224)$$

the resulting formulas are identical with the corresponding ones for the free slice.

It should be noted that the relations (equations 222 to 224) need be satisfied only in certain cases where the state of stress depends on one or more of the physical properties of the material. These special cases are as follows.

From the differential equation 213 and equations 209 to 211, it may be seen that the components of stress σ_x, σ_y, τ_{xy} will depend on Poisson's ratio when either the body-force potential or the temperature distribution is not harmonic (that is, $\nabla^2 V \neq 0$ or $\nabla^2\theta \neq 0$). An example of a harmonic body-force potential is that of the uniform gravitational attraction of the earth, whereas a nonharmonic body-force potential is illustrated by that of the centrifugal force in a rotating body. A steady-state temperature distribution is harmonic while a nonsteady-state distribution is not harmonic.

It should also be noted that, even if V and θ are harmonic, there may be dependence on Poisson's ratio under the circumstances listed in the following.

From equations 219, 220, and 221 it may be seen that, in a multiply connected slice, the stress will depend on Poisson's ratio if any one of the following line integrals does not vanish (unless, of course, they vanish in the combinations that appear in those equations):

$$\int_{C_i} \bar{X}\,ds \qquad \int_{C_i} \bar{Y}\,ds$$

$$\int_{C_i} \frac{\partial V}{\partial \nu}\,ds \qquad \int_{C_i} \dot{V}l\,ds \qquad \int_{C_i} Vm\,ds$$

$$\int_{C_i} \left(y\frac{\partial V}{\partial \nu} - x\frac{\partial V}{\partial s} \right) ds \qquad \int_{C_i} \left(y\frac{\partial V}{\partial s} + x\frac{\partial V}{\partial \nu} \right) ds$$

The first two of these are the x and y components of the resultant force on the internal boundary C_i. Hence, in a multiply connected slice stressed only by boundary loading, the stress will be independent of the elastic constants if the resultant force on each internal boundary vanishes.

The third integral represents the flux of the body force across the boundary C_i, while the fourth and fifth integrals are the x and y components of the resultant body force on C_i. The last two integrals are nonvanishing only if the body-force potential has singularities inside C_i of the order of a doublet or less.

Again from equations 219 to 221, the stress will depend on both Poisson's ratio and Young's modulus if any one of the following quantities does not vanish (unless they vanish in the combinations that appear in those equations):

$$a_i \qquad b_i \qquad c_i$$

$$\int_{C_i} \frac{\partial \theta}{\partial \nu}\,ds \qquad \int_{C_i} \left(y\frac{\partial \theta}{\partial \nu} - x\frac{\partial \theta}{\partial s} \right) ds \qquad \int_{C_i} \left(y\frac{\partial \theta}{\partial s} + x\frac{\partial \theta}{\partial \nu} \right) ds$$

Hence, if there is a dislocation (a_i, b_i, or c_i) the stress depends on both elastic constants. Also, the first integral represents the total flow of heat across C_i while the second and third integrals are nonvanishing only if the temperature distribution has a singularity inside C_i of the order of a doublet or less.

Finally, if θ is harmonic, and the body is simply connected, the coefficient of expansion does not affect the components of stress σ_x, σ_y, τ_{xy}. In fact, these components have zero values, and the only component of stress that appears is in a constrained slice where, from equation 165,

$$\sigma_z = -E\alpha\theta$$

Most of the foregoing conclusions regarding dependence of stress on elastic and thermal constants were pointed out by M. A. Biot in the papers listed under his name in the bibliography.[53, 54, 55]

R. Analogy between Body Forces and Boundary Loads and Dislocations

44. Formulation of the Analogy. M. A. Biot has shown[53, 54] how a two-dimensional state of stress resulting from body-force loading (for example, the earth's gravitational pull on a structure) can be reproduced by applying boundary loads and in some cases, dislocations. If the body-force potential is harmonic ($\nabla^2 V = 0$) the analogy may be derived from equations 198 to 203 and 166 to 168, in the following manner.

When the stresses are the result of only boundary loadings and a harmonic body-force potential, the equations governing the plane-strain function φ become

$$\nabla^4\varphi = 0 \tag{225}$$

$$\varphi_{C_i} = \int_0^s (B_i l - A_i m)\, ds + \alpha_i x + \beta_i y + \gamma_i$$

$$(i = 0, 1, 2, \cdots, n) \tag{226}$$

$$\frac{\partial \varphi}{\partial \nu}\bigg]_{C_i} = A_i l + B_i m + \alpha_i l + \beta_i m \qquad (i = 0, 1, 2, \cdots, n) \tag{227}$$

$$A_i = -\int_0^s (\bar{Y} - Vm)\, ds \qquad B_i = \int_0^s (\bar{X} - Vl)\, ds \tag{228}$$

$$\int_{C_i} \frac{\partial(\nabla^2\varphi)}{\partial \nu}\, ds = -\frac{1-2\mu}{1-\mu}\int_{C_i} \frac{\partial V}{\partial \nu}\, ds \qquad (i = 1, 2, 3, \cdots, n) \tag{229}$$

$$\int_{C_i}\left(y\frac{\partial(\nabla^2\varphi)}{\partial \nu} - x\frac{\partial(\nabla^2\varphi)}{\partial s}\right) ds = -\frac{1-2\mu}{1-\mu}\int_{C_i}\left(y\frac{\partial V}{\partial \nu} - x\frac{\partial V}{\partial s}\right) ds$$

$$-\frac{1}{1-\mu}\int_{C_i}(\bar{Y} - Vm)\, ds \qquad (i = 1, 2, 3, \cdots, n) \tag{230}$$

$$\int_{C_i}\left(y\frac{\partial(\nabla^2\varphi)}{\partial s} + x\frac{\partial(\nabla^2\varphi)}{\partial \nu}\right) ds = -\frac{1-2\mu}{1-\mu}\int_{C_i}\left(y\frac{\partial V}{\partial s} + x\frac{\partial V}{\partial \nu}\right) ds$$

$$-\frac{1}{1-\mu}\int_{C_i}(\bar{X} - Vl)\, ds \qquad (i = 1, 2, 3, \cdots, n) \tag{231}$$

$$\sigma_x = \frac{\partial^2\varphi}{\partial y^2} + V \tag{232}$$

$$\sigma_y = \frac{\partial^2\varphi}{\partial x^2} + V \tag{233}$$

$$\tau_{xy} = -\frac{\partial^2\varphi}{\partial x\,\partial y} \tag{234}$$

Let us now consider a state of stress in a geometrically similar model, expressed in terms of an Airy function φ', resulting from only boundary loadings and dislocations. Then, identifying quantities pertaining to the model by prime ($'$) or subscript ($_1$) we have

$$\nabla_1{}^4\varphi' = 0 \tag{235}$$

$$\varphi_{c_i}' = \int_0^{s_1} (B_i'l - A_i'm)\, ds_1 + \alpha_i'x_i + \beta_i'y_i + \gamma_i'$$
$$(i = 0, 1, 2, \cdots, n) \tag{236}$$

$$\frac{\partial\varphi'}{\partial\nu_1}\bigg]_{c_i'} = A_i'l + B_i'm + \alpha_i'l + \beta_i'm \qquad (i = 0, 1, 2, \cdots, n) \tag{237}$$

$$A_i' = -\int_0^{s_1} \bar{Y}'\, ds_1 \qquad B_i' = \int_0^{s_1} \bar{X}'\, ds_1 \tag{238}$$

$$\int_{c_i'} \frac{\partial(\nabla_1{}^2\varphi')}{\partial\nu_1}\, ds_1 = \frac{E_1 c_i'}{1 - \mu_1{}^2} \qquad (i = 1, 2, 3, \cdots, n) \tag{239}$$

$$\int_{c_i'} \left(y_1 \frac{\partial(\nabla_1{}^2\varphi')}{\partial\nu_1} - x_1 \frac{\partial(\nabla_1{}^2\varphi')}{\partial s_1} \right) ds_1 = \frac{E_1(a_i' + y_i'c_i')}{1 - \mu_1{}^2}$$
$$- \frac{1}{1 - \mu_1} \int_{c_i'} \bar{Y}'\, ds_1 \qquad (i = 1, 2, 3, \cdots, n) \tag{240}$$

$$\int_{c_i'} \left(y_1 \frac{\partial(\nabla_1{}^2\varphi')}{\partial s_1} + x_1 \frac{\partial(\nabla_1{}^2\varphi')}{\partial\nu_1} \right) ds_1 = \frac{-E_1(b_i' - x_i'c_i')}{1 - \mu_1{}^2}$$
$$- \frac{1}{1 - \mu_1} \int_{c_i'} \bar{X}'\, ds_1 \qquad (i = 1, 2, 3, \cdots, n) \tag{241}$$

$$\sigma_{x_1}' = \frac{\partial^2\varphi'}{\partial y_1{}^2} \quad (242) \qquad \sigma_{y_1}' = \frac{\partial^2\varphi'}{\partial x_1{}^2} \quad (243) \qquad \tau_{x_1y_1}' = -\frac{\partial^2\varphi'}{\partial x_1\,\partial y_1} \quad (244)$$

Let the ratio of lengths in the x, y plane of the prototype to corresponding lengths in the x_1, y_1 plane of the model be λ. Then, comparing equations 225 to 234 with equations 235 to 244, Biot observed that the stress function φ' can be made directly proportional to φ if the boundaries of the model are made geometrically similar to those of the prototype (with scale ratio λ) and if the following relations are satisfied:

(a). *In a simply connected slice:*

$$\bar{X} - Vl = \Upsilon\bar{X}' \qquad \bar{Y} - Vm = \Upsilon\bar{Y}' \tag{245}$$

where Υ is a scale factor for stress.

(b) *In a multiply connected slice*, equation 245 is satisfied on all boundaries, and, in addition, if there is a resultant force on an internal boundary,

$$\mu = \mu_1 \tag{246}$$

Also, dislocations a_i', b_i', c_i' will be required, of magnitudes

$$a_i' = -y_i'c_i' - \frac{(1+\mu)(1-2\mu)}{\Upsilon\lambda E_1} \int_{C_i} \left(y \frac{\partial V}{\partial \nu} - x \frac{\partial V}{\partial s} \right) ds \tag{247}$$

$$b_i' = x_i'c_i' + \frac{(1+\mu)(1-2\mu)}{\Upsilon\lambda E_1} \int_{C_i} \left(y \frac{\partial V}{\partial s} + x \frac{\partial V}{\partial \nu} \right) ds \tag{248}$$

$$c_i' = -\frac{(1+\mu)(1-2\mu)}{\Upsilon E_1} \int_{C_i} \frac{\partial V}{\partial \nu} ds \tag{249}$$

if the integrals in equations 247 to 249 do not vanish. If these conditions are satisfied and if we set

$$\varphi' = \frac{\varphi}{\Upsilon\lambda^2} \tag{250}$$

equations 235 to 244 become identical with equations 225 to 234.

Finally, subtracting equations 242 to 244 from equations 232 to 234, respectively, and using equation 250, we find the following simple relations between the stress in the prototype and the stress in the model:

$$\sigma_x = \Upsilon\sigma_{x_1}' + V \tag{251}$$

$$\sigma_y = \Upsilon\sigma_{y_1}' + V \tag{252}$$

$$\tau_{xy} = \Upsilon\tau_{x_1y_1}' \tag{253}$$

Equations 245, which give the boundary loading to be applied to the model, have a simple physical meaning. The equations state that *the stresses applied to the boundaries of the model shall be everywhere proportional to the sum of the corresponding boundary stresses on the prototype and a normal pressure of magnitude V.*

45. Constrained and Free Slices. The conversion formulas 246 to 249 are for the case where both the prototype and the model are constrained slices. If both prototype and model are free slices, then according to equations 222 to 224, μ should be replaced by $\bar{\mu}$, μ_1 by $\bar{\mu}_1$ and E_1 by $\bar{E}_1$ where

$$\bar{\mu} = \frac{\mu}{1+\mu} \tag{254}$$

$$\bar{\mu}_1 = \frac{\mu_1}{1+\mu_1} \tag{255}$$

$$\bar{E}_1 = \frac{E_1(1+2\mu_1)}{(1+\mu_1)^2} \tag{256}$$

If the prototype is a constrained slice and the model is a free slice (the most likely case), then, in equations 246 to 249, μ_1 and E_1 should be replaced by $\bar{\mu}_1$ and $\bar{E}_1$ where $\bar{\mu}_1$ and $\bar{E}_1$ are again given by equations 255 and 256.

46. Arbitrary Poisson's Ratios in Model and Prototype. It should be observed that Biot's analogy requires a definite relation to exist between the Poisson's ratios of the materials of model and prototype. When both the model and the prototype are constrained slices, or when both are free slices, the Poisson's ratios must be the same (see equation 246). If the prototype is a constrained slice and the model is a free slice, the required relation is

$$\mu = \frac{\mu_1}{1 + \mu_1} \tag{257}$$

It is usually difficult to guess the magnitude of the errors that may be introduced if the required relation is not satisfied. However, Biot's analogy may be altered so that no restriction is placed on the values of Poisson's ratios. To do this it is only necessary to compare, again, equations 225 to 234 with 235 to 244 and observe that we can once more make

$$\varphi' = \frac{\varphi}{\Upsilon \lambda^2}$$

if we set

$$\bar{X} - Vl = \Upsilon \bar{X}' \qquad \bar{Y} - Vm = \Upsilon \bar{Y}' \tag{258}$$

$$c_i' = -\frac{(1 - \mu_1^2)(1 - 2\mu)}{\Upsilon E_1(1 - \mu)} \int_{C_i} \frac{\partial V}{\partial \nu}\, ds \tag{259}$$

$$a_i' = -y_i'c_i' - \frac{(1 - \mu_1^2)(1 - 2\mu)}{\Upsilon \lambda E_1(1 - \mu)} \int_{C_i} \left(y\frac{\partial V}{\partial \nu} - x\frac{\partial V}{\partial s} \right) ds$$
$$- \frac{(\mu - \mu_1)(1 + \mu_1)}{\Upsilon \lambda E_1(1 - \mu)} \int_{C_i} (\bar{Y} - Vm)\, ds \tag{260}$$

$$b_i' = x_i'c_i' + \frac{(1 - \mu_1^2)(1 - 2\mu)}{\Upsilon \lambda E_1(1 - \mu)} \int_{C_i} \left(y\frac{\partial V}{\partial s} + x\frac{\partial V}{\partial \nu} \right) ds$$
$$+ \frac{(\mu - \mu_1)(1 + \mu_1)}{\Upsilon \lambda E_1(1 - \mu)} \int_{C_i} (\bar{X} - Vl)\, ds \tag{261}$$

The following properties of these conversion formulas may be observed:

1. The defect in satisfying Biot's relations between Poisson's ratios is countered by introducing additional dislocations.

2. If the Poisson's ratio relations are satisfied, the additional dislocations disappear, and the formulas 259 to 261 reduce to formulas 247 to 249.

3. The additional integrals in equations 260 and 261 are proportional to the components of the resultant forces on the internal boundaries of the model. If these components vanish, the additional dislocations are not required. If these components do not vanish, their magnitudes can be calculated (from

the known values of $\bar{X}$ and $\bar{Y}$) and an estimate can be made of the errors introduced by ignoring the additional dislocations. Alternatively, the dislocations can be produced physically in the model and the resulting stresses measured.

4. Equations 259 to 261 are written for the case in which both the prototype and model are constrained slices. If this is not the case, the procedure described in article 45 should be followed.

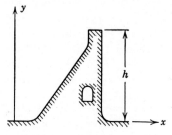

FIG. 16-30.   Section of a Gravity Dam

47. Application to Gravity Stresses. Biot has shown an ingenious application in which the distributed gravity loading of a body's own weight is replaced by fluid pressure on its boundaries. As an example, consider the gravity dam shown in Fig. 16-30. Owing to the gravity's dam's own weight, the body-force components in the dam are $X = 0$, $Y = -\rho g$, where ρ is the density of the material, and g is the gravitational acceleration (both assumed constant). The body-force potential is then $V = \rho gy$, a function for which the integrals in equations 247 to 249 vanish. Hence, no dislocations are required in the model if the body is simply connected or if the Poisson's ratio relation is satisfied in the case of multiply connected bodies. Then, all that is necessary is to apply, to the model, boundary stresses:

$$\bar{X}' = (\bar{X} - \rho gyl)/\Upsilon \tag{262}$$

$$\bar{Y}' = (\bar{Y} - \rho gym)/\Upsilon \tag{263}$$

On the unloaded faces of the prototype, $\bar{X}$ and $\bar{Y}$ are zero. Therefore, the loading on the corresponding faces of the model is a hydrostatic pressure of magnitude ρgy, that is, increasing linearly with y. This may be achieved by inverting the model (constructed to scale λ) and immersing it in a fluid as shown in Fig. 16-31. If the ratio of the density of the model to the density of the fluid is small enough so that stresses due to the former are negligible, the required loading is obtained. If the density of the fluid is

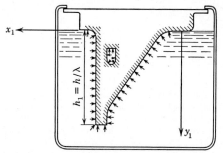

FIG. 16-31.   Model of a Gravity Dam Inverted and Immersed in a Dense Fluid

called ρ_1, the constant Υ is

$$\Upsilon = \frac{\rho\lambda}{\rho_1} \tag{264}$$

Hence, if σ_{x_1}', σ_{y_1}', $\tau_{x_1y_1}'$ are the observed components of stress in the model, the components of stress in the prototype are

$$\sigma_x = \frac{\rho\lambda}{\rho_1}\sigma_{x_1}{}' + \rho g\lambda y_1 \tag{265}$$

$$\sigma_y = \frac{\rho\lambda}{\rho_1}\sigma_{y_1}{}' + \rho g\lambda y_1 \tag{266}$$

$$\tau_{xy} = \frac{\rho\lambda}{\rho_1}\tau_{x_1y_1}{}' \tag{267}$$

The average traction across the base of the model, as a result of the total upward push of the fluid, is equal to $\rho_1/\rho\lambda$ times the average traction on the base of the prototype, but the distributions may be different if the modes of support are not analogous.

It should be observed that, if there is a hole in the model, it must be filled with fluid which is connected with the outside fluid so that hydrostatic equilibrium is maintained between the two. This is necessary in order to satisfy equations 262 and 263 on all boundaries.

48. Poisson's Ratio Correction for Gravity Stresses. If there are holes in the slice, and the Poisson's ratio relation is not satisfied, we must investigate the values of the integrals,

$$\int_{C_i} \frac{\partial V}{\partial \nu}\, ds \qquad \int_{C_i}\left(y\,\frac{\partial V}{\partial \nu} - x\,\frac{\partial V}{\partial s}\right) ds \qquad \int_{C_i}\left(y\,\frac{\partial V}{\partial s} + x\,\frac{\partial V}{\partial \nu}\right) ds$$

$$\int_{C_i} (\bar{X} - Vl)\, ds \qquad \int_{C_i} (\bar{Y} - Vm)\, ds$$

in equations 258 to 261. If the faces of the hole in the prototype are not loaded, $\bar{X}$ and $\bar{Y}$ are zero. Since $V = \rho gy$, all the integrals vanish except the last which becomes

$$-\rho g \int_{C_i} ym\, ds = \rho g A_i$$

where A_i is the area enclosed by the ith hole in the prototype. Hence, the integral is equal to the weight (per unit thickness) of the material of the prototype that is absent from the hole. According to equation 260, the model requires a discontinuity in the displacement u, of magnitude

$$a_i' = \frac{(\mu_1 - \mu)(1 + \mu_1)}{\Upsilon\lambda E_1(1 - \mu)}\,\rho g A_i$$

If equation 264 is used, this becomes

$$a_i' = \frac{(\mu_1 - \mu)(1 + \mu_1)}{E_1(1 - \mu)}\,\rho_1 g A_i'$$

where $A_i' = A_i/\lambda^2$, that is, the area enclosed in the hole in the model. The quantity $\rho_1 g A_i'$ is simply the weight per unit of thickness of the fluid enclosed in the hole in the model.

The required dislocation may be produced in the model by cutting a slit from the outer boundary into the hole and displacing the cut surfaces parallel to the x_1 axis by an amount a_i' as shown in Fig. 16-32.

The stress in the model resulting from the dislocation is to be added to that caused by the fluid pressure. If the magnitude of a_i' and the shape of the slice are known, it is often possible to estimate the magnitude and extent of the dislocation stress without actually performing the experiment.

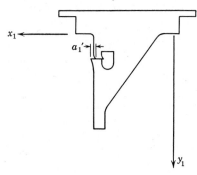

49. Nonharmonic Body-Force Potential. An important case of body-force distribution is that of the centrifugal force in a rotating body. In this case,

$$\nabla^2 V = -2\rho\omega^2$$

where ω is the angular speed, and, hence,

$$\nabla^4\varphi = \frac{2(1 - 2\mu)\rho\omega^2}{1 - \mu}$$

Fig. 16-32. Dislocation Producing State of Stress in Gravity-Dam Model for Poisson's Ratio Correction

Thus, the Airy function for centrifugal stress is not biharmonic. Such a state of stress cannot be replaced by a state of stress arising from boundary loads and dislocations alone since the latter two are represented by a biharmonic Airy function. The present analogy then breaks down. However, it can be revived by a device similar to that used in converting from a pressure membrane to a zero-pressure membrane in the torsion analogy (see article 6).

S. Analogy between Thermal and Dislocation Stresses

50. Formulation of the Analogy. Another analogy discovered by M. A. Biot[53, 54] is that which exists between the stresses produced by a two-dimensional steady-state temperature distribution and the stresses produced by dislocations. By means of this analogy steady-state "thermal" stresses may be induced in a model by means of a simple mechanical device.

To find the conditions governing the Airy function for steady-state thermal stresses in a constrained slice, we use equations 198 to 203 with

$$\bar{X} = \bar{Y} = V = \nabla^2\theta = a_i = b_i = c_i = 0 \tag{268}$$

and, hence, $A_i = B_i = 0$. Then,

$$\nabla^4\varphi = 0 \tag{269}$$

$$\varphi_{c_i} = \alpha_i x + \beta_i y + \gamma_i \qquad (i = 0, 1, 2, \cdots, n) \tag{270}$$

$$\left.\frac{\partial\varphi}{\partial\nu}\right]_{c_i} = \alpha_i l + \beta_i m \qquad (i = 0, 1, 2, \cdots, n) \tag{271}$$

$$\int_{C_i} \frac{\partial(\nabla^2\varphi)}{\partial\nu}\, ds = -\frac{E\alpha}{1-\mu}\int_{C_i}\frac{\partial\theta}{\partial\nu}\, ds \qquad (i = 1, 2, 3, \cdots, n) \quad (272)$$

$$\int_{C_i}\left(y\,\frac{\partial(\nabla^2\varphi)}{\partial\nu} - x\,\frac{\partial(\nabla^2\varphi)}{\partial s}\right)ds = -\frac{E\alpha}{1-\mu}\int_{C_i}\left(y\,\frac{\partial\theta}{\partial\nu} - x\,\frac{\partial\theta}{\partial s}\right)ds$$
$$(i = 1, 2, 3, \cdots, n) \quad (273)$$

$$\int_{C_i}\left(y\,\frac{\partial(\nabla^2\varphi)}{\partial s} + x\,\frac{\partial(\nabla^2\varphi)}{\partial\nu}\right)ds = -\frac{E\alpha}{1-\mu}\int_{C_i}\left(y\,\frac{\partial\theta}{\partial s} + x\,\frac{\partial\theta}{\partial\nu}\right)ds$$
$$(i = 1, 2, 3, \cdots, n) \quad (274)$$

We now consider a model geometrically similar and constructed to scale ratio λ. The Airy function φ' in the model for dislocation stresses only is governed by

$$\nabla_1{}^4\varphi' = 0 \tag{275}$$

$$\varphi c_i{}' = \alpha_i{}'x_1 + \beta_i{}'y_1 + \gamma_i{}' \qquad (i = 0, 1, 2, \cdots, n) \quad (276)$$

$$\frac{\partial\varphi'}{\partial\nu_1}\bigg]_{C_i{}'} = \alpha_i{}'l + \beta_i{}'m \qquad (i = 0, 1, 2, \cdots, n) \quad (277)$$

$$\int_{C_i{}'}\frac{\partial(\nabla_1{}^2\varphi')}{\partial\nu_1}\, ds_1 = \frac{E_1 c_i{}'}{1-\mu_i{}^2} \qquad (i = 1, 2, 3, \cdots, n) \quad (278)$$

$$\int_{C_i{}'}\left(y_1\,\frac{\partial(\nabla_1{}^2\varphi')}{\partial\nu_1} - x_1\,\frac{\partial(\nabla_1{}^2\varphi')}{\partial s_1}\right)ds_1 = \frac{E_1(a_i{}' + y_i{}'c_i{}')}{1-\mu_i{}^2}$$
$$(i = 1, 2, 3, \cdots, n) \quad (279)$$

$$\int_{C_i{}'}\left(y_1\,\frac{\partial(\nabla_1{}^2\varphi')}{\partial s_1} + x_1\,\frac{\partial(\nabla_1{}^2\varphi')}{\partial\nu_1}\right)ds_1 = \frac{-E_1(b_i{}' - x_i{}'c_i{}')}{1-\mu_i{}^2}$$
$$(i = 1, 2, 3, \cdots, n) \quad (280)$$

Comparing equations 275 to 280 with equations 268 to 274, we see that, if we set

$$c_i{}' = -\frac{(1-\mu_1{}^2)E\alpha}{\Upsilon E_1(1-\mu)}\int_{C_i}\frac{\partial\theta}{\partial\nu}\, ds \tag{281}$$

$$a_i{}' = -y_i{}'c_i{}' - \frac{(1-\mu_1{}^2)E\alpha}{\Upsilon\lambda E_1(1-\mu)}\int_{C_i}\left(y\,\frac{\partial\theta}{\partial\nu} - x\,\frac{\partial\theta}{\partial s}\right)ds \tag{282}$$

$$b_i{}' = x_i{}'c_i{}' + \frac{(1-\mu_1{}^2)E\alpha}{\Upsilon\lambda E_1(1-\mu)}\int_{C_i}\left(y\,\frac{\partial\theta}{\partial s} + x\,\frac{\partial\theta}{\partial\nu}\right)ds \tag{283}$$

$$\varphi' = \frac{\varphi}{\Upsilon\lambda^2} \tag{284}$$

equations 269 to 274 become identical with equations 275 to 280. In these formulas, Υ is again an arbitrary scale factor for stress.

The relations between the components of stress in the prototype (produced by temperatures θ) and the components of stress in the model (produced by the dislocations a_i', b_i', c_i') are simply

$$\sigma_x = \Upsilon\sigma_{x_1}' \tag{285}$$

$$\sigma_y = \Upsilon\sigma_{y_1}' \tag{286}$$

$$\tau_{xy} = \Upsilon\tau_{x_1y_1}' \tag{287}$$

If the prototype is a constrained slice,

$$\sigma_z = \mu(\sigma_x + \sigma_y) - E\alpha\theta \tag{288}$$

whereas, if the prototype is a free slice, $\sigma_z = 0$.

51. Free and Constrained Slices. Equations 281 and 283 hold when both prototype and model are constrained slices. In other cases the rules set down in article 43 should be followed. For example, if both prototype and model are free slices, replace E by $\bar{E}$, μ by $\bar{\mu}$, α by $\bar{\alpha}$, E_1 by $\bar{E}_1$ and μ_1 by $\bar{\mu}_1$, where

$$\bar{E} = \frac{E(1 + 2\mu)}{(1 + \mu)^2} \tag{289}$$

$$\bar{\mu} = \frac{\mu}{1 + \mu} \tag{290}$$

$$\bar{\alpha} = \frac{\alpha(1 + \mu)}{1 + 2\mu} \tag{291}$$

$$\bar{E}_1 = \frac{E_1(1 + 2\mu_1)}{(1 + \mu_1)^2} \tag{292}$$

$$\bar{\mu}_1 = \frac{\mu_1}{1 + \mu_1} \tag{293}$$

If the prototype is a constrained slice and the model is a free slice, then in equations 281 to 283 replace E_1 by $\bar{E}_1$ and μ_1 by $\bar{\mu}_1$, where $\bar{E}_1$ and $\bar{\mu}_1$ are given by equations 292 and 293. In this case the constant multiplying the integral in equation 281 becomes

$$\frac{E\alpha}{\Upsilon E_1(1 - \mu)} \tag{294}$$

and the constants multiplying the integrals in equations 282 and 283 become

$$\frac{E\alpha}{\Upsilon\lambda E_1(1 - \mu)} \tag{295}$$

52. General Properties of Two-Dimensional Thermal Stress. Biot has established some general theorems which are very useful in studying steady-state thermal stresses in two dimensions.   These theorems appear on inspection of equations 269 to 274.

Theorem I.   If a solid cylinder is heated either uniformly or not, but in such a way that a steady-state temperature distribution exists, the same in every cross section, the only stress produced is a tension (or compression) σ_z, acting normally to the cross section and equal to $-E\alpha\theta$.

To verify this theorem, we observe that, since the section is solid, equations 272 to 274 do not apply, and, from equations 269 to 271, Airy's function is linear in x and y.   Hence, $\sigma_x = \sigma_y = \tau_{xy} = 0$, and, from equation 288, $\sigma_z = -E\alpha\theta$.

Theorem II.   Theorem I holds for a hollow cylinder provided: (1) *The total amount of heat flowing in or out of each hole is zero:*

$$\int_{C_i} \frac{\partial\theta}{\partial\nu}\, ds = 0 \tag{296}$$

and (2) *The following line integrals around each hole are zero:*

$$\int_{C_i} \left(y\frac{\partial\theta}{\partial\nu} - x\frac{\partial\theta}{\partial s} \right) ds = 0 \tag{297}$$

$$\int_{C_i} \left(y\frac{\partial\theta}{\partial s} + x\frac{\partial\theta}{\partial\nu} \right) ds = 0 \tag{298}$$

Since theorem II deals with a hollow section, equations 272 to 274 apply in addition to equations 269 to 271.   The integral (equation 296) is proportional to the total heat flux across C_i.   If this integral vanishes, no stress arises from the requirement that equation 272 be satisfied, as may be confirmed by noting, from equation 281, that the analogy requires no rotational dislocation.

The integrals (equations 297 and 298) are nonvanishing if the temperature distribution contains singularities of the order of a doublet or less inside an internal boundary C_i.   If these integrals vanish along with equation 296, no stress is implied by equations 273 and 274, as may be verified by noting that, in the analogy, the translational dislocations (equations 282 and 283) vanish.   Hence, if all three integrals vanish for each internal boundary, the components of stress $\sigma_x, \sigma_y, \tau_{xy}$ will all be zero.

If any one of the integrals does not vanish, there will be stress corresponding to the appropriate dislocation.   For example if equations 297 and 298 are zero, but there is a source or sink within a boundary, there will be stress corresponding to a rotational dislocation.

On the other hand, if equation 296 vanishes but either equation 297 or equation 298 does not, there will be stress corresponding to a translational dislocation.   However, if the hole, around which there is a nonvanishing integral, is filled with a fluid of the same thermal conductivity as that of the material of the cylinder, this stress will disappear because the temperature distribution can no longer contain singularities.

53. Application. Following a suggestion made by Biot,[55] E. E. Weibel[56] has used this analogy in conjunction with the photoelastic method to determine thermal stresses in circular and rectangular tubes under various conditions of temperature. Free-slice models of Bakelite were used, and the dislocations were applied by means of a mechanical device similar to a Beggs deformeter but more rugged on account of the large forces involved.

A drawing of Weibel's deformeter is shown in Fig. 16-33. The dislocations c' and b' are produced by inserting pins in the 90° V grooves. The grooves

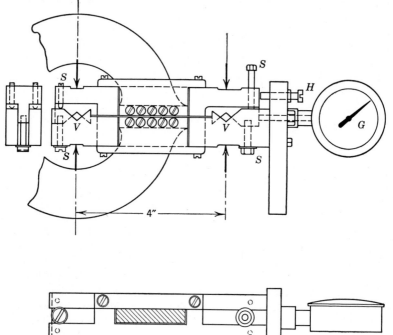

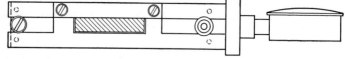

FIG. 16-33. Weibel's Deformeter for Producing Dislocations

are sloped to accommodate standard taper pins, thus permitting continuous variation of c' and b'. Loading of the model is facilitated by the vertical adjusting screws S which may also be used to fix c' and b' and thus permit the addition of a dislocation a'. The latter is introduced by the horizontal adjusting screw H, and its magnitude is recorded by the removable dial gage G. The magnitudes of b' and c' are measured with micrometer calipers across the deformeter at the sections where the taper pins are inserted, as indicated by the arrows.

In the case of a cylinder with uniform temperature on its circular external and internal boundaries, for which the mathematical solution is known, Weibel's experimental values had a maximum deviation of 3.7 per cent from the theoretical and an average deviation of 2.7 per cent.

T. The Slab Analogy

54. Formulation of the Analogy.   The slab analogy is based on the similarity between the equations governing Airy's function and those governing the deflections of a thin plate (slab).   In the approximate theory of the bending of thin slabs,[2] the displacement (ζ) normal to the middle plane of the slab, is governed by the differential equation,

$$D\nabla_1^4 \zeta = Z \tag{299}$$

where Z is the transverse loading on the surface of the slab (force per unit of area), and D is the flexural rigidity of the slab:

$$D = \frac{Eh^3}{12(1-\mu_1)^2}$$

in which h is the slab thickness, and μ_1 is Poisson's ratio for the material of the slab.   In equation 299,

$$\nabla_1^4 = \nabla_1^2\nabla_1^2 = \left(\frac{\partial^2}{\partial x_1^2} + \frac{\partial^2}{\partial y_1^2}\right)\left(\frac{\partial^2}{\partial x_1^2} + \frac{\partial^2}{\partial y_1^2}\right)$$

where x_1 and y_1 are rectangular coordinates in the middle plane of the slab.

In the neighborhood of a point of the surface of the slab, the shape of the surface is given, to a sufficient approximation, by

$$\zeta = \frac{\kappa_{x_1}}{2}x_1^2 + \frac{\kappa_{y_1}}{2}y_1^2 - \kappa_{x_1y_1}$$

where the constants κ_{y_1}, κ_{x_1}, $\kappa_{x_1y_1}$ are the components of the curvature at the point under consideration.   Hence,

$$\kappa_{y_1} = \frac{\partial^2\zeta}{\partial y_1^2} \tag{300}$$

$$\kappa_{x_1} = \frac{\partial^2\zeta}{\partial x_1^2} \tag{301}$$

$$\kappa_{x_1y_1} = -\frac{\partial^2\zeta}{\partial x_1 \partial y_1} \tag{302}$$

We note that, if we set

$$\sigma_x - V = \Upsilon\kappa_{y_1} \tag{303}$$

$$\sigma_y - V = \Upsilon\kappa_{x_1} \tag{304}$$

$$\tau_{xy} = \Upsilon\kappa_{x_1y_1} \tag{305}$$

$$\varphi = \Upsilon\lambda^2\zeta \tag{306}$$

$$(1-\mu)^{-1}[(1-2\mu)\nabla^2 V + E\alpha\nabla^2\theta] = -\frac{\Upsilon Z}{\lambda^2 D} \tag{307}$$

in equations 187 and 166 to 168, these equations become identical with equations 299 to 302. In equations 303 and 304, Υ is a scale factor between curvature of the slab surface and stress in the slice, and λ is the geometrical scale ratio, that is, the ratio of a length in the x, y plane of the slice to the corresponding length in the x_1, y_1 plane of the slab.

From equations 306, 199, and 200, the boundary conditions, for each point on a boundary of the slab, become

$$\Upsilon \zeta_{C_{i'}} = \int_0^{s_1} (B_i{}'l - A_i{}'m)\, ds_1 + \alpha_i{}'x_1 + \beta_i{}'y_1 + \gamma_i{}'$$
$$(i = 0, 1, 2, \cdots, n) \quad (308)$$

$$\Upsilon \frac{\partial \zeta}{\partial \nu_1}\bigg]_{C_{i'}} = A_i{}'l + B_i{}'m + \alpha_i{}'l + \beta_i{}'m \qquad (i = 0, 1, 2, \cdots, n) \quad (309)$$

where

$$A_i{}' = -\int_0^{s_1} (\bar{Y} - Vm)\, ds_1$$
$$B_i{}' = \int_0^{s_1} (\bar{X} - Vl)\, ds_1$$

For a simply connected slice, these equations complete the analogy. The slab outline is made geometrically similar to the outline of the slice (to scale ratio λ), and the edges are deflected and inclined in accordance with equations 308 and 309. The constants $\alpha_o{}'$, $\beta_o{}'$, $\gamma_o{}'$ may be taken equal to zero for the simply connected case, because they constitute only a rigid-body translation and rotation of the whole slab and, hence, do not contribute to the curvatures.

If the temperature is steady state and the body-force potential is harmonic, $Z = 0$, that is, no loading is required on the surface of the slab. If either $\nabla^2 V$ or $\nabla^2 \theta$ is not zero, transverse loading is required in accordance with equation 307. For example, a centrifugal body force in the slice is represented by a uniform pressure on the slab (see article 49). Alternatively, surface pressures on the slab may be converted to additional boundary elevations and slopes by a procedure similar to that used in converting from a pressure membrane to a zero-pressure membrane in the membrane analogy for torsion (see article 6).

Note that, if the slice is a free slice, μ and α in equation 307 must be replaced by $\bar{\mu}$ and $\bar{\alpha}$ as given in equations 223 and 224.

55. Multiply Connected Slices. If the slice contains a hole or holes, the three additional conditions (equations 201 to 203) must be satisfied on each internal boundary, and these will determine the unknown constants $\alpha_i{}'$, $\beta_i{}'$, $\gamma_i{}'$ $(i = 1, 2, 3, \cdots, n)$. As may be seen from equations 308 and 309, Michell's constants specify a rigid-body translation and rotation of each boundary of the slab. Such rigid-body movements may be effected by applying, on a plug inserted in each hole, a resultant force normal to the middle plane of the slab and a couple about an axis properly oriented in the plane of the slab (see Fig. 16-34). To determine the magnitudes of the force and the x_1 and y_1 components of the couple, we require the expressions for these quantities in terms of the deflection of the slab.

At a point on a boundary of the slab, the shearing force N normal to the middle plane, the flexural couple G and the torsional couple H (all per unit of arc length s_1, of the boundary, see Fig. 16-35) are[2]

$$N = -D \frac{\partial}{\partial \nu_1} (\nabla_1^2 \zeta) \tag{310}$$

$$G = -D \left[\frac{\partial^2 \zeta}{\partial \nu_1^2} + \mu_1 \left(\frac{\partial^2 \zeta}{\partial s_1^2} + \frac{1}{\rho_1'} \frac{\partial \zeta}{\partial \nu_1} \right) \right] \tag{311}$$

$$H = (1 - \mu_1)D \frac{\partial}{\partial \nu_1} \left(\frac{\partial \zeta}{\partial s_1} \right) \tag{312}$$

where ρ_1' is the radius of curvature of the boundary of the unflexed slab at the point considered and μ_1 is Poisson's ratio for the material of the slab.

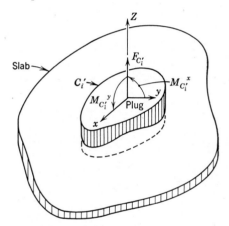

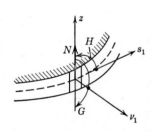

Fig. 16-34. Plug Inserted in Hole of Equivalent Slab to Force Correct Variation of Boundary Ordinates and Slopes

Fig. 16-35. Shearing Force, Flexural Couple, and Torsional Couple at the Edge of a Plate

The resultant force normal to the slab and the x_1 and y_1 components of the resultant couple on a complete boundary C_i' are[2] (see Fig. 16-34)

$$F_{C_i'} = \int_{C_i'} \left(N - \frac{\partial H}{\partial s_1} \right) ds_1 \tag{313}$$

$$M_{C_i'^{x_1}} = \int_{C_i'} \left[y_1 \left(N - \frac{\partial H}{\partial s_1} \right) + G \frac{\partial x_1}{\partial s_1} \right] ds_1 \tag{314}$$

$$M_{C_i'^{y_1}} = \int_{C_i'} \left[G \frac{\partial y_1}{\partial s_1} - x_1 \left(N - \frac{\partial H}{\partial s_1} \right) \right] ds_1 \tag{315}$$

Substituting equations 310 to 312 in equations 313 to 315, we have, for each boundary

$$F_{C_{i'}} = -D \int_{C_{i'}} \left[\frac{\partial}{\partial \nu_1} (\nabla_1{}^2 \zeta) + (1 + \mu_1) \frac{\partial}{\partial s_1} \frac{\partial}{\partial \nu_1} \left(\frac{\partial \zeta}{\partial s_1} \right) \right] ds_1 \qquad (316)$$

$$M_{C_{i'}{}^{x_1}} = -D \int_{C_{i'}} \left\{ y \left[\frac{\partial}{\partial \nu_1} (\nabla_1{}^2 \zeta) + (1 - \mu_1) \frac{\partial}{\partial s_1} \frac{\partial}{\partial \nu_1} \left(\frac{\partial \zeta}{\partial s_1} \right) \right] \right.$$
$$\left. + \frac{\partial x_1}{\partial s_1} \left[\frac{\partial^2 \zeta}{\partial \nu_1{}^2} + \mu_1 \left(\frac{\partial^2 \zeta}{\partial s_1{}^2} + \frac{1}{\rho_1'} \frac{\partial \zeta}{\partial \nu_1} \right) \right] \right\} ds_1 \quad (317)$$

$$M_{C_{i'}{}^{y_1}} = -D \int_{C_{i'}} \left\{ \frac{\partial y_1}{\partial s_1} \left[\frac{\partial^2 \zeta}{\partial \nu_1{}^2} + \mu_1 \left(\frac{\partial^2 \zeta}{\partial s_1{}^2} + \frac{1}{\rho_1'} \frac{\partial \zeta}{\partial \nu_1} \right) \right] \right.$$
$$\left. - x_1 \left[\frac{\partial (\nabla_1{}^2 \zeta)}{\partial \nu_1} + (1 - \mu_1) \frac{\partial}{\partial s_1} \frac{\partial}{\partial \nu_1} \left(\frac{\partial \zeta}{\partial s_1} \right) \right] \right\} ds_1 \quad (318)$$

These are the required expressions for the force and the components of the couple in terms of the slab deflections. We have now to transform equations 316 to 318 into expressions in terms of the boundary conditions on the slice.

56. Resultant Force on a Boundary of the Slab. Replacing ζ by $\varphi/\Upsilon\lambda^2$ and $\nu_1, s_1, \nabla_1{}^2$ by $\nu/\lambda, s/\lambda, \lambda^2\nabla^2$, respectively, in equation 316, we have

$$F_{C_{i'}} = -\frac{D}{\Upsilon} \int_{C_i} \left[\frac{\partial (\nabla^2 \varphi)}{\partial \nu} + (1 - \mu_1) \frac{\partial}{\partial s} \frac{\partial}{\partial \nu} \left(\frac{\partial \varphi}{\partial s} \right) \right] ds \qquad (319)$$

Now,

$$\int_{C_i} \frac{\partial}{\partial s} \frac{\partial}{\partial \nu} \left(\frac{\partial \varphi}{\partial s} \right) ds = 0$$

because we are considering only continuous stresses in the slice. Hence,

$$F_{C_{i'}} = -\frac{D}{\Upsilon} \int_{C_i} \frac{\partial}{\partial \nu} (\nabla^2 \varphi) ds$$

Therefore, from equation 201,

$$\frac{\Upsilon}{D} F_{C_{i'}} = -\frac{E c_i}{1 - \mu^2} + \frac{1 - 2\mu}{1 - \mu} \int_{C_i} \frac{\partial V}{\partial \nu} ds + \frac{E\alpha}{1 - \mu} \int_{C_i} \frac{\partial \theta}{\partial \nu} ds$$
$$(i = 1, 2, 3, \cdots, n) \quad (320)$$

Thus, we have the resultant force on an internal boundary of the slab expressed in terms of quantities that are known for the slice. It may be seen that a nonzero force is required if there is a rotational dislocation or if there is a nonvanishing flux of body force or of heat across the boundary.

57. x Component of Couple on a Boundary of the Slab. Substituting $\varphi/\Upsilon\lambda^2$ for ζ and $x/\lambda, y/\lambda, \nu/\lambda, s/\lambda, \rho'/\lambda$, and $\lambda^2\nabla^2$ for $x_1, y_1, \nu_1, s_1, \rho_1'$, and $\nabla_1{}^2$

in equation 317, we have

$$M_{c_i'^{z_1}} = -\frac{D}{\Upsilon\lambda}\int_{C_i}\left\{y\left[\frac{\partial(\nabla^2\varphi)}{\partial\nu} + (1-\mu_1)\frac{\partial}{\partial s}\frac{\partial}{\partial\nu}\left(\frac{\partial\varphi}{\partial s}\right)\right]\right.$$
$$\left.+\frac{dx}{ds}\left[\frac{\partial^2\varphi}{\partial\nu^2} + \mu_1\left(\frac{\partial^2\varphi}{\partial s^2} + \frac{1}{\rho'}\frac{\partial\varphi}{\partial\nu}\right)\right]\right\}\,ds \quad (321)$$

We now introduce the boundary conditions on the slice by eliminating

$$\int_{C_i} y\,\frac{\partial}{\partial\nu}\,(\nabla^2\varphi)\,ds$$

between equations 321 and 202. The result is

$$\frac{\Upsilon\lambda M_{c_i'^{z_1}}}{D} = -\int_{C_i}\left\{x\,\frac{\partial(\nabla^2\varphi)}{\partial s} + (1-\mu_1)\,y\,\frac{\partial}{\partial s}\frac{\partial}{\partial\nu}\left(\frac{\partial\varphi}{\partial s}\right)\right.$$
$$+\frac{dx}{ds}\left[\frac{\partial^2\varphi}{\partial\nu^2} + \mu_1\left(\frac{\partial^2\varphi}{\partial s^2} + \frac{1}{\rho'}\frac{\partial\varphi}{\partial\nu}\right)\right]\right\}\,ds - \frac{E(a_i + y_i c_i)}{1-\mu^2}$$
$$+\frac{1-2\mu}{1-\mu}\int_{C_i}\left(y\,\frac{\partial V}{\partial\nu} - x\,\frac{\partial V}{\partial s}\right)ds + \frac{E\alpha}{1-\mu}\int_{C_i}\left(y\,\frac{\partial\theta}{\partial\nu} - x\,\frac{\partial\theta}{\partial s}\right)ds$$
$$+\frac{1}{1-\mu}\int_{C_i}(\bar{Y} - Vm)\,ds \quad (322)$$

Now, integrating by parts gives

$$\int_{C_i}\left[x\,\frac{\partial(\nabla^2\varphi)}{\partial s} + (1-\mu_1)\,y\,\frac{\partial}{\partial s}\frac{\partial}{\partial\nu}\left(\frac{\partial\varphi}{\partial s}\right)\right]ds$$
$$= [x\nabla^2\varphi]_0^0 + (1-\mu_1)\left[y\,\frac{\partial}{\partial\nu}\left(\frac{\partial\varphi}{\partial s}\right)\right]_0^0$$
$$-\int_{C_i}\left[\frac{dx}{ds}\nabla^2\varphi + (1-\mu_1)\frac{dy}{ds}\frac{\partial}{\partial\nu}\left(\frac{\partial\varphi}{\partial s}\right)\right]ds$$

The terms outside the integrals vanish because the stresses in the slice are continuous. Therefore the first integral on the right-hand side of equation 322 becomes

$$\int_{C_i}\left\{(1-\mu_1)\frac{dy}{ds}\frac{\partial}{\partial\nu}\left(\frac{\partial\varphi}{\partial s}\right) + \frac{dx}{ds}\left[\nabla^2\varphi - \frac{\partial^2\varphi}{\partial\nu^2} - \mu_1\left(\frac{\partial^2\varphi}{\partial s^2} + \frac{1}{\rho'}\frac{\partial\varphi}{\partial\nu}\right)\right]\right\}\,ds \quad (323)$$

On a boundary of the slice,

$$\nabla^2\varphi = \frac{\partial^2\varphi}{\partial\nu^2} + \frac{1}{\rho'}\frac{\partial\varphi}{\partial\nu} + \frac{\partial^2\varphi}{\partial s^2} \quad (324)$$

so that equation 323 becomes

$$(1-\mu_1)\int_{C_i}\left[\frac{dy}{ds}\frac{\partial}{\partial\nu}\left(\frac{\partial\varphi}{\partial s}\right) + \frac{dx}{ds}\left(\frac{\partial^2\varphi}{\partial s^2} + \frac{1}{\rho'}\frac{\partial\varphi}{\partial\nu}\right)\right]\,ds \quad (325)$$

However, along a boundary,

$$\frac{\partial}{\partial \nu}\left(\frac{\partial \varphi}{\partial s}\right) = -\tau_{\nu s} \tag{326}$$

$$\frac{\partial^2 \varphi}{\partial s^2} + \frac{1}{\rho'}\frac{\partial \varphi}{\partial \nu} = \sigma_\nu - V \tag{327}$$

and

$$\frac{dy}{ds}\tau_{\nu s} - \frac{dx}{ds}\sigma_\nu = \bar{Y} \tag{328}$$

where σ_ν and $\tau_{\nu s}$ are the normal and shearing components of stress on the boundary of the slice. Hence equation 325 becomes

$$-(1 - \mu_1)\int_{C_i}(\bar{Y} - Vm)\,ds$$

Substituting back in equation 322, we have, finally,

$$\frac{\Upsilon\lambda M_{C_i'{}^{x_1}}}{D} = -\frac{E(a_i + y_i c_i)}{(1 - \mu^2)} + \frac{1 - 2\mu}{1 - \mu}\int_{C_i}\left(y\frac{\partial V}{\partial \nu} - x\frac{\partial V}{\partial s}\right)ds$$

$$+ \frac{E\alpha}{1 - \mu}\int_{C_i}\left(y\frac{\partial \theta}{\partial \nu} - x\frac{\partial \theta}{\partial s}\right)ds - \left(1 - \mu_1 - \frac{1}{1 - \mu}\right)\int_{C_i}(\bar{Y} - Vm)\,ds$$

$$(i = 1, 2, 3, \cdots, n) \tag{329}$$

Thus, we have the x component of the moment, to be applied to the ith plug, in terms of the known boundary stresses, body forces, temperatures, and dislocations of the slice.

58. y Component of Couple on a Boundary of the Slab. Substituting $\varphi/\Upsilon\lambda^2$ for ζ and x/λ, y/λ, ν/λ, s/λ, ρ'/λ, and $\lambda^2\nabla^2$ for x_1, y_1, ν_1, s_1, ρ_1', and ∇_1^2 in equation 318, we have

$$M_{C_i'{}^{y_1}} = -\frac{D}{\Upsilon\lambda}\int_{C_i}\left\{\frac{dy}{ds}\left[\frac{\partial^2 \varphi}{\partial \nu^2} + \mu_1\left(\frac{\partial^2 \varphi}{\partial s^2} + \frac{1}{\rho'}\frac{\partial \varphi}{\partial \nu}\right)\right]\right.$$

$$\left. - x\left[\frac{\partial(\nabla^2\varphi)}{\partial \nu} + (1 - \mu_1)\frac{\partial}{\partial s}\frac{\partial}{\partial \nu}\left(\frac{\partial \varphi}{\partial s}\right)\right]\right\}ds \tag{330}$$

Eliminating

$$\int_{C_i}x\frac{\partial}{\partial \nu}(\nabla^2\varphi)\,ds$$

between equations 330 and 203, we have

$$\frac{\Upsilon\lambda M_{C_i'{}^{y_1}}}{D} = -\int_{C_i}\left\{y\frac{\partial(\nabla^2\varphi)}{\partial s} - (1 - \mu_1)x\frac{\partial}{\partial s}\frac{\partial}{\partial \nu}\left(\frac{\partial \varphi}{\partial s}\right)\right.$$

$$\left. + \frac{dy}{ds}\left[\frac{\partial^2 \varphi}{\partial \nu^2} + \mu_1\left(\frac{\partial^2 \varphi}{\partial s^2} + \frac{1}{\rho'}\frac{\partial \varphi}{\partial \nu}\right)\right]\right\}ds - \frac{E(b_i - x_i c_i)}{1 - \mu^2}$$

$$- \frac{1 - 2\mu}{1 - \mu}\int_{C_i}\left(y\frac{\partial V}{\partial s} + x\frac{\partial V}{\partial \nu}\right)ds - \frac{E\alpha}{1 - \mu}\int_{C_i}\left(y\frac{\partial \theta}{\partial s} + x\frac{\partial \theta}{\partial \nu}\right)ds$$

$$- \frac{1}{1 - \mu}\int_{C_i}(\bar{X} - Vl)\,ds \tag{331}$$

Now,

$$\int_{C_i} \left[y \frac{\partial(\nabla^2 \varphi)}{\partial s} - (1 - \mu_1)x \frac{\partial}{\partial s} \frac{\partial}{\partial \nu} \left(\frac{\partial \varphi}{\partial s} \right) \right] ds$$

$$= [y \nabla^2 \varphi]_0^0 - (1 - \mu_1) \left[x \frac{\partial}{\partial \nu} \left(\frac{\partial \varphi}{\partial s} \right) \right]_0^0$$

$$- \int_{C_i} \left[\frac{dy}{ds} \nabla^2 \varphi - (1 - \mu_1) \frac{dx}{ds} \frac{\partial}{\partial \nu} \left(\frac{\partial \varphi}{\partial s} \right) \right] ds \quad (332)$$

The terms outside the integrals in equation 332 vanish because the stresses are continuous. Therefore, the first integral on the right-hand side of equation 331 becomes

$$\int_{C_i} \left\{ \frac{dy}{ds} \left[\nabla^2 \varphi - \frac{\partial^2 \varphi}{\partial \nu^2} - \mu_1 \left(\frac{\partial^2 \varphi}{\partial s^2} + \frac{1}{\rho'} \frac{\partial \varphi}{\partial \nu} \right) \right] - (1 - \mu_1) \frac{dx}{ds} \frac{\partial}{\partial \nu} \left(\frac{\partial \varphi}{\partial s} \right) \right\} ds \quad (333)$$

Then, if we use equations 324, 326, and 327 and note that

$$\tau_{\nu s} \frac{dx}{ds} + \sigma_\nu \frac{dy}{ds} = \bar{X} \quad (334)$$

equation 333 may be written in the form

$$(1 - \mu_1) \int_{C_i} (\bar{X} - Vl) \, ds \quad (335)$$

Substituting back in equation 331, we have

$$\frac{\Upsilon \lambda M_{c_i'^{y_1}}}{D} = - \frac{E(b_i - x_i c_i)}{1 - \mu^2} - \frac{1 - 2\mu}{1 - \mu} \int_{C_i} \left(y \frac{\partial V}{\partial s} + x \frac{\partial V}{\partial \nu} \right) ds$$

$$- \frac{E\alpha}{1 - \mu} \int_{C_i} \left(y \frac{\partial \theta}{\partial s} + x \frac{\partial \theta}{\partial \nu} \right) ds + \left(1 - \mu_1 - \frac{1}{1 - \mu} \right) \int_{C_i} (\bar{X} - Vl) \, ds$$

$$(i = 1, 2, 3, \cdots, n) \quad (336)$$

59. Recapitulation. The components of stress in a constrained slice are given in terms of the curvatures of a slab by

$$\sigma_x - V = \Upsilon \kappa_{y_1} \quad (337)$$

$$\sigma_y - V = \Upsilon \kappa_{x_1} \quad (338)$$

$$\tau_{xy} = \Upsilon \kappa_{x_1 y_1} \quad (339)$$

if the following conditions are satisfied on the slab:

1. There is a transverse force per unit of area Z, in the positive z direction, on the surface of the slab, where

$$Z = - \frac{\lambda^2 D}{\Upsilon(1 - \mu)} [(1 - 2\mu)\nabla^2 V + E\alpha \nabla^2 \theta] \quad (340)$$

2. At each point of *each* boundary of the slab, the transverse displacement of the edge and the slope normal to the edge are made to be

$$\Upsilon \zeta_{c_{i'}} = \int_0^{s_1} (B_i'l - A_i'm)\, ds_1 + \alpha_i'x_1 + \beta_i'y_1 + \gamma_i' \tag{341}$$

$$\Upsilon \frac{\partial \zeta}{\partial \nu_1}\bigg]_{C_{i'}} = A_i'l + B_i'm + \alpha_i'l + \beta_i'm \tag{342}$$

where

$$A_i' = \int_0^{s_1} (\bar{Y} - Vm)\, ds_1 \tag{343}$$

$$B_i' = \int_0^{s_1} (\bar{X} - Vl)\, ds_1 \tag{344}$$

3. On each *internal* boundary of the slab a resultant force $F_{c_{i'}}$ and couples $M_{c_{i'}^{x_1}}$ and $M_{c_{i'}^{y_1}}$ are applied, of magnitudes,

$$\frac{\Upsilon F_{c_{i'}}}{D} = -\frac{Ec_i}{1-\mu^2} + \frac{1-2\mu}{1-\mu} \int_{C_i} \frac{\partial V}{\partial \nu}\, ds + \frac{E\alpha}{1-\mu} \int_{C_i} \frac{\partial \theta}{\partial \nu}\, ds \tag{345}$$

$$\frac{\Upsilon \lambda M_{c_{i'}^{x_1}}}{D} = -\frac{E(a_i + y_i c_i)}{1-\mu^2} + \frac{1-2\mu}{1-\mu} \int_{C_i} \left(y\frac{\partial V}{\partial \nu} - x\frac{\partial V}{\partial s} \right) ds$$

$$+\frac{E\alpha}{1-\mu} \int_{C_i} \left(y\frac{\partial \theta}{\partial \nu} - x\frac{\partial \theta}{\partial s} \right) ds - \left(1 - \mu_1 - \frac{1}{1-\mu} \right) \int_{C_i} (\bar{Y} - Vm)\, ds \tag{346}$$

$$\frac{\Upsilon \lambda M_{c_{i'}^{y_1}}}{D} = -\frac{E(b_i - x_i c_i)}{1-\mu^2} - \frac{1-2\mu}{1-\mu} \int_{C_i} \left(y\frac{\partial V}{\partial s} + x\frac{\partial V}{\partial \nu} \right) ds$$

$$-\frac{E\alpha}{1-\mu} \int_{C_i} \left(y\frac{\partial \theta}{\partial s} + x\frac{\partial \theta}{\partial \nu} \right) ds + \left(1 - \mu_1 - \frac{1}{1-\mu} \right) \int_{C_i} (\bar{X} - Vl)\, ds \tag{347}$$

If the slice is a free slice instead of a constrained slice E, μ and α are to be replaced by $\bar{E}$, $\bar{\mu}$, and $\bar{\alpha}$ where the latter are given by equations 222 to 224. (Note that μ_1 is Poisson's ratio for the material of the slab and remains the same whether the slice is free or constrained.)

60. Transformation of Curvatures. At a point P of the slab surface, the quantity

$$\kappa_{x_1} = \frac{\partial^2 \zeta}{\partial x_1^2} \tag{348}$$

is the curvature of the intersection, with the surface, of the plane containing the normal to the surface at P and parallel to the x_1 axis. For brevity κ_{x_1} will be called the curvature in the x_1 direction. The curvature

$$\kappa_{x_1'} = \frac{\partial^2 \zeta}{\partial x_1'^2} \tag{349}$$

in a direction x_1' making an angle θ with the x_1 axis may be found by a transformation of coordinates. Referring to Fig. 16-36, let x_1', y_1' be a set of rectangular axes making an angle θ with the x_1, y_1 axes. Then,

$$x_1 = x_1' \cos \theta - y_1' \sin \theta \quad (350)$$

$$y_1 = x_1' \sin \theta + y_1' \cos \theta \quad (351)$$

Now,

$$\frac{\partial \zeta}{\partial x_1'} = \frac{\partial \zeta}{\partial x_1} \frac{\partial x_1}{\partial x_1'} + \frac{\partial \zeta}{\partial y_1} \frac{\partial y_1}{\partial x_1'}$$

$$= \cos \theta \frac{\partial \zeta}{\partial x_1} + \sin \theta \frac{\partial \zeta}{\partial y_1} \quad (352)$$

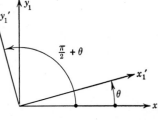

FIG. 16-36. Rotation of Coordinates

and, therefore,

$$\frac{\partial^2 \zeta}{\partial x_1'^2} = \left(\cos \theta \frac{\partial}{\partial x_1} + \sin \theta \frac{\partial}{\partial y_1} \right) \left(\cos \theta \frac{\partial \zeta}{\partial x_1} + \sin \theta \frac{\partial \zeta}{\partial y_1} \right)$$

$$= \cos^2 \theta \frac{\partial^2 \zeta}{\partial x_1^2} + \sin^2 \theta \frac{\partial^2 \zeta}{\partial y_1^2} + 2 \sin \theta \cos \theta \frac{\partial^2 \zeta}{\partial x_1 \partial y_1} \quad (353)$$

From equations 353, 349, and 300 to 302, we have

$$\kappa_{x_1'} = \kappa_{x_1} \cos^2 \theta + \kappa_{y_1} \sin^2 \theta - 2\kappa_{x_1 y_1} \sin \theta \cos \theta \quad (354)$$

It may be seen, from equation 354, that curvatures transform just like stresses and strains (see Appendix I, equation 17). It should be noted, however, that the curvature in a specified direction in the slab corresponds to the component of stress at right angles to that direction in the slice (see equations 337 to 339).

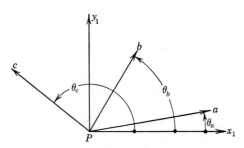

FIG. 16-37. Curvature Rosette

From equation 354 we find that the principal curvatures are

$$\kappa_1, \kappa_2 = \frac{\kappa_{x_1} + \kappa_{y_1}}{2} \pm \frac{1}{2} \sqrt{(\kappa_{x_1} - \kappa_{y_1})^2 + 4\kappa_{x_1 y_1}^2} \quad (355)$$

and their directions are given by

$$\tan 2\theta = \frac{2\kappa_{x_1 y_1}}{\kappa_{y_1} - \kappa_{x_1}} \quad (356)$$

As in the case of surface stresses, three independent measurements are required to specify the curvature at a point on the surface of the slab. These may be three curvature measurements $\kappa_a, \kappa_b, \kappa_c$ in three directions a,b,c making angles $\theta_a, \theta_b, \theta_c$ with the x_1 axis (see Fig. 16-37). Then,

$$\kappa_a = \kappa_{x_1} \cos^2 \theta_a + \kappa_{y_1} \sin^2 \theta_a - 2\kappa_{x_1y_1} \sin \theta_a \cos \theta_a \tag{357}$$

$$\kappa_b = \kappa_{x_1} \cos^2 \theta_b + \kappa_{y_1} \sin^2 \theta_b - 2\kappa_{x_1y_1} \sin \theta_b \cos \theta_b \tag{358}$$

$$\kappa_c = \kappa_{x_1} \cos^2 \theta_c + \kappa_{y_1} \sin^2 \theta_c - 2\kappa_{x_1y_1} \sin \theta_c \cos \theta_c \tag{359}$$

Once the three measurements $\kappa_a, \kappa_b, \kappa_c$ have been made at known angles $\theta_a, \theta_b, \theta_c$, these equations may be solved for $\kappa_{x_1}, \kappa_{y_1}, \kappa_{x_1y_1}$. The components of stress in the slice are then given by

$$\sigma_x - V = \Upsilon \kappa_{y_1} \tag{360}$$

$$\sigma_y - V = \Upsilon \kappa_{x_1} \tag{361}$$

$$\tau_{xy} = \Upsilon \kappa_{x_1y_1} \tag{362}$$

and the principal stresses (σ_1, σ_2) are given by

$$\sigma_1, \sigma_2 = \Upsilon \left[\frac{\kappa_{x_1} + \kappa_{y_1}}{2} \pm \frac{1}{2} \sqrt{(\kappa_{x_1} - \kappa_{y_1})^2 + 4\kappa_{x_1y_1}} \right] + V \tag{363}$$

The directions of the principal stresses are given by equation 356, but it should be remembered that the direction of the algebraically larger principal stress is that of the algebraically lesser principal curvature.

61. Applications. The slab analogy was first applied, by K. Wieghardt[57] in 1908, to the determination of stresses in a U frame acted on by spreading forces near the free ends of its legs. The slab was made of a brass sheet and was clamped in a frame whose boundary ordinates and slopes were made to conform with equations 341 and 342. One surface of the brass sheet was polished, and slopes of the surface were determined optically, point by point, by measuring angles of incidence and reflection with a

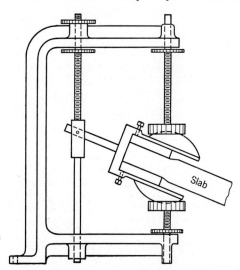

FIG. 16-38. Bureau of Reclamation Fixture for Forcing Correct Deflection and Slope at Edge of Slab

telescope. Curvatures were determined from the slopes by graphical and numerical differentiation.

In spite of its broad applicability, the analogy does not appear to have been used again until it was revived by H. M. Westergaard and V. P. Jensen in 1931.[50] Their applications were to the determination of stresses in a disk and in a slice of the Boulder Canyon Dam. The work was continued by the United States Bureau of Reclamation.[58] The Boulder Canyon slab model was made of rubber $\frac{3}{4}$ in. thick and about 30 in. in its longest surface dimension. The slab was supported in a vertical plane. Edge deflections and slopes were produced by individual clamps (Fig. 16-38) spaced every 3 or 4 in. along the boundary. Curvature was determined by measuring the relative displacement of scratch marks on the ends of a pair of pins driven into the rubber (Fig. 16-39).

H. Cranz[59] in 1939 made improvements in technique in an application to the measurement of the stress concentration in a long notched plate under tension (Fig. 16-40). He observed that, according to equations 341 and 342 (taking $\alpha_i = \beta_i = \gamma_i = 0$ since the plate is simply connected), a free boundary such as $abcde$ (Fig. 16-40) has a constant slope in the y direction while the displacement varies linearly with y. Along a uniformly loaded boundary, such as $a-a$ or $e-e$, the displacement follows a parabolic law while the slope, normal to the edge, is zero. These edge conditions may be reproduced by applying pure bending to a rectangular slab by means of flat clamps shaped to the contour $abcde$

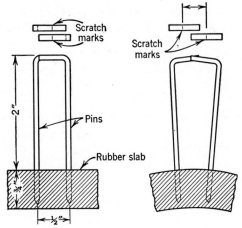

FIG. 16-39. Bureau of Reclamation Gage for Measuring Slab Curvature

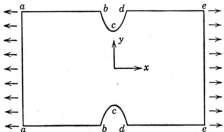

FIG. 16-40. Problem of Notched Slice under Tension to Which Cranz Applied the Slab Analogy

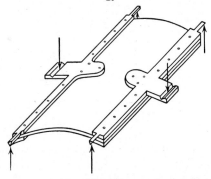

FIG. 16-41. Clamping and Loading Technique Used by Cranz to Obtain Required Deflections and Slopes of Slab Boundaries

(see Fig. 16-41).   The slab material was a polished Plexiglas sheet 1 or 1.5 mm thick.   Curvatures were measured by a direct optical method described in the next section.

62. Optical Measurement of Curvature.   Cranz measured curvatures with an optical instrument described by Einsporn.[60]   With reference to Fig. 16-42, a light source S is collimated by a lens L_1.   The rays are reflected from the slab P, and an image of the source is brought to focus by a lens L_2 distant a from the slab.   If the slab were plane, the image would be at a distance from

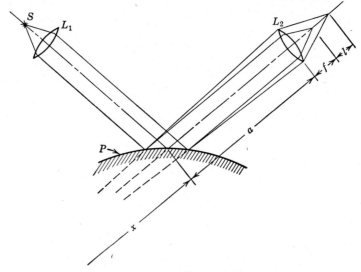

FIG. 16-42.   Optics of Einsporn's Spherometer

L_2 equal to its focal length f since the source appears at infinity.   If the slab is convex, the apparent source comes in from infinity to a distance x from the slab, and the lens L_2 brings the image to focus at $f + l$, where

$$\frac{1}{f+l} + \frac{1}{a+x} = \frac{1}{f}$$

(364)

or

$$x = \frac{f^2}{l} + f - a$$

(365)

The length l is measured with a traveling Ramsden ocular.

The distance x is determined by the curvature of the slab.   From the geometry of Fig. 16-43 we find, from the law of sines,

$$x = m\,\frac{\cos\left(\alpha + \dfrac{3\epsilon}{2}\right)}{\sin 2\epsilon}$$

(366)

where α is the angle of incidence, and

$$m = 2R \sin \frac{\epsilon}{2} \tag{367}$$

in which R is the radius of curvature of the slab in the plane of the incident

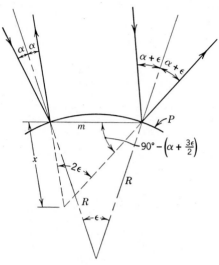

FIG. 16-43. Geometry of Einsporn's Spherometer

and reflected rays. Hence,

$$x = \frac{R \cos \left(\alpha + \dfrac{3\epsilon}{2} \right)}{2 \cos \dfrac{\epsilon}{2} \cos \epsilon} \tag{368}$$

Now, ϵ can be made small in absolute value and also small in comparison with α. Then,

$$x \approx \frac{R}{2} \cos \alpha = \frac{f^2}{l} + f - a \tag{369}$$

Hence, the radius of curvature is given by

$$R = \frac{2f^2}{l \cos \alpha} + \frac{2(f - a)}{\cos \alpha} \tag{370}$$

An ingenious optical instrument for measuring slab curvatures has been developed by Professor Martinelli of the University of Rome. This instrument measures the principal curvatures and their orientations directly. It avoids the need for measuring the angle of incidence and eliminates errors due to astigmatism that occur in the Einsporn instrument. A diagram of the Martinelli instrument is shown in Fig. 16-44. In this figure A is the curved

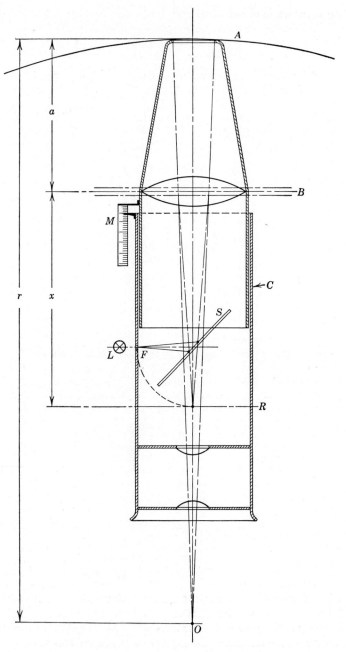

FIG. 16-44. Martinelli's Spherometer

reflecting surface of the slab, and B is a lens kept at a fixed distance a from A. A slit F is illuminated by a light source L, and rays from F are reflected through lens B by a half-silvered plane reflector S. After passage through lens B, the rays are reflected from the surface A and pass back through lens B and mirror S, forming a real image at the plane R where cross-wires are located. The image and cross-wires are viewed through a Ramsden ocular. The light source, slit, mirror, and cross-wires are fixed to a sliding tube C whose position is read on a scale M. Calling x the variable distance between the lens and the cross-wires and f the focal length of lens B, we have

$$\frac{1}{x} - \frac{1}{r-a} = \frac{1}{f} \tag{371}$$

where r is the radius that is to be measured. In the instrument, a is made equal to f. Hence, the curvature ($\kappa = 1/r$) is given by

$$\kappa = \frac{f-x}{f^2} \tag{372}$$

Measuring the displacement of tube C from an origin at $x = f$ and setting $x' = f - x$, we have

$$\kappa = \frac{x'}{f^2}. \tag{373}$$

The procedure for measuring curvatures is as follows. With the objective end of the instrument in contact with the plate (or at a fixed distance from it) the device is tilted and rotated until a faint image of the slit appears at the center of the cross-wires. The sliding tube is then moved to the position nearest the lens at which the slit is in focus. The direction perpendicular to the image of the slit is the direction of maximum curvature, and the magnitude of this curvature is computed by equation 373 from the observed value of x' and the known value of f. The sliding tube is then moved back (away from lens B), and the slit image will be observed to rotate. When the slit image is at right angles to its previous direction, the new value of x' gives the minimum curvature (from equation 373).

IV. ELECTRIC-NETWORK ANALOGUE OF THE ELASTIC FIELD

U. KRON'S ANALOGY

G. Kron[61] has devised a scheme of electric networks representing the most general elastic field. This includes two- or three-dimensional transient, sinusoidally oscillating or static fields arising from boundary loadings, body forces, or boundary displacements.

In the analogy, stresses are represented by currents in the electric circuit and strains by voltage drops. The stress equations of equilibrium correspond to Kirchhoff's current law which states that the sum of the currents I, entering each junction of the circuit, is zero. The compatibility conditions correspond to Kirchhoff's voltage law which states that the sum of the voltage drops E, around each mesh, is zero. Hooke's law corresponds to Ohm's law $I = YE$, so that the elastic constants are represented by lumped admittances Y.

Of the many possible circuits indicated by Kron, a case of static plane strain is chosen for detailed description here.

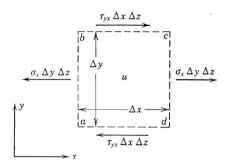

FIG. 16-45. Components of Force on a u block in a Homogeneous Stress Field

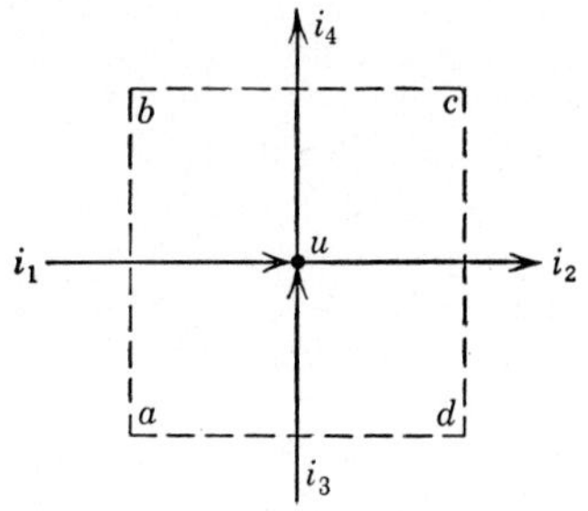

FIG. 16-46. Currents Entering and Leaving a u Block

63. Specification of Stress. Consider the elastic body, of constant thickness Δz, to be made up of small rectangular blocks with edges, of lengths Δx and Δy, parallel to the axes of an x, y rectangular coordinate system. On each block let us consider, first, only the stress components acting parallel to the x axis. Such a block will be called a u *block*. The integrals of these stresses over the areas on which they act are indicated in Fig. 16-45. The force

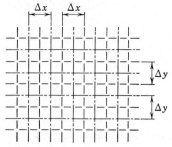

$\sigma_x \Delta y \Delta z$, on the rear face ab perpendicular to the x axis, is represented by a current i_1 entering the block in the positive x direction (Fig. 16-46). The force $\sigma_x \Delta y \Delta z$ on the front face cd is represented by a current i_2 leaving the block in the positive x direction. The forces $\tau_{yx} \Delta x \Delta z$ are represented by currents i_3 and i_4 entering and leaving the block in the positive y direction.

We write

FIG. 16-47. Division of a Two-Dimensional Body into u and v blocks

$$mi_1 = -\sigma_x \Delta y \Delta z \qquad (374)$$

$$mi_3 = -\tau_{yx} \Delta x \Delta z \qquad (375)$$

where m is a factor to convert force units to current units. The dimensions of m are, say, pounds per ampere. In a homogeneous state of stress, $i_1 = i_2$, $i_3 = i_4$.

In order to represent the components of stress that act parallel to the y axis, the whole body is divided all over again into another system of blocks of dimensions Δx and Δy, but shifted by amounts $\Delta x/2$ and $\Delta y/2$ in the x

and y directions, respectively. These blocks are called v blocks. In Fig.
16-47 the system of u blocks is bounded by dashed lines, and the v blocks are
bounded by dot–dashed lines.

On each v block we consider only the components of stress acting in the y

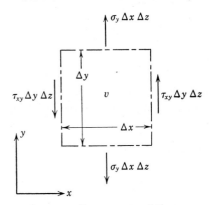

direction (Fig. 16-48). The stress
integrals $\sigma_y \Delta x \Delta z$ are represented by
currents i_5 and i_6 entering and leaving
the v block in the positive y direction,
and the stress integrals $\tau_{xy} \Delta y \Delta z$ are

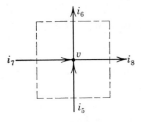

FIG. 16-48. Components of Force on
a v Block in a Homogeneous Stress
Field

FIG. 16-49. Currents En-
tering and Leaving a v
Block

represented by currents i_7 and i_8 entering and leaving the v block in the
positive x direction, as shown in Fig. 16-49. We write

$$mi_5 = -\sigma_y \Delta x \Delta z \tag{376}$$

$$mi_7 = -\tau_{xy} \Delta y \Delta z \tag{377}$$

In a homogeneous state of stress $i_5 = i_6$, $i_7 = i_8$.

The current intersection points u and v (Figs.
16-46 and 16-49) are junction points of two networks (thus far not connected) as shown in Fig.
16-50. The circuit does not represent, at any
one junction, all the components of stress
acting on an element of the elastic body. It
represents only the components of stress either
in the x direction on one block or in the y direction on another block. However, these blocks
are so interspersed that the total stresses on any
block are represented to half-block accuracy.

64. Equilibrium of Moments. By considering the equilibrium of moments acting on an
element of the elastic solid, we obtain the condition of equality of cross-shears:

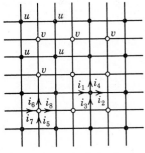

FIG. 16-50. Independent u
and v Networks

$$\tau_{xy} = \tau_{yx} \tag{378}$$

Now, τ_{yx} appears as a current i_3 in the u network, and τ_{xy} appears as a current
i_7 in the v network. In order to satisfy the condition expressed by equation

378 the two networks must be connected. Figure 16-51 shows a connection between a y-direction line of the u network and an x-direction line of the v network. The boxes inserted in the main and connecting lines represent admittances g_1, g_2, c_1, c_2, f, and b which have to be adjusted so that

$$\frac{i_4}{\Delta x} = \frac{i_7}{\Delta y} \tag{379}$$

$$\frac{i_3}{\Delta x} = \frac{i_8}{\Delta y} \tag{380}$$

as required by equations 374 to 377 and 378 for a homogeneous state of stress. (Note that the connection between the u and v networks could also be made

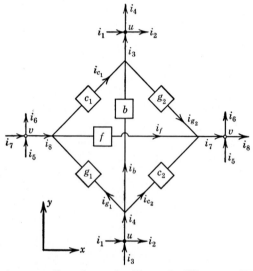

FIG. 16-51. Interconnection of u and v Networks Where a y-Direction Line of the u Network Crosses an x-Direction Line of the v Network

by introducing mutual inductance between b and f while omitting the loop c_1, g_1, c_2, g_2.)

From Fig. 16-51 and Kirchhoff's current law,

$$i_4 = i_{g_1} + i_b + i_{c_2} \tag{381}$$

$$i_7 = i_{g_2} + i_f + i_{c_2} \tag{382}$$

Hence, equation 379 requires

$$\frac{i_4}{\Delta x} - \frac{i_7}{\Delta y} = \frac{i_{g_1}}{\Delta x} - \frac{i_{g_2}}{\Delta y} + \frac{i_b}{\Delta x} - \frac{i_f}{\Delta y} + i_{c_2}\left(\frac{1}{\Delta x} - \frac{1}{\Delta y}\right) = 0$$

or

$$\Delta y\left(i_{g_1} - \frac{\Delta x}{\Delta y}i_f + i_{c_2}\right) - \Delta x\left(i_{g_2} - \frac{\Delta y}{\Delta x}i_b + i_{c_2}\right) = 0 \tag{383}$$

Since equation 383 must be true for all values of Δx and Δy, we must have

$$i_{g_1} - \frac{\Delta x}{\Delta y} i_f + i_{c_2} = 0 \tag{384}$$

$$i_{g_2} - \frac{\Delta y}{\Delta x} i_b + i_{c_2} = 0 \tag{385}$$

Now, by Kirchhoff's voltage law, (if we refer to Fig. 16-51),

$$E_{g_1} + E_f - E_{c_2} = 0$$

$$E_b + E_{g_2} - E_{c_2} = 0$$

and, hence, by Ohm's law,

$$\frac{i_{g_1}}{g_1} + \frac{i_f}{f} + \frac{i_{c_2}}{c_2} = 0 \tag{386}$$

$$\frac{i_b}{b} + \frac{i_{g_2}}{g_2} - \frac{i_{c_2}}{c_2} = 0 \tag{387}$$

In view of equations 386 and 387, equations 384 and 385 will be satisfied if

$$g_1 = -f \frac{\Delta x}{\Delta y} = -c_2$$

$$g_2 = -b \frac{\Delta y}{\Delta x} = -c_2$$

that is, if

$$g_1 = g_2 = -f \frac{\Delta x}{\Delta y} = -b \frac{\Delta y}{\Delta x} = -c_2 \tag{388}$$

Similarly, equation 380 requires that

$$g_1 = g_2 = -f \frac{\Delta x}{\Delta y} = -b \frac{\Delta y}{\Delta x} = -c_1 \tag{389}$$

Hence, the requirement of equality of cross-shears is satisfied in the electric circuit if the u and v networks are connected in the manner shown in Fig. 16-51, provided the admittances satisfy the relations

$$g_1 = g_2 = -f \frac{\Delta x}{\Delta y} = -b \frac{\Delta y}{\Delta x} = -c_1 = -c_2 \tag{390}$$

65. Equilibrium of Forces. Figure 16-52 represents the forces acting on a u block, and Fig. 16-53 represents the corresponding currents at a u junction, for a nonhomogeneous state of stress.   We write

$$mi_1 = -\sigma_x \, \Delta y \, \Delta z \tag{391}$$

$$mi_2 = -\left(\sigma_x + \frac{\partial \sigma_x}{\partial x} \Delta x\right) \Delta y \, \Delta z \tag{392}$$

$$mi_3 = -\tau_{yx} \, \Delta x \, \Delta z \tag{393}$$

$$mi_4 = -\left(\tau_{yx} + \frac{\partial \tau_{yx}}{\partial y} \Delta y\right) \Delta x \, \Delta z \tag{394}$$

Now, by Kirchhoff's current law,

$$i_1 + i_3 - i_2 - i_4 = 0 \tag{395}$$

Hence, from equations 391 to 394 and 395, we obtain

$$\frac{\partial \sigma_x}{\partial x} + \frac{\partial \tau_{xy}}{\partial y} = 0$$

which is the required equation of equilibrium for components of stress in the x direction.   Similarly, for a v block and a v junction, the currents in the network satisfy the stress equation of equilibrium in the y direction.

Hence the currents in the u and v networks satisfy all the conditions of equilibrium if they are

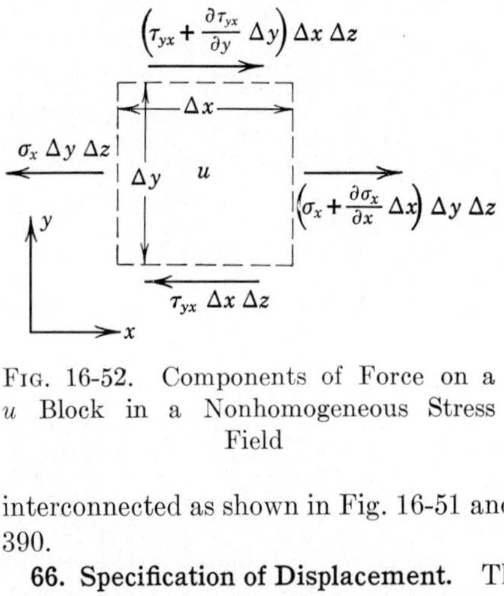

FIG. 16-52.   Components of Force on a u Block in a Nonhomogeneous Stress Field

FIG. 16 53.   Currents Entering and Leaving a Junction of the u network

interconnected as shown in Fig. 16-51 and if the admittances satisfy equation 390.

66. Specification of Displacement.   The absolute potential e_u (or e_v), above ground, of a u (or v) junction, is taken to represent the component of displacement in the x (or y) direction of the corresponding point in the elastic body. Hence,

$$ne_u = u \tag{396}$$

$$ne_v = v \tag{397}$$

where n is a conversion factor in units, say, of inches per volt.

67. Specification of Strain. Consider Fig. 16-54, which represents a portion of a network. Each u junction is identified by a symbol $(e_u)_{r,\,s}$ ($r = 1, 2, 3 \cdots$, $s = 1, 2, 3 \cdots$) representing the potential of the junction. Similarly $(e_v)_{r,s}$ is the potential of a v junction.

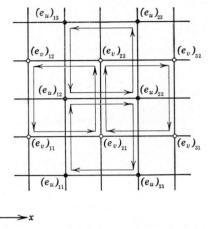

The potential difference between two adjacent u junctions along the x direction is $(e_u)_{r+1,\,s} - (e_u)_{r,\,s}$. We now write

$$(e_u)_{r+1,\,s} - (e_u)_{r,\,s} = \frac{\partial e_u}{\partial x}\Delta x \tag{398}$$

Then, from equations 398 and 396,

$$(e_u)_{r+1,\,s} - (e_u)_{r,\,s} = \frac{1}{n}\frac{\partial u}{\partial x}\Delta x \tag{399}$$

Fig. 16-54. Potentials of the Junctions of the u and v Networks

Now, the unit elongation of the elastic solid in the x direction is given by

$$\epsilon_x = \frac{\partial u}{\partial x} \tag{400}$$

Hence, from equations 400 and 399,

$$\epsilon_x = \frac{n}{\Delta x}\left[(e_u)_{r+1,\,s} - (e_u)_{r,\,s}\right] \tag{401}$$

Similarly, considering the potential difference between a pair of adjacent v junctions along the y direction, we find

$$\epsilon_y = \frac{\partial v}{\partial y} = \frac{n}{\Delta y}\left[(e_v)_{r,\,s+1} - (e_v)_{r,\,s}\right] \tag{402}$$

To find the analogue of the shearing component of strain,

$$\gamma_{xy} = \frac{\partial v}{\partial x} + \frac{\partial u}{\partial y} \tag{403}$$

in the network, we consider the potential difference between two adjacent u junctions along the y direction and the potential difference between two adjacent v junctions along the x direction:

$$(e_u)_{r,\,s+1} - (e_u)_{r,\,s} = \frac{\partial e_u}{\partial y}\,\Delta y = \frac{\Delta y}{n}\frac{\partial u}{\partial y} \tag{404}$$

$$(e_v)_{r+1,\,s} - (e_v)_{r,\,s} = \frac{\partial e_v}{\partial x}\,\Delta x = \frac{\Delta x}{n}\frac{\partial v}{\partial x} \tag{405}$$

Therefore, from equations 403 to 405,

$$\gamma_{xy} = n\left\{\frac{1}{\Delta y}\left[(e_u)_{r,\,s+1} - (e_u)_{r,\,s}\right] + \frac{1}{\Delta x}\left[(e_v)_{r+1,\,s} - (e_v)_{r,\,s}\right]\right\} \tag{406}$$

68. Compatibility Conditions.   The u and v networks must be so constituted that the compatibility condition,

$$\frac{\partial^2 \epsilon_y}{\partial x^2} + \frac{\partial^2 \epsilon_x}{\partial y^2} - \frac{\partial^2 \gamma_{xy}}{\partial x\,\partial y} = 0 \tag{407}$$

is satisfied.   Since equation 407 is simply a necessary condition for the single-valuedness of the displacements u and v, it will be satisfied automatically in the circuit because the potential above ground of any junction can have only one value.   However, it is instructive to verify this by using Kirchhoff's voltage law.   Referring to Fig. 16-54 and equation 402, we have

$$\frac{n}{\Delta y}\left[(e_v)_{12} - (e_v)_{11}\right] = \epsilon_y \tag{408}$$

$$\frac{n}{\Delta y}\left[(e_v)_{22} - (e_v)_{21}\right] = \epsilon_y + \frac{\partial \epsilon_y}{\partial x}\Delta x \tag{409}$$

$$\frac{n}{\Delta y}\left[(e_v)_{32} - (e_v)_{31}\right] = \left(\epsilon_y + \frac{\partial \epsilon_y}{\partial x}\Delta x\right) + \frac{\partial}{\partial x}\left(\epsilon_y + \frac{\partial \epsilon_y}{\partial x}\Delta x\right)\Delta x \tag{410}$$

Adding equations 408 and 410 and subtracting twice equation 409, we have

$$\frac{n}{\Delta x}\left\{\left[(e_v)_{32} - (e_v)_{31}\right] - 2\left[(e_v)_{22} - (e_v)_{21}\right] + \left[(e_v)_{12} - (e_v)_{11}\right]\right\} = \frac{\partial^2 \epsilon_y}{\partial x^2}\Delta x\,\Delta y \tag{411}$$

Again, from Fig. 16-54 and equation 401,

$$\frac{n}{\Delta x}\left[(e_u)_{21} - (e_u)_{11}\right] = \epsilon_x \tag{412}$$

$$\frac{n}{\Delta x}\left[(e_u)_{22} - (e_u)_{12}\right] = \epsilon_x + \frac{\partial \epsilon_x}{\partial y}\Delta y \tag{413}$$

$$\frac{n}{\Delta x}\left[(e_u)_{23} - (e_u)_{13}\right] = \left(\epsilon_x + \frac{\partial \epsilon_x}{\partial y}\Delta y\right) + \frac{\partial}{\partial y}\left(\epsilon_x + \frac{\partial \epsilon_x}{\partial y}\Delta y\right)\Delta y \tag{414}$$

Adding equations 412 and 414 and subtracting twice equation 413, we have

$$\frac{n}{\Delta y}\{[(e_u)_{23} - (e_u)_{13}] - 2[(e_u)_{22} - (e_u)_{12}] + [(e_u)_{21} - (e_u)_{11}]\} = \frac{\partial^2 \epsilon_x}{\partial y^2} \Delta x\, \Delta y \quad (415)$$

Finally, from Fig. 16-54 and equation 406,

$$\frac{n}{\Delta y}[(e_u)_{12} - (e_u)_{11}] + \frac{n}{\Delta x}[(e_v)_{21} - (e_v)_{11}] = \gamma_{yx} \quad (416)$$

$$\frac{n}{\Delta y}[(e_u)_{13} - (e_u)_{12}] + \frac{n}{\Delta x}[(e_v)_{22} - (e_v)_{12}] = \gamma_{xy} + \frac{\partial \gamma_{xy}}{\partial y}\Delta y \quad (417)$$

$$\frac{n}{\Delta y}[(e_u)_{22} - (e_u)_{21}] + \frac{n}{\Delta x}[(e_v)_{31} - (e_v)_{21}] = \gamma_{xy} + \frac{\partial \gamma_{xy}}{\partial x}\Delta x \quad (418)$$

$$\frac{n}{\Delta y}[(e_u)_{23} - (e_u)_{22}] + \frac{n}{\Delta x}[(e_v)_{32} - (e_v)_{22}] = \gamma_{xy} + \frac{\partial \gamma_{xy}}{\partial x}$$
$$+ \frac{\partial}{\partial y}\left(\gamma_{xy} + \frac{\partial \gamma_{xy}}{\partial x}\Delta x\right)\Delta y \quad (419)$$

Adding equations 416 and 419 and subtracting equations 417 and 418 from the sum, we obtain

$$\frac{n}{\Delta y}\{[(e_u)_{23} - (e_u)_{13}] - 2[(e_u)_{22} - (e_u)_{12}] + [(e_u)_{21} - (e_u)_{11}]\}$$
$$+ \frac{n}{\Delta x}\{[(e_v)_{32} - (e_v)_{31}] - 2[(e_v)_{22} - (e_v)_{21}] + [(e_v)_{12} - (e_v)_{11}]\}$$
$$= \frac{\partial^2 \gamma_{xy}}{\partial x\, \partial y}\Delta x\, \Delta y \quad (420)$$

Now, add equations 411 and 415 and subtract equation 420 to obtain

$$\frac{n}{\Delta y}\{[(e_u)_{23} - (e_u)_{13}] + [(e_u)_{13} - (e_u)_{12}] + [(e_u)_{12} - (e_u)_{22}] + [(e_u)_{22} - (e_u)_{23}]\}$$
$$+ \frac{n}{\Delta y}\{[(e_u)_{21} - (e_u)_{11}] + [(e_u)_{11} - (e_u)_{12}] + [(e_u)_{12} - (e_u)_{22}] + [(e_u)_{22} - (e_u)_{12}]\}$$
$$+ \frac{n}{\Delta x}\{[(e_v)_{32} - (e_v)_{31}] + [(e_v)_{31} - (e_v)_{21}] + [(e_v)_{21} - (e_v)_{22}] + [(e_v)_{22} - (e_v)_{32}]\}$$
$$+ \frac{n}{\Delta x}\{[(e_v)_{11} - (e_v)_{21}] + [(e_v)_{21} - (e_v)_{22}] + [(e_v)_{22} - (e_v)_{12}] + [(e_v)_{12} - (e_v)_{11}]\}$$
$$= \left(\frac{\partial^2 \epsilon_x}{\partial y^2} + \frac{\partial^2 \epsilon_y}{\partial x^2} - \frac{\partial^2 \gamma_{xy}}{\partial x\, \partial y}\right)\Delta x\, \Delta y \quad (421)$$

Each quantity in braces in equation 421 represents the four voltage drops around a four-element closed loop in the network, as shown by the arrows in Fig. 16-54. Hence, by Kirchhoff's voltage law, each quantity in braces vanishes and the left-hand side of equation 421 is equal to zero. Comparing equation 421 with equation 407, we see that the circuit satisfies the compatibility condition.

69. Stress-Strain Relations. The circuit and its constants must be chosen so as to satisfy Hooke's law. For a state of plane strain, the stress–strain relations may be written as

$$\sigma_x = (\lambda + 2G)\epsilon_x + \lambda\epsilon_y \tag{422}$$

$$\sigma_y = (\lambda + 2G)\epsilon_y + \lambda\epsilon_x \tag{423}$$

$$\tau_{xy} = G\gamma_{xy} \tag{424}$$

where

$$\lambda = \frac{\mu E}{(1 + \mu)(1 - 2\mu)} = \frac{2\mu G}{1 - 2\mu} \tag{425}$$

We have now to convert the stress–strain relations to their circuit equivalents.

70. Relation between Shear Stress and Shear Strain. If equations 406 and 375 are used, and it is remembered that $\tau_{yx} = \tau_{xy}$, equation 424 becomes

$$\frac{mi_3}{\Delta x\, \Delta z} = -nG\left\{\frac{1}{\Delta y}[(e_u)_{r,\,s+1} - (e_u)_{r,\,s}] + \frac{1}{\Delta x}[(e_v)_{r+1,\,s} - (e_v)_{r,\,s}]\right\} \tag{426}$$

Referring to Fig. 16-51, we write

$$E_b = [(e_u)_{r,\,s+1} - (e_u)_{r,\,s}]$$

$$E_f = -[(e_v)_{r+1,\,s} - (e_v)_{r,\,s}]$$

$$i_3 = i_{g_1} + i_b + i_{c_2} = g_1 E_{g_1} + bE_b + c_2 E_{c_2}$$

If these substitutions are made in equation 426, the latter becomes

$$\frac{m}{\Delta x\, \Delta z}[g_1 E_{g_1} + bE_b + c_2 E_{c_2}] = nG\left[\frac{E_b}{\Delta y} + \frac{E_f}{\Delta x}\right] \tag{427}$$

We can eliminate E_{c_2} from equation 427 by noting, from Fig. 16-51, that Kirchhoff's voltage law requires

$$E_{c_2} = E_f + E_{g_1}$$

Then equation 427 becomes

$$E_b\left[\frac{1}{\Delta y} - \frac{mb}{nG\,\Delta x\, \Delta z}\right] + E_f\left[\frac{1}{\Delta x} - \frac{mc_2}{nG\,\Delta x\, \Delta z}\right] - \frac{mE_{g_1}}{nG\,\Delta x\, \Delta z}(g_1 + c_2) = 0 \tag{428}$$

Equation 428 and, hence, also equation 424 will be satisfied if

$$b = \frac{n\,\Delta x\, \Delta z}{m\,\Delta y}G \tag{429}$$

$$c_2 = \frac{n\,\Delta z}{m}\,G \tag{430}$$

$$g_1 = -\frac{n\,\Delta z}{m}\,G \tag{431}$$

It may be observed that equations 429 to 431 are compatible with the condition of equality of cross-shears as expressed by equation 390. Equations 390 and 429 to 431 determine the values of all the admittances in the link between the u and v networks illustrated in Fig. 16-51. We have

$$b = \frac{n\,\Delta x\,\Delta z}{m\,\Delta y}\,G \tag{432}$$

$$f = \frac{n\,\Delta y\,\Delta z}{m\,\Delta x}\,G \tag{433}$$

$$c_1 = c_2 = \frac{n\,\Delta z}{m}\,G \tag{434}$$

$$g_1 = g_2 = -\frac{n\,\Delta z}{m}\,G \tag{435}$$

71. Relations between Normal Components of Stress and Unit Elongations. We transform the stress–strain relations (equations 422 and 423) to equations relating currents and voltages by using equations 374, 376, 401, and 402 with the result:

$$\frac{mi_1}{\Delta y\,\Delta z} = -\frac{n(\lambda + 2G)}{\Delta x}\,[(e_u)_{r+1,\,s} - (e_u)_{r,\,s}] - \frac{n\lambda}{\Delta y}\,[(e_v)_{r,\,s+1} - (e_v)_{r,\,s}] \tag{436}$$

$$\frac{mi_5}{\Delta x\,\Delta z} = -\frac{n(\lambda + 2G)}{\Delta y}\,[(e_v)_{r,\,s+1} - (e_v)_{r,\,s}] - \frac{n\lambda}{\Delta x}\,[(e_u)_{r+1,\,s} - (e_u)_{r,\,s}] \tag{437}$$

These equations express relations between voltage drops along an x-direction line of the u network and a y-direction line of the v network. In order to satisfy equations 436 and 437, it is necessary to have a suitable connection between the two networks at those points where an x-direction line of the u network crosses a y-direction line of the v network. Such a connection is shown in Fig. 16-55. Referring to this figure, we may write

$$(e_u)_{r+1,\,s} - (e_u)_{r,\,s} = -E_a$$

$$(e_v)_{r,\,s+1} - (e_v)_{r,\,s} = -E_e$$

$$i_1 = i_2 = i_a + i_{d_1} + i_{h_2} = aE_a + d_1E_{d_1} + h_2E_{h_2}$$

$$i_5 = i_6 = i_e + i_{d_2} - i_{h_2} = eE_e + d_2E_{d_2} - h_2E_{h_2}$$

$$i_5 = i_e + i_{d_1} - i_{h_1} = eE_e + d_1E_{d_1} - h_1E_{h_1}$$

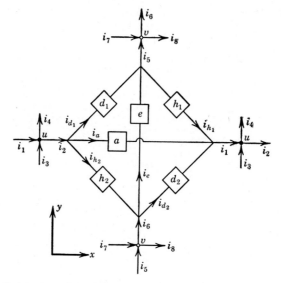

FIG. 16-55. Interconnection of the u and v Networks Where an x-Direction Line of the u Network Crosses a y-Direction Line of the v Network

If these relations are substituted into equations 436 and 437, the latter become

$$\frac{m}{\Delta y \, \Delta z}[aE_a + d_1E_{d_1} + h_2E_{h_2}] = \frac{n(\lambda + 2G)E_a}{\Delta x} + \frac{n\lambda E_e}{\Delta y} \qquad (438)$$

$$\frac{m}{\Delta x \, \Delta z}[eE_e + d_2E_{d_2} - h_2E_{h_2}] = \frac{n(\lambda + 2G)E_e}{\Delta y} + \frac{n\lambda E_a}{\Delta x} \qquad (439)$$

$$\frac{m}{\Delta x \, \Delta z}[eE_e + d_1E_{d_1} - h_1E_{h_1}] = \frac{n(\lambda + 2G)E_e}{\Delta y} + \frac{n\lambda E_a}{\Delta x} \qquad (440)$$

Now, by Kirchhoff's voltage law,

$$E_e - E_{d_1} + E_{h_2} = 0 \qquad (441)$$

$$E_a - E_{d_2} - E_{h_2} = 0 \qquad (442)$$

$$E_a - E_{d_1} - E_{h_1} = 0 \qquad (443)$$

Eliminating E_e between equations 438 and 441, E_a between equations 439 and 442, and E_a between equations 440 and 443, we find

$$\left[\frac{ma}{\Delta y \, \Delta z} - \frac{n(\lambda + 2G)}{\Delta x}\right]E_a + \left[\frac{md_1}{\Delta y \, \Delta z} - \frac{n\lambda}{\Delta y}\right]E_{d_1} + \left[\frac{mh_2}{\Delta y \, \Delta z} + \frac{n\lambda}{\Delta y}\right]E_{h_2} = 0$$

$$(444)$$

$$\left[\frac{me}{\Delta x\,\Delta z} - \frac{n(\lambda + 2G)}{\Delta y}\right] E_e + \left[\frac{md_2}{\Delta x\,\Delta z} - \frac{n\lambda}{\Delta x}\right] E_{d_2} - \left[\frac{mh_2}{\Delta x\,\Delta z} + \frac{n\lambda}{\Delta x}\right] E_{h_2} = 0$$

(445)

$$\left[\frac{me}{\Delta x\,\Delta z} - \frac{n(\lambda + 2G)}{\Delta y}\right] E_e + \left[\frac{md_1}{\Delta x\,\Delta z} - \frac{n\lambda}{\Delta x}\right] E_{d_1} - \left[\frac{mh_1}{\Delta x\,\Delta z} + \frac{n\lambda}{\Delta x}\right] E_{h_1} = 0$$

(446)

If equations 444 to 446 are satisfied, so will the stress–strain relations (equations 422 and 423). The former will be satisfied, for all values of voltage drops E, if all the bracketed quantities vanish, that is, if

$$a = \frac{n\,\Delta y\,\Delta z}{m\,\Delta x}\,(\lambda + 2G)$$

(447)

$$e = \frac{n\,\Delta x\,\Delta z}{m\,\Delta y}\,(\lambda + 2G)$$

(448)

$$d_1 = d_2 = \frac{n\,\Delta z\lambda}{m}$$

(449)

$$h_1 = h_2 = -\frac{n\,\Delta z\lambda}{m}$$

(450)

72. Positive and Negative Admittances. It may be seen, from equations 449, 450, 434, and 435 that both positive and negative admittances are required. In order to avoid the necessity for negative resistances an a-c circuit is used rather than a d-c circuit. In an a-c circuit, positive and negative resistances are supplied by inductances and capacitances. As a simple example, consider the two circuits shown in Figs. 16-56a and b in

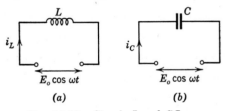

Fig. 16-56. Simple L and C Loops

which L is a pure inductance and C is a pure capacitance while the impressed voltage is in each case a steady oscillation of frequency ω. The equations governing the currents, are respectively,

$$L\frac{di_L}{dt} = E_o \cos \omega t$$

(451)

$$\frac{1}{C}\int i_c\,dt = E_o \cos \omega t$$

(452)

Hence, the steady-state currents are

$$i_L = \left(\frac{E_o}{\omega L}\right)\sin \omega t$$

(453)

$$i_c = -E_o C\omega \sin \omega t$$

(454)

Thus, the inductance corresponds to a positive admittance while the capacitance corresponds to a negative admittance, and we can satisfy the requirement $c_1 = -g_1$ (see equations 434 and 435) by getting $1/LC = \omega^2$.

Since all real coils and capacitors have resistive losses, the circuits of Fig. 16-56 are better represented by Fig. 16-57a and b. The currents are then determined by

$$L \frac{di_L}{dt} + R_L i_L = E_o \cos \omega t \tag{455}$$

$$\frac{1}{C} \int i_c \, dt + R_c i_c = E_o \cos \omega t \tag{456}$$

for which the steady-state solutions are

$$i_L = \left(\frac{E_o}{\sqrt{R_L{}^2 + \omega^2 L^2}} \right) \sin (\omega t + \alpha) \qquad \alpha = \tan^{-1} \frac{R_L}{\omega L} \tag{457}$$

$$i_c = -\left(\frac{E_o C \omega}{\sqrt{1 + R_c{}^2 C^2 \omega^2}} \right) \sin (\omega t - \beta) \qquad \beta = \tan^{-1} R_c C \omega \tag{458}$$

On account of the phase differences α and β, we cannot satisfy a relation such as $c_1 = -g_1$ exactly, nor can we maintain a 90° phase difference between voltage and current as required by equations 451 to 454. This is the major difficulty in constructing a real analogous circuit.

73. A-C Network. If we assume negligible resistive losses, the complete analogous circuit is formed by adding, to the network of Fig. 16-50, the cross connections shown in Figs. 16-51 and 16-55

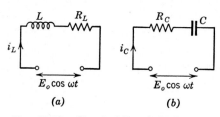

Fig. 16-57. Simple LR and CR Loops

with coils for admittances a, b, c_1, c_2, d_1, d_2, e, f and capacitors for g_1, g_2, h_1, h_2, all having values as prescribed by equations 432 to 435 and 447 to 450. The resulting circuit is shown in Fig. 16-58.

It may be seen that diagonal coils always occur in parallel pairs and the same applies to the capacitors. The members of each pair may be combined to form the simplified circuit shown in Fig. 16-59. In the simplified circuit, the stresses cannot be measured directly as currents, but the strains can still be measured as voltage drops, and the stresses may be calculated from the strains.

74. Boundary Conditions. Boundary shapes and boundary loadings are realized by cutting appropriate network lines and supplying appropriate currents. Consider, for example, a *free* boundary parallel to the x axis (that is, $y = $ constant). On such a boundary we require $\sigma_y = 0$ and $\tau_{xy} = 0$. The normal component of stress σ_y is a current flowing into a v junction along a vertical line of the v network. Hence, all the vertical lines of the v network should be cut at junctions $y = $ const and left free. Vertical lines of the u network carry currents τ_{xy} into u junctions. Hence, all vertical lines of the u network should be cut at $y = $ const and left free. In Fig. 16-60, the dashed

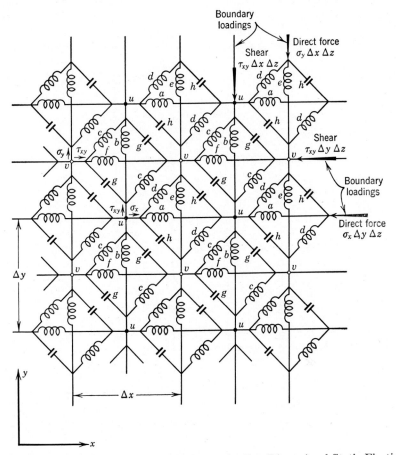

FIG. 16-58. Kron's A-C Network Analogue of a Two-Dimensional Static Elastic Field

wavy line marked $y = $ const shows where the network should be cut to form a free boundary $y = $ const.

If the boundary $y = $ const is to have prescribed normal and shearing stresses on it, instead of being free, normal components (σ_y) are introduced as currents supplied to the cut lines of the v network, and shearing components (τ_{xy}) are introduced as currents supplied to the cut lines of the u network. Such boundary stresses are shown in Fig. 16-58.

To form a free boundary $x = $ const, horizontal lines of the u network are cut at a junction and left free in order to annul σ_x, and horizontal lines of the v network are cut at a junction and left free to annul τ_{xy}. The dashed wavy line marked $x = $ const, in Fig. 16-60, crosses the lines to be cut for such a boundary. If boundary stresses are prescribed, σ_x is applied as a current entering the u network, and τ_{xy} is applied as a current entering the v network, as shown in Fig. 16-58.

If the mesh of the network is fine enough, curved boundaries may be formed by cutting across the mesh at junction points as indicated by the dotted line

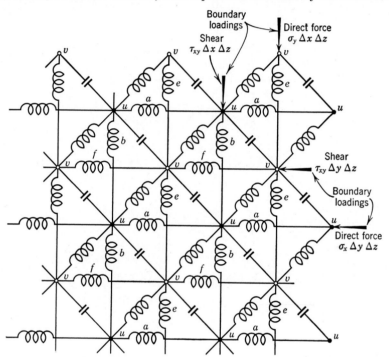

FIG. 16-59. Kron's Simplified Network Analogue of a Two-Dimensional Static Elastic Field

in Fig. 16-60. Kron suggests the possibility of having a permanent network and forming boundaries for each special problem simply by opening and closing switches.

75. Applications. Several experiments are reported by G. K. Carter[62] in which he used a standard a-c network analyzer to reproduce simple states of stress. A bar in simple tension, a bar in pure bending, and a thick-walled cylindrical tube under internal and external pressure were analyzed. The difficulty with resistive losses, mentioned in article 72, was encountered. Ideally, all the voltages in the circuit should be exactly 90° out of phase with the currents, but, owing to losses in the circuit elements, the ideal phase relation is not realized. Carter was able to overcome the discrepancies by supply-

ing additional currents in phase with the voltage. For example, the results of
the experiment with simple tension (σ_y) are shown in Fig. 16-61. The v junctions at the lower end of the network were grounded (zero displacement) while
voltages were applied to the v junctions at the upper end. At the latter,
currents entered the network, 90° out of phase with the voltage (as indicated
by the symbol jI) and with magnitudes as shown in the figure. Voltages
were measured at all the u and v junctions of the network and compared with
the theoretical displacements. In the latter, Young's modulus was taken as
30×10^6 psi and Poisson's ratio as 0.38. In order to bring the experimental

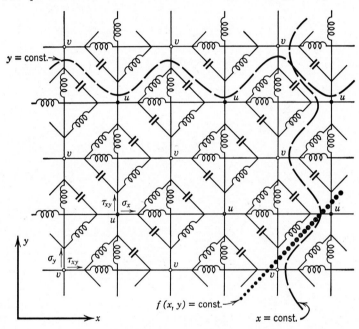

FIG. 16-60. Formation of Boundaries in Kron's Network

results close to the theory, an additional current, in phase with the voltage,
had to be applied at the center u junction in the lowest row, as indicated in
the figure. By adjusting this current to a optimum value (20.6), the displacements shown in the figure were recorded. These are to be compared with the
theoretical values shown in parentheses.

Carter states that no simple and easily applied rule was found for determining the optimum position and magnitude of the loss-replacing currents.

76. D-C Network Analogue of a Shear-Lag Problem. R. E. Newton[63] has
devised an electric network for determining the stress distribution in a plane
sheet reinforced by a set of parallel stringers. The combination has an axis
of geometric and elastic symmetry parallel to the stringers and is loaded in
its plane by forces parallel to and distributed symmetrically with respect to
the axis of geometric and elastic symmetry. The assumption is made that

the displacement perpendicular to the axis of symmetry is zero.　This problem is known in aeronautical engineering as a shear-lag problem.

As in Kron's analogy, stress is represented by current, displacement by potential, strain by voltage drop, and elastic constants by admittances.　The

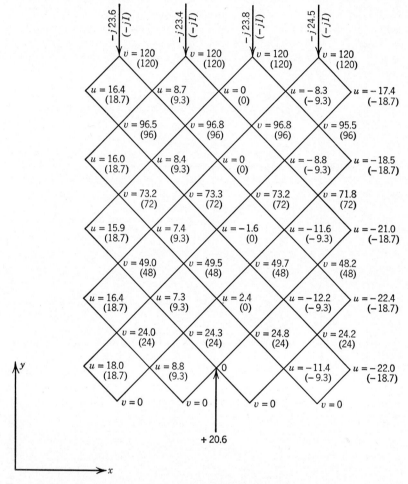

FIG. 16-61.　Comparison of Theoretical Displacements (in Parentheses) for Simple Tension with Potentials Measured by Carter in Kron's Equivalent Network after Applying Loss-Replacing Current

equations of equilibrium are represented by Kirchoff's current law, Hooke's law by Ohm's law, and the conditions of compatibility by Kirchhoff's voltage law.

Since only one component of displacement (say v) is nonzero, only one network is required.　Thus, in Fig. 16-58, the u network is removed and all admittances disappear except e and f.   The necessity for positive and negative admittances does not arise since there are no interconnections between networks.   Hence, a d-c network may be used, and e and f may be conductances. Since e is proportional to the cross-sectional area of a stringer, and f is proportional to the thickness of the sheet, Newton is able to accommodate variations of these dimensions from point to point by appropriate choice of resistors.

V. ELECTRIC-NETWORK ANALOGUES OF FRAMED STRUCTURES

V. Bush[64] has devised electric networks which are equivalent to pin-connected and rigid-joint structural frames.   A special circuit is available for the solution of each of the following problems:

1. Equilibrium of pin-connected statically determinate structures.
2. Equilibrium of pin-connected structures with redundant members.
3. Equilibrium of rectangular frameworks.
4. Motion of pin-connected structures, with or without redundant members.

There are many circuit arrangements which can be made to represent a single structure.   The choice of circuit depends in part on the relative importance assigned to the simplicity of the circuit and on the ease of constructing the circuit by inspection of the structure.   For this reason circuits vary from fixed arrangements for solving a system of simultaneous, linear, algebraic equations to sets of subcircuits representing individual structural members. In the former case each structural problem must first be transformed to mathematical form.   In the latter case the circuit is built up by connecting the "structural members" to form the "framework," and this convenience is likely to be gained at the expense of simplicity of the circuit.

V. EQUILIBRIUM OF PIN-CONNECTED STATICALLY DETERMINATE STRUCTURES

The analysis of structures, in which the forces in the members are determined by considerations of static equilibrium alone, is so simple that it is not necessary to resort to an analogue calculating machine.   However, the study of one example will simplify the subsequent study of indeterminate structures.

At each pinned joint of a plane framework the sum of the horizontal components of force must vanish, and the sum of the vertical components of force must vanish.   In Bush's analogy, current corresponds to force.   Thus the equilibrium conditions at a joint are represented by Kirchhoff's current law.   Two networks are required: one for horizontal forces and one for vertical forces.   Horizontal members appear only in one network and vertical members only in the other.   Since a diagonal member has both horizontal and vertical components, it appears in both networks.

To construct the electrical analogue of the Pratt truss shown in Fig. 16-62, first lay out two sets of 12 terminals, representing the 12 panel points.   One set of 12 terminals is for horizontal forces, and the other set is for vertical forces.   In the horizontal network connect each pair of terminals which correspond to panel points that are connected by a horizontal member in the structure.   Similarly, in the vertical network, connect each pair of terminals which correspond to panel points that are connected by a vertical member. In *both* networks connect each pair of terminals which correspond to the ends of a diagonal member, but interpose a transformer with its primary coil in the horizontal network and its secondary coil in the vertical network. The transformer ratio (ratio of secondary to primary current) is made equal to the tangent of the angle (α) of inclination of the diagonal member with the horizontal. This completes the circuit. Forces are applied by inserting alternating currents at the load and support points. In the Pratt truss of

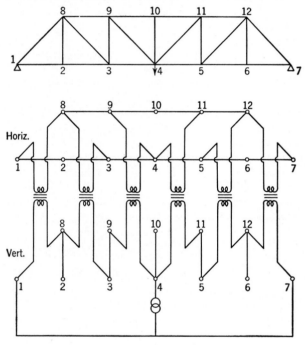

Fig. 16-62. A Pin-Connected Statically Determinate Structure and Bush's Equivalent Circuit

Fig. 16-62, these are at terminals 1, 4, and 7 of the vertical network, since the forces are vertical and are applied at panel points 1, 4, and 7. The currents should be proportional to the external forces and should all be in phase. If the ratio of external force to current inserted is Υ, the force in a horizontal or vertical member is equal to Υ times the current measured between the appropriate terminals. The force in a diagonal member is obtained by measuring the current between the corresponding terminals in the vertical, or horizontal network and multiplying by $\Upsilon \operatorname{cosec} \alpha$ or $\Upsilon \sec \alpha$, respectively.

In this type of problem the only circuit elements that appear are current transformers. The only voltage drops are those due to leakage reactance and internal resistance. These should be small.

"Ideal" transformers appear in all of Bush's equivalent circuits. They may be constructed to the required degree of accuracy by using nickel–iron-alloy cores and closely coupled windings. The flux density should be low and the primary turns sufficient so that the exciting current is negligible in comparison with the work current. Frequency should be high enough to make the size of the transformer small but not so high that currents flowing through distributed capacities will be appreciable in comparison with the work current.

W. Equilibrium of Pin-Connected Frames with Redundant Members

If a pin-connected structure has redundant members, the forces in the members are influenced by their changes in length. In a single member the relation between axial force P and change of length Δ is

$$\Delta = \frac{Pl}{AE} \qquad (459)$$

where l, A, and E are, respectively, the length, cross-sectional area, and modulus of elasticity of the member.

To form the analogy, force, as before, is taken proportional to current:

$$P = \Upsilon_1 I \qquad (460)$$

where Υ_1 is a scale factor, and change of length of a member is taken proportional to voltage drop (V) between terminals:

$$\Delta = \Upsilon_2 V \qquad (461)$$

The analogue of equation 459 is Ohm's law:

$$V = IR \qquad (462)$$

Thus, electrical resistance R corresponds to compliance (l/AE):

$$R = \frac{\Upsilon_1}{\Upsilon_2} \frac{l}{AE} \qquad (463)$$

The circuit is constructed exactly as in the statically determinate case except that, wherever two terminals were connected before, the appropriate

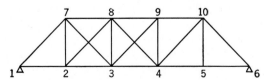

Fig. 16-63. A Pin-Connected Statically Indeterminate Structure

resistance (given by equation 463) is inserted between them. Thus, for the Pratt truss with two redundant panels shown in Fig. 16-63, the redundant panels are represented by the circuit shown in Fig. 16-64. Note that *each* of the two connections representing a single diagonal member has inserted in it the resistance given by equation 463.

Equations 459 to 463 represent the analogy for a single member. The extension to a framework follows from energy considerations.

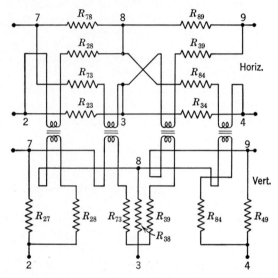

FIG. 16-64. Bush's Circuit Equivalent of the Two Indeterminate Panels of the Truss Shown in Fig. 16-63

The potential energy stored in a member is $P^2l/2AE$. If subscripts h, v, d refer to horizontal, vertical, and diagonal members, respectively, the total energy of deformation of the structure is

$$\sum_h \frac{P_h{}^2 l_h}{2A_h E_h} + \sum_v \frac{P_v{}^2 l_v}{2A_v E_v} + \sum_d \frac{P_d{}^2 l_d}{2A_d E_d}$$

The forces in the members will assume such values as to make the total energy of deformation a minimum. Hence,

$$\delta \left\{ \sum_h \frac{P_h{}^2 l_h}{2A_h E_h} + \sum_v \frac{P_v{}^2 l_v}{2A_v E_v} + \sum_d \frac{P_d{}^2 l_d}{2A_d E_d} \right\} = 0 \qquad (464)$$

In the electric circuit the power dissipated in an element is $I^2 R$. The total power dissipation in the horizontal network will be a minimum:

$$\delta \left\{ \sum_h I_h{}^2 R_h + \sum_d I_{hd}{}^2 R_d \right\} = 0 \qquad (465)$$

where I_{hd} is the current in the dth diagonal element of the horizontal network.

Similarly, the total power dissipated in the vertical network will be a minimum:

$$\delta \left\{ \sum_v I_v{}^2 R_v + \sum_d I_{vd}{}^2 R_d \right\} = 0 \qquad (466)$$

where I_{vd} is the current in the dth diagonal element of the vertical circuit. Now,

$$\Upsilon_1 I_h = P_h$$

$$\Upsilon_1 I_v = P_v$$

$$\Upsilon_1{}^2 (I_{hd}{}^2 + I_{vd}{}^2) = P_d{}^2$$

$$\frac{\Upsilon_2 R_h}{\Upsilon_1} = \frac{l_h}{A_h E_h}$$

$$\frac{\Upsilon_2 R_v}{\Upsilon_1} = \frac{l_v}{A_v E_v} \quad \text{and} \quad \frac{\Upsilon_2 R_d}{\Upsilon_1} = \frac{l_d}{A_d E_d}$$

Hence, substituting in equations 465 and 466, adding the two equations, and canceling the scale factors, we arrive at equations 464. The analogy is thus complete.

In constructing the circuit for the truss shown in Fig. 16-63, Bush used resistances ranging from ¾ to 3½ ohms and commercial instrument transformers rated at 5 amperes and 80 watts. Since the diagonals were at 45° to the horizontal, nominal 1:1 transformers were used. The error in ratio was less than 0.1 per cent at 3.2 ohms load from 0.5 to 5.0 amperes. With 13 ohms load the error was less than 2 per cent at 0.5 amperes and decreased with increase of current. However, the transformers were found to have excessive leakage reactance, so that, with pure resistance representing compliance, the necessary condition was not satisfied that the impedance angles be the same in all branches of the circuit. To make the impedance angles the same, each branch was made up of a resistance and an inductance. The latter were so chosen that, together with the leakage inductance, the resulting impedance angles were all equal. Bush calls attention to the method developed by Mallock[65] for automatically compensating for imperfect transformer action.

Compared with a mathematical solution of the truss in Fig. 16-63, Bush's results were in error by 0 to 3.5 per cent, the larger percentage errors occurring only in the low-stressed members.

X. Equilibrium of Rectangular Frameworks

To analyze simple and multiple rigid-frame bents, Bush has devised an electric-circuit equivalent of the slope-deflection equations. These equations may be derived by considering the equilibrium and deformation of a single structural member.

In Fig. 16-65 the member AB, of length L, is acted on by moments M_A and M_B at ends A and B, respectively. Both moments are taken positive clockwise. To be in equilibrium under moments and transverse forces applied only at its ends, a shear force S is required such that

$$M_A + M_B + SL = 0 \tag{467}$$

Positive S tends to rotate the member clockwise. The curvature of the member at any section is assumed to be proportional to the bending moment at that section, the factor of proportionality being the flexural rigidity EI.

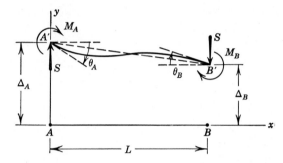

Fig. 16-65. Plane Deformation of a Slender Uniform Bar Acted on by Flexural Couples and Transverse Forces at Its Ends

Using the approximate expression for curvature, we may then write the Bernoulli–Euler equation:

$$EI \frac{d^2y}{dx^2} = M \tag{468}$$

Taking the origin of coordinates at A, we have

$$M = M_A + Sx$$

Integrating equation 468 once and using the boundary conditions,

$$\frac{dy}{dx}\Big]_{x=0} = -\theta_A$$

$$\frac{dy}{dx}\Big]_{x=L} = -\theta_B$$

we find

$$\theta_A - \theta_B = \frac{M_A L}{EI} + \frac{SL^2}{2EI} \tag{469}$$

where θ_A and θ_B are the rotations of the tangents to the elastic curve at A and B, respectively, both positive clockwise.

Integrating again and using the boundary conditions,

$$y]_{x=0} = \Delta_A \qquad y]_{x=L} = \Delta_B$$

we find

$$\Delta_A - \Delta_B = \theta_B L + \frac{M_A L^2}{2EI} + \frac{SL^3}{3EI} \qquad (470)$$

$\Delta_A - \Delta_B$ is the relative transverse displacement of the two ends of the member, considered positive for clockwise rotation of the line joining the ends of the member. Equations 467, 469, and 470 are the slope-deflection equations.

In Bush's analogy, force, moment, rotation, and displacement are all represented by currents. Calling Υ_1, Υ_2, Υ_3, Υ_4 the scale factors between current and shear, moment, rotation and displacement, respectively, we write

$$S = \Upsilon_1 I_s \qquad (471)$$

$$M_A = \Upsilon_2 I_{M_A} \qquad (472)$$

$$M_B = \Upsilon_2 I_{M_B} \qquad (473)$$

$$\theta_A = \Upsilon_3 I_{\theta_A} \qquad (474)$$

$$\theta_B = \Upsilon_3 I_{\theta_B} \qquad (475)$$

$$\Delta_A = \Upsilon_4 I_{\Delta_A} \qquad (476)$$

$$\Delta_B = \Upsilon_4 I_{\Delta_B} \qquad (477)$$

where the I's are currents representing the quantities indicated by the subscripts.

Substituting equations 471 to 477 in equations 467, 469, and 470 we have the electrical equivalents of the slope-deflection equations:

$$I_{M_A} + I_{M_B} + \left(\frac{\Upsilon_1 L}{\Upsilon_2}\right) I_s = 0 \qquad (478)$$

$$I_{\theta_A} - I_{\theta_B} = \left(\frac{\Upsilon_2 L}{\Upsilon_3 EI}\right) I_{M_A} + \left(\frac{\Upsilon_1 L^2}{2\Upsilon_3 EI}\right) I_s \qquad (479)$$

$$I_{\Delta_A} - I_{\Delta_B} = \left(\frac{\Upsilon_3 L}{\Upsilon_4}\right) I_{\theta_B} + \left(\frac{\Upsilon_2 L^2}{2\Upsilon_4 EI}\right) I_{M_A} + \left(\frac{\Upsilon_1 L^3}{3\Upsilon_4 EI}\right) I_s \qquad (480)$$

Bush's equivalent circuit is shown in Fig. 16-66, in which the four upper terminals represent the end A, and the four lower terminals represent the end B of the member. Positive shear is represented by current I_s entering at A and leaving at B. Positive moment is represented by current I_{M_A} entering at A and I_{M_B} entering at B. Positive rotation is represented by current I_{θ_A} entering at A and I_{θ_B} leaving at B. Positive transverse displacement is represented by current I_{Δ_A} entering at A and I_{Δ_B} leaving at B, so that $I_{\Delta_A} - I_{\Delta_B}$ represents positive relative transverse displacement (that is, clockwise rotation of the member).

Six current transformers are used, with ratios T_1, $\cdots$, T_6 given by the six quantities in parentheses in equations 478 to 480. Thus:

$$T_1 = \frac{\Upsilon_1 L}{\Upsilon_2} \qquad T_4 = \frac{\Upsilon_3 L}{\Upsilon_4}$$

$$T_2 = \frac{\Upsilon_1 L^2}{2\Upsilon_3 EI} \qquad T_5 = \frac{\Upsilon_2 L^2}{2\Upsilon_4 EI}$$

$$T_3 = \frac{\Upsilon_2 L}{\Upsilon_3 EI} \qquad T_6 = \frac{\Upsilon_1 L^3}{3\Upsilon_4 EI}$$

With these transformer ratios, it may be verified readily, by applying Kirchhoff's current law, that the circuit satisfies the equivalent slope-deflection equations 478 to 480.

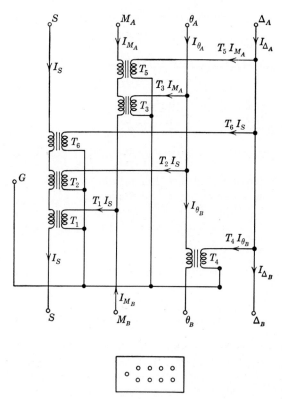

FIG. 16-66. Bush's Circuit Equivalent of the Slope-Deflection Equations

The nine terminals in Fig. 16-66 are used for connecting the member to adjacent members, G being a common terminal. Thus if terminals G and θ_B are connected to terminals G' and θ_A' of an adjacent member, the current I_{θ_B} is forced to be equal to $I_{\theta'_A}$ and, thus, the rotation θ_B is made equal to the rotation θ_A', as required by continuity.

In drawing circuit diagrams for frameworks it is convenient to use a symbol, shown in the lower part of Fig. 16-66, to represent a member.   The nine terminals in the symbol represent the nine terminals in the corresponding positions in the preceding circuit.

Consider, first, four members meeting at a rigid joint, as shown in the upper part of Fig. 16-67.   The equivalent circuit is shown in the lower part of the same figure.   The sum of all the moments acting on the joint is made equal to zero by joining the four corresponding terminals at M.   The rotations of

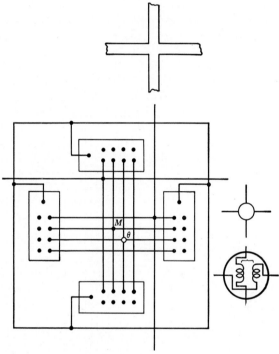

Fig. 16-67.   Connections Required in Bush's Equivalent Circuit When Four Members Meet at a Rigid Joint

all members meeting at the joint are made equal by using a 1:1 transformer connection at θ.   The connection at θ is indicated by a circle, the actual connecting circuit being shown at the right.   The transverse displacements of adjoining vertical members are made equal by series connection, and the same is done for adjoining horizontal members, but the two connections are not joined, since the displacements are at right angles and not necessarily equal. The shear connections depend on the distribution of applied loads in a complete structure.

A problem of wind loads on a nine-panel bent is shown in Fig. 16-68.   In the circuit the sum of the moments at each joint is made equal to zero by interconnection as described previously.   Rotations of adjoining members are made equal by series connection in the case of two members and by transformer connection in the case of three or four. Where two vertical members meet, the transverse displacements are made equal by series connection. The transverse displacements of all the horizontal members must be zero; so the corresponding circuits of members 1–9 are left open. At each floor level the lateral displacements of all vertical members are made equal by transformer

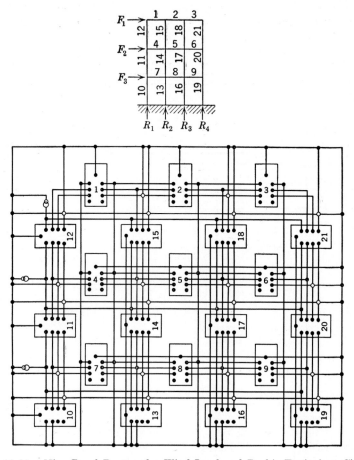

Fig. 16-68. Nine-Panel Bent under Wind Load and Bush's Equivalent Circuit

connections. The displacements and rotations of the lower ends of the first-story columns are assumed to be zero, and so the corresponding terminals are left unconnected. The applied loads are represented by adjustable sources of alternating current, F_1, F_2, F_3, held strictly in phase. The currents which appear at R_1, R_2, R_3, R_4 are proportional to the foundation reactions.

The sum of the shears in members 12, 15, 18, and 21 is made equal to the load F_1 by connecting the five terminals together. Similarly, for reaction R_1

and the shears in 1, 4, 7. The sum of the shears in 11, 14, 17, 20 minus the sum of the shears in 12, 15, 18, 21 is made equal to F_2 by connecting all the terminals representing these forces. The load F_3 and the reactions R_2 and R_3 are treated similarly. Attention must be paid to algebraic signs in making connections. In solving this problem Bush made use of symmetry conditions with resulting simplification of the circuit.

The cores of the transformers were made of continuous annular laminations $2\frac{1}{16}$ in. outside diameter, $1\frac{3}{4}$ in. inside diameter, and 0.005 in. thick of Hypernick, annealed and lacquered. The basic winding was 222 turns of no. 19

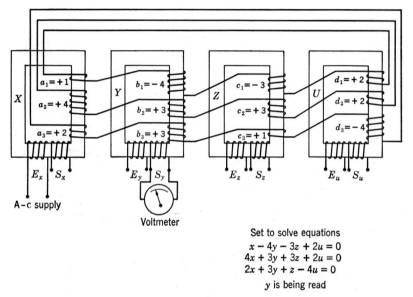

Set to solve equations
$$x - 4y - 3z + 2u = 0$$
$$4x + 3y + 3z + 2u = 0$$
$$2x + 3y + z - 4u = 0$$
$$y \text{ is being read}$$

FIG. 16-69. Principle of Mallock's Electric Computer for Solving Simultaneous Linear Algebraic Equations, Illustrated for Three Equations

B. & S., enameled and cotton-covered, doubled, for both primary and secondary windings. The coil was wound by hand, carrying the four strands through together, both to insure a one-to-one ratio and to produce a minimum of leakage reactance. At 500 cps the error in transformer ratio averaged about 0.5 per cent maximum for a load equivalent to five times the resistance of a single transformer, over the design range of currents.

In measuring currents in the circuit, a low-resistance shunt and a vacuum-tube amplifier were used. Great care had to be taken to ensure low-resistance connections as the resistance everywhere in the circuit had to be low.

The final results for shear, moment, displacement, and rotation had errors ranging from 0 to 30 per cent, but the larger percentage errors were always associated with the smaller magnitudes.

Y. Analogue Machines for Solving Simultaneous Linear Algebraic Equations

The determination of stresses in a statically indeterminate structure under static loading is equivalent to the solution of a system of simultaneous linear algebraic equations. Such equations appear in many branches of engineering and physics, and several machines are available for their solution. A few of the more recent machines are described here.

77. Mallock's Machine.[65] The fundamental principle of operation of this machine is illustrated in Fig. 16-69 for the case of three equations. X, Y, Z, U are four small a-c transformers and a_1, b_1, c_1, $\cdots$ are coils having, respectively, a_1, b_1, c_1, $\cdots$ turns. The transformer design is such that the stray flux is very small, and, hence, in any transformer the flux through each turn is essentially the same. Voltage drops in the coils, due to resistance, are counteracted by a compensator (not shown) consisting of an amplifier and another transformer for each of the main transformers.

Each of the three sets of coils, a_1, b_1, c_1, d_1; a_2, b_2, c_2, d_2; a_3, b_3, c_3, d_3, is connected in series and short-circuited, as shown in the diagram. The direction in which a coil is connected corresponds to the sign of the symbol representing the number of turns.

If an alternating voltage is applied to an independent coil E_x, on the transformer X, a current will flow in the coil and will induce a flux in the core of X; this flux will induce electromotive forces and, consequently, currents in the circuits a_1, b_1, c_1, d_1, $\cdots$, and these currents will induce fluxes in the other cores. After a short time a steady state will be attained.

With no stray flux and resistance losses perfectly compensated, the electromotive force induced in any coil of a given transformer is proportional to the number of turns in the coil, and the potential difference of the coil is equal to the induced electromotive force. If x, y, z, u are the electromotive forces induced in single turns of the four transformers, the potential difference of a coil a_1 will be a_1x, and the potential difference of the four coils in series will be $a_1x + b_1y + c_1z + d_1u$. Since the circuit is short-circuited, this sum must be zero, so that we have

$$a_1x + b_1y + c_1z + d_1u = 0$$

and, similarly,

$$a_2x + b_2y + c_2z + d_2u = 0$$

$$a_3x + b_3y + c_3z + d_3u = 0$$

If we now measure the electromotive forces induced in an additional coil S_x on X and corresponding coils S_y, S_z, S_u on Y, Z, U, each of these coils having the same number of turns, we can find the ratios x/u, y/u, z/u, and these will be the roots x, y, z of the equations:

$$a_1x + b_1y + c_1z + d_1 = 0$$

$$a_2x + b_2y + c_2z + d_2 = 0$$

$$a_3x + b_3y + c_3z + d_3 = 0$$

A machine, based on this principle, for solving ten equations was manufactured by the Cambridge Instrument Co., Ltd.

78. The Consolidated Computer.[66]   The fundamental operations that occur in the solution of systems of linear algebraic equations are the multiplication of pairs of numbers and the addition or subtraction of the resulting products. These operations may be carried out by simple resistor networks.   In Fig. 16-70 is shown a circuit for producing a product proportional to ax, where a and x are introduced by the two potentiometers: x, for example being the fraction of the total resistance of the x potentiometer.   In Fig. 16-71 is shown a circuit for obtaining an open-circuit voltage proportional to the sum

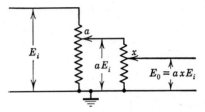
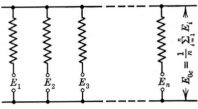

FIG. 16-70.   Circuit for Producing a Voltage Proportional to the Product ax

FIG. 16-71.   Circuit for Summing (Averaging) Voltages

of a number of voltages.   In Fig. 16-72 combinations of these circuits are connected to form the equivalent of

$$a_1 x + b_1 y + c_1 z = d_1$$

when the null indicator N reads zero.   In the case of three equations there would be three such circuits.

The procedure for operating the network is based on the Gauss–Seidel method of iteration.   For a three-equation network the values of all the coefficients are first set into the 12 a_1, b_1, c_1, d_1 potentiometers.   Tentative values y_0 and z_0 are set into the first equation, and x is adjusted to a value x_1 which gives a null reading on the indicator.   The indicator is then switched to the second equation, z_0 and x_1 are inserted, and y is adjusted to y_1 for null. When the indicator is switched to the third equation, x_1 and y_1 are inserted, and z is adjusted to z_1 for null.   We now have a first approximation for x_1, y_1, z_1.   The process is then repeated, by switching to the first equation, inserting y_1 and z_1, and adjusting the x potentiometer to the value x_2 that gives a null reading, then proceeding to the second and third equations, and ending with a second approximation x_2, y_2, z_2.   The cycle is repeated as many times as is necessary to satisfy all three equations.   If the main diagonal coefficients are large in comparison with the sum of the absolute values of the side terms along the same row or column, the convergence will be rapid.   Not every system yields a convergent sequence.   It is possible, but impractical, to bring the system to a suitable form by normalization of the equations.

A machine of this type for 12 equations is manufactured by the Consolidated Engineering Corporation.

79. Murray's Machine.[12] A resistance network based on another principle, in which the iterative process always converges, has been devised by F. J. Murray. The basic circuit is illustrated for two equations in Fig. 16-73.

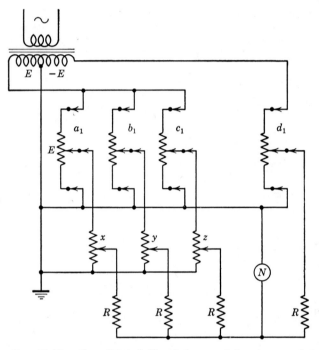

FIG. 16-72. Consolidated Circuit for $a_1 x + b_1 y + c_1 z = d_1$

The "variable-boxes," x and y, produce alternating voltages and, by a summing network, voltages proportional to

$$\epsilon_1 = a_1 x + b_1 y - d_1 t$$

$$\epsilon_2 = a_2 x + b_2 y - d_2 t$$

are produced (t is a scale variable.) ϵ_1 and ϵ_2 are amplified and fed to the plates of a diode, and, by square law rectification, a direct current proportional to

$$\bar{\mu} = \epsilon_1{}^2 + \epsilon_2{}^2$$

is obtained and read on a microammeter. The variables x, y are adjusted in rotation to minimize $\bar{\mu}$.

The resistances R_g are the output grid resistors of the amplifiers. Each is joined to the plate of the final amplifying stage by a blocking condenser.

Each variable-box has the circuit shown in Fig. 16-74. Power is obtained from a stepdown transformer across the line. The double-pole switch determines the sign, and the potentiometer P_2 determines the magnitude of the variable.

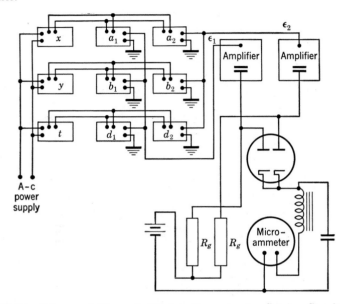

FIG. 16-73. Scheme of Murray's Electric Computer for Solving Simultaneous Linear Algebraic Equations, Illustrated for Two Equations

Each coefficient box contains the circuit shown in Fig. 16-75. The switch is set according to the sign of the coefficient, and the potentiometer determines the magnitude. The grounds in the coefficient boxes locate the variable circuits relative to ground and permit addition by averaging the voltages a_1x, b_1y and d_1t through the resistances R_2, which are identical for all the coefficient boxes.

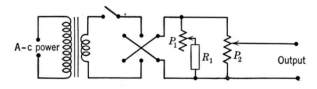

FIG. 16-74. Circuit in Murray's Variable Box

A 12-equation machine of this type has been built in the Watson Scientific Computing Laboratory at Columbia University.

80. Mechanical Linear-Equation Solvers. Since multiplication and addition can be accomplished with gear trains and differentials, purely mechanical devices can be constructed to solve simultaneous linear algebraic equations.

Backlash makes most of these impractical, but this defect has been avoided in one machine devised by Wilbur.[67] In this device, each variable is represented by the sine of the angle of rotation of a shaft, and each equation is

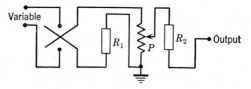

FIG. 16-75.   Circuit in Murray's Coefficient Box

represented by a continuous steel tape which passes over the shafts and over pulleys in such a manner as to form an endless-chain adder.

Z. VIBRATIONS OF STRUCTURES

Bush has proposed the solution of problems of vibration of pin-connected structures by electric-network analogies.   The mass of the structure is considered to be concentrated at the panel points, and the compliances are those of the individual members.   The validity of the assumption of concentrated masses is debatable, but, if it is granted, the problem is reduced to the construction of one of the many analogies between lumped mechanical and electric

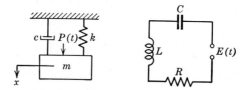

FIG. 16-76.   Analogous Lumped Mechanical and Lumped Electric Systems

systems.[3-5]   The most common of these is obtained by noting the similarity between the second-order linear ordinary differential equations governing the one-degree-of freedom mechanical and electric systems shown in Fig. 16-76. The displacement in the mechanical system is governed by

$$m\frac{d^2x}{dt^2} + c\frac{dx}{dt} + kx = P(t)$$

and the charge in the electrical system by

$$L\frac{d^2q}{dt^2} + R\frac{dq}{dt} + \frac{q}{C} = E(t)$$

One equation may be transformed to the other by making inductance L proportional to mass m, resistance R proportional to viscosity coefficient c, capacity C inversely proportional to spring rate k, displacement x proportional to charge q, velocity $(v = dx/dt)$ proportional to current $(i = dq/dt)$ and force P proportional to voltage E.

A permanent installation capable of solving systems of second-order linear ordinary differential equations has been built at the Westinghouse Electric Company in East Pittsburgh, Pa.

BIBLIOGRAPHY

1. J. Pérès, "Les Méthodes d'analogie en mécanique appliquée," *Proc 5th Int. Congress Applied Mechanics*, John Wiley & Sons, New York, 1939, pp 9–19. A review of analogies in applied mechanics with more than 50 references, including several to early philosophical speculations. Contains description of work with electrolytic tanks conducted at the Institut de Mécanique in Paris.

2. A. E. H. Love, *A Treatise on the Mathematical Theory of Elasticity*, 4th ed, Cambridge, England, 1927, ch 19. References to Kirchhoff's kinetic analogue. Also, pp 460, 465, and 487, approximate theory of the bending of thin slabs.

3. Th. von Kármán and M. A. Biot, *Mathematical Methods in Engineering*, McGraw-Hill Book Co, New York, 1940, pp 228–233, 372–74. Analogy between mechanical and electrical oscillations.

4. H. F. Olson, *Dynamical Analogies*, D. Van Nostrand Co, New York, 1943. Analogies among mechanical, electrical, and acoustical systems.

5. H. E. Criner, G. D. McCann, and C. E. Warren, "A New Device for the Solution of Transient–Vibration Problems by the Method of Electrical–Mechanical Analogy," *J Applied Mechanics*, v 12, n 3, pp A-135–41, 1945. Description of a machine, for the solution of simultaneous ordinary differential equations of the second order, composed of a bank of LCR circuits with means for repetitive insertion of data.

6. Lord Rayleigh, "On the Flow of Viscous Fluids, Especially in Two Dimensions," *Phil Mag* series 5, v 36, 1893, p 354. Contains an exposition of the analogy between the steady motion of a viscous liquid and the flexure of an elastic plate, with applications. Also: J. N. Goodier, "An Analogy between the Slow Motions of a Viscous Fluid in Two Dimensions and Systems of Plane Stress," *Phil Mag*, series 7, v 17, 1934, pp 554–76. A presentation of the analogy with numerous applications, including theory for measurements by photoelasticity.

7. T. Alfrey, "Non-Homogeneous Stresses in Visco-Elastic Media," *Quarterly of Applied Mathematics*, v 2, 1944, pp. 113–19. Analogy between incompressible elastic and viscoelastic bodies. Also:
R. D. Mindlin, "A Mathematical Theory of Photo-Viscoelasticity," *J Applied Physics*, v 20, n 2, 1949, pp. 206–16. Extension of Alfrey's analogy with applications to photoelasticity.

8. C. B. Biezeno and R. Grammel, *Technische Dynamik*, Julius Springer, Berlin, 1939, pp 180–225. Contains several sections on mechanical, electrical, and optical methods of stress analysis.

9. M. Hetényi, "On Similarities between Stress and Flow Patterns," *J Applied Physics*, v 12, 1941, pp 592–95. A review of analogies between stress and fluid flow.

10. S. Timoshenko, *Theory of Elasticity*, McGraw-Hill Book Co, New York, 1934, pp 263–65. Contains a brief description of hydrodynamical analogues of torsion, with references.

11. A. Nádai, *Plasticity*, McGraw-Hill Book Co, New York, 1931, p 132. Also: M. A. Sadowsky, "An Extension of the Sand-Heap Analogy in Plastic Torsion Applicable to Cross Sections Having One or More Holes." *J Applied Mechanics*, v 8, n 4, p A-166, 1941.

12. F. J. Murray, *The Theory of Mathematical Machines*, King's Crown Press,

New York, 1947.   In this book are described the theory and operation of a large number of calculating devices, ranging from the abacus to the most elaborate modern analyzers.

13. F. S. Woods, *Advanced Calculus*, Ginn and Co, Boston, Mass, 1932, ch 8.

14. L. Prandtl, "Zur Torsion von prismatischen Stäben," *Physikalische Zeitschrift*, 4, 1903, pp 758–59.   Original proposal of the pressure–membrane analogy for torsion.

15. H. Anthes, "Versuchsmethode zur Ermittlung der Spannungsverteilung bei Torsion prismatischer Stäbe," *Dinglers Polytechnisches Journal*, 1906, pp 342–45, 356–59, 388–92, 441–44, 455–59, 471–75.   A description of the pressure-membrane torsion analogy and of the first series of experiments applied to many commonly used sections.   Contains the checkerboard photographic and graphical method.

16. F. Vening-Meinesz, "De verdeeling der spanningen in een lichaam dat zich volgens de wet van Hooke gedraagt," *De Ingenieur*, n 26–3, 1911, pp 180–85. Original derivation of zero-pressure membrane analogue of bending.

17. A. A. Griffith and G. I. Taylor: (a) "The Use of Soap Films in Solving Torsion Problems," *Great Brit Rep and Mem Aeronautical Research Comm (Lond) Reports and Memoranda* v 3, n 333, pp 920–70, 1917–18.   (b) "The Determination of the Torsional Stiffness and Strength of Cylindrical Bars of Any shape," *Great Brit Rep and Mem Aero Res Comm*, v 3, n 334, 1917–18. (c) "The Problem of Flexure and Its Solution by the Soap-Film Method," *Great Brit Rep and Mem Aero Res Comm*, v 3, n 399, 1917–18, p 950.   (d) "The Application of Soap Films to the Determination of the Torsion and Flexure of Hollow Shafts," *Great Brit Rep and Mem Aero Res Comm*, v 3, n 392, 1918, p 938.   (e) "The Use of Soap Films in solving Torsion Problems," *Proc Inst Mech Engrs* (Lond), pp 755–809.   (a) and (b) contain a complete description of the apparatus and methods of measurement devised by the authors, together with experimental results in torsion by the pressure-membrane analogy.   (c) Contains the independent discussion of the flexure analogy originally proposed by Vening–Meinesz, together with experiments on propeller–blade models.   (d) contains the extension of the soap-film analogy to multiply connected regions.   (e) is a résumé of the papers on the pressure-membrane–torsion analogy.

18. A. Piccard and L. Baes, "Mode expérimental nouveau relatif à l'application des surfaces à courbure constante à la solution du problème de la torsion des barres prismatiques," *Proc 2nd Int Congress Applied Mechanics*, (Zurich, 1926, pp 195–200.   First proposal and application of the meniscus method.   Description of collimator for the automatic registration of lines of constant slope. Experiments on circular, square, and triangular sections.

19. G. W. Trayer and H. W. March, "The Torsion of Members Having Sections Common in Aircraft Construction," *U.S. 15th Annual Report Nat Advisory Commit for Aeronautics*, 1929, pp 675–719.   Applications of Griffith and Taylor apparatus and techniques in pressure-membrane analogy.

20. P. A. Cushman, "Shearing Stresses in Torsion and Bending by Membrane Analogy," *ASME advance paper*, June 1932 meeting.   Application of pressure and pressureless membrane techniques in torsion and bending to circular and square sections.

21. H. Quest, "Eine experimentelle Lösung des Torsionsproblems," *Ingenieur-Archiv*, v 4, 1933, pp 510–20.   Description of pressure-membrane apparatus using an accurate collimator,   Applications to hollow rectangular sections and special sections of steel cutters.

22. E. Kopf and E. Weber, "Verfahren zur Ermittlung der Torsionsbeanspruchung mittels Membranmodell," *Verein Deutscher Ingenieure Zeitschrift*, v 78, pt 2, 1934, pp 913–14.   Molding of membrane shape in melted paraffin and measurement of contours by slicing.   Applications to square sections and notched circular sections.

23. J. G. McGivern and H. L. Supper, "A Membrane Analogy Supplementing Photoelasticity," *J Franklin Inst*, v 217, 1934, pp 491–504. Zero-pressure rubber-membrane measurements for the determination of the sum of the principal stresses in photoelasticity. Discussion of experimental errors.

24. A. Thiel, "Photogrammetrisches Verfahren zur versuchsmässigen Lösung von Torsions Aufgaben (Nach einem Seifenhautgleichniss von L. Föppl)," *Ingenieur-Archiv*, v 5, 1934, pp 417–29. Detailed description of a photogrammetric procedure and camera for measurements on zero-pressure membranes.

25. F. Englemann, "Verdrehung von Stäben mit einseitigringförmigen Querschnitt," *Forschung auf dem Gebiete des Ingenieurwesens*, v 6, 1935, pp 146–54. Zero-pressure membrane applied to eccentric annuli.

26. B. G Johnston, "Torsional Rigidity of Structural Sections," *Civil Eng*, v 5, 1935, pp 698–701. Brief description of pressure-membrane techniques, especially volume measurement.

27. H. Reichenbächer, "Selbstättige Ausmessung von Seifenhautmodellen," *Ingenieur-Archiv*, v 7, 1936, pp 257–72. Description of photographic apparatus for the automatic recording of lines of equal slope.

28. S. Negoro, "Method of Solving Torsion and Bending Problems of a Bar with Axial Holes," *Tohoku Univ Science Report* 12, 1938, pp 517–28. Discussion of membrane analogy in torsion and bending for multiply connected sections.

29. C. Sunatani, T. Matuyama, and M. Hatamura, "The Solution of Torsion Problems by Means of a Liquid Surface," *Tohoku Univ Tech Report* 12, 1938, pp 374–96. Description of apparatus and techniques of pressure and pressureless meniscus measurements. New photographic method for the simultaneous determination of slopes at all points of meniscus.

30. H. Deutler, "Zur versuchsmässigen Lösung von Torsionsaufgaben mit Hilfe des Seifenhautgleichnisses," *Ingenieur-Archiv*, v 9, 1938, pp 280–82. Description of simplified method of building boundary ordinates for pressureless-membrane analogy. Application to triangular section.

31. T. J. Higgins, "Analogic Experimental Methods in Stress Analysis as Exemplified by Saint-Venant's Torsion Problem," *Experimental Stress Analysis*, v 2, n 2, pp 17–27, 1944. Review of literature on the subject and complete bibliography.

32. J. C. Slater and N. H. Frank, *Introduction to Theoretical Physics*, McGraw-Hill Book Co, New York, 1933, pp 211–12.

33. G. Hepp, "Measurements of Potential by Means of the Electrolytic Tank," *Phillips Tech Rev*, v 4, 1939, pp 223–30. Description of a modern electrolytic tank designed to plot potential fields to an accuracy of 1 per cent.

34. C. B. Biezeno and J. J. Koch, "Über einige Beispiele zur elektrischen Spannungsbestimmung," *Ingenieur-Archiv*, v 4, 1933, pp 384–93. Description of an electric apparatus using a manganin plate as conductor. Applications to torsional stresses in rectangular cross sections, to sum of principal stresses in photoelasticity, and to bending stresses in an angle.

35. H. Cranz, "Experimentelle Lösung von Torsions Aufgaben," *Ingenieur-Archiv*, v 4, 1933, pp 506–09. Description of an electric apparatus using a metal plate. Applications to torsional stresses in ellipse and lune.

36. S. Negoro and K. Sato, "The Use of Electric Bath in Solving Torsion and Bending Problems," *Trans Soc Mech Engrs Japan*, v 2, 1936, pp S–38, 112–16. Description of an electrolytic tank and application to torsional and bending stresses in equilateral triangle, circular ring, and airfoil section.

37. H. Meyer and F. Tank, "Über ein verbessertes elektrisches Verfahren zur Auswertung der Gleichung $\nabla^2 \varphi = 0$ und seine Anwendung bei photoelastischen Untersuchungen," *Helvetica Physica Acta*, v 8, 1935, pp 315–17. The authors suggest the use of a slightly conducting material on the boundaries of the tank in order to obtain a smooth distribution of boundary potentials.

38. H. Cranz, "Modellversuche zur Lösung von Aufgaben der ebenen Potentials," *Ingenieur-Archiv*, v 7, 1936, pp 432–33. Description of an electric apparatus

using a metal plate. Applications to conformal mapping of eccentric annulus and lune.

39. U. Hohenemser, "Experimentelle Lösung ebenes Potentialaufgaben," *Forschung auf dem Gebiete des Ingenieurwesens*, v 2, 1931, pp 370–71. Description of tank apparatus.

40. J. H. Jeans, *The Mathematical Theory of Electricity and Magnetism*, Cambridge Univ Press, 2d ed, 1911, pp 342 and 345.

41. J. H. Michell, "The Uniform Torsion and Flexure of Incomplete Tores, with Application to Helical Springs," *Proc London Math Soc*, v 31, 1899, pp 141–42. Derivation of the boundary-value problem for the torsion of axially symmetrical bars.

42. A. Föppl, "Über die Torsion von runden Stäben mit veränderlichen Durchmesser," *Sitzungsberichter bayerischen Akademie der Wissenschaften*, München, v 35, 1905, pp 249–304. Derivation of the boundary-value problem for the torsion of axially symmetrical bars and complete discussion of the stress distribution.

43. L. S. Jacobsen, "Torsional Stress Concentrations in Shafts of Circular Cross Section and Variable Diameter," *Trans ASME*, v 47, pp 619–41, 1925. Derivation of the electric analogy equations and description of experiments.

44. A. Thum and W. Bautz, "Die Ermittlung von Spannungsspitzen in Verdrehbeanspruchten Wellen durch ein elektrisches Modell," *Verein Deutscher Ingenieure*, v 78, 1934, pp 17–9. Statement of the analogy and description of tank experiments.

45. G. Solet, "Determination des pointes de tension dans les arbres de revolution soumis à torsion au moyen d'un modèle électrique." *Bul de l'Assn Technique Maritime et Aeronautique*, v 40, 1936, pp 341–50. Description of tank experiments and investigation of the influence of the length of the model on stress-concentration factors.

46. G. Solet, "Amélioration de la méthode de détermination des pointes de tension dans les arbres de revolution soumis à torsion au moyen d'un modèle électrique," *Bul de l'Assn Technique Maritime et Aeronautique*, v 41, 1937, pp 295–303. Improvement of Saul's extrapolation formula for the determination of stress-concentration factors.

47. F. A. Willers, "Die Torsion eines Rotationskörper um seine Achse," *Zeitschrift für Math und Physik*, v 55, 1907, p 225. Approximate analytical evaluation of stress-concentration factors.

48. J. H. Michell, "On the Direct Determination of Stress in an Elastic Solid, with Application to the Theory of Plates," *Proc London Math Soc*, v 31, 1899, pp 100–24. Derivation of the boundary conditions on the Airy stress function for multiply connected regions.

49. R. D. Mindlin, "The Analogy between Multiply-Connected Slices and Slabs," *Quarterly of Applied Mathematics*, v 4, n 3, pp 279–90, 1946; and v 5, n 2, p 238, 1947. Extension of Michell's boundary conditions to include dislocations and thermal dilatations, and application to slab analogy.

50. H. M. Westergaard, "Graphostatics of stress functions," *Trans ASME*, v 56, n 3, pp 141–50, 1934. Contains discussions of a variety of analogies, including that between free and constrained slices.

51. E. G. Coker and L. N. G. Filon, *A Treatise on Photo-Elasticity*, Cambridge University Press, Cambridge, 1931, pp 124–30, 503–24. Introduction to Airy's stress function and general theory of multiply connected slices.

52. R. V. Southwell, *Theory of Elasticity*, Oxford University Press, Oxford, 1936, pp 368–71. Discussion of z dependence of Airy's function for a free slice (plane stress).

53. M. A. Biot, "Distributed Gravity and Temperature Loading in Two-Dimensional Elasticity Replaced by Boundary Pressures and Dislocations," *J Applied Mechanics*, v 2, 1935, pp A-41–5.

54. M. A. BIOT, "A General Property of Two-Dimensional Thermal Stress Distribution," *Phil Mag*, v 19, 1935, pp 540–49.
55. M. A. BIOT, "Propriété générale des tensions thermiques en régime stationnaire dans les corps cylindriques. Application a la mésure photoélastique de ces tensions," *Annales Société Scientifique Bruxelles*, series B, v 54, 1934, pp 14–18.
56. E. E. WEIBEL, "Thermal Stresses in Cylinders by the Photoelastic Method," *Proc 5th Int Congress Applied Mechanics*, Cambridge, Mass., 1938, pp 213–20. Application of Biot's analogy to tubes of circular and rectangular cross sections.
57. K. WIEGHARDT, "Über ein neues Verfahren, verwickelte Spannungsverteilungen in elastischen Körpern auf experimentellem Wege zu finden," *Mitteilungen über Forschungsarbeiten an den Gebiete des Ingenieurwesens*, v 49, 1908, pp 15–30. First application of slab analogy.
58. "Slab Analogy Experiments," Bul 2, and "Stress Studies for Boulder Dam," Bul 4, *U. S. Dept of Interior Final Report*, part 5, Technical Investigations, Bureau of Reclamation, Boulder Canyon Project.
59. H. CRANZ, "Die experimentelle Bestimmung der Airyschen Spannungsfunktion mit Hilfe des Plattengleichnisses," *Ingenieur-Archiv*, v 10, 1939, pp 159–66.
60. E. EINSPORN, "Ebenheit," *Zeitschrift für Instrumentenkunde*, v 57, 1937, pp 265–85.
61. G. KRON, "Equivalent Circuits of the Elastic Field, "*J Applied Mechanics*, v 11, n 3, 1944, pp A–149–61.
62. G. K. CARTER, "Numerical and Network Analyzer Solution of the Equivalent Circuits for the Elastic Field," *J Applied Mechanics*, v 11, n 3, 1944, pp A-162–67.
63. R. E. NEWTON, "Electrical Analogy for Shear Lag Problems," *Proc Soc Exp Stress Analysis*, v 2, n 2, 1945, pp 71–80.
64. V. BUSH, "Structural Analysis by Electric Circuit Analogies," *J Franklin Inst*, v 217, v 3, 1934, pp 289–329. Description of a-c networks for the solution of problems of equilibrium and motion of statically determinate and indeterminate structural frameworks.
65. R. R. M. MALLOCK, "An Electrical Calculating Machine," *Proc Royal Soc (Lond)*, s A, v 140, 1933, pp 457–83. A voltage-transformer network for solving simultaneous linear algebraic equations.
66. C. E. BERRY, D. E. WILCOX, S. M. ROCK, AND H. W. WASHBURN, "A Computer for Solving Linear Simultaneous Equations," *J Applied Physics*, v 17, n 4, 1945, pp 261–72. A description of the Consolidated Engineering Corporation's resistance-network analogue of the Gauss–Seidel iteration method.
67. J. B. WILBUR, "The Mechanical Solution of Simultaneous Equations," *J Franklin Inst*, v 222, 1936, pp 715–24. Description of the application of the endless tape adder to the solution of simultaneous linear algebraic equations.

CHAPTER 17

PHOTOELASTICITY

I. Fundamentals and Two-Dimensional Applications

By T. J. Dolan and W. M. Murray

II. Three-Dimensional Photoelasticity

By D. C. Drucker

I. FUNDAMENTALS AND TWO-DIMENSIONAL APPLICATIONS

By T. J. Dolan and W. M. Murray

A. INTRODUCTION

The discovery of the photoelastic effect is credited to Sir David Brewster, who in 1816 published an account of his finding that clear stressed glass when examined in polarized light exhibited colored patterns. The possibility of valuable engineering applications, however, was not immediately recognized, and few practical problems were investigated with photoelasticity prior to 1900. The underlying theory, however, was well developed by investigators such as Neumann, Maxwell, Wertheim, and other noted physicists who formulated the concept that the optical retardation producing the color effects is proportional to the difference of the principal stresses existing in the glass.

Of all those who have applied this optical method of stress analysis, Professor E. G. Coker, of the University of London has been outstanding both for his many practical investigations and for the development of many techniques which made engineering applications possible. His introduction of celluloid for models and the use of monochromatic light have led to the modern laboratory methods which make photoelasticity a powerful engineering tool.

In recent years the development of new synthetic resins (plastics), which possess desirable photoelastic characteristics, has helped the engineer to expand the application of the method to an ever wider variety of problems. The invention of "Polaroid," which provides a relatively inexpensive means of producing large beams of polarized light, has so reduced the cost of the necessary equipment that even small firms and design offices can take advantage of this tool as an aid in design.

1. Field of Application. The photoelastic method of stress analysis represents one type of model testing in which the models are fashioned from

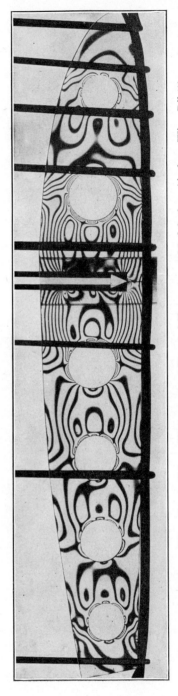

FIG. 17-1. Photoelastic Fringe Photograph of Stressed Transparent Model of an Airplane-Wing Rib[111] Nonuniformly distributed load applied through the (dark) wires, and reaction transferred to the spar at location shown by white arrow

flat sheets of some appropriate transparent elastic material. Primarily the experimental techniques of photoelasticity are best suited to the determination of the boundary stresses in two-dimensional (plane stress) problems; with the aid of certain supplementary experimental or analytical techniques the stresses at interior points may be evaluated. However, the two-dimensional methods of stress analysis can be applied to certain three-dimensional problems to give a useful picture of some of the stress distribution.[86, 96] Furthermore, recently developed methods have been devised (see part II) for the direct application of photoelasticity to three-dimensional models.

The transparent photoelastic model is made of elastic material (usually about $\frac{1}{4}$ in. thick) and must have the contours of the model geometrically similar to those of the prototype in which the stress distribution is desired. The model is then examined in a field of polarized light with loads applied in a manner similar to those existing on the prototype. Under these conditions a series of brilliant bands having different color tints will be observed in white light (or alternate bright and dark bands called interference "fringes," in monochromatic light, as shown in Fig. 17-1). These optical effects may be readily interpreted to give a graphic representation of the stress distribution either qualitatively or quantitatively. Direct visual observation is sufficient to locate regions of high and low stress. By a relatively simple process of counting colored bands or fringes and multiplying by a calibration factor, the corresponding stress intensities may be accurately evaluated (for example, see Fig. 17-2).

For a great many problems involving contours of irregular form which cannot be solved analytically, photoelasticity is of untold value in determining stresses and in the evaluation of stress-concentration factors for certain standard types of abrupt changes in section. In this manner the method forms a connecting link between the mathematical theory of elasticity (which can be applied only to certain regular shapes) and the elastic stresses prevailing in irregular shapes which may be required for design. As a tool to aid in machine design, photoelasticity can be utilized to considerable advantage for locating regions of low stress from which material may be removed for the purpose of reducing weight.

As in other experimental methods of stress analysis, the question may be raised: "Are the stresses developed in a small transparent model the same as those in a metal member under a similar loading, or do the differences in elastic constants and size influence the results?" For the great majority of cases, the problems of similarity between stresses in model and prototype are not difficult. In general, the stresses due to external forces in an elastic system in two dimensions are functions of the geometry of the contour and

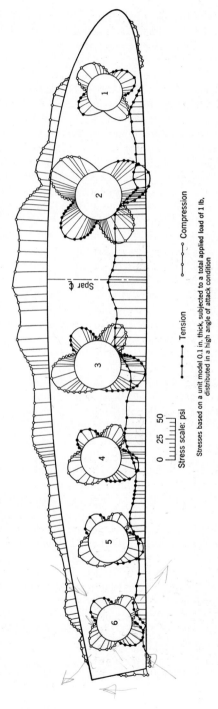

Stress scale: psi
0 25 50

———•——— Tension   ———∘——— Compression

Stresses based on a unit model 0.1 in. thick, subjected to a total applied load of 1 lb, distributed in a high angle of attack condition

Fig. 17-2. Curves of Boundary Stresses for Wing Rib Shown in Fig. 1[111]

of the intensity of the load. Thus, the stress pattern in the model per inch
of thickness should be identical with that in the prototype if the loads are in
proportion to the scale or size ratio. For a limited number of cases in which
the body investigated has a hole or a boundary on which the externally
applied loads are not in equilibrium, a minor correction is necessary to take
account of the differences in elastic properties of the model and prototype.

As with all other experimental methods, great care must be taken to insure
the model being accurately similar to the prototype both in physical dimensions and in locations and types of loading applied. Unknown frictional
forces in the loading mechanism or at the points of load application to the
model may materially influence the stresses. It should be emphasized that,
if the stresses exceed the elastic strength in either the model or the prototype,
the magnitudes and distribution in the region of peak stress will be materially
altered and cannot be accurately determined by the presently available techniques used in photoelasticity.

Among the chief advantages of the photoelastic method of stress analysis
are that it provides a means of:

1. Obtaining an over-all visual picture of the shearing-stress distribution
throughout the body.

2. Measurement of stress at a point with consequent possibility of finding
actual peak values even in regions of high stress gradient.

3. Determination of stresses in two-dimensional problems that cannot be
solved analytically.

4. Accurate stress determination in irregular members comparable to
results obtained with precise strain-gage techniques.

5. Readily obtaining qualitative results for location of minimum- and
maximum-stress locations or for the determination of changes in stress distribution caused by minor alterations in shape of the model to aid in the process
of developing a satisfactory design.

The shortcomings of this experimental technique and some of the disadvantages appear to be as follows:

1. It is an indirect method requiring the use of accurate scale models and
subsequent interpretation of data for the prototype.

2. The experimental procedure is readily applied only to two-dimensional
conditions, since the three-dimensional methods require rather involved and
carefully developed techniques.

3. The separation of the individual principal stresses at interior points in
the model becomes rather troublesome if great accuracy is required.

4. For proper application a carefully developed experimental procedure
must be followed including the necessity of preparing models that are
stress-free.

5. The applications of the method are limited to the determination of
elastic stresses due to externally applied forces. The method will not yield
information relative to the influences of surface conditions on the prototype
(such as microscopic corrosion pits and machining scratches), nor can it be
used to determine the residual stresses or the elastic redistribution of stress

that occurs after the prototype has undergone some plastic deformation, heat treatment, or welding operation.

In presenting the photoelastic method of stress analysis, the diversity of the subject matter has made it difficult to arrange in a logical sequence. The method is based on a rather careful and fixed routine of (1) preparation of model, (2) examination, and (3) interpretation in terms of the analysis of the behavior of a beam of light in accordance with the electromagnetic-wave theory. A somewhat reverse sequence of arrangement of these steps is found in the interdependent sections of part I of this chapter, in which the discussions and applications will be limited to *two-dimensional* stress systems.

In section B the elementary concepts of light are presented and the equations developed that are necessary for an understanding of section C which discusses the photoelastic effect and the functions of the elements in a polariscope. These relationships lead directly to the fundamental photoelastic equations in section D and the interpretation of the photoelastic-stress pattern from color bands or interference fringes. Supplementary methods of finding fractional orders of interference are discussed in section E. For the interpretation of the photoelastic effect in terms of numerical values of stress, a fringe constant may be evaluated by the methods suggested in section F. In sections G and H are presented methods for the determination of the individual principal stresses at interior points since the information obtained from the photoelastic-stress pattern gives only the difference of the two principal stresses. Comments on photoelastic materials and laboratory equipment together with suggestions for preparation and photographing of models are presented in sections I, J, and K. Several supplementary optical methods that have been employed by various investigators are listed in section L, and a brief review of the wide variety of problems that have been analyzed by photoelasticity is compiled in section M. For a complete understanding of the theory and experimental techniques, the reader is referred to the references listed at the end of this chapter, especially the excellent books by Coker and Filon[1] and Frocht.[3]

B. Elementary Concepts of Light

According to the electromagnetic-wave theory, light is considered an electromagnetic disturbance consisting of transverse waves which are propagated along straight lines called rays. Actually, there are two companion effects, one magnetic and the other electric, which exist simultaneously in planes at right angles such that the line of intersection of the planes is parallel to the direction of the light ray. Since both the electric and magnetic effects correspond to transverse waves, either may be represented by a vector at a given place and time,[1] though the electric vector is considered at the light vector.[19, 20]

2. Polarization. The term "polarization" is used to imply that some kind of control over the light vector exists or that the vector obeys some definite law, as indicated in Fig. 17-3. For example:

(a) *Plane Polarization.* Light is said to be plane-polarized when the light vector is confined to a single plane. The plane containing the light vector

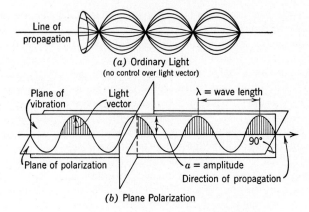

(a) Ordinary Light
(no control over light vector)

(b) Plane Polarization

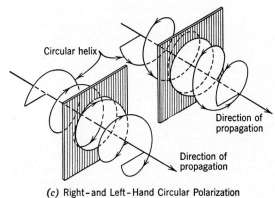

(c) Right-and Left-Hand Circular Polarization

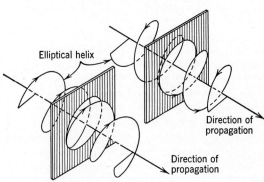

(d) Right-and Left-Hand Elliptical Polarization

FIG. 17-3.   Representation of Different Types of Polarization

is known as the plane of vibration, and the plane at right angles is the plane of polarization.* Ordinary or common light may be considered as being made up of an infinite number of plane-polarized components whose planes of polarization have every conceivable orientation.

(b) *Circular Polarization.* For circularly polarized light the light vector rotates around the line of propagation, and its magnitude remains constant. If, at some given instant, the light vector is plotted at various positions along the line of propagation, the tips of the vectors thus drawn will lie along a circular helix. Or, if at a given location (that is, on a given plane perpendicular to the light ray), the successive positions of the light vector are plotted, the tips of the various vectors will lie on a circle. Circularly polarized light may be resolved into components in any two directions at right angles, and the components will always have the same amplitudes.

(c) *Elliptical Polarization.* This is essentially similar to circular polarization with the exception that the magnitude of the light vector changes periodically during the rotation. The tips of the vectors plotted along the line of propagation, at a given instant, will describe an elliptical helix, and at any given location the successive positions of the tip of the vector will trace an ellipse. Elliptical polarization may be considered a general condition of which plane and circular polarization are special cases. If, when one looks along the line of propagation *towards* the light source, the vector rotates clockwise, the polarization is said to be right handed. If the vector rotates anticlockwise, the polarization is left handed.

3. Color and Wave Length. Daylight (or white light) is made up of a number of constituent vibrations possessing different frequencies which can be distinguished from one another through the sense of color. In the case of visible light the entire range of colors which can be seen in the spectrum runs from a frequency of approximately 390×10^{12} cps (deep red) to approximately 770×10^{12} cps (deep violet).

Reference can be made to each color by its frequency of vibration, but it is usual to employ the corresponding wave length in a vacuum since all electromagnetic disturbances have the same velocity in evacuated space. Accordingly, the following relation exists:

$$\lambda \cdot f = c = \text{approximately } 3 \times 10^{10} \text{ cm/sec (about 186,000 miles per second)}$$

where c = the velocity of light in vacuum
$\quad \lambda$ = the wave length
$\quad f$ = the frequency
Therefore,

$$\lambda = \frac{c}{f} = \frac{3 \times 10^{10}}{f} \tag{1}$$

which means that the wave lengths of visible light run from about 3.9×10^{-5} cm to about 7.7×10^{-5} cm. Expressed in angstroms (angstrom unit 10^{-8} cm), this gives a range of from 3900 for extreme violet to 7700 for extreme red,

* Reference 20, p 317.

from which it is seen that all visible light has its wave length in four-digit numbers in angstroms.

Monochromatic or homogeneous light consists of one wave length only. In practice this is probably never completely realized, but good approximations can be made. The monochromatic light may be plane-, circularly, or elliptically polarized. White or polychromatic light consists of a mixture of light of several different wave lengths. The intensity of the light is proportional to the square of the amplitude of vibration.

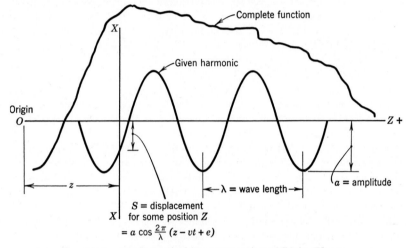

FIG. 17-4. Mathematical Representation of Light Wave

When light passes from one medium into another of different density, there is a change in velocity. The ratio of these velocities is called the index of refraction. Therefore,

$$\text{Index of refraction} = \frac{\text{velocity in 1st medium}}{\text{velocity in 2d medium}} \qquad (2)$$

Since light is considered as composed of waves, its individual components may be represented mathematically in the form,

$$S = a \cos \frac{2\pi}{\lambda} (z - vt + e) \qquad (3)$$

as illustrated diagrammatically in Fig. 17-4. A complicated condition can be expressed by the combination of an infinite number of elements such that

$$S = \sum_{i=1}^{i=\infty} a_i \cos \frac{2\pi}{\lambda_i} (z - v_i t + e_i) \qquad (4)$$

where S = magnitude of the displacement given by the vector
z = distance along the light ray from some reference point

v = velocity of propagation
a = amplitude of vibration
t = time
e = a constant

In the case of monochromatic light under the special circumstance in which z and e both happen to be zero, equation 3 reduces to the simplified form,

$$S = a \cos \frac{2\pi v}{\lambda} t = a \cos (2\pi f)t$$
$$= a \cos pt \tag{5}$$

which shows that the magnitude of the displacement indicated by the light vector varies harmonically with time, and the light has a color dependent on the frequency, as indicated by the proportionality factor p.

C. THE PHOTOELASTIC EFFECT

4. Wave Plates. Plates made of certain crystalline materials, such as mica, have the property of resolving the light (which falls on them at normal incidence) into two components and transmitting it on planes at right angles. This phenomenon is referred to as "double refraction" or "birefringence." Furthermore, the optical properties on the two planes of transmission will, in general, be different, so that the two components will be transmitted with different velocities. Therefore, when they emerge from the plate there is a difference in phase between the two waves that is proportional to the thickness of the plate traversed by the light. Plates which possess this characteristic are called wave or retardation plates and may be further designated in accordance with the amount of relative retardation which they produce between the two component vibrations.

For example, if, for a given wave length of light there is a relative displacement of a quarter of a wave length, as shown in Fig. 17-5, then the plate is defined as a "quarter-wave plate" ($\lambda/4$ plate), or, for a half-wave length relative retardation, it would be described as a half-wave plate ($\lambda/2$ plate), and so on. It should be noted that a wave plate can have a specified relative retardation for only one given wave length; for all other wave lengths the retardation will be a slightly different fraction of the length.

By producing a phase shift of $\lambda/4$ (for a given wave length) a quarter-wave plate will convert plane-polarized light into circularly polarized light if the original plane of vibration is inclined at 45° to the planes of transmission of the wave plate. Figure 17-5 illustrates these relationships graphically.

Plane-polarized monochromatic light entering the crystal with the plane of vibration at 45° to the planes of transmission (Fig. 17-5b) is resolved into equal components as shown in Fig. 17-5c, which travel through the thickness h with different velocities. If the plate is of a suitable thickness, the emerging waves will have a phase-difference (relative retardation) of $\frac{1}{4}\lambda$ and equal amplitudes in planes at right angles as indicated in Fig. 17-5a. These waves may be represented by vectors as in Fig. 17-5d and can be combined to form a resultant vector,

$$\text{Resultant} = \sqrt{\left(\frac{a}{\sqrt{2}}\sin pt\right)^2 + \left(\frac{a}{\sqrt{2}}\cos pt\right)^2}$$

$$= \frac{a}{\sqrt{2}} \tag{6}$$

and

$$\tan \theta = \frac{\dfrac{a}{\sqrt{2}}\sin pt}{\dfrac{a}{\sqrt{2}}\cos pt} = \tan pt \tag{7}$$

Thus, θ is proportional to the time t, which indicates that the light vector remains constant in amplitude and rotates uniformly with time. This corresponds to the definition of circular polarization, and, hence, the transmitted light is circularly polarized.

The effect of a half-wave plate is similar to that of a quarter-wave plate, except the relative retardation is one-half wave length. If plane-polarized

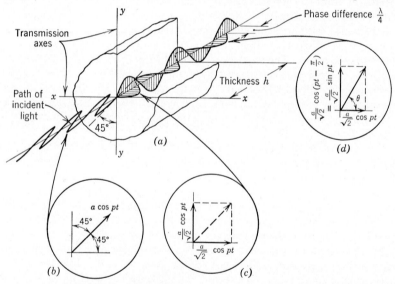

FIG. 17-5.   What Happens in a Quarter-Wave Plate

Difference in optical properties on the two planes of transmission causes one component to travel faster than the other, setting up a phase difference. The relative retardation is proportional to the thickness h and will be exactly $\lambda/4$ only for one given thickness and light of a given wave length λ

        (a) Light Traversing a Quarter-Wave Plate
        (b) Plane-Polarized Monochromatic Light
        (c) Components within the Crystal
        (d) Transmitted Light

light is transmitted through a half-wave plate, the only influence is to rotate the plane of vibration, whose orientation will be revolved through twice the angle between the original plane of vibration and one of the axes of the wave plate.

5. Fundamental Optical Laws of Photoelasticity. Almost all transparent materials such as glass, Celluloid, Bakelite, and many other synthetic resins temporarily have to some extent the same optical effect on a beam of light as a crystal when these materials are subjected to stress. The double-refracting effect, although temporary, is similar to that which takes place in a wave plate, except the retardation depends on the nature and intensity of the stress; on release of load the double refraction disappears. For normal incidence on flat plates subjected to plane stress within the elastic limit, the transmission of light obeys the following two laws which form the basis of photoelastic stress determination:

1. The light is polarized in the directions of the *principal-stress* axes and is transmitted only on the planes of principal stress.

2. The velocity of transmission in each principal plane is dependent on the intensities of the *principal stresses* in these two planes and obeys the following equations which have been simplified from the general case (see part II) to terms of plane stress.

$$\delta_1 = N_1 - N_0 = A\sigma_1 + B\sigma_2 \tag{8}$$

$$\delta_2 = N_2 - N_0 = B\sigma_1 + A\sigma_2 \tag{9}$$

where δ_1 = change of refractive index on no. 1 principal plane
δ_2 = change of refractive index on no. 2 principal plane
N_0 = refractive index of unstressed material
N_1 = refractive index on no. 1 principal plane
N_2 = refractive index on no. 2 principal plane
σ_1 and σ_2 = the principal stresses
A and B = the photoelastic constants of the material

By subtracting equation 9 from equation 8, one finds that the difference between the refractive indices on the two principal planes is given by the equation:

$$\delta_1 - \delta_2 = N_1 - N_2 = (A - B)(\sigma_1 - \sigma_2)$$

$$= C(\sigma_1 - \sigma_2) \tag{10}$$

where C = the differential-stress optical constant

From the definition in equation 2 this relation may be expressed in terms of the velocity of transmission of the light, as

$$\frac{v(v_2 - v_1)}{v_1 v_2} = C(\sigma_1 - \sigma_2) \tag{11}$$

where v_1 and v_2 = the velocities of transmission on the principal planes of stress

and v = the velocity of transmission in the surrounding medium

Thus, the difference in velocities of transmission $v_1 - v_2$ (and the resulting phase difference) is seen to be directly related to the difference of the two principal stresses $\sigma_1 - \sigma_2$.

6. Stresses in a Plane.   Since the photoelastic effects are related only to *principal* stresses, a brief review is desirable of the relationship between stresses

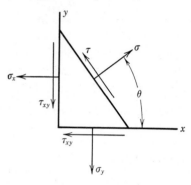

on the various planes that may be passed through any given point in a body. This discussion (and all the analyses in part I of this chapter) is limited to two-dimensional stress systems such as are closely approximated by a thin flat model loaded in the plane of the model.

At a given point in a member, the stresses existing on two rectangular coordinate planes, x and y, may be represented, in general, by normal and shearing components, as shown in Fig. 17-6. On any other plane at this point a normal stress σ and a shearing stress τ of different intensity exist.   From equilibrium

FIG. 17-6.   Stresses at a Point in a Two-Dimensional System

considerations the relationships between these stresses are as follows:*

$$\sigma = \tfrac{1}{2}(\sigma_x + \sigma_y) + \tfrac{1}{2}(\sigma_x - \sigma_y)\cos 2\theta + \tau_{xy}\sin 2\theta \tag{12}$$

$$\tau = \tfrac{1}{2}(\sigma_y - \sigma_x)\sin 2\theta + \tau_{xy}\cos 2\theta \tag{13}$$

In this latter relation τ becomes zero, and only a normal stress σ exists on the plane when

$$\tan 2\theta = \frac{2\tau_{xy}}{\sigma_x - \sigma_y} \tag{14}$$

Differentiating equation 12 with respect to θ and setting the result equal to zero constitutes one way of determining the values of θ for which σ becomes a maximum (or a minimum) algebraic value.   The results turns out to be identical with equation 14.   Thus, the algebraic maximum (and minimum) normal stresses at the point under consideration exist on planes for which the shearing stresses vanish, and these normal stresses are then called *principal stresses*.   Since there are two possible values (less than 360°) for the angle 2θ obtained from equation 14, which differ by 180°, it follows that there are *two principal stresses* lying on *principal planes* at 90° to each other.   One of these is the maximum principal stress σ_1 (+ stresses are regarded as tensile stresses), and the other is the minimum principal stress σ_2 (if σ_2 is negative, it is the largest compressive stress existing at the point).   The values of the principal stresses are obtained by substituting equation 14, in equations 12

* See reference 23, article 9, or reference 3, chapter 1.

and 13; they become

$$\sigma_1 = \tfrac{1}{2}(\sigma_x + \sigma_y) + \tfrac{1}{2}[(\sigma_x - \sigma_y)^2 + 4\tau_{xy}{}^2]^{1/2} \qquad (15)$$

$$\sigma_2 = \tfrac{1}{2}(\sigma_x + \sigma_y) - \tfrac{1}{2}[(\sigma_x - \sigma_y)^2 + 4\tau_{xy}{}^2]^{1/2} \qquad (16)$$

The maximum shearing stresses at any point may be shown[3, 23] to occur on planes bisecting the planes of principal stress and to have a magnitude

$$\tau_m = \tfrac{1}{2}[(\sigma_x - \sigma_y)^2 + 4\tau_{xy}{}^2]^{1/2} = \tfrac{1}{2}(\sigma_1 - \sigma_2) \qquad (17)$$

At any free (unloaded) boundary of a member there are no shearing stresses acting tangent to the edge. Hence, the normal stresses acting in directions tangent to and perpendicular to the boundary are principal stresses. Furthermore, since the principal stress perpendicular to the boundary is zero, it follows that the difference between the principal stresses is numerically equal to the principal stress acting tangent to the edge.

7. The Plane Polariscope and the Photoelastic Effect. The device or optical system most frequently employed to produce the necessary polarized beams of light and to interpret the photoelastic effect in terms of stress is called a *polariscope*. It may take a variety of different forms, depending on the desired use; however, in general, it consists of a light source, a polarizing device called the polarizer, the photoelastic model, and a second polarizing device known as the analyzer. In addition, there may be a system of lenses, a viewing screen, and other adjuncts for convenient visual observation or photographic recording.

The relation between the optical effects and the stresses prevailing in the model may be illustrated by analyzing the passage of light through a plane polariscope. Although this is the simplest case, the corresponding analyses for other more complicated arrangements of the polariscope can be made in a similar manner.

Figure 17-7 shows diagrammatically how light directed from the source is plane-polarized by the polarizer (usually a Nicol prism or Polaroid disk), then resolved by the model into two components in the directions of the principal stress axes, and transmitted on the principal planes. If the principal stress intensities are not equal, then the optical properties on the two principal planes will be different, and the velocity of transmission on one principal plane will be greater than on the other (as indicated by equations 8 to 11). This results in a phase difference between the two component vibrations as they emerge from the model.

This phase difference is proportional to the difference between the principal stresses and is measured by introducing the analyzer which brings part of each component vibration into interference in a single plane. Since white light consists of many wave lengths, each of which will be influenced in a similar manner, the analysis will be made on the basis of monochromatic light using the very simplest form of mathematical representation.

Let us assume a source of monochromatic light at Q (Fig. 17-7a) and investigate the effect produced as the light passes, at normal incidence, through a point in the photoelastic model. When the polarizer P has been traversed, the vibration has been confined to a single plane in the direction of and with amplitude proportional to OA, Fig. 17-7b. In symbols this is represented by the simple equation:

$$S = a \cos pt \qquad (18)$$

When the light arrives at the model, in general, its plane of vibration will not coincide with either principal plane of stress. Therefore, since the stressed

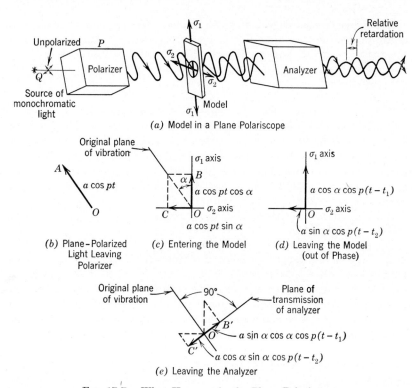

(a) Model in a Plane Polariscope

(b) Plane-Polarized Light Leaving Polarizer

(c) Entering the Model

(d) Leaving the Model (out of Phase)

(e) Leaving the Analyzer

FIG. 17-7. What Happens in the Plane Polariscope

model only transmits light on the principal planes, the original vibration is immediately resolved into two components as it enters the model. These will be

$$a \cos \alpha \cos pt \quad \text{(parallel to the no. 1 principal plane)} \qquad (19)$$

and

$$a \sin \alpha \cos pt \quad \text{(parallel to the no. 2 principal plane)} \qquad (20)$$

where α = the angle between the original plane of vibration and the no. 1 principal plane (see Fig. 17-7c).

Now, if t_1 and t_2 represent the time required for transmission on the no. 1

and no. 2 principal planes, respectively, then the two component vibrations leaving the model will be represented by the equations:

$$a \cos \alpha \cos p(t - t_1) \text{ (parallel to the no. 1 principal plane)} \tag{21}$$

and $\quad a \sin \alpha \cos p(t - t_2)$ (parallel to the no. 2 principal plane) $\tag{22}$

These will be observed to have a phase difference, $p(t_1 - t_2)$, which can be shown to be proportional to the difference between the principal stresses σ_1 and σ_2.

If h represents the thickness of the photoelastic model along the path of the light, then,

$$t_1 = \frac{h}{v_1} \quad \text{and} \quad t_2 = \frac{h}{v_2} \tag{23}$$

whence
$$t_1 - t_2 = h \left(\frac{1}{v_1} - \frac{1}{v_2} \right)$$

$$= h \left(\frac{v_2 - v_1}{v_1 v_2} \right) \tag{24}$$

and, by substituting for the velocities the value from equation 11, we have

$$t_1 - t_2 = \frac{hC}{v} (\sigma_1 - \sigma_2) \tag{25}$$

Therefore, the phase difference, $p(t_1 - t_2)$, of the waves emerging from the model is seen to be directly proportional to the difference between the principal stresses $(\sigma_1 - \sigma_2)$; the phase difference is also proportional to the model thickness h (and to the optical constant C/v for the material and surrounding medium). Hence, *any method that can be employed to determine this phase difference can be used as a measure of the difference between the principal stresses.*

By introducing the analyzer in the system (Fig. 17-7) in the proper orientation, the phase difference of the two waves can be made evident by the interference effects of their components in the plane of the analyzer; the amplitude of the resultant vibration is a function of $p(t_1 - t_2)$. If the analyzer's plane of transmission is at right angles to that of the polarizer, the components of the two vibrations emerging from the model that will be transmitted by the analyzer may be represented by

$$. \quad a \cos \alpha \sin \alpha \cos p(t - t_1) \tag{26}$$

and $\quad a \sin \alpha \cos \alpha \cos p(t - t_2)$ $\tag{27}$

both of which have the same amplitude. Since the two vibrations lie in the same plane, they may be added algebraically (or subtracted arithmetically since the vectors are opposed in direction) to give the expression for the resultant vibration:

$$a \cos \alpha \sin \alpha [\cos p(t - t_1) - \cos p(t - t_2)], \quad \text{or}$$

Resultant:

$$a \sin 2\alpha \sin p \left(\frac{t_1 - t_2}{2} \right) \sin p \left(t - \frac{t_1 + t_2}{2} \right) \qquad (28)$$

Thus, the amplitude of the resultant vibration leaving the analyzer is a function of both the angle α and the phase difference $p(t_1 - t_2)$, and, hence, it is influenced by the directions of the principal stresses and by the difference between the principal stresses at the given point in the model.

The intensity of the light transmitted through any given point in the model is proportional to the square of the amplitude of vibration, and a dark spot will be observed on the model's image for every point at which

$$a \sin 2\alpha \sin p \left(\frac{t_1 - t_2}{2} \right) = 0 \qquad (29)$$

Such dark points are, in general, linked together to form loci representing one of two conditions, namely: (1) loci of constant stress direction called "isoclinics" (when $\alpha = 0°$, or $90°$), or (2) loci of constant difference $(\sigma_1 - \sigma_2)$ between the principal stresses and referred to as "isochromatics" (for those cases in which $p \left(\frac{t_1 - t_2}{2} \right) = 0°, 180°$, etc.). The interpretation of equations 28 and 29 is considered in more detail in section D.

Since it becomes desirable for many applications to use several different arrangements of optical equipment for the polariscope that are slightly more complex than the plane polariscope of Fig. 17-7, several of the commonly used types of equipment are briefly described in the next section.

8. Polariscope Arrangements. A variety of arrangements of optical equipment that have been employed for photoelastic analyses are illustrated diagrammatically in Fig. 17-8, and a brief summary of the principal features of some of these is listed in Table 17-1.

Thus far we have considered only photoelastic effects at a given point in a model. However, for engineering applications it is desirable to have a large-diameter parallel beam of polarized light in which the greater portion of the model can be observed, and, hence, supplementary lenses are inserted in the systems of Fig. 17-8. Photographs of typical circular polariscopes are shown in Figs. 17-9, 17-10, and 17-43. Some of the uses for which these principal arrangements of Table 17-1 are employed are as follows:

(a) *The Plane Polariscope.* This is the simplest form of instrument, and it can be used to determine the following quantities in the photoelastic model:

1. The directions of the principal stresses at all points (isoclinics).

2. The difference between the principal stresses at all points (isochromatics).

3. The individual values of the principal stresses along free boundaries where the directions are either normal or tangent to the edge. (On the free

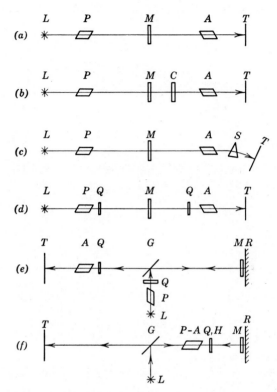

Fig. 17-8. Arrangements of the Essential Parts of a Photoelastic Polariscope
(R.D. Mindlin[5])

(a) Plane polariscope
(b) Plane polariscope with compensator
(c) Plane polariscope with spectroscopic analyzer
(d) Circular polariscope
(e) Nörrenberg doubler
(f) Reflection polariscope

L = light source	S = prism
P = polarizer	Q = quarter-wave plate
A = analyzer	G = glass plate
M = model	R = reflector
T = screen	H = half-wave plate
C = compensator	D = spherical reflector

boundary the principal stress normal to the boundary has zero for its value, and consequently the difference between the principal stresses represents the actual numerical value along the boundary.)

The polarizer and analyzer may be cartooned as a pair of slots set at right angles to each other, each of which pass only those components of the light wave which are parallel to the slot.   Thus, with no specimen in the polariscope,

FIG. 17-9.   Circular Polariscope Employing Large-Diameter Polarizers (H.
Becker[110])

 (a) Light source
 (b) Polarizer and quarter-wave plate
 (c) Model
 (d) Loading frame
 (e) Tension compensator
 (f) Quarter-wave plate and analyzer

and the transmission planes of the polarizer and analyzer at 90°, the light is
completely extinguished.   When a stressed model is placed in the field, however, the plane-polarized light passing through the first "slot" is broken up
into two rays, the planes of which coincide with the directions of principal
stresses in the model, as illustrated in Fig. 17-7.   The rays in these new planes
may have components parallel to the "slot" in the analyzer, and thus some
light is transmitted through the analyzer and produces the interference fringes

TABLE 17-1

SUMMARY OF POLARISCOPE ARRANGEMENTS

Type of Polariscope	Arrangement	Field	Isoclinics	With Monochromatic Light, Black Isochromatics Represent
Plane	Polarizer and analyzer crossed at 90°	Dark	Black	Integral orders of interference
	Polarizer and analyzer parallel	Light	Light	Half orders of interference
Circular	Equivalent of crossed polarizer and analyzer with λ/4 plates in opposition	Dark	Not shown	Integral orders of interference
	Equivalent of crossed polarizer and analyzer with λ/4 plates augumenting each other	Light	Not shown	Half orders of interference
	Equivalent of parallel polarizer and analyzer with λ/4 plates augumenting each other	Dark	Not shown	Integral orders of interference
	Equivalent of parallel polarizer and analyzer with λ/4 plates in opposition	Light	Not shown	Half orders of interference
Doubling	Single polarizing unit	Light	Light	Integral and half orders* of interference
	Single polarizing unit and single λ/4 plate	Dark	Not shown	Integral and half orders* of interference
	Independent plane polarizer and plane analyzer			All effects obtainable with either arrangement of the ordinary plane polariscope*
	Independent circular polarizer and circular analyzer			All effects obtainable with any arrangement of the circular polariscope*

* In calculating the stress values use twice actual thickness of model.

(or isochromatic color effects in white light) on the screen. At some points in the model one of the planes of principal stress will coincide with the plane of polarization of the incident light passed through the first "slot." At these points the light is not rotated or split up in passing through the model and will be completely extinguished by the analyzer, leaving black spots on the image of the model. In general, the stress directions in a loaded member vary continuously so that these dark points will form one or more continuous lines on the image. These lines are known as "isoclinics" or loci of all points having their principal stresses acting on planes of equal inclination (parallel to the planes of polarization).

Unfortunately, the isoclinic lines representing stress direction and the isochromatic lines representing stress magnitude are superimposed on each other. If monochromatic light is used, the resulting combination of black lines representing two different conditions may be confusing. However, when white light is used, the isoclinic lines will be represented by black whereas the isochromatic lines will be colored. The plane polariscope is used chiefly to locate isoclinics for determining directions of principal stresses. Photographs of typical isoclinic lines produced by this instrument are illustrated in Figs. 17-13 and 17-15. (In these figures the isochromatics are not evident, because relatively light loads were employed on a model of low sensitivity to the photoelastic effect.)

(b) *The Circular Polariscope.* The addition of quarter-wave plates to the plane polariscope converts the instrument into what is known as the circular polariscope (Table 17-1). With this equipment one may determine:

1. The difference between the principal stresses at all points.
2. The individual values of the principal stresses along free boundaries

FIG. 17-10.   Polariscope Utilizing Small-Diameter Polarizers and Lens System
(At Columbia University, R. D. Mindlin[5])

The photoelastic stress pattern produced by this instrument is independent of the directional effect of the stresses and, as a consequence, does not include the isoclinic lines. The image, therefore, consisting only of isochromatic lines, represents stress magnitudes alone. Typical isochromatics (interference-fringe patterns) are shown in Figs. 17-11 and 17-12.

The circular polariscope is in general use for finding the magnitudes of the stresses in the model. It has the characteristic that, when used with the wave length of light for which the quarter-wave plates were designed, the angular orientation of the circular analyzer (combination of quarter-wave plane and analyzing unit) is independent of the orientation of the circular polarizer (combination of quarter-wave plate and polarizer). For other wave lengths (including white light) the polarization will be slightly elliptical, and it will not be possible to produce a completely dark field. In this case, rotation of the circular analyzer relative to the circular polarizer will produce a slight variation in the illumination of the field, but for some position a minimum can be reached. Fortunately, from the engineering point of view, the

Fig. 17-11. Isochromatic-Fringe Photograph of a Short Cantilever Beam Using a Circular Polariscope with Light Field

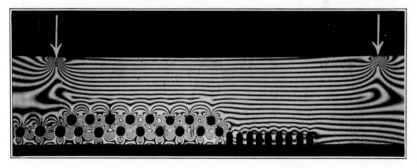

Fig. 17-12. Isochromatic-Fringe Photograph of a Beam with Multiple Holes Using a Circular Polariscope with Dark Field

requirement for the circular polarization is not rigid, and even the elliptical polarization produced with white light is not objectionable since the isoclinic lines will still be eliminated without excessive alteration of isochromatic fringes (particularly those of higher order in regions of high stress).

In selecting the quarter-wave plates for a given application it is much more important that the two wave plates match each other than that they correspond precisely to one quarter of the wave length of the light being used. If the quarter-wave plates do not match, the polariscope becomes optically unbalanced and the stress pattern of uncertain meaning.[21]

(c) *The Doubling Polariscope.* For examination of very thin models a doubling polariscope (Table 17-1 and Fig. 17-8) has the advantage that it produces twice as many interference fringes (isochromatics) as the conventional type. This result is accomplished by passing the light twice through the model and, thereby, doubling the effective thickness. The observations which can be made with this instrument will be similar to those which can be made with the ordinary plane and circular polariscopes.[22] The doubling polariscope is somewhat more difficult to use; the reflecting surface behind the model must be accurately positioned perpendicular to the beam of light, or diffusion will produce blurring of fringes. Some diffusion may also be caused by double reflections from the two faces of the glass plate G, in Figs. 17-8e and 17-8f.

(d) *Light Field versus Dark Field.* The three kinds of polariscope just described all may have variations in the arrangement of the parts. In Table 17-1 a number of the arrangements are indicated with the corresponding characteristics which one may expect.* If the optic axes of the two quarter-wave plates are crossed (in the usual simple circular polariscope with polarizer and analyzer crossed), the emerging background or field is extinguished. Conversely, if the quarter-wave plates are arranged to augment each other, they produce a total of a half-wave retardation resulting in a bright field of transmitted light.

Although the dark-field arrangement was often used by early investigators, the light-field arrangement has the advantage that the edge of the model can often be more readily seen. In many cases, fine isochromatic lines near a boundary may be obscured if the model is not perfectly aligned. With the dark field the shadow of the edge of the model cannot be observed, and, if closely spaced isochromatics are obscured in this shadow, the condition may go undetected, whereas with the light field the sharpness of the boundary or edge can be readily observed and corrected. The dark-field arrangement has the characteristic that with monochromatic light the zero and integral orders of interference will be represented by isochromatic lines in black, whereas with a light field the isochromatics are light (the integral isochromatics are always the same color as the field or background around the model).

D. INTERPRETATION OF THE PHOTOELASTIC-STRESS PATTERN

9. Isoclinic Lines. By reconsidering the resultant amplitude of vibration of the intensity of light transmitted through a model and plane polariscope as represented by equations 28 and 29, it may be observed that these become

zero when $a = 0$; $\sin 2\alpha = 0$; or $\sin p\left(\dfrac{t_1 - t_2}{2}\right) = 0$. If a were zero, then no

---

* Reference 3, pp 382-5.

light would be transmitted from the polarizer to the model; hence, for practical applications we need only examine the other two conditions.

For a first condition let us assume that $\sin p \left(\dfrac{t_1 - t_2}{2} \right)$ is not zero.   Then if $\sin 2\alpha = 0$, α must be $0°$ or $90°$.   This means that, if the planes of transmission of the polarizer and analyzer are parallel to the directions of the principal planes of stress, on the image of the model there will be dark spots corresponding to all points at which the principal-stress directions coincide with the planes of transmission of the polarizer and analyzer.   Such points are linked up and form a locus of all points having the same directions for the principal stresses, that is (with a dark-field arrangement), an isoclinic line

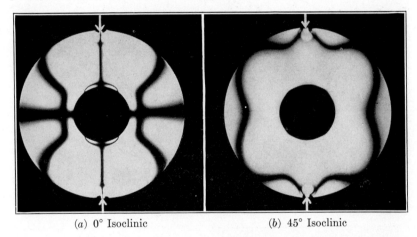

(a) 0° Isoclinic   (b) 45° Isoclinic

FIG. 17-13.   Isoclinics in a Diametrically Compressed Ring Material: Methyl Methacrylate Resin (Lucite) without Plasticizer (M. Hetényi)

will be represented by a black rather broad line on the image of the model, as shown by Fig. 17-13.

In Fig. 17-14 are shown diagrammatically several isoclinic lines corresponding to inclinations (rotation of the polarized field by angles)ϕ_1, ϕ_2, etc., from some fixed reference line or axis.   It may be observed that at all points on line ϕ_1 the planes of principal stress have the constant orientation ϕ_1, and on ϕ_2 the orientation is ϕ_2, etc., as is indicated by the small crosses drawn at several points on each isoclinic.   The directions of the principal stresses change from point to point as shown by the stress trajectories in this figure. A straight free boundary of a model may also be regarded as an isoclinic since it represents a line along which the principal stresses are constant in direction.

By adjusting the orientation of the polarizer and analyzer (but always keeping them, respectively, at right angles), the isoclinic line corresponding to any desired stress inclination may be determined.   It is customary practice to put a sheet of tracing paper on the viewing screen of the polariscope and to trace on this the isoclinic lines for each selected inclination.   The

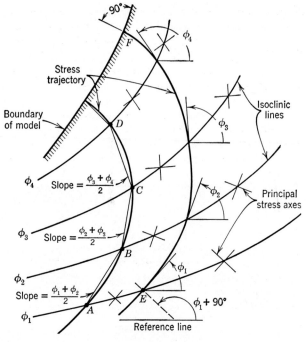

Fig. 17-14.   Relation between Isoclinics and Stress Trajectories

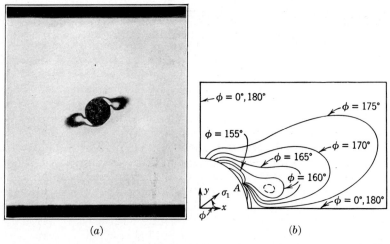

(a)   (b)

Fig. 17-15.   Isoclinics around a Small Hole in a Plate in Tension (R. D. Mindlin[5])
       (a) Photograph of 165° isoclinic
       (b) Sketch of a set of isoclinics in one quarter of the plate

increment of inclination between the stress directions represented by any two isoclinics lines can be selected at will, and the pattern will repeat itself every time the polarizer and analyzer have been rotated through 90°. A typical set of isoclinic lines differing by 5° in the orientations of the stresses they represent are shown in Fig. 17-15b; these represent a complete survey for the model of a tension plate with a hole for which a photograph of one of the isoclinics is shown in Fig. 17-15a.

Actually, except in the regions of rapidly changing stress direction, the isoclinic lines are represented by dark zones for which it is necessary to determine the mean. The existence of small residual stresses in the model may change the orientation of the net stress sufficiently to shift an isoclinic appreciably on a model. For these reasons the determination of the principal-stress orientations is more susceptible to error than the other values determined by photoelastic analysis.

White light is generally used when tracing the isoclinic lines so that the black bands may be readily distinguishable from the colored isochromatics which remain stationary as the polarizer and analyzer are rotated. For convenience of observation, it is much better to use the dark-field arrangement of the polariscope (which produces black isoclinics) in preference to the light field which makes them bright. In the laboratory the isoclinics can be seen more clearly if one looks at the screen from a position slightly to one side of the center line of the polariscope.

Some of the properties of isoclinic lines are:

1. The isoclinic lines do not intersect one another (except at an isotropic point).

2. The isoclinic lines only intersect a free boundary where it has the inclination indicated for the isoclinic (except at a point of zero stress where all isoclinics may run into the boundary).

3. A straight free boundary is also an isoclinic line.

4. All isoclinic lines intersect at an isotropic point. (At an isotropic point the two principal stresses are equal and are inclined in every conceivable direction representing a condition similar to a two-dimensional hydrostatic pressure.)

5. An axis which is symmetrical with respect to both the loads and geometry of the model coincides with one isoclinic.

10. Stress Trajectories and Determination of Stress Directions. Unfortunately, it is necessary to reinterpret the isoclinic lines in order to obtain a direct representation of the stress directions. They furnish data from which the network of stress directions may be obtained by a graphical construction. The "isostatics" (commonly called stress trajectories) are lines parallel or normal to the two principal-stress directions at all points through which they pass, and as such they give a graphic representation of the directions of the principal stresses (see for instance Fig. 17-16 and Fig. 17-19).

The stress trajectories may be sketched in (as shown by line *EF* in Fig. 17-14) to intersect each isoclinic in a direction tangent to that indicated by the value of ϕ (tangent to the crosses drawn to indicate the respective orientations of the principal stresses).

A somewhat more systematic method of tracing the isostatics is also illustrated in Fig. 17-14 by the line $ABCD$ which was constructed as follows: Take any point A, at which one wishes to start the construction of a stress trajectory, on the first isoclinic, and draw a straight line with a slope equal to the average between isoclinics 1 and 2, to point B on the second isoclinic. From B draw another straight line to C on the third isoclinic such that the slope of BC is the average between the second and third isoclinics. This process is repeated until a series of short straight lines have been drawn. Then

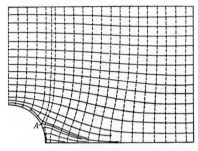

fair in a smooth curve such that the previously drawn straight lines are chords between isoclinics. If the isoclinic lines are relatively close together, the curve thus drawn will represent a stress trajectory. This trajectory must intersect all the isoclinic lines which it cuts at the proper inclination to the reference axis (that is, at the angle designated by each isoclinic). Furthermore, all stress trajectories form an orthogonal network (intersect only at right angles to each other and at 90° to a free boundary).

Fig. 17-16.   Stress Trajectories from the Isoclinics of Fig. 17-15 (R. D. Mindlin[5])

A set of isostatics constructed from the isoclinics of Fig. 17-15 are shown in Fig. 17-16 for the tension plate with a hole, and sample isoclinics and stress trajectories for knee frames are shown in Fig. 17-19.

11. Isochromatic Lines. Let us again consider equations 28 and 29 for the resultant transmitted light but this time assume that both a and $\sin 2\alpha$ are other than zero. Under these conditions, at a point in the photoelastic model, no light will be transmitted through a plane polariscope when

$$\sin p\left(\frac{t_1 - t_2}{2}\right) = 0 \tag{30}$$

in which case a dark spot will be shown on the image. This condition will prevail for all points at which

$$p\left(\frac{t_1 - t_2}{2}\right) = 0 \quad \text{or } n\pi, \text{ where } n = \text{any integer} \tag{31}$$

Conversely, a maximum intensity of transmitted light will take place at all points for which

$$p\left(\frac{t_1 - t_2}{2}\right) = \frac{\pi}{2} \quad \text{or } (n + \tfrac{1}{2})\pi \tag{32}$$

In general, all points of a model having a constant retardation $p(t_1 - t_2)$ form a continuous band or line. Thus, a dark line or locus appears on the image of the model for each value of n in equation 31, and, similarly, a bright band or locus appears for each value of n in equation 32. When examined in *white* light the various fractional orders of retardation are each made evident by a brilliant band of a particular color or hue, and, hence, they have been designated by the name "*isochromatics.*" The alternate bright and dark lines formed in monochromatic light are also isochromatics (though sometimes called interference "fringes") and are distinguished from one another accord-

Fig. 17-17.   Typical Isochromatic-Fringe Photograph of Circular Discontinuity in a Field of Pure Shear (Photo made in collaboration with A. J. Durelli)

ing to the value of n; consequently, they are often referred to as the isochromatic of zero, first, second order of interference, and so on.

By comparing equations 25 and 31 (or 32) it may be observed that, since

$$p\left(\frac{t_1 - t_2}{2}\right) \text{ is proportional to } (\sigma_1 - \sigma_2) \qquad (33)$$

the order of interference is, therefore, directly proportional to the difference between the principal stresses; consequently, *the isochromatic line may be defined as the locus of all points having a constant value for the difference between the two principal stresses.* From equation 25 this may be written in the form:

$$(\sigma_1 - \sigma_2) = \frac{v}{Ch}(t_1 - t_2) = \frac{f}{h} \times n \qquad (34)$$

in which f = a "fringe constant" for the material, $\left(\dfrac{\text{lb}}{\text{in.} \times \text{order}}\right)$

h = thickness of the photoelastic model, inches

n = order of interference

For materials which possess a linear relation between stress-magnitude and optical-retardation effects, the change in the difference between the principal stresses when progressing from any given isochromatic line to its neighbor is

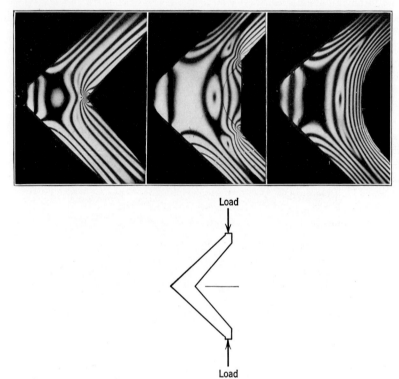

Load

Load

FIG. 17-18. Isochromatics for Several Shapes of Knee Frame[109]

a constant. One may, therefore, regard the isochromatic diagram as a contour map of the photoelastic model in which the isochromatic lines represent contour lines of constant difference between the principal stresses. Since the maximum shearing stress that occurs at any point in a two-dimensional body is equal to half the difference in the principal stresses at the point (as shown by equation 17), the isochromatic lines may also be interpreted as loci of constant intensity of *maximum* shearing stresses.

Isochromatic diagrams obtained with circularly polarized monochromatic light (Figs. 17-11, 17-17, 17-18) have no indication of reference or datum. This must be established through observation in the laboratory or by other means as is discussed in the following. However, since there is the same change in shear stress between isochromatics, it is evident that wherever the lines are gathered together closely there will be a high stress gradient and a correspondingly high stress in the region.

Since isoclinic lines also appear on a model examined in *plane*-polarized light, these are usually eliminated by using a circular polariscope for photographing or evaluating isochromatics. As indicated by equation 29, the isochromatics have maximum contrasting intensities in a plane polariscope only at points where the principal stresses are oriented at 45° to the planes of polarization. These difficulties make it desirable to use circular polarization when it is desired to observe a large portion of the model at one time. One may, however, distinguish between isoclinics and isochromatics in the plane polariscope by rotating the planes of polarization or by changing the load on the model. Isoclinics will change position on the model only as the planes of polarization are rotated, whereas the isochromatics change position only as the loads are varied.

(*a*) *Calculation of Stress Magnitude.* The evaluation of the difference between the principal stresses (equation 34) depends on determining the order of interference n (fringe order) for a given model of thickness h and on knowing the fringe constant f for the particular material. Detailed methods of evaluating n and f are presented in sections E and F. For the present, let it be assumed that these quantities have been determined, and it is desired to find the difference between the principal stresses in a photoelastic model for the following conditions:

Order of interference at the point, $n = 4$
Thickness of the model, $h = 0.375$ in.

Finge constant for the material, $f = 84 \dfrac{\text{lb}}{\text{in.} \times \text{order}}$

From equation 34 we find

$$\sigma_1 - \sigma_2 = \frac{84 \times 4}{0.375} = 896 \text{ psi} \tag{35}$$

The isochromatic diagram does not give any information concerning the sign of σ_1 or σ_2 but merely indicates the difference in value. *The order of interference (or fringe order) is always taken as positive.* This agrees with the definition that σ_1 is the algebraically larger principal stress and that $\sigma_1 - \sigma_2$ will always be a positive quantity, irrespective of whether σ_1 and σ_2 are both tension, σ_1 tension and σ_2 compression, or both stresses compression.

(*b*) *Free Boundary.* In a free (unloaded) boundary the principal stresses lie along and normal to the edge. The principal stress normal to a free edge is always zero, and consequently equation 34 can be used to calculate the value of the principal stress tangent to the edge. Although the fringe order is positive, the stress along the edge may be tension or compression. In many cases the sign of the stress (whether tension or compression) along a free boundary may be determined by inspection of the geometry of the model and the manner of loading. However, if this is not obvious or certain, a

Coker or Babinet compensator (see section E) may be used to determine the
type of stress.

12. Evaluation of the Fringe Order.   Although it is not always possible to
make a photographic record of the photoelastic-stress pattern, this is a most
desirable procedure.   In all cases such a record should be supplemented by
studying the formation of the fringe pattern in the polariscope as the loads
are applied to the model.   The procedure of making a stress analysis from a
single isochromatic diagram is open to serious doubt unless a good deal is
known about the stress distribution under consideration.

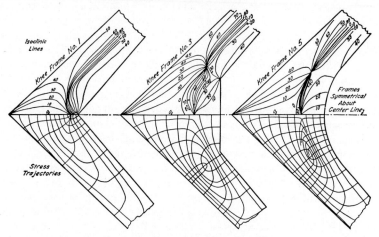

FIG. 17-19.   Isoclinics and Stress Trajectories for Knee Frames of Fig. 17-18

The determination of the isochromatic fringe order at any particular point
can be accomplished in a number of ways.   The following applicable methods
may be employed:

1. Locate a line corresponding to the isochromatic of zero order, and count
isochromatic lines from it.   The zero-order line will not be distinguishable
from isochromatics of higher order with monochromatic light; however, with
a sufficient change in load, all other points in the model will change in brightness indicating a change in fringe order with loading.   If it is inconvenient
to change the load, or if this test is not sufficiently sensitive, the line can be
checked by using white light in the circular polariscope (and a dark-field
arrangement).   Under these conditions the line of zero order is the only one
represented in *black* with orange–yellow tints on both sides of it.

2. Find an isotropic point ($\sigma_1 = \sigma_2$), and count fringe orders to the neighboring isochromatics from this point.   With monochromatic light the isotropic
point will be represented by a black dot in the dark-field polariscope.   This
may lead to confusion with other black dots representing higher orders of
interference (sinks or sources); however, if when the load is changed the same
position in the model continues to remain dark, an isotropic point is indicated.
If this check is not satisfactory, or if the load cannot be changed, an examina-

tion in white light (as in method 1) may settle the question, since the isotropic point is black, and all points corresponding to higher orders of interference will be colored.   A further check may be obtained by removing the quarter-wave plates and determining whether all the isoclinic lines pass through the point.   If all the isoclinic lines intersect at this location than an isotropic point is indicated.

3. At any external (projecting) square corner on a free boundary there will be an isotropic point from which the order of each isochromatic line may be counted.   Care must be exercised in using this method since residual stresses or time-edge effects may move the isochromatic of zero order a slight distance from the corner.

4. Count the fringes as they are formed at some given location during the gradual application of the load.   This is a useful method when the isochromatic lines disappear off a boundary of the model or move out of the field of the polariscope.   An example of this nature is found in a thick hollow cylinder subjected to internal pressure.   In this case the isochromatics are concentric circles which form at the bore and more outwards and ultimately go off the outer edge as the load is increased.

5. As a variation of method 4, it is also possible to change the load by a known increment sufficient to produce a given change in interference fringe order (the number of fringes to pass the point) at some particular location. One can thus determine the load increment per fringe and by direct proportion compute the expected fringe order for any given load.   In certain cases the stress at some location can be computed analytically and the corresponding fringe order calculated and used as a reference.

6. The interference order may be determined by using a Coker or Babinet compensator (see section E).   These instruments are particularly useful for evaluating isochromatic order when the load cannot be changed to alter the stress pattern, and for low-order fringes.

Once the order of interference and the thickness of the model have been determined, the difference between the principal stresses can be calculated if the fringe constant for the material is known.   The relationships between the various types of photoelastic data and the resulting analysis are illustrated in Fig. 17-18 to 17-20 which show the original isochromatics and isoclinics for a particular problem and the resulting stress trajectories and values of stress computed from the observations.

13. The Isotropic Point.   By definition, an isotropic point is a location at which the two principal stresses are equal ($\sigma_1 = \sigma_2$).   In the photoelastic model this is represented by the zero order of interference.   If it is desired to determine whether the principal stresses in addition to being equal to each other, are equal to zero at the isotropic point, the following three methods may be employed.

1. If a lateral strain gage shows no change in thickness at the isotropic point as the model is loaded, then $\sigma_1 - \sigma_2 = 0 = \sigma_1 + \sigma_2$, and $\sigma_1 = \sigma_2 = 0$.

2. If a small hole is carefully drilled in the model at the isotropic point, and no change in the stress pattern results, then $\sigma_1 = \sigma_2 = 0$.   If $\sigma_1 = \sigma_2 \neq$

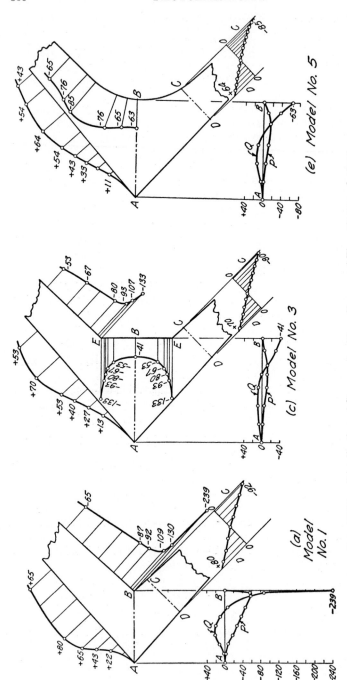

Fig. 17-20. Distribution of Stresses for Knee Frames of Figs. 17-18 and 17-19

Values shown are in pounds per square inch per pound of load. Stresses P are the principal stresses in the direction AB, and those designated as Q are normal to AB. In proceeding from A to B, the algebraically larger principal stress σ_1 is represented by Q until the isotropic point is reached. From there on it is represented by P; the principal stress axes rotate through 90° at the isotropic point

0, the presence of the small hole will produce concentric isochromatic lines in the immediate vicinity of the discontinuity. Experimentally, it is difficult to drill a sufficiently small hole in the model without developing machining stresses or removing excessive area of material, both of which would tend to develop new isochromatic lines around the hole making interpretation difficult.

3. Drucker's oblique incidence method (which is described in section L.)

At an isotropic point the stress is oriented equally in all directions (all isoclinics pass through the point), and this sometimes leads to confusion in constructing the stress trajectories in the neighborhood of the point. In general, the networks of stress trajectories form either *interlocking* hairpin loops around the point (as shown near the center of one leg of the frames 3 and 5 in Fig. 17-19) or *noninterlocking* curves which diverge in an abrupt manner as they approach the point instead of circling around it. An example of noninterlocking stress trajectories is shown at point *A* in Figs. 17-15 and 17-16. These two different types of arrangement of the network around an isotropic point can usually be readily distinguished in the construction, but the specific configuration can be determined by the manner in which the isoclinics are grouped through the isotropic point. Definite rules or procedure for determining whether the trajectories are interlocking or noninterlocking have been formulated and are outlined by Frocht,* by Mindlin,† and by Sadowski.[27]

E. Methods of Finding Fractional Orders of Interference

In certain cases involving very thin models, or optically insensitive materials such as glass, the number of integral or half-order isochromatics will be too small to permit of convenient interpretation or accurate interpolation. Under conditions of this nature the following methods of determining fractional orders of interference may be found useful.

14. The Coker Compensator. A tension compensator consists of a small strip of photoelastic material arranged in a loading frame in such a manner that it can be placed in series with the light passing through the photoelastic model in the polariscope as illustrated at *e* in Fig. 17-9. Figure 17-21 shows details of another form of tension compensator.

The procedure employed is to orient and load the tensile strip in such a manner that the relative retardation produced in it just neutralizes the effect at the point to be investigated in the photoelastic model. The method represents a point-by-point procedure and involves the following steps for each point in question:

1. With the quarter-wave plates removed and using a white-light source determine which isoclinic line passes through the point and the corresponding directions of the principal stresses.

2. Replace the quarter-wave plates in their correct orientations with respect to the polarizer and analyzer. Then mount the compensator in the light

* Reference 3, article 6-12.
† Reference 5, p 241.

beam with the tension axis parallel to the direction of one of the principal stresses at a given point in the model.

3. Apply load to the compensator until the neutral line (black with yellow on both sides) is observed at the point. The order of interference in the compensator is then the same as that in the model. If the load on the compensator is known, together with its cross-sectional dimensions and the fringe constant for its material, the interference order n can be computed by rewriting equation 34 in the form:

$$n = \left(\frac{\sigma_1 - \sigma_2}{f}\right) \times h \qquad (36)$$

For the tension strip, $\sigma_2 = 0$ and hence,

$$\sigma_1 - \sigma_2 = \sigma_1 = \frac{P}{bh} \qquad (37)$$

where P = total load on compensator strip, pounds
b = breadth of strip, inches
h = thickness of strip (traversed by the light), inches
f = fringe constant for the material, pounds per inch per order

Therefore, the interference order may be obtained as

$$n = \frac{P}{fb} \qquad (38)$$

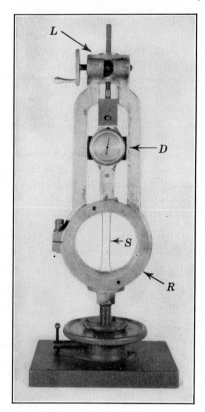

FIG. 17-21. The Coker Tension Compensator
L is a load-changing device; D is a dial to indicate the load; S indicates the tension bar; and R is a ring to allow rotation of the assembly and measurement of angles

If a neutral line is not observed, then the compensator should be rotated 90° in its own plane (lined up parallel to the direction of the other principal stress) and the loading process repeated. In the direction of one of the two principal stresses the neutral effect will appear.

One will observe that the determination of the fringe order (fractional or integral) with the compensator does not require the model and compensator to be of the same thickness nor of the same material. If, however, the compensator be made of the same material and thickness as the model, the value of $(\sigma_1 - \sigma_2)$ for the model is identical with the value for tensile stress in the compensating bar at the point where a neutral line (black band) is obtained by the foregoing procedure. The method works well up to about the fourth order of interference. The chief disadvantage in the use of a tensile-bar compensator, however, lies in the possible errors that may be introduced by optical creep (added retardation) in the bar under sustained load; this effect is particularly troublesome in certain plastics.

The tension compensator can be used to study any point in a photoelastic model. However, for points along a free boundary it has the useful characteristic of being able to indicate the difference between tension and compression. If, in order to produce neutralization,the tension axis of the compensator must be positioned perpendicular to the free boundary, then the edge is in tension. If, on the other hand, the compensator must be oriented parallel to the boundary, the edge is in compression. One will observe that, in going along a free boundary from a region of tension to compression, or vice versa, the compensator must be rotated through 90° at the transition point of zero stress.

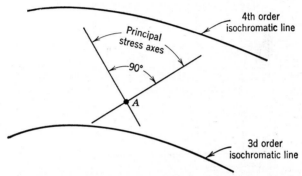

FIG. 17-22. Determination of Fractional Order of Interference by Rotation of the Analyzer

15. Use of the Analyzer as a Compensator. Another simple point-by-point method of determining fractional orders of interference is available by rotation of the analyzer.[28-30] However, this method will only determine the fractional order relative to the nearest integral or half-order isochromatic line. In connection with studies on glass the method has been extremely useful.

Let us assume that it is desired to find the fractional order of interference at some point A (Fig. 17-22) located between isochromatics of the third and fourth order. The following steps will be necessary:

1. Determine the directions of the principal-stress axes at A.

2. Line up the planes of polarization of the polarizer and analyzer parallel and perpendicular to the principal-stress axes at A. Then orient the quarter-wave plates properly (at 45°) with respect to the polarizer and analyzer.

3. With monochromatic-light source the integral orders of interference will be observed in black if the quarter-wave plates are set for dark field.

4. By rotating the analyzer only, (quarter-wave plates should *remain fixed* in orientation) extinction can be achieved at point A, and the angle of rotation

will be proportional to the difference in order of interference between A and one of the adjacent isochromatics.

For example, if one observes, under conditions similar to those indicated by the isochromatics in Fig. 17-22, that, by rotating the analyzer clockwise through 36°, extinction is transferred from the third-order isochromatic to the point A, then the order of interference at A will be

$$n = 3 + \frac{\text{angle of rotation}}{180}$$

$$= 3 + \tfrac{36}{180} = 3.20 \tag{39}$$

If the analyzer had been rotated in the opposite direction the point of extinction would have moved from the fourth-order isochromatic into the

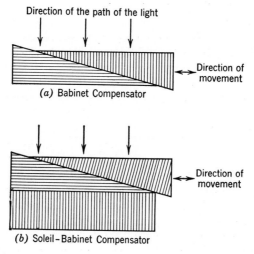

Direction of the path of the light

Direction of movement

(*a*) Babinet Compensator

Direction of movement

(*b*) Soleil–Babinet Compensator

FIG. 17-23. Schematic Diagrams of Babinet and Soleil–Babinet Compensators (Micrometer-screw mechanism for adjusting relative positions of wedges is not shown)

region of lower order at A. In this case the angle of rotation would have been 144° = (180 − 36), and the corresponding order at A would have been observed as

$$n = 4 - \tfrac{144}{180} = 3.20 \tag{40}$$

Every time the analyzer is rotated through 180° the isochromatic diagram will be completely repeated. If one starts with the dark field, then a 90° rotation will produce a light field in which the isochromatics in black represent the half orders (that is, $n = \tfrac{90}{180} = \tfrac{1}{2}$).

16. Babinet and Soleil–Babinet Compensators. For measuring very small retardations these optical instruments will have better application than either of the two methods previously described; they consist of a pair of wedge-shaped quartz (or other crystal) plates with the polarizing axes arranged as indicated in Fig. 17-23. In the Babinet compensator the fast and slow axes of the two wedges are arranged to oppose each other, whereas in the Soleil–Babinet instrument they augment each other, and, in addition, there is a third crystal plate.

If circularly polarized light (or plane-polarized light with its plane of vibration at approximately 45° to the polarizing axes of the crystal plates) is directed at normal incidence through the pair of wedges, it will be resolved into two equal components in the directions of the axes of transmission. In the Babinet compensator, when the light traverses the first wedge, one component is advanced relative to the other. However, in passing through the second wedge the component which was previously advanced is retarded so that the final result is a relative retardation, depending on the distance traveled in each wedge. When white light is used, this effect produces a series of colored bands across the compensator. In the location at which the effect in the second wedge just neutralizes that in the first wedge, a black band will appear with yellow on both sides of it. It is convenient to locate this neutral line with white light, but precise observations should be made with monochromatic light.

By moving the wedges relative to each other the interference lines can be displaced, and relative retardations can be measured by this means, according to the equation.

$$R = \frac{M}{M_o} \qquad (41)$$

where R = the retardation produced by the compensator in wave lengths
M_o = the wedge displacement from the neutral position necessary to produce one wave length retardation.
M = the measured displacement from the neutral position

The Soleil–Babinet compensator is constructed so that the relative retardation over the entire field is the same for any given setting of wedges and, in effect, produces a uniform color (in white light) across the field; however, with this exception it may be used in the same manner as described previously for the Babinet compensator.

F. Determination of the Fringe Constant

The problem of determining the quantitative meaning of the isochromatic lines in terms of stress intensity is common to all problems in which absolute stress values, instead of relative values, are required. Equations 34 and 36 relate the difference between the principal stresses to the order of interference of the isochromatic lines. Evaluation of the *fringe constant f* is really a calibration of a stress-optic constant for the material.

The fringe constant may be interpreted as the change in the difference between the principal stresses that will produce a change of one order of interference at a given point in a piece of the material having unit thickness. Its units are pounds per square inch per inch thickness per fringe order, or simply $\dfrac{\text{force}}{\text{length} \times \text{order}}$. From the point of view of utilization one may also consider the fringe constant as the proportionality factor which is multiplied by the order of interference and divided by the thickness of the model to obtain the value of the difference between the principal stresses.

It should be noted that the following discussion relates only to those materials having a linear relation between stress and the optical-retardation effect. As long as this condition prevails, a single value of the fringe constant can be used since the increment in stress between all orders of interference will be the same. With a nonlinear relationship a different value of the constant must be used for each order and thickness. Theoretically this is no disadvantage, but it makes the arithmetical computation more tedious. Other considerations which influence values of fringe constants listed in the literature are:

1. The value of the constant is dependent on the wave length of the light used during the calibration. This should be taken into account if the photoelastic test is to be conducted with light of another wave length.

2. Some authors quote values in terms of maximum shear stress which is just half the difference between the principal stresses. This procedure sometimes leads to confusion when comparison is made with certain classes of plastics whose constants are in the ratio of about 2 to 1.

Theoretically, any model for which there is a known analytical solution for the stress distribution may be used for evaluating the fringe constant. However, in practice there are some limitations of experimental techniques and available equipment which may govern the selection. The optical sensitivity of the material and its other mechanical properties will sometimes determine the method which should be employed.

By rearranging equation 34 the following relation is obtained for the fringe constant:

$$f = \frac{(\sigma_1 - \sigma_2)h}{n} \quad \left(\frac{\text{lb}}{\text{in.} \times \text{order}}\right) \tag{42}$$

(The units of this quantity are sometimes written lb/in./order.) It is frequently found desirable in practice to determine changes of fringe order corresponding to known increments of $(\sigma_1 - \sigma_2)$ and to substitute these increments directly in the right side of equation 42.

One might make a rough division of the methods of calibration into three classes, depending on the relative values of fringe constant. If we remember that the relatively insensitive materials require a large change in stress to produce an optical change of one order of interference, it is evident that the very sensitive materials will have low fringe constants, whereas those which are not so sensitive will possess higher values. For convenience the following subdivision according to optical sensitivity is made:

Class	Approximate Range of Fringe Constant, lb/in./order	Characteristic
a	Up to 35	Rather sensitive
b	35–125	Intermediatly sensitivity
c	Above 125	Relatively insensitive

17. Calibration in Tension. A common method for determining the fringe constant for material is to employ a tension bar; this type of calibration is best suited to intermediate and relatively insensitive materials. It involves simple calculations and can be made quite independent of residual stress and the "time-edge" effect.

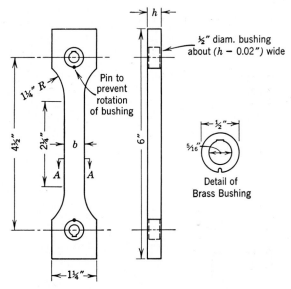

FIG. 17-24. Specimen for Calibration in Tension
Thickness h is usually about $\frac{1}{4}$ to $\frac{3}{8}$ in., and width, b is approximately $\frac{1}{2}$ in.

In this form of model the algebraically larger principal stress σ_1 is equal to the load divided by the area, (and $\sigma_2 = 0$); hence (from equation 42),

$$f = \frac{\sigma_1 h}{n} = \frac{P}{bh} \cdot \frac{h}{n} = \frac{P}{bn} \qquad (43)$$

where $P =$ the load (assumed uniformly distributed)
and $b \times h =$ the area of cross section

Figure 17-24 shows a drawing of a typical calibration specimen of an average size. Two brass bushings are located near the ends to take the loading pins about $\frac{1}{4}$ in. in diameter. These bushings should have a snug fit and yet press in easily with the fingers. The flats which are filed on the insides of the brass bushings are for the purpose of allowing the operator to shift or adjust the line of action of the applied forced by rolling the loading pins slightly. This feature is rather desirable since it permits establishing an axial loading, and, in consequence, uniform distribution of stress over the entire area of cross section in the reduced portion (section $A–A$).

If the specimen is free from residual stress, and no edge stress has developed, the entire image should appear dark in the polariscope (with the dark-field arrangement) when no load is applied. Actually this condition is very difficult to obtain, and one can usually see a bright outline of the model on the screen of the polariscope. However, this will not have an appreciable affect on the value obtained for the fringe constant (the reason for this is explained in the following).

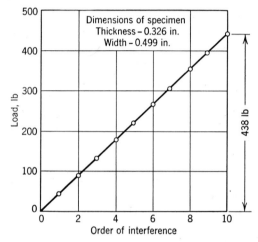

Fig. 17-25. Calibration Curve for Bakelite BT-61-893 in Tension Using light of wave length 5461 A traversing the thickness of 0.326 in.

(a) *Procedure for Materials of Intermediate Sensitivity.* The model should first be checked for central loading by applying a small load and observing the formation of the isochromatics. If these appear symmetrically from the fillets and on either side of the center line, then the line of action of the applied force is in the correct position, but, if the appearance is unsymmetrical, there is misalignment, and bending is present. To eliminate misalignment the loading pins can be rotated slightly until the isochromatics become symmetrical.

After adjusting for symmetry, the load should be reduced as nearly as possible to zero. The calibration is then performed by gradually increasing the load while at the same time watching a convenient reference point on the model. (It is best to choose a point of reference preferably near midlength and, to minimize any effect of bending, on the center line.) As the load is gradually applied, the point of reference will become alternately light and dark. Every time it becomes completely dark there is a change of one order of interference from the previous like condition, and the load corresponding to each condition should be recorded. These values of load may then be plotted against the order of interference and the slope of the line determined. It is advisable to make a series of observations with increasing and with decreasing loads and then to plot the average loads for each order of interference as indicated in Fig. 17-25.

From this plot the slope of the line represents P/n in equation 43, and the final fringe constant is obtained by dividing this by the width of specimen b. Thus, from the data in Fig 17-25, the slope is $43\,8\!\!/_{10}$, and hence,

$$f = \frac{43.8}{0.499} = 87.7 \text{ lb/in./order} \quad (44)$$

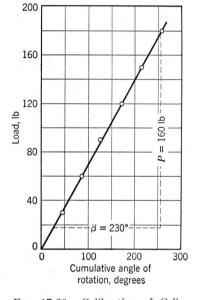

(b) *Procedure for Relatively Insensitive Materials.* For materials which are relatively insensitive the determination of the fringe constant can be made quite satisfactorily by a slight modification of the procedures described just previously and in section E. All the precautions relative to proper alignment of the specimen should be taken, and in addition the polarizing axes of the polarizer and analyzer should be lined up parallel and perpendicular to the axis of the calibration specimen, that is, parallel and perpendicular to the directions of the principal stresses. The quarter-wave plates should be oriented accurately with respect to the polarizer and analyzer (preferably for dark field, but the light-field arrangement may also be used).

With no load on the model the whole should appear dark on the screen of

Fig. 17-26. Calibration of Celluloid Specimen by Rotation of the Analyzer (Tardy Method)
Width of specimen 0.50 in.; thickness in path of light 0.253 in.; wave length of light 5461 A

the dark-field polariscope as long as there is no residual birefringence or edge effect. If either of these conditions prevail, portions of the image will appear light, in which case the analyzer only should be rotated slightly until extinction is obtained at the reference point; the quarter-wave plates should be maintained fixed in direction. The angular orientation of the analyzer should then be observed, as this will be the zero or reference reading.

After calculating or determining what will be the maximum permissible load to apply to the model from the strength and optical characteristics, the bar is gradually loaded. At the same time the analyzer only (without changing orientation of quater-wave plates) is rotated in the direction in which it is possible to maintain extinction while the load is being applied. At definite intervals of load (usually increments of about one-tenth the maximum permissible load) the cumulative angular displacement of the analyzer from the initial position is recorded. The loads and corresponding analyzer orientations can then be plotted as shown in Fig. 17-26.

Corresponding to each increment of change in angular orientation of the analyzer β, the change in order of interference will be

$$\frac{\beta}{180} \quad \text{(if the angle is measured in degrees)} \tag{45}$$

The value of the fringe constant is then found by substitution in equation 42 with the result,

$$f = \frac{P}{b} \times \frac{180}{\beta} \tag{46}$$

From this relation and the data plotted in Fig. 17-26 the fringe constant for this calibration is seen to be

$$f = \frac{160}{0.500} \times \frac{180}{230} = 250 \text{ lb/in./order} \tag{47}$$

18. Photographic Recording of Data for Finding the Fringe Constant. Unfortunately, calibration by means of a tensile specimen does not lend itself conveniently to photographic recording of the observations. However, the following methods are available for evaluation of the fringe constant by interpretation of fringe photographs.

(a) *Beam in Pure Bending.* The use of a beam in pure bending, as shown in Fig. 17-27 is a favorite and widely used means for calibrating materials of medium and high sensitivity. The positions of the isochromatic lines throughout the depth of the beam may be plotted, and by extrapolation the total change in interference order n from top to bottom may be found. The fringe constant is then determined from equation 42, with σ_1 taken as the total increment in calculated stress between the two extreme fibers of the beam (and $\sigma_2 = 0$), as follows:

$$f = \frac{2M}{Z} \times \frac{h}{n} = \frac{12M}{d^2 n} \tag{48}$$

where Z = section modulus = $\frac{1}{6}hd^2$, inches³
d = depth of beam, inches
h = thickness of beam, inches
M = bending moment on beam, inch-pounds

Several variations in application of this method of calibration may be adopted. If small amounts of initial birefringence exist, it may be found (by plotting from the zero-order fringe at mid-depth) that the fringe order at the top and bottom edges are slightly different. It is desirable, therefore, to plot from the zero-order fringe and extrapolate to the top and bottom fibers. This difference in fringe order gives a measure of the residual stresses present.

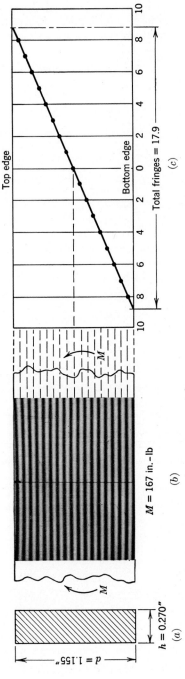

$M = 167$ in.-lb

(a) $d = 1.155''$ $h = 0.270''$

(b)

Total fringes = 17.9

(c)

FIG. 17-27. Calibration by Means of a Beam in Pure Bending (Bakelite BT-61-893)

(a) Cross section
(b) Photoelastic-fringe pattern (M = bending moment = 167 in.-lb; integral orders of retardation are light bands with a light-field arrangement of the polariscope)
(c) Plot of fringe orders across depth of beam

If the data shown in Fig. 17-27 are used, the total change in fringe order from top to bottom is found to be 17.9 for a bending moment of 167 in.-lb. Therefore, from equation 48, the fringe constant may be computed as

$$f = \frac{12 \times 167}{17.9(1.155)^2} = 83.9 \text{ lb/in./fringe} \tag{49}$$

It should be noted that it is desirable to use as large a value of n (and corresponding high stress) as possible for calibration to improve the accuracy. For instance, an error of 0.1 fringe order in determining n leads to a difference of 2 per cent in the computed value of f if only 5 fringes are used, whereas this difference becomes only 1 per cent if n is 10. However, difficulties from optical creep and inelastic behavior become pronounced as the stresses are increased, as is discussed in section I. Consequently, the maximum stresses in the calibration beam (or in the model) must not exceed certain limits which depend on the plastic and viscous characteristics of the material.

(b) *Concentrated Load on a Semi-Infinite Plate.* Another method of calibration usable for materials of medium and moderately high sensitivity is provided by applying a concentrated force, in the normal direction, to the free edge of a semi-infinite plate. The corresponding analytical solution for the stress distribution shows that the isochromatic lines are circles (Fig. 17-28) with their centers on the line of action of the force and all tangent to the boundary at the point of application of the load.

On the axis of symmetry, the relation between the load and the difference between the principal stresses is given by the equation,

$$\sigma_1 - \sigma_2 = \frac{2P}{\pi r} \tag{50}$$

where P = the load per unit thickness, pounds per inch
       r = the distance from the point of loading, inches

By plotting the logarithm of interference order against the logarithm of r, as shown in Fig. 17-28c, one obtains a straight line. From equation 50 the corresponding change in stress difference, between two given points may be found. The fringe constant is then computed by direct substitution in equation 42. For the example in Fig. 17-28 this gives the following data:

	r, in.	$\sigma_1 - \sigma_2$, psi	n, order
	0.12	4020	14.0
	0.7	690	2.68
Increments		3330	11.32

whence

$$f = \frac{3330 \times 0.291}{11.32} = 85.5 \text{ lb/in./order} \tag{51}$$

In cases where the determination of the fringe constant by a concentrated load is inconvenient or impractical, a *uniformly distributed load* (Fig. 17-29) may be applied to the boundary of a semi-infinite plate. Such a uniform distribution of load may be accomplished by means of a rectangular bucket with a thin rubber bottom. By partially filling the bucket with water or mercury the hydrostatic pressure at the bottom will be transmitted through the membrane to the photoelastic material.

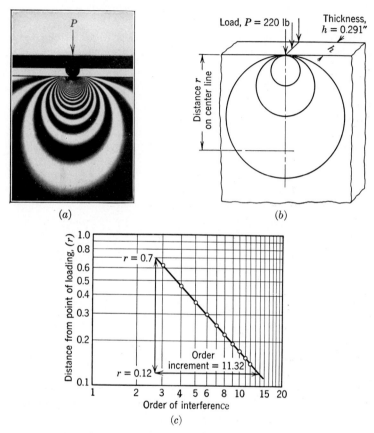

FIG. 17-28. Calibration with a Concentrated Load on a Semi-Infinite Plate
  (a) Isochromatic pattern
  (b) Isochromatic diagram, according to theory
  (c) Logarithmic plot of orders of interference at distance r on center line

For this type of loading the isochromatic lines will be circles passing through the limits of the loaded area. The difference between the principal stresses will be given by the equation,

$$\sigma_1 - \sigma_2 = \frac{-2q}{\pi} \sin \beta \tag{52}$$

where q = the intensity of loading, pounds per square inch (compression) and β = the angle indicated in Fig. 17-29, radians.

The maximum order of interference will be equivalent to $0.638q$, and the corresponding isochromatic line will cross the center line at a distance from the loaded edge equal to half the width of the loaded zone.

(c) *Dead Weight in Compression.* For those ultrasensitive materials in which the gravitational body forces will produce several orders of interference, a rectangular prism on end may be used as the calibration specimen. In this case the stress is uniformly distributed over every horizontal cross section, and the intensity is proportional to the weight per unit volume and the dis-

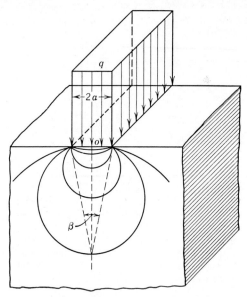

Fɪɢ. 17-29.   Uniformly Distributed Load on a Semi-Infinite Plate

tance from the top. By plotting the orders of interference against distance from the top of the prism the relation between stress and the optical effect, that is, the fringe constant, may be established.

G. Determination of the Sum of the Principal Stresses by Lateral Strain Measurement

For interior points of a model the polariscope only furnishes information relative to the directions of and *differences* between the principal stresses. If it is desired to evaluate each principal stress *independently* for points within the boundaries of a photoelastic model, it is necessary to use auxiliary data. In most cases the stresses at interior points are of academic interest only, since the maximum stresses occur at boundaries of the model. However, a number of useful auxiliary methods for determining stresses at interior points are discussed in this section and in section H.

As the change in thickness of the model is proportional to the sum of the principal stresses, the measurement of lateral strain provides a quick and simple method for securing the auxiliary information necessary to evaluate individual principal stresses.   This procedure requires a strain gage of high sensitivity and a device for changing the load on the model.   For a few observations it is probably the quickest of the methods of determining the sum of the principal stresses, and it has the advantage that it is a point-by-point procedure in which an error at one location will not be carried on to the next position.   It depends on Hooke's law, and, in consequence, for materials which do not possess a linear stress–strain relationship (or for cases in which the proportional limit is exceeded) there is an inherent error in addition to that which may result from the laboratory technique.

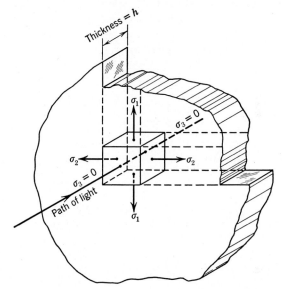

FIG. 17-30.   Element in a Photoelastic Model

Consider a small rectangular prism in the photoelastic model, taken in the manner shown in Fig. 17-30, with its two ends in the surfaces of the model (perpendicular to the direction of the path of the light) and the other faces parallel to the planes of the principal stresses.   If the principal stresses in the plane of the model are σ_1 and σ_2, then the direction of σ_3 coincides with the direction of the path of the light.   Since the model is subjected to forces only in its own plane, $\sigma_3 = 0$, and the corresponding strain is given by the equation:

$$\epsilon_3 = -\frac{\mu}{E}(\sigma_1 + \sigma_2) \tag{53}$$

The strain in the direction of the path of light may also be expressed as the ratio:

$$\frac{\text{Change in thickness}}{\text{Original thickness}} = \frac{\Delta h}{h} = \epsilon_3 \tag{54}$$

Therefore, $(\sigma_1 + \sigma_2) = -\dfrac{E}{\mu} \cdot \dfrac{\Delta h}{h} = -k \dfrac{\Delta h}{h}$ (55)

which means that the sum of the principal stresses is proportional to the percentage change in thickness of the model, and k is the proportionality constant which depends on the elastic properties of the material.

If E and μ are known for a given material the measurement of h and Δh will enable one to determine the value of $(\sigma_1 + \sigma_2)$. Fortunately one can evaluate $(\sigma_1 + \sigma_2)$ even if E and μ are unknown, since a direct calibration for the constant k, in terms of strain-gage reading on a simple tension bar, can be made. The lateral constant k may also be regarded as a proportionality factor relating the reading of the lateral strain gage to the sum of the principal stresses and thickness of model, according to equation 55. It may include the multiplication constant of the lateral strain gage making it unnecessary to convert the readings to the same units as h. Thus, the relation may be written

$$(\sigma_1 + \sigma_2) = -k \cdot \frac{\text{gage increment}}{h}$$ (56)

In this form the lateral constant represents the change in sum of the principal stresses required to produce a change of one division on the lateral strain gage for material of unit thickness; its units are $\dfrac{\text{force}}{\text{length} \times \text{units on gage}}$.

Since, for the general run of photoelastic models, the change in thickness will be less than 1 μin. (millionth) for a change of 1 psi in the sum of the principal stresses, lateral extensometers or strain gages must be rather sensitive instruments. However, in most cases, the stress values with which one has to deal will be of the order of several thousand pounds per square inch, so that the lateral extensometer should be capable of precise determination of changes in thickness of a few ten-thousandths of an inch. To do this, the instrument should indicate to about 5 μin.

A very usual pitfall in the determination of the change in thickness of the model lies in the technique of applying the gage. Slightly rounded points and a light clamping spring of low spring constant should be used. Any appreciable change in contact pressure as the model changes thickness will lead to error in values for $(\sigma_1 + \sigma_2)$. The suspension of the gage should be such as to allow it complete freedom to follow any movements of the model.

If the gage points are sharp, even with moderate spring pressure, the local stress intensity in the region of contact is so high that the soft photoelastic material will creep, and the points will sink into the material slightly, producing appreciable error. Likewise, a clamping spring of too great a stiffness will cause false readings.[31, 32]

19. The Interferometer Strain Gage. The instrument illustrated in Fig. 17-31 was developed by Schaid[36] and is somewhat similar to that of Vose.[32] Since the measurement depends on the wave length of light, the interferometer gage represents a primary means of determining small changes in distance.   In addition, it is very rugged and extremely simple mechanically. The device consists of a pair of small steel levers, connected together at the middle by a crossed-plate fulcrum which gives rigidity in one direction and freedom of motion at right angles.   To one end of each lever a small optical

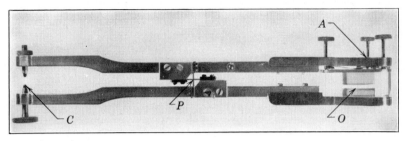

Fig. 17-31.   Lateral Interferometer Strain Gage (R. J. Schaid[36])
A, adjustable mounting for optical flat; C, contact points; O, optical flats; P, cross-spring pivot

flat is attached and at the other end an adjustable point for attachment to the model.   The instrument shown in Fig. 17-31 incorporates a small pointer and reference line at the end opposite the contact points to insure setting of the contact points to the same (light) pressure for each reading.

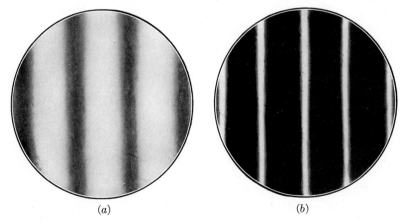

(a)   (b)

Fig. 17-32.   Appearance of the Interference Fringes in the Field of the Lateral Interferometer Strain Gage (R. J. Schaid[36])
(a) Reflected light with uncoated optical surfaces
(b) Transmitted light with coated optical surfaces (reflectivity over 85 per cent)

When the optical flats are illuminated with monochromatic light at normal incidence and an observer looks through a telescope at them he sees the image of a pair of cross-hairs, etched on one of the optical flats, and a series of shadow bands or interference fringes as shown in Fig. 17-32.   Vose observed light reflected from the optical flats giving fringes as shown in Fig. 17-32a, whereas Schaid utilized the transmitted light with coated optical flats having a high reflectivity and obtained sharper fringes as shown in Fig. 17-32b.

Strains are read with the gage by observing the passage of the bands over the intersection of the cross-hairs and counting them as they go by.[33]   The number of bands counted will be directly proportional to the change in thickness of the model.   For a gage with a lever ratio of 1:1 and with monochromatic green light of 5461 angstroms wave length, each band passing the cross-hairs corresponds to a movement of the gage points of $\Delta h = 0.00001075$ in. For other lever ratios and for other wave lengths of light the gage factor will be proportional to these variables.

20. The de Forest–Anderson Lateral Extensometer.[34]   This instrument is merely a special adaptation of the wire-resistance strain gage described in

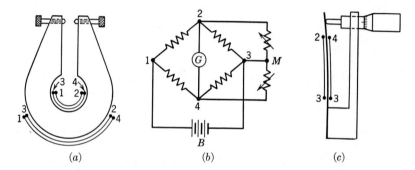

(a) (b) (c)

Fig. 17-33.   The deForest–Anderson Lateral Extensometer

(a) Gage, showing location of resistance wires for bridge circuit
(b) Wiring diagram (G is galvanometer; B is battery; M represents balancing screw)
(c) Balancing screw

Chapter 5.   The extensometer itself consists of a small horseshoe-shaped aluminum frame to which strain-gage wire is attached as indicated in Fig. 17-33a.   The entire strain-gage bridge (Fig. 17-33b) is mounted on the frame of the extensometer in order to achieve temperature compensation and maximum sensitivity.

The observations are obtained from a micrometer screw (Fig. 17-33c) actuating balancing resistors which are mounted in a control box.   These readings are just numbers, but they are directly proportional to the lateral strain and can be evaluated in terms of the sum of the principal stresses by means of the lateral constant (equation 56).

21. Other Lateral Extensometers.   A number of high-sensitivity extensometers can be adapted, by suitable clamps and frames, to the measurement of lateral strain.   Of these, the adaptation of the Huggenberger tensometer as carried out by Peterson and Wahl[35] is especially convenient.

A very elaborate lateral extensometer using a combination of mechanical-

and optical-lever systems with drum recording has been developed and successfully used by Coker and Filon.[*]

22. Determination of the Lateral Constant. Although the lateral constant can be evaluated in a number of different ways, the simplest method is that

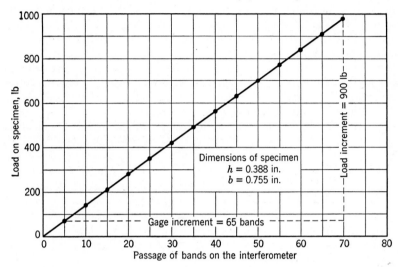

FIG. 17-34. Determination of Lateral Constant with Interferometer Strain Gage

involving a tensile specimen and a procedure similar to that used for finding the fringe constant.

For the case of a tensile strip, $\sigma_1 = \dfrac{\text{load}}{\text{area}} = \dfrac{P}{bh}$, and $\sigma_2 = 0$. Therefore, from equation 56,

$$\sigma_1 = \frac{P}{bh} = -k\,\frac{\text{gage increment}}{h} \tag{57}$$

or

$$k = -\frac{P}{b \times \text{gage increment}} \tag{58}$$

By plotting the load on the tension specimen versus gage reading, the corresponding load increment for any given gage increment may be determined as the slope of the straight line. The lateral constant k is then numerically equal to this slope divided by the specimen width b, as indicated by equation 58. This is illustrated in Fig. 17-34 for which the values chosen were a passage of 65 interference bands for a load increment of 900 lb. The value from equation 58 is then

$$k = -\frac{900}{0.755 \times 65} = 18.4 \text{ lb/in./band} \tag{59}$$

[*] Reference 1, pp 170–8.

H. Determining Stresses at Interior Points by Auxiliary Methods Involving Equations of Equilibrium

In addition to the lateral-strain measurements mentioned in the preceding section, there are numerous analytical methods involving the use of equations of equilibrium for stresses in a two-dimensional state that can be employed for determining the stresses at interior points in a photoelastic model. These methods may be regarded as supplements to the general procedure of photo-elastic analysis; their application to a specific problem involves numerical or graphical integration along fixed lines of the member or may utilize the lateral deflections of a stretched membrane by means of an analogy between the differential equations for the two cases.

Several methods are outlined in this section which are based only on equations of equilibrium, and hence are not dependent on maintaining purely elastic conditions and are not influenced by elastic constants. However, the experimental data from which the analysis is made are obtained from a photo-elastic model which should be kept within the elastic range for the data to be utilizable. The difficulties encountered in applying these methods are those usually inherent in all graphical integration: small errors of observation will be accumulated as the integration proceeds, and hence the original experimental data must be very accurate regarding both location of isoclinics and magnitudes of the fringe orders.

For two-dimensional stress states the equations of equilibrium (which may be found in standard texts on theory of elasticity[23]) are as follows:

$$\frac{\partial \sigma_x}{\partial x} + \frac{\partial \tau_{xy}}{\partial y} + X = 0 \tag{60}$$

$$\frac{\partial \sigma_y}{\partial y} + \frac{\partial \tau_{xy}}{\partial x} + Y = 0 \tag{61}$$

where σ_x and σ_y are the normal stresses on the x and y planes, τ_{xy} is the shearing stress intensity on the x and y planes, and X and Y are the body forces per unit volume in the x and y directions, as shown in Fig. 17-35.

In most cases the body forces can be neglected since their influence is usually small in comparison with the effect of the applied load. When this is the case, equations 60 and 61 may be simplified by assuming $X = 0$ and $Y = 0$.

23. The Shear Difference Method. Solutions of equations 60 and 61, if body forces are neglected, may be obtained in the form,

$$\sigma_x = (\sigma_x)_o - \int \frac{\partial \tau_{xy}}{\partial y}\, dx \tag{62}$$

and

$$\sigma_y = (\sigma_y)_o - \int \frac{\partial \tau_{xy}}{\partial x}\, dy \tag{63}$$

where $(\sigma_x)_o$ and $(\sigma_y)_o$ represent the values of σ_x and σ_y at a given location (for which the stress values are known or may be obtained). In both equations 62 and 63 the value of the integral can be represented by the area under a curve for which the ordinates are the "rate of change of shear in a direction normal to direction of integration" and the abscissas are distances along the path of integration.

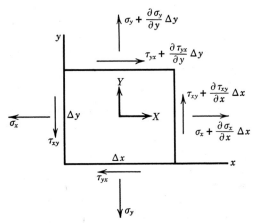

FIG. 17-35.   Stresses Acting on a Small Rectangular Element in the x–y Plane
$\tau_{xy} = \tau_{yx}$ numerically

In the case of a small finite particle (as shown in Fig. 17-35) equations 62 and 63 which contain integrals can be closely approximated by the following similar expressions containing summations of finite increments:

$$\sigma_x = (\sigma_x)_o - \sum \frac{\Delta \tau_{xy}}{\Delta y} \cdot \Delta x \qquad (64)$$

$$\sigma_y = (\sigma_y)_o - \sum \frac{\Delta \tau_{xy}}{\Delta x} \cdot \Delta y \qquad (65)$$

These equations may be used to determine the distribution of the normal stresses over any plane section through the model from data obtained with the polariscope alone.

It should be emphasized that the values of τ_{xy} in the previous relationships are *not* the *maximum* shearing stresses at the point as given by equation 17 but are the tangential stresses on the x and y planes at the point. These values τ_{xy} are related to the principal stresses by the following equation:

$$\tau_{xy} = \frac{(\sigma_1 - \sigma_2)}{2} \sin 2\theta \qquad (66)$$

in which θ is the acute angle between the direction of the principal stress σ_1 and the plane on which τ_{xy} acts. The values of $(\sigma_1 - \sigma_2)$ may be obtained from the isochromatic-fringe orders, and the values of θ may be determined from the isoclinics by correcting the angles of rotation ϕ by an amount equal to the difference in orientation between the direction of τ_{xy} and the reference axis used in determining the isoclinics. Care must be taken in a graphical integration to maintain the proper algebraic sign for τ_{xy}. This can often be determined by inspection, but the sign will reverse when passing across an isotropic point.

The following steps outline a suggested procedure for applying equations 64 and 65:

1. On a large-scale drawing of the model, draw in the line $A-A$ (Fig. 17-36) along which it is desired to determine the distribution of the stresses. Divide

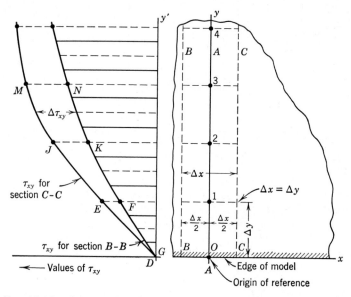

FIG. 17-36. Stress at Interior Points by the Shear-Difference Method

$A-A$ into a number of equal parts (ten equal parts will generally be most convenient), and arrange the coordinate axes and origin conveniently, so that the origin falls at one end of $A-A$ (at an edge of the model) and one of the axes along it.

2. On either side of $A-A$ draw $B-B$ and $C-C$ at equal distances from $A-A$, and separated by a total distance equal to the length of the uniform intervals already marked out along $A-A$. This procedure makes $\Delta x = \Delta y$ (numerically), and equation 65 will be simplified to the form,

$$\sigma_y = (\sigma_y)_o - \Sigma \, \Delta\tau_{xy} \tag{65a}$$

where $\Delta\tau_{xy}$ is the difference in the average shearing stress (on the xy planes) between the left and the right sides of an elemental particle (from $B-B$ to $C-C$), and $(\sigma_y)_o$ is the initial value of σ_y at station O.

3. Determine the positions at which the isochromatic and isoclinic lines

intersect sections B–B and C–C, and for each section plot separate curves of fringe order and for angle of orientation θ, both as functions of distance along the section (y in this case).   In these plots it is desirable to minimize the error by fairing in smooth curves to represent the mean values of the observations.

4. From these curves one may scale off ordinates at convenient increments (usually at the midpoints of the intervals chosen for integration), and compute values of τ_{xy} from equation 66.   These values may then be plotted along the y axis for section B–B and for section C–C, as shown at the left in Fig. 17-36, and these curves represent the distributions of the shearing stresses along the two sides of the rectangular elements chosen.   (It is not necessary to plot these stresses if the values are computed for the midpoints of each interval between stations 1, 2, 3, etc.)

5. The difference in shearing stress from B–B to C–C at points corresponding to the middle of each interval represents $\Delta\tau_{xy}$ as given in equation 65a and is numerically equal to $\Delta\sigma_y$, the change in normal stress in the y direction along section A–A from one station to the next.   By starting at a boundary $(\sigma_y)_o = 0$, and, hence, the summation of the values $\Delta\tau_{xy}$ will give the value of σ_y at an interior point as indicated by equation 65a.

6. A more exact procedure for finding the increments $\Delta\sigma_y$ would be to employ equation 65 directly to the diagram in Fig. 17-36.   The area enclosed (in the curves for values of τ_{xy}) by the letters $DEFG$ represents the $\Sigma \, \Delta\tau_{xy} \cdot \Delta y$ for the interval from points zero to 1 and, hence, when divided by the (constant) distance Δx, is the change in σ_y from point 0 to 1.   Similarly area $EJKF/\Delta x$ represents the change in σ_y from point 1 to 2, etc.

7. When the values of σ_y have been obtained for all desired points, the value of σ_x (the normal stress at right angles to section A–A) can be computed from the equation:

$$\sigma_x = \sigma_y + (\sigma_1 - \sigma_2) \cos 2\theta \tag{67}$$

(This relation is obtained by subtracting equation 16 from equation 15, substituting the value of τ_{xy} from equation 66, squaring the result, and simplifying).   The principal stresses can be found from the equations,

$$\sigma_1 = \frac{\sigma_x + \sigma_y}{2} + \frac{\sigma_1 - \sigma_2}{2} \tag{68}$$

and

$$\sigma_2 = \frac{\sigma_x + \sigma_y}{2} - \frac{\sigma_1 - \sigma_2}{2} \tag{69}$$

(These relations are obtained directly from equations 15 and 16 by substituting for the radical the value $(\sigma_1 - \sigma_2)$ from equation 17.)

Note of Caution.   Since the value of σ_y determined by this method may represent the evaluation of a small difference between two relatively large quantities, the percentage error may be great.   Therefore, for those cases in which the results depend largely on σ_y, one should be prepared to expect appreciable errors.   If σ_y is small relative to $(\sigma_1 - \sigma_2) \cos 2\theta$, then relatively precise results may be expected for σ_x.   Decreasing the size of the intervals along A–A should lead to greater accuracy if the experimental data obtained for isoclinics and isochromatics are sufficiently exact to facilitate employing small increments.

24. The Membrane Analogy.   This experimental technique provides a very simple and useful method for determining the sum of the principal stresses at points within the boundaries of photoelastic models.[39–43]   It is based on the similarity between the differential equations for the lateral ordinates of a stretched membrane with equal pressures on both sides and the sum of the principal stresses in an elastic plate (two-dimensional case) in which the body forces are neglected (or negligible).

The differential equation for the stretched membrane is of the form,

$$\frac{\partial^2 z}{\partial x^2} + \frac{\partial^2 z}{\partial y^2} = 0 \tag{70}$$

where z = the lateral ordinate
and x and y = any arbitrarily chosen directions normal to z and at right
                     angles to each other

The differential equation for the sum of the principal stresses $(\sigma_1 + \sigma_2)$ is

$$\frac{\partial^2(\sigma_1 + \sigma_2)}{\partial x^2} + \frac{\partial^2(\sigma_1 + \sigma_2)}{\partial y^2} = 0 \tag{71}$$

In order for the analogy to be used quantitatively, the boundary conditions for the membrane must be similar to the boundary conditions for the stress problem.   Under these circumstances, the similarity in the forms of equations 70 and 71 indicates that lateral ordinates of the membrane will be proportional to the sum of the principal stresses at the corresponding points in the photoelastic model.   It is necessary, of course, to establish the correct datum from which to make observations.   The lateral deflections of the membrane must be interpreted in the same scale ratio as that used in establishing the boundary conditions.   Contours of the membrane at a given elevation represent the locus of all points having the same value for $(\sigma_1 + \sigma_2)$ and are often referred to as "isopachic" lines.

For the purpose of setting up the boundary conditions it is necessary to have a frame over which to stretch the membrane.   The plan view of this frame should be geometrically similar to the contour of the photoelastic model, and its elevations should represent the sum of the principal stresses at corresponding points around the boundary.   Since one of the principal stresses is zero along a free boundary, the sum and difference will be the same, and the isochromatic diagram (photoelastic stress pattern) may be used to establish these elevations around the boundary.

Membranes of soap film or thin rubber have both been used with success. Rubber is more durable but requires stretching carefully to produce a uniform biaxial tension.   A soap solution which has been found satisfactory can be made by mixing about 1 cc of triethanolamine oleate dissolved in about 5 cc of water, with another 5 cc of glycerin.   The solution is said to produce bubbles which last from 3 hr to 3 days and which resist prickling with the depth gage, used to measure lateral ordinates. For rubber membrane, Dental Dam, which will sustain better than 100 per cent elastic deformation, has been found very useful.

Note of Caution. Since equation 70 is developed on the assumption of very small slope in the membrane, the maximum inclination should be kept below about 18°. On this account the method may be subject to considerable error in regions of high stress concentration if the scale factor has been chosen for use in the remainder of the model. A way of surmounting this difficulty is to set up two membranes, one with a scale suitable for all locations except the regions of stress concentration and the second for regions of high stress gradient and concentration.

25. The Method of Iteration. Although the membrane analogy provides a very simple means of finding the sum of the principal stresses, nevertheless, the construction of a frame for enforcing the boundary conditions may involve considerable time and effort.

The method of iteration, which is an arithmetical procedure, in effect determines the elevations of the membrane (and hence the values of $\sigma_1 + \sigma_2$) at a network of points by a simple process of computation.[45,46] The actual time required to solve a given problem by iteration will be somewhat longer than that necessary to measure the lateral ordinates of the stretched membrane, but it will probably be somewhat less than the time required to make the frame for the membrane, particularly if a calculating machine is used to speed up the computation.

From the practical point of view a very convenient feature of the iteration process lies in the fact that it is self-correcting; if a mistake should be made in the early stages, this will not alter the ultimate result, although it will likely increase the time required for solution. This means that an engineer can set up a problem and then turn it over to an untrained assistant for solution without having to check the calculations in detail.

As in the membrane analogy, the sum of the principal stresses at the boundaries of the model are first determined from the isochromatic-fringe pattern, and these are used as known values along the boundary of the member. In Fig. 17-37 is illustrated the procedure for a small portion of a model which is known to be symmetrical (with respect to both loads and geometry) about the line $Y-Y$. A network of equally spaced points is laid out on the diagram of the model; the horizontal rows of points may be designated for convenience by letters A, B, C, etc., and the columns by numbers 1, 2, 3, etc. Square boxes are drawn around each point merely to avoid confusion in tabulating the values relating to each point. A procedure that may be followed in determining the sum of the principal stresses at interior points is as follows:

1. The known values of the sum of the principal stresses on the *boundary* are entered on the diagram (at points marked by crosses). One then estimates the value for the sum of the principal stresses at each *interior* station and enters this in the box surrounding each point. A good estimate will hasten the convergence and thus reduce the amount of labor involved for the final

solution, but any arbitrary values can be assigned initially to the stations representing interior points.

2. The values at interior stations may now be improved by going over the entire network in definite sequence and at each station averaging the four nearest surrounding values (see special conditions for curved boundaries later) to produce a better approximation. For example, if

ψ = the value of the sum of the principal stresses at a boundary station
      or an approximation to the value of $(\sigma_1 + \sigma_2)$ at an interior station

and ψ' = an improved value of ψ at an interior station

then, at station $C3$ the improved value will be

$$\psi_{C3}' = \tfrac{1}{4}\{\psi_{C2} + \psi_{B3} + \psi_{C4} + \psi_{D3}\} \tag{72}$$

3. In order to produce as rapid an improvement as possible, newly computed values should be substituted in equation 72 as soon as they are obtained.

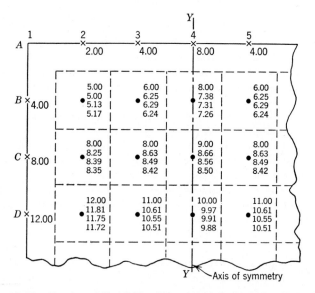

FIG. 17-37.   Portion of Small Net Illustrating the Iteration Procedure

Boundary points at which values are known are indicated by crosses; interior points of the net shown by small dots. Squares around each point facilitate grouping of numbers relating to that point. The body and loading are symmetrical about line Y–Y

By repeatedly recomputing all interior points over the entire network, the individual values will converge or eventually tend to repeat themselves to the required number of significant figures. If greater precision is required the net spacing can be halved to give four times the number of stations and the process again repeated.

For example, the data in Fig. 17-37 have been computed from the boundary values by the previous general procedure. In the first traverse to obtain improved values we have:

For point $B2$, $\frac{1}{4}(4 + 2 + 6 + 8) = 5.00$

and for point $B3$, $\frac{1}{4}(5 + 4 + 8 + 8) = 6.25$

Since column 4 is an axis of symmetry we can immediately enter this same value for point $B5$ and use it in obtaining the improved value for $B4$; thus

For point $B4$, $\frac{1}{4}(6.25 + 8 + 6.25 + 9) = 7.38$ etc.

In calculating an improved value at any point the previously altered values are used wherever these are available. Thus in the fourth traverse, the value for point $C3$ would be obtained as

$$\frac{1}{4}(8.35 + 6.24 + 8.56 + 10.55) = 8.42$$

and (because of symmetry) this value is also utilized as the new improved value for $C5$.

Existence of axes of symmetry will materially reduce the work, since one may assume that values at points equally spaced on opposite sides of an axis of symmetry converge to the same value and are improved *simultaneously*. The computations may, therefore, be reduced one half by working with stations on one side of the axis only. The evaluation of improved values of ψ for the axis of symmetry involves a doubling of the value on one side of the axis. As an example, for point $B4$ in Fig. 17-37, an improved value is obtained from the relation:

$$\psi_{B4}' = \frac{1}{4}[2\psi_{B3} + \psi_{A4} + \psi_{C4}] \tag{73}$$

Various methods have been worked out to cut down the time required for close convergence of the values (see Weller and Shortley[44]), but, in general, one should *start with a very coarse network* and obtain the best result possible from it before going on to a finer spacing of the points. A net with intervals of spacing half as great should converge to values having errors (with respect to a true continuous solution of the differential equation) of only about one-fourth those of the coarser net.

(*a*) *Nonrectangular Boundaries.* For the case of models which do not have rectangular boundaries some of the interior stations, like station O in Fig. 17-38, may be nearer the edge than the normal net spacing. Under these conditions, since the four nearest surrounding stations are not equidistant from the point at which an improved value is to be obtained, their influences will be different, and one must apply weighting factors according to the formula.[45]

$$\psi_o' = C_r\psi_r + C_\sigma\psi_\sigma + C_t\psi_t + C_s\psi_s \tag{74}$$

if s and t represent the ratios of the distances of the nearest points on the boundary to the net spacing d, as indicated in Fig. 17-38, then the constants or weighing factors in equation 74 are given by

$$C_\tau = \frac{st}{s+t}\left(\frac{1}{1+t}\right) \tag{75}$$

$$C_\sigma = \frac{st}{s+t}\left(\frac{1}{1+s}\right) \tag{76}$$

$$C_t = \frac{st}{s+t} \cdot \frac{1}{t(1+t)} \tag{77}$$

$$C_s = \frac{st}{s+t} \cdot \frac{1}{s(1+s)} \tag{78}$$

In computing the values of the weighting factors, one has a convenient check on the values obtained since

$$C_\tau + C_\sigma + C_t + C_s = 1 \tag{79}$$

In order to obtain an exact check, if s and t are originally determined in fractions, they should remain such when the values of the constants are computed. After the sum of the weighting factors has been proved equal to unity, then it may be more convenient to use the nearest decimal equivalents.

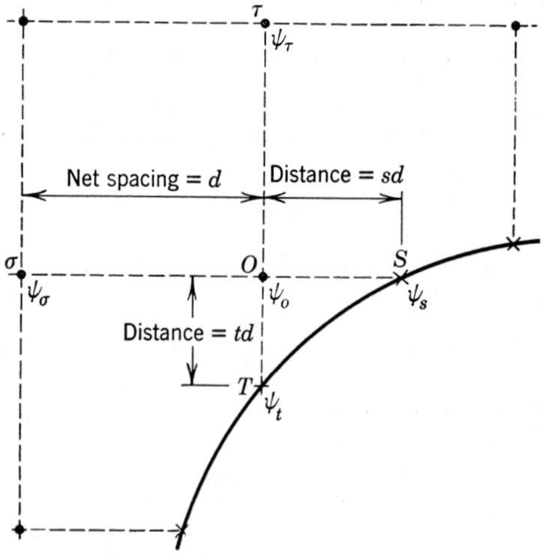

26. Application in Polar Coordinates. Certain problems are more easily solved in terms of polar coordinates,

Fig. 17-38. Procedure for a Point O near an Irregular Boundary

See equations 74 to 79

in which case the equations of equilibrium for plane stress are

$$\frac{\partial \sigma_r}{\partial r} + \frac{\sigma_r - \sigma_\theta}{r} + \frac{1}{r}\frac{\partial \tau_{r\theta}}{\partial \theta} + R = 0 \tag{80}$$

and

$$\frac{1}{r}\frac{\partial \sigma_\theta}{\partial \theta} + \frac{2\tau_{r\theta}}{r} + \frac{\partial \tau_{r\theta}}{\partial r} + T = 0 \tag{81}$$

where σ_r and σ_θ = the normal stresses in the radial and tangential directions, respectively

$\tau_{r\theta}$ = the shearing stress in the radial and circumferential directions

r = the radial coordinate to the point

R and T = the body forces per unit volume in the radial and tangential directions, respectively

θ = angular coordinate measured from a fixed radial direction

(a) *Polar Symmetry.* For conditions of polar symmetry in which the stress distribution is a function of radius only, σ_r and σ_θ will be principal stresses, and equation 80 is then reduced to the form:

$$\frac{\partial \sigma_r}{\partial r} + \frac{\sigma_r - \sigma_\theta}{r} + R = 0 \qquad (82)$$

If the body force R can be neglected, a further simplification results by letting $R = 0$, and the solution will be of the form,

$$\sigma_r = (\sigma_r)_o - \int \frac{\sigma_r - \sigma_\theta}{r}\, dr \qquad (83)$$

where $(\sigma_r)_o$ = some initial (known) value of σ_r

and $\sigma_r - \sigma_\theta$ = the difference between the principal stresses*

The information available from an isochromatic-stress pattern may be used to evaluate the integral.

TABLE 17-2

Work Sheet for Problem in Polar Coordinates Involving Radial Symmetry

Bakelite Ring Subjected to Internal Pressure of 600 psi

Inside Radius of Ring—1.50 in.   Thickness—0.375 in.
Outside Radius of Ring—2.25 in.   Fringe Constant—87.7 lb/in./order

Radius (1)	Fringe Order (2)	$(\sigma_\theta - \sigma_r)$, psi (3)	$\dfrac{\sigma_\theta - \sigma_r}{r}$, lb/in.³ (4)	Radial Location in. (5)	$\dfrac{(\sigma_\theta - \sigma_r)}{r} \Delta r$ $= \Delta \sigma_r$, psi (6)	σ_r, psi (7)	$(\sigma_\theta - \sigma_r)$, psi (8)	σ_θ psi (9)
1.52	9	2110	1395	1.5		−600	2160	1560
1.61	8	1870	1160	1.6	130	−470	1900	1430
1.72	7	1640	955	1.7	108	−362	1680	1318
1.86	6	1405	755	1.8	90	−272	1500	1228
2.04	5	1170	575	1.9	77	−195	1345	1150
				2.0	66	−129	1215	1086
				2.1	57	− 72	1105	1033
				2.25	72	0	965	965

(−) Indicates compression.

The following example in Table 17-2 will illustrate the method as applied to a bakelite ring subjected to internal pressure to find the distribution of radial and tangential stresses across a section. The observed isochromatic-fringe orders and their radial locations are listed in the first two columns; from these data the general procedure is:

1. Determine the differences $(\sigma_\theta - \sigma_r)$ between the principal stresses (by

* The algebraically larger principal stress might be either σ_θ or σ_r. The value of the difference between the principal stresses has therefore been kept in terms of $(\sigma_r - \sigma_\theta)$ rather than $(\sigma_1 - \sigma_2)$ in order to avoid confusion with the sign of the quantity under the integral.

equation 34) for each fringe, and plot these values for each radial position. Compute also the values of $\dfrac{\sigma_\theta - \sigma_r}{r}$ as tabulated in column 4.

2. Plot a curve, as shown in Fig. 17-39, having values of $\dfrac{\sigma_\theta - \sigma_r}{r}$ as ordinates and the corresponding values of r as the abscissas. Areas under this curve represent values of the integral in equation 83. Each element of area (such as $ABCD$, Fig. 17-39) represents the change in σ_r across this interval in r.

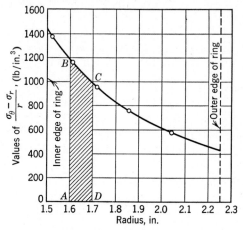

3. Establish definite intervals of integration along the radius, as indicated by the radial positions in column 5 of Table 17-2, and tabulate (column 6) the changes $\Delta\sigma_r$ obtained from the areas under the curve of Fig. 17-39.

4. The initial value of $(\sigma_r)_o$ at the inside edge is the internal pressure in this case (-600 psi). By starting with this value and adding the increments from column 6 the magnitude of σ_r at each radial position is obtained (column 7).

5. The values of $(\sigma_\theta - \sigma_r)$ in column 8 for each radial position (obtained from the curve plotted in step 1) may be added to the computed values for σ_r to obtain the distribution of σ_θ shown in column 9.

FIG. 17-39.   Integration for Principal Stress in Problem of Radial Symmetry
From data in Table 17-2 for Bakelite ring subjected to internal pressure. Shaded area $ABCD$ represents change in σ_r between the locations $r = 1.6$ in. and $r = 1.7$ in.

Extrapolation of the curves of $(\sigma_\theta - \sigma_r)$ and $\dfrac{\sigma_\theta - \sigma_r}{r}$ to the boundaries may sometimes be inaccurate. In some problems these may be straight lines when plotted on logarithmic scales and therefore may be more readily extrapolated.

27. Application in Curvilinear Coordinates. In the previous example of polar symmetry the integration along a radius coincided with integration along a straight stress trajectory. In general, stress trajectories are not usually straight lines, but Filon's method of graphical integration[48-50] is adapted to integration for separation of the principal stresses along any isostatic if the experimental data have been recorded with sufficient accuracy. The equations relating the principal stresses along an isostatic (if body forces are neglected) are as follows:

$$\sigma_1 = (\sigma_1)_o + \int (\sigma_1 - \sigma_2) \cot \gamma_1 \, d\phi \tag{84}$$

$$\sigma_2 = (\sigma_2)_o - \int (\sigma_1 - \sigma_2) \cot \gamma_2 \, d\phi \tag{85}$$

where $(\sigma_1)_o$ and $(\sigma_2)_o$ = initial values of the principal stresses

γ_1 and γ_2 = the angles between the stress trajectories of σ_1 or σ_2, respectively, and the isoclinic line measured anti-clockwise (see Fig. 17-40).

ϕ = the angle of the tangent to the stress trajectory with respect to some reference.

One may integrate either along the trajectory of σ_1, or along the trajectory of σ_2. Sometimes it is desirable to start on one trajectory and then proceed along the other from an interior point if a convenient check can be established on the accuracy of the results.

The procedure to be adopted for the σ_1 trajectory is as follows (and that for the σ_2 trajectory is similar):

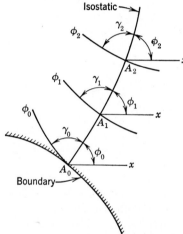

1. From some point at which σ_1 is known, (such as at A_o in Fig. 17-40) establish the isostatic along which it is desired to integrate. Then divide it into a number of uniform intervals to establish a set of equally spaced stations along its length.

2. Superimpose the isostatic on the isochromatic diagram, and, from the locations at which the isochromatic lines intersect, plot a curve of order of interference as a function of distance along the trajectory.

3. Superimpose the isostatic on the isoclinic diagram and plot curves of ϕ, the direction of the tangent to the trajectory, and γ_1, the angle between the isostatic and the isoclinic lines, as a function of distance along the trajectory.

FIG. 17-40.   Filon's Integration along an Isostatic (R. D. Mindlin[5])

Integration along trajectory of the stress σ_1, starting from point A_0

4. From the curves plotted in items 2 and 3 determine the average value of $(\sigma_1 - \sigma_2)$ and γ_1 for each interval, (that is, the values halfway between stations) and $\Delta\phi$, the change in the inclination of the isostatic from beginning to end of each interval.

5. From the values obtained in item 4 determine the increment in σ_1 over each interval, from the relation,

$$\Delta\sigma_1 = (\sigma_1 - \sigma_2) \cot \gamma_1 \Delta\phi \qquad (86)$$

in which $\Delta\phi$ must be expressed in radians.

6. The summation $(\sigma_1) + \Sigma \Delta\sigma_1$ will give the value of σ_1, at any station along the trajectory. Since $(\sigma_1 - \sigma_2)$ is known from step 2, the value of σ_2 may also be found for each station.

The major disadvantages of Filon's method are the inaccuracies introduced by errors in determining the angles ϕ and γ. Since the isoclinics are often poorly defined in a model, it becomes difficult to measure the required angles with precision, and all errors are accumulated as the integration proceeds.

(a) *Alternate Method.* If the angle between the isostatic and the isoclinic lines is very small, the procedure just outlined may result in large errors. To overcome this difficulty one may integrate along the trajectory of σ_2; however, if this is inconvenient an alternative method following somewhat the same procedure is available.

When the isoclinic lines are nearly parallel to the trajectory of σ_1,

$$\Delta\sigma_1 = (\sigma_1 - \sigma_2)\frac{\Delta S}{\Delta L}\Delta\phi_1 \tag{87}$$

where ΔS = distance between stations along the trajectory
      ΔL = the intercept perpendicular to the trajectory to the nearest isoclinic line
      $\Delta\phi_1$ = the change in parameter to the nearest isoclinic line (this should not exceed 10°) expressed in radians, (that is, the difference in orientation of the stress at the nearest known isoclinic)

This alternative method is useful when exploring the variations in principal stress along a trajectory that happens to be an axis of symmetry with respect to loads and geometry. For instance, the values of the principal stresses (P and Q) along the axis of symmetry in the example shown in Fig. 17-20 were determined by means of equation 87. In this procedure a convenient check on the accuracy of the result exists since the principal stress P (along line AB in Fig. 17-20) is zero at both boundaries. Hence, by integrating from A to B any accumulated errors are reflected in the amount by which the stress at B differs from zero.

(b) *Neuber's Method.* Another graphical procedure using the equations of equilibrium in a slightly different form has been developed by Neuber.[51, 52] According to this method the lines of constant sum of the principal stresses (isopachics) are determined. The method is somewhat more laborious in that it requires measurements of distance between successive isoclinics and successive isochromatics, plus the measurement of angles between isostatics, isoclinics, and isochromatics. These quantities are substituted in two equations of equilibrium which are solved simultaneously to determine a direction and a spacing for the isopachic. When the procedure has been repeated for many points throughout the model, the isopachic lines may be sketched in (by starting from known boundary conditions) in much the same manner as the isostatics are drawn from the isoclinic lines. As with Filon's method, errors or faults in the original data for measurement of angles and spacings of lines may lead to accumulation of appreciable errors in computation.

I. PHOTOELASTIC MATERIALS

28. Desirable Characteristics of Photoelastic Materials. The photoelastic material selected for a given model is always the result of a compromise to secure the largest number of desirable properties with the fewest undesirable characteristics.

Although the choice of material may be governed by the individual problem under consideration, nevertheless, there are certain general properties which should be sought for even if they cannot all be obtained. In general, the following characteristics must be given consideration in the selection of a material for the model:

1. The model must transmit light; clear materials transmitting the maximum amount of light are preferable to colored or partially opaque materials.

2. It must possess the necessary birefringent effect; that is, when under stress it must polarize light and transmit it on the principal planes with velocities dependent on the principal-stress magnitudes.

3. The material should be easy to fabricate into the desired form for the model, whether this is by machining, casting, or joining of several pieces.

4. Usually it is desirable to have a low fringe constant, but frequently this requirement will have to be modified in view of other (mechanical-strength) properties also required.

5. The material should have a linear stress–strain characteristic so that it conforms to the elastic theory, on which this method of analysis is dependent for similarity in stress pattern between model and prototype.

6. A high proportional limit is very desirable so that reasonably large applied stresses can be sustained.

7. A high modulus of elasticity is particularly desirable to maintain approximately the same geometrical form under the applied loading.

8. The material should possess a linear relation between stress and optical effect so that the same value of fringe constant may be applied to all orders of interference.

9. The effect of creep must be negligible within the limits of the stresses to be applied. In other words, the material should recover its initial condition immediately, both physically and optically, on release of load.

10. It is preferable to have a material which can be obtained free from residual stress or residual birefringence; however, if such is impossible, the material should be of such a nature that it can be annealed to eliminate these undesirable effects.

11. The material should resist the formation of residual stresses which tend to develop with time along the boundaries. Unfortunately, there are few materials suitable for photoelasticity which do not gradually develop residual birefringent effects along the edges shortly after being machined. However, the degree to which this influence prevails varies tremendously with different plastics. In some materials the "time-edge effect" can be considerably retarded, but the only way to eliminate it entirely is to machine a small amount off the edge immediately before using the model.

12. It is desirable that the material be available in large sheets with highly polished flat surfaces.

When a photoelastic model cut from a synthetic material has been stored for some time (without external load), it is usually found that, even though the model were originally stress-free, it will have developed some residual birefringence along the boundaries. As noted previously, this is known as the *time-edge effect* and is apparently caused by transfer of water or other volatile constituents to or from the surroundings.

Except for remachining the edge no means has yet been found for completely eliminating this effect, although it can be accelerated or retarded by appropriate storage conditions.[59, 60] In the case of Bakelite, storage in clean light oil or in a desiccator will frequently retard the effect. With Celluloid, coating the edges of the model with Vaseline, has also been found useful in retarding the effect.

A great many of the synthetic resins sold under numerous trade names possess useful optical characteristics, but the majority of them suffer from disadvantages such as creep, low modulus of elasticity, and low strength.[3, 53] A few of the plastics, however, are relatively satisfactory and have been utilized in the great majority of photoelastic analyses in recent years. The approximate properties of a number of materials that have been used for photoelastic models are summarized in Table 17-3 and are discussed briefly in the following paragraphs.

TABLE 17-3

APPROXIMATE PHYSICAL PROPERITIES OF SOME PHOTOELASTIC MATERIAL

This table of approximate values has been prepared as a rough guide for use in the selection of a material. Because considerable variation in properties may exist between different lots of the same material, and because variations in temperature, humidity age, and manner of annealing and testing all influence the results, it is recommended that each investigator make independent observations of the properties of the material actually selected.

Material	Tensile Strength, psi	Modulus of Elasticity, psi	Poisson's Ratio	Fringe Constant, f, lb/in./order for $\lambda = 5461$ Å
Bakelite:				
BT-61-893 @ 70°F	15,000	620,000	0.36	86
BT-46-001	16,000	620,000	0.36	83
BT-41-001 @ 70°F	14,000	620,000	0.36	65
BT-48-005 @ 70°F	......	300,000	....	55
BT-61-893 @ 230°F	400	1,100	0.5	3.33
Catalin	4,000	200,000	....	45
Cellulose nitrate	7,000	280,000	....	224
Columbia resin—39	......	350,000	....	85
Gelatin—water 65% glycerin 14%	......	15	0.5	0.19
Glass	10,000	10,000,000	0.4	1150
Lucite	8,000	300,000	....	High
Marblette—annealed	....	500,000	0.4	70
unannealed	4,500	160,000	0.4	42

29. Comments on a Few Photoelastic Materials. (*a*) *Glass* is the original photoelastic material. Although available in a tremendous number of varieties, it is now used only to a very limited extent because of the difficulty in machining to intricate shapes and because it is relatively insensitive optically (high fringe constant) in comparison with some of the synthetic resins now available. Glass, however, has the advantage that it shows very clearly defined isoclinic lines and, in addition, is one of the few materials which do not exhibit the time-edge effect. Its strength and elastic characteristics are superior to those of most other photoelastic materials.

(b) *Bakelite BT-61-893*.* At the present time, in the United States, this particular one of the numerous types of Bakelite seems to be preferred over all other materials for the general run of photoelastic problems. It has good strength properties, a relatively high modulus of elasticity, and, optically, is moderately sensitive to stress. For stresses below 4000 psi the creep effect is negligible in a period of a few hours, although over longer periods of time it becomes quite noticeable. The machining properties are reasonably good, and its susceptibility to the time-edge effect is not excessive. The latter can often be retarded somewhat by storage in a desiccator or in oil. The material may be obtained in sheets approximately 7 in. $\times$ 11 in. and up to about 1 in. in thickness which must be polished prior to using.

A peculiar characteristic of this material is to be found in its physical properties at temperatures just in excess of 212°F. If one raises the temperature (above 70°F) creep influence becomes more and more pronounced until a temperature of approximately 200°F is reached; above this temperature its behavior corresponds closely to that of an elastic body. That is, on being loaded, it takes up its full deformation almost immediately and recovers its initial condition rather rapidly where the load is removed. If the material is subjected to load at the elevated temperature and then gradually cooled down to room temperature, the strains (except for $\frac{1}{640}$ part due to elastic recovery as the load is removed) will be locked into the material as well as the photoelastic effect (26 times as great) which it possessed at the elevated temperature. These peculiar properties make the material suitable for three-dimensional stress analyses by the "fixation method" in which the isochromatic-fringe pattern is locked into the model before the load is removed (see part II of this chapter and reference 58).

(c) *Bakelite BT-48-005*. This plastic possesses properties somewhat analogous to those of BT-61-893, but the physical constants are very different. It possesses the disadvantage of poor creep characteristics, but on the other hand it can be obtained in fairly large pieces. Owing to residual-stress effects these large pieces may not always be in a stable state of stress internally and as a consequence may develop cracks when machining operations are performed.

(d) *Catalin* plastic has somewhat lower mechanical-strength properties than Bakelite (BT-61-893), but it is somewhat more sensitive optically to the influence of stress. It can be obtained in much larger sheets than Bakelite and with the surfaces highly polished (ready for use without buffing). If it is not loaded excessively, or the load is not maintained too long, it will give good results in spite of a tendency towards creep.

(e) *Celluloid*. This trade name includes several plastics of the cellulose nitrate type. Although not so sensitive optically as Bakelite, the Celluloids

* Recently this material has also been marketed under the trade name Catalin 61-893.

are much easier to machine and may be obtained in large (20-in. $\times$ 50-in. or larger) polished sheets in thicknesses from $\frac{1}{8}$ in. (or less) up. Celluloid has the great advantage that it can be fused together by softening the surfaces with acetone or amyl acetate. This feature makes it useful for simulating built-up plate structures of welded steel.[57]

FIG. 17-41.   Fringe Photograph of Bakelite Model Taken through Lucite Holders
(Photograph by Gideon Hoffman)

(f) *Columbia Resin CR-39* is a beautifully clear material having about the same optical sensitivity as Bakelite (BT-61-893) but about half the modulus of elasticity.[64a] Like Bakelite it cannot readily be satisfactorily welded together; it is a little harder to machine owing to the tendency to chip along the edges (brittleness), and the material has a tendency to creep under load.

(g) *Lucite* is beautifully clear and can be obtained in large sheets with polished surfaces. Its relative inactivity from the photoelastic point of view (high fringe constant) practically precludes its direct use for photoelastic-stress determination. However, it is satisfactory for observing the isoclinic lines which appear more clearly in materials of low sensitivity (see Fig. 17-13) and for transparent loading fixtures for Bakelite models (see Fig. 17-41). The latter application is very useful since the stress pattern in Bakelite can be photographed through two $\frac{1}{4}$ in. thicknesses of Lucite under stress with practically no distortion.

(h) *Marblette* has characteristics somewhat akin to Bakelite BT-48-005, but its properties can be varied tremendously by heat treatment.[62] It can be cast into intricate forms but is likely to develop high residual stresses on solidifying.

(i) *Gelatin.* For applications involving stresses produced by the dead weight of a structure, such as in gravity dams and foundations, the use of gelatin as a photoelastic material has been successful. Its extreme sensitivity produces a reasonable number of isochromatic lines corresponding to the stresses developed by the dead weight. In general, models made of gelatin will be much larger and thicker than those made from other substances. Since the characteristics of gelatin change with variation of the moisture content, it is essential that models from this material be kept in an atmosphere at constant temperature and humidity.[64, 54]

J. EQUIPMENT FOR THE LABORATORY

30. Polariscope. The essential piece of equipment for the photoelastic laboratory is a polariscope. This may be an exceedingly simple apparatus

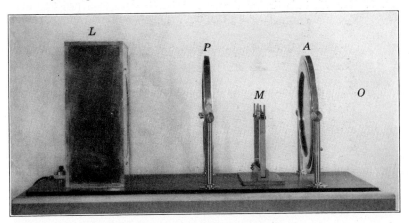

FIG. 17-42.   Simple Polariscope
L is light source; P, polarizing disk; M, model in loading fixture; A, analyzer; O, position of observer

as shown in Fig. 17-42 consisting only of polarizers and light source, or it may include an elaborate optical bench with a complicated lens system as shown in Fig. 17-10 and Fig. 17-43. The physical forms or schematic arrangements of a number of typical polariscopes are illustrated in references 3 and 5.

If lenses are employed in the polarized field (between the polarizer and

FIG. 17-43a. Photoelastic Polariscope and Loading Machine (Timken Roller Bearing Co., O. J. Horger)

FIG. 17-43b. Photoelastic Polariscope, Loading Frame, and Remote Controls (Courtesy B. R. Lee, Newport News Shipbuilding & Dry Dock Co.)

analyzer), they should be of good quality and "strain-free," since any initial birefringence will add to the retardations observed. Lenses between light source and polarizer need not be of high quality or strain-free. The most inexpensive polariscopes, therefore, utilize large-size Polaroid disks for polarization and dispense with expensive lenses in the polarized field of light.

31. Polarizers (or Analyzers). These may be Nicol, Ahrens, or other prisms, a pile of glass plates[1] or Polaroid.[66] In general, prisms are of small diameter and require a more elaborate lens system in order to produce a field of sufficient size for studying photoelastic models. Glass plates and Polaroid have the advantages that they can produce large beams of polarized light without lenses. Polaroid gives sufficiently good polarization for photoelastic work in either large- or small-field polariscopes. It is compact, not too expensive, and obtainable in large sheets mounted in plastic or glass. In addition, quarter-wave plates in corresponding large sizes are obtainable from manufacturers.

A very convenient adjunct to the polarizer and analyzer is the inclusion of means whereby they may be rotated simultaneously in such a manner that their axes remain crossed. This is very helpful in studying the isoclinic lines, and some systems using mechanical linkage or Selsyn motors have been developed by individual investigators.

32. Quarter-Wave Plates. In small sizes, sheets of mica or other natural crystal, split to the proper thickness (which must be uniform throughout the area) make excellent quarter-wave plates. In large or small diameters synthetic plates prepared by the Polaroid Corporation give adequate results. Other artificial quarter-wave plates have been produced by stressing glass[67] and by crossing two sheets of cellophane at the appropriate angle.[68] Single sheets of cellophane about 0.0005 in. thick (about half the thickness of the usual commercial wrapping material) also can be made suitable for quarter-wave plates.

33. Light Sources. It will be found convenient to have the polariscope equipped with sources of both white and monochromatic light which can be interchanged quickly and easily. For white light an incandescent projection-type bulb of about 500 watts capacity is satisfactory for most installations. Monochromatic light can be obtained from a d-c mercury-arc or the type H-4 a-c lamps produced by General Electric and Westinghouse, but filters should be used to mask out radiations other than the "green" line. Sodium-vapor lamps can be utilized but generally do not have a sufficiently concentrated source of high intensity for photographic work. Whatever the source of light, it should be of high intensity and concentrated at as nearly a point source as possible to enable the lens system to produce parallel rays in the polarized field.

34. Filters. In order to obtain sharply defined fringes in the isochromatic diagrams the use of a color filter along with a mercury lamp is essential. Many investigators prefer optically flat glass filters, but good success can be obtained economically with a gelatin filter mounted between glass plates or with inexpensive Corning glass filters that are not ground optically flat.

Since the filter can be placed anywhere in the optical system, residual stresses in the glass plates protecting a gelatin filter (or in a cheap glass filter) will have no effect if the filter is not located between the polarizer and analyzer. The filters listed in Table 17-4 will be found useful in photoelastic work[65] for obtaining a monochromatic green light from a mercury-vapor lamp.

TABLE 17-4

LIGHT FILTERS FOR MERCURY GREEN LINE

Wratten No.	Remarks
62	Transmits about 10 per cent of the mercury green line and about 0.05 per cent of the yellow.
77	Transmits about 72 per cent of the mercury green line and only about 0.5 per cent of the yellow lines.
77A	Transmits about 68 per cent of the mercury green line and completely absorbs the yellow lines.
77 +58 or 77A+58	If the red light given off by the quartz in the lamp is objectionable, filter no. 58 can be superimposed on no. 77 or no. 77A.

35. Loading Frames. The devices used to apply the external loads to a model vary a great deal to suit individual requirements or special models, but the types most commonly used consist of a rectangular framework to which is attached an adjustable single lever as shown in Figs. 17-9 and 17-43a. Provision should be made for moving the whole frame vertically and laterally in its own plane to position the model in the light beam while the load is applied. Sufficient versatility should be incorporated in the possible positions of loading lever and loading accessories to allow for universal testing in tension, compression, or bending, of a variety of sizes of models.

The actual load is usually applied to the lever by calibrated dead weights or through a good spring balance. A calibrated elastic ring or, as shown in Fig. 17-10, a flat leaf spring may be readily adapted for loading directly without a lever arrangement. In order to produce a smooth gradual loading and unloading Frocht[3] has used water tanks as dead weights with a remote control of water level to enable close observation of the formation of fringes. A pneumatic system or sylphon-bellows arrangement may be similarly employed. Loads are usually transferred to the model through cylindrical pins (or steel balls with one side ground flat for contact with the model). Care must be taken to minimize any frictional effects at loading points (and to keep the loading lever in a horizontal position) to insure that the actual action line of the load corresponds accurately with that assumed.

Although the polariscope and loading frame are the primary essentials for the photoelastic laboratory, the following items are also necessary if quantitative results are to be obtained:

1. A good view camera (preferably 5 in. × 7 in. or larger) for photographing isochromatics in the polariscope.
2. A darkroom with photographic developing and printing equipment.
3. A clock with large illuminated dial and second hand.

4. A small annealing oven (for stress-relieving materials for models).

5. Small hand tools and equipment for cutting out accurate models.

In addition, several of the following items will often prove to be useful accessories in special applications or for more complete and accurate analyses:

1. Lateral extensometer.

2. Coker (or other) tension compensator.

3. Polishing equipment (for polishing models; see Fig. 17-44).

4. Weighing scales and spring balances.

5. Dial gages.

6. Small machine shop including lathe, milling machine, drill press, hand tools, and micrometers.

K. Preparation and Photography of Models

Unfortunately, the technique of preparation of photoelastic models has not received publicity comparable with other aspects of this type of analysis. Each individual seems to prefer the methods which have been worked out in his own laboratory; consequently, variations in procedure are about as numerous as investigators. The following comments have been written from the point of view of what has been found convenient in one laboratory, and no claim is made that the methods outlined are the best but rather that this procedure has been found workable under a given set of laboratory conditions.

Although the following statements are intended primarily for the preparation of models in Bakelite BT-61-893, they apply in a similar manner to other materials.[3, 69]

36. Cutting Sheets of Material. Ordinary sawing procedures by hand generally are satisfactory if the pitch of the sawteeth is not too fine and the teeth are well set. Bakelite, although soft, has a great tendency to dull the saw which should be kept sharp. A power-driven jig saw is not recommended since rapid strokes usually produce too much heat in the cut surfaces. About $\frac{1}{16}$ to $\frac{1}{8}$ in. and sometimes more material should be allowed between the line of the saw cut and the edge of the finished model if the influence of the sawing is to be avoided. Some investigators prefer to do the sawing under water, but slow-speed dry cutting is generally more satisfactory.

37. Sizing of Sheets. Materials that can be obtained in sheets with polished surfaces are usually of sufficient uniformity in thickness so that no sizing operations are necessary. However, Bakelite, which is rough cut from a large slab, may vary so much in thickness that machining of the faces is necessary prior to annealing and polishing. Small pieces can be brought to uniform thickness by turning on the face plate of a lathe. Larger pieces can be faced on a milling machine with an end mill. Surface grinding has been tried but is likely to generate too much local heat for satisfactory results unless extremely small cuts and slow feed are used. Pieces of Bakelite which do not vary in thickness by more than about 0.02 in. can be brought to uniform size by hand operations with moderately coarse sandpaper.

38. Annealing. With Bakelite and several other plastics, residual stresses can be removed by a suitable annealing process. Sometimes it is preferable to anneal large sheets of Bakelite prior to sizing, since any warpage may be overcome in the sizing operation. For models requiring a piece of material 5 in. × 5 in. or less it will usually be best to do the sizing first and the annealing second, so that the piece will rest on an even flat surface during the anneal. Some investigators follow the practice of annealing after machining the edges of the model; however, if the machining technique has been satisfactory, this should not be necessary. The advantage gained by this attempt to remove machining stresses along the boundary is usually more than offset by the added stresses developed by the time-edge effect.

Annealing of Bakelite BT-61-893 is accomplished by heating to about 240°F, soaking at that temperature for a few hours, and then cooling slowly. The process may be carried on in air or in an oil bath, but the latter is preferred since it provides better control of the temperature and minimizes surface defects due to contact of the Bakelite with supports while it is in a softened condition. In either case the Bakelite should be placed flat on a sheet of plate glass to minimize warping, and sheets of material should not be stacked one on top of another. The rate at which the temperature is raised seems to be relatively unimportant, but the success of the annealing process does depend on a slow rate of cooling. Although various elaborate temperature–time cycles have been applied, satisfactory results have been obtained on sheets up to ½ in. thick by raising the temperature in about 2 hr, soaking for 2 or 3 hr, and cooling slowly for at least 12 hr (overnight). With thicker material it may be desirable to prolong the cycle slightly, particularly in cooling.

A small insulated furnace is very desirable for annealing Bakelite. By making the oil bath of sufficient capacity one can eliminate the necessity for an automatic time–temperature control if there is sufficient oil in the bath (or insulation in the furnace) to prolong the cooling. One investigator has reduced the annealing process to an extremely simple form by hanging the Bakelite in a wide mouth Thermos jar into which hot oil is poured. The heat of the oil brings the Bakelite up to temperature, and the rate of cooling is sufficiently slow to give good results.

By using very small models it may be possible to cut them from portions of the plates where residual birefringence effects are small. However, this procedure is likely to be wasteful of an expensive material and for large models is impractical. Occasionally a piece of material will be found such that the annealing process just described will not be successful. If this happens, the desired results can perhaps be achieved by repeating the process and soaking the material for a longer time at a higher temperature, which for Bakelite should not be above 350°F.

For an oil bath any nonvolatile clean oil like Nujol is satisfactory. Heavy dark oils are to be avoided, since some of them tend to stain the material, and care should be taken to check the temperature at which the oil will flash to insure against fire in the annealing tank.

39. Polishing. The advantage of performing the polishing operation before machining the contour of the edges lies in the reduction or elimination of time-edge effect since the model can be photographed as soon as the contours have been shaped. Also the unavoidable rounding of the surfaces near the edge produced by polishing may be removed when the contour is machined. The disadvantage lies in the possibility of scratching the highly polished surfaces during the machining operations.

Since the polishing of large sheets of material is a tedious and lengthy process, much time can be saved by sawing out the piece of material for the model, allowing about $\frac{1}{4}$ in. excess beyond the proposed final contour. The rough-cut jagged edges may be rounded with a file for ease of handling.

The surfaces should first be made parallel, flat, and smooth by hand grinding on sheets of several successively finer grades of sandpaper or emery cloth. (Except in the case of a very experienced technician, a power sander should not be used; rapid abrasion generates heat which induces appreciable thermal stresses.) The sandpaper or emery cloth should be mounted on a piece of plate glass or other smooth flat surface. The same result may also be achieved on a power-driven wet lapping wheel, by using a coarse grinding compound, but is somewhat slower during the initial stages. The plastic rapidly loads up and destroys the cutting effect of sandpaper or emery cloth, and fresh sheets should be used at frequent intervals. Excellent results can be obtained with power-driven abrasive-belt machines which perform these initial operations under water; but the expense of this equipment is not usually warranted.

Final polishing operations can be best performed on a power-driven lapping wheel (Fig. 17-44). These may consist of an intermediate operation for producing a smooth flat translucent surface, and a final lapping in which the surfaces are polished to a high degree of transparency.

The intermediate operation can be carried out very successfully on a cast-iron lapping wheel using water and no. 600 flour of emery as the abrasive agent. The water and the emery are mixed together in the ratio of about three parts to one, respectively, by volume, and the solution is liberally sprinkled or dripped on the lapping wheel. By grinding carefully until all deep scratches are removed, a saving of time can be effected in the subsequent buffing. At the conclusion of the intermediate lapping (and also prior to this operation) meticulous care must be taken in washing all abrasive from the model (and the hands), since even a few particles remaining may spoil not only the final finish on the model but also the polishing wheel.

The final polishing can be accomplished in several different ways, depending on the degree of surface finish desired. A reasonably good polish can be obtained using a wet-canvas-covered lapping wheel (a metallurgical lapping wheel is excellent if of sufficient diameter) and levigated alumina in water as the polishing agent. A somewhat better result will be achieved by finishing on a velvet-covered wheel with the levigated alumina and water. If a still better degree of surface finish is desired, a velvet wheel and rouge can subsequently be used; however, except in special cases, the slight improvement in surface finish is more than offset by the added time and trouble encountered.

Cloth-covered lapping wheels all have the disadvantage of tending to round the edges of the model. If the final machining is done prior to polishing, this effect may be very harmful since the boundaries will be obscured in the photograph of the isochromatic diagram. By using a lapping wheel covered with beeswax (and levigated alumina in water) this trouble can be minimized, as the wax-covered wheel has less tendency to round the edges of the model. It will be a little slower in polishing and will only produce a degree of surface finish about equivalent to that obtained with the canvas-covered wheel. In using the wax wheel best results are achieved by allowing the lap to become dry in the final stages and, at the same time, taking care that the wax is not driven into the surface of the model.

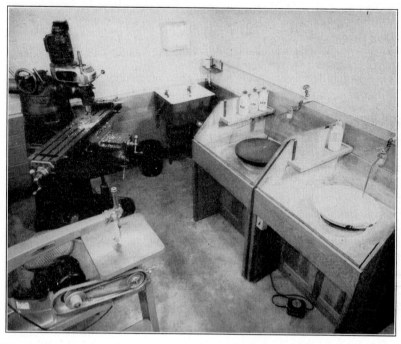

Fig. 17-44. Equipment for Preparation of Photoelastic Models—Saw, Milling Machine, and Polishing Laps (Courtesy B. R. Lee, Newport News Shipbuilding & Dry Dock Co.)

40. Machining. There appears to be no generally accepted machining procedure, except most technicians agree that the cutting tools used for making photoelastic models should be very sharp and should not be used on metals or other materials. Whenever the material must be held in a clamp or vise, it should be protected by pieces of blotting paper on each clamped face; only smooth jaws and light pressures should be applied. Blotting paper will help to distribute the clamping force evenly, and it is sometimes helpful to insert wood strips on both sides of the blotters to aid in preventing the edges from chipping as they are cut.

Careful hand filing of the model to a template (metal) will yield excellent results and freedom from edge stress as long as one does not have to maintain the contour of the boundary within very close tolerances.   A rotary filing machine, with the template, will improve the precision, but care must be taken to avoid the introduction of machining stresses by localized heating. Small rotary filing cutters mounted in a drill press have also been used satisfactorily for light cuts in hand operations.

Bakelite can be readily turned in a lathe if a sharp tool is used.   One should be careful not to force the material onto a mandrel nor to grip it too tightly in the jaws of a chuck since local residual stress effects may be produced. For producing straight edges and certain curved contours, a milling machine is most desirable.   End- or side-milling cutters with straight- or spiral-cutting edges can be used with or without lubrication.   Machine oil, lard oil, and soda water have all been used as cooling and cutting fluids, but there is considerable difference of opinion as to the desirability of using cutting fluids on synthetic plastics.   Dry cutting has been found satisfactory on Bakelite, but a jet of air directed on to the cutting tool at the point of contact with the model will aid materially in clearing away chips and avoid machining stresses. In any turning or milling operations it is essential to take very light cuts especially as one approaches the final dimension.   Approximate depths of the last three cuts might well be 0.005, 0.003 and 0.001 in.

41. Photographing the Model.   A wide variety of techniques in the actual photographic recording of the isochromatic stress pattern is available so that the following remarks should only be considered as suggestions.

Accurate loading of the model is naturally of prime importance in attaining good results.   In tension there is not likely to be much trouble but one should make provision for slight adjustment of the line of action of the applied force. With symmetrical models (and loading) it is relatively simple to adjust the applied force until the stress pattern is symmetrical.   In compression one has to cope with the tendency towards lateral buckling of the model.   Consequently, it may be necessary to adjust the action line of the load very carefully relative to the thickness of the model.   If isotropic points tend to merge into the first-order isochromatic, this usually indicates variation in stress throughout the thickness of the model and the necessity for adjustment in load.   A more sensitive test is to examine the isoclinic lines passing through the isotropic point.   If all isoclinics are visible and well defined, the loading is probably correct.

For isochromatic diagrams in green light ($\lambda = 5461$ angstroms), Gavaert plates, Kodalith, and Super Press Ortho films all give good results; in general all orthochromatic or panchromatic films of good *contrast* are suitable.   The time of exposure must be worked out for each particular setup.   However, after a few trials on a given polariscope it will be a simple matter to estimate the time required for future work.   Isoclinics can best be photographed by overexposure of the isochromatics in a plane polariscope, preferably in white light.   Changing the load on the model during the exposure will assist in diffusing the isochromatics if this can be accomplished without noticeable deflections or movement of the model; any movement will produce a fuzzy image of the edges.

The sharpness and general appearance of the photoelastic stress patterns can be greatly improved by coating the surfaces of the model with a light clear oil such as Nujol or Halowax and then wiping them clean. This serves the double purpose of removing finger marks and filling up many tiny scratches. If the surfaces of the model are really rough, as in the case of a slice from a three-dimensional model with locked-up stress, excellent pictures may be obtained by immersion in Halowax oil RD-11-1.

Very often the interpretation of the stress pattern can be made much easier if fine reference or location lines are ruled on the model. These may take the form of a single line, a line with divisions on it, or a network of squares. A light pressure on a sharp-drawing compass point will produce the desired result. The lines scratched on the model appear on the photograph and should be narrow and shallow, or they may either interfere with the stress pattern or mark out very fine isochromatic fringes.

L. Other Optical Methods

42. Direct Measurement of the Principal Stresses. (*a*) *Favre's Method.* The fundamental principle on which Favre's method[71] is based depends on the direct determination of the changes in the refractive indices on the two principal planes. That is, the evaluation of the equations 8 and 9 of section C. This is accomplished by using a rather elaborate and expensive interferometer of the type shown diagrammatically in Fig. 17-45. In this apparatus a polarized beam of light is divided into two parts, one of which is passed around the model and the other through it on one of the principal planes. The absolute retardation produced on each principal plane is determined. Monochromatic light from the source S is plane-polarized and transmitted through a lens L whose focal length is such that the point of focus is within the photoelastic model. This produces, as nearly as possible, point illumination.

The light arriving at the first half-silvered optical parallel, PL_1, is divided into two parts, one of which is transmitted and the other reflected. The beam which is reflected from PL_1 is directed on to the fully silvered optical flat F_1, and, thence, reflected to and transmitted through the unsilvered parallel PL_3 and, finally, the half-silvered parallel PL_4.

The light which passed through PL_1 is transmitted through the unsilvered parallel PL_2 and reflected from the fully silvered optical flat F_2. Following reflection from F_2 the light goes through a half-wave plate whose purpose is to rotate the plane of polarization so that the plane of vibration coincides with the direction of one of the principal stresses. By means of the half-wave plate, it is therefore possible to transmit the light through the model, on either principal plane at will. After passing through the model, the light beam traverses a second half-wave plate which restores the plane of vibration to its original position. This is necessary in order that, on reflection from the half-silvered parallel $PL_{,4}$ interference will be established with the light beam which went around the model.

When an observer looks through the eyepiece, a pair of cross-hairs and a series of shadow bands are seen. (These shadow bands have the same appear-

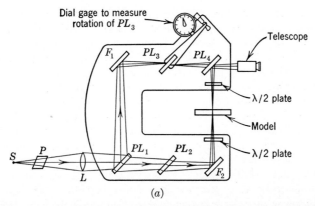

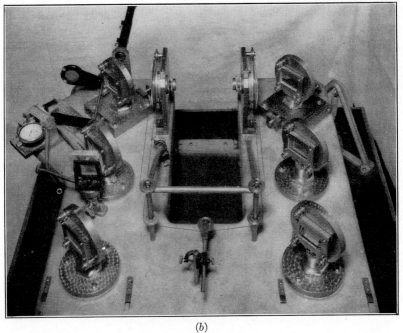

(b)

Fig. 17-45.   Favre Interferometer as Modified by Brahtz and Soehrens[72]
(a) Diagrammatic Sketch (S, source of monochromatic light; P, plane polarizer; L, lens; F_1, F_2, are full-silvered mirrors PL_1 and PL_4 are half-silvered mirrors, optically flat)
(b) Photograph of apparatus (Courtesy U. S. Bureau of Reclamation)

ance as those shown for the interferometer strain gage in Fig. 17-32.)   With
change in load on the model the shadow bands will move over the intersection
of the cross-hairs.   An observation is made on the instrument by counting
the number of bands passing the reference, for a given change in load.   For
each point at which the principal stresses are to be determined one observation
is made on each principal plane, and the principal stresses are then computed
from equations 8 and 9.

As a variation of this technique, it has been found less tiring for the observer
to rotate the parallel PL_3, so that the bands observed in the eyepiece appear
to remain steady.   The corresponding observations are then made as readings
on the dial gage.   Determination of the constants A and B in terms of the
dial-gage reading can be obtained from a simple tensile calibration specimen.
For any other model it is then possible to find σ_1 and σ_2 from the observations
on the interferometer.   For actual operation of the instrument it has been
found useful to construct a simple chart for evaluation of the principal stress
magnitudes directly from the dial-gage readings.

At the Bureau of Reclamation in Denver Bakelite models have been used
with pneumatic loading to eliminate vibration.   At Zürick glass models have
been used almost extensively.   The reader's attention is drawn to the necessity of a slightly more elaborate procedure required for evaluating the stresses
in the glass models.[72, 73]

(b) *Drucker's Oblique-Incidence Method.*   Rotation of a two-dimensional
model about an axis in its plane has been utilized by Drucker[74] as a simple and
rapid means of obtaining the individual principal stresses at interior points
of the model.   A determination of fringe orders in oblique positions is all
that is required in addition to the usual fringe photographs and isoclinics.
The relative retardation (interference order) for light at normal incidence to
the model (Fig. 17-46a) is given by equation 34 as

$$n = \frac{(\sigma_1 - \sigma_2)h}{f} \tag{34}$$

For convenience in solving for fringe orders corresponding to each of the
separate principal stresses, let

$$n_1 = \frac{\sigma_1 h}{f} \quad \text{and} \quad n_2 = \frac{\sigma_2 h}{f} \tag{88}$$

and equation 34 then may be written

$$n = n_1 - n_2 \tag{89}$$

If the model is rotated about the principal stress σ_1 through some angle θ,
the principal stresses (see part II) in the plane perpendicular to the light
normal will be σ_1 and $\sigma_2 \cos^2 \theta$.   The light then travels through a thickness
$h/\cos \theta$ as shown in Fig. 17-46b.   Thus, the fringe order n_0 for oblique incidence due to rotation through an angle θ about σ_1 will be

$$n_0 = \frac{\sigma_1 - \sigma_2 \cos^2 \theta}{f} \cdot \frac{h}{\cos \theta} = \frac{n_1 - n_2 \cos^2 \theta}{\cos \theta} \tag{90}$$

By solving these relationships for the fringe orders corresponding to the principal stresses we have

$$n_1 = \frac{\cos \theta (n_0 - n \cos \theta)}{\sin^2 \theta} \tag{91}$$

and

$$n_2 = \frac{n_0 \cos \theta - n}{\sin^2 \theta} \tag{92}$$

from which the stresses may be evaluated individually by substituting these values in equation 88.

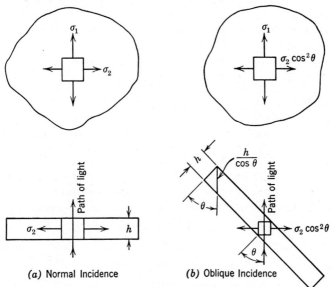

(a) Normal Incidence   **(b) Oblique Incidence**

FIG. 17-46.   Stresses Producing Retardation for Oblique Incidence

Similarly, if the model is rotated through an angle θ about the axis of the principal stress σ_2, the order of interference n_0' is

$$n_0' = \frac{n_1 \cos^2 \theta - n_2}{\cos \theta} \tag{93}$$

and the fringe orders corresponding to the values of principal stress become

$$n_1 = \frac{n - n_0' \cos \theta}{\sin^2 \theta} \tag{94}$$

and

$$n_2 = \frac{\cos \theta (n \cos \theta - n_0')}{\sin^2 \theta} \tag{95}$$

The variations of stress that occur along the light path when observations are made with oblique incidence are not troublesome except for very thick models or for observations near boundaries having a high stress gradient. In general, however, the errors to be expected are no greater than those encountered with normal incidence in attempting to evaluate the maximum fringe order at a boundary in a region of high stress gradient.

(c) *Fabry's Interferometer Method.* A point-by-point method of separately determining principal stresses at interior points has been described by Fabry.[75] In this method the model must be accurately polished (with surfaces plane and parallel) and the two faces are half silvered. Parallel light passed through the model at normal incidence produces interference between the rays transmitted directly through the model and those which undergo two reflections as indicated in Fig. 17-47.

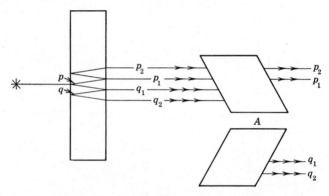

FIG. 17-47. Interference Produced by Reflections in Fabry's Method (R. D. Mindlin[5])

Light entering the front face of the model is divided into two component waves p and q, each of which is plane-polarized on the planes of principal stress. These in turn are partially transmitted (p_1 and q_1) and partially reflected (p_2 and q_2) at the rear face of the model. The waves p_2 and q_2 are again reflected at the front face and partially transmitted in the original direction to the analyzer A. By rotating the analyzer to the proper orientation, the waves q_1 and q_2 may be extinguished, and interference between p_1 and p_2 (due to the difference in lengths of path through the plate) may be observed. Similarly, by rotating the analyzer 90°, the interference between q_1 and q_2 can be observed and evaluated. The method has not been widely used in practice owing to the great difficulty of preparing the special model required.

43. Direct Determination of Isopachic Lines. An *isopachic line* is the locus of points having a given value for the sum of the principal stresses. On the photoelastic model it is also the locus of all points having the same change in thickness as the load is applied. If the isochromatic and isopachic lines for a given model and loading are known, it becomes a simple matter to evaluate the two principal stresses at any point by direct addition and subtraction of the equivalent values in terms of stress. The following two methods have been utilized for observing optical phenomena from which the isopachic lines may be determined.

(a) *Method of Sinclair and Bucky.* This system has the advantage that it can be used for photographic recording of either the isochromatic or isopachic diagrams over the entire field. The apparatus is somewhat similar to that used by Favre; however, two models and two quartz rotators are employed. Here, again, the light is divided into parts, one of which is passed around the models, and the other through them; the corresponding interference effect is then observed.

In order to determine the isopachic lines the arrangement indicated in Fig. 17-48 is employed. The light on entering the first model is broken up

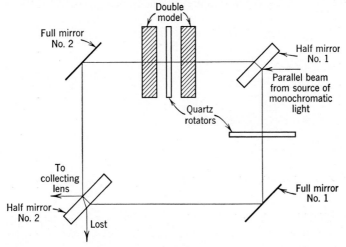

FIG. 17-48. Schematic Diagram of Interferometer Used by Sinclair and Bucky[76]

into two components, in the directions of σ_1 and σ_2. The rotator placed between the models revolves the component vibrations leaving the first model through 90°, so that the component wave which came through the first model on the σ_1 axis goes through the second on the σ_2 axis, and vice versa. Therefore, the component vibrations leaving the second model will both be subjected to the same change in optical path. This will be the sum of the effects taking place on the two principal planes. The rotator in the path around the models is for the purpose of compensating for the influence of its counterpart between the models.

If one neglects products of relatively small quantities, the combined change in optical path produced by stress in the two models is directly proportional to the sum of the principal stresses for any given pair of *identical* models and given wave length of light.

If the quartz rotators are removed, the outside path of the light interrupted, and two sheets of crossed Polaroid are inserted on either side of the models, the apparatus becomes an ordinary transmission polariscope with two identical models in series. Since the sum and the difference of the principal stresses are the same along the free boundaries, the isochromatic diagram can be obtained and used to calibrate the isopachics from the boundary values. For a complete discussion of the advantages and disadvantages of the method references 76 and 77 should be consulted.

(b) *Isopachic Lines Produced by Interference.* For small models whose surfaces can be polished *optically flat,* the isopachic lines may be made evident by direct-interference effects.[78, 79] Before the load is applied to the model, an optical flat is placed on its (optically flat) surface, as indicated in Fig. 17-49. After the load has been applied, the surface of the model becomes distorted, with the result that there is a variation in the air-gap thickness between the model and the optical flat resting on it. When monochromatic light is directed

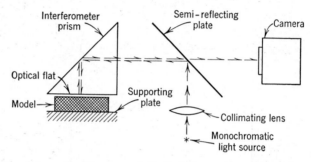

FIG. 17-49. Schematic Diagram of Optical System for Observing Isopachic Lines

at normal incidence through the optical flat to the surface of the model, there will be reflections from both surfaces. For given thicknesses of the air gap, interference will be produced, and a pattern of shadow bands representing lines of constant air-gap thickness will result. As long as the model does not buckle, (that is, it must retain its inherent plane of symmetry), the lines of constant air gap thickness will also be isopachics.

The method has the advantage that the model need not be of transparent material; in fact, Frocht[78] has actually used stainless steel. Furthermore, a complete set of isopachic lines are obtained by the method. As with other methods, the stress values corresponding to the isopachic lines can be determined from the boundary conditions in the isochromatic diagram. However, for accurate results an extremely careful specimen preparation is essential, and a delicate technique of observation must be developed to eliminate errors due to surface imperfections, slight temperature gradients, and misalignment of specimen and optical flat.

M. Some Problems That Have Been Analyzed by Photoelastic Methods

The field of application of the photoelastic method of stress analysis has covered such a diversity of subjects that it is futile to attempt to cover the entire range in a short summary. For convenience therefore the applications may be broadly classified in five main categories as follows:

1. The determination of localized stresses for regular geometric shapes or discontinuities.[80-88]

2. Stress analyses for the design of specific machine parts.[89-99]

3. Analysis of the stresses in engineering structures (including foundations) and aircraft frames.[100-114]

4. Studies of stresses of short-time duration or those due to dynamic action.[115-120]

FIG. 17-50. Stress Concentration around a Hole in a Tension Bar (Fringe photograph by M. M. Frocht)

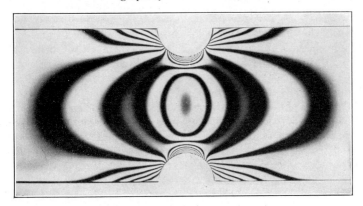

FIG. 17-51. Stress Concentrations at Semicircular Notches in a Tension Bar (Fringe photograph by M. M. Frocht)

5. Miscellaneous applications of the photoelastic effect to solve (by analogy) problems involving other physical phenomena such as fluid flow and thermal stresses.[121-128]

The references for part I are not intended to represent a complete tabulation; they should be regarded only as representative samples of many of the types of work that have been done in two-dimensional photoelasticity.

As examples of the type of analyses under class 1, Frocht[85] has determined stress-concentration factors for holes, fillets, and grooves (see Figs. 17-50 and 17-51) in tension and bending; Wahl and Beeuwkes[87] for holes and notches; and Weibel[88] for fillets in tension and bending; whereas Baud[80] has studied the

FIG. 17-52.   Fringe Photographs of Curved Bars Subjected to Bending Loads of Varying Eccentricity[84]

reduction in localized stress at a fillet caused by introducing a transition curve (spiral) in place of the usual circular fillet. Several investigators have studied the stress distributions in curved beams which do not conform to the conditions for which mathematical analyses are available (see for instance reference 84 and Fig. 17-52).

In the design of machine parts Boor and Stitz[89] and Dolan and Broghamer[90] have determined the localized stresses in gear teeth (see Fig. 17-53). Solakian and Karelitz[97] have studied the shearing stresses in keys and keyways, and Peterson and Wahl[96] and Horger and Buckwalter[92] investigated the effect of shape of hub-and-shaft seat on the effective stresses developed in a press fit. Stresses in noncircular press fits,[98] curved links,[95] rollers[92] of the types in Figs 17-54 and 17-55, car wheels[99] (Fig. 17-56), turbine-generator design,[91] and miscellaneous automotive parts[93, 94] have all been studied by means of photoelastic models.

In the field of structures a wide variety of useful applications are possible.[100] Stresses in composite members such as reinforced-concrete beams[101] and the possible use of gelatin models for foundation studies[54, 64, 104] are particularly interesting. Adequate analyses of statically indeterminate structures and frames[102, 105, 110] can be readily made, including the localized stresses not ordi-

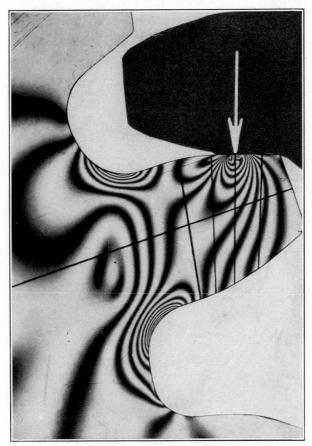

FIG. 17-53.   Localized Stresses in the Fillets of a Gear Tooth[90]

narily computed by the usual analytical methods of design. Hydraulic structures,[107] welded joints,[106, 108] and special details of rigid frames[109] (see Figs. 17-18 to 17-20) have all been the subjects of special investigations. In the airframe field, studies of bulkheads[110, 112] (see Fig. 17-57), wing ribs[111] (see Figs. 17-1 and 17-2), and the stresses at cutouts in webs of beams of high shear[113] indicate some of the types of applications in the past. Mesmer[114] has made an interesting study of the stresses around a hole in a box beam built of plastic by means of a reflection-type polariscope.

FIG. 17-54.   Contact Stresses with a Hollow Roller (M. Hetényi)

In the field of transient stresses, photographic records of stresses due to impact have been made by Frocht[115] and by Tuzi and Nisida.[119]   Dynamic stresses in rotating disks have been evaluated by Frost and Whitcomb,[116] and fringe photographs for forced vibrations of a beam have been obtained by Murray.[117]

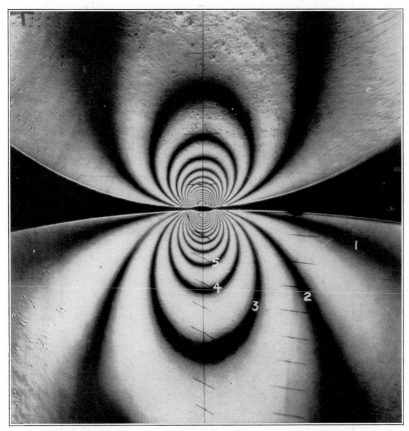

Fig. 17-55.   Contact Stresses in Rollers of Different Radii (O. J. Horger[92])

Some of the most interesting potentialities of the photoelastic effects lie in its possible use for solving problems other than those of simple stress analysis. There exist certain similarities between the differential equations for stress and those for fluid-flow problems.   Therefore, two-dimensional plane-stress systems are found to have features analogous to nonviscous potential-flow fields on one hand and to viscous flows on the other hand.[121, 128]   Thus the isochromatics, isoclinics, and isopachics of a rigid photoelastic model can be reinterpreted for certain conditions involving the solution of problems of fluid flow.

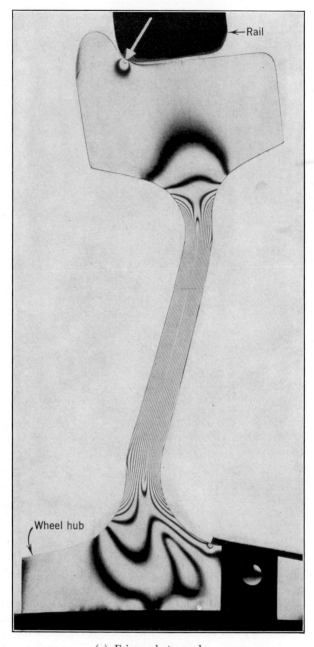

(a) Fringe photograph

FIG. 17-56.   Stresses in Model of Radial Section of a Railway-Car Wheel[99]

Weller[122] has utilized the photoelastic methods of analysis in studying the flow of fluids by making use of the double refraction developed in certain fluids by viscous shear.   This "photoviscous" effect can be observed through glass walls in a liquid tunnel, and the flow around obstructions can be analyzed from the retardations measured in a polariscope.   Leaf[123] has made practical application of the method for improving the design of locomotive fire boxes.

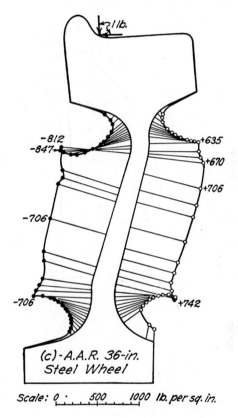

Scale: 0 :   500   1000 lb. per sq. in.

(b) Distribution of boundary stresses

Fig. 17-56.   (Continued)

Stresses produced by body forces (gravitation) or due to temperature gradients may be analyzed by methods proposed by Biot,[124] using photoelastic models in which it is not necessary to reproduce the gravity forces or the thermal effects.   Gravity stresses are determined from the stresses produced by loading a small model with boundary forces varying linearly with the depth.   Steady-state thermal stresses are determined by slitting a model between inner and outer boundaries and displacing or rotating the two edges of the slit with respect to each other by controlled amounts.   This method

(Fig. 17-58) has been applied by Weibel[125] to several cross-sectional shapes. In addition to the dislocation, boundary loadings may be applied to simulate stress conditions for transient conditions of thermal stress.

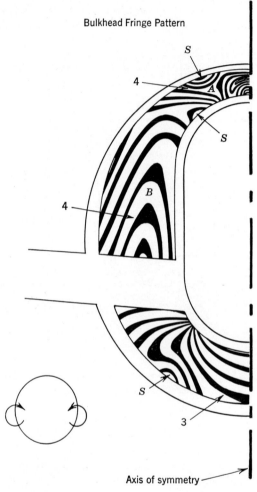

Bulkhead Fringe Pattern

(a) Fringe pattern for one half of a moment loaded bulkhead
FIG. 17-57.   Stresses in a Spar Bulkhead (H. Becker)[110]

The photoelastic effect has proved useful in the manufacture and inspection of high-quality glass products[127] as a means of detecting and measuring inherent residual stresses, and an interesting application to stress measurement in rubber has utilized the natural birefringence of the rubber as a photoelastic material.[126]

The general field of applications that have been made to specific products also includes such items as arches, slabs, hooks (see Fig. 17-59), bolts, dams, retaining walls, specimens for materials testing, shafts (Fig. 17-60), riveted and welded joints, bridge rockers, and many other parts of engineering structures. One of the most advantageous uses of the method is the facility with which several modifications of a given design may be reproduced by a sequence of cuts on a single model, and the corresponding redistribution of stress rapidly determined for selection of the optimum design of the member.

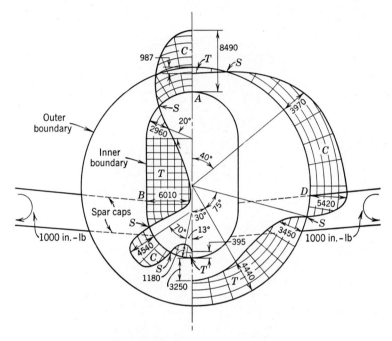

(b) Distribution of boundary stresses

Fig. 17-57. (*Continued*)

As a visual aid the photoelastic method is outstanding in its ability to help in educating the engineer to the dangers of localized stresses by vividly portraying the entire stress situation in any two-dimensional member in a striking manner.

Acknowledgements. The authors wish to thank the many investigators who have been kind enough to contribute photographs of apparatus and photoelastic observations for use as illustrations in this section and whose names appear under the titles of many of the figures. Especial acknowledgement is made of numerous suggestions and comments received from Dr. M. Hetényi relative to the content of the manuscript.

FIG. 17-58. Application of the Thermal Stress Analogy to a Circular Tube (E. E. Weibel[125])

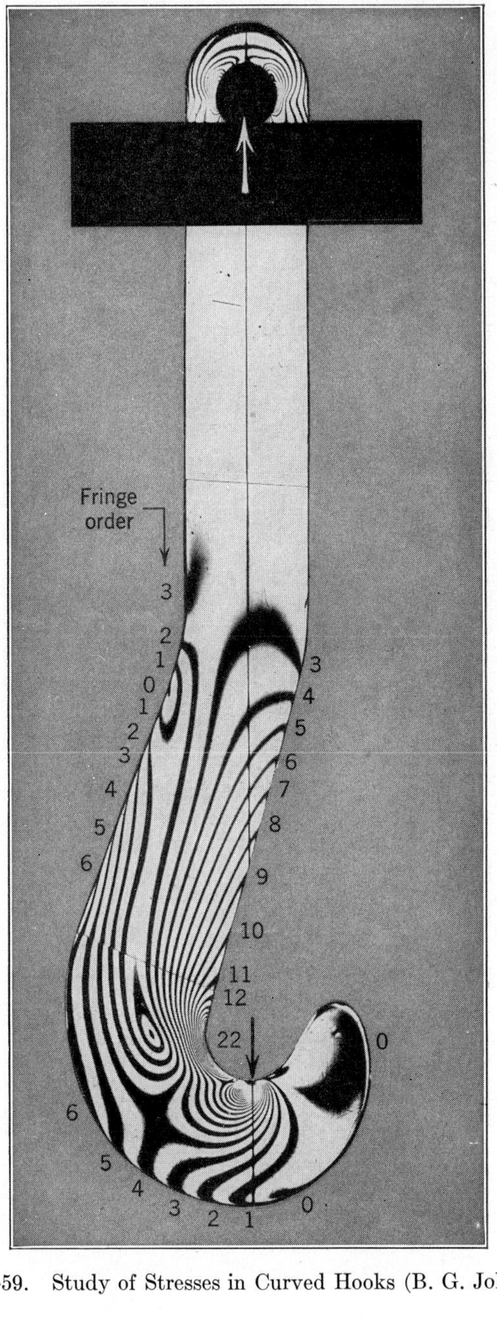

FIG. 17-59.   Study of Stresses in Curved Hooks (B. G. Johnston)

FIG. 17-60. Stresses in a Fillet of a Shaft in Bending (M. Hetényi)

II. THREE-DIMENSIONAL PHOTOELASTICITY

By D. C. Drucker

N. INTRODUCTION

In this part, only the truly photoelastic methods of three-dimensional analysis are considered in detail. The very useful auxiliary techniques, such as membrane analogy, relaxation nets, lateral-strain measurements, or their equivalents, which are often required for the successful completion of a photoelastic problem, are mentioned only in passing to give the reader an understanding of their function. They are fully discussed in the first part of this chapter.

The approach to the subject is partly historical, but has as its main objective the acquainting of the reader with the fundamentals of the art so that, as the present specific techniques are improved and new ones are developed, he should find little difficulty keeping up with its progress. Applications are cited to show what has been accomplished so far and to demonstrate the possibilities for the future. Comparisons are made with other methods to indicate the proper place of three-dimensional photoelasticity in the field of stress analysis.

A bibliography is included which gives a very short description of most of the important articles on theory, technique, and application.

O. The Two-Dimensional Approach

In most problems, the important stresses occur on the free boundary of the structure or machine part. Therefore, a method of determining the boundary or surface stresses with reasonable accuracy and speed would often be sufficient. As the normal and shear stresses acting on the surface are zero in these regions of interest, the state of stress in the surface is two dimensional.

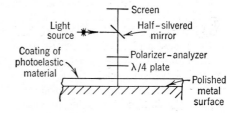

Fig. 17-61. (Mesnager[154])

A first and most logical approach to the solution of three-dimensional problems is, therefore, the application by simple extension of previously developed two dimensional techniques.

44. Photoelastic Materials Applied as Surface Coatings or Sheets. (a) *Surface Coatings.* Mesnager[154] suggested the use of a coating of photoelastic material on a polished model or portion of a prototype (Fig. 17-61). The strain in the coating and in the surface of the model is almost the same, and, therefore, the resulting birefringence in the coating determines the surface-stress differences.

Many difficulties have prevented general successful application of this procedure, although Oppel[158] did use it to determine the stress at the root of a notch. Even with the reflection-type polariscope which doubles the effective relative retardation, the sensitivity is low because the strain is small; the coating must usually be thin; and the strain-optical sensitivity of most plastics is too low for them to show appreciable birefringence.

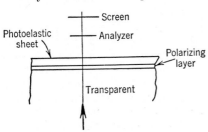

Fig. 17-62. (Timby and Hedrick[162])

Worse still, the accuracy is poor because the coating is variable in thickness, and it is extremely difficult to get good adhesion, good reflection, and good transparency. A further objection, which is not always serious, is that usually only the difference between the principal stresses in the surface can be found and not the principal stresses themselves.

Mesnager stated that Tardy's polariscope could be used to obtain the required accuracy, but, as Mindlin[22] points out, the image is blurred in regions where the stress gradient is high. A reflection polariscope with a single unit acting as both polarizer and analyzer is more convenient than a Nörrenberg doubler which has separate units.

(b) *Surface Sheets.* Timby and Hedrick[162] proposed the cementing of a polarizing layer over a transparent model and cementing of a sheet of photo-elastic material over the polarizing layer (Fig. 17-62). Light emerging from the body of the model is polarized and then affected by the stresses in the surface layer. An isochromatic or fringe photograph will give the difference between the principal stresses in the boundary directly.

The main difficulties encountered would be the obtaining of proper adhesion and of sufficient shear strength in the polarizing layer, which of necessity must have appreciable thickness. Other troubles are the cost of preparation of the model and the interference of the isoclinics with the isochromatics because of the use of plane-polarized light. However, only an ordinary transmission polariscope without a polarizer is required.

45. Surface Insertions and Attachments. Mabboux[150] embedded blocks of photoelastic material in the surface of concrete structures. Although the problems of accuracy involving thickness of material, good reflection, and good adhesion are greatly simplified, the information obtained is very limited. The insertion acts merely as a strain gage and would rarely have any advantage over present electrical or mechanical gages that would warrant its use.

The foregoing statement applies to projecting attachments of photoelastic material also. They too act as a substitute for the point-by-point mechanical- or electrical-strain-gage techniques and are generally more difficult to use.

46. Body Insertions. Favre[136] proposed the insertion of optically sensitive prisms in a transparent and insensitive three-dimensional body (Pockel's glass). The difficult technique required makes it unlikely that this method will have successful application, although the insertion of a sheet of sensitive plastic in an insensitive one is a possibility.

47. Laminated Constructions—Especially for Plates. In general, the integrated retardation over a considerable thickness can be interpreted in terms of maximum-stress difference, or of stress difference at some particular point, only if the law of stress distribution is known. For example, the bending stress in a thin plate varies linearly with the distance z from the middle plane, and the direction of the principal stresses p and q in planes parallel to the middle plane remains constant. Therefore, the integrated relative retardation in fringes (wave lengths of the light used) through the half thickness of the plate, $t/2$ will be a simple sum,

$$\Delta = \int_0^{t/2} (p - q) \, dz/C = \tfrac{1}{2}(\sigma_1 - \sigma_2)t/2C \qquad (96)$$

where C is the stress-optical coefficient of the model material, and σ_1 and σ_2 are the principal bending stresses at the surface of the plate. The retardation is only half as large as for a plate subject to a plane-stress field $\sigma_1 - \sigma_2$ because of the linear variation of stress from zero to a maximum, but the maximum-bending-stress difference can be calculated just as directly from the integrated relative retardation.

(a) *Combinations of Materials of Different Stress-Optical Coefficients.* If the materials and cements are available,[160, 161] an improvement on the method of Timby and Hedrick previously discussed would be the use of a sandwich of two materials, one of high and one of low optical sensitivity (Fig. 17-63). The materials must have the same elastic moduli, that is, the same Young's modulus and the same Poisson's ratio. A difference in Poisson's ratio will probably have little effect, but it is necessary to make sure that the modulus of elasticity is closely the same for both. As annealing of photoelastic materials often changes their physical properties,[56, 160] Marblette could be joined to a much less sensitive phenolic resin by a transparent Marblette cement, or Marblette and cellulose nitrate sheet could be combined.

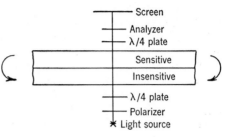

Fig. 17-63. A Method for Determining Bending Stress in Plates

Still another possibility is insensitive Lucite (Plexiglas) with cellulose nitrate (Celluloid, Pyralin).

(b) *Reflecting Surfaces or Layers.* Instead of employing transparent sandwiches it is possible to use one of the layers as an opaque reflector, but the intensity of the reflected light will be quite low.

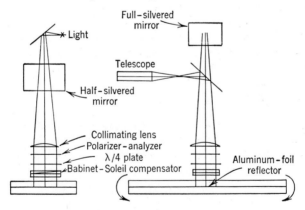

Fig. 17-64. (Goodier and Lee)[142]

The only method that has been successfully employed to an appreciable extent is the use of cemented layers of cellulose nitrate sheets with reflecting surfaces of aluminum foil between them (Fig. 17-64).[142] The following technique is given by Goodier and Lee.

Two plates of photoelastic material, preferably cellulose nitrate sheets, are cemented together with a layer of reflecting material between them. A rather thin acetone–cellulose nitrate material mixture is found to be satisfactory. The aluminum-foil reflecting layer is first cemented to one of the plates, and then the two plates are joined. Sufficient pressure to force all air bubbles out of the seal can be applied with an ordinary washing-machine ringer. The completed composite plate should be aged for several weeks to insure thorough drying of the cement.

An excellent bond is obtained between the sheets themselves, but a weak bond only between them and the foil. In regions of stress concentrations the shearing forces perpendicular to the plate become large, and the maximum shearing stress, which acts in the plane of weakness, may be sufficient to cause the cement bond to fail. If this does occur, the concentration factor will be too high, corresponding to the plane-stress case and not to bending.

The reflection polariscope used in the experiments should be very light because of the appreciable change in slope of the plate when it is bent. It is suggested that a very small light polariscope be attached to the model with vacuum cups. A strong white-light source and compensator are used to obtain visibility and accuracy.

Separation of the principal bending stresses can be accomplished in many of the same ways as for plane stress, because the sum of the bending moments G_x and G_y satisfies the same equation as the sum of the normal stresses in the two-dimensional case, that is $(\partial^2/\partial x^2 + \partial^2/\partial y^2)(G_x + G_y) = 0$. As bending stress is directly proportional to bending moment, membrane analogy or iteration can be employed using the experimentally determined and known values of the bending stress on the boundaries.

48. Summarizing Remarks on Two-Dimensional Extensions. As can be seen from the preceding discussion, many two-dimensional extensions have been proposed, but very few have had even limited successful application to practical problems other than the analysis of plate bending. A really three-dimensional technique is required to obtain the answers to most three-dimensional problems.

However, the possibility of the use of other means of measurement must always be kept in mind. For example, if the object of the experiment is to determine stresses at a few exposed points only, electrical or mechanical gages will be found much more suitable than photoelastic means. Also, if a qualitative picture is wanted of the stresses on free boundaries, brittle lacquer coatings will be more convenient.

P. BASIC THREE-DIMENSIONAL LAWS

49. Homogeneous State of Stress. (*a*) *Plane Stress Viewed Obliquely.* The reader is assumed to be familiar with elementary two-dimensional photo-elasticity. Therefore, the transition to three dimensions will be made by considering the problem of plane stress from a general viewpoint (oblique incidence).

For simplicity, assume that the state of stress is uniform over the region of the two-dimensional model being considered (homogeneous stress) and also that in the unloaded state there is complete absence of initial stress and initial optical effect. The relative retardation produced by the stressed model when light enters at normal incidence, (Fig. 17-65a) is $\Delta_n = (p - q)t/C$ where t is the thickness of the model, C is the stress-optical coefficient of the model material, and p and q are the maximum and minimum principal stresses, respectively. If the model is rotated about p so that the light normal through the model makes an angle θ with the normal to the plane (Fig. 17-65b) the light path becomes $t/\cos \theta$ long. The light is then subject to "principal" stresses in the plane perpendicular to the light normal, p and $q \cos^2 \theta$. Such stresses are called secondary principal stresses to distinguish them from the

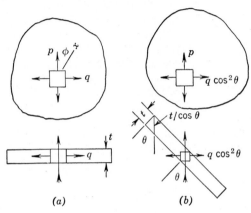

FIG. 17-65. Plane Stress Viewed
(a) Normally
(b) Obliquely

true principal stresses p, q, and 0. The relative retardation in the oblique position is

$$\Delta_0 = (p - q \cos^2 \theta)(t/\cos \theta)/C$$

This simple example illustrates two very important related fundamental points. The retardation per unit length of travel of the light is a constant multiplied by the difference between the secondary principal stresses; and additional information of value is obtained by oblique incidence.

In the case of plane stress, oblique-incidence information combined with normal incidence gives two equations in p and q and, therefore, enables determination of each.[74] Naturally, more measurements must be made for more general states of stress.

The types of measurements and their interpretation are described in detail in the discussions of actual methods of analysis.

(b) *Stress-Optical Laws in Three Dimensions—the Index Ellipsoid*.[156] Stress transforms the originally isotropic photoelastic material into an artificial crystal whose axes coincide with the axes of principal stress. A crystalline material is doubly refracting; that is, in general, there are two wave velocities for each wave normal, these velocities being different for wave normals in different directions. Each of the two waves is plane-polarized; the directions of vibration are perpendicular to each other and to the wave normal. A point source of light will, therefore, spread out as a two sheeted surface (Fig.

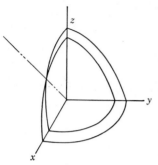

17-66). It is more convenient to think in terms of index of refraction n, which is essentially the reciprocal of velocity, $n = v_{\text{vacuum}}/v$. There are thus two indices of refraction for each wave normal, and the optics of the artificial crystals can be understood in terms of the index ellipsoid (Fig. 17-67) whose principal axes OA, OB, OC coincide with the axes of principal stress σ_1, σ_2, σ_3 at the point. The semiaxes OD, OE of any central section ODE are in the directions of vibration of the transmitted light and in length are the indices of refraction for each of the two waves whose wave normal ON is perpendicular to the sectioning plane. These semiaxes coincide with the directions of secondary principal stress.

FIG. 17-66. Wave Surface for a Biaxial Crystal

If the radius of the index sphere before stress is applied is n_0, the following

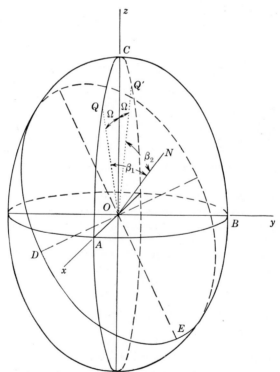

FIG. 17-67.   Index Ellipsoid[155]

stress-optical relationships hold (note their similarity to the stress–strain equations as though the original index sphere were actually deformed by the stresses):

$$n_A - n_0 = C_1\sigma_1 + C_2(\sigma_2 + \sigma_3)$$

$$n_B - n_0 = C_1\sigma_2 + C_2(\sigma_3 + \sigma_1)$$

$$n_C - n_0 = C_1\sigma_3 + C_2(\sigma_1 + \sigma_2) \tag{97}$$

where n_A, n_B, n_C are the three principal indices of refraction along the 1, 2, 3 directions and C_1 and C_2 are stress-optical coefficients.

For the general wave normal ON,

$$n_D - n_0 = C_1\sigma_D + C_2(\sigma_E + \sigma_N)$$

$$n_E - n_0 = C_1\sigma_E + C_2(\sigma_N + \sigma_D)$$

or

$$n_D - n_E = (C_1 - C_2)(\sigma_D - \sigma_E)$$

and the relative retardation in wave lengths through a thickness t is

$$\Delta = \frac{(n_D - n_E)t}{\lambda} = \frac{(C_1 - C_2)t(\sigma_D - \sigma_E)}{\lambda}$$

or

$$\Delta = \frac{t}{C}(\sigma_D - \sigma_E) \tag{98}$$

where λ is the wave length of the light, and C is the commonly used stress-optical coefficient, $1/C = (C_1 - C_2)/\lambda$.

If, by definition, $n_C > n_B > n_A$, that is, $OC > OB > OA$, the plane OCB contains the largest principal axis and the intermediate. From symmetry there must be two circular sections the normals to which, OQ, OQ', lie in the OAC plane and are at some angle Ω to OC. These normals, or directions along which the material acts toward light as though it were isotropic, are called the optic axes and the angle between them 2Ω is the optic axial angle. The planes of polarization for any wave normal bisect internally and externally the angle between the planes formed by the wave normal and each of the optic axes.

As $n_C - n_B$ and $n_C - n_A$ are small in photoelastic work, 0.002 or smaller,

$$\sin^2 \Omega = \frac{n_B - n_A}{n_C - n_A} \qquad \cos^2 \Omega = \frac{n_C - n_B}{n_C - n_A} \tag{99}$$

and, in general,

$$n_D - n_E = (n_C - n_A) \sin \beta_1 \sin \beta_2 \tag{100}$$

where β_1 and β_2 are the angles between the normal and the optic axes.

These relationships lead to equations for the difference between the principal stresses,

$$\sigma_3 - \sigma_1 = \frac{\sigma_D - \sigma_E}{\sin \beta_1 \sin \beta_2}$$

$$\sigma_2 - \sigma_1 = \frac{(\sigma_D - \sigma_E) \sin^2 \Omega}{\sin \beta_1 \sin \beta_2} \tag{101}$$

50. Nonhomogeneous Stress. (*a*) *Correction to the Elementary Law of Retardation.* If the stress field is perfectly uniform through the thickness t of the model or portion being investigated, the relative retardation will be given by $\Delta = (p - q)t/C$ and is dependent entirely on the magnitude of the secondary principal-stress difference, $p - q$.

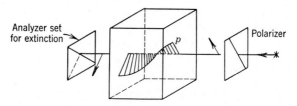

FIG. 17-68. Light Vector Follows Stress[134]

If p and q vary in magnitude along the wave normal but remain fixed in direction, the retardation sums simply point by point so that

$$\Delta = \int_t (p - q) \, dt/C \tag{102}$$

However, if there is rotation, along the wave normal, of the axes of (secondary) principal stress in planes perpendicular to the wave normal, the relative retardation is increased.[134] The assumption of a constant rate of rotation along the wave normal leads to the form

$$\Delta = \Delta' \sqrt{1 + 4R^2} = \Delta'S \tag{103}$$

where Δ' is the relative retardation for zero rotation, and R is the dimensionless ratio of rotation to retardation per unit length. S is, therefore, rarely appreciably larger than unity.

(*b*) *The Direction of the Light Vector.* Although the effect of the rotation on the retardation is generally very small, its influence on the light vector is great and often very important. In almost all practical cases the light vector will follow the change in direction of the (secondary) principal stresses.[134] For example, if plane-polarized light enters a model at a point where the direction of vibration of the light coincides with a secondary principal-stress direction, the direction of vibration will continue to coincide with the stress direction as it rotates through very large angles (Fig. 17-68). When the magnitude of the secondary principal-stress difference is constant and the orientation changes at a constant rate along the wave normal, the intensity of light vibrating perpendicularly to this direction is less at all points than

$4R^2/(1 + 4R^2)$ of the total intensity of the light.[134] R, as before, is the ratio of the rotation to the retardation. It will almost always be less than 5 per cent (18° rotation per fringe) in regions of interest, so that the intensity at right angles to the main vibration will be less than 1 per cent of it and is entirely negligible.

No solution has as yet been obtained for general variations of orientation and magnitude of the secondary principal stresses. Coker and Filon* derive the differential expressions

$$d\gamma = -\cos \rho \, d\varphi$$

$$d\rho = 2 \operatorname{ctn} 2\gamma \sin \rho \, d\varphi + \frac{2\pi}{\lambda} (n_1 - n_2) \, dz \qquad (104)$$

in which $\tan \gamma$ is the ratio of the amplitudes of vibration along the secondary principal-stress directions 1 and 2; φ is the angle between the 1 direction and an arbitrary axis; $\frac{2\pi}{\lambda} (n_1 - n_2) \, dz$ is the relative retardation that would occur in the length dz if the axes of principal stress did not rotate; and ρ is the relative retardation in radians actually occurring. φ and $n_1 - n_2$ are functions of z.

Mindlin and Goodman[168] obtain a more useful pair of equations which, as expected, show R to be the controlling variable.

Q. Techniques of Three-Dimensional Analysis

Two general practical methods are in use at the present time for the photo-elastic determination of three-dimensional states of stress. In one the stresses are fixed or "frozen" in the model, and slices cut from the model are analyzed. In the other the phenomenon of scattering of light is employed, and the slicing is done optically. As the technique of measurement required is different for the two methods of slicing or probing, they are discussed separately. However, both procedures depend on the previously discussed effects of stress on the propagation of light which are independent of the means of observation of these effects.

51. The Fixation Method or "Stress Freezing." (a) *The Behavior of Heat-Hardening Resins.* In 1850 Maxwell[151] reported on an experiment with a jelly of isinglass between two concentric cylinders. A torque was applied to the inner cylinder while the isinglass was allowed to cool and dry. On removal of the torque, Maxwell found that the optical pattern corresponded to the elastic optical pattern and apparently was not a system in equilibrium. However, he was unable to explain his results, and the matter was dropped until 1935 when Solakian[160] heated a circular bar of Marblette to 180°F, twisted it, and cooled it under load. A slice taken perpendicularly to the axis of the bar showed a fringe pattern. This experiment was the start of the fixation method, even though no pattern appears with such a slice if the strains are

* Reference 1, p 256.

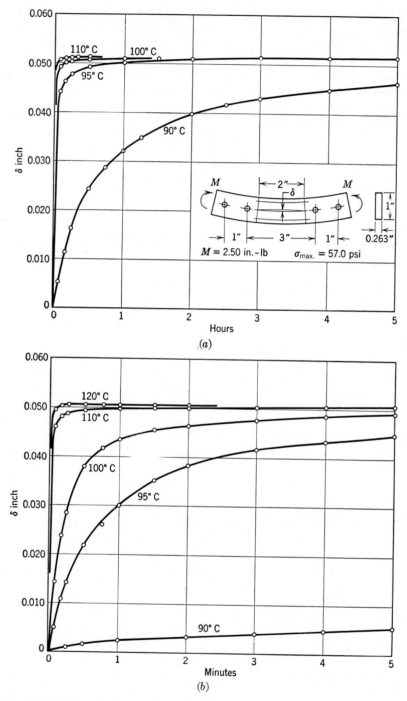

FIG. 17-69.   Time–Deflection Curves for Bakelite BT-61-893 at Elevated Temperature (M. Hetényi[58])

small and the incident light is normal.   Oppel[157] in 1936 was the first to state
that cutting a frozen model does not disturb its fringe pattern, and Kuske[148]
and Hetényi[58] supplied the theoretical explanation of the phenomenon.

At room temperatures or lower the most commonly used heat-hardening
plastic, BT-61-893,* exhibits practically no creep in the usual short-time tests
at stresses under 3000 psi.   The phenolic resins are not so good in this respect,
but the creep rate is quite low.

This rate apparently increases considerably with temperature,[56] but
Hetényi[58] found that surprisingly an upper limit of deformation exists; that
is, an increase in temperature merely decreases the time required to reach this
maximum deformation but does not have an appreciable effect on its magnitude
(Fig. 17-69).

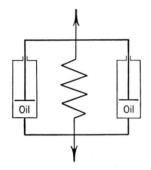

FIG. 17-70.   Model for Behavior of Heat-Hardening
Resins (M. Hetényi[58])

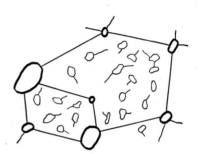

FIG.   17-71.   Primary   and   Fusible
Phases (Houwink[129])

This peculiar and possibly unexpected behavior can be explained by a very
simple model (Fig. 17-70), a spring and dashpots in parallel.   At low temperatures the viscosity of the oil in the dashpots is so high that creep proceeds
extremely slowly.   The spring remains almost unchanged in length and,
therefore, only slightly stressed.   As the temperature is increased, the oil
becomes less viscous, and deformation can proceed more rapidly.   The more
the deformation, the more the stress in the spring.   Eventually, at either
sufficient time or temperature, all the load is taken by the spring and none
by the oil.   If the spring material is perfectly elastic, no further deformation
can take place at the given load.   Therefore, at high temperatures, the model
will be perfectly elastic, but its modulus will be quite low.

That the behavior of a heat-hardening resin can be explained by a three-
dimensional arrangement of springs and dashpots is, of course, not accidental.
Such a resin has a strong primary network (polymerized phase) permeated by
a fusible and soluble phase (Fig. 17-71).   It, therefore, is essentially a spring
of low modulus (because of its form) embedded in a viscous material.[129]

Knowledge of the structure of this type of resin indicates that, if the mate-

* BT-61-893 is now called Catalin 61-893.

rial is heated to a temperature at which the fusible phase has negligible viscosity, loaded so that all the load is carried by the primary network, and then cooled slowly under load, the fusible portion will set and hold the primary network in place when the load is removed. The internal stress in the network is balanced microscopically by a small stress in the fusible phase.

From the photoelastic point of view, the important fact is that this system of stresses in equilibrium at each point produces an optical pattern which is proportional to the elastic optical pattern under load at room temperature. The retardation is produced by the primary network and is almost as great as under load at the elevated temperature at which the pattern was "frozen." Because the stresses balance internally on a microscopic scale, careful sawing of the model, avoiding the generation of appreciable heat, will not affect the retardation pattern (Fig. 17-72). A model can, therefore, be analyzed slice by slice or point by point as the optical properties of a region will not be altered by its removal from the model. Subsequent loading of the model or of a portion of it at room temperature will be carried almost entirely by the fusible phase and will produce additional retardation which will add to that already fixed in the resin.[135] The effects add in the same manner as two systems of stresses add.

The fusible portion of BT-61-893 has a very high strain-optical sensitivity compared with the infusible as may be seen from the following figures:

$$\text{At room temperature} \quad E = 650{,}000 \text{ psi} \quad C = 85 \quad \text{lb/in./fringe}$$
$$\text{At } 115°C \qquad\qquad E = \quad 1{,}100 \text{ psi} \quad C = 3.3 \text{ lb/in./fringe}$$

an increase in stress-optical sensitivity at the elevated temperature of approximately $26\times$ but an increase in strain for a given stress of $600\times$, therefore, almost a 25-fold increase in deformation for a given retardation.

On the other hand, the fusible portion of the styrene–alkyd resins developed by Westinghouse seems practically insensitive; the optical properties of the material are due almost solely to the infusible network. As reported by Leven,[166] for sebacic Fosterite, the stress-optical coefficient $C = 3.0$ lb/in./fringe at 100°C when the modulus E is close to 2000 psi. At other temperatures both E and C increase but are closely in ratio so that the strain-optical coefficient remains almost constant. On the reasonable assumption that the optical effect caused by the primary network is determined by the strain it is subjected to, all the birefringence is accounted for, and there can be no contribution from the very large viscous component.

It should be noted that other materials, such as cellulose nitrate, which are thermoplastic, do show similar effects to those observed in the thermosetting resins. A frozen pattern can be set in, which at the time is only slightly disturbed by careful sawing. However, the patterns will eventually disappear, and the model will distort.

Mindlin[169] has studied the photoviscoelastic problem and reached the conclusion that cross-linked polymers are not required for the fixation method. An "elastic" pattern will be obtained if all loads on a viscoelastic model are changed and kept in ratio.

(b) *Experimental Procedure.* The preferred procedure for BT-61-893 is first to heat the model at 240–260°F (115–127°C) for a sufficient period of time to obtain a reasonably uniform distribution of temperature, and then to load and cool slowly under load. The optimum temperature for the styrene–

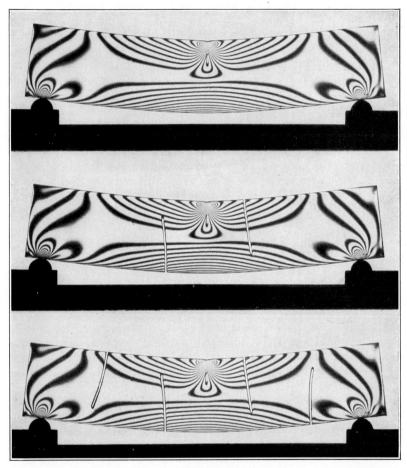

FIG. 17-72. Illustrations Showing that Careful Sawing Does not Disturb the Frozen Stress Pattern. Material: Adipic Fosterite (M. Hetényi)

alkyd resins is in the neighborhood of 100°C and depends on the particular acid used.

Either air or liquid-bath heating is usually employed, but dielectric heating would have the great advantages of both speed and uniformity. The liquid, if one is used, must have a low rate of evaporation at 120°C and should not decompose at this temperature. A heavy mineral oil, or possibly better, some of the newly developed silicones can be used. Air heating is easily adaptable to most existing loading devices because leakage is not especially objectionable and proper insulation can be provided. If the problem calls for a simple type of loading or a very special small frame, the entire setup may be placed in a standard heating or annealing oven.

After the optical pattern is fixed in the cooled model, slices can be cut and analyzed. Although careful cutting will not have an appreciable effect on the optical pattern except at the very surface, the slice will generally not be sufficiently transparent. Clear photographs can be obtained by immersing the slice in a fluid of the same refractive index (for example, Halowax Company RD-11 for BT-61-893) or by coating it with lacquer or oil. Polishing may be necessary if extremely good visibility at the boundaries is required. Ordinary polishing, however, will round the edges too much unless a wax-coated lap is used. It should be kept in mind that polishing itself is a process of plastic flow and, of necessity, must destroy the frozen-stress pattern at the very surface if the previous cutting has not already done so. The depth affected is extremely small, and no report has been published in which this disturbance of a thin surface layer has been said to cause trouble. To avoid chipping of the edges when cutting slices, Meriam[153] cast a model in a Wood's metal before slicing. The particular Wood's metal used had a melting point of 160°F obtained with a composition of 50% Bi, 25% Pb, $12\frac{1}{2}\%$ Cd, $12\frac{1}{2}\%$ Sn.

Appreciable edge stresses, which almost completely obscure the boundary fringe values, are produced in BT-61-893 during the heating and cooling period and subsequent slicing. However, Frocht[3] has discovered that these "time stresses" are materially reduced and often completely eliminated if the slice is allowed to stand for a few days before measurements are made (Fig. 17-73). Apparently no new edge effects are introduced if the slice is kept in oil. Frocht also shows the relief of induced internal stress when original surface layers are machined off, demonstrating that large elastic stresses are produced by polymerization and changes in water content of the outer layers of BT-61-893 and similar plastics.

Mönch[170, 171] uses layers of oil and aluminum foil to protect the model and prevent edge effect.

One enormous advantage of the best styrene–alkyd resins is that practically no edge effect results from heating, cooling, and slicing. This factor alone would be sufficient reason for changing from Bakelite and allied plastics in most applications of the freezing method. In addition, the Fosterites have been cast in 6-in.-diameter rods, whereas the maximum available thickness for BT-61-893 is only a little over 1 in. Many problems can be investigated now that these practical difficulties have been overcome, although what is really required and not yet available is a resin which can be cast in large complicated shapes.

Kriston, an allyl ester resin, has many desirable properties[174] and can be cast fairly well.

(c) *Methods of Analysis—Accuracy.*[176] Methods of analysis can be classified as point by point or region by region. The distinction is in the method of

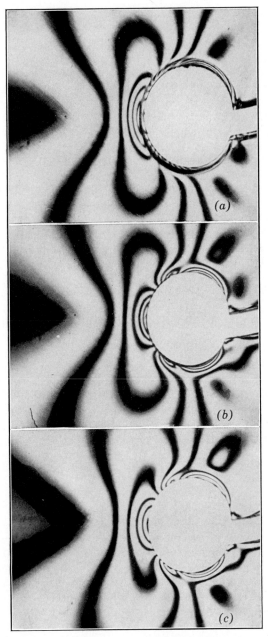

Fig. 17-73.   Reduction of Edge Effect (Time Stresses) in Frozen Pattern (Frocht, ref. 3 vol. 2)

(a) Slice cut from BT-61-893 model immediately on removal from oven
(b) Same slice a few days later
(c) Slice reduced in thickness showing still further elimination of edge effect

measurement on the model and not in the calculations necessary for stress determination. If the apparatus enables useful readings to be obtained at one point only, a fairly complete analysis will take a long time. If an entire plane or region can be observed at once, a qualitative picture is obtained quickly. Some point-by-point methods have high accuracy and may be used at points of greatest interest to supplement the regional exploration where practicable.

If a plane of principal stress can be chosen as the middle plane of a slice, a normal incidence photograph will give the same information as it does for a two-dimensional plane-stress model—the difference between two true principal stresses. The stress normal to the plane does not affect the retardation (nor would a shearing stress on the plane). If the slice is sufficiently thin that the directions of the principal stresses do not change appreciably through the thickness, an isoclinic pattern can be obtained in the usual two-dimensional manner. If the directions change through the thickness, it is necessary to use the fact that the light vector follows the principal stress directions through the slice. Polarizer and analyzer must be rotated separately until extinction is obtained at any point. White light should be used to avoid interference by the isochromatics. The polarizer will then give the direction of one of the principal stresses on its side of the slice, and the analyzer the perpendicular to the correspondingly principal stress on its side (Fig. 17-68). It is not possible in the general case to obtain isoclinics directly, point by point exploration is necessary.

However, even for the simpler and more usual case of a sufficiently thin slice, the stress normal to the plane is not known, and, therefore, one additional measurement must be made at each point of interest to determine the three principal stress differences. A photograph at oblique incidence will give this information at all points.

When the incident light is normal to the slice (Fig. 17-74abc) the total relative retardation through the thickness t at any point is (equation 98)

$$\Delta_n = (\sigma_1 - \sigma_2)t/C \tag{105}$$

measured in fringes. σ_1 is the algebraically larger and σ_2 the algebraically smaller (true) principal stress in the plane of the slice.

If the slice is rotated about some arbitrary axis x, at an angle ϕ to the σ_1 direction at the point considered, so that the wave normal makes an angle θ with the σ_3 direction (normal to the slice), the light path becomes $t/\cos\theta$ long. The component stresses affecting the light change from σ_x, σ_y, and τ_{xy} to σ_x, $\sigma_y \cos^2\theta + \sigma_3 \sin^2\theta$, and $\tau_{xy} \cos\theta$ (Fig. 17-74def).

The formulas for the transformation of stress (see Professor Timoshenko's chapter on elasticity) give the difference between the secondary principal stresses, the diameter of Mohr's circle, as

$$p - q = \sqrt{[\sigma_x - (\sigma_y \cos^2\theta + \sigma_3 \sin^2\theta)]^2 + 4\tau_{xy}^2 \cos^2\theta} \tag{106}$$

and the relations,

$$\sigma_x = \sigma_1 \cos^2 \phi + \sigma_2 \sin^2 \phi = (\sigma_1 - \sigma_2) \cos^2 \phi + \sigma_2$$

$$\sigma_y = \sigma_1 \sin^2 \phi + \sigma_2 \cos^2 \phi = (\sigma_1 - \sigma_2) \sin^2 \phi + \sigma_2$$

$$\tau_{xy} = \frac{\sigma_1 - \sigma_2}{2} \sin 2\phi \tag{107}$$

Also

$$\tan 2\psi = \frac{2\tau_{xy} \cos \theta}{\sigma_x - (\sigma_y \cos^2 \theta + \sigma_3 \sin^2 \sigma)} \tag{108}$$

where ψ is the angle between the maximum secondary principal stress p and the x axis. Both ϕ and ψ are measured positively in the same direction, counterclockwise from x to the maximum principal stress.

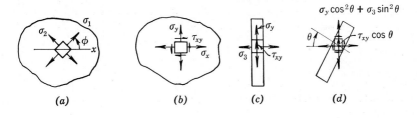

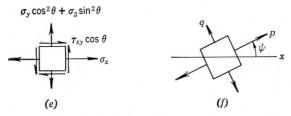

(e)   (f)

FIG. 17-74.   Principal Slice Viewed Normally and Obliquely

The relative retardation through the thickness $t/\cos \theta$ is

$$\Delta_\theta = (p - q)t/C \cos \theta \tag{109}$$

Substituting for $p - q$, after algebraic manipulation, leads to

$$\sigma_2 - \sigma_3 = \frac{C}{t \sin^2 \theta} \{ \pm \cos \theta \sqrt{\Delta_\theta^2 - \Delta_n^2 \sin^2 2\phi} - \Delta_n[1 - \sin^2 \phi(1 + \cos^2 \theta)]\} \tag{110}$$

The indeterminate sign before the square root is troublesome when ϕ is not close to $0°$ or $90°$, unless an approximate isoclinic pattern is obtained in the oblique position as explained in the following.

Transformation of equation 108 gives another expression for $\sigma_2 - \sigma_3$

$$\sigma_2 - \sigma_3 = \frac{\sigma_1 - \sigma_2}{\sin^2 \theta} \left\{ \frac{\sin 2\phi}{\tan 2\psi} \cos \theta - [1 - \sin^2 \phi (1 + \cos^2 \theta)] \right\} \quad (111)$$

As $\sigma_1 - \sigma_2 = \Delta_n C/t$, comparison of the two expressions for $\sigma_2 - \sigma_3$ shows that

$$\pm \sqrt{\Delta_\theta^2 - \Delta_n^2 \sin^2 2\phi} \equiv \Delta_n \frac{\sin 2\phi}{\tan 2\psi} \quad (112)$$

or the sign of the square root is given by the sign of $\sin 2\phi / \tan 2\psi$ where ϕ and ψ are determined experimentally.

Equation 111 apparently could be used directly without recourse to the measurement of the retardation in the oblique position. Actually this is not practical except for ψ near $45°$ because of the extremely poor accuracy of determination of $\sin 2\phi / \tan 2\psi$ in regions of $\phi = 0°$ or $90°$.

Note that, as ϕ approaches zero, if ψ approaches zero, this ratio is positive (but not unity), and, if ψ approaches $90°$, the ratio is negative. Also, as ϕ approaches $90°$, if ψ approaches $90°$, the ratio is negative (but again not unity), and, if ψ approaches zero, the ratio is positive. These two cases, in which high accuracy can be obtained, lead to expressions which are very useful in point-by-point exploration:

$$(\sigma_2 - \sigma_3)_0 = \frac{C}{t \sin^2 \theta} (+\Delta_\theta \cos \theta - \Delta_n)$$

$$(\sigma_2 - \sigma_3)_{90} = \frac{C}{t \sin^2 \theta} (-\Delta_\theta \cos \theta + \Delta_n \cos^2 \theta) \quad (113)$$

In the previous equations Δ_n is always positive by definition, and Δ_θ is positive when the algebraically larger principal stress is in the same direction as for normal incidence, and negative when it turns through $90°$, that is, if as the slice is rotated the fringe order decreases to zero and then increases again. This question is quickly and easily settled when the pattern is not observed during rotation by the use of white light or a simple-tension compensator.

The accuracy that is attainable with this general procedure at any point in a plane of principal stress can be estimated by considering the effect of errors in each of the measured quantities Δ_θ, Δ_n, ϕ, and θ. Using the notation δ for error gives

$$\delta(\sigma_2 - \sigma_3) = \frac{\partial(\sigma_2 - \sigma_3)}{\partial \Delta_\theta} \delta \Delta_\theta + \frac{\partial(\sigma_2 - \sigma_3)}{\partial \Delta_n} \delta \Delta_n$$

$$+ \frac{\partial(\sigma_2 - \sigma_3)}{\partial \phi} \delta \phi + \frac{\partial(\sigma_2 - \sigma_3)}{\partial \theta} \delta \theta \quad (114)$$

if the errors are reasonably small.

As the determination of the isoclinics is usually not very precise, the most interesting term is $\frac{\partial(\sigma_2 - \sigma_3)}{\partial \phi} \delta \phi$. This term is found to be zero at both $\phi = 0$ and $90°$, showing that a small error in ϕ will not have an appreciable effect on the experimentally determined value of $\sigma_2 - \sigma_3$ in such cases and indicating the advisability of choosing the axis of rotation to make ϕ either zero or 90° at important points of the stress field. However, the term becomes large at intermediate values of ϕ. For example, at 45°, which is not quite the worst case,

$$\frac{\partial(\sigma_2 - \sigma_3)}{\partial \phi} = \frac{\Delta_n(1 + \cos^2 \theta) \, C^*}{t \sin^2 \theta} = (\sigma_1 - \sigma_2) \frac{1 + \cos^2 \theta}{\sin^2 \theta} \tag{115}$$

so that, for $\theta = 45°$, the error in $\sigma_2 - \sigma_3$ due to the error in ϕ is

$$\delta(\sigma_2 - \sigma_3) = (\sigma_1 - \sigma_2) \, 3\delta\phi$$

A reasonable value for the maximum error of determination of ϕ is 3° so that $\delta(\sigma_2 - \sigma_3) \approx \frac{1}{6}(\sigma_1 - \sigma_2)$, a large error but not so large that the general method is necessarily unusable.

The error produced by an incorrect setting of θ will not be excessive if $\delta\theta$ does not exceed $\frac{1}{2}°$, and so it can be made very small with proper care.

Errors in the determination of retardation cause an inaccuracy of a different type from those caused by errors in angle, (equation 115), as shown by

$$\frac{\partial(\sigma_2 - \sigma_3)}{\partial \Delta_\theta} = \frac{C}{t \sin^2 \theta} \left\{ \pm \frac{\Delta_\theta \cos \theta}{\sqrt{\Delta_\theta^2 - \Delta_n^2 \sin^2 2\phi}} \right\} \tag{116}$$

In a sense, the error is absolute, for it is independent of the magnitude of the stresses or the retardation they produce, being a function of the numeric error in fringe determination. The larger the stress, therefore, the less the importance of these terms, but they may make the method of oblique incidence useless in regions of small stress except for ϕ of 0° or 90°.

At ϕ of 0° or 90° and θ of 45°, the error in $\sigma_2 - \sigma_3$ is

$$\delta(\sigma_2 - \sigma_3) = (1.4C/t) \, \delta\Delta_\theta + (2C/t) \, \delta\Delta_n$$

This means simply that the error of determination of the difference between these principal stresses is less than 3.4 times as large as for direct determination by light incident along the normal to the 2–3 plane. Actually, such an error is not very large because $\delta\Delta_\theta$ and $\delta\Delta_n$ are the errors in the measurement of the fringe order that is present regardless of why it exists. In other words, initial optical effect, errors in loading, etc. which may result in considerable departure from the true value of Δ do not enter here. Therefore, the use of both dark- and light-field photographs, from which fringe order can be determined to the nearest $\frac{1}{10}$ or $\pm\frac{1}{20}$ fringe without especial difficulty, reduce the error at ϕ of 0° or 90° to a sufficiently small quantity for truly accurate work.

However, at ϕ of 45° the error is multiplied by a factor $\Delta_\theta/\sqrt{\Delta_\theta^2 - \Delta_n^2}$ which may become very large.

From the preceding discussion it can be seen that, the closer the axis of rotation for oblique incidence to the direction of a principal stress, the less the final error for given errors of observation.

The difference between the principal stresses can also be determined by measurements of retardation alone. There are three photoelastic unknowns for a principal slice, and three independent retardation measurements are required. As the normal to the slice is an axis of optical symmetry, fringe photographs at $\pm\theta$ will be identical, and, therefore, three incident directions in a single plane will be useful only if each is at a different angle to the normal. A photograph at normal incidence and two at oblique incidence, one in the xz and the other in the yz plane, will also provide the necessary information.

Norris and Voss[175] suggest using three retardations and one orientation value to obtain a simple formula. Drucker[176] has shown that calculations employing retardations alone are usually more accurate.

In the more general case of an arbitrary slice, the equations are more complicated, more observations are required because less is known about the state of stress, and the accuracy is lower. There is wide latitude in the choice of the five necessary observations. Simplest to interpret in terms of the usual picture of stresses on the faces of a cube is the addition of orientation measurements to the one normal- and two oblique-incidence observations which alone are sufficient for a plane of principal stress. Starting with the cube on whose faces act the stresses σ_x, σ_y, σ_z, τ_{xy}, τ_{zx} of the general state of stress (Fig. 17-75), normal incidence gives

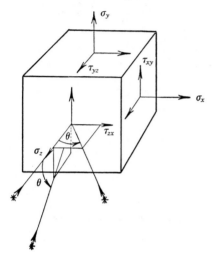

FIG. 17-75. The General State of Stress Oblique Incidence in yz and xz Planes is indicated

$(p-q)_n$ by measurement of retardation, and the orientation ϕ_n of p_n from the isoclinic. $\sigma_x - \sigma_y$ and τ_{xy} can be calculated from

$$\sigma_x - \sigma_y = (p-q)_n \cos 2\phi_n$$
$$\tau_{xy} = \tfrac{1}{2}(p-q)_n \sin 2\phi_n \quad (117)$$

Oblique incidence in the yz plane at some angle θ to z gives $(p-q)_0$ and ϕ_0 which can be transformed into

$$\sigma_x - \sigma_0 = (p-q)_0 \cos 2\phi_0$$
$$\tau_{x0} = \tfrac{1}{2}(p-q)_0 \sin 2\phi_0 \quad (118)$$

Measurements at two angles θ_1 and θ_2 in addition to normal incidence will give three components of the shearing stress τ_{xy}, τ_{zx} (one can be used as a check), and three normal-stress differences which can be used to calculate

$\sigma_x - \sigma_z$ and τ_{yz} in addition to $\sigma_x - \sigma_y$. Fig. 17-76 shows the information obtained. The reader is referred to Chapter 9 by Dr. Meier on "Strain Rosettes" that he may choose the method he prefers for the computation of $\sigma_z, \tau_{yz}, \sigma_y$ from $\sigma_{01}, \sigma_{02}, \sigma_y$ or actually in this case $\sigma_x - \sigma_z, \tau_{yz}, \sigma_x - \sigma_y$ from $\sigma_x - \sigma_{01}, \sigma_x - \sigma_{02}, \sigma_x - \sigma_y$. The shearing stress τ_{zx} is computed from

$$\tau_{zx} = (\pm\tau_{x1} \cos \theta_2 - \tau_{x2} \cos \theta_1)/\sin (\theta_1 + \theta_2) \tag{119}$$

and the check is

$$\tau_{xy} = (+\tau_{x1} \sin \theta_2 + \tau_{x2} \sin \theta_1)/\sin (\theta_1 + \theta_2) \tag{120}$$

The formulas for the stresses become very simple when θ_1 and θ_2 are each 45°.

$$\sigma_z = (\sigma_{01} + \sigma_{02}) - \sigma_y$$

$$\tau_{yz} = \frac{\sigma_{01} - \sigma_{02}}{2}$$

or

$$(\sigma_x - \sigma_z) = (\sigma_x - \sigma_{01}) + (\sigma_x - \sigma_{02}) - (\sigma_x - \sigma_y)$$

$$\tau_{yz} = \frac{-(\sigma_x - \sigma_{01}) + (\sigma_x - \sigma_{02})}{2}$$

and

$$\tau_{zx} = \frac{\sqrt{2}}{2} (\tau_{x1} - \tau_{x2}) \tag{121}$$

Signs of the stresses must always be taken into account.

The three principal-stress differences and the orientations of the principal stresses can be calculated from the normal-stress differences $\sigma_x - \sigma_y, \sigma_x - \sigma_z$ and the shearing stresses $\tau_{xy}, \tau_{yz}, \tau_{zx}$ in the same manner as the principal stresses from the components of stress.

An alternate procedure would be to take one oblique picture in the yz and one in the xz plane in addition to normal incidence. Shear stresses $\tau_{xy}, \tau_{yz}, \tau_{zx}$ can then be computed directly and $\sigma_x - \sigma_z$ from $\sigma_x - \sigma_{01}, \sigma_x - \sigma_y, \tau_{yz}$ or $\sigma_y - \sigma_z$ from $\sigma_y - \sigma_{03}, \sigma_x - \sigma_y, \tau_{zx}$.

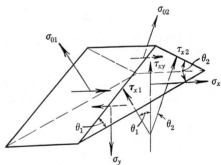

FIG. 17-76.   Information Obtained from One Observation at Normal and Two at Oblique Incidence

Measurement of retardation for five directions of the wave normal will generally determine the principal stresses with greater accuracy than retardation and orientation measurements for three directions, because the accuracy of determination of the directions of secondary principal stress is not very high. However, the equations for calculating the three principal-stress differences become very much more involved, and the process cannot be followed through step by step for each point at which calculations are made.

The present alternatives to oblique incidence, which itself is a very effective and accurate point-by-point method if a compensator is used, are two definitely point-by-point methods. The easiest to visualize and understand is to mount a portion of the model on a universal stage in the parallel field of the polariscope and by trial establish the direction of observation for minimum and maximum retardation per unit thickness of model. Because of the variation of thickness with orientation this procedure offers some difficulty, but if it is successful the desired answer is obtained immediately as

$$\sigma_1 - \sigma_3 = \frac{\text{(maximum retardation in fringes) } C}{\text{(thickness traversed) } S}$$

$$\sigma_2 - \sigma_3 = \frac{\text{(minimum retardation in fringes) } C}{\text{(thickness traversed) } S} \tag{122}$$

where S is the correction (equation 103) for rotation of the directions of principal stress and is very close to unity at all important points. In practice, the orientation of the faces of the portion of the model or the details of the universal stage will often prevent observation along the maximum or minimum directions.

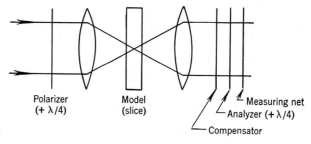

Polarizer
(+ λ/4)

Model
(slice)

Measuring net
Analyzer (+ λ/4)
Compensator

FIG. 17-77. Apparatus for the Use of Convergent Light (Hiltscher[147])
Note that the apex of the cone is in the middle plane of the slice to minimize stress-gradient effects

Another procedure proposed by Hiltscher[146, 147] and improved on by Kuske[149] employs the crystallographic technique of convergent light (Figs. 17-77 and 17-78). In his first paper Hiltscher made direct use of a petrographic microscope. The method is essentially oblique incidence with an infinite number of wave normals and, therefore, has a great advantage if a point-by-point analysis is not objectionable. Simple oblique incidence is probably preferable when the slice is a principal plane, but the rather lengthy calculations required for a general plane will often offset the desirable feature of observing the entire slice at once. To visualize the fringe patterns that will be obtained with convergent light, it is necessary to consider the index ellipsoid (Fig. 17-67) and the surfaces of equal relative retardation for a point source of light. Fig. 17-79 shows such a surface for the general case of a biaxial crystal; that is, all three principal stresses have different values. It goes out to infinity along each of the optic axes as there is no relative retardation along these directions. It is closest to the point source along the normal to the plane containing the maximum and the minimum principal stress. The fringe patterns obtained by convergent light are intersections of these surfaces with a plane, perpendicular to the central ray of the cone of light, at a distance from the origin equal to the thickness of the slice. Figure 17-80 is a drawing of these intersections for cuts parallel to the principal planes.

Measurement of the angle between two rays from the position of their points of emergence on these fringe patterns is facilitated by

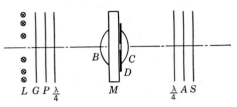

Fig. 17-78.   Apparatus for Convergent Light (Kuske[149])

L—Light source with greater intensity at the boundary than at the center

G—Ground glass plate

P—Polarizer

$\dfrac{\lambda}{4}$—Quarter-wave plate

B, C—Lenses of approximately 4 cm focal length

D—Diaphragm of 2 mm diameter opening

M—Model slice

A—Analyzer

S—Screen

A fluid is used between B and M and between M and C to obtain a large apex angle for the cone

Kuske's measuring net (Fig. 17-81) which is the gnomonic projection (on a plane) of lines of equal latitude and longitude on a sphere. The center of the net is placed over the center of the fringe pattern, that is, the point of emergence of the central and, therefore, normal ray. The net is then rotated until the points of emergence of the two rays are on the same straight line of longitude. The angle between the two rays is read from the scale for the curved lines of equal latitude. If the optical system is imperfect, but the distortion produced is radially symmetric, a corrected net can be obtained by placing a very accurately ruled net in the plane of the slice and photographing or tracing its enlarged image.

If the two points of emergence of the optic axes appear in the pattern, the optic-axial angle 2Ω can be read off directly, the point of emergence of the ray along an axis of principal stress can be determined, and its retardation can be measured. Equations 98 and 99 will then give the differences between the principal stresses. This simple procedure can be used whenever both optic axes appear, even when the pattern

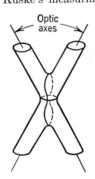

Fig. 17-79.   Surface of Equal Relative Phase Difference —Biaxial Crystal

is skewed because the axis of principal stress is inclined to the normal or central ray.

In the more usual case of only one optic axis or none appearing, the analysis of the patterns is more difficult. If an axis of symmetry can be spotted, measurements are made that correspond identically to those discussed under oblique incidence for a principal slice, and the same type of formulas hold for their interpretation. However, there is difficulty in locating the point of emergence of an axis of symmetry exactly, although the region in which it is located may be obvious, unless the axis is normal to the slice. When the

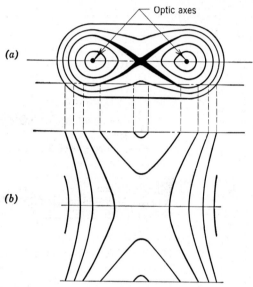

FIG. 17-80. Sections of Surfaces of Equal Relative Phase Difference (Fringe Patterns)

(a) By a plane perpendicular to the plane of the optic axes
(b) By a plane parallel

ray makes an angle with the normal, the relative retardation upon exit depends on this angle and not on the difference between the indices of refraction only. Therefore, points of maximum or minimum relative retardation do not indicate points of emergence of rays along principal directions. Kuske[149] points out that it is necessary to measure retardation at a number of points in the region and use the angle between the corresponding rays and the normal to determine where the difference between the indices of refraction is maximum or minimum. This problem is the same one that arises in the use of the universal stage procedure with a parallel beam of light. However, despite the number of trials and calculations required, the method has the great advantage of measuring a principal-stress difference practically directly.

A universal stage may be used in combination with the convergent-light method, but it is difficult to make angular measurements on the patterns.

If neither an optic axis nor a point of emergence of an axis of symmetry is apparent, measurements corresponding to oblique incidence for a general slice will give sufficient information, but Hiltscher[146] suggests moving on to a more favorable point. His paper contains a detailed description of many possible patterns and methods of interpretation. The reader should become familiar with them, before using convergent light, by consulting both the paper and a book on optical crystallography.[130, 131] The isogyres, used extensively in crystallography, correspond to the isoclinics of the two-dimensional patterns and are useful at times to indicate the points of emergence of optic

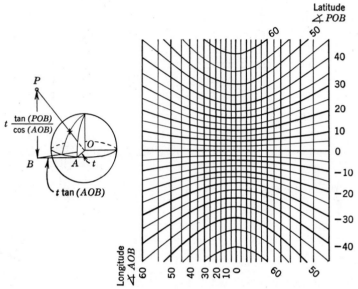

FIG. 17–81.   Net for Measuring Angles between Rays from Their Points of Emergence on the Fringe Pattern in Convergent Light (Kuske[149])
Projection of the circles of latitude and longitude on a plane, all projecting rays originating at the center of the sphere

and principal axes. When they interfere with the fringe pattern, they may be removed by use of circularly polarized light. Isogyres, in the sense of continuous black lines, are not formed if the secondary principal-stress directions change through the thickness.

The method of convergent light will not work very satisfactorily in a region of stress gradient because of the marked distortion of the fringe patterns. However, all the alternatives also become difficult to use. Measurements with oblique rays are reliable only when the rays are oblique in a plane approximately perpendicular to the line of maximum change of stress. In the region of stress concentration due to a discontinuity, this plane fortunately is the tangent to the boundary and because of the interference by the boundary with rays strongly oblique in other directions is sometimes the only usable one. It will often be necessary to choose a small θ to stay within a region of reasonably constant stress through the thickness although the accuracy of measurement must be high to obtain a good final result.

(d) *Additional Measurements to Obtain the Principal Stresses Themselves.* The methods described so far give principal-stress differences, that is, shearing stresses, but, unless one of the principal stresses is known, they do not give the principal stresses themselves.

Measurement of the principal indices of refraction in the stressed and unstressed state by very precise means could conceivably accomplish the desired result (equation 97). However, it must be kept in mind that the birefringence produced in photoelastic materials is very small, and the change of index of refraction is rarely much larger than 0.001. Therefore, to obtain results within a 10 per cent error it would be necessary to measure the index of refraction to much better than 0.0001.

Kuske[148] has proposed reheating the slice to release the stresses frozen in the infusible phase and measuring the resulting increase in thickness dt. This experimental procedure is capable of good accuracy. The expression,

$$-dt = (1/E')[\sigma_z - \nu'(\sigma_x + \sigma_y)] \tag{123}$$

gives the added relation between σ_x, σ_y, and σ_z or σ_1, σ_2, and σ_3. The values of E' and ν' can be determined with a simple tension-calibration specimen.

(e) *Advantages and Disadvantages of the Fixation Method.* The main and obvious advantage of the fixation method is the ability to get directly to the regions of greatest interest and observe them in the most convenient manner without the encumbrance of a loading fixture. Body-force problems can be dealt with by use of a centrifuge for constant or linearly varying body forces or by direct setup for turbines, superchargers, and the like. Observation during rotation is not necessary, and so a stroboscopic source with its relatively low equivalent intensity is dispensed with in favor of simple observation in the usual type of polariscope.

The main disadvantage is the visibly large distortion of the model, necessary for sufficient retardation, which may occasionally vitiate the results. Circular holes, for example, may become too elliptical to trust the results; fillets also may distort unduly. Rarely, however, will these effects be too large for the obtaining of practical answers to industrial problems. Another disadvantage, when the model is sliced, is the distortion of the layers at the very surface. In regions of high stress and of variation in direction of the principal stresses, this disturbance may cause difficulty in the obtaining of the orientation of the principal stresses. Careful sawing without heating the material and the choice of a reasonable thickness of slice will minimize the effect.

A further disadvantage, of a different type, is that true dynamic problems cannot be investigated. If the state of stress at a point varies with time, a fixation method is unusable.

52. The Scattering Method. (a) *Scattering of Light in Plastics.* Light passing through a plastic causes submicroscopic particles to vibrate and re-emit light. Except for a relatively small scattering background, the re-emitted light at each point can be considered as coming from a particle vibrating in the same manner as the light incident at the point. The amplitudes of vibration are proportional to the incident amplitudes, so that diagrams of the incident-light vector can be thought of as pictures of the motion of the scattering particle (Fig. 17-82). If one looks at this particle along a direction at right angles to the wave normal of the transmitted light, the scattering vibration would be seen edge on; that is, plane-polarized light would reach the eye of the observer. If the light entering the model is unpolarized (no directional properties), the amplitude of the scattered light is independent of the position of observation in the plane at right angles to the incident wave normal. If, however, the light entering the stressed model is polarized, and therefore, the light incident on the particle is elliptically polarized, the observed amplitude of scattering is clearly a function of position. This amplitude is proportional to the projection of the ellipse, traced by the tip of the light vector, on a plane perpendicular to the direction of observation.

The scattering can, therefore, be used to produce a plane-polarized source of light inside the model, or it can be used to analyze the elliptical vibration resulting from the transmission of polarized light. A collimated beam of small diameter or a sheet of light of small width is required for either procedure.

If the scattering is used as a polarizer, an analyzer outside the model will give the integrated effect of the principal stresses over the path between the point of scattering and the boundary of the model. Unless the type of distribution of stress is known, as it is in the case of thin plates in bending (article

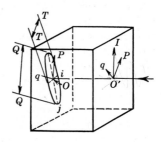

Fig. 17-82. Scattering of Light[134]

The entering vibration $O'I$ breaks up into two components, one along P, the other along q. At any point O in the model the two components, in general, will combine to form an elliptic vibration with axes Oi and Oj in the plane perpendicular to the wave normal $O'O$. The intensity of scattered light seen by an observer is proportional to the square of the projection of the ellipse (for example, QQ or TT) on a plane perpendicular to the direction of observation

47) the resulting retardation cannot be interpreted directly in terms of stress. If the sheet of light is close to the boundary of the model, close enough that the stresses can be considered as constant from the points of scattering to the boundary, then an isochromatic pattern is obtained for the two-dimensional state of stress in the boundary layer. This procedure corresponds to the proposal of Timby and Hedrick (article 44b, Fig. 17-62).

Although the integrated effect determined from one isochromatic pattern cannot be interpreted in terms of stress in the interior of the model, if the point of scattering is moved a definite distance t along the path of observation, the change in retardation $d\Delta$ determines the state of stress between the two points of scattering:

$$d\Delta = (p - q)t/C \tag{124}$$

If the secondary principal stresses, p and q are not constant in orientation in the distance t, a generally small factor S (equation 103) must be inserted in the multiplying expression. This procedure has many disadvantages that are quite apparent. Measurement of small change in retardation is subject to large inaccuracy unless point-by-point accurate compensation is employed. The location of the scattering source is not well defined because of the width of the sheet of light, and, when the stress varies, the equivalent displacement is not necessarily the motion of the source. Also, isoclinics will tend to obscure the isochromatic patterns that are obtained. However, the procedure has the advantage of giving patterns that have the same meaning as in two-dimensional analysis; the order of interference determines the magnitude of the principal-stress differences.

The alternate procedure, in which the scattering is used as an analyzer, results in fringe patterns of an entirely different kind but is to be preferred in practically all cases, because information about the points of scattering is obtained directly. Formation of the fringe pattern and its interpretation can be best understood by reference to simple models and stress distributions. The simplest is the two-dimensional tension specimen. A beam of polarized light, of small diameter, is sent through the model perpendicularly to the axis of tension and parallel to the plane of the model (Fig. 17-83). Suppose first (Fig. 17-83a) that the entering light is plane-polarized, the direction of vibration coinciding with the direction of the tension.

As the vibration of the entering light is in the direction of a principal stress in the plane perpendicular to the wave normal (the other principal stress in this plane is zero), it will suffer an absolute retardation but will not be broken up into two components. If the direction of observation is perpendicular to the plane of the model, the eye will see the full intensity of the scattered light as all the small particles are vibrating linearly at right angles to this direction. If the direction of observation is rotated about the wave normal of the light transmitted through the model, always being kept perpendicular to it, the little oscillators will be seen more and more end on, and the apparent amplitude of scattering will decrease with the angle from the perpendicular to the plane of the model, becoming zero for the physically impossible case of 90° or observation along the direction of vibration. The intensity of the light seen by the observer will be the same at every point of the model; it varies only with the direction of observation and, therefore, gives the orientation but no information about the magnitude of the tensile stress in the model.

Suppose now that plane-polarized light enters as in the previous case, but the direction of vibration is at 45° to the tension axis. The light will immediately be split into two components, one vibrating along the tension direction, the other along the perpendicular to the model. As each is subject to a different stress, it will be retarded by a different amount, and there will be a varying relative retardation between the two waves. Progressing along the path through the model, the originally plane-polarized light, point A, Fig. 17-83b, will become elliptically polarized; point B, then circularly polarized;

point C, (the amplitudes of the two components are equal because of the 45° angle) elliptical, then plane-polarized; point D, but at right angles to the vibration on entrance, elliptical, circular at point E, elliptical, and back to plane-polarized at point F as it was at A. If the direction of observation is again chosen as perpendicular to the plane of the model, the component of vibration along the tension direction is seen fully at all points along the path; the perpendicular component is seen end on and contributes nothing to the light

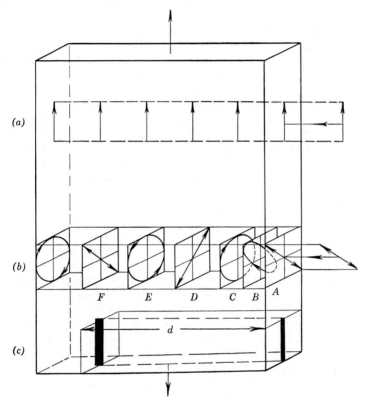

FIG. 17-83.   Fringe Formation in a Simple Tension Specimen

reaching the observer.   As before, there will be no variation in intensity along the path, and no information will be obtained about the magnitude of the stress.   If, however, the direction of observation is at 45°, that is, along the direction of the entering vibration, a fringe pattern will appear that will be a measure of the stress.   At point A the vibration is seen end on, and the point will be black, as apparently there is no emission of light.   At B the ellipse will have a small projection, and a small amount of light will be seen. At C the projection is the diameter of the circle so that the amplitude is equal to the maximum amplitude of scattering divided by $\sqrt{2}$.   The intensity, proportional to the square of the amplitude, will therefore be one-half the maximum intensity of scattering. The intensity will continue to increase to point D where the full vibration is seen. After this brightest point, the intensity decreases to one half at E and down to zero at F where the cycle starts over again. Dark points, therefore, appear at intervals over which the relative retardation is 1 wave length of the monochromatic light used. Calling this interval or fringe spacing d, we have

$$d = \frac{C}{\sigma_t} \quad \text{or} \quad \sigma_t = \frac{C}{d} \tag{125}$$

where as before C is the usual stress-optical coefficient.

If a sheet of light is used instead of a beam of small diameter, the plane of the sheet parallel to the plane of the model, dark parallel bands or fringes will appear instead of isolated points (Fig. 17-83c).

On the basis of this simple model it is clear that to obtain a fringe pattern the direction of observation must not coincide with a direction of (secondary) principal stress at all points, nor can the entering light coincide with such a direction. Note that although the clarity of the fringe pattern and also the position of the fringes change as the direction of observation is changed, the fringe spacing is always a measure of the stress.

The direction of the principal stresses can be found from the absence of a fringe pattern when the entering vibration is properly oriented, which in a sense is similar to the two-dimensional determination of isoclinics. As in the plane-stress case, this effect of orientation can be eliminated by the use of circularly polarized light and choice of a proper direction of observation.

If the direction of the principal stresses in the entering boundary vary, as they generally will in a three-dimensional problem, it is not possible to send plane-polarized light vibrating at 45° except at isolated points, but circularly polarized light entering a stressed model is always broken up into two equal components. In the case of the simple-tension model, the fringe pattern is merely shifted through a small distance, the point C or the point E moves over to point A and takes the whole pattern with it. Observation along the perpendicular to the model will again result in an absence of fringe pattern.

If we consider a general plane-stress model, instead of the simple-tension specimen, with the sheet of light in the plane of the model, the transmitted light along x is subject to secondary principal stresses σ_y and zero. This is equivalent to a state of simple tension which varies in magnitude along the path. The distance d between fringes can be calculated from

$$\Delta = 1 = \int_{x_o}^{x_o+d} \frac{\sigma_y \, dx}{C} \tag{126}$$

or the stress σ_y at some point between the two fringes one at x_o and one at $x_o + d$ is given by

$$\sigma_y = C/d \tag{127}$$

Generalizing still further, if the plane is a plane of principal stress, that is, there is a normal stress σ_z acting on the plane but no shearing stress, then the transmitted light is affected by the stresses σ_y and σ_z. The difference between them at some point intermediate between two fringes will be

$$\sigma_y - \sigma_z = C/d \qquad (128)$$

In all these elementary examples the directions of the stresses affecting the light remained constant, parallel to y and z at every point along the wave normal. In the general problem of three-dimensional analysis these directions will change continuously. A vibration along a secondary principal-stress direction follows that direction as it changes (Fig. 17-68) so that the orientation of the principal stresses can be traced through the model. The spacing between the fringes is decreased a small amount by the rotation so that the difference between the secondary principal stresses is given by

$$p - q = \frac{C}{dS} \qquad (129)$$

where as before, (equation 103) $S = \sqrt{1 + 4R^2}$ where R is the ratio of the rotation to the retardation, or $\alpha/2\pi$ where α is the total angular rotation (radians) of the secondary principal-stress directions between the two fringes spaced d apart.

(b) *Experimental Procedure.* A typical apparatus used by Weller[163] is shown in Fig. 17-84. The polarizing system is vertical and the viewing system horizontal for convenience. An intense light source is collimated by a lens system and then filtered, and a slit is placed in the parallel beam either before or after the polarizing unit. A camera is mounted in a horizontal plane and can be rotated about the axis of the polarizing system. The model is submerged in a fluid to eliminate undesirable reflections and refractions of the light on entering and leaving. The loading frame is not required when the model has the optical pattern frozen in it.

In more detail, the light source is a 1000-watt H-6 water-cooled lamp. The manufacturer will advise on the necessary auxiliary apparatus and the desirable automatic controls to avoid burning out of the lamp in case of a failure of the water supply. It is necessary to use these bright lamps because of the low intensity of scattering. The two condensing lenses are 6.5 in. in diameter, the lamp being placed at the focal point of the combination.

The filters are a combination of Wratten no. 77 with a Wratten B for photographing, the 77 alone for visual observation. Filters are needed because of the dispersion of chromatic light which produces a blur instead of fringe pattern at high orders of interference. The exposure required with a 0.1 in. slit is approximately 1 min with high-speed film. The immersion fluid is a mixture of Halowax oil and mineral oil (RD 11).

A difficulty in accurate work is that the light source is a line and not a point so that its entire length cannot be collimated. If the slit is oriented parallel to the line source, the sheet of light will contain rays at large angles to the axis of the system. These rays are acted on by different states of stress and may confuse the picture greatly. If the slit is perpendicular to the light source, the intensity is reduced markedly but the sheet of light will contain practically parallel rays. An intermediate position of the slit as a compromise is often satisfactory.

(c) *Methods of Analysis.* As in the fixation method, entire planes or regions may be investigated at one time, or the analysis may proceed point by point

Fig. 17-84. Apparatus for Scattered Light (Weller.[163] Courtesy National Advisory Committee for Aeronautics)

experimentally. Corresponding to oblique incidence would be the photographing of entire planes for different directions of the wave normal in the illuminated plane. Circularly polarized light should be used for fringe spacing; plane-polarized to obtain the orientation of the principal stresses.

In the case of plane stress, if the central plane is illuminated by a sheet of light with wave normals parallel to x, the fringe spacing will give the difference between the secondary principal stresses in the yz plane, which is perpendicular to the wave normal, $\sigma_y - \sigma_z = \sigma_y$ as σ_z is zero. Similarly σ_x could be found by sending the light in parallel to y, that is, rotate the model 90° about z. A third wave-normal direction would also be required because there are, in general, three unknowns: σ_x, σ_y, and τ_{xy} or the corresponding σ_1, σ_2, and their orientation ϕ. The accuracy would be better if the three wave normals were taken as 120° (or 60°) apart, rather than 45°.

If the illuminated plane is a plane of principal stress in a three-dimensional model, σ_z is not zero, and the three observations in the directions x, ξ, and η (Fig. 17-85), give $\sigma_x - \sigma_z$, $\sigma_y - \sigma_z$, and τ_{xy} or $\sigma_1 - \sigma_z$, $\sigma_2 - \sigma_z$, and ϕ the angle between σ_1 and the x axis. The formulas for wave normals 45° apart are

$$\sigma_1 - \sigma_z = \frac{C}{2}\left\{\left(\frac{1}{d_\xi}+\frac{1}{d_\eta}\right) + \sqrt{\left[\left(\frac{1}{d_x}-\frac{1}{d_\xi}\right)+\left(\frac{1}{d_x}-\frac{1}{d_\eta}\right)\right]^2 + \left(\frac{1}{d_\xi}-\frac{1}{d_\eta}\right)^2}\right\}$$

$$\sigma_2 - \sigma_z = \frac{C}{2}\left\{\left(\frac{1}{d_\xi}+\frac{1}{d_\eta}\right) - \sqrt{\left[\left(\frac{1}{d_x}-\frac{1}{d_\xi}\right)+\left(\frac{1}{d_x}-\frac{1}{d_\eta}\right)\right]^2 + \left(\frac{1}{d_\xi}-\frac{1}{d_\eta}\right)^2}\right\}$$

$$\tan 2\phi = \frac{\dfrac{1}{d_\xi}-\dfrac{1}{d_\eta}}{\left(\dfrac{1}{d_x}-\dfrac{1}{d_\xi}\right)+\left(\dfrac{1}{d_x}-\dfrac{1}{d_\eta}\right)} \qquad (130)$$

and, for the more accurate 60° case,

$$\sigma_1 - \sigma_z = \frac{C}{3}\left\{\left(\frac{1}{d_x}+\frac{1}{d_\xi}+\frac{1}{d_\eta}\right) \right.$$
$$\left. + \sqrt{2\left[\left(\frac{1}{d_x}-\frac{1}{d_\xi}\right)^2+\left(\frac{1}{d_\xi}-\frac{1}{d_\eta}\right)^2+\left(\frac{1}{d_\eta}-\frac{1}{d_x}\right)^2\right]}\right\}$$

$$\sigma_2 - \sigma_z = \frac{C}{3}\left\{\left(\frac{1}{d_x}+\frac{1}{d_\xi}+\frac{1}{d_\eta}\right) \right.$$
$$\left. - \sqrt{2\left[\left(\frac{1}{d_x}-\frac{1}{d_\xi}\right)^2+\left(\frac{1}{d_\xi}-\frac{1}{d_\eta}\right)^2+\left(\frac{1}{d_\eta}-\frac{1}{d_x}\right)^2\right]}\right\}$$

$$\tan 2\phi = \frac{\sqrt{3}\left(\dfrac{1}{d_\xi}-\dfrac{1}{d_\eta}\right)}{\left(\dfrac{1}{d_x}-\dfrac{1}{d_\xi}\right)+\left(\dfrac{1}{d_x}-\dfrac{1}{d_\eta}\right)} \qquad (131)$$

In all cases the fringe spacings d have sign $+$ for increasing, $-$ for decreasing fringe order in the direction of travel of the light. The correction factor S does not enter into these formulas, because the directions of secondary principal stress along the wave normal remain constant.

The accuracy of the result for the principal-stress differences depends on the accuracy of determination of the fringe spacing and direction of the wave normal. A microphotometer trace of the photographic plate can be used to give spacing precisely if required, and a small error in angle will not have much effect.

If nothing is known about the state of stress, five measurements must be made to determine the five photoelastic quantities $\sigma_x - \sigma_z$, $\sigma_y - \sigma_z$, τ_{xy}, τ_{yz}, τ_{zx} or $\sigma_1 - \sigma_2$, $\sigma_1 - \sigma_3$ and the orientation of the principal stresses.

The procedure analogous to that proposed for the fixation method is to use three directions of the wave normal in a single plane and, in addition, determine the orientations of the secondary principal stresses. The alternative method, for the slice, of oblique incidence in two planes is not convenient here because information is obtained about only one line in the plane of interest instead of the entire plane.

It is possible to increase accuracy at points of low stress by a method similar to the use of a compensator for two-dimensional models. Accurate retardation plates can be inserted between the polarizing unit and the model to shift the fringe pattern a known amount. Their axes would most conveniently

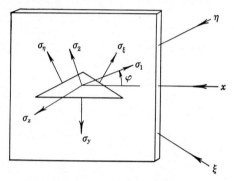

FIG. 17-85.   Analysis of a Plane of Principal Stress[*][8]

σ_z is perpendicular to the plane; ξ and η are conveniently at 45° or 60° to x

coincide with the axes of principal stress on entrance to the model which will usually require a line-by-line exploration rather than a true plane by plane. The equivalent of dark- and light-field photographs can be taken either by rotation of the camera through 90° about the axis of the polarizing system or, more simply, by reversing the direction of the entering circularly polarized light. These methods are useful in the determination of boundary stresses also.

Two point-by-point methods have been proposed for the analysis of models with scattered light. One is Weller's suggestion of universal rotation of the model to determine by trial and error in a systematic way when the fringe spacing at the point of interest is a minimum. The other by Menges[152] is to determine the ellipse of polarization at neighboring points along the wave normal with a photometer mounted in place of a camera so that it can be rotated about the wave normal as an axis and use a graphical solution of equations 104. Saleme[167] advocates similar measurements. There is no apparent advantage in such a method from the viewpoint of convenience or accuracy over either universal rotation or plane-by-plane methods. The scattering background is a complicating factor in such an analysis.

(d) *Advantages and Disadvantages of the Scattering Method.* If scattering is compared with physical slicing, the advantage is that the model is not destroyed. However, the intensity of light is low, especially in regions far from the point of entrance.

If the large distortions of the fixation method are not permissible, the scattering procedure can be used on an elastically deformed model, but it has the disadvantage of requiring observation with a loading device in place which may interfere with the most desirable procedure of analysis.

At present it would be possible to analyze steady-state vibrations by scattering and possibly eventually to analyze transients if still more intense light sources and more sensitive photographic materials are developed.

Combination of this optical method of slicing or probing and actual physical slicing is often advantageous.

R. ILLUSTRATIVE APPLICATIONS

53. Similarity of Model and Prototype. The subject of similarity is discussed in detail in the appendix, part II, by Professor Goodier and should be thoroughly understood by all experimenters. In very brief summary, complete similarity requires that all dimensionless variables and dimensionless combinations of variables be the same in model and prototype. Geometric combinations require that models be made to scale, a condition that usually is not too troublesome. However, stress (or load divided by some area) and Young's modulus have the same dimensions and, therefore, must be in the same ratio for model and prototype in the general case. Compliance with this requirement is not desirable because of the low modulus of most photoelastic materials. Even BT-61-893, which is one of the best materials available has a modulus only $\frac{1}{45}$ that of steel. If the maximum stress in the steel is to be kept below 20,000 psi, the maximum stress in the bakelite model would have to be below 450 psi, and the resulting birefringence would be very weak and correspondingly difficult to determine. Fortunately, if the problem is a linear one, that is, stress at all points is proportional to load, and most practical problems are, this limitation on the stress in the model no longer holds. However, if contact stress is involved and is significant in the experiment, linearity does not exist, and the ratio of stress to modulus must be adhered to. More accurate methods of measurement will often have to be employed. Another troublesome quantity in three-dimensional work is Poisson's ratio which is dimensionless, and should have the same value for the model material as for the prototype. As there are so few suitable photoelastic materials presently available, it is generally not possible to satisfy this requirement. Little is known about the effect of this neglect.

54. Typical Studies. Frocht has investigated several fundamental and practical problems of stress concentration with the fixation and slicing procedure. His excellent photographs and agreement with theory[138-141] demonstrate conclusively that good accuracy and useful results can be obtained with the proper technique.

Hetényi was the first to make successful application of the fixation method to the solution of industrial problems. He has analyzed the stress distribution in threaded fastenings[145] and the centrifugal stresses in rotating disks.[91, 144]

Work along similar lines has been carried out by Newton[118] on rotating disks and Meriam[153] on a supercharger impeller.

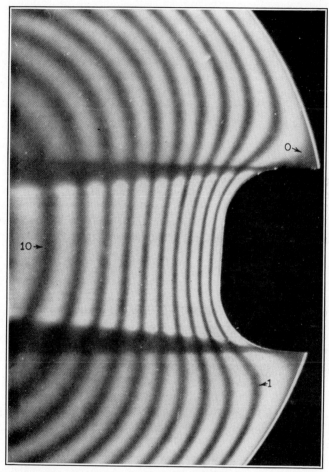

FIG. 17-86. Scattered Pattern of Transverse Section of Fosterite Shaft with Keyway in Pure Torsion

Thickness of slice = 0.110 in.; D = 3.00 in. Slice immersed in Halowax oil no. 1000; 100-watt H-4 mercury-vapor lamp; exposure time 3 min at $f5.6$. Plane-polarized light

A number of fundamental problems were investigated by Weller to show the practicability of the scattering procedure,[163, 164] but there are few reports of other experimental work. Frigon[137] and also Drucker and Frocht[165] have studied the torsion of prismatic bars, and Rosenberg has analyzed shrink fits.[159]   However, no one has published truly well-defined scattering patterns comparable in clarity to the fringe photographs obtained in two-dimensional photoelastic analysis, until the very recent photographs of Leven,[177] Fig. 17-86.

55. Special Solutions.   The fundamental ideas of three-dimensional photoelasticity can be applied in special cases to obtain solutions where ordinary methods fail or are exceedingly cumbersome.   For example, the photoelastic analysis of the transverse bending of plates, previously discussed, can be carried out with an ordinary transmission polariscope[135] simply by starting

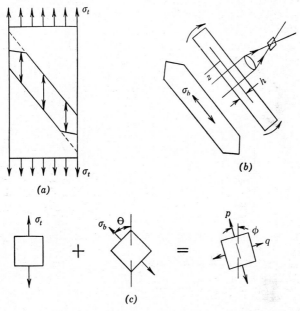

FIG. 17-87.   Superposition of Bending on Initial Frozen Tension[135]

with a plate of thermosetting material in which a state of uniaxial tension has been frozen (Fig. 17-87).   The model is then cut from this larger plate at some angle Θ to the direction of the tension.   When this smaller plate is placed in a polariscope and bent transversely, it will be found that the fringe order appearing on the screen will increase as the bending moment increases although not in direct proportion.   The tension side in bending no longer cancels the compression side.

The basic physical reason for this useful fact is shown in Fig. (17-88). When there is no frozen tension, the direction of the principal stresses through the thickness of the plate remains constant, and the compression side presents a picture which is simply the negative of the tension side and nullifies it. The frozen tension, on the other hand, produces a continuous change in the direction of the principal stresses through the thickness.   The light vector follows this change in direction, and, therefore, the canceling effect disappears.

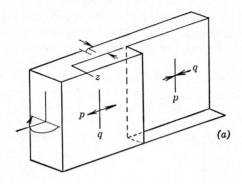

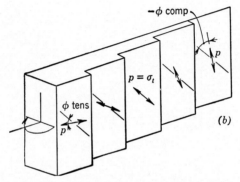

Fig. 17-88. Bending without (a) and with (b) Frozen Tension σ_t[135]

The following relations are easily derived:

$$\Delta = \Delta_t F \left[\frac{(\sigma_1 - \sigma_2)_m}{\sigma_t} \Theta \right]$$

$$\tan 2\phi_{\text{tens}} = \frac{\dfrac{(\sigma_1 - \sigma_2)_m}{\sigma_t} \sin 2\Theta}{1 + \dfrac{(\sigma_1 - \sigma_2)_m}{\sigma_t} \cos 2\Theta}$$

$$\tan 2\phi_{\text{comp}} = \frac{\dfrac{-(\sigma_1 - \sigma_2)_m}{\sigma_t} \sin 2\Theta}{1 - \dfrac{(\sigma_1 - \sigma_2)_m}{\sigma_t} \cos 2\Theta}$$

$$\sin 2\Theta = \frac{\left[\dfrac{(\sigma_1 - \sigma_2)_m}{\sigma_t} \right]^2 - 1}{2 \dfrac{(\sigma_1 - \sigma_2)_m}{\sigma_t}} \tan 2(\phi_{\text{comp}} - \phi_{\text{tens}}) \qquad (132)$$

where Δ is the fringe order observed when the plate is bent and Δ_t is the fringe order fixed at the start, $\Delta_t = \sigma_t \times$ plate thickness$/C$. F, a function of the ratio of the maximum bending-stress difference to the equivalent initial tension, $(\sigma_1 - \sigma_2)_m/\sigma_t$, and of the smallest angle between the frozen tensile stress and either of the bending stresses, is plotted as Fig. 17-89. Values of Θ from $0°$ to $45°$ are sufficient, as $\pm\Theta$, $\pm(90 - \Theta)$ all lead to the same F. ϕ_{tens} is the angle between the algebraically larger principal stress p and the frozen tension direction on the tension side of the bent plate, and ϕ_{comp} is the angle between the rotated p direction and the frozen tension on the compression side.

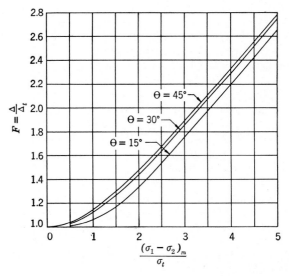

FIG. 17-89. Bending of Plates Retardation as a Function of the Ratio of the Maximum Principal Bending Stress Difference to the Initial Tension and of the Angle between the Tension and Either Principal Bending Stress

Various experimental procedures can be worked out on the basis of the equations. Measurement of retardation and of orientation on entrance and on leaving the model can easily be made. If Θ is known, as it will be at many important points (free boundaries, axes of symmetry, and regions away from disturbance), a measurement of retardation determines the maximum bending-stress difference. If Θ is not known, two measurements must be made. The most convenient and accurate method is to measure the retardation and the change in orientation of the principal stress, $\phi_{comp} - \phi_{tens}$, although measurement of ϕ_{comp} and ϕ_{tens} individually is sufficient. However, independent rotation of the polarizer and the analyzer of a plane polariscope is required to obtain complete extinction of the light at a general point; the polarizer must pass light vibrating in a principal-stress direction on entrance to the model and the analyzer stop light vibrating in the rotated position of this principal direction on exit (Fig. 17-68). At points where the retardation

Δ is a whole number, $\phi_{comp} - \phi_{tens}$, on the other hand, is found very simply, as there is some position of the analyzer which will extinguish the light for each position of the polarizer. Therefore, the change in direction of the principal stress is found by keeping the polarizer fixed and recording the change in analyzer extinction position from the crossed position without a model, an even simpler procedure than for the isoclinics in a two-dimensional case.

Figure 17-89 shows that Θ may be considerably in error without appreciably affecting the result for the magnitude of the bending-stress difference so that the accuracy that can be obtained is close to that for photoelastic analysis of plane stress.

As in plane-stress analysis, accurate clear fringe photographs can be obtained[135] for the entire model, a great advantage over point-by-point methods.

A similar procedure can be used, although not so conveniently, for bars in torsion for directions in which the shearing stress varies linearly with the distance from the axis of the bar. However, it is easily shown that the scattering fringes obtained with any cross-sectional sheet of light correspond exactly to the contour lines of membrane analogy.[165] Therefore, other photoelastic methods are neither so general nor so convenient.

S. Remarks on the Present and Future State of the Art

The art of three-dimensional photoelasticity is still in its infancy. Unlike the electrical resistance gage, the war years have given relatively little impetus to its development. Full-scale testing of aircraft, for example, required the gage but not photoelasticity. It seems reasonable that model analysis will be more fully utilized in all fields when cost of production as well as large volume becomes important again. This will certainly mean an extended use of photoelastic analysis.

It is to be expected that there will be a very great increase in the number of investigations using the stress-freezing or fixation method as soon as heat-hardening plastics are fully developed which can be cast into fairly large and complicated shapes without initial optical effect. Resins such as Kryston are a significant step in this direction. Under these conditions, in fact, it is quite probable that it will become standard practice to so analyze and redesign all highly stressed castings that are to be produced in very large quantity or which are individually very expensive. Such a plastic with good scattering properties would similarly provide the necessary stimulus to analysis by the scattering method.

Unfortunately, three-dimensional photoelasticity requires a much greater knowledge of the theory of elasticity and of optics than does two-dimensional work. Also, the experimental technique is much more difficult because the information sought for is generally a complex and not a simple state of stress. The adequate training of technicians is, therefore, a considerably longer process.

However, there are many fundamental problems which are too involved or for which it would be too time-consuming to obtain solutions by elastic theory. Among these are some of the problems of stress concentration in bodies with three-dimensional discontinuities (holes, fillets, or notches) and the associated practical consideration of the proper type and depth of surface or general treatment. More than just surface information is required, and three-dimensional photoelastic methods will probably provide the answer.

BIBLIOGRAPHY

GENERAL REFERENCES

1. E. G. COKER AND L. N. G. FILON, *A Treatise on Photoelasticity*, Cambridge Univ Press, London, 1931. Contains a comprehensive development of fundamental theory, graphical and analytical methods, apparatus, and numerous applications to specific problems.
2. L. N. G. FILON, *A Manual of Photoelasticity for Engineers*, Cambridge Univ Press, London, 1936. Very much abridged version of Ref 1.
3. M. M. FROCHT, *Photoelasticity*, v 1 and 2, John Wiley & Sons, New York, 1941, 1948. Well-illustrated modern textbooks on practical two- and three-dimensional photoelastic analysis. Contain many excellent detailed examples of specific methods of analysis.
4. N. ALEXANDER, *Photoelasticity*, Rhode Island State College, Kingston, R I, 1936. Elementary text for undergraduate students outlining basic theory and technique.
5. R. D. MINDLIN, "A Review of the Photoelastic Method of Stress Analysis," *J Applied Physics*, v 10, Apr 1939, pp 222–41 and May 1939, pp 273–94. An excellent concise summary of photoelastic methods and applications; includes an extensive bibliography.
6. E. E. WEIBEL, "Developments in Photoelasticity," *Stephen Timoshenko 60th Anniversary Volume*, Macmillan Co, 1938, pp 257–67. A brief outline of methods, materials, equipment, and applications.
7. S. TIMOSHENKO AND G. H. MacCULLOUGH, *Elements of Strength of Materials*, D. Van Nostrand Co, New York, 1940, Ch 13.
8. *J Applied Physics* (a) v 10, n 4, Apr 1939; (b) v 10, n 5, May 1939; (c) v 12, n 8, Aug 1941. (a) and (b) contain a variety of articles on several phases of photoelasticity. (c) contains six papers presented at the 11th Eastern Photoelasticity Conference.
9. *Proc 9th, 10th, 13th, 14th, 15th, 16th Eastern Photoelasticity Conf*, 1939–42, Addison–Wesley Press, Cambridge, Mass. Articles covering many phases of methods and applications.

In French

10. H. L. SUPPER, "Photoélasticimétrie et apsidométrie," *Publications scientifiques et techniques du Ministère de l'air*, n 106, Paris, 1937.
11. P. HEYMANS, G. BOTHY, *Photoélasticimetrie*, Brussells, 1921.
12. PIERRE LAURENT AND A. POPOFF, "La photoélasticité. Principes, methodes, et applications," *Révue de métallurgie*, Aug 1938, p 363; Sept 1938, p 407; Oct 1938, p. 448.
13. H. LeBOITEUX AND R. BOUSSARD, *Élasticité et photoélasticimétrie*, Hermann & Cie, Paris, 1940.
14. M. BRICAS, *La Théorie de l'Élasticité bidimensionnelle*, Pyrsos, Athens, 1936.
15. A. J. DURELLI, *Contribution a'l étude du Béton traité—Essai Photoélasticimétrique*, Thesis, Univ Paris, 1936. Contains good bibliography of French, English, German, Spanish, and Italian references.

In Spanish

16. Raul Buich, *La Investigacíon de las Tensiónes, Elásticas Mediante La Lyz Polarizáda*, Thesis, University Press, Buenos Aires, 1929.

In German

17. L. Föppl and H. Neuber, *Festigkeitslehre Mittels Spannungsoptik*, R. Oldenbourg, Berlin, 1935.
18. G. Mesmer, *Spannungsoptik*, Julius Springer, Berlin, 1939.

OPTICS AND POLARISCOPES

19. J. K. Robertson, *Introduction to Physical Optics*, D. Van Nostrand Co, New York, 1929.
20. F. A. Jenkins and H. E. White, *Fundamentals of Physical Optics*, McGraw-Hill Book Co, New York, 1937.　References 19 and 20 are complete texts on optics and cover basic theories of polarization and double refraction.
21. R. D. Mindlin, "Distortion of Photoelastic Fringe Pattern in an Optically Unbalanced Polariscope," *J Applied Mechanics, Trans ASME*, v 4, n 4, pp A-170–72, Dec 1937.　Effect of inaccuracies in quarter-wave plates on the isochromatic-fringe pattern.
22. R. D. Mindlin, "A Reflection Polariscope for Photoelastic Analysis," *Rev Sci Inst*, v 5, n 6, pp 224–28, June 1934.　Presents the optical arrangement and basic theory of the reflection polariscope in which the polarizer also acts as the analyzer.

INTERPRETATION OF PHOTOELASTIC OBSERVATIONS

23. S. Timoshenko, *Theory of Elasticity*, McGraw-Hill Book Co, New York, 1934, pp 123–26.
24. S. Timoshenko, *Strength of Materials*, pt 2, D. Van Nostrand Co, New York, 1930, pp 641–45.
25. Wm. MacGregor Murray, "Seeing Stresses with Photoelasticity," *Metal Progress*, v 39, n 2, pp 195–200, Feb 1941.
26. R. E. Orton, "Photoelastic Analysis in Commercial Practice," pt 1, *Machine Design*, v 12, n 3, p 33, March 1940, and continued in April and May issues. References 23 to 26 contain simplified presentations of general photoelastic methods and interpretation of fringe patterns.
27. M. Sadowsky. "Classification of Isotropic Points as Defined by $\sigma_1 - \sigma_2 = 0$ within a Regular Region," *J Applied Physics*, v 12, Aug 1941, pp 605–09. Mathematical investigation of the network of isostatics around an isotropic point.
28. R. W. Goranson and L. H. Adams, "A Method for the Precise Measurement of Optical Path–Difference, Especially in Stressed Glass," *J Franklin Inst*, v 216, n 4, pp 475–504 Oct 1933.　Rotation of analyser.
29. A. J Durelli, "Distribution of Stresses in Partial Compression," pt 4, *Proc 13th Eastern Photoelasticity Conf*, 1941, pp 42–5.　Rotation of analyzer.
30. H. L. Tardy, "Methode pratique d'examen et de la birefringence des verres d'optique," *Revue d'optique*, v 8, 1929, pp 59–69.　References 28 to 30 present methods of determining retardation by rotation of the analyzer.

DETERMINATION OF STRESSES AT INTERIOR POINTS

Lateral Extensometers

31. E. E. Weibel, "Characteristics of Lateral Extensometers," *Proc 16th Eastern Photoelasticity Conference*, 1942, p 47.
32. R. W. Vose, "An Application of the Interferometer Strain Gage in Photoelasticity," *J Applied Mechanics, Trans ASME*, v 2, n 3, p A-99, Sept 1935.

Deformations measured by interference fringes in reflection from two optical flats on gage frame.

33. H. E. DAVIS, G. E. TROXELL, AND C. T. WISKOCIL, *Testing and Inspection of Engineering Materials*, McGraw-Hill Book Co, New York, 1941, pp 59 and 65.

34. A. V. DE FOREST AND A. R. ANDERSON, "A New Lateral Extensometer," *Proc 10th Eastern Photoelasticity Conf*, 1939, p 31.   See also *J Applied Mechanics*, v 3, n 4, p A-152, Dec 1941.   Deformations measured by wire-resistance gages on a U-shaped frame.

35. R. E. PETERSON AND A. M. WAHL, "Fatigue of Shafts at Fitted Members with a Related Photoelastic Analysis," *J Applied Mechanics, Trans ASME*, v 2, n 1, p A-1, Mar 1935.   Lateral extensometer employing Huggenberger tensometer.

36. R. J. SCHAID, *Development of an Interferometer Strain Gage*, Master of Science Thesis, Northwestern Univ, 1947.   An improved transmission-type interferometer gage with partially reflecting optical flats.

Shear-Difference Method

37. M. S. KETCHUM, "Procedures for Recording Data and Calculating Internal Stresses by the Photoelastic Method," *Proc 10th Eastern Photoelasticity Conf*, 1939, p 1.

38. M. M. FROCHT, "The Shear Difference Method," *Proc 13th Eastern Photoelasticity Conf*, 1941, p 51.

Membrane Analogy

39. S. TIMOSHENKO, *Theory of Elasticity*, McGraw-Hill Book Co, New York, 1934, Articles 38 and 76.

40. J. G. McGIVERN AND H. L. SUPPER, "A Membrane Analogy Supplementing Photoelasticity," *J Franklin Inst*, v 217, Apr 1934, p 491.   See also *Trans ASME*, v 56, n 8, APM 56–9, p 601, Aug 1934.

41. E. E. WEIBEL, "Studies in Photoelastic Stress Determination," *Trans ASME*, v 56, 1934, pp 637–58.

42. D. H. PLETTA AND F. J. MAHER, "The Torsional Properties of Round Edged Flat Bars," *Bul Va Polytechnic Inst* Eng Exp Sta 50, v 35, n 7, Mar 1942.

43. C. G. VREEDENBURGH, "Eenige experimenteele Onderzoekingens-Methoden in de Mechanica," *De Ingenieur*, v 45, n 43, pp A-392–397, October 24, 1930.

Method of Iteration

44. G. H. SHORTLEY AND R. WELLER, "Calculation of Stresses within the Boundary of Photoelastic Models," *J Applied Mechanics, Trans ASME*, v 6, n 2, p A-71, June 1939.   Discusses procedures for increasing speed and accuracy of numerical solution for sum of principal stresses.

45. G. H. SHORTLEY, R. WELLER, AND B. FRIED, "Numerical Solution of Laplace's and Poisson's Equations," *Ohio State Univ Studies*, Eng Series v 9, n 5, *Eng Exp Sta Bull* 107, Sept 1940.

46. M. M. FROCHT AND M. M. LEVEN, "A Rational Approach to the Numerical Solution of Laplace's Equation," *J Applied Physics*, v 12, n 8, p 596, August 1941.

47. C. E. GROSSER, "Determination of the Sum of Principal Stresses by Graphical and Mechanical Means," *Proc 15th Eastern Photoelasticity Conf*, 1942, p 43.

Filon's Graphical Integration

48. E. G. COKER AND L. N. G. FILON, *Treatise on Photoelasticity*, Cambridge Univ Press, London, 1931, Articles 2.29–2.31.

49. L. N. G. FILON, *A Manual of Photoelasticity for Engineers*, Cambridge Univ Press, London, 1936, Articles 3.06, 3.09, and 3.10.

50. M. M. Frocht, *Photoelasticity*, v 1, ch 2 and 9, John Wiley & Sons, New York, 1941.

51. H. Neuber, "New Method of Determining Stresses Graphically from Photoelastic Observations," *Proc Royal Soc (Lond.)*, v 131, 1933, p 314.

52. H. Neuber, "Exact Construction of ($\sigma_1 + \sigma_2$) Network from Photoelastic Observations," *Trans ASME*, v 56, 1934, p 733.

MATERIALS, MODELS, AND EQUIPMENT

53. R. A. Frigon, "Report of the Eastern Photoelasticity Conference Committee on Materials Research," *Proc 13th Eastern Photoelasticity Conf*, 1941, pp 62–66. Lists properties of the most suitable photoelastic materials for models.

54. F. B. Farquharson and R. G. Hennes, "Gelatin Models for Photoelastic Analysis of Stress in Earth Masses," *Civil Eng*, v 10, n 4, p 211–14, 1940.

55. E. E. Weibel, "Studies in Photoelastic Stress Determination," *Trans ASME*, v 56, n 8, pp 637–58, 1934. Describes apparatus for studies of stresses in fillets and presents data on properties of Phenolite and C-25 Bakelite.

56. G. H. Lee and C. W. Armstrong, "Effect of Temperature on Physical and Optical Properties of Photoelastic Materials," *J Applied Mechanics, Trans ASME*, v 5, n 1, pp A-11–12, 1938. Variation in mechanical properties of Marblette and Bakelites at temperatures ranging from 32° to 140°F.

57. R. H. G. Edmonds and B. T. McMinn, "Celluloid as a Medium for Photoelastic Investigation," *Univ Washington Eng Exp Sta Bul* 63, 1932. Characteristics of celluloid.

58. M. Hetényi, "The Fundamentals of Three-Dimensional Photoelasticity," *J Applied Mechanics, Trans ASME*, v 5, n 4, pp A-149–155, 1938 (also discussion, v 6, pp A-133–35). Describes properties and "fixation" procedure for Bakelite at elevated temperature. Test results and photographs show that the diphase theory is in accord with experiment. See also *Proc 5th Int Congress Applied Mechanics*, 1938, John Wiley & Sons, New York, pp 208–12.

59. W. Leaf, "The Time Edge Effect: Its Cause and Prevention," *Proc 15th Eastern Photoelasticity Conf*, 1942, pp 20–2.

60. W. Leaf, "Additional Data on the Time Edge Effect," *Proc 16th Eastern Photoelasticity Conf*, 1942, pp 31–4.

61. W. N. Findley, "The Load Resisting Properties of Cellulose Acetate," *Proc 16th Eastern Photoelasticity Conf*, 1942, pp 16–9.

62. A. G. Solakian, "A New Photoelastic Material," *Mech Eng*, v 57, n 12, pp 767–71, December 1935. Discusses properties of Marblette for models.

63. R. B. Carleton, "Suitability of Materials for Photoelastic Investigation," *Rev Sci Instr*, v 5, n 1, pp 30–2, 1934.

64. T. R. Cuykendall, "Gelatin Models," *Proc 9th Eastern Photoelasticity Conf*, May 1939, pp 13–7.

64a. D. J. Coolidge, Jr., "An Investigation of the Mechanical and Stress-Optical Properties of Columbia Resin CR-39," *Proc Exp Stress Analysis*, v 6, n 1, pp 74–82.

65. *Wratten Light Filters*, Eastman Kodak Co, 16th ed, revised, Rochester, NY, 1940, p 12. See also: *Glass Color Filters*, Corning Glass Works, Corning, NY.

66. M. Grabau, *Introduction to Polarized Light and Its Application*, Polaroid Corp, Cambridge, Mass, 1940.

67. Z. Tuzi and M. Nisida, "On a New Apparatus for Photoelasticity—Stress-Type Quarter-Wave Plate of Large Field," *Sci Papers Inst of Phys and Chem Research*, Tokyo, v 31, n 676, pp 99–107, 1937. Uses stressed-glass plate for quarter-wave plate.

68. Z. Tuzi and H. Oosima, "On the Artificial Quarter-Wave Plate for Photoelasticity Apparatus, and Its Theory," *Sci Papers Inst Phys Chem Research*, Tokyo, v 36, n 905, p 72, 1939.

69. M. L. Price, "Preparation of Photoelastic Models," *Proc 9th Eastern Photo-*

elasticity Conf, 1939, p 23. Details of apparatus and procedures used in one laboratory.

70. A. CALDWELL, "Photoelasticity and Design of Apparatus," *J Royal Tech College*, v 4, pt 3, Jan 1939, p 501.

SUPPLEMENTARY OPTICAL METHODS

71. H. FAVRE, "Sur une Nouvelle Méthode optique de détermination des tensions interieures," *Revue d'optique*, v 8, n 5, 6, 7; May, June, July; 1929, p 193 and p 241.

72. J. H. A. BRAHTZ AND J. E. SOEHRENS, "Direct Optical Measurement of Individual Principal Stresses," *J Applied Physics*, v 10, n 4, p 242, Apr 1939. References 71 and 72 describe Favre's interferometer method.

73. J. H. A. BRAHTZ AND J. R. BRUGGEMAN, "The Bureau of Reclamation Photoelastic Laboratory," *Proc 13th Eastern Photoelasticity Conf*, 1941, p 67. Describes polariscopes, interferometer, compensaters, membrane analogy, and other supplementary equipment at the Bureau of Reclamation.)

74. D. C. DRUCKER, "Photoelastic Separation of Principal Stresses by Oblique Incidence," *J Applied Mechanics, Trans ASME*, v 10, n 3, pp A-156–60, Sept 1943. See also: M. M. FROCHT, Discussion of Ref 74, *J Applied Mechanics*, v 11, n 2, p A-125, June 1944. Demonstrates the applicability of the oblique-incidence method by use of a plane-stress model. High accuracy is obtained under favorable conditions.

75. C. FABRY, "Sur une Nouvelle Méthode poùr l'étude expérimentale des tensions élastiques," *Comptes rendus*, Paris, v 190, 1930, pp 457–60.

76. D. SINCLAIR AND P. B. BUCKY, "Photoelasticity and Its Application to Mine–Pillar and Tunnel Problems," *Am Inst Mining and Met Eng Tech Publ* 1140, Jan 1940.

77. D. SINCLAIR, "A New Optical Method for the Determination of the Principal Stress Sum," *Proc 10th Eastern Photoelasticity Conf*, 1939, pp 8–16.

78. M. M. FROCHT, "On the Optical Determination of Isopachic Stress Patterns," *Proc 5th Int Congress Applied Mechanics*, John Wiley & Sons, New York, 1939, p 221. See also: M. M. FROCHT, "Isopachic Stress Patterns," *J Applied Physics*, v 10, n 4, p 248, Apr 1939.

79. H. B. MARIS, "Photoelastic Investigations of the Tensile Test Specimen, the Notched Bar, the Ship Propeller Strut, and the Roller Path Ring," *J Optical Soc of America*, v 15, 1927, pp 194–200.

APPLICATIONS OF PHOTOELASTICITY TO SPECIFIC PROBLEMS

Localized Stresses in Regular Geometric Shapes

80. R. V. BAUD, "Fillet Profiles for Constant Stress," *Prod Eng*, Apr 1934, p 133. Fillet stresses reduced by adding a spiral to the circular contour.

81. A. J. DURELLI AND W. M. MURRAY, "Stress Distribution around a Circular Discontinuity in Any Two-Dimensional System of Combined Stress," *Proc 14th Eastern Photoelasticity Conf*, Dec 1941, pp 21–36.

82. A. J. DURELLI AND W. M. MURRAY, "Stress Distribution around an Elliptical Discontinuity in Any Two-Dimensional, Uniform and Axial, System of Combined Stress," *Proc Soc Exp Stress Analysis*, v 1, n 1, p 19.

83. T. J. DOLAN, "Influence of Certain Variables on the Stresses in Gear Teeth," *J Applied Physics*, v 12, Aug 1941, pp 584–91. Variation in stresses at fillet caused by altering flank angle, load position, fillet radius, etc.

84. T. J. DOLAN AND R. E. LEVINE, "A Study of the Stresses in Curved Beams," *Proc 13th Eastern Photoelasticity Conf*, June 1941, pp 90–8. Maximum stresses produced by combined axial and bending loads.

85. M. M. FROCHT, "Factors of Stress Concentration Photoelastically Determined," *J Applied Mechanics, Trans ASME*, v 2, n 2, p A-67, June 1935, Localized stresses at fillets, holes, or grooves, in tension or bending.

86. R. E. Peterson and A. M. Wahl, "Two- and Three-Dimensional Cases of Stress Concentration and Comparison with Fatigue Tests," *J Applied Mechanics, Trans ASME*, v 3, 1936, pp A-15–22. Holes and fillets in shafting.
87. A. M. Wahl and R. Beeuwkes, "Stress Concentration Produced by Holes and Notches," *Trans ASME*, v 56, 1934, pp 617–25.
88. E. E. Weibel, "Studies in Photoelastic Stress Determination," *Trans ASME*, v 56, 1934, pp 637–58. Fillets in tension and bending; also utilizes membrane analogy.

Design of Machine Parts

89 F. H Boor and E. O. Stitz, "Stress Distribution in Spur Gear Teeth," *Proc Soc Exp Stress Analysis*, v 3, n 2, pp 28–39.
90. T. J. Dolan and E. L. Broghamer, "A Study of the Stresses in Gear Tooth Fillets," *Proc 14th Eastern Photoelasticity Conf*, Dec 1941, pp 1–14.
91. M. Hetényi, "Some Applications of Photoelasticity in Turbine-Generator Design," *J Applied Mechanics, Trans ASME*, v 61, Dec 1939, pp A-151–55. Stress in a rotor is investigated by the fixation method.
92. O. J. Horger and T. V. Buckwalter, "Photoelasticity as Applied to Design Problems," *Iron Age*, May 23, 1940, pp 42–9. General applications to rollers, press fits, and localized stresses.
93. C. Lipson, "Application of Photoelasticity to Automotive Engineering," *Proc 13th Eastern Photoelasticity Conf*, June 1941, pp 105–12. Apparatus for examination of miscellaneous parts.
94. S. Oldberg and C. Lipson, "Structural Evolution of a Crankshaft," *Proc Soc Exp Stress Analysis*, v 2, n 2, pp 118–38, 1944. Contains some photoelastic analyses of crankshafts.
95. R. E. Orton, "Photoelasticity as a Designer's Tool," *Proc Soc Exp Stress Analysis*, v 2, n 1, pp 32–9, 1944. Applications to curved links and forming dies.
96. R. E. Peterson and A. M. Wahl, "Fatigue of Shafts at Fitted Members with a Related Photoelastic Analysis," *J Applied Mechanics, Trans ASME*, v 57, 1935, pp A-1–11.
97. A. G. Solakian and G. B. Karelitz, "Photoelastic Study of Shearing Stresses in Keys and Keyways," *Trans ASME*, v 54, 1931, pp 97–123.
98. E. E. Weibel and W. B. Coolbaugh, "Stresses and Torsional Resistance of Non-Circular Press Fitted Members," *Proc 13th Eastern Photoelasticity Conf*, June 1941, pp 126–30.
99. T. J. Dolan and Rex L. Brown, "An Investigation of Wrought Steel Railway Car Wheels," *Univ Ill Eng Exp Sta Bul* 312, Aug 1939.

Stresses in Structures

100. J. H. A. Brahtz, "Photoelastic Determination of Stress," *Trans ASCE*, v 102, 1937, pp 1227–238. General discussion of applications to structures.
101. A. H. Beyer and A. G. Solakian, "Photoelastic Analysis of Stresses in Composite Materials," *Trans ASCE*, v 99, 1934, pp 1196–1211. Tests of a model of a reinforced-concrete beam.
102. M. M. Frocht, "The Place of Photoelasticity in the Analysis of Statically Indeterminate Structures," *Carnegie Inst Tech Eng Bul*, 1938, 53 pp.
103. M. M. Frocht, "A Photoelastic Investigation of Shear and Bending Stresses in Centrally Loaded Simple Beams," *Carnegie Inst Tech, Eng Bul*, 1937, 20 pp.
104. D. P. Krynine, "Photoelasticity in Foundation Studies," *Proc 14th Eastern Photoelasticity Conf*, December 1941, pp 42–6. Discusses precautions and limitations of photoelastic applications to foundations.
105. J. J. Polivka, "Use of Photoelasticity in the Analysis of Hyperstatic Structures," *Proc 13th Eastern Photoelasticity Conf*, June 1941, pp 57–61.

106. E. G. Coker and R. Russell, "Stress Distributions in Fusion Joints of Plates Connected at Right Angles," Institution of Naval Architects, v 5, 1933, pp 1–8.
107. J. E. Soehrens, R. T. Cass, and J. E. Sower, "Photoelastic Analysis of Twin Concrete Conduit, Bull Lake Dam Outlet Works," Civil Eng Sept 1936, p 594.
108. A. G. Solakian, "Photoelastic Analysis of Stress in the Lap Plates of Fillet Welded Joints," Welding J, Sept 1939.
109. F. E. Richart, T. A. Olson, and T. J. Dolan, "Tests of Reinforced Concrete Knee Frames and Bakelite Models," Univ Ill Eng Exp Sta Bul 307, 1938. Analyses of stresses in frames simulating the action of the upper corners of a rigid-frame bridge.

Aircraft Frames

110. H. Becker, "Photoelastic Analysis of a Spar Bulkhead in a Semi-Monocoque Airplane Fuselage," Proc Soc Exp Stress Analysis, v 4, n 1, pp 36–48.
111. T. J. Dolan and D. G. Richards, "A Photoelastic Study of the Stresses in Wing Ribs," J Aeronautical Sciences, v 7, n 8, pp 340–46, June 1940.
112. B. F. Ruffner, "Stress Analysis of Monocoque Fuselage Bulkheads by the Photoelastic Method," Nat Advisory Commit for Aeronautics Tech Note 870, Dec 1942.
113. B. F. Ruffner and C. L. Schmidt, "Stresses at Cut-outs in Shear Resistant Webs as Determined by the Photoelastic Method," Nat Advisory Commit for Aeronautics Tech Note 984, Oct 1945.
114. G. Mesmer, "Andwendung des Spannungsoptischen Verfahrens im Luftfahrzeugbau," Yahrbuch der Lilienthal Gesellschaft für Luftfahrtforschung, 1936, pp 147–53. Analysis of stress around a hole in a box beam with built-up plastic model and reflection-type polariscope.

Dynamics and Transient Stresses

115. M. M. Frocht, "Kinematography in Photoelasticity," Trans ASME, v 54, 1939, pp 54–9. Photographic records of fluctuating stresses due to impact.
116. T. H. Frost and K. F. Whitcomb, "The Stresses in Rotating Disks," Trans ASME, v 53, 1931, pp 1–11.
117. W. M. Murray, "A Photoelastic Study in Vibrations," J Applied Physics, v 12, Aug 1941, pp 617–22. Forced vibrations of a cantilever beam.
118. R. E. Newton, "A Photoelastic Study of the Stresses in Rotating Disks," J Applied Mechanics, Trans ASME, v 62, 1940, pp A-57–60. Fixation technique applied to the determination of centrifugal stresses in disks of uniform thickness having symmetrically placed noncentral holes.
119. Z. Tuzi and M. Nisida, "Photoelastic Study of Stresses Due to Impact," Phil Mag, v 21, 1936, pp 448–73.
120. F. S. Wyle, "Some Photoelastic Studies in Dynamics," Proc 13th Eastern Photoelasticity Conf, June 1941, pp 13–6. Utilizes stroboscopic high-speed light source.

Other Applications of the Photoelastic Effect

121. M. Hetényi, "On Similarities between Stress and Flow Patterns," J Applied Physics, v 12, Aug 1941, pp 592–5. Analogies between plane stress systems and nonviscous potential flow or to viscous flow.
122a. R. Weller, "The Optical Investigation of Fluid Flow," J. Applied Mechanics, Trans ASME, v 14, June 1947, p A-103. Liquids and methods for photoelastic study of fluid flow.
122b. R. Weller, D. J. Middlehurst, and R. Steiner, "The Photoviscous Properties of Fluids," Nat Advisory Comm for Aeronautics Tech Note 841, 1942. Velocity distribution in moving fluid studied by photoelastic effects.

123. W. Leaf, "Fluid Flow Studies of Locomotive Fire Box Design," *Proc Soc Exp Stress Analysis*, v 1, n 1, pp 116–17.

124. M. A. Biot, "Distributed Gravity and Temperature Loading in Two-Dimensional Elasticity Replaced by Boundary Pressures and Dislocations," *J Applied Mechanics, Trans ASME*, v 2, 1935, pp 41–5. Gravitational stresses calculated from stresses in model loaded on boundaries with linear pressure distribution; thermal stresses found from model by controlled displacement or rotation of the two edges of an artificial slit which joins inner and outer boundaries.

125. E. E. Weibel, "Thermal Stresses in Cylinders by the Photoelastic Method," *Proc 5th Int Congress Applied Mechanics*, Cambridge, 1938. Application of Biot's dislocation method for several shapes of cross section.

126. W. E. Thibodeau and L. A. Wood, "Photoelastic Determination of Stresses around Circular Inclusion in Rubber," *Nat Bur Standards J Research*, v 20, n 3, paper 1083, p 393, Mar 1938. Utilizes rubber as a photoelastic material.

127. F. E. Wright, "The Manufacture of Optical Glass and Optical Systems," *Ordnance Dept Document* 2037, U. S. Government Printing Office, 1924, ch 4.

128. J. N. Goodier, "An Analogy Between the Slow Motions of Viscous Fluids in Two-Dimensions and Systems of Plane Stress," *Phil Mag*, v 17, 1934, p 554.

THREE-DIMENSIONAL PHOTOELASTICITY

Books

129. R. Houwink, *Elasticity, Plasticity, and Structure of Matter*, Cambridge Univ Press, 1937. Very complete discussion of diphase theory and high elasticity.

130. A. Johannsen, *Manual of Petrographic Methods*, McGraw-Hill Book Co, New York, 1918.

131. E. E. Wahlstrom, *Optical Crystallography*, John Wiley & Sons, New York, 1943.

132. R. W. Wood, *Physical Optics*, Macmillan Co, New York, 1934.

Articles

133. R. E. Arthur, "Introduction to the Theory of Photoelasticity and its Application to Problems of Stress Analysis," *J Royal Aeronautical Soc*, v 47, 1943, pp 263–72. Summarizes fundamentals and presents photographs of models of wave surfaces for propagation of light in a crystal.

134. D. C. Drucker and R. D. Mindlin, "Stress Analysis by Three-Dimensional Photoelastic Methods," *J Applied Physics*, v 11, 1940, pp 724–32. Basic photoelastic theory is extended to include rotation of the direction of the secondary principal stresses along the wave normal. Investigation of entire planes at once (oblique incidence) is proposed.

135. D. C. Drucker, "The Photoelastic Analysis of Transverse Bending of Plates in the Standard Transmission Polariscope," *J Applied Mechanics, Transactions ASME*, v 64, 1942, pp A-161–64. An initial tension is frozen in a bakelite sheet, and the model is cut from it at some angle to the tension direction. The laws of three-dimensional photoelasticity are used to calculate the bending stress from fringe photographs taken in the usual transmission polariscope.

136. H. Favre, "Sur une Méthode optique de détermination des tensions intérieures dans les solides à trois dimensions," *Comptes Rendus*, Paris, v 190, 1930, pp 1182–184. Proposes insertion of prisms of optically sensitive material in the interior of a transparent optically insensitive model (Pockels glass).

137. R. A. Frigon, "Some Three-Dimensional Studies with Scattered Light," *Proc 15th Semi-Annual Eastern Photoelasticity Conf*, Addison–Wesley Press,

Cambridge, Mass, June 1942, pp 68–73. Summarizes theory and gives application to torsion of prismatic bars. Fringe photographs, obtained by the scattering method, are presented for four cross-sectional shapes.

138. Max M. Frocht and M. M. Leven, "On the State of Stress in Thick Bars," *J Applied Physics*, v 13, 1942, pp 308–13. Results of a photoelastic investigation using both elastic and frozen-stress patterns are reported. Factors of stress concentration are found to be the same as in thin bars.

139. Max M. Frocht, "Studies in Three Dimensional Photoelasticity—Stress Concentrations in Shafts with Transverse Circular Holes in Tension," *J Applied Physics*, v 15, 1944, pp 72–88. Obtains excellent photographs of fringe patterns using fixation method, slicing and viewing both the slices and the remaining portion.

140. Max M. Frocht, "Studies in Three-Dimensional Photoelasticity," *J Applied Mechanics, Trans ASME*, v 66, 1944, pp A-10–6. Stresses in bent circular shafts with transverse holes are determined by the fixation method. See also *Proc Soc Exp Stress Analysis*, v 2, n 1, pp 128–38, 1944.

141. Max M. Frocht, "Studies in Three-Dimensional Photoelasticity—Torsional Stresses by Oblique Incidence," *J Applied Mechanics, Trans ASME*, v 66, 1944, pp A-229–34. Applies the oblique incidence method to the known case of a circular bar in torsion. Excellent fringe photographs give a clear indication of the precision possible with the fixation and slicing procedure. Experimental results are in close agreement with known theory.

142. J. N. Goodier and G. H. Lee, "An Extension of the Photoelastic Method of Stress Measurement to Plates in Transverse Bending," *J Applied Mechanics, Trans ASME*, v 63, 1941, pp A-27–9, discussion p A-187. Plates are built up of cemented laminations with reflecting surfaces of aluminum foil between the laminations. Good results are obtained with celluloid sheets, poor results with Bakelite.

143. M. Hetényi, "Photoelastic Stress Analyses Made in Three Dimensions," *Machine Design*, v 10, 1938, pp 40–1. Fringe photographs are shown of slices taken from a shaft with a transverse hole and one with a sled-runner keyway.

144. M. Hetényi, "The Application of Hardening Resins in Three-Dimensional Photoelastic Studies," *J Applied Physics*, v 10, 1939, pp 295–300. Contains experimental results and fringe photographs in addition to basic theory. Demonstrates the applicability of the fixation method to the determination of centrifugal stresses in rotating disks.

145. M. Hetényi, "A Photoelastic Study of Bolt and Nut Fastenings," *J Applied Mechanics, Trans ASME*, v 65, 1943, pp A-93–100. Six different designs investigated by fixation and slicing method. Design is found which minimizes stress at root of thread. See also *Proc Soc Experimental Stress Analysis*, v 1, n 1, pp 147–156, 1943.

146. R. Hiltscher, "Polarisationsoptische Untersuchung des räumlichen Spannungszustandes im konvergenten Licht," *Forschung auf dem Gebiete des Ingenieurwesens*, v 9, 1938, pp 91–103. Presents the methods of determining principal stress differences and orientations using convergent light, preferably with a petrographic microscope.

147. R. Hiltscher, "Vollständige Bestimmung des ebenen Spannungszustandes nach dem Achsenbildverfahren," *Forschung auf dem Gebiete des Ingenieurwesens*, v 15, 1944, pp 12–7. Applies the method of convergent light to the analysis of plane stress. Fringe patterns (axis pictures) are shown for the various possible signs and relative magnitudes of the principal stresses.

148. A. Kuske, "Das Kunstharz Phenolformaldehyd in der Spannungsoptik," *Forschung auf dem Gebiete des Ingenieurwesens*, v 9, 1938, pp 139–49. Suggests reheating the slice cut from the model and measuring the change in thickness accompanying the relief of stress in the infusible polymerized phase.

This information combined with the principal stress differences gives the principal stresses themselves.

149. A. Kuske, "Vereinfachte Auswerteverfahren räumlicher spannungsoptischer Versuche," *Vereines deutscher Ingenieure Zeitschrift*, v 86, 1942, pp 541–44. Shows an apparatus for using convergent light to analyze slices and gives a simple method for measuring angles on the image obtained. Discusses some of the difficulties arising in the analysis of a general slice.

150. Georges Mabboux, "Applications de la photoélasticimétre à l'étude des ouvrages en béton," *Revue d'Optique*, v 11, 1932, pp 501–07. Proposes insertion of photoelastic blocks in the surface of concrete structures and the use of a Nörrenberg doubler to measure the stress.

151. J. C. Maxwell, "On the Equilibrium of Elastic Solids," *Trans Royal Soc of Edinburgh*, v 20, pt 1, 1849–50, p 87. First mention of a residual optical pattern that corresponds to the elastic stress distribution and not to the residual stress.

152. H. J. Menges, "Die experimentelle Ermittlung räumlicher Spannungszustande an durchsichtigen Modellen mit Hilfe des Tyndalleffects," *Zeitschrift fur angewandte Mathematik und Mechanik*, v 20, 1940, pp 210–17. Uses a photometer to determine ellipse of vibration at neighboring points of scattering.

153. J. L. Meriam, "Centrifugal Stresses in a Supercharger Impeller," *Proc 15th Semiannual Eastern Photoelasticity Conf*, Addison–Wesley Press, Cambridge Mass, June 1942, pp 1–19. Three-dimensional BT-61-893 model is analyzed by fixation and slicing methods. Complete technique is given, and photographs of fringe patterns are shown.

154. A. Mesnager, "Sur la Détermination optique des tensions intérieures dans des solides à trois dimensions," *Comptes Rendus*, Paris, v 190, 1930, p 1249. Proposes coating a polished metal slab with a transparent photoelastic material to determine the surface stresses.

155. Raymond D. Mindlin, "A Review of the Photoelastic Method of Stress Analysis," *J Applied Physics*, v 10, 1939, pp 222–47 and 273–94. A concise complete easily understood summary and report of both two- and three-dimensional photoelastic theory and technique. Necessary reading for all photoelasticians.

156. Raymond D. Mindlin, "Optical Aspect of Three-Dimensional Photoelasticity," *J Franklin Inst*, v 233, 1942, pp 349–64. Discusses crystal optics and stress-optical relationships. Uses ideas based on the orientation of the optic axes of the artificial crystal.

157. G. Oppel, "Photoelastic Investigation of Three-Dimensional Stress and Strain Conditions," *Nat Advisory Commit Aeronautics Tech Memo* 824, 1937. A translation by J. Vanier of Oppel's article in *Forschung auf dem Gebiete des Ingenieurwesens*, v 7, 1936, pp 240–48. First to propose the fixation method. Applies it to the case of a ball pressed against a block.

158. G. Oppel, "Das polarisationsoptische Schichtverfahren zur Messung der Oberflächenspannung am beanspruchten Bauteil ohne Modell," *Vereines deutscher Ingenieure, Zeitschrift*, v 81, 1937, pp 803–04. Applies Mesnager's suggestion of coating a polished portion of a machine part with photoelastic material.

159. P. R. Rosenberg, "Study of a Shrink Fit Model by the Scattered Light Method," *Proc 13th Semiannual Eastern Photoelasticity Conf, Mass Inst of Tech*, Cambridge, Mass, June 1941, pp 99–103. Fringe photographs are shown for each of the two models investigated. Despite use of microphotometer to determine fringe spacing, accuracy is said to be "not as good as expected."

160. A. G. Solakian, "A New Photoelastic Material," *Mech Eng*, v 57, 1935, pp 767–71. As a secondary point, a photograph is shown of a frozen-stress

pattern obtained from a bar in torsion, the first such photograph ever published.   Also, the properties of several photoelastic materials are given.
161. A. G. SOLAKIAN, "Photoelastic Models with Cemented Elements," *Photoelastic J*, v 1, n 1, pp 14–7, 1938.   Investigation of plate with circular hole, reinforced with rings of square and rectangular cross section.
162. E. K. TIMBY AND I. G. HEDRICK, JR., "Photoelastic Analysis Broadened," *Eng News-Rec*, v 121, 1938, pp 179–81.   Proposes coating a model with polarizing material (or cementing it to the surface) and cementing a sheet of photoelastic material over the polarizing layer.   An ordinary transmission polariscope without a polarizer can be used to obtain surface stresses.
163. R. WELLER AND J. K. BUSSEY, "Photoelastic Analysis of Three-Dimensional Stress Systems Using Scattered Light," *Nat Advisory Commit Aeronautics Tech Note* 737, Washington, D.C., Nov 1939.   Outlines the basic experimental technique of the scattering method.   Analysis is given of beams in bending showing agreement with elementary theory.   However, as this note followed so closely after Weller's initial announcement of his discovery of the scattering technique (letter to editor, *J Applied Physics*, v 10, 1939, p 266) it naturally does not contain a discussion of more advanced theory and procedure.
164. R. WELLER, "Three-Dimensional Photoelasticity Using Scattered Light," *J Applied Physics*, v 12, 1941, pp 610–16.   Essentially the same as ref 163.
165. D. C. DRUCKER AND MAX M. FROCHT, "Equivalence of Photoelastic Scattering Patterns and Membrane Contours for Torsion," *Proc Soc Exp Stress Analysis*, v 5, n 2.   For St. Venant torsion, the scattering fringes observed for any cross-sectional sheet of light are shown to be identical with equal difference in elevation contours of the analogous membrane.
166. M. M. LEVEN, "A New Material for Three-Dimensional Photoelasticity," *Proc Soc Exp Stress Analysis*, v 6, n 1.   Fosterites, styrene-alkyd resins, are shown to be more desirable for the fixation technique than BT-61-893.   They exhibit little edge effect and can be cast in large rods or blocks.
167. E. M. SALEME, "Three-Dimensional Photoelastic Analysis by Scattered Light," *Proc Soc Exp Stress Analysis*, v 6, n 1.
168. R. D. MINDLIN AND L. E. GOODMAN, "The Optical Equations of Three-Dimensional Photoelasticity," *J. Applied Physics*, v 20, 1949, pp 89–95.   The nature of the approximations required for the passage from Maxwell's to Neumann's equations is disclosed.   A simple pair of equations is developed from which solutions to problems of wave propagation in photoelastic models can be found.
169. R. D. MINDLIN, "A Mathematical Theory of Photo-Viscoelasticity," *J. Applied Physics*, v 20, n 2, Feb 1949, pp 206–16.   The conclusion is reached that cross-linked polymers are not required for the fixation method.   A proper frozen pattern can be obtained if all the loads on the model are increased in ratio.
170. E. MÖNCH, "Räumliche Spannungsoptik mit Phenol-Kunstharz bei Anwendung einer Schutzhülle," *Kunststoffe*, v 9, pp 181–9.   Layers of oil and aluminum foil wrapped around the model eliminate most of the edge effect produced by heating and cooling.
171. E. MÖNCH, "Praxis des spannungsoptischen Versuch mit Dekorit als Modellwerkstoff," *Ingenieur Archiv*, v 16, 1948, pp 267–86.   Elevated temperature behavior and properties of this phenolic resin are given.
172. W. A. P. FISHER, "Basic Physical Properties Relied upon in the Frozen Stress Technique," *Proc Inst Mech Engineers*, v 158, 1948, pp 230–35.   Properties of Catalin 800 are discussed and some experimental results are given.
173. R. B. HEYWOOD, "Modern Applications of Photoelasticity," *Proc Inst Mech Engnrs*, v 158, 1948, pp 235–40.   Contains a discussion of stress freezing.
174. C. E. TAYLOR, E. O. STITZ, AND R. O. BELSHEIM, "A Casting Material for

Three-Dimensional Photoelasticity," to appear *Proc Soc Exp Stress Analysis*. An allyl-ester resin called Kriston is shown to have many desirable properties for the fixation technique.

175. C. B. Norris and A. W. Voss, "An Improved Photoelastic Method for Determining Plane Stresses," *Nat Advisory Commit Aeronautics Tech Note* 1410, Jan 1948. An oblique incidence formula for rotation about two axes using retardation and orientation values.

176. D. C. Drucker, "The Method of Oblique Incidence in Photoelasticity," to appear in *Proc Soc Exp Stress Analysis*. Discusses the accuracy attainable for principal slices and plane-stress systems. Calculations based on retardation alone are shown to be generally best for double oblique incidence.

177. M. M. Leven, "Stresses in Keyways by Photoelastic Methods and Comparison with Numerical Solutions," to appear in *Proc Soc Exp Stress Analysis*. Contains excellent fringe photographs obtained with scattered light.

CHAPTER 18

X-RAY ANALYSIS

By Charles S. Barrett

X rays have served the stress analyst in two main fields: the detection of internal flaws in materials by radiography and the determination of stresses by X-ray diffraction. These are treated in separate sections below.

Radiography consists in sending radiation through an object and recording the shadow image of the object on a photographic film placed so as to receive the transmitted beam. There are several methods of testing that are closely related to radiography: fluoroscopy, in which the transmitted beam is registered on a fluorescent screen and is studied visually; microradiography, in which a thin sample is radiographed on fine-grain films or plates that are studied after enlargement; and other methods in which the transmitted beam or the back-scattered beam is measured with electrical instruments.

Stress analysis by X-ray diffraction consists in directing a beam of X rays of known wave length at an object and recording the rays reflected by the object in such a way that the spacings between planes of atoms in the object can be measured; since these spacings are altered by applied or residual stresses, they serve as a strain gage and permit strain and stress determinations similar to those made by using the more common types of strain gages.

A. RADIOGRAPHY

1. General Principles of Radiography. X rays, like visible light, are electromagnetic radiation and differ from light in that their wave lengths lie in a range about 1/10,000 the wave length of light radiation. Because of their short wave length they are able to penetrate materials that are opaque to ordinary light. Gamma rays from radium and other radioactive substances are the same in nature and are more penetrating than most X rays.

X rays are generated by a vacuum tube in which electrons are driven against a target at high speed. In the usual form of tube the electrons are supplied from a filament which is heated to incandescence. They are concentrated into a small stream by a focusing cup surrounding the filament and are driven against the target in a small spot called the focal spot. The target in radiographic X-ray tubes is of tungsten or is a tungsten button imbedded in a copper anode. The electrons are propelled through the vacuum from the incandescent cathode to the anode by charging these electrodes to a high potential; the negatively charged electrons are repelled by the negatively charged cathode and attracted by the positively charged anode.

The current of electrons through the tube, measured in milliamperes, is increased by increasing the temperature of the filament, and this is accomplished by controlling the voltage applied to the filament. The maximum current permissible in a given tube is limited by the ability of the target to carry away the heat generated by the electron impacts and is increased by water-cooling or oil-cooling the target. More heat can be dissipated if the focal spot is large than if it is small, but for radiographic work small focal spots are desirable for they produce sharply defined shadows.

The electrons are accelerated from filament to target by voltages measured in kilovolts (thousands of volts). The higher the voltage, the greater the speed of the electrons, the greater the intensity of the X rays produced, and the greater the penetrating power of the rays, but the lower the contrast in a radiograph between sound material and defective material or between two different thicknesses of material in the object being radiographed.

The voltages required are provided by a high-voltage transformer, usually connected to the tube through a rectifier so that pulsating (or sometimes constant) direct current reaches the tube. The transformer is attached to the ordinary a-c lines through suitable control units that provide for a wide variation in the voltage. Power requirements are usually modest.

The rays leave the surface of the target in all directions. All but a small cone of the rays are absorbed in lead or lead-impregnated housings, and the cone of emerging rays is directed at the object to be radiographed. As they pass through the object, they are absorbed at a rate dependent on the density of the object and the atomic number of the materials within the object. Absorption is negligible when the rays pass through holes in the material; therefore, the rays that emerge from the far side of the object are stronger behind holes, cracks, or porous areas. The same is true to a lesser degree when the rays encounter slag inclusions or other light inclusions, or regions in which lighter elements are segregated. Thus, these regions cast "shadows" of greater intensity than the sound metal, and, conversely, heavy inclusions cast shadows of lower-radiation intensity.

The shadows are registered on X-ray films, suitably protected from exposure to daylight by cassettes. The rate of darkening of the films by the radiation is increased by placing lead sheets or fluorescent screens in very uniform close contact with both sides of the film—and sometimes also by using two films, one behind the other so as to make simultaneously two duplicate pictures which can be superimposed for viewing. In an alternative technique, the shadows are viewed directly on a fluorescent screen which emits light when irradiated by X rays. (The relative merits of this method are discussed later under "Fluoroscopy.")

Films are usually developed, washed, and fixed in tanks while suspended from film hangers. For the small foundry or welding shop where only occasional radiographs are made, using a rented capsule of radium and developing

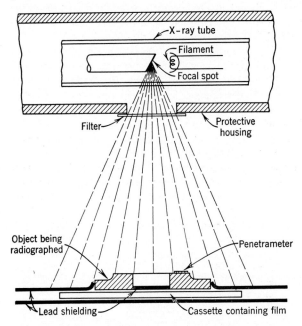

FIG. 18-1. Arrangement for X-Ray Radiography, Showing Method of Protecting Film from Direct and Scattered Rays

in darkroom trays are adequate, whereas in the largest installations, where film costs run as high as $20 to $100 per day or more, automatic film developing and drying units are found to be worth while.

For viewing the films it is very desirable to have an illuminator in which the intensity of the light can be varied over a wide range. Films that appear almost dead black in ordinary light may have excellent detail when viewed with sufficient lighting behind them.

The nature of a defect is determined from the appearance of its shadow; thus, cracks appear as wavy black lines on the film, holes as black spots, and so on. The size of the defect is shown by the size of its image (there is almost no enlargement when the image is formed because the object is very close to the film and far from the X-ray tube). The thickness of the defect in the direction of the rays is estimated from the contrast in the image; comparison with standard films of previously studied objects is useful in this connection. The distance a defect lies below the surface can be determined, if desired, by taking two radiographs with the X-ray tube shifted a measured amount between the two exposures. If markers are placed on both surfaces of the object, shifting the tube will shift the shadow image of a defect an amount that depends on the location of the defect: if the defect is at the back (nearest the film), the shadow image will shift only as much as the marker on the back surface; if the defect lies at the front, the shadow will shift more (as much as the shadow of the front marker), and, if it lies at any intermediate position, the shadow will shift an intermediate amount, in direct proportion to the distance of the defect from the back.

2. Equipment in Common Use. (*a*) *X-Ray Radiography.* The choice of equipment for a given task is governed chiefly by the range of voltages that can be applied to the X-ray tube. Light metals require operation at low voltages, because high contrast is required and low penetrating power is sufficient. Steel, brass, and other heavy metals require greater penetrating power and, hence, higher voltages. The approximate ranges of thickness that can be inspected by different X-ray units can be determined from Table 18-1. The higher the voltage, the faster any given object can be radiographed, and the greater the thickness that can be penetrated, but the more elaborate must be the protection of the operator from the rays. Principles are now thoroughly established for the safeguarding of personnel from the dangerous effects of exposure to X rays. Remote controls, barrier walls or pits or isolated buildings, and safety switches on the doors of the X-ray room are common safety measures.

TABLE 18-1

THICKNESSES RADIOGRAPHED WITH DIFFERENT VOLTAGES

| Voltage on X-Ray Tube, kv | Magnesium Alloys | Maximum Thickness, in. | | Copper Alloys |
		Aluminum Alloys	Steel	
85	3	2	$\frac{1}{2}$	$\frac{3}{8}$
140	$6\frac{1}{2}$	$4\frac{1}{2}$	$1\frac{1}{2}$	1
220		12	3	2
400			$5\frac{1}{4}$	$4\frac{3}{4}$
1,000			8 or 9	7
20,000			20	

An important feature of radiographs is their sensitivity. Sensitivity may be defined as the smallest decrease in thickness of a metal section (expressed as a per cent) that can be detected on a radiograph. This varies from 0.5 per cent or better in sections less than $\frac{1}{2}$ in. thick to about 1 per cent in 2-in. sections and continues to deteriorate as thickness increases; the figures quoted are common values, but it must be emphasized that much variation is possible when radiographic technique is altered. For example, the slower fine-grained X-ray films provide better sensitivity than the fast coarse-grained films, and lower voltages with longer exposures give better sensitivity than the shorter exposures that are possible with higher voltages. Improved radiographs also result from careful shielding of the film from direct and scattered radiation, proper filtering of the rays, and careful film-processing procedures. Since smaller defects can be seen when the shadow images are sharp than when they

FIG. 18-2. A Million-Volt Installation for X-Ray Radiography (General Electric X-Ray Corp.)

are diffuse, it is important to consider this factor at all times in the work. Sharpness (definition) is increased by increasing the distance from tube to specimen and decreasing the distance from specimen to film (or, more precisely, from defect to film); it is greater for fine-grain films than for coarse-grain films, and better with paper-covered or lead-sheet-covered films than when intensifying screens are used against the films (a practice that is resorted to when short-exposure times are required). The degree of sensitivity obtained is determined by placing penetrameters—test strips containing drilled holes —on the object to be tested. From the shadow of the penetrameter holes on the film it is easy to tell whether or not proper sensitivity has been reached. The design of penetrameters has been carefully studied and standardized, and their use is obligatory in many inspection problems.

High-voltage electron accelerators such as the Betatron can accomplish remarkable feats in radiography but are unlikely to find widespread use in

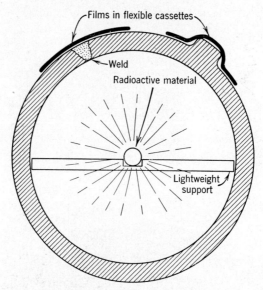

FIG. 18-3. A Typical Arrangement for Radiography with Radium or Artificially Radioactive Material
Whenever possible, the source is placed on the center line of cylindrical objects, with films around the periphery

engineering because of their great initial expense. The penetration possible with a Betatron extends as high as 20 in. of steel, and it is possible to detect a difference in thickness of $\frac{1}{32}$ in. in any penetrable thickness of steel. The focal spot is extremely small, so that sharp radiographs are obtained even with thick samples.

(b) *Gamma-Ray Radiography.* Gamma rays are highly penetrating rays produced by the disintegration of natural or artifically made radioactive elements. The most common source of gamma rays is radium (usually in the form of radium sulphate or radium bromide) which is sealed tightly in a small capsule. When the pellet is placed at a suitable distance from an object to be radiographed, and an X-ray film in its holder is placed against the opposite

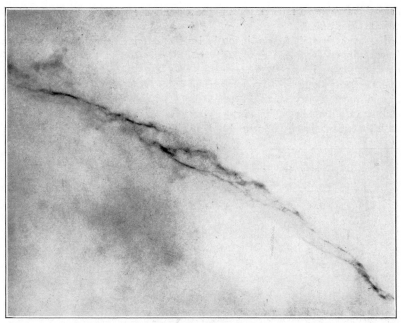

FIG. 18-4. A Crack in a Steel Casting 1½-in. Thick Radiographed with Radium

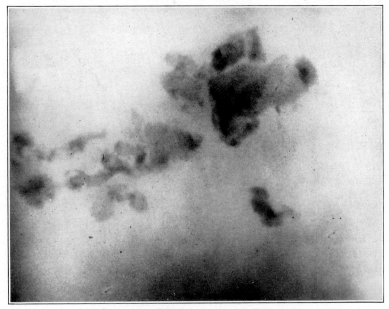

FIG. 18-5. Sand Inclusions in a Steel Casting
Radiographed with radium

side of the object, a radiograph is produced that resembles one made by high-voltage X rays.

Radiation is emitted continuously by the radioactive material (the rays from radium decrease to half intensity only after 1600 years) and is not "turned off" but is merely absorbed in the walls of a container when not in use. An operator can handle the capsule by strings or long tongs so as to avoid exposing himself to the rays when taking radiographs. Capsules of suitable size, 25 to 500 mg of radium or equivalent, may be purchased or rented; exposure times with these capsules are measured in hours or days instead of minutes as with

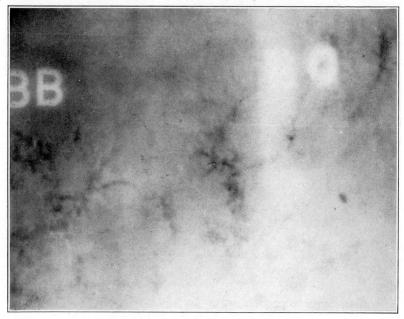

FIG. 18-6. Shrinkage in a Large Cast-Steel Cylinder
Wall thickness 7 in. Radiographed with radium. Reduced to ⅓-in. reproduction

X rays. However, by surrounding the source of rays with many objects to be tested or with a cylindrical or globular object, it is possible to take many radiographs simultaneously and thus accelerate the work.

Gamma-rays are capable of inspecting steel objects up to 8 or 10 in. thick if sufficiently long exposure times are used. Because of favorable scattering characteristics, gamma-ray radiography requires a less elaborate technique than most X-ray work and frequently meets the needs of the manufacturer who has only occasional use for radiography. Its extreme portability is of importance in various applications, such as inspection in the field and in constricted places that cannot be reached by the larger heavier X-ray units. Gamma-ray radiographs have low contrast, resembling those taken with

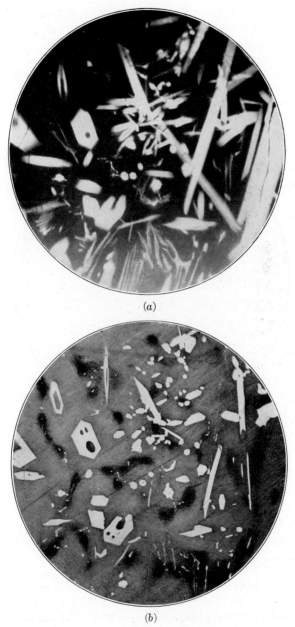

(a)

(b)

FIG. 18-7.   Photomicrograph and Microradiograph of a Bearing Alloy × 70
(a) Microradiograph with X ray from chromium tube at 20 kv
(b) Photomicrograph of same area.   Composition: Sn-base alloy with 9.2% Cu,
8.5% Sb, 0.3% Fe (R. Smoluchowski)

high-voltage X rays (low contrast always goes with high penetrating power). This makes the method inferior to X rays for inspection of thin specimens, where defects are small and high contrast is desired.

(c) *Microradiography*. Microradiography is the radiography of thin sections of metal with fine-grained photographic films or plates and the viewing of the image after enlargement (10 to 200 times). Cracks, gas porosity, shrink porosity, and nonmetallic inclusions can be seen and identified on a microscopic scale. With the proper choice of voltage on the tube it is possible to

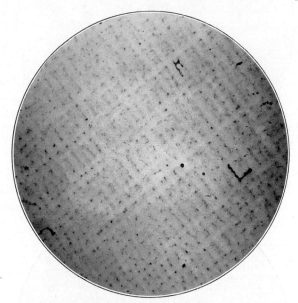

FIG. 18-8. Microradiograph of a Turbine Bucket for High-Temperature Service, X 100
Alloy containing 64% Co, 26% Cr, 5% Mo, 2% Ni, 1% Fe plus impurities; cast into hot mold; transverse section of turbine bucket radiographed with copper tube at 15 kv. Some dendritic segregation that can be identified by comparing pictures taken with different radiations (R. Smoluchowski)

register heterogeneity in composition of alloys, showing the distribution of heavy and light phases and impurities, dendrites and other microscopic segregations of constituents in a way closely related to metallography. Unlike metallography, the method records the structures throughout the thickness penetrated, (metallography reveals the structure only at a prepared surface); this requires sawing and grinding metal specimens down to a thickness of 0.003 to 0.005 in. before exposing. Voltages used lie in the range below 50 kv.

(d) *Electric Recording of Rays*. Electric devices can record with precision the intensity of X-ray and gamma-ray radiation. Electroscopes and ionization chambers connected to sensitive electrometers were first used and were cumbersome; the advent of vacuum-tube amplifiers increased the convenience of operation, but the outstanding improvement came from the use of the tube counters (Geiger–Mueller counting tubes), which can be arranged for direct reading of intensity or for automatic recording. By scanning the back of an object that is being irradiated with X rays or gamma rays the detecting device locates the larger flaws in the object (but not the ones smaller than about $\frac{1}{2}$ in. in diameter). Measuring the intensity of transmitted or back-scattered rays leads, by calibration, to determinations of thickness of sheet metals, tubing, walls of drums, tanks, and pipes. The accuracy attained is about plus or minus 3 per cent.

(e) *Fluoroscopy.* The visual examination of X-ray shadow images by means of a fluorescent screen has been applied mainly to the inspection of fruit, packages of food, mail, the fitting of shoes, the checking of mechanical assemblies and molded parts, and so on, but has also been extended to metals.

The principal uses of fluoroscopy in the metals field lie in the inspection of light-metal castings. As the images are formed directly on a screen and no films are required, the cost of inspection is lower than in the ordinary methods which involve both film and film-processing costs. The inspection, however, is less thorough. The screen provides a less sharply defined image than can be obtained on films, and the effective contrast is lower. Whereas a sensitivity of 2 per cent or better is nearly always obtained in radiographic inspection of ordinary thicknesses of metal when films are used, the usual sensitivity with fluoroscopic machines is about 10 per cent, and only under ideal conditions does it reach 5 per cent. The very limited thicknesses that can be inspected by fluoroscopy constitute another disadvantage of the method. The upper limit of thickness is given by various investigators from 2 to $3\frac{1}{2}$ in. of aluminum and magnesium alloys, and from $\frac{3}{8}$ to $\frac{1}{2}$ in. of steel.

It is characteristic of the method that the intensity of light from the fluoroscopic image is very weak and can be seen properly only after a person has thoroughly accommodated his eyes to the dark. This requires spending about 20 min in the dark or in red light (by wearing red goggles) before beginning work with a fluoroscope.

The equipment must be provided with carefully designed protective features so the operator is not exposed to direct or scattered radiation. This can be adequately accomplished with the aid of mirrors, lead sheet, and lead-glass partitions. It is also necessary in most cases to provide for turning the object in the rays by remote control or at least providing for more than one orientation of the object in the rays. Ordinary installations are built around a belt conveyor which moves objects under the viewing screen at a rate that is under the control of the inspector. Operating voltages for the inspection of $\frac{1}{2}$-in. aluminum castings are of the order of 85 kv and increase with increasing thicknesses up to 220 kv. Tube-to-screen distances are usually 18 to 30 in.

Fluoroscopy serves as a low-cost method of control of foundry technique and is also used for final inspection of some light-metal castings (rarely of heavy metals). In the metals field it is reliable only for gross defects and, hence, is not recommended as the sole test for highly stressed castings such as aircraft parts. On the other hand, for industrial castings where the primary requirement is the absence of gross defects, fluoroscopy can reduce machine-shop losses by eliminating castings in which defects would be exposed by machining.

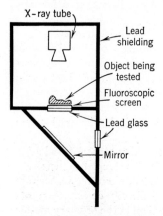

Fig. 18-9. A Simple Cabinet for Fluoroscopic Examination of Light Metals or Thin Sections
Operator is protected by lead sheet and lead glass and works in a darkened room

3. Defects Revealed. Radiographs reveal and permit the identification of the following defects in metal castings: cracks; hot tears; shrinkage cavities, gas cavities, and holes of various types; porosity from various causes; slag, sand, and other inclusions; segregation of alloy constituents or impurities; plugs, unfused chaplets, and internal chills; faulty repair welds. Radiographs of welds reveal cracks, porosity, slag and other inclusions, incomplete fusion, lack of penetration, and undercut. In spot welds the size of the fused portion and the general nature of the weld can be seen.

A uniform and precisely defined terminology for the defects seen on industrial radiographs has long been needed. A cooperative effort of committees of the American Society for Testing Materials, the American Foundrymen's Association, and the Canadian Research Council has been working toward a standard terminology and

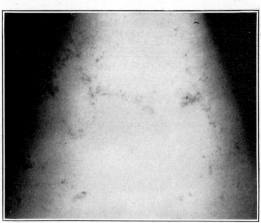

Fig. 18-10. Dross in an Aluminum-Alloy Casting Radiographed with 100-kv X Rays.

published a preliminary list in the *ASTM Symposium on Radiography* in 1942. It now seems likely that a smaller list will replace this, with defects listed somewhat as follows: gas cavities, gas porosity, shrinkage cavities, interdendritic shrinkage, shrinkage plus gas, shrinkage porosity, heterogeneities (inclusions, oxide, segregation), sharp discontinuities (cracks, cold shuts), hot cracks, misruns (failure to fill the section).

Modified forms of this classification have been used in various laboratories with considerable success for both castings and welds, and, when films are on file as standards of the types of defects and their ratings with regard to their effect on serviceability, the reliability of interpretation is greatly increased.

4. Standards for Acceptance and Rejection. A uniform rating for acceptance and rejection of all radiographed objects is not possible because of the different service conditions to which the objects are subjected. For each product the most reliable interpretation of radiographs requires comparison with standard films of samples that have been subjected to mechanical tests. Not only the nature of the defects must be considered, but also their distribution in regard to the areas of higher stress during service.

Nondestructive testing reveals many causes for loss of strength but not all. The correlation of measured strengths with radiographic ratings falls short of being perfect even with the best standardization if important metallurgical factors vary which are not registered on the films. Nevertheless, the value of radiographic inspection is very great, and boiler codes and various specifications

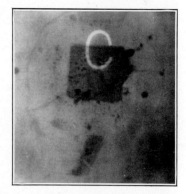

FIG. 18-11. Unfused Chaplet (Dark Square), Cold Shuts (Hook-Shaped Black Lines), Blow Holes (Circular), and Cracks in a Steel Casting

have effectively defined acceptable and nonacceptable radiographic quality in numerous classes of welds and castings.

5. Limitations; Supplementary Methods. X-ray inspection is limited in the thickness that can be penetrated (Table 18-1). To raise this limit radiographers must resort to gamma rays, which require inconveniently long exposure time, or to expensive X-ray installations that exceed one million volts.

Radiography does not detect differences in heat treatment unless segregation is altered by the heat treatment. Radiographs are not a reliable substitute for the hydraulic test for leaks, although they supplement this test. Some engineers feel that radiography is inferior to magnetic-powder inspection for welds in thin materials, while others require it in the specifications for such welds. It appears certain that radiographic testing is not fully reliable in detecting extremely fine cracks. When fine-grained film can be applied and the sections are thin, this deficiency is lessened, but for the most rigorous inspection for small cracks and discontinuities the radiographic method is

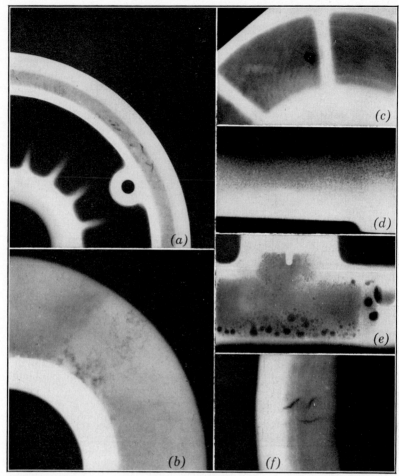

FIG. 18-12. Some Important Defects Revealed by X-Ray Radiography
(a) Zinc die casting with sharp discontinuities that would act as stress raisers.
(b) Sponginess resulting from shrinkage in a steel casting. (c) Microshrinkage
in a cast magnesium-alloy supercharger housing. (d) Hydrogen porosity in an
aluminum casting. (e) Gas in a steel casting arising from steam from the sand
mold. (f) Hot tears in a steel casting $\frac{3}{4}$–$1\frac{1}{2}$ in. thick (General Electric X-Ray
Corp.)

supplemented or replaced by methods using fluorescent powders, magnetic
powders, or by other magnetic tests.

Ordinary radiographs sometimes fail to distinguish clearly between fine-
scale porosity from different causes (gas porosity, microshrinkage), and a
supplementary investigation by microradiography may be useful for the
purpose; this involves thin slices of metal cut from the sample and is, therefore,
a destructive test, unlike nondestructive radiography.

X-ray inspection is not well suited to forgings, for laminations and folds in forgings are not detected with certainty, and it is the usual practice to supplement or substitute this inspection with magnetic tests and with the examination of etched cross sections of pilot forgings.

The quality of radiographs depends greatly on the care and skill used in setting up the sample for exposure, applying proper penetrameters to insure that the required sensitivity to defects is attained, and processing and viewing the films. Some Government agencies have established a certification procedure to assure that radiographic laboratories meet required standards of technique; more commonly, the interpreter relies on seeing the shadow of standard penetrameters on each film to ascertain that the technique has been adequate to provide the required sensitivity. The more complete specifications for acceptance of large or important castings and welded structures wisely contain statements of what areas are to be radiographed and what positions of radiation source, films, and penetrameters are to be used.

6. Product Improvement and Final Inspection with Radiography. Widespread use is made of radiography in the foundry to study pilot castings. By recognizing the nature of defects that occur, changes can be made in casting technique or in design to correct the faults or to shift the defects into harmless areas, and rapid improvement of the product usually follows such study. Indirect benefits also accrue, for the skill of the foundryman and designer is continually increased by development work of this kind.

The Army Ordnance Department has made extensive use of radiography in the inspection of cast armor in recent years, and the aircraft industry has made very effective use of radiographic control of the quality of castings for aircraft. Statistical analysis of radiographic rejections have proved valuable in determining the relative ability of various suppliers to make sound castings and to see how the quality of each supplier's product varies from month to month. In a study of statistical control by an aircraft manufacturer it was concluded that the best control was a continuous plotting of a control chart for each type of casting, that is, a graph of number of rejections versus lot number. By such statistical analysis the effect of changing an important variable in production may become immediately obvious. It was found by one manufacturer, for example, that aircraft castings made with loose patterns averaged lower in quality than those made with permanent metal-plate or wood-board patterns, and so the loose patterns were abandoned. The decrease in rejections resulting from this one change of policy was enough to pay the entire cost of the statistical investigations.

In the welding shop, with both manual and automatic welding, the development of technique is aided greatly by radiography, and periodic checks on the quality of welds are valuable even when the welding machines are believed to be in adjustment or when the welders have passed qualification tests. Some of the possible sources of defects that can be detected on radiographs are lack of adequate preheating for certain grades of steel, excessive nonmetallic inclusions, defective welding rods or coatings, and improper welding technique. On the other hand, there are microstructural conditions and embrittling constituents that cannot be detected by radiography and yet seriously affect weld quality—an example is the presence of nitride needles. Wide use is made of radiography in the repair of defective objects. If defective areas are chipped out in preparation for making a repair weld, it is difficult to tell by visual inspection when all the defective metal has been removed, owing to the great tendency for a chipping hammer and even a grinding wheel to smear over all fine cracks and porosity. It is wise to take a radiograph of the chipped-out area before beginning the repair weld, to see if the removal has been complete, since stress concentrations will occur at fine cracks that are left. After the repair welding is completed, another radiographic inspection is needed to check the quality of the repair work.

Since 1930 radiographic inspection has been written into many specifications and codes for pressure vessels and welded assemblies that could cause possible loss of life or serious property damage if failure occurred. Structural units that require expensive machining are also frequently subjected to radiographic tests to provide early recognition of the presence of any defects that will be uncovered during machining or will seriously weaken the machined part.

The bibliography at the end of this chapter lists the better-known treatises on radiography and a selection of research and review papers of recent years that cover the various engineering applications in greater detail than the books. In the interest of brevity most of the foreign literature has been omitted, and only a few articles on technique have been included.

B. STRESS MEASUREMENT BY X RAYS

7. Characteristics of the Method.[1-6] X rays may be diffracted from metals and other crystalline solids under conditions that make it possible to use the distances between atoms as gage lengths. Strains may be determined by measuring the changes in these interatomic distances.

As a strain gage, the X-ray-diffraction method has unusual characteristics compared with the common types of gages. It measures elastic strains only, whereas the usual gages record both elastic and plastic strains. It is the only method of determining stresses that does not require measurements of the unstressed metal, and, thus, it is the only method of determining residual stresses in an object without cutting or drilling the object to relieve the stresses. It uses a spot about $1/8$ in. in diameter on the surface of the test object, an area much smaller than the area covered in most strain gages. It registers the conditions in an extremely thin layer (usually less than 0.001 in.) at the surface. It is used at the present time almost exclusively on steels of lower hardness than Rockwell 45 C and on other metals that yield reasonably sharp diffraction lines because of the inaccuracies obtained when lines are diffuse. With fine-grained annealed steel an accuracy of 2000 or 3000 psi can be expected, but with the diffuse broad lines of cold-worked or quenched steels the error is increased to four or five times this; coarse-grained metals also introduce difficulties in technique and lower the accuracy.

As is discussed in later sections of this chapter, the simplest technique of

X-ray stress measurement yields the sum of the two principal stresses in the surface layer of an object. To obtain this result it is necessary to make one X-ray measurement of the object in the stressed condition and to make a separate X-ray measurement in the stress-free condition. A more precise knowledge of the stress pattern in the surface layers can be obtained without studying the stress-free material, if a pair of X-ray exposures are made, one with the X-ray beam directed perpendicularly onto the surface and the other with the beam striking the surface at an angle (usually about 45°). From this pair of exposures it is possible to compute the component of stress that lies parallel to the surface and in the direction toward which the beam is tilted. This method is treated in article 10.

X-ray diffraction when used in another way sometimes can furnish qualitative or semiquantitative information on plastic strain. It is frequently possible to tell by a glance at a diffraction film whether or not an annealed metal object has been subjected to a stress that has elongated it more than 1 or 2 per cent. On the other hand, if cold-worked metal has been heated, diffraction studies will indicate whether the heating has produced complete recrystallization, thereby replacing the strained metal completely with strain-free grains, or whether there has merely been a recovery of the metal from severe microstresses without appreciable recrystallization. These uses of diffraction are treated in article 17.

Throughout the following sections the subject is presented as if the diffracted rays are always recorded on a photographic film. This has been the only method used in the past, but at present there is a strong tendency to use electric recording of the rays, and there is much reason to believe it will displace film recording in many instances of stress analysis. Electric recording is usually by means of the Geiger counter, a device which is extremely sensitive to low-intensity radiation. When a counter is connected through suitable circuits to an automatic recorder, it traces a plot of intensity on a graph and by suitable instrumentation the graph may be made to read intensity versus diffraction angle, just as is desired for stress analysis. Since the interpretation of such records is fundamentally the same as the interpretation of films, it is not given a separate treatment in this discussion.

8. General Principles. X-ray diffraction from a crystal occurs when Bragg's law is fulfilled:

$$n\lambda = 2d \sin \theta \qquad (1)$$

where n is an integer, λ is the wave length of the X-ray beam, d is the spacing between the planes of atoms that reflect X rays from the crystal, and θ is the angle of incidence of the beam on these atomic planes. When the left side of the equation is constant, a variation in interplanar spacing, caused by stresses, will bring about a proportional variation in $\sin \theta$. As $\sin \theta$ approaches 1, that is, as θ approaches 90°, a given elastic strain causes greater and greater change in θ; hence, maximum sensitivity in the measurement of strain is obtained in a back-reflection camera, where θ is nearly 90°, and where 2θ, the angle between incident and diffracted beams, is nearly 180°. Good conditions are obtained when the characteristic radiation from a cobalt target tube is directed at iron or steel ($\theta = 80° 37.5'$), copper ($\theta = 81° 46.5'$) or brass; when copper radiation is used for aluminum alloys ($\theta = 81°$); when nickel is used for brass, and when iron is used for magnesium ($\theta = 83°$). The wave lengths in most common use are given in Table 18-2.

TABLE 18-2

X-Ray Tube Target	Wave Lengths in Angstroms (10^{-8} cm)	
	$K\alpha_2$ (Strong)	$K\alpha_1$ (Very Strong)
Chromium	2.29352	2.28962
Iron	1.93991	1.93597
Cobalt	1.79279	1.78890
Nickel	1.66168	1.65783
Copper	1.54434	1.54050
Molybdenum	0.71354	0.70926

The apparatus consists essentially of a film in a lighttight cassette mounted perpendicularly to the incoming X-ray beam, with a hole through which the pinhole system is inserted that collimates the beam, Fig. 18-13. The film records the rays diffracted by the specimen, and shows, on development, almost circular rings. The diameter of a diffraction ring divided by the distance from the film to the specimen gives $2 \tan (180 - 2\theta)$ from which θ is obtained for insertion in equation 1. For best results it is advisable to oscillate the film (15° to 30°) using the metal tube containing the pinholes as the axis of oscillation. This removes much of the spottiness of the diffraction lines, but, if the grain size of the specimen is large, it may also be necessary to oscillate the specimen a few degrees, keeping the distance from the film to the irradiated spot on the specimen strictly constant. This distance can be measured by inside micrometers, or can be adjusted to a predetermined distance by means of a special gage inserted between the cassette and the specimen.[57] Another method frequently employed is to compute the distance from specimen to film by measuring the diameter of a calibrating ring of known θ on the film. In this method a strain-free powder is placed on the surface of the test object. The powder is chosen to yield a ring near $\theta = 90°$ that does not interfere with measurements of the ring produced by the specimen. Gold powder is sometimes used with steel, since it gives a convenient reflection at $\theta = 78° 46'$ with cobalt $K\alpha_1$ radiation as illustrated in Fig. 18-14; tungsten

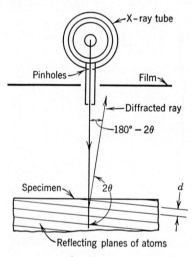

FIG. 18-13. Principle of the Back-Reflection Camera for Stress Measurement with Incident Beam Normal to Specimen Surface

and brass powders are also used, and silver powder is used with aluminum alloys, steel, and brass specimens. When the distance from specimen to film is obtained from such calculation, there are no errors introduced by film shrinkage, but these are seldom considered important in any event.

For maximum accuracy, the surface of the test object should be free from cold work introduced by machining or abrasion since sharp diffraction lines are necessary. If the surface is not in suitable condition, electropolishing is probably the best way to condition it, but good results are also obtained by etching the surface, provided the etching does not leave etch pits so deep that they relieve the surface stresses (see article 13).

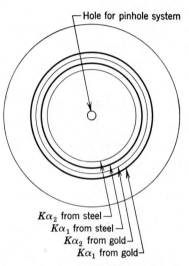

Although a few investigators have resorted to microphotometers for reading the films, it is generally agreed that it is satisfactory to read them by eye, moving a very fine cross-hair or scratch over the film under conditions of good illumination. Suitable films are prepared with a specimen placed at a distance of about 5 cm and with pinholes of about 1 mm diameter. Exposure times have been reduced to 15 min or so with carefully designed cameras mounted snugly on small X-ray tubes, and for rough work, with a larger pinhole and an overloaded X-ray tube, exposure times as short as 3 to 5 min have been reported. With rapid drying of films, simplified reading, and appropriate charts or tables to eliminate the necessity of computations, the method can be made quite rapid.

FIG. 18-14. Sketch of Back-Reflection Film Showing Diffraction Rings from Steel and Calibration Rings from Gold Powder

9. **Determining the Sum of the Principal Stresses.**[51, 55, 56] The simplest X-ray method of stress analysis measures the sum of the two principal stresses parallel to the surface of the object tested, that is, $(\sigma_1 + \sigma_2)$. The measurement is accomplished by taking back-reflection photographs with the beam directed perpendicularly at the surface as in Fig. 18-13. One film is exposed while the surface is in the stressed condition, and another when the surface is unstressed.

For measurement of the unstressed state it is necessary to remove any applied loads, and in objects containing residual stresses these stresses must be released by appropriate machining operations or by stress-relief annealing. If annealing is used, it should not alter the concentration of the elements in solid solution, for this might alter the unstressed value of the interplaner spacings and, thus, in effect alter the gage length during the test. The rate of cooling from the annealing temperature must be slow enough to avoid reintroducing stresses. If machining is used it must be done with a sharp cutting tool or a fine-toothed saw in such a manner as to minimize the straining and cold working of the testpiece. It is difficult to accomplish this properly, and considerable care is required: for example, it was found that a saw cut made with a hair-fine jeweler's saw in magnesium stressed the surface of a piece at considerable distances from the cut, introducing an error of 400 psi for cuts $\frac{1}{2}$ in. from the surface, 1300 psi for cuts $\frac{1}{8}$ in. from the surface, and 1900 psi for cuts $\frac{1}{16}$ in. from the surface.[58] These errors were removed by a careful approximately isothermal etching of the cut surfaces in all except the $\frac{1}{16}$-in. slices.

From the diameter of the diffraction rings on the film, the measured or calculated distance from film to irradiated spot on the test object, and the wave length of the X rays equation 1 gives value of interplanar spacings, d_z and d_o for the stressed and unstressed states, respectively. The strain is then

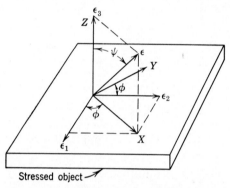

$$\epsilon = (d_z - d_o)/d_o \qquad (2)$$

and is the average elastic strain in the directions midway between the diffracted beams and the direction normal to the surface. Since the diffracted beams themselves are very nearly perpendicular to the surface, this strain very closely approximates the strain normal to the surface; hence, the sum of the principal stresses $(\sigma_1 + \sigma_2)$ can be directly computed from this strain by using Poisson's ratio ν and Young's modulus E in the equation for isotropic elastic solids,

FIG. 18-15. Rectangular Coordinate System, X, Y, Z, in Relation to Directions of Principal Strains ϵ_1, ϵ_2, ϵ_3, and the Arbitrary Direction along Which the Strain Is ϵ

$$\sigma_1 + \sigma_2 = -\epsilon E/\nu \qquad (3)$$

For uniaxial stresses $(\sigma_2 = 0)$ this method gives the required value of σ_1. For biaxial stresses produced by torsion, where $\sigma_1 = -\sigma_2$, the method obviously cannot be used. It has been employed in a number of instances to indicate in a general way the magnitude and distribution of biaxial stresses in metals and to show the reduction of biaxial residual stresses by annealing and by other treatments.

10. Determining a Stress Component.[54, 55, 57, 59, 61] The stress σ_x in any direction in the plane of the surface, either in the direction of a principal stress or otherwise, can be determined by an equation derived from the approximate equation for the ellipsoid of strain in isotropic materials,

$$\epsilon = a_1{}^2\epsilon_1 + a_2{}^2\epsilon_2 + a_3{}^2\epsilon_3 \qquad (4)$$

where a_1, a_2, and a_3 are the direction cosines of the direction in which ϵ is measured with respect to the directions of the principal strains ϵ_1, ϵ_2, ϵ_3. In the notation of Fig. 18-15,

$$a_1 = \sin \psi \cos \phi$$

$$a_2 = \sin \psi \sin \phi$$

$$a_3 = \cos \psi$$

Substituting in equation 4 gives

$$\epsilon = (\epsilon_1 \cos^2 \phi + \epsilon_2 \sin^2 \phi) \sin^2 \psi + \epsilon_3 \cos^2 \psi \tag{5}$$

The strain in the direction of the X axis, which is at an angle ϕ from the principal strain ϵ_1, as in Fig. 18-15, is

$$\epsilon_x = \epsilon_1 \cos^2 \phi + \epsilon_2 \sin^2 \phi$$

Thus equation 5 reduces to

$$\epsilon = \epsilon_x \sin^2 \psi + \epsilon_3 \cos^2 \psi$$

$$= \epsilon_x \sin^2 \psi + \epsilon_3 - \epsilon_3 \sin^2 \psi$$

and, since $\sigma_z = 0$ at the surface, where X-ray reflection takes place, this can be put in the form:

$$E(\epsilon - \epsilon_3) = \{\sigma_x - \nu\sigma_y + \nu(\sigma_x + \sigma_y)\} \sin^2 \psi \tag{6}$$

$$= (1 + \nu)\sigma_x \sin^2 \psi$$

Two X-ray exposures are made, one with the incident beam falling perpendicularly on the surface of the specimen, as in Fig. 18-13, and the other with the beam inclined at an angle to the surface. The first measures the spacings of the planes whose normals are approximately along the Z axis d_z. The second exposure is indicated in Fig. 18-16. The lower part of the film at B receives the diffracted rays from the atomic planes whose normals lie along OA, at an angle of ψ from the Z axis and midway between the original beam and the diffracted beam OB; if this portion of the film is measured, the atomic spacings d_ψ may be computed. (Obviously, the film cannot be rotated during this exposure nor even oscillated through a very large angle, for then the portion of the diffraction ring at B will have received radiation from planes at angles other than ψ.)

Now if d_o is the unstressed lattice spacing, we may write;

$$\epsilon - \epsilon_3 = \frac{d_\psi - d_o}{d_o} - \frac{d_z - d_o}{d_o} = \frac{d_\psi - d_z}{d_o}$$

and there is negligible error introduced by substituting d_z for d_o in the denominator of this expression. If we substitute in equation 6, the stress component

σ_x in terms of known and measurable quantities is then

$$\sigma_x = \frac{E}{1 + \nu} \cdot \frac{1}{\sin^2 \psi} \cdot \frac{d_\psi - d_z}{d_z} \qquad (7)$$

(This is the stress component parallel to the surface, in the direction toward which the initial beam was tilted, and may or may not be one of the principal stresses.)

It should be noted that the stress can be computed by this equation without determining the lattice spacing in the unstressed condition. It is, therefore, not necessary to cut the specimen or otherwise reduce the stress in the specimen to zero.

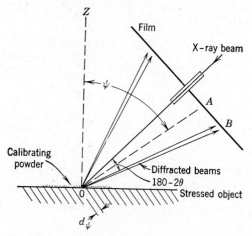

FIG. 18-16. Back-Reflection Camera with Inclined Beam for Measuring a Stress Component

Diffraction rings from object and calibrating powder are measured at B, where reflections are registered from planes at angle ψ to the surface

In practice, the inclined exposure is usually made with the reflection taking place from planes inclined about 45° to the surface, so that ψ is approximately 45°. The value of d_z may be obtained with sufficient accuracy from an exposure made with the incident beam normal to the surface, even though, as indicated in Fig. 18-13, the spacing thus measured is not exactly parallel to the Z axis.

On a film exposed in the inclined position, the diffraction rings are measured on one side only, not from one side across the diameter to the other. This is done by producing a diffraction ring from a calibrating powder that has been laid on the specimen during the exposure and measuring the distance from the calibrating ring to the specimen ring at the point B corresponding to the maximum value of ψ. A powder having known lattice constants produces a line at a known diffraction angle; hence, the diameter of the ring permits one to compute the effective distance from specimen to film under conditions where direct measurement would be difficult.   It is advisable to oscillate the film a few degrees around the beam as an axis to smooth the lines, but wide-angle oscillation or complete rotation would introduce considerable error.[59] When the grains in the specimen are large, it may also be necessary to oscillate the specimen, as Frommer and Lloyd have done,[60] or even to scan the surface.   Figure 18-17 shows the marked improvement of the back-reflection rings sometimes obtained when oscillation of the film is employed and when this is combined with a small oscillation of the specimen about an axis lying

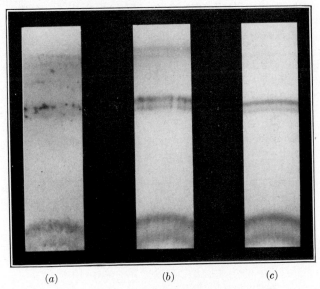

(a)   (b)   (c)

FIG. 18-17.   Appearance of Lines in a Back-Reflection Photograph of a Mag-
nesium-Alloy Casting (J. B. Hess)
(a) Casting and film stationary
(b) Casting stationary, film oscillated
(c) Casting and film oscillated

in the plane of the specimen surface.   The specimen in this case was a mag-nesium-alloy casting.

As has been explained previously, if one exposure is made with the incident beam inclined from the perpendicular toward the X axis, and another is made with a perpendicular beam, equation 7 may be used to compute the stress component in the direction X.   Similarly, an exposure with a perpendicular beam combined with two exposures made with the beam inclined toward each of the two principal stresses in turn permits the calculation of both principal stresses.   If the directions of the principal stresses are unknown, it is necessary to use at least three inclined exposures and a perpendicular one. Then both the magnitude and directions of the principle stresses may be determined by using the standard formulas discussed elsewhere in this handbook.

In carrying out a series of stress determinations it is convenient to simplify the equations and reduce the calculations as much as possible. For example, when merely the sum of the principal stresses is being measured, using a beam at normal incidence and a standard distance from specimen to film, a measured change in the diffraction-ring diameter is directly proportional to the sum of the stresses, to a very close approximation, and a single slide-rule computation yields the answer. Simple computations are possible in the other methods also,[61] when standard conditions are established.

11. Values of the Elastic Constants. The preceding equations assume isotropic material. In general, this assumption is not valid for the individual grains of a metal even when it is valid for the metal as a whole. This fact together with the fact that a diffracted beam comes from only those grains having certain orientations in the specimen, has given rise to much uncertainty concerning the correct values to use for Young's modulus and Poisson's ratio. Some investigators, including Bohlenrath and Hauk,[67] have concluded that the effective values of the constants vary with the carbon content of steels, their heat treatment, the radiation used, and the angle of incidence of the radiation on the surface, and recommend that the operator always calibrate his apparatus for the given set of conditions that he uses. Certain other investigators, including Norton and his collaborators, have found that the ordinary values of the elastic constants are satisfactory to use in X-ray work. It is possible that some of the apparent variations of the elastic constants that have been observed by some are due to variations in the roughness of the surface produced by etching[60] (see article 12 on surface stresses).

Until further research is available on the subject, it appears proper to assume that the ordinary mechanical values of the elastic constants for polycrystalline metals will produce errors no greater than the errors from reading the films.[60, 61] Nevertheless, in precise work, it is always advisable to check apparatus, technique, and effective value of the constants by making a calibration experiment. This may be done on a test specimen under a known tensile or compressive load or with a beam bent to a known curvature.

12. Surface Stresses. The penetration of the X rays used in stress analysis is very slight; usually the penetration does not exceed one or two thousandths of an inch. Because of this, the preparation of the surface before stresses are measured is an important matter. If the surface has been roughly etched so that there are deep etch pits, the pits may partially relieve the stresses in the material between the pits. The higher and the narrower the microscopic peaks that project out from the surface, the more complete is the relief of stress in the peaks. If the surface is prepared by etching, it should be made as smooth as possible. For steel, it has been found that a 10 per cent solution of nitric acid in alcohol is satisfactory, but a 30 per cent solution is poor.[60]

When electrolytic polishing can be used, it is preferable to etching, for it leaves no pits. Small areas an inch or less in diameter can be polished on the surface of an object at the place where stresses are to be measured if one confines the electrolyte in a small pool at this place.

The shallow penetration makes it possible to study the surface stresses introduced by machining, shot peening, and the like. One investigation showed that a machined surface of steel contained a layer less than 0.010 in. deep with a stress that differed from the stress in the underlying layers by 60,000 psi. Surface stresses of 12,000 psi have been discovered even after a simple elongation in a tensile machine. (This is discussed in article 13.)

When X-ray measurements of residual stresses differ from strain-gage measurements, a system of shallow surface stresses is immediately suspected. In such cases the subdivision or boring-out methods may not have been carried in such a way as to reduce the surface layer to a stress-free state. Unless this is done, the mechanical sectioning methods cannot yield true absolute values of the stresses; but X-ray measurements always yield absolute values.

It is a general rule that plastic flow always tends to reduce residual stresses. Hence, surveys of the initial stress pattern may have little or nothing to do with failure of an object in service when the service involves any plastic flow in the object. On the other hand, studies of the initially stressed state may be of prime importance when an object is subject to failure by stress corrosion. Stresses in the outer skin of an object are probably more important than underlying stresses in season-cracking or stress-corrosion investigations, although it may be some time before a complete understanding of the situation is reached.

13. Distribution of Residual Stresses within an Object. X rays can be employed with various sectioning procedures to determine the distribution of internal stress in the interior of an object. For example, Rosenthal and Norton[66] devised a method for sectioning objects that involves cutting out rectangular blocks and then slicing layers from them, with stress measurements made after each cut. Their results on a butt weld in a welded 1-in. plate showed a maximum residual stress at mid-thickness (Fig. 18-18). The assumptions employed in developing the formulas used increase the inaccuracies when either the stress gradients are high or the plate thickness is great. Shearing stresses can also be computed from these data for points throughout the interior of the object. There has been no nondestructive method developed for determining stresses at interior points; the X rays that are used diffract only from surface layers.

14. Variations in Stresses during Service. The nondestructive feature of the X-ray method is valuable in applications where changes in stresses during service are important. X-ray tests reveal only *elastic* strain and not the plastic component of the strain and thereby differ from ordinary strain-gage measurements which concern the sum of the elastic and plastic components, that is, the total elongation. This feature is important when X rays are used to trace the relaxation of residual stresses during heat treatment or service, for the methods that reveal only the sum of the strains do not permit a calculation of the stress from time to time during the life of the object, as is possible with X rays.

An early use of the method abroad was to study the changes in residual stresses around a drilled hole during the life of a fatigue specimen. In this study the slight plastic flow accompanying the cyclic stressing caused major changes in the residual-stress pattern.

The changes in residual stresses caused by the application of a tensile stress are nicely indicated by the tests of Norton and Rosenthal summarized in Fig. 18-19. In these tests a system of stresses was introduced in a mild-steel strip by placing it between two cylindrical electrodes of a welding machine and heating locally with a current of 3000 amperes for a few seconds. Figure 18-19a, curve I, shows the transverse component of the stresses along a line through the center of the heated zone after this local heating; Fig. 18-19b, curve I, shows the longitudinal component. Curves II, III, IV, and V give the residual stresses after the strip is loaded successively to 7200, 16,000, 29,500, and 38,300 psi and then unloaded. It is seen that stresses in the neighborhood of the tensile yield point (which was 35,000

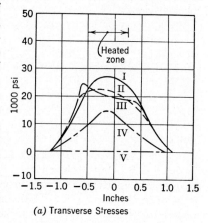

(a) Transverse Stresses

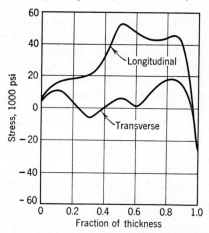

Fig. 18-18. Longitudinal and Transverse Stresses across the Thickness of a Weld in a 1-in. Mild-Steel Plate (D. Rosenthal and J. T. Norton)

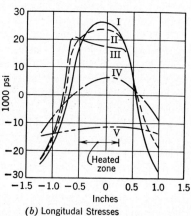

(b) Longitudal Stresses

Fig. 18-19. Residual Stresses around a Heated Zone in a Mild-Steel Strip
I—Directly after stresses were introduced by local heating. II—After applying 7200 psi tensile stress to the strip. III—After 16,000 psi. IV—After 29,500 psi. V—After 38,300 psi (J. T. Norton and D. Rosenthal)

psi) have reduced the residual stresses and, in fact, have replaced them by small longitudinal compressive stresses. These, of course, are stresses at the surface.

15. Miscellaneous Industrial Applications. X-ray methods have been made use of for indicating residual stresses in castings, such as valve bodies, and for studying how the stresses are altered by design, foundry technique, and heat treatment. The laboratories of the automotive and the aircraft industries have employed X-ray methods in similar instances and in studies of forgings, extrusions, and welds.[61] [65] Research on stresses in railroad rails has also been conducted with X rays, and the methods are applicable to residual stresses in car wheels and their alteration during service.

With sufficient care it appears possible to determine stresses in heat-treated steels having hardnesses somewhat above the usually accepted limit of Rockwell C 45. McCutcheon estimates that an accuracy of ± 8000 psi. was obtained on SAE 1045 steel at a hardness of Rockwell C 49, by careful measurement of densitometer traces.[65] There is a possibility that high-hardness steels might be investigated by using the diffraction pattern from the carbide particles in the steels, which may be expected to yield sharper lines than the strained austenite, ferrite, or martensite.

Because of the smallness of the irradiated spot, studies can be made of stresses around holes, notches, or other points where stress concentrations arise. There have been residual-stress measurements of this type completed on specimens before and after fatigue stressing.

Measurements of residual stresses produced or altered by peening, shot blasting, surface rolling, and other surface treatments cannot be made with high precision by X rays because the deformation introduces microscopically distributed stresses which broaden the diffraction lines. With care, however, useful information can sometimes be obtained.

Many industrial problems of the sort discussed in this section can be adequately solved by the simplest X-ray techniques. This applies particularly to problems dealing with the reduction of residual stresses by annealing or by modification in manufacturing procedure. If the unstressed value of the lattice constant has been determined, a measurement of the sum of the principal stresses may be sufficient, and this then requires only a single exposure with the X-ray beam perpendicular to the surface.

It perhaps should be mentioned here that residual stresses are by no means always detrimental. Some improve the load-carrying capacity as in the antofrettage of guns. In many instances they are quite unimportant. Norton and Rosenthal conclude[64] that residual stresses will not effect the safety of a ductile material subjected to a static impact or repeated load if the material is homogeneous and without notches and if the stresses are merely biaxial and not triaxial.

X-rays have seldom been used for the measurement of live loads, although some mention has been found of their use on railway bridges in Germany. It is possible to measure peak values of cyclic stresses if one synchronizes the electric impulse to an X-ray tube with the peak stress to be measured; the rays are then diffracted only when the metal is under maximum stress, and the diffraction pattern is then not blurred by the range of stresses that would have been recorded by a continuous exposure.

16. Plastic Strain and X-Ray Diffraction. Plastic deformation, resulting from stressing a metal beyond its elastic limit, alters X-ray diffraction patterns in various ways: (1) Individual diffraction spots become distorted; (2) diffraction lines ("Debye rings") become blurred, widened and, weakened in intensity; (3) reorientation of grains occurs, tending to develop a preferred orientation characteristic of the type of strain and the particular metal used.

The distortion of spots and the blurring of lines have fundamentally different causes.[55] The blurring of spots is caused by warping and bending of atomic planes—fundamentally by a range of orientation of the atomic planes in a grain; the blurring of diffraction lines is caused by a variation of the stresses from point to point in a grain, the so-called "microstresses."

1. The blurring of spots is illustrated in Fig. 18-20 which compares the Laue pattern of an annealed-aluminum wire before and after plastic strain of

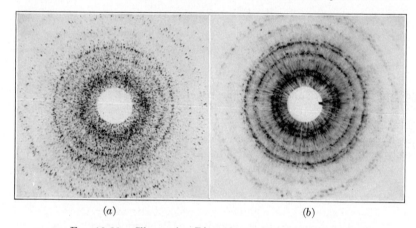

(a)   (b)

Fig. 18-20.   Illustrating Distortion of Spots (Asterism)
Diffraction by transmission through a 1-mm wire of aluminum.   Molybdenum X-ray tube, unfiltered, 45 kv
(a) As recrystallized by annealing
(b) After straining the wire to a 3 per cent permanent elongation

3 per cent.   The appearance of the strained spots is frequently called "asterism."   The effect is related to the range of orientation of layers or of blocks of varying size in the grains (like the reflection of light from a wrinkled mirror or from a mosaic mirror), and it is impossible to compute the intensity of the microstresses responsible for it.   In fact, if a specimen such as this is given an anneal which relieves the stresses without causing recrystallization, the appearance will not be greatly changed.

The distortion of spots is inappreciable at stresses below the elastic limit and increases steadily with increasing plastic deformation and, hence, is a semiquantitative indication of the severity of the strain.   However, the correlation between appearance and amount of strain is not free of complicating factors.   The appearance is altered by changing the voltage on the X-ray tube and by inserting a filter in the X-ray beam; asterism is more easily seen with specimens of large grain size than of small.   Asterism may also arise from imperfections of growth of a grain, or from microstrains accompanying age hardening or transformations in the grain, or from absorption and release of gases, and in these cases the asterism is present, of course, before external stress has been applied.

Distortion of spots is sometimes produced in cyclic stressing in fatigue tests, as, for example, in Fig. 18-21. When it is seen, it is an indication of plastic deformation at the point X-rayed, but most authorities agree that the amount of cold work a metal will stand before damage sets in or failure occurs varies

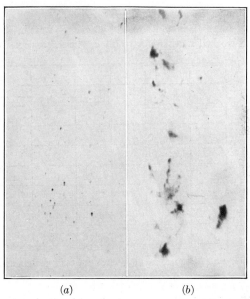

(a)   (b)

FIG. 18-21.   Distortion of Spots by Fatigue Stressing
Aluminum alloy (2S-0) photographed with molybdenum X-ray tube, an oscillating specimen and a stationary film
  (a) Unstressed
  (b) After 505,000,000 cycles at 4000 psi, within the safe range of stresses

greatly from one material to another and may even be negligible; hence, X-ray indications of this cold work do not correlate directly with the likelihood that an object will fail.   No universal rule can be stated that will enable one to predict impending fatigue failure from X-ray patterns nor to predict that failure will not occur.   A rule might be established for a given alloy after a given heat treatment by careful calibration experiments in the laboratory, which duplicated service conditions closely; however, this would be possible only if it is found that appreciable cold work always precedes failure.   Even then it would be difficult to trust the information in practice, for fatigue failure in engineering structures is not usually accompanied by widespread damage to the metal, but rather by very localized damage.   The X rays would have to be directed at the spot where damage is localized and where the crack would ultimately start, the spot where stress concentration is the greatest.

2. The widening of diffraction lines can be measured by plotting the intensity of diffraction against the diffraction angle as the angle is varied through the value for maximum intensity and by taking the width of the peak at half maximum intensity as the index of the blurring. Line widths increase with increasing plastic deformation, as in the example shown in Fig. 18-22. Considerable care is required to get good measurements of this kind, and difficulties are encountered with specimens of large grain size; for best results it is necessary to use high diffraction angles (large θ values).

After lengthy research it is now agreed by most workers in the field that line widening in cold-worked metals is a result of the microstresses in the metal,

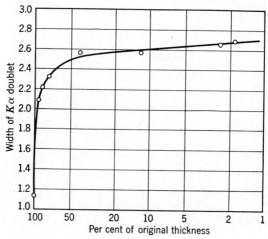

FIG. 18-22. Diffraction-Line Widening Produced by Cold Rolling of Permalloy Widths of back-reflection lines between points of half maximum intensity (F. E. Haworth)

the stresses which vary on a scale of 10^{-5} cm or more. Crystal-lattice distortions that vary on a scale of 10^{-6} cm to 10^{-8} cm, that is, from atom to atom or within small groups of atoms, are studied not by line widths, but by line intensities. There is little doubt that microstresses play an important role in the physical properties of cold-worked metals, but only a statistical average can be deduced with any certainty from the line-width measurements.

3. Preferred orientation is induced only by strains of considerable magnitude. Rolled-sheet steel begins to show this when the reduction in thickness by cold rolling has reached 30 to 60 per cent, if the beam is passed through the sheet in a direction perpendicular to the surface. The diffraction pattern passes from rings of uniform intensity to rings on which maxima of intensity occur at certain positions, the maxima becoming more distinct with increasing deformation. After reductions above 70 to 80 per cent the pattern of rolled steel resembles that in Fig. 18-23. These intensity maxima may be seen with

lesser rolling if certain favored directions are chosen for the initial beam; for example, if the beam is inclined about 10° from the sheet normal and 80° from the rolling direction in the sheet. Simultaneously with the development of a preferred orientation, the metal develops directional properties (anisotropy). These characteristics are not lost until the metal is annealed at a high enough temperature to cause recrystallization—and even recrystallization may bring about merely a change in the type of orientation, rather than a complete return to random orientation. Passing a steel through the phase

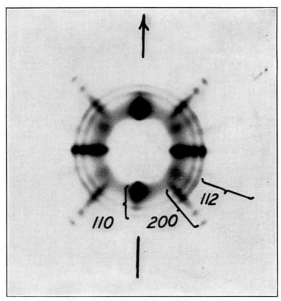

FIG. 18-23.   Indication of Highly Developed Preferred Orientation in Cold-Rolled Steel Sheet
Molybdenum tube, beam normal to sheet, 110, 200, and 112 reflection circles indicated.   Rolling direction indicated by the arrow

change to austenite and back, as in normalizing, is more effective than recrystallization below the critical temperature in removing preferred orientation.

17. Estimation of Plastic Strain. The distortion of spots is the most sensitive X-ray indication of cold work. Considerable distortion occurs, for example, as a result of the plastic flow at the lower yield point in iron and steel, even though this seldom exceeds a few per cent elongation. Spot distortion is most sensitive with recrystallized metal that is free from the imperfections that arise during freezing or during phase transformations in the solid state. It can be studied only with grains that are large enough to give separate spots on the diffraction pattern. Either back-reflection cameras or cameras for reflection from the surface with glancing incidence of the rays on the surface, or cameras in which the beam penetrates a thin etched specimen will serve. The widening of lines is measurable at strains slightly exceeding the yield point and increases rapidly in the first 50 per cent or so of elongation or reduction in thickness (see Fig. 18-22). The reduction of diffraction-line intensity has not been extensively investigated as a function of the amount of strain, and the interpretation of intensities is less straightforward because the intensity may also be altered to some extent by variations in "extinction," an effect that is related to the perfection of the lattice.

The development of preferred orientations is usually expected only after deformation has proceeded until the preceding effects have reached a nearly stable final value. With sufficient strain this too reaches an end value which is not increased with further cold work. Some tests indicate that a given reduction in thickness of a sheet by deep drawing may yield a more pronounced orientation than the same reduction by rolling.

In the foregoing discussion, all plastic deformation is presumed to be at temperatures below the recrystallization temperature, and thus cold work rather than hot work. True hot work leaves strain-free grains and, generally, a low degree of preferred orientation.

X-ray diffraction provides rather direct evidence for the effects of annealing with most polycrystalline metals. If a metal containing high microstresses, for example, a cold-worked metal, is annealed so as to produce recovery, the diffraction lines will lose their diffuseness and sharpen (provided the metal is homogeneous as to composition). If the metal is annealed so as to recrystallize the grains, the lines will split up into discrete spots, as in Fig. 18-20a. The two processes may or may not be concurrent in any given metal. If an alloy is heat-treated so as to age-harden, it usually shows distorted spots and widened lines. If a phase change occurs, the pattern of diffraction lines will be altered in accordance with the diffraction patterns of the various phases present.

BIBLIOGRAPHY

General Treatises

1. G. L. CLARK, *Applied X-Rays*, McGraw-Hill Book Co, New York, 1940. Principles and applications.
2. G. E. DOAN, "Gamma Ray Radiographic Testing," *J Franklin Inst*, v 216, 1933, pp 183–216. Review of early radium radiography.
3. R. GLOCKER, *Material Prüfung mit Röntgenstrahlen*, Julius Springer, Berlin, 1936. German practice
4. H. R. ISENBURGER, *Bibliography on Industrial Radiography*, St. John X-Ray Service, Long Island City, New York, 1946. Extensive bibliography.
5. A. ST. JOHN AND H. R. ISENBURGER, *Industrial Radiology*, John Wiley & Sons, New York, 1943. General survey of practice.
6. W. T. SPROULE, *X-Rays in Practice*, McGraw-Hill Book Co, New York, 1945. Principles and practice of X-ray and radium inspection. Authoritative.
7. *Symposium on Radiography*, ASTM, 1936, 1942. Good articles on the subject by specialists in various branches of engineering.
8. O. ZMESKAL, "Radiographic Inspection of Metals," Harper Bros, 1943. Clear and concise; good text for elementary course.

Technique and Equipment

9. L. W. BALL, "High Sensitivity in Radium Radiography of Castings," *ASTM Bul*, May 1942, pp 29–32. Technique.

10. L. W. BALL, "A Study of Secondary Radiation in Relation to the Radiography of Aircraft Castings," *ASTM Bul*, Mar 1942, pp 27–33.

11. C. S. BARRETT, R. A. GEZELIUS, AND R. F. MEHL, "The Technique of Radiography by Gamma Rays," *Metals and Alloys*, v 1, 1930, 872–9. Principles, technique, early results.

12. E. E. CHARLESTON, W. F. WESTENDORP, L. E. DEMPSTER, AND G. HOTALING, "New 1,000,000 Volt X-Ray Unit," *J Applied Physics*, v 10, 1939, pp 374–85. Design and operating characteristics.

13. A. F. COTA, "Control of Radiographic Quality through Direct Density Checks," *Indus Radiography*, v 4, n 2, pp 11–7. fall 1945. Technique.

14. EHRKE AND SLACK, "Radiography at High Speed," *Elec Eng*, v 60, 1941, pp 432–35. Examples of radiography in 1 μsec with cold-cathode tube.

15. A. J. MOSES, "Ten Years Progress in Radiography," *Metal Progress*, Nov 1941, pp 771–76. Review.

16. "Radium Protection," Handbook 23, National Bureau of Standards; "X-Ray Protection," Handbook 20, National Bureau of Standards.

17. H. E. SEEMAN, "Reduction of Secondary Radiation and of Excessive Radiographic Contrast by Filtration," *Proc ASTM* v 40, pp 1289–96. Useful information on filter technique.

18. H. E. SEEMAN, "Some Physical and Radiographic Properties of Metallic Intensifying Screens," *J Applied Physics*, v 8, Dec 1937, pp 836–45. Measurements on the properties and effectiveness of metal foil screens of various metals and thicknesses.

19. H. E. SEEMAN, "General Properties of Industrial Radiographic Films," *ASTM Bul*, May 1945, pp 17–27. Principles of film action and processing.

20. L. S. TAYLOR, "Industrial X-Ray Protection," *ASTM Bul*, Aug 1939, pp 23–31. Principles; protection required for different voltages; lead equivalents of different materials.

21. E. F. THILO, "Ultra High Speed Radiography," *Indus Radiography*, winter 1945–46, pp 40–43. Brief summary of Frankford Arsenal use of microsecond exposures.

22. R. C. WOODS AND V. C. CETRONE, "Radiography of Light Alloys," *Indus Radiography*, summer 1943, pp 32–8; *Iron Age*, v 151, 1943, pp 52–8. Choice of radiation.

Applications

See also the books listed under "General Treatises."

23. L. W. BALL, "The Interpretation of Radiographs, Particularly Aircraft Parts," *Am Soc Metals Preprint*, 1944. A system for identifying defects, with illustrations.

24. B. C. BOULTON, "X-Ray of Aircraft Castings, its Control and Value," *J Aeronautical Sciences*, v 9, June 1942, pp 271–83. Statistical analysis of results of radiography.

25. R. S. BUSK, "A Correlation of Mechanical Properties and Radiographic Appearance of Magnesium Alloy Castings," *Proc ASTM*, v 42, 1942, pp 1076–083; *Indus Radiography*, v 2, n 3, pp 33–7, 1943–44. A method of rating porosity and the correlation of the rating with physical properties.

26. O. R. CARPENTER, "Radiographic Examination of Heavy Plate," *Welding J*, v 20, 1941, pp 717–23.

27. A. E. CARTWRIGHT, "Fluoroscopic Examination of Light Alloy Castings," *Trans Am Foundrymen's Asso*, v 51, 1943, pp 133–50. Design of installations; practicability and limitations; technique.

28. C. B. CLASON, "X-Ray Testing of Welds," *Indus Radiography*, fall 1942, pp 14–20; *Welding Engr*, Aug 1942, pp 27–31. Typical weld defects described and illustrated.

29. J. J. Chyle, "Quality Control of Metallic Arc Welds by Radiographic Examination," *Indus Radiography*, v 3, n 3, pp 13–22, 1944–45.
30. R. W. Emerson, "Gamma-Ray Radiography of Welded High Pressure Power Plant Piping," *ASTM Preprint*, 1942. Method and results.
31. C. L. Frear, "Radiographic Specifications and Standards for Naval Materials," *Trans Am Foundrymen's Assoc*, v 52, 1944–45, p 1078–110. Describes Navy inspection and standards.
32. R. Jackson, *Application of Radiography to Improvement of Foundry Technique*, Iron & Steel Institute, advance copy, Jan 1945. Principles of interpretation; examples; remedies in the foundry technique that proved effective; many sketches of castings showing location of defects.
33. R. Katz, "X-Ray Inspection of Castings," *Metal Progress*, July 1943, pp 89–94.
34. F. R. Mansfield, "X-Rays in Light Alloy Foundry," *Indus Radiography*, v 3, n 4, 1945, pp 36–43; "X-Rays in Light Alloy Foundry," *Light Metals*, v 6, 1943, pp 469–78. Plant technique, interpretation and evaluation; improvement of quality by radiography.
35. D. M. McCutcheon, "The Use of Radiography in the Development of Castings for Mass Production," *ASTM Bul*, Mar 1940, pp 13–6. Experience at Ford Motor Co plant.
36. W. Montgomery, "The Use of X-Rays in the Foundry," *Foundry Trade J*, Oct 22, 1942, pp 159–70. General survey of applications.
37. "Radiographic Requirements," (Bureau of Ships) *Indus Radiography*, summer 1942, pp 23–9. Radiography from the standpoint of naval requirements.
38. D. W. Smith and F. Keller, "Correlation of Metallographic and Radiographic Examinations of Spot Welds in Aluminum Alloys," *Welding J Research Supp*, Dec 1942, pp 573–83-s. Tests on Alclad 24S and 42S alloys; useful correlation shown.
39. "Radiographic Inspection of Fusion Welds," ASME Boiler Construction Code, 1940.
40. "Tentative Methods of Radiographic Testing of Metal Castings," Committee E7, ASTM, 1939, Standards, pp 1225–229. Recommended practice.
41. "Testing with X-Ray Counting Tubes," *Iron Age*, June 10, 1943; *Indus Radiography*, v 2, n 2, p 39–41, 1943. On Geiger counter applications.
42. G. H. Tenney, "Radiography of Radioactive Heavy Metals," *Indus Radiography*, v 5, spring 1947, pp 33–6. Use of radium in radiographing uranium.
43. K. R. Van Horn, "Recent Developments in X-Ray Inspection," *Metal Progress*, Jan 1944, pp 78–82. Review.
44. R. C. Woods, J. C. Barrett, and T. W. Dietz, "Radiography of Spot Welds," *Metals and Alloys*, Sept 1942, p 442; *Indus Radiography*, v 1, n 3, p 42; n 4, p 17, 1943. Judging spot-weld quality from radiographs. Illustrations.

Microradiography

45. L. W. Ball, "X-Ray Micrography as a Tool for Foundry Control," *Trans Am Foundrymen's Assoc*, v 52, 1945, pp 1111–1123. Diagnosis of cause of microcavities by magnification of radiographs of 0.005-in. to 0.050-in. slices.
46. S. T. Gross and G. L. Clark, "Technique and Practice of Microradiography," *Indus Radiography*, v 1, n 2, p 21, 1942; also *Indus and Eng Chem*, analytic ed, v 14, 1942, pp 676–83. An early report on technique and possibilities; illustrations.
47. S. E. Maddigan, "The Technique of Microradiography," *J Applied Physics*, v 15, 1944, pp 43–54. Method and theory.
48. S. E. Maddigan and B. R. Zimmerman, "Microradiography, a New Metallurgical Tool," *Trans AIME*, v 156, 1944, pp 33–58. Method and applications to nonferrous alloys.

49. R. C. Woods and V. C. Cetrone, "Microradiography of Alloys," *Metals and Alloys*, Dec 1943, pp 1318–325. Covers use of tungsten-target X-ray tube as well as diffraction tubes.

50. R. Smoluchowski, C. M Lucht, and J. M Hurd, "Composition and Diffraction Effects in X-Ray Micrographs," *J Applied Physics*, v 17, 1946, pp 864–70. Segregation in alloys.

Stress Measurement by X Rays

51. G. Sachs and J. Weerts, "Elastizitätsmessungen mit Röntgenstrahlen," *Zeitschrift für Physik*, vol 64, 1930, p 344. Theory and experiments, using exposures of stress-free metal and of stressed metal.

52. C. S. Barrett and M Gensamer, *Physics*, v 7, 1936, p 1 Mathematical formulas for stiess analysis by X rays.

53. R. Glocker and E Oswald, "Einzelbestimmung der elastischen Hauptspannungen mit Röntgenstrahlen," *Zeitschrift für technische Physik*, v 16, 1935, pp 237–42 Mathematical formulas for magnitude and direction of principal stresses from perpendicular and inclined exposures.

54. F. Gisen, R. Glocker, and E. Osswald, "Einzelbestimmung von elastische Spannungen mit Röntgenstrahlen II," *Zeitschrift für technische Physik*, v 17, 1936, pp 145–55. Determining lattice constants for stress-free material, stress determination; avoiding graininess; errors introduced by oscillation; accuracies obtained.

55. C. S. Barrett, *Structure of Metals*, McGraw-Hill Book Co, New York, 1943. A review.

56. F. Wever and H. Moller, "Ueber ein Verfahren zum Nachweis innerer Spannungen," *Archiv für das Eisenhüttenwesen*, v 5, 1931–32, pp 215–18. Determination of $(\sigma_1 + \sigma_2)$; errors.

57. D. E. Thomas, "The Measurement of Stress by X-Rays," *J Sci Instr*, v 18, 1941, pp 135–38. Technique; use of gage instead of reference material.

58. G. H. Found, *Experimental Stress Analysis*, v 2, n 1, p 203, 1944. Discussion. Strains introduced by sawing in magnesium.

59. R. Glocker, B. Hess, and O. Schaaber, "Einzelbestimmung von elastischen Spannungen mit Röntgenstrahlen III," *Zeitschrift für technische Physik*, v 19, 1938, pp 194–204. Stress components from single exposures; determining magnitudes and directions of principal stresses and the unstressed lattice dimensions; errors from oscillation; application to hexagonal metals.

60. J. T. Norton, "X-Ray Methods in the Field of Residual Stresses," *Experimental Stress Analysis*, v 2, n 1, pp 157–60, 1944. Discussion of elastic constants, surface preparation, applications.

61. L. Frommer and E. H. Lloyd, *J Inst Metals*, (Lond.) v 70, 1944, p 91. Method and applications.

62. J. T. Norton and D. Rosenthal, "Stress Measurement by X-Ray Diffraction," *Experimental Stress Analysis*, v 1, n 2, pp 73–6, 1944. Technique. Advantages and limitations of X-ray method. "Applications of the X-Ray Diffraction Method of Stress Measurement to Problems Involving Residual Stresses in Metals," *Experimental Stress Analysis*, v 1, n 2, pp 77–81, 1944. Experimental results on sheet steel heated in small areas; reduction of residual stresses by plastic deformation.

63. J. T. Norton and B. M. Loring, "Stress Measurement in Weldments by X-Rays," *Welding J Research Supp*, v 20, 1941, pp 284-s–88-s. Technique and results.

64. J. T. Norton and D. Rosenthal, "An Investigation of the Behavior of Residual Stresses under External Load and Their Effect on Safety," *J Am Welding Soc*, v 22, n 2, pp 63-s–78-s, 1943. Results of X-ray measurements

of stress components in simulated welds correlated with static, impact, and fatigue properties.

65. D. M. McCutcheon, *Industrial Radiography*, spring 1946, p 9. Experiments with high-hardness steels.
66. D. Rosenthal and J. T. Norton, "A Method of Measuring Triaxial Residual Stress in Plates," *Welding J Research Supp*, v 24, 1945, pp 295-s–307-s. A sectioning method using X-rays or strain gages.
67. W. T. Sproull, *X-Rays in Practice*, McGraw-Hill Book Co, New York, 1946. Review.

APPENDIX I

FUNDAMENTALS OF THE THEORY OF ELASTICITY

By S. P. Timoshenko

1. Stress. Let Fig. A-1 represent a body in equilibrium under the action of external forces, P_1, $\cdots$ P_7. Such a body is said to be in a *condition of stress*. To study the *internal forces* produced in the body, let us divide the body by a plane m–m into two parts A and B and consider one of these parts, say, part A. This part is in equilibrium under the action of external forces P_5, $\cdots$ P_7 and the internal forces, continuously distributed over the plane

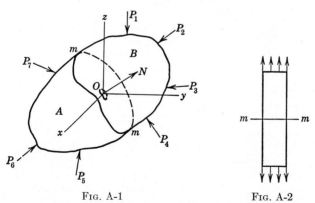

FIG. A-1   FIG. A-2

m–m and representing the actions of the material of part B on the material of part A. The magnitude of the latter forces is defined by their intensity, that is, by the amount of force per unit area of the plane on which they act. This intensity, usually measured in pounds per square inch is called stress. In the simple case of a prismatical bar submitted to tension by forces uniformly distributed over the ends (Fig. A-2), the internal forces are also uniformly distributed over any cross section m–m of the bar, and the stress can be obtained by dividing the total tensile force P by the cross-sectional area A. In the general case of Fig. A-1 the stress is not uniformly distributed over the plane m–m and to obtain stress at any point O of that plane we take an elemental area δA at that point and assume that the forces acting across this area and representing the action of particles of the side B on the particles of the side A are reduced to a resultant δP. If we now continuously contract the elemental area δA, the limiting value of the ratio $\delta P/\delta A$ gives us the magnitude of the stress acting on the plane m–m at the point O. The direction of the resultant δP is the direction of this stress. Generally, the direction of stress is inclined to the area δA, on which it acts, and we usually will resolve it into two components: a *normal stress* perpendicular to the area δA, and a *shearing stress* acting in the plane of the area.

2. Symbols for Forces and Stresses. We shall distinguish two kinds of external forces which may act on a body. Forces distributed over the surface of the body, such as hydrostatic pressure or the pressure of one body on another, are called *surface forces*. Forces distributed over the volume of a body; such as gravitational forces; magnetic forces; inertia forces, in the case of a body in motion; are called *body forces*. The surface forces per unit area we will usually resolve into three components parallel to the coordinate axes and use for these components the notations $\bar{X}$, $\bar{Y}$, $\bar{Z}$. Concentrated forces acting on the surface of the body represent a particular case of surface forces in which a finite force is distributed over a very small area so that the intensity of the force becomes very large. The body forces per unit volume we also shall resolve into three orthogonal components and will denote these components by X, Y, Z.

In dealing with stresses we shall use the letter σ to denote normal stress and the letter τ for shearing stress. To indicate the direction of the plane on which the stress is acting, subscripts to σ and τ symbols will be used. These subscripts and also the directions of stresses which in the future will be considered as positive are shown in Fig. A-3, representing an infinitesimal element cut out of the stressed body by planes perpendicular to the orthogonal x, y, z axes. If we consider, for example, the side of the element perpendicular to the x axis, the normal component of stress, acting on this side, is denoted by σ_x, the subscript x indicating that this stress is acting on a plane normal to the x axis. The normal stress is taken positive when it produces tension and negative when it produces compression.

The shearing stress is resolved into two components τ_{xy} and τ_{xz} parallel to the coordinate axes y and z. Two subscript letters are used in this case, the first indicating the direction of the normal to the plane under consideration and the second indicating the direction of the stress. The positive directions of the components of shearing stress on any side of the element are taken as the positive directions of the coordinate axes if a tensile stress on the same side would have the positive direction of the corresponding axis. If the tensile stress has the direction opposite to the positive axis, the positive directions of the shearing-stress components should be reversed. Following this rule, the positive directions of all the stress components acting on the right-hand side of the element in Fig. A-3 coincide with the positive directions of the coordinate axes. The positive directions are all reversed if we are considering the left-hand side of the same element.

3. Six Stress Components. From the preceding discussion we see that, for each pair of parallel sides of an element, such as in Fig. A-3, one symbol is needed to denote the normal component of stress and two more symbols to denote the two components of shearing stress. To define the stresses acting on all six sides of the element we used three symbols σ_x, σ_y, σ_z for normal stresses and six symbols, $\tau_{xy}, \tau_{xz}, \tau_{yx}, \tau_{yz}, \tau_{zx}, \tau_{zy}$, for shearing stresses. From the condition of equilibrium of the element it can be concluded that the required number of symbols for shearing-stress components can be reduced from six to three. Considering moment about the x axis of all forces acting on the element, we have to take only forces corresponding to the stress components shown in Fig. A-4. Body forces, such as the weight of the element, can be neglected in this case. This follows from the fact that, when we are reducing the dimensions of the element, the body forces acting on it diminish as the cube of the linear dimensions, while the surface forces diminish as the square of the linear dimensions. Hence, for an infinitesimal element, body forces are small quantities of higher order than surface forces and can be neglected.

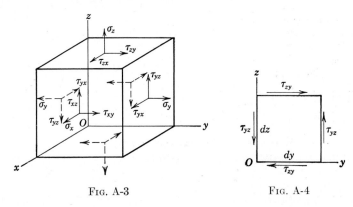

FIG. A-3   FIG. A-4

Similarly, moments due to nonuniformity of distribution of stresses over the sides of the element can be neglected, and in calculation of forces acting on any side of the element we multiply the area of the side by the magnitude of stress at the center of the side. Denoting by dx, dy, dz, the dimensions of the element, we find that the equation of equilibrium for moments about the x axis (Fig. A-4) is

$$\tau_{yz} \, dx \, dy \, dz - \tau_{zy} \, dx \, dy \, dz = 0$$

Similar equations can be written also for the y and z axes. From these three equations of equilibrium we find

$$\tau_{xy} = \tau_{yx}, \quad \tau_{xz} = \tau_{zx}, \quad \tau_{yz} = \tau_{zy} \tag{1}$$

We see that for, any two perpendicular sides of the element, the components of shearing stress perpendicular to the intersection line of these sides are equal. The six quantities,

$$\sigma_x, \quad \sigma_y, \quad \sigma_z, \quad \tau_{xy} = \tau_{yx}, \quad \tau_{xz} = \tau_{zx}, \quad \tau_{yz} = \tau_{zy}$$

are, therefore, sufficient to define the stresses acting on the three perpendicular planes passing through any point O of a body. These six quantities are called the *components of stress* for that point.

If these six components are known, the stress on any inclined plane through the same point can be calculated from equations of statics, as follows. Let O be a point of the stressed body, and suppose that the stresses for three coordinate planes are known (Fig. A-5). To obtain the stress for any inclined plane through O, we take a plane BCD parallel to it at a small distance from O, so that this latter plane, together with the coordinate planes, cuts out from the body a very small tetrahedron $BCDO$. We assume that stresses vary continuously in the body. Then the stress acting on the plane BCD approaches the stress on the parallel plane through O as the distance between the planes becomes infinitesimal.

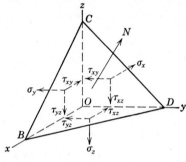

FIG. A-5

In writing equations of equilibrium of the elemental tetrahedron we proceed as in the preceding article, neglect the body forces, and assume that the stresses are uniformly distributed over the sides of the element. The forces acting on the tetrahedron can, therefore, be determined by multiplying the stress components by the areas of the faces. If A denotes the area of the face BCD of the tetrahedron, the areas of the three other faces are obtained by projecting the area A on the three coordinate planes. Let N be the normal to the plane BCD directed as shown in Fig. A-5. Introducing then for the direction cosines of this normal the notations,

$$\cos (Nx) = l, \quad \cos (Ny) = m, \quad \cos (Nz) = n$$

we find the areas of the three other faces of the tetrahedron, Al, Am, An, perpendicular to the x, y, z axes, respectively. Let $\bar{X}$, $\bar{Y}$, $\bar{Z}$ be the three components of the stress acting on the inclined face BCD. Then the component in the x direction of the force acting on face BCD is $A\bar{X}$. The components in the x direction of the forces acting on the three other faces of the element are $-Al\sigma_x$, $-Am\tau_{xy}$, $-An\tau_{xz}$. The corresponding equation of equilibrium is

$$A\bar{X} - Al\sigma_x - Am\tau_{xy} - An\tau_{xz} = 0$$

Similar equations can be written also for the y and z axes. After canceling the factor A, we obtain the following expressions for the components $\bar{X}$, $\bar{Y}$, $\bar{Z}$ of the stress acting on an inclined plane, the aspect of which is defined by the direction cosines l, m, n.

$$\bar{X} = \sigma_x l + \tau_{xy} m + \tau_{xz} n$$
$$\bar{Y} = \tau_{xy} l + \sigma_y m + \tau_{zy} n \qquad (2)$$
$$\bar{Z} = \tau_{xz} l + \tau_{yz} m + \sigma_z n$$

4. Principal Stresses. *Maximum Shear.* Having the components $\bar{X}$, $\bar{Y}$, $\bar{Z}$ of the stress acting on an inclined plane (equations 2), we can obtain the normal stress on that plane by projecting $\bar{X}$, $\bar{Y}$, $\bar{Z}$ on the direction of the normal N, which gives

$$\sigma_n = \bar{X}l + \bar{Y}m + \bar{Z}n$$

Substituting for $\bar{X}$, $\bar{Y}$, $\bar{Z}$ their expressions 2, we obtain

$$\sigma_n = \sigma_x l^2 + \sigma_y m^2 + \sigma_z n^2 + 2\tau_{yz}mn + 2\tau_{zx}ln + 2\tau_{xy}lm \qquad (3)$$

The variation of σ_n with the direction of the normal N can be represented geometrically as follows. Let us put from the origin O (Fig. A-5) in the direction of N a vector whose length r is inversely proportional to the square root of the absolute value of the stress σ_n; then,

$$r = \frac{k}{\sqrt{|\sigma_n|}} \qquad (a)$$

where k is an arbitrary selected constant. The coordinates of the end of this vector will be

$$x = lr, \quad y = mr, \quad z = nr \qquad (b)$$

and we obtain

$$l = \frac{x}{r}, \quad m = \frac{y}{r}, \quad n = \frac{z}{r}$$

Substituting these values into equation 3 and using equation a, we find

$$\pm k^2 = \sigma_x x^2 + \sigma_y y^2 + \sigma_z z^2 + 2\tau_{yz}yz + 2\tau_{zx}zx + 2\tau_{xy}xy \qquad (4)$$

As the plane BCD rotates about the point O, the end of the vector r always lies on the surface of the second degree given by equation 4. This surface is completely defined by the stress condition at the point O (Fig. A-5) and is independent of the selection of coordinate axes x, y, z. If the directions of these axes are changed, the surface (equation 4) remains unchanged and only the components of stress σ_x, σ_y, σ_z, τ_{yz}, τ_{zx}, τ_{xy}, appearing as coefficients in equation 4, will alter. From geometry it is known that, in the case of a surface of second degree, such as given by equation 4, it is always possible to select for the axes x, y, z such directions that the terms in this equation containing products of coordinates will vanish. This means that we can always find three perpendicular planes for which τ_{yz}, τ_{zx}, τ_{xy} vanish, that is, the corresponding resultant stresses are perpendicular to the planes on which they act. These planes we call *principal planes* and the stresses acting on them *principal stresses*. The corresponding coordinate axes are called *principal axes*.

If x, y, z, are principal axes, τ_{yz}, τ_{zx}, τ_{xy} vanish, and equations 2 give

$$\bar{X} = l\sigma_x, \quad \bar{Y} = m\sigma_y, \quad \bar{Z} = n\sigma_z \qquad (5)$$

We see that, knowing the principal directions and principal stresses σ_x, σ_y, σ_z, we can calculate the stress components on any inclined plane, and the resultant stress s will be found from the equation:

$$s^2 = \bar{X}^2 + \bar{Y}^2 + \bar{Z}^2 = l^2\sigma_x^2 + m^2\sigma_y^2 + n^2\sigma_z^2 \qquad (6)$$

The component σ_n of this stress in the direction normal to the plane, from equation 3, is

$$\sigma_n = l^2\sigma_x + m^2\sigma_y + n^2\sigma_z \qquad (7)$$

The square of the shearing stress acting on the same plane will be

$$\tau^2 = s^2 - \sigma_n^2 = l^2\sigma_x^2 + m^2\sigma_y^2 + n^2\sigma_z^2 - (l^2\sigma_x + m^2\sigma_y + n^2\sigma_z)^2 \qquad (8)$$

Using this expression, it can be proved that the maximum shearing stress acts on the plane bisecting the angle between the largest and the smallest principal stresses and is equal to half the difference between these two principal stresses.

5. Strain. *Strain Components.* In discussing deformation of an elastic body we assume that there are enough constraints to prevent motion as a rigid body, so that no displacements of particles of the body are possible without deformation. Only small deformations such as occur in engineering structures will be considered. The small displacements of particles during deformation of a body we resolve into components u, v, w, parallel to the coordinate axes x, y, z, respectively. It may be assumed that these small quantities vary continuously over the volume of the body. Consider an infinitesimal element $dx\,dy\,dz$ at point O of a body (Fig. A-6). If the body undergoes deformation, and u, v, w are the components of the displacement of the point O, the displacement in the x direction of an adjacent point A on the x axis will be

$$u + \frac{\partial u}{\partial x}\,dx$$

The increase in length of the element OA due to deformation is, therefore, $(\partial u/\partial x)\,dx$. Hence, the *unit elongation*, or *strain* at point O in the x direction

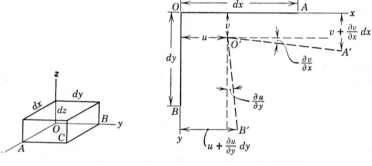

Fig. A-6   Fig. A-7

is $\partial u/\partial x$. In the same manner it can be shown that the unit elongations in the y and z directions are given by the derivatives $\partial v/\partial y$, $\partial w/\partial z$.

Let us consider now the change in angle between the two elements OA and OB (Fig. A-7) which were perpendicular before the deformation of the body. If u and v are the displacements of point O in the x and y directions, the displacement of point A in the y direction and of the point B in the x direction are $v + (\partial v/\partial x)\,dx$ and $u + (\partial u/\partial y)\,dy$, respectively. Owing to these displacements, the new direction $O'A'$ of the element OA is inclined to the initial direction by the small angle indicated in the figure, equal to $\partial v/\partial x$. In the same manner we find that the direction $O'B'$ is inclined to OB by the small angle $\partial u/\partial y$. From this we see that the initially right angle AOB between the two elements OA and OB is diminished by the amount $\partial v/\partial x + \partial u/\partial y$. This represents the *shearing strain* between the planes xz and yz. The shearing strains between the planes xy and xz and the planes yx and yz can be obtained in similar manner.

We shall use the letter ϵ for unit elongation and the letter γ for shearing strain.   To indicate the directions the same subscripts to these letters as for stress components will be used, and we obtain:

$$\epsilon_x = \frac{\partial u}{\partial x}, \quad \epsilon_y = \frac{\partial v}{\partial y}, \quad \epsilon_z = \frac{\partial w}{\partial z}$$

$$\gamma_{xy} = \frac{\partial u}{\partial y} + \frac{\partial v}{\partial x}, \quad \gamma_{yz} = \frac{\partial v}{\partial z} + \frac{\partial w}{\partial y}, \quad \gamma_{xz} = \frac{\partial u}{\partial z} + \frac{\partial w}{\partial x} \tag{9}$$

These six quantities are called *components of strain*.   If they are known, the elongation in any direction and the change in angle between any two directions can be calculated.

6. Hooke's Law.   In our further discussion we assume that structural materials are perfectly elastic and homogeneous; we assume also that their elastic properties are the same in all the directions, that is, that the materials are *isotropic*.   Experiments show that a specimen of isotropic material in the form of rectangular parallelepiped retains its right angles under the action of normal stresses uniformly distributed over the sides of the specimen.   Assume that a specimen of that kind with sides parallel to the coordinate axes is submitted to the action of normal stress σ_x uniformly distributed over two opposite ends.   Experiments show that the magnitude of strain ϵ_x is proportional to the stress applied, and we have

$$\epsilon_x = \frac{\sigma_x}{E} \tag{10}$$

where E is the *modulus of elasticity in tension*.   This extension in the x direction is accompanied by lateral contractions:

$$\epsilon_y = \epsilon_z = -\mu \frac{\sigma_x}{E} \tag{11}$$

The constant factor μ is called *Poisson's ratio*.   For structural steel it can be taken equal to 0.3.   Equations 10 and 11 can be used also for compressive stress.   Longitudinal compression will be accompanied by lateral expansion, the constants E and μ remaining the same as in the case of tension.

If the specimen is submitted to the action of normal stresses σ_x, σ_y, σ_z uniformly distributed over the sides, we superpose the strains produced by each of these stresses and obtain

$$\epsilon_x = \frac{1}{E}[\sigma_x - \mu(\sigma_y + \sigma_z)]$$

$$\epsilon_y = \frac{1}{E}[\sigma_y - \mu(\sigma_x + \sigma_z)] \tag{12}$$

$$\epsilon_z = \frac{1}{E}[\sigma_z - \mu(\sigma_x + \sigma_y)]$$

These equations represent *Hooke's law* for the case of isotropic materials.   It is seen that relations between strains and stresses are completely defined by two constants E and μ, which are called *elastic constants*.

The same constants can also be used to define the relation between shearing strain and shearing stress.   Let us consider the particular case of deformation of the rectangular parallelepiped in which $\sigma_y = -\sigma_z$ and $\sigma_x = 0$ (Fig. A-8). Cutting out an element $abcd$ by planes parallel to the x axis and at $45°$ to the y and z axes, we can see, from Fig. A-8b, by summing up the forces along and perpendicular to bc, that the normal stresses on the sides of this element vanish and the shearing stress is

$$\tau = \tfrac{1}{2}(\sigma_z - \sigma_y) = \sigma_z$$

We say that the element $abcd$ is in condition of *pure shear*. The angle between

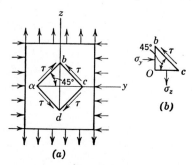

(a)

(b)

Fig. A-8

the sides ab and bc changes, and the corresponding shearing strain γ will be found from the triangle Obc, from which

$$\frac{Oc}{Ob} = \tan\left(\frac{\pi}{4} - \frac{\gamma}{2}\right) = \frac{1 + \epsilon_y}{1 + \epsilon_z} \qquad (a)$$

Substituting, from equations 12,

$$\epsilon_z = -\epsilon_y = \frac{1}{E}(\sigma_z - \mu\sigma_y) = \frac{(1 + \mu)\sigma_z}{E}$$

and observing that for small γ

$$\tan\left(\frac{\pi}{4} - \frac{\gamma}{2}\right) = \frac{1 - \dfrac{\gamma}{2}}{1 + \dfrac{\gamma}{2}}$$

we find

$$\gamma = \frac{2(1 + \mu)\sigma_z}{E} = \frac{2(1 + \mu)\tau}{E} \qquad (13)$$

This gives the required relation between shearing strain and shearing stress. Often the notation,

$$G = \frac{E}{2(1 + \mu)} \qquad (14)$$

is used, and this constant is called *modulus of elasticity in shear*. The relations between the shearing strain components and shearing stress components then are

$$\gamma_{xy} = \frac{1}{G}\tau_{xy}, \quad \gamma_{xz} = \frac{1}{G}\tau_{xz}, \quad \gamma_{yz} = \frac{1}{G}\tau_{yz} \tag{15}$$

These components are independent of elongations 12 and the general case of strain is obtained by superposing the three elongations, given by equations 12, on the three shearing strains, given by equations 15.

PLANE STRESS AND PLANE STRAIN

7. Plane Stress. The problems of the theory of elasticity are considerably simplified if the stresses are all parallel to one plane. There are many engineering problems in which the stress distribution is essentially plane. This is always the case if a thin plate of uniform thickness is submitted to the action of forces applied at the boundary, parallel to the plane of the plate and distributed uniformly over its thickness (Fig. A-9). In such a case the stress components σ_z, τ_{xz}, τ_{yz} vanish on both surfaces of the plate, and without substantial error it can be assumed that they vanish through the entire thickness

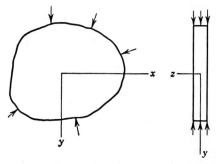

FIG. A-9

of the plate, that is the stress distribution is plane and defined by the three stress components $\sigma_x, \sigma_y, \tau_{xy}$, which can be considered constant across the thickness of the plate. The thickness of the plate is then of no importance, and in the following discussion this dimension is usually considered equal to the unity of length.

8. Plane Strain. The same simplification of the problem as in the case of thin plates, discussed in the preceding article, is encountered also when we go to the other extreme in which the dimension of the body in the z direction is very large. If a long cylindrical or prismatical body is loaded by forces which are perpendicular to the z axis and whose intensity does not vary along the length of the body, the portion of the body at a considerable distance from the ends suffers essentially a *plane deformation;* that is, the particles of the body

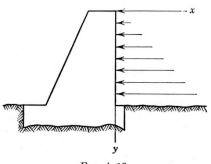

FIG. A-10

move during deformation in the planes perpendicular to the length of body. An example of this kind is a retaining wall submitted to the action of lateral pressure, constant along the length of the wall, Fig. A-10. It is easy to see that in this case the deformation occurs in planes perpendicular to the length of the wall. Cross sections remote from the ends of the wall remain plane, and in studying stress distribution it is sufficient to consider only one slice of the wall between two adjacent cross sections unit distance apart. The components u and v of the displacements are functions of the coordinates x and y and do not depend on the longitudinal coordinate z. At the same time the component w vanishes, and we have

$$\gamma_{yz} = \frac{\partial v}{\partial z} + \frac{\partial w}{\partial y} = 0, \quad \gamma_{xz} = \frac{\partial u}{\partial z} + \frac{\partial w}{\partial x} = 0, \quad \epsilon_z = \frac{\partial w}{\partial z} = 0$$

There will be only three strain components ϵ_x, ϵ_y, γ_{xy} different from zero. If they are found, the corresponding stress components σ_x, σ_y, τ_{xy} can be readily calculated from equations 12 and 15. It should be noted that the normal stress σ_z does not vanish here, as in the case of thin plates; moreover, substituting $\epsilon_z = 0$ in the third of equations 12, we obtain

$$\sigma_z = \mu(\sigma_x + \sigma_y) \tag{16}$$

These are the normal stresses distributed over cross sections perpendicular to the z axis and keeping these cross sections plane during the deformation.

9. Stress at a Point. It was shown in the preceding discussion that in the case of plane stress or plane strain we have to consider only three stress components σ_x, σ_y, τ_{xy}. If these components are known at any point O of the plate, the stress acting on any plane through this point perpendicular to the plate and inclined to the x and y axes can be calculated from the equations of equilibrium of an infinitesimal element in the form of a triangular prism cut out from the plate by the three planes perpendicular to the plate (Fig. A-11). These equations are obtained from the first two of equations 2 by substituting $n = 0$, which gives

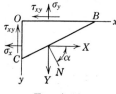

Fig. A-11

$$\bar{X} = \sigma_x l + \tau_{xy} m = \sigma_x \cos \alpha + \tau_{xy} \sin \alpha$$

$$\bar{Y} = \tau_{xy} l + \sigma_y m = \tau_{xy} \cos \alpha + \sigma_y \sin \alpha$$

Projecting the components $\bar{X}$ and $\bar{Y}$ on the normal N and on the perpendicular to it, we obtain

$$\sigma_n = \sigma_x \cos^2 \alpha + \sigma_y \sin^2 \alpha + 2\tau_{xy} \sin \alpha \cos \alpha$$
$$\tau = \tau_{xy}(\cos^2 \alpha - \sin^2 \alpha) + (\sigma_y - \sigma_x) \sin \alpha \cos \alpha \tag{17}$$

It may be seen that the angle α can be chosen in such a manner that the shearing stress τ on the corresponding plane vanishes. For this purpose we have only to put

$$\tau_{xy}(\cos^2 \alpha - \sin^2 \alpha) + (\sigma_y - \sigma_x) \sin \alpha \cos \alpha = 0$$

which gives

$$\tan 2\alpha = \frac{2\tau_{xy}}{\sigma_x - \sigma_y} \tag{18}$$

From this equation the two principal directions are obtained. If the principal directions are taken as the x and y axis, τ_{xy} vanishes in equations 17, and we obtain

$$\sigma_n = \sigma_x \cos^2 \alpha + \sigma_y \sin^2 \alpha$$
$$\tau = \tfrac{1}{2}(\sigma_y - \sigma_x) \sin 2\alpha \tag{19}$$

These normal and shearing components of stress are given by the coordinates of point D of the circle shown in Fig. A-12a. In the construction of this circle we take the τ axis positive in the upward direction and consider shearing stresses as positive when they give a couple in the clockwise direction, as on the sides bc and ad of the element $abcd$ (Fig. A-12b). Shearing stresses of opposite direction, as on the sides ab and dc of the element, are considered as negative.* As the angle α, in Fig. A-11, varies from O to $\pi/2$, the point D in Fig. A-12a moves from A to B, so that the lower half-circle represents the stress variation for all values of α within these limits. The upper half of the circle gives stresses for $O > \alpha > -\dfrac{\pi}{2}$. Prolonging the radius CD to the point D_1, Fig. 12a; that is, if the angle $\pi + 2\alpha$ is taken instead of 2α, the stresses on the plane perpendicular to BC, in Fig. A-11, are obtained. This shows that the shearing stresses on two perpendicular planes are numerically equal. As

for normal stresses, we see from the figure that their sum remains constant when the angle α changes. The maximum shearing stress on the planes perpendicular to the plate is given in Fig. A-12 by the maximum ordinate of the circle and is equal to

$$\tau_{\max} = \frac{\sigma_x - \sigma_y}{2}$$

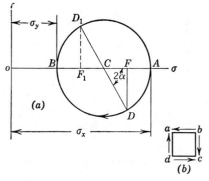

(a)

(b)

Fig. A-12

The circle can be used also for determining the principal directions. If x and y axes are not the principal axes, and we know σ_x, σ_y, τ_{xy}, the two points, such as D and D_1 in Fig. A-12, can be plotted. This gives us the diameter DD_1 of the circle. Making the corresponding circle, we obtain points A and B defining the magnitudes of principal stresses and the angle 2α defining the directions of these stresses.

10. Differential Equations of Equilibrium. We considered, previously, only the stress at one point of a body; let us discuss now the variation of the stress components σ_x, σ_y, τ_{xy} as we slightly change the position of the point. For this purpose the equations of equilibrium of an infinitesimal rectangular parallelepiped with the sides dx, dy, 1, Fig. A-13, will be considered. The stresses acting at the centers of the sides of this element and their positive directions are shown in the figure. Here we take into account the small changes in the stress components corresponding to small increments dx and dy of the coordinates. In calculating the forces acting on the sides of the element, we multiply the stress at the center of a side by the area of that side. It should be noted that the body forces, acting on the element, which were

* This rule is used only in construction of the stress circle, otherwise the rule illustrated in Fig. A-3 holds.

neglected before in derivation of equations 2 as small quantities of higher order, must now be taken into consideration since they are of the same order as the terms due to the small variations of the stress components, which we are considering. Denoting by X, Y the components of the body force per unit volume of the body and summing up all the forces acting on the element in the direction of the x axis, we obtain the equation:

$$\left(\sigma_x + \frac{\partial \sigma_x}{\partial x}\, dx\right) dy - \sigma_x\, dy + \left(\tau_{xy} + \frac{\partial \tau_{xy}}{\partial y}\, dy\right) dx - \tau_{xy}\, dx + X\, dx\, dy = 0$$

The second equation of equilibrium can be written in a similar manner. These two equations reduce to

$$\frac{\partial \sigma_x}{\partial x} + \frac{\partial \tau_{xy}}{\partial y} + X = 0$$

$$\frac{\partial \sigma_y}{\partial y} + \frac{\partial \tau_{xy}}{\partial x} + Y = 0 \tag{20}$$

These are the differential equations of equilibrium for two-dimensional problems of elasticity.

In practical applications the gravity force is usually the only body force. Denoting the weight per unit volume of the body by Δ and taking the y axis downward, we obtain the equations of equilibrium for this case in the following form:

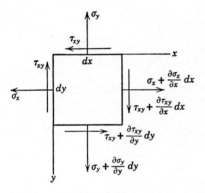

FIG. A-13.

$$\frac{\partial \sigma_x}{\partial x} + \frac{\partial \tau_{xy}}{\partial y} = 0$$

$$\frac{\partial \sigma_y}{\partial y} + \frac{\partial \tau_{xy}}{\partial x} + \Delta = 0 \tag{21}$$

11. Compatibility Equations. Two equations of equilibrium 20 are not sufficient for the determination of three unknown stress components. The necessary third equation can be derived only if we take into account the elastic properties of the body. In the case of two-dimensional problems we have to consider only three strain components, from equations 9, namely,

$$\epsilon_x = \frac{\partial u}{\partial x}, \quad \epsilon_y = \frac{\partial v}{\partial y}, \quad \gamma_{xy} = \frac{\partial u}{\partial y} + \frac{\partial v}{\partial x} \tag{a}$$

Differentiating the first of these equations twice with respect to y, the second twice with respect to x, and the third once with respect to x and once with respect to y, we find the *compatibility equation:*

$$\frac{\partial^2 \epsilon_x}{\partial y^2} + \frac{\partial^2 \epsilon_y}{\partial x^2} = \frac{\partial^2 \gamma_{xy}}{\partial x\, \partial y} \tag{22}$$

Assuming now the case of plane stress, we have, from Hooke's law,

$$\epsilon_x = \frac{1}{E}(\sigma_x - \mu\sigma_y), \quad \epsilon_y = \frac{1}{E}(\sigma_y - \mu\sigma_x), \quad \gamma_{xy} = \frac{2(1+\mu)}{E}\tau_{xy}$$

Substituting into equation 22, we obtain

$$\frac{\partial^2}{\partial y^2}(\sigma_x - \mu\sigma_y) + \frac{\partial^2}{\partial x^2}(\sigma_y - \mu\sigma_x) = 2(1+\mu)\frac{\partial^2\tau_{xy}}{\partial x\,\partial y} \tag{b}$$

This equation can be put in a simpler form by using differential equations of equilibrium. Assuming that there is only gravity force acting, we differentiate the first of equations 21 with respect to x, the second with respect to y, and add them together. This gives

$$\frac{\partial^2\sigma_x}{\partial x^2} + \frac{\partial^2\sigma_y}{\partial y^2} = -2\frac{\partial^2\tau_{xy}}{\partial x\,\partial y}$$

Substituting into equation b, we obtain the *compatibility equation in terms of stress components:*

$$\left(\frac{\partial^2}{\partial x^2} + \frac{\partial^2}{\partial y^2}\right)(\sigma_x + \sigma_y) = 0 \tag{23}$$

In the general case of body forces, we use equations 20 and obtain

$$\left(\frac{\partial^2}{\partial x^2} + \frac{\partial^2}{\partial y^2}\right)(\sigma_x + \sigma_y) = -(1+\mu)\left(\frac{\partial X}{\partial x} + \frac{\partial Y}{\partial y}\right) \tag{24}$$

Equation 23 or 24 together with equations 21 or 20 give us the required system of three equations for determining the three stress components σ_x, σ_y, $_{xy}$ in the case of a plane-stress problem.

In the case of plane deformation (article 8) we have equation 16, and Hooke's law gives

$$\epsilon_x = \frac{1}{E}\{(1-\mu^2)\sigma_x - \mu(1+\mu)\sigma_y\}$$

$$\epsilon_y = \frac{1}{E}\{(1-\mu^2)\sigma_y - \mu(1+\mu)\sigma_x\}$$

$$\gamma_{xy} = \frac{2(1+\mu)}{E}\tau_{xy}$$

Substituting into equation 22 and using equations 21 we conclude that equation 23, obtained for the plane-stress problem, holds also for the plane-strain problem. In the general case of body forces, we use equations 20 and obtain

$$\left(\frac{\partial^2}{\partial x^2} + \frac{\partial^2}{\partial y^2}\right)(\sigma_x + \sigma_y) = -\frac{1}{1+\mu}\left(\frac{\partial X}{\partial x} + \frac{\partial Y}{\partial y}\right) \tag{25}$$

12. Solution of Two-Dimensional Problems by Using a Stress Function.
It was shown in the preceding article that a solution of two-dimensional prob-

lems of theory of elasticity reduces to the integration of the differential equations of equilibrium together with the compatibility equation. Limiting ourselves to the case where the gravity force is the only body force, the equations to be satisfied are

$$\left.\begin{array}{l} \dfrac{\partial \sigma_x}{\partial x} + \dfrac{\partial \tau_{xy}}{\partial y} = 0 \\[3mm] \dfrac{\partial \sigma_y}{\partial y} + \dfrac{\partial \tau_{xy}}{\partial x} + \Delta = 0 \end{array}\right\} \tag{a}$$

$$\left(\frac{\partial^2}{\partial x^2} + \frac{\partial^2}{\partial y^2}\right)(\sigma_x + \sigma_y) = 0 \tag{b}$$

To solve these equations we introduce a new function, called the *stress function*. As is easily verified, equations a are satisfied by taking any function ϕ of x and y^* and putting for the stress components the following expressions:

$$\sigma_x = \frac{\partial^2 \phi}{\partial y^2}, \quad \sigma_y = \frac{\partial^2 \phi}{\partial x^2}, \quad \tau_{xy} = -\frac{\partial^2 \phi}{\partial x\, \partial y} - \Delta x \tag{26}$$

Substituting these expressions into equation b, we find that the stress function ϕ must satisfy the equation:

$$\frac{\partial^4 \phi}{\partial x^4} + 2\frac{\partial^4 \phi}{\partial x^2\, \partial y^2} + \frac{\partial^4 \phi}{\partial y^4} = 0 \tag{27}$$

All two-dimensional problems, in which the weight of the body is the only force, can be reduced to the solution of equation 27. There are many different forms of solution of this equation. To each of these solutions there corresponds a particular case of a two-dimensional problem. The problem becomes definite if the shape of the plate and the force distribution along the boundary of the plate are given. We have then to select such a solution of equation 27 that, after substituting it in expression 26, we will obtain the stresses which balance at the boundary the applied external forces.

13. Particular Solutions. In solving two-dimensional problems we usually assume various particular solutions of equations 27. Then using equations 26, we can establish what external forces must be applied to produce stresses corresponding to the assumed solutions. Combining such particular solutions we may eventually obtain solutions for problems of practical importance. In the case of rectangular plates some useful solutions were obtained by taking the stress function in the form of a polynomial. Take, for example, a polynomial of second degree:

$$\phi = ax^2 + bxy + cy^2 \tag{a}$$

This expression evidently satisfies equation 27. Substituting it into equations 26, and assuming that there are no body forces, we obtain

$$\sigma_x = 2c, \quad \sigma_y = 2a, \quad \tau_{xy} = -b \tag{b}$$

If we take only the first term in expression a and put $b = c = 0$, we obtain constant tensile stress in the x direction. To produce such a stress in a

---

* The function must have continuous derivatives up to the fourth order.

rectangular plate, we have to apply at the ends uniformly distributed tensile forces of intensity $2c$ as shown in Fig. A-14a. By taking only the second term in expression a, we obtain the case of pure shear shown in Fig. A-14b.

In a similar manner we can discuss the solution of equation 27 in the form of a polynomial of third degree. Taking only one term of that polynomial and putting $\phi = ay^3$, we obtain, in the absence of body forces, $\sigma_x = 6ay$, $\sigma_y = \tau_{xy} = 0$. To produce such stresses we have to apply at the ends of the plate the forces shown in Fig. A-15. Only in this way can equilibrium between internal and external forces at the boundary be accomplished. We see that

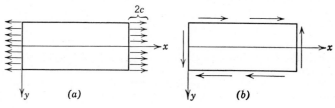

FIG. A-14

in this case the assumed solution represents pure bending of the plate in its plane.

Taking the solution of equation 27 in the form $\phi = axy^3$, we obtain, from equations 26, $\sigma_x = 6axy$, $\tau_{xy} = -3ay^2$. To satisfy the conditions at the boundary, we have to apply the forces shown in Fig. A-16   Along the longitudinal sides of the plate we have to apply shearing forces of intensity $-3ac^2$. Along the ends we have to apply shearing and normal forces, as shown. An important case can be obtained by superposing the forces shown in Fig. A-14b and those in Fig. A-16. If we take $b = -3ac^2$, the shearing forces will vanish

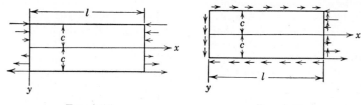

FIG. A-15   FIG. A-16

along the longitudinal sides of the plate; at the end $x = 0$ we will get only shearing stresses of magnitude:

$$(\tau_{xy})_{x=0} = -b - 3ay^2 = 3a(c^2 - y^2) \tag{c}$$

At the end $x = l$ we obtain not only shearing stresses of this magnitude but also normal stresses:

$$\sigma_x = 6ly \tag{d}$$

We obtain bending of a cantilever by a force P applied at the end (Fig. A-17). Assuming the thickness of the plate equal to 1 in. and the width equal to $2c$, we find

$$P = \int_{-c}^{c} \tau_{xy} dy = \int_{-c}^{c} 3a(c^2 - y^2)\, dy = 4ac^3 \tag{e}$$

Treating the plate as a cantilever beam, we find at the built-in end $(x = l)$ a bending moment Pl and bending stresses,

$$\sigma_x = \frac{Ply}{I} = 12\,\frac{Ply}{(2c)^3} = 6ly$$

which coincides with equation d. The usual elementary solution coincides with the preceding rigorous solution if the load applied at the end of the cantilever is distributed in accordance with equation c. Combining this equation with equation e, we obtain

$$(\tau_{xy})_{x=0} = \frac{3P}{4c^3}\,(c^2 - y^2) \tag{f}$$

This again is the same shear-stress distribution as given by elementary-beam theory for rectangular beams.

By using a polynomial of fifth degree the stress distribution in a uniformly loaded beam can be discussed, and it can be shown that the elementary-beam formulas for stresses and deflections do not coincide with the rigorous solution, but the discrepancy is small and can be neglected in practical application.

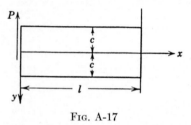

FIG. A-17

By using equation 27 a considerable number of two-dimensional problems are rigorously solved. These solutions have proved especially important in studying stress distribution around small holes, at grooves, and at fillets where high-stress concentration takes place and where cracks usually begin to develop under the action of pulsating forces.

The rigorous theory proves also that in all cases of plates with simply connected boundaries the stress distribution, as obtained by using equation 27, is independent of the elastic constants of materials and can be applied to structures of any isotropic material. This conclusion serves as a basis for experimental stress analysis by the *photoelastic* method.

STRESS AND STRAIN IN THREE DIMENSIONS

14. Differential Equations of Equilibrium. In articles 4 and 5 the stress at a point of an elastic body was discussed. Let us consider now the variation of stress with change in position of the point. For this purpose the conditions of equilibrium of a small rectangular parallelepiped with the sides dx, dy, dz are studied (Fig. A-18). Proceeding as in article 10 and observing the small changes in stress components, shown in the figure, we obtain, by summing up all the forces acting on the element in the x direction, the following equation of equilibrium:

$$\left(\sigma_x + \frac{\partial \sigma_x}{\partial x}\,dx\right)dy\,dz - \sigma_x\,dy\,dz + \left(\tau_{xy} + \frac{\partial \tau_{xy}}{\partial y}\,dy\right)dx\,dz - \tau_{xy}\,dx\,dz$$
$$+ \left(\tau_{xz} + \frac{\partial \tau_{xz}}{\partial z}\,dz\right)dx\,dy - \tau_{xz}\,dx\,dy + X\,dx\,dy\,dz = 0$$

In the same manner the equations of equilibrium for the y and z directions can be written. After simplifications, the three equations of equilibrium can be presented in the following forms:

$$\frac{\partial \sigma_x}{\partial x} + \frac{\partial \tau_{xy}}{\partial y} + \frac{\partial \tau_{xz}}{\partial z} + X = 0$$

$$\frac{\partial \sigma_y}{\partial y} + \frac{\partial \tau_{xy}}{\partial x} + \frac{\partial \tau_{yz}}{\partial z} + Y = 0 \tag{28}$$

$$\frac{\partial \sigma_z}{\partial z} + \frac{\partial \tau_{xz}}{\partial x} + \frac{\partial \tau_{yz}}{\partial y} + Z = 0$$

These are *differential equations of equilibrium in terms of stresses.* Sometimes it is advantageous to have equations of equilibrium in terms of displacements.

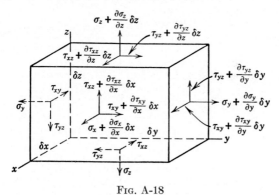

Fig. A-18

To derive these we substitute into equations 28 for stress components their expressions through strain components. To simplify writing, the following notations are used:

$$e = \epsilon_x + \epsilon_y + \epsilon_z \tag{29}$$

$$\lambda = \frac{\mu E}{(1 + \mu)(1 - 2\mu)} \tag{30}$$

Then, from equations 12,

$$\sigma_x = \lambda e + 2G \frac{\partial u}{\partial x}$$

$$\tau_{xy} = G\gamma_{xy} = G\left(\frac{\partial u}{\partial y} + \frac{\partial v}{\partial x}\right)$$

$$\tau_{xz} = G\gamma_{xz} = G\left(\frac{\partial w}{\partial x} + \frac{\partial u}{\partial z}\right)$$

and the first of equations 28 gives

$$(\lambda + G) \frac{\partial e}{\partial x} + G\left(\frac{\partial^2 u}{\partial x^2} + \frac{\partial^2 u}{\partial y^2} + \frac{\partial^2 u}{\partial z^2}\right) + X = 0 \tag{31}$$

In a similar manner the two other equations can be written. If there are no body forces, these equations can be written in the following simplified form:

$$\left.\begin{array}{c} (\lambda + G)\dfrac{\partial e}{\partial x} + G\nabla^2 u = 0 \\[2mm] (\lambda + G)\dfrac{\partial e}{\partial y} + G\nabla^2 v = 0 \\[2mm] (\lambda + G)\dfrac{\partial e}{\partial z} + G\nabla^2 w = 0 \end{array}\right\} \tag{32}$$

where the symbol ∇^2 stands for the sum of the second derivatives; that is,

$$\nabla^2 = \frac{\partial^2}{\partial x^2} + \frac{\partial^2}{\partial y^2} + \frac{\partial^2}{\partial z^2}$$

Sometimes we have to consider stresses produced in an elastic body by temperature changes. Let T denote the temperature at any point of a body measured from a certain specified constant temperature representing the initial unstressed condition of the body. The strain components will depend in this case not only on stresses, but also on the temperature change T, and, instead of equations 12, we obtain

$$\epsilon_x = \frac{1}{E}\{\sigma_x - \mu(\sigma_y + \sigma_z)\} + \alpha T$$

$$\epsilon_y = \frac{1}{E}\{\sigma_y - \mu(\sigma_x + \sigma_z)\} + \alpha T$$

$$\epsilon_z = \frac{1}{E}\{\sigma_z - \mu(\sigma_x + \sigma_y)\} + \alpha T$$

where α is the coefficient of linear temperature expansion. Solving these equations for stress components and substituting into equations 28, we obtain, in the absence of body forces, the following equations:

$$\left.\begin{array}{c} (\lambda + G)\dfrac{\partial e}{\partial x} + G\nabla^2 u - \dfrac{\alpha E}{1 - 2\mu}\dfrac{\partial T}{\partial x} = 0 \\[3mm] (\lambda + G)\dfrac{\partial e}{\partial y} + G\nabla^2 v - \dfrac{\alpha E}{1 - 2\mu}\dfrac{\partial T}{\partial y} = 0 \\[3mm] (\lambda + G)\dfrac{\partial e}{\partial z} + G\nabla^2 w - \dfrac{\alpha E}{1 - 2\mu}\dfrac{\partial T}{\partial z} = 0 \end{array}\right\} \tag{33}$$

These equations are to be used in discussing thermal stresses.

15. Conditions of Compatibility. If in the discussion of elasticity problems equations 28 are used, it is necessary to observe that the six stress components are not independent but are subject to relations which follow from the fact that the six strain components are represented by three functions u, v, w (see equations 9). Proceeding as shown in article 12, we obtain the following six relations:

$$\frac{\partial^2\epsilon_x}{\partial y^2} + \frac{\partial^2\epsilon_y}{\partial x^2} = \frac{\partial^2\gamma_{xy}}{\partial x\,\partial y}, \quad 2\frac{\partial^2\epsilon_x}{\partial y\,\partial z} = \frac{\partial}{\partial x}\left(-\frac{\partial\gamma_{yz}}{\partial x} + \frac{\partial\gamma_{xz}}{\partial y} + \frac{\partial\gamma_{xy}}{\partial z}\right)$$

$$\frac{\partial^2\epsilon_y}{\partial z^2} + \frac{\partial^2\epsilon_z}{\partial y^2} = \frac{\partial^2\gamma_{yz}}{\partial y\,\partial z}, \quad 2\frac{\partial^2\epsilon_y}{\partial x\,\partial z} = \frac{\partial}{\partial y}\left(\frac{\partial\gamma_{yz}}{\partial x} - \frac{\partial\gamma_{xz}}{\partial y} + \frac{\partial\gamma_{xy}}{\partial z}\right) \qquad (34)$$

$$\frac{\partial^2\epsilon_z}{\partial x^2} + \frac{\partial^2\epsilon_x}{\partial z^2} = \frac{\partial^2\gamma_{xz}}{\partial x\,\partial z}, \quad 2\frac{\partial^2\epsilon_z}{\partial x\,\partial y} = \frac{\partial}{\partial z}\left(\frac{\partial\gamma_{yz}}{\partial x} + \frac{\partial\gamma_{xz}}{\partial y} - \frac{\partial\gamma_{xy}}{\partial z}\right)$$

These are the *conditions of compatibility in terms of strain components.*

Substituting for strain components their expressions 12 and 15 through stress components and using equations of equilibrium, we can obtain the *compatibility conditions in terms of stress components.* If there are no body forces, these conditions can be presented in the following form:

$$(1 + \mu)\nabla^2\sigma_x + \frac{\partial^2\theta}{\partial x^2} = 0 \qquad (1 + \mu)\nabla^2\tau_{yz} + \frac{\partial^2\theta}{\partial y\,\partial z} = 0$$

$$(1 + \mu)\nabla^2\sigma_y + \frac{\partial^2\theta}{\partial y^2} = 0 \qquad (1 + \mu)\nabla^2\tau_{xz} + \frac{\partial^2\theta}{\partial x\,\partial z} = 0 \qquad (35)$$

$$(1 + \mu)\nabla^2\sigma_z + \frac{\partial^2\theta}{\partial z^2} = 0 \qquad (1 + \mu)\nabla^2\tau_{xy} + \frac{\partial^2\theta}{\partial x\,\partial y} = 0$$

where

$$\theta = \sigma_x + \sigma_y + \sigma_z \qquad (36)$$

16. Uniqueness of Solution. If the forces acting on an elastic body are known and we have to find stresses produced by these forces, we apply equations of equilibrium 28. The six stress components entering in these equations must satisfy the six compatibility conditions, discussed in the preceding article, and also the conditions at the boundary of the body. The expressions for the stress components must be such that, when an element of the body at the boundary is taken, the conditions of equilibrium between the applied surface forces and the internal forces are satisfied. If l, m, n, are the cosines which the outer normal to the surface of the body at the point under consideration makes with the x, y, z axes, the required conditions of equilibrium are given by equations 2. A more elaborate analysis shows that equations of equilibrium 28, together with the compatibility conditions and the boundary conditions, completely determine the stresses in the body. This indicates that, if we have found by some means such expressions for the stress components that the equations of equilibrium together with the compatibility conditions are satisfied at every point of the body and the surface conditions 2 are satisfied at every point of the surface of the body, those expressions represent the only possible rigorous solution of the problem.

Sometimes we can guess about the expressions for some of the six stress components, and, if the remaining components can be found in such form that all of the previously discussed equations are satisfied, this will show that the expressions, initially assumed as a guess, represent a portion of the rigorous solution of the problem. The method of solution in which initial assumptions about some of the stress components are taken and the remaining components are determined so as to satisfy all elasticity equations is called the *semi-*

inverse method. It has been successfully used in the solution of several important problems. Its application to the problem of torsion of prismatical bars will now be discussed.

17. Torsion of Prismatical Bars. Assume that a prismatical bar of any cross section is fixed at O (Fig. A-19) and twisted as shown. The elementary theory of torsion of a circular bar states that, in this case,

$$\sigma_x = \sigma_y = \sigma_z = \tau_{xy} = 0 \tag{a}$$

and that only the two stress components τ_{xz} and τ_{yz} do not vanish. Let us assume now that this holds also for prismatical bars of any cross section. Equations of equilibrium 28, in the absence of body forces, then give

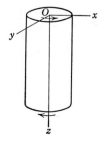

$$\frac{\partial \tau_{xz}}{\partial z} = 0, \quad \frac{\partial \tau_{yz}}{\partial z} = 0, \quad \frac{\partial \tau_{xz}}{\partial x} + \frac{\partial \tau_{yz}}{\partial y} = 0 \tag{b}$$

To satisfy the first two of these equations, we must have the stress components depending only on x and y.

To satisfy also the third of equations b we introduce a stress function ψ of x and y and select for stress components the expressions:

Fig. A-19

$$\tau_{xz} = \frac{\partial \psi}{\partial y} \qquad \tau_{yz} = -\frac{\partial \psi}{\partial x} \tag{c}$$

In this way all three equations of equilibrum will be satisfied. Let us consider now the compatibility conditions 35. With assumption a regarding the stress components, these conditions reduce to the following two equations:

$$\nabla^2 \tau_{yz} = 0 \qquad \nabla^2 \tau_{xz} = 0$$

Substituting expressions c, we obtain

$$\frac{\partial}{\partial x}\left(\frac{\partial^2 \psi}{\partial x^2} + \frac{\partial^2 \psi}{\partial y^2}\right) = 0 \qquad \frac{\partial}{\partial y}\left(\frac{\partial^2 \psi}{\partial x^2} + \frac{\partial^2 \psi}{\partial y^2}\right) = 0$$

This means that the expression in the parenthesis must be a constant, and the introduced stress function must satisfy the equation,

$$\frac{\partial^2 \psi}{\partial x^2} + \frac{\partial^2 \psi}{\partial y^2} = c \tag{d}$$

in which c is a constant.

Consider now the boundary conditions. We assume that torsion of the bar is produced by forces applied at the ends. Then, the lateral surface of the bar is free from forces, and the components $\bar{X}$, $\bar{Y}$, $\bar{Z}$ in equations 2 vanish. The cosine n in those equations vanishes also, since the normal to the cylindrical surface is perpendicular to the z axis. With our assumptions a the first two of equations 2 are satisfied, and the third one gives

$$\tau_{xz}l + \tau_{yz}m = 0 \tag{e}$$

This equation states that the resultant shearing stress at the boundary of the cross section (Fig. A-20) is in the direction of the tangent of the boundary.

From Fig. A-20 we see also that when we move clockwise along the boundary of the cross section, the cosines l and m are

$$l = \frac{dy}{ds} \qquad m = -\frac{dx}{ds}$$

Substituting these expressions together with expressions c into equation e, we find the following condition at the boundary:

$$\frac{\partial \psi}{\partial y}\frac{dy}{ds} + \frac{\partial \psi}{\partial x}\frac{dx}{ds} = \frac{d\psi}{ds} = 0 \tag{f}$$

which indicates that the stress function must be constant along the boundary.

We see that the equations of equilibrium 28, the compatibility equations 35, and the conditions on the lateral surface are satisfied by taking for stress components the values a and c and by selecting the stress function so as to satisfy

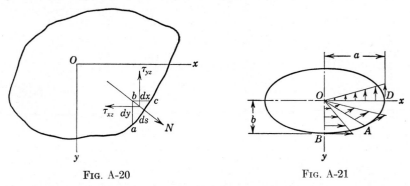

FIG. A-20   FIG. A-21

equation d at every point of the cross section and condition f at the boundary of the cross section. In every particular case of torsion we have to find such a solution of equation d which satisfies the boundary condition f.

Take, as an example, torsion of a bar of elliptical cross section (Fig. A-21). The boundary equation is

$$\frac{x^2}{a^2} + \frac{y^2}{b^2} - 1 = 0 \tag{g}$$

For a stress function we take

$$\psi = \frac{ca^2b^2}{2(a^2 + b^2)}\left(\frac{x^2}{a^2} + \frac{y^2}{b^2} - 1\right) \tag{h}$$

which satisfies equation d. This function vanishes on the boundary by virtue of equation g so that the boundary condition f is also satisfied. We conclude, then, that expression h is the required stress function for bars of elliptical cross section. The constant c in this expression depends on the magnitude of torque acting on the bar. This torque is

$$M_t = \int\int (x\tau_{yz} - y\tau_{xz})\,dx\,dy = -\int\int\left(x\frac{\partial \psi}{\partial x} + y\frac{\partial \psi}{\partial y}\right)dx\,dy$$

Integrating this by parts, and observing that ψ vanishes at the boundary, we find

$$M_t = 2\int\int\psi\ dx\ dy$$

Substituting for ψ its expression h, we obtain

$$M_t = -\frac{\pi a^3 b^3 c}{2(a^2 + b^2)}$$

from which

$$c = -\frac{2M_t(a^2 + b^2)}{\pi a^3 b^3}$$

Substituting into expression h and using equations c, we then obtain

$$\tau_{xz} = -\frac{2M_t y}{\pi ab^3} \qquad \tau_{yz} = \frac{2M_t x}{\pi a^3 b}$$

This stress distribution is shown in Fig. A-21. The maximum stress occurs at the ends of the smaller axis of the ellipse.

There exists a very useful experimental method of determining torsional stresses, introduced by L. Prandtl and based on the fact that equation a is identical with that for deflections of a uniformly stretched and uniformly loaded membrane.

APPENDIX II

DIMENSIONAL ANALYSIS

By J. N. Goodier

1. Introduction. The construction and testing of small models for the purpose of predicting stresses, deformations, vibrational and buckling characteristics of their prototypes raises questions such as:

(a) Must the model be geometrically similar in all respects?

(b) Must it be made of the same material?

(c) How must the loads be scaled down?

(d) Can the model give useful results if the elastic limit is exceeded, or if buckling occurs, or if the deformations are large?

(e) How must a model subject to fluid forces, as in flutter of aircraft wings, or wind vibrations in bridges, be tested?

The answers can sometimes be given readily. It may obviously be sufficient simply to reduce loads according to the square of the model scale and observe that the stresses and, hence, the strains, will then be the same and the displacements in proportion to the scale. The more difficult questions, such as d and e are most satisfactorily dealt with by means of the method of dimensional analysis, as developed by E. Buckingham[1] and P. W. Bridgman.[2] A brief account of the application of this method to structural models is given here. Various general types are discussed, but it will be understood that most actual models will involve special considerations, both theoretical and practical.

2. Method of Dimensional Analysis. The rules for model construction and testing, the "conditions of structural similarity," are reached by two steps. We first contemplate the derivation of a general formula which will apply to model and prototype alike, just as the familiar beam formulas apply to small or large beams. It is not necessary that we should be able to derive the actual formula; in fact, if we could, the model tests would hardly be necessary. It is sufficient that there must be such a formula if only we could find it. It is to be valid in any unit system—if, for instance, it yields in a given case the number 2000 (pounds per square inch) when the pound and inch are used, it must yield the number 144 (tons per square foot) when the ton and foot are used. This requirement, commonplace as it is, means that the formula must possess certain features. We then find that these lead to useful conclusions as to what must happen when the size of the system is changed; that is, we are able to deduce rules of similarity. The method is now illustrated by applying it to the problem of determining stresses, strains, displacements, or redundant forces or reactions, in any elastic structure of material obeying Hooke's law.

3. Elastic Structures. The structure itself may be specified by the elastic constants E (Young's modulus) and μ (Poisson's ratio), by one length a, and the ratios r_1, r_2, etc., of all other required lengths to a. The loads may be specified by one of them P, and the ratios r_1', r_2', etc., of the others to P. The directions may be specified by ratios r_1'', r_2'', etc. A particular stress component σ is to be found at some point x, y, z. A formula for this would be a relation between the quantities:

$$\sigma, x, y, z, E, \mu, a, r_1, r_2 \cdots, P, r_1', r_2' \cdots, r_1'', r_2'' \cdots \qquad (1)$$

Only two fundamental units are required for the measurement of all these quantities, and these can be force and length. There is a theorem[1,2] that dimensionless groups can be formed from the list of symbols to a number equal to the number of symbols minus the number of fundamental units. In the present problem this means two less, and the groups are

$$\frac{\sigma a^2}{P}, \frac{x}{a}, \frac{y}{a}, \frac{z}{a}, \mu, \frac{P}{Ea^2}, r_1, r_2 \cdots, r_1', r_2' \cdots, r_1'', r_2'' \cdots \qquad (2)$$

Any other dimensionless groups will be merely products of powers of these and so are not independent. The sense of dimensionless is simply that the numerical value remains the same when the units are changed.

The stress formula must take the form of a relation between these groups, not merely a relation between the original symbols 1. Thus,

$$\frac{\sigma a^2}{P} = f_1\left(\frac{x}{a}, \frac{y}{a}, \frac{z}{a}, \mu, \frac{P}{Ea^2}, r_1\, r_2, \cdots, r_1', r_2' \cdots, r_1'', r_2'' \cdots \right) \qquad (3)$$

where the right-hand side denotes a function of unknown form, definite in a given problem although we may not be able to find it. For instance, the beam formula $\sigma = My/I$ for a simple beam of rectangular cross section (width b, depth a, span c) simply supported and loaded by a central force P becomes, written in the form 3,

$$\frac{\sigma a^2}{P} = 6\frac{x}{a} \cdot \frac{y}{a} \cdot \frac{1}{r_1} \qquad \left(0 < x < \frac{c}{2}\right)$$

where $r_1 = b/a$ and σ is the fiber stress evaluated at a section x from one end, at a depth y below the neutral axis.

It is clear that, if the units are changed so that the numerical values of the symbols in formula 1 change, the numerical values of the dimensionless groups remain unchanged, and formula 3 remains a true relation. The theorem known as Buckingham's Π theorem shows[1,2] that the form 3 is the only form the relation can take if it is to be true in all unit systems.

The formula 3 is now applied to both model and prototype. Although the functional form is unknown, it is the same for both. If, therefore, the groups on the right of formula 3 are made the same for both, it will follow that the group on the left is also the same for both.

Making r_1, $r_2 \cdots$ the same for both means geometrical similarity (but it is pointed out later that complete similarity is often not needed); making r_1',

$r_2' \cdots$, r_1'', $r_2'' \cdots$ the same for both means an obvious similarity of load distribution. Making x/a, y/a, z/a the same means that the stress is to be taken at the point in the model corresponding to the point in the prototype at which the stress is required. These conditions, of course, are usually taken for granted, but the method of dimensional analysis, being free from such assumptions, insures that there are no unnecessary restrictions. Next μ must be the same for both, if it matters. Otherwise, it is not required in the list of symbols. Finally P/Ea^2 must be the same for both. If the subscript m is used for the model and p for the prototype, this means

$$\frac{P_m}{E_m a_m^2} = \frac{P_p}{E_p a_p^2} \quad \text{or} \quad \frac{P_m}{P_p} = \frac{E_m}{E_p} \frac{a_m^2}{a_p^2} \tag{4}$$

The loads must, therefore, be scaled down according to this rule. We are free to make the model of a different material. The change is allowed for in the factor E_m/E_p, but Poisson's ratio must be kept the same if it is significant.

All dimensionless groups on the right of formula 3 being now the same for model and prototype, it follows that the group on the left is also the same, that is

$$\frac{\sigma_m a_m^2}{P_m} = \frac{\sigma_p a_p^2}{P_p} \quad \text{or} \quad \frac{\sigma_m}{\sigma_p} = \frac{P_m}{P_p} \cdot \frac{a_p^2}{a_m^2} \tag{5}$$

Introducing equation 4 we obtain

$$\frac{\sigma_m}{\sigma_p} = \frac{E_m}{E_p} \tag{6}$$

from which σ_p may be calculated when σ_m has been measured.

The analysis is carried out in a similar way for quantities other than stress. For a displacement u, the dimensionless group u/a is used instead of $\sigma a^2/P$. For a strain e, e itself may be used, and for a force R, the ratio R/P. Then instead of formula 3 we should find

$$\frac{u}{a} = f_2\left(\frac{x}{a}, \frac{y}{a}, \frac{z}{a}, \mu, \frac{P}{Ea^2}, r_1, r_2 \cdots, r_1', r_2' \cdots, r_1'', r_2'' \cdots\right) \tag{7}$$

$$e = f_3(\cdots) \tag{8}$$

$$\frac{R}{P} = f_4(\cdots) \tag{9}$$

where f_2, f_3, f_4 denote other functional forms.

The similarity rules up to and including equation 4 must again be observed, and it then follows that

$$\frac{u_m}{a_m} = \frac{u_p}{a_p}, \quad e_m = e_p, \quad \frac{R_m}{P_m} = \frac{R_p}{P_p} \tag{10}$$

The displacements have not been assumed small. These similarity rules, therefore, apply not only to small deformations, but also to the large deformations of flexible structures (of material obeying Hooke's law), where the stresses, displacements, and forces or reactions are not in general proportional to the loads. Very flexible steel springs and rings, thin plates compressed beyond buckling or transversely loaded to large deflections are in this class so long as the proportional limit of the material is not exceeded.

The dimensional analysis also indicates how curves obtained in model tests may be plotted so as to be immediately applicable to the prototype. If for instance a stress σ is plotted against a load P, the curve showing $\sigma a^2/P$ as a function of P/Ea^2 is a graphical representation of the formula 3 and, the similarity conditions being satisfied, is identical with the corresponding curve which might be obtained from the prototype. This is exactly analogous to the plotting of dimensionless force, moment, or pressure coefficients versus Reynold's number which is customary in aerodynamics. In fact, the number P/Ea^2 plays a role very much like that of Reynold's number and might well have a special name, such as "strain number." A model and its prototype are "structurally similar" at the same strain number, similarity of form and load distribution (and identity of Poisson's ratios where significant) being taken for granted. The deformed shapes are geometrically similar by equation 7, and the strains at similarly situated points are the same. The assumption of concentrated loads P, r_1P, r_2P, etc., will not always be appropriate. The formation of dimensionless groups to replace P/Ea^2 when the loads are distributed as pressures, or force per unit length, or when they are moments will be obvious.

4. Linear Structures. The commonest type of stress-analysis problem is concerned with stiff structures, such as tension, torsion, or bending members, or pressure vessels, where the deformations do not significantly affect the action of the loads, and the stresses, strains, displacements, redundant reactions, and the like are known to be linear functions of the loads*—that is, the principle of superposition holds. This supplementary knowledge may be used in conjunction with the dimensional analysis. In formula 3 for instance, $\sigma a^2/P$ must be *independent* of P, since σ must be proportional to P. Thus, the group P/Ea^2 must not appear in the function on the right. The similarity condition 4 is not required. The remaining groups on the right being made the same for model and prototype—geometrical similarity and similarity of load distribution—the function becomes a constant k_1, the same for model and prototype, and $\sigma a^2/P = k_1$. The model test may now be regarded as a test to determine k_1. The model may be made of any material obeying Hooke's law, except that μ, if it has any influence, must be the same as for the prototype.

An analogous argument applies to equation 9, leading to $R/P = k_4$, a constant for model and structure alike. When we turn to equations 7 and 8, however, the requirements that u and e shall be proportional to P mean that in each case the group P/Ea^2 must appear on the right as a simple factor, and

$$\frac{u}{a} = \frac{P}{Ea^2}\,k_2 \qquad e = \frac{P}{Ea^2}\,k_3$$

where k_2 and k_3 are also constants for model and structure alike. We, thus, arrive at the well-known results that stresses and forces, such as redundant reactions (for rigid supports), are independent of Young's modulus and that

---

* This follows as well where the formulas are not known as where they are, from the linearity of the fundamental differential equations and boundary conditions of the theory of elasticity.

displacements and strains are inversely as Young's modulus. We can also say that if $\sigma a^2/P$, u/a, e, R/P are plotted versus P/Ea^2, from tests on the model, $\sigma a^2/P$ and R/P are represented by straight lines parallel to the P/Ea^2 axis, and u/a and e by inclined lines, and the lines are the same for the prototype.

5. Relaxation of Similarity Conditions. So far we have accepted the requirement in equations 3, 7, 8, and 9 that all dimensionless groups on the right must be made the same for model and prototype to justify the conclusion that the groups on the left will be the same. The requirement includes complete geometrical similarity. Suppose, however, that the prototype is a truss, all members carrying simply tension or compression. It is clear that the geometrically similar model may be modified by changing the cross-sectional shape of the members, so long as their sectional areas remain unchanged. If the prototype is a rigid frame with members acting in tension, compression, and bending, the cross-sectional shape in the model may be changed so long as the area and flexural rigidity remain the same. If it is a framework with members subject also to torsion, the torsional rigidity must also be kept the same. It will be apparent that sometimes the over-all form of members may be changed so long as their over-all tensional, flexural, and torsional stiffnesses are correct. It has been found convenient to make such modifications in airship models.[3, 4]

6. Gravity and Surface Loads. When the load includes the weight of the structure itself, as in a dam or bridge, it may be represented by a weight per unit volume w. This adds another symbol without increasing the number of fundamental units, and another dimensionless group must be included, for instance, wa/E or wa^3/P. If the former is taken, it is convenient to use σ/E instead of $\sigma a^2/P$, and R/Ea^2 instead of R/P. Instead of formulas 3, 7, 8, and 9 we shall now have formulas of the types,

$$\left.\begin{array}{l} \dfrac{\sigma}{E} = f_1\left(\dfrac{x}{a}, \dfrac{y}{a}, \dfrac{z}{a}, \mu, \dfrac{P}{Ea^2}, \dfrac{wa}{E}, r_1, r_2 \cdots, r_1', r_2' \cdots, r_1'', r_2'' \cdots\right) \\[2mm] \dfrac{u}{a} = f_2(\cdots) \\[2mm] e = f_3(\cdots) \\[2mm] \dfrac{R}{Ea^2} = f_4(\cdots) \end{array}\right\} \quad (11)$$

The rules of similarity now require geometric similarity, similarity of load distribution, and

$$\frac{P_m}{E_m a_m{}^2} = \frac{P_p}{E_p a_p{}^2} \qquad \frac{w_m a_m}{E_m} = \frac{w_p a_p}{E_p} \qquad (12)$$

Free choice of a different material for the model, irrespective of scale, is now not possible. It is necessary to find a material to satisfy the second relation in equation 12. Again the discussion has not been limited to small deformations.

However, the structure will usually be a "solid" one such as a dam, having small deformations which do not affect the action of the loads. The stresses will then be linear both as to P and w, and the problem is divisible into two parts, one to evaluate the effects of loads P_1, $r_1'P$, etc., only, and the other to evaluate the effects of gravity only. In the dam problem the surface loading would be water pressure, which can be described by a greatest pressure p together with mere ratios. The latter may be omitted as naturally the same for the model as for the prototype when a corresponding pressure *distribution* is provided. Instead of P/Ea^2, p/E may be used. Consider in particular a stress component σ at x, y, z. Since this is to be linear in both w and p, it follows that

$$ \frac{\sigma}{E} = \frac{wa}{E} f\left(\frac{x}{a}, \frac{y}{a}, \frac{z}{a}, \mu, r_1, r_2 \cdots \right) + \frac{p}{E} F\left(\frac{x}{a}, \frac{y}{a}, \frac{z}{a}, \mu, r_1, r_2 \cdots \right) \quad (13) $$

The E now cancels, and it follows that the stress is independent of it. We are free to choose the model material as to E, but it must have the same Poisson's ratio μ if significant, and there must be geometrical similarity. The functions f and F will then have the same value for model and prototype (considering the stress at a chosen point), and may be replaced by c_1 and c_2. Then,

$$ \sigma = c_1 wa + c_2 p \quad (14) $$

The values of c_1 and c_2 may be determined by separate tests on the model, using material of any convenient density, or producting w centrifugally (or by replacing the gravity problem by a surface-load problem 5. Different models of different materials may be used for the two tests, provided constancy of μ is observed to a reasonable approximation. It is evidently not necessary to put any restrictions on the means by which the pressure p on the model is created, although, if the system is taken as a single solid-fluid system, it might appear at first sight that the weight per unit volume w_f of the fluid must be included in the list of symbols and then that a fluid of suitable density must be used to make the additional dimensionless group w_f/w the same for model as for prototype.

7. Composite Structures. If the structure is not all of the same material it will be necessary to include in the list of symbols the several Young's moduli and Poisson's ratios. Let these be E, E_1, E_2, etc., and μ, μ_1, etc. The dimensionless groups E_1/E, E_2/E, etc., and μ, μ_1, etc., now appear, and the similarity conditions require that these shall be the same for model and prototype. In a model of a reinforced-concrete structure these correspond to the requirement that the ratio of Young's moduli should be the same, the Poisson's ratio being treated as unimportant.

8. Prescribed Displacements. So far the problem has been considered as that of prescribed loads, although the loaded body may have any number of fixed points such as rigid supports. If instead certain displacements, defined by one of them U and the ratios of the others to it, are prescribed, the problem becomes that of determining a stress σ, displacement u, strain e, or force R, in terms of U, the ratios (which may be at once taken as necessarily the same for model and prototype), and the symbols specifying the structure. The formulas will be of the types,

$$\left.\begin{array}{l}
\dfrac{\sigma}{E} = f_1\left(\dfrac{U}{a}, \dfrac{x}{a}, \dfrac{y}{a}, \dfrac{z}{a}, \mu, r_1, r_2 \cdots\right) \\[3mm]
\dfrac{u}{a} = f_2(\ \cdots\ ) \\[3mm]
e = f_3(\ \cdots\ ) \\[3mm]
\dfrac{R}{Ea^2} = f_4(\ \cdots\ )
\end{array}\right\} \qquad (15)$$

and, when there is no restriction to small deformations, there must be geometrical similarity (subject to relaxation if appropriate) and identity of the μ's and of the U/a values. The latter condition means that the model must be brought to a geometrically similar *deformed* state. Then, the quantities on the left become identical for model and prototype. If the prototype is linear, we can introduce the knowledge that σ, u, e, and R must be proportional to U, so that U/a must be a simple factor on the right, and we can write equations 15 as

$$\sigma = K_1 \frac{EU}{a}, \quad u = K_2 U, \quad e = K_3 \frac{U}{a}, \quad R = K_4 EUa \qquad (16)$$

representing linear relationships in which K_1, K_2, K_3, K_4 are the same for the model as for the prototype. The quantities evaluated are, of course, at similarly situated points in the two, and, if Poisson's ratio is significant, it must be the same for both.

9. Curved Stress–Strain Relations—Loading beyond the Proportional and Elastic Limits. If the ordinary tensile or compressive stress–strain line of the material is curved, it can be expressed in the form,

$$\frac{\sigma}{E} = f(e)$$

in a chosen unit system, where E is any appropriate "Young's modulus" such as the initial slope of the curve, and $f(e)$ involves suitable numbers, as, for instance, in $\sigma/E = e - 0.01e^2$. This relation will be valid even when the unit of stress is changed, since σ and E will retain the same ratio. Curved stress–strain relations between all six components of stress and all six components of strain can be similarly expressed in terms of a selected E and mere numbers which do not change with change of unit system. E having this new meaning, the arguments used in all the preceding sections, except, of course, those concerned with linear problems, take the same form, since the list of symbols and the dimensionless groups are the same except for the changed meaning of E. Geometrical similarity (relaxed as appropriate) is required, and then in the problem of prescribed loads (article 3) the groups $\sigma a^2/P$ for model and prototype are identical at the same strain number (P/Ea^2). Alternatively, curves of $\sigma a^2/P$ (and u/a, e, R/p) versus P/Ea^2 are the same for both model and prototype. There is, of course, no freedom to choose a different material for the model. The numbers appearing in the stress–strain law must be the same for both. Even this condition can be somewhat relaxed however,[6] similarity being possible when the stress–strain line of the model material can be brought into coincidence with that of the prototype material by uniform strain of the sheet on which it is drawn in the direction of one or both axes.

If parts of the structure are in the plastic range, they can still be covered by the curved stress–strain law. However, if the loading process does not steadily increase the stress at some point but increases it into the plastic range and then decreases it, the decrease will sometimes, as for steel, follow a line different from the increase. Even then, if the model goes through the same values of the strain number P/Ea^2 in the same order, the dimensional reasoning shows that the similarity is preserved. When the material is the same for model and prototype, the E is the same and may be dropped from the strain number. We can then say that at the same "nominal stress" P/a^2, model and structure will have the same stress distribution ($\sigma a^2/P$ the same), geometrical similarity of deformation (u/a the same), and forces such as statically indeterminate reactions or forces in members in proportion to the loads (R/P the same). Thus, tensile test specimens of different sizes (of the same material) show geometrically similar deformed shapes at the same nominal stress (Barba's law) and yield the same stress–strain relation.

The conclusions as to curved stress–strain relations may be applied to large deflections of rubber springs, the rubber being bonded to steel. The latter may be treated as rigid, and so its elastic constants are not involved. Two such springs of the same rubber, of different size but geometrically similar, are in structurally similar states when loaded to similar deformed shapes, or when loaded to the same strain number P/Ea^2, that is, to the same nominal stress or average strain. The distribution of stress throughout and, in particular, over the bonded surface will usually not be uniform, but it will be similar under the foregoing conditions of similarity, and the maximum stresses will be the same.

10. Buckling. It was shown in article 3 that for a structure with given loads the curves of $\sigma a^2/P$, u/a, e, R/P versus P/Ea^2 obtained from the model would also be valid for the prototype, even when the displacements are large. A buckling phenomenon would appear as a sudden increase of u/a at some value of the strain number P/Ea^2. Since the curve is valid for all geometrically similar elastic (Hooke's law material) structures, it follows that all similar structures will buckle in the same way at the same value of P/Ea^2, or

$$\frac{P_{cr}}{Ea^2} = C \qquad P_{cr} = CEa^2$$

where C is the same for the whole set of similar structures (it is a dimensionless number). Critical loads for such a set are, thus, proportional to the Young's modulus and to the square of a representative length.

In virtue of article 9 this conclusion can be extended to buckling in the plastic range or to a partly plastic partly elastic state, except that now the material should be the same for model and prototype. Then, the two buckle (in the same mode), at the same value of P/a^2, that is, at the same critical *stress*.

Buckling at a definite strain number is entirely analogous to the onset of turbulence at a definite Reynold's number in a given type of fluid flow.

11. Vibration Due to Aerodynamic Forces. When the structure is not in motion, forces applied to the prototype by a fluid may be reproduced on the model in any convenient way, and the problem may be regarded as one of given forces. On the other hand, dynamical phenomena such as flutter of airfoils, or oscillation of suspension bridges in a wind, may require consideration of structure and fluid as a single system. It may not be sufficient to provide structural similarity for dynamical behavior in vacuo, together with identity of Reynold's number. This will be merely illustrated here by means of a simple example. The system, as indicated in the figure, consists of a mass suspended by a spring, subject to damping, and set into up-and-down oscillation by a steady airstream.* Consider first the free damped vibrations of the mass without the airstream. The required symbols (ignoring gravity) are

ρ_1 = the density of the mass
a = a linear dimension
$r_1, r_2,$ etc. = ratios of other significant linear dimensions to a
k = the spring constant
c = the viscous damping coefficient (damping force for unit velocity)
$\dfrac{x_1}{x_2}$ = the ratio of two successive amplitudes (the decrement)

Apart from the ratios r_1, r_2, etc., there are five symbols, and, since the problem is one of dynamics (with 3 fundamental units), there will be 5–3 or 2 dimensionless groups. One of these is x_1/x_2, the quantity we wish to evaluate here. The other may be taken as $c^2/k\rho_1 a^3$. This is essentially the ratio of c^2 to the square of the critical damping. The formula must, therefore, take the form,

$$\frac{x_1}{x_2} = f\left(\frac{c^2}{k\rho_1 a^3}\right) \qquad (17)$$

or $x_1/x_2 = f(c^2/km)$ where $m = \rho_1 a^3$ is proportional to the mass. The actual solution of this problem is, of course, well known and is, in fact,

$$\frac{x_1}{x_2} = \exp\left\{ -\pi \sqrt{\frac{c^2/4km}{1 - \dfrac{c^2}{4km}}} \right\}$$

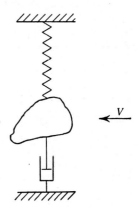

Fig. B-1. Oscillation
Due to an Airstream
To illustrate similarity
when solid and fluid
form a single system

It follows from equation 17 that the decrement is the same for model and prototype when $c^2/k\rho_1 a^3$ is the same.

Now consider oscillation of the mass maintained by the airstream, and let it be required to find the amplitude x_0. The list of symbols, other than r_1, r_2, etc., is now

$$x_0,\ k,\ \rho_1,\ c,\ a,\ V,\ \rho_2,\ \mu_2$$

where V, ρ_2, μ_2 are the velocity, density, and viscosity of the fluid. There are eight symbols and so there must be 5 dimensionless groups. If we take the first five symbols, which refer to the structure only, it is possible to form only

---

* A system of this type is used by J. P. Den Hartog (*Mechanical Vibrations*, McGraw-Hill, 2d ed., p 343) as a model of the "galloping transmission line."

5–3 or 2 groups from them. These may be x_0/a and $c^2/k\rho_1 a^3$. If we take the last four symbols, it is possible to form only one group from them $V\rho_2 a/\mu_2$ (Reynold's number). Thus, there must be two more groups which can only be formed by combining the symbols referring to the structure with those referring to the fluid, and these may be taken as ρ_1/ρ_2 and $k/V^2\rho_2 a$. The amplitude formula must, therefore, take the form,

$$\frac{x_0}{a} = f\left(\frac{c^2}{k\rho_1 a^3}, \quad \frac{V\rho_2 a}{\mu_2}, \quad \frac{\rho_1}{\rho_2}, \quad \frac{k}{V^2\rho a}\right) \tag{18}$$

Giving the groups on the right the same value for model and prototype means that
1. The decrements in free vibration must be the same.
2. The Reynold's numbers must be the same.
3. The ratio of densities ρ_1/ρ_2 must be the same.
4. The values of $k/V^2\rho_2 a$ must be the same.

Suppose now that it is proposed to test the model in air. Then item 3 means that ρ_1 must be the same for model and prototype. However, since the exact distribution of mass in the model will not matter, the group ρ_1/ρ_2 may be changed to $\rho_1 a^3/\rho_2 a^3$ or $m/\rho_2 a^3$. Then m/a^3 must be the same, that is,

$$\frac{m_m}{a_m{}^3} = \frac{m_p}{a_p{}^3} \quad \text{or} \quad \frac{m_m}{m_p} = \frac{a_m{}^3}{a_p{}^3} \tag{19}$$

Identity of Reynold's numbers will mean

$$V_m a_m = V_p a_p \quad \text{or} \quad \frac{V_m}{V_p} = \frac{a_p}{a_m} \tag{20}$$

and so the airstream must be faster (for the same x_0/a) in the small model system. Finally, identity of the values of group 4 means

$$\frac{k_m}{V_m{}^2 a_m} = \frac{k_p}{V_p{}^2 a_p} \tag{21}$$

which reduces to
$$\frac{k_m}{k_p} = \frac{a_p}{a_M}$$

so that the model spring must have a greater stiffness than the prototype spring.

When these conditions are satisfied, we can be sure that the pattern of flow about the model is the same as in the prototype system. If at some airspeed the model does not vibrate, the prototype will not vibrate at the corresponding airspeed V_p determined from equation 20.

Additional knowledge of aerodynamic behavior may, of course, modify such conclusions. For instance, the flow about an airfoil may be independent of the Reynold's number over a range of values of this number—that is, until the flow pattern suddenly changes.

BIBLIOGRAPHY

1. E. BUCKINGHAM, (a) "On Physically Similar Systems; Illustrations of the Use of Dimensional Equations," *Phys Rev*, Series 2, vol 4, 1914, pp. 345–76; (b) "Model Experiments and the Forms of Empirical Equations," *Trans ASME*, v 37, 1915,

pp 263–96.   In (a) the method of dimensional analysis is developed.   In (b) several engineering applications are discussed.

2. P. W. BRIDGMAN, *Dimensional Analysis*, Yale Univ Press, 1931.   Discusses exhaustively the mathematical basis of dimensional analysis and applies the method to a variety of physical problems.   Includes models.

3. L. H. DONNELL, E. L. SHAW, AND W. C. POTTHOFF, "Stress Model of Complete Airship Structure," *Trans ASME*, v 60, 1938, p A-67.

4. O. W. LOUDENSLAGER, "Structural Model Testing," *J Soc Automotive Engrs*, v 54, n 1, Jan 1946, p 18.   Bibliography items 3 and 4 describe model members specially designed to give required extensional flexural and torsional stiffnesses.   Item 4 contains a list of references.

5. M. A. BIOT, "Distributed Gravity and Temperature Loading in Two-Dimensional Elasticity Replaced by Boundary Pressures and Dislocations," *Trans ASME*, v 57, 1935, p A-41.   Shows how gravity may be replaced by external normal loads corresponding to a hydrostatic pressure.

6. J. N. GOODIER AND W. T. THOMSON, "Applicability of Similarity Principles to Structural Models," *Nat Advisory Commit for Aeronautics Tech Note* 933, 1944.   A systematic account of the use of dimensional analysis in constructing similarity conditions for models and structures, with a report on tests on square thin sheets buckling in shear, with and without holes.   With certain exceptions the measurements follow closely the indications of the similarity principles.   Contains a list of references.

APPENDIX III

THE PRECISION OF MEASUREMENTS

By M. Hetényi

1. Errors of Measurements. It is generally recognized in experimental work that the "true" value of an object of measurement can never be exactly established. If a number of direct measurements are made on a physical quantity, all with equal care and with full utilization of the sensitivity of the measuring instruments, it will be found that such measurements invariably lead to discordant results. In spite of the contradictions among the individual readings, however, it is clear that through a greater number of measurements we will know more about the unknown quantity, and will be in position to give a more precise "estimate" of its value than that obtainable through any single measurement. The purpose of this chapter is to present briefly the fundamentals of the mathematical theory by which the *best estimate* of a measured quantity and the *degree of precision* of this estimate may be established from results of repeated measurements.

The discrepancies between the results of repeated observations are due to *errors* inherent in any measurement. The error of an observation is defined as the difference between the observed and the "true" value of the physical quantity in question, and, accordingly, errors may have positive or negative values. An analysis of possible sources of error is, of course, of great importance when an improvement in precision is desired. Errors are usually classified in two main groups, as systematic and accidental errors.

Systematic errors generally enter with the same sign, and often with the same magnitude, into the records, and therefore they are most effective in disturbing the results. They may be due to *instrumental errors*, such as faulty graduation of scales, defective screws, inaccurate standards; or to *personal errors*, such as the inclination of an observer to respond to a time signal too soon, or to estimate a fractional distance too short.* In experimental work every effort should be made to trace the sources of systematic errors and to eliminate their effect. Sometimes the error is nearly constant and may be easily taken into account by a suitable correction, or it may have other regular features, like the afore-mentioned idiosyncrasies of the observer, which may be studied and their effect defined by a "personal equation."

There are two general procedures by which the influence of systematic errors may be largely eliminated. These are the method of symmetry and

---

* J. Volger[6] found a general and outspoken tendency among observers to read 0.3 and 0.4 one-tenth too low and to read 0.6 and 0.7 one-tenth too high. For other positions errors were comparatively rare.

the method of substitution. The *method of symmetry* consists of repeating the test in a symmetrical or reversed manner with respect to the particular condition that is suspected as a source of systematic error, such as taking strain-gage readings during unloading as well as during loading of a testpiece, or making weight measurements by interchanging the pans in the scale. The principle of the *method of substitution* is to replace the object of measurement by quantities of known magnitudes, that is, essentially repeated calibration.

Accidental errors are due to irregular causes, too many in number and too complex in nature for their origin to be traced. The chief characteristic of accidental errors is that they are as often positive as negative, and for this reason they are likely to have a negligible effect on the value of the arithmetic

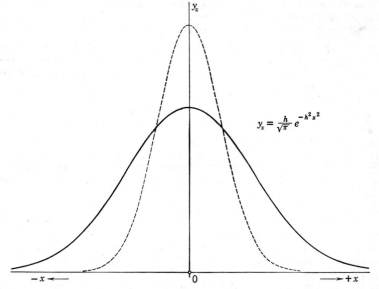

$$y_x = \frac{h}{\sqrt{\pi}} e^{-h^2 x^2}$$

Fig. C-1. Normal Frequency Distribution of Errors

mean of a set of measurements. The principal object of experimental precautions is to reduce errors of measurement to the accidental class, which can then be treated by the probability theory, to deduce the most probable value of the object of observation.

2. The Normal Frequency Distribution of Errors. If we assume that an accidental error is the algebraic sum of an infinite number of independent elemental errors, each of which is as likely to be positive as negative, it can be shown that for a very large number of measurements, which contain only accidental errors, the errors will follow the so-called normal distribution law,

$$y_x = \frac{h}{\sqrt{\pi}} e^{-h^2 x^2} \tag{1a}$$

where x denotes the value of an error (the difference between the observed and the true value of the quantity), y_x is the probability of occurrence of the error of magnitude x, h is a constant associated with the particular set of observations in question, and e is the base of natural logarithms. Since hx

must be an absolute number, it follows that the dimensions of h and y_x will be reciprocal of that of x. For example, if x is measured in inches, the dimensions of h and y_x will be $1/\text{in}$.

A graphical representation of y_x as a function of x is shown by the full curve in Fig. C-1. It may be seen that small errors are more frequent than large ones and that positive and negative errors of the same magnitude occur with the same frequency. The area under the curve is equal to unity, expressing the condition that all errors lie between the $+\infty$ and $-\infty$ limits. The value of y_x at $x = 0$ is equal to $h/\sqrt{\pi}$ where h is a characteristic of the particular set of observations the curve represents. If for another set of measurements, shown by the dotted curve in Fig. C-1, h has a larger value, it will mean that this second set of observations has a greater number of measurements with small errors, and, consequently, this set should be regarded as a more accurate one. The constant h may be looked on, therefore, as an *index of precision*, which enables us to compare the reliability of different sets of measurements. For convenience of computation, however, it is usually preferred to use other quantities as measures of precision, which all bear certain relations with h and which are discussed in the next article.

Since the difference between the two curves in Fig. C-1 is due to the difference in the respective values of h, a table for all normal frequency curves may be set up if hx is considered as the independent variable. Thus we get

$$y_{hx} = \frac{1}{h} y_x = \frac{1}{\sqrt{\pi}} e^{-h^2 x^2} \tag{1b}$$

values of which are shown in Table C-1.

TABLE C-1

NORMAL FREQUENCY DISTRIBUTION OF ERRORS*

hx	y_{hx}	hx	y_{hx}	hx	y_{hx}
0.0	0.5642	1.0	0.2076	2.0	0.0103
0.1	0.5586	1.1	0.1682	2.1	0.0069
0.2	0.5421	1.2	0.1337	2.2	0.0045
0.3	0.5156	1.3	0.1041	2.3	0.0028
0.4	0.4808	1.4	0.0795	2.4	0.0018
0.5	0.4394	1.5	0.0595	2.5	0.0011
0.6	0.3936	1.6	0.0436	2.6	0.0007
0.7	0.3456	1.7	0.0314	2.7	0.0004
0.8	0.2975	1.8	0.0221	2.8	0.0002
0.9	0.2510	1.9	0.0153	2.9	0.0001

* The value of h for a set of n measurements can be calculated from equation 4. If, instead of h, the standard derivation s or the probable error p is used as a basis of reference, one may put, from equations 6 and 7, $hx = x/s\sqrt{2}$ or $hx = 0.477x/p$, respectively. The same substitutions can be used also in Table C-2.

Since the y_x curve represents the frequency of errors, the probability P_x of an error being between the limits $+x$ and $-x$ is defined by the area of the y_x curve between these limits, that is,

$$P_x = \frac{h}{\sqrt{\pi}} \int_{-x}^{x} e^{-h^2 x^2} \, dx \tag{2a}$$

The influence of h as parameter can be eliminated from the previous formula if we regard hx as an independent variable, in the same manner as it was done for y_x. Thus, we can write

$$P_x = P_{hx} = \frac{2}{\sqrt{\pi}} \int_0^{hx} e^{-(hx)^2} \, d(hx) \tag{2b}$$

Values of P_{hx}, corresponding to given values of hx, are shown in Table C-2. The use of Table C-2 may be illustrated as follows. If, in a large set of measurements of a distance in inches, the modulus of precision h is found to be $h = 8$ in.$^{-1}$, the probability of occurrence of a positive error lying between the limits $x = +0.02$ in. and $x = +0.03$ in. will be $\frac{1}{2}(P_{hx=0.24} - P_{hx=0.16})$ $= \frac{1}{2}(0.2657 - 0.1790) = 0.0434$. The probability of occurrence of an error between the same numerical limits but irrespective of sign will be, of course, twice the previously obtained value.

In the foregoing formulas the error x was defined as the difference between the observed and the true value of the measured quantity. The use of these

TABLE C-2*

VALUES OF THE PROBABILITY INTEGRAL $P_{hx} = \dfrac{2}{\sqrt{\pi}} \displaystyle\int_0^{hx} e^{-h^2 x^2} \, d(hx)$

hx	0.00	0.01	0.02	0.03	0.04	0.05	0.06	0.07	0.08	0.09
0.0	0.0000	0.0113	0.0226	0.0338	0.0451	0.0564	0.0676	0.0789	0.0901	0.1013
0.1	0.1125	0.1236	0.1348	0.1459	0.1569	0.1680	0.1790	0.1900	0.2009	0.2118
0.2	0.2227	0.2335	0.2443	0.2550	0.2657	0.2763	0.2869	0.2974	0.3079	0.3183
0.3	0.3286	0.3389	0.3491	0.3593	0.3694	0.3794	0.3893	0.3992	0.4090	0.4187
0.4	0.4284	0.4380	0.4475	0.4569	0.4662	0.4755	0.4847	0.4937	0.5027	0.5117
0.5	0.5205	0.5292	0.5379	0.5465	0.5549	0.5633	0.5716	0.5798	0.5879	0.5959
0.6	0.6039	0.6117	0.6194	0.6270	0.6346	0.6420	0.6494	0.6566	0.6638	0.6708
0.7	0.6778	0.6847	0.6914	0.6981	0.7047	0.7112	0.7175	0.7238	0.7300	0.7361
0.8	0.7421	0.7480	0.7538	0.7595	0.7651	0.7707	0.7761	0.7814	0.7867	0.7918
0.9	0.7969	0.8019	0.8068	0.8116	0.8163	0.8209	0.8254	0.8299	0.8342	0.8385
1.0	0.8427	0.8468	0.8508	0.8548	0.8586	0.8624	0.8661	0.8698	0.8733	0.8768
1.1	0.8802	0.8835	0.8868	0.8900	0.8931	0.8961	0.8991	0.9020	0.9048	0.9076
1.2	0.9103	0.9130	0.9155	0.9181	0.9205	0.9229	0.9252	0.9275	0.9297	0.9319
1.3	0.9340	0.9361	0.9381	0.9400	0.9419	0.9438	0.9456	0.9473	0.9490	0.9507
1.4	0.9523	0.9539	0.9554	0.9569	0.9583	0.9597	0.9611	0.9624	0.9637	0.9649
1.5	0.9661	0.9673	0.9684	0.9695	0.9706	0.9716	0.9726	0.9736	0.9745	0.9755
1.6	0.9763	0.9772	0.9780	0.9788	0.9796	0.9804	0.9811	0.9818	0.9825	0.9832
1.7	0.9838	0.9844	0.9850	0.9856	0.9861	0.9867	0.9872	0.9877	0.9882	0.9886
1.8	0.9891	0.9895	0.9899	0.9903	0.9907	0.9911	0.9915	0.9918	0.9922	0.9925
1.9	0.9928	0.9931	0.9934	0.9937	0.9939	0.9942	0.9944	0.9947	0.9949	0.9951
2.0	0.9953	0.9955	0.9957	0.9959	0.9961	0.9963	0.9964	0.9966	0.9967	0.9969

* This table is based on *Tables of Probability Functions*, Vol. 1, Federal Works Agency, Work Projects Administration for the City of New York, 1941. In the use of this table, when not hx but x/s or x/p is given, see footnote to Table C-1.

terms has, however, certain limitations. In one class of physical problems the "true" value may be approximated but never exactly established, which leaves also the errors undefined. In other types of problems, such as the determination of the strength of a testpiece, it is entirely illusory to speak of a "true" value, because each test result was equally true under the given circumstances. In such cases it is more correct to say that the object of repeated tests was to find the "best estimate" or the "most probable value" of strength that a randomly chosen piece in the series is likely to exhibit. Since in the theory of measurements the difference between the observed value and the best estimate of a quantity is defined as the *deviation* (or sometimes *residual*), the previous x values are referred to in the subsequent articles more often as deviations.

Though the normal frequency-distribution curve adequately covers the majority of physical problems, there are exceptions where this law evidently cannot apply. In those instances we usually find that the nature of the problem is such that it contradicts one of the following three characteristic features of the normal law, namely: (*a*) that there is an equal probability for positive and negative deviations, (*b*) that very large deviations, though less likely, are possible, and (*c*) that the frequency curve has only one peak at $x = 0$. Methods of analysis of such problems, which are at variance with the normal distribution law, may be found in references 1, 2, and 5 in the bibliography.

3. The Most Probable Value and Indexes of Precision. It can be shown on the basis of the normal frequency law, that, if a large number of n measurements, $X_1, X_2, \cdots X_n$, are taken, all with equal skill and care, of a quantity X, *the most probable value of the quantity is* X_0, *the arithmetic mean of all measurements:*

$$X_0 = \frac{X_1 + X_2 + \cdots + X_n}{n} = \frac{\Sigma X}{n} \tag{3}$$

Denoting the deviations from the mean as $x_1 = X_1 - X_0$, $x_2 = X_2 - X_0$ and $x_n = X_n - X_0$, we also find that the foregoing choice for the most probable value makes the combined probability of occurrence of these deviations the greatest, or the sum of squares of the deviations a minimum, which is the basis of the well-known *method of least squares*. As the number of observations n becomes very large, the arithmetic mean X_0 coincides with the true value X, and the deviations can be regarded as the actual values of the errors.

Once the deviations, $x_1, x_2, \cdots x_n$, are obtained, the following precision indexes can be calculated by the so-called *standard* of Bessel's formulas:

$$\text{Modulus of precision } h = \sqrt{\frac{n-1}{2\Sigma x^2}} \tag{4}$$

$$\text{Average deviation of a single observation } a = \frac{\Sigma|x|}{n} \tag{5}$$

$$\text{Standard deviation of a single observation } s = \frac{1}{h\sqrt{2}} = \sqrt{\frac{\Sigma x^2}{n-1}} \tag{6}$$

$$\text{Probable error of a single observation } p = 0.6745s = 0.6745\sqrt{\frac{\Sigma x^2}{n-1}} \tag{7}$$

Thus, the average deviation a is defined as the mean of the absolute values of all deviations, and the standard deviation s (often denoted by σ) is obtained as the square root of the sum of squared deviations divided by $n - 1$. The probable error of a single observation is a deviation of such magnitude that the probability of a deviation being greater than it equals the probability of lesser deviations. The term is not altogether fitting, and a name like "median error" would describe more correctly the nature of this deviation, since the most probable accidental error in a series of measurements is actually zero.

It can be shown that the precision indexes for the mean value X_0 of a set of n measurements is $1/\sqrt{n}$ times the corresponding indexes for an individual observation in the set, that is:

$$\text{Average deviation of the mean } a_0 \ = \ \frac{\Sigma|x|}{n\sqrt{n}} \tag{8}$$

$$\text{Standard deviation of the mean } s_0 = \sqrt{\frac{\Sigma x^2}{n(n-1)}} \tag{9}$$

$$\text{Probable error of the mean } p_0 \ = 0.6745\sqrt{\frac{\Sigma x^2}{n(n-1)}} \tag{10}$$

Approximate values of the precision indexes may be more rapidly calculated from the following formulas of Peters, based on the sum of the absolute values of the deviations, $\Sigma|x| = |x_1| + |x_2| + \cdots + |x_n|$, instead of the sum of the squares of deviations used in the standard formulas.

$$h = \frac{\sqrt{n(n-1)}}{\sqrt{\pi}\,\Sigma|x|} \tag{11}$$

$$s = \frac{1.2533\,\Sigma|x|}{\sqrt{n(n-1)}} \qquad s_0 = \frac{1.2533\,\Sigma|x|}{n\sqrt{n-1}} \tag{12a, b}$$

$$p = \frac{0.8453\,\Sigma|x|}{\sqrt{n(n-1)}} \qquad p_0 = \frac{0.8453\,\Sigma|x|}{n\sqrt{n-1}} \tag{13a, b}$$

Example. A distance X is measured 20 times with equal care by a tape reading $\frac{1}{10}$ in. The following table shows the results of measurement, the x deviations of these values from their arithmetic mean, and the squares of the deviations.

X_i in.	$x_i = X_i - X_0$ in.	x_i^2 in.^{2}	X_i in.	$x_i = X_i - X_0$ in.	x_i^2 in.^{2}
71.4	−0.1	0.01	71.1	−0.4	0.16
71.3	−0.2	0.04	71.8	+0.3	0.09
71.6	+0.1	0.01	71.5	0.0	0.00
71.5	0.0	0.00	71.4	−0.1	0.01
71.3	−0.2	0.04	71.7	+0.2	0.04
71.8	+0.3	0.09	71.6	+0.1	0.01
71.6	+0.1	0.01	71.2	−0.3	0.09
71.4	−0.1	0.01	71.5	0.0	0.00
71.7	+0.2	0.04	71.6	+0.1	0.01
71.6	+0.1	0.01	71.4	−0.1	0.01

The most probable value of the distance X_0 is obtained as the arithmetic mean of the measurements $X_0 = \Sigma X_i/n = 1430.0/20 = 71.50$ in. We also find that the sum of the deviations $\Sigma x = 0$, $\Sigma|x| = 3.00$ in., and that $\Sigma x^2 = 0.68$ in.^{2} For the probable error of the mean we have from the standard formula (equation 10): $p_0 = 0.0285$ in. and from Peters' approximate formula (equation 13b): $p_0 = 0.0291$ in. The final result of this series of observation can thus be stated as $X = 71.50 \pm 0.029$ in., which denotes that there is a 50 per cent probability that the true value of the distance is between the values of 71.53 and 71.47 in.

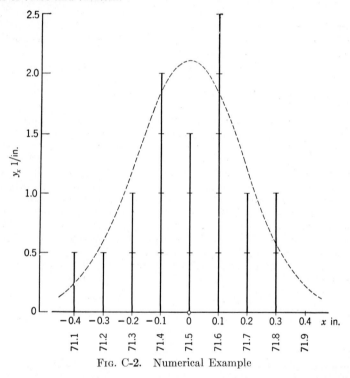

FIG. C-2. Numerical Example

The relative frequency of the foregoing measurements may be represented as shown in Fig. C-2. Since in 20 observations the value 71.4 in. was obtained 4 times, its relative frequency per least count, that is per 0.1 in., is $(4/20) \times (1/0.1 \text{ in.}) = 2.0 \text{ in.}^{-1}$, which is marked as a corresponding ordinate in the graph, and frequency values for all the other readings are found in a similar manner. This observed frequency distribution can be compared with the theoretical curve by calculating h from equation 4 as $h = \sqrt{(n-1)/2\Sigma x^2} = 3.74 \text{ in.}^{-1}$ (the approximate formula in equation 11 gives $h = 3.66 \text{ in.}^{-1}$), and then finding the ordinates of the y_x curve by interpolating in Table C-1. The calculation in the tabular form follows, and the results indicated by the dotted curve in Fig. C-2. Such comparisons between observed and theoretical frequency distributions of deviations are often used to establish whether a set of measurements is likely to contain constant or systematic errors.

$x^{\text{in.}}$	hx	y_{hx}	$y_x = hy_{hx}\text{in.}^{-1}$
0	0	0.56	2.11
0.1	0.374	0.49	1.83
0.2	0.748	0.32	1.20
0.3	1.122	0.16	0.60
0.4	1.496	0.06	0.22

4. Rejection of Observations. It is frequently found in a series of measurements that one or two individual readings differ widely from the others, which gives rise to the question whether it may be justified to reject such incongruous readings in calculating the most probable value of the observed quantity.

The mere fact that an observation differs considerably from the others seems to be not a sufficient reason for its rejection, since the normal frequency distribution clearly indicates the possibility of deviations occurring between the $+\infty$ and $-\infty$ limits. However, the normal distribution curve was derived on the assumption of an infinitely large number of observations, and for a finite number of measurements the probability of occurrence of large deviations should be, of course, accordingly limited. If in 10 measurements, for instance, a deviation of such magnitude is found that is likely to occur only once in 100 readings, the influence of this discordant value in the small set of readings would evidently distort the results, and better estimate of the observed quantity can be derived by rejecting such a value from the record.

Of the various criteria proposed for the limits of rejection of observations the most widely accepted one is by Chauvenet, which states that if in a series of n measurements the probability of occurrence of a deviation of x magnitude is less than one half, then the observation exhibiting such deviation should be rejected. Since the probability of a deviation of magnitude less than x among n measurements is defined by the normal distribution law as nP_x, where P_x is the probability integral, the foregoing limiting condition can be written in the form:

$$n(1 - P_x) = \tfrac{1}{2} \quad \text{or} \quad P_x = \frac{2n - 1}{2n} \tag{14}$$

TABLE C-3

CHAUVENET'S CRITERION

If any individual deviation x in a set of n measurements exceeds the values of hx, x/s, or x/p given in the table, the observation exhibiting such a deviation should be rejected. The symbols h, s, and p denote the modulus of precision, the standard deviation and the probable error, respectively, for a single observation in the set and can be calculated from equations 4, 6, and 7.

n	hx	x/s	x/p	n	hx	x/s	x/p
5	1.16	1.68	2.44	15	1.51	2.13	3.16
6	1.22	1.73	2.57	16	1.53	2.16	3.20
7	1.27	1.79	2.68	17	1.54	2.18	3.22
8	1.32	1.86	2.76	18	1.56	2.20	3.26
9	1.35	1.92	2.84	19	1.57	2.22	3.29
10	1.39	1.96	2.91	20	1.58	2.24	3.32
11	1.42	2.00	2.98	25	1.64	2.32	3.44
12	1.44	2.03	3.02	30	1.69	2.39	3.55
13	1.47	2.07	3.08	40	1.77	2.50	3.70
14	1.49	2.10	3.12	50	1.82	2.58	3.82

Hence P_x can be found for any n value from Table C-2, and the ratio be determined between the permissible error x and the modulus of precision h, the standard deviation s or the probable error p, for any given set of n measurements as shown in Table C-3.

Example. The following table shows the results of 10 measurements, $i = 1, 2, 3 \cdots 10$, made on an X quantity; the deviation of each of these measurements, $x_i = X_i - X_0$, from the mean value X_0; and the squares of the deviations.

i	1	2	3	4	5	6	7	8	9	10
X_i	45.3	47.2	46.3	48.9	46.9	45.8	46.7	47.1	45.7	45.1
$x_i = X_i - X_0$	−1.2	0.7	−0.2	2.4	0.4	−0.7	0.2	0.6	−0.8	−1.4
x_i^2	1.44	0.49	0.04	5.76	0.16	0.49	0.04	0.36	0.64	1.96

We find $X_0 = \Sigma X/n = 46.5$ and $\Sigma x^2 = 11.38$. The standard deviation for an individual reading in this set is calculated from equation 6 as

$$s = \sqrt{\Sigma x^2 / n - 1} = 1.12.$$

The maximum permissible deviation is, therefore, obtained from Table C-3 as $x = 1.12 \times 1.96 = 2.20$. Since observation number 4 gives a deviation of 2.40, that is, larger than this value, that observation should be rejected from the set.

The same procedure may be repeated now to check whether any of the remaining 9 observations show an unduly large deviation from their mean value. Thus, we have:

i	1	2	3	5	6	7	8	9	10
X_i	45.30	47.20	46.30	46.90	45.80	46.70	47.10	45.70	45.10
$x_i = X_i - X_0$	−0.93	0.97	0.07	0.67	−0.43	0.47	0.87	−0.53	−1.13
x_i^2	0.865	0.941	0.005	0.449	0.185	0.221	0.757	0.281	1.277

Now $X_0 = 46.23$, $\Sigma x^2 = 4.981$, $s = 0.789$, and, since, from Table C-3, the limit of permissible deviations $x = 0.789 \times 1.92 = 1.575$ is larger than the maximum deviation 1.13 in the above set, none of the remaining observations should be rejected.

5. Weighted Measurements. In the preceding articles it was assumed that each measurement in a set was made with equal care and precaution, thus deserving the same degree of confidence. However, this is not always so, and there are instances when certain observations are known to be more reliable than others. In such cases evidently a better estimate of the observed quantity may be derived if the more trustworthy measurements are allowed to exert a greater influence on the result. This can be accomplished by assigning relative degrees of reliability of "weights" to each measurement in the set. These weights are usually chosen as integer numbers, and by assigning to a given observation a weight w we signify the fact that this observation is equivalent in importance to a w number of observations, each of unit weight. In calculating the most probable value of the quantity such an observation should be counted, therefore, w times compared to those of unit weight.

Thus, if a series of X_1, X_2, $\cdots X_n$ measurements is made with relative weights w_1, w_2, $\cdots w_n$, the most probable value of the quantity is found to be the *weighted arithmetic mean:*

$$X_0 = \frac{w_1 X_1 + w_2 X_2 \cdots + w_n X_n}{w_1 + w_2 + \cdots + w_n} = \frac{\Sigma w X}{\Sigma w} \tag{15}$$

Denoting by $x_i = X_i - X_0$ the difference between the ith observation in the foregoing set and the weighted mean value, the modulus of precision for the set is obtained as

$$h = \sqrt{\frac{n - 1}{2 \Sigma w x^2}} \tag{16}$$

whereas for an observation of unit weight we have the following values of the standard deviation s_1 and the probable error p_1:

$$s_1 = \sqrt{\frac{\Sigma w x^2}{n - 1}} \tag{17}$$

$$p_1 = 0.6745 \sqrt{\frac{\Sigma w x^2}{n - 1}} \tag{18}$$

Since the standard deviations or probable errors of individual observations in the same series are inversely proportional to the square root of their weights, the standard deviation s_0 and the probable error p_0 of the weighted mean will be

$$s_0 = \sqrt{\frac{\Sigma w x^2}{(n - 1) \Sigma w}} \tag{19}$$

and

$$p_0 = 0.6745 \sqrt{\frac{\Sigma w x^2}{(n - 1) \Sigma w}} \tag{20}$$

By substituting $\Sigma w = n$, the foregoing expressions are reduced to the standard formulas for equally weighted measurements given in equations 4 to 10.

6. Indirect Observations on One Unknown Quantity. If an unknown quantity U is not directly accessible to measurement, but it has a known functional relationship to X, Y, and Z measurable quantities,

$$U = f(X, Y, Z) \tag{21}$$

the most probable value for the unknown, U_0, can be obtained by substituting the most probable values of the measured quantities, X_0, Y_0, and Z_0 into the foregoing equation. The standard deviation s_{0U} and the probable error p_{0U} will then have the following correlations with the corresponding values of s_{0X}, s_{0Y}, s_{0Z} and p_{0X}, p_{0Y}, p_{0Z} of the mean values X_0, Y_0, and Z_0:

$$s^2{}_{0U} = \left(\frac{\partial U}{\partial X}\right)^2 s^2{}_{0X} + \left(\frac{\partial U}{\partial Y}\right)^2 s^2{}_{0Y} + \left(\frac{\partial U}{\partial Z}\right)^2 s^2{}_{0Z} \tag{22}$$

and
$$p^2{}_{0U} = \left(\frac{\partial U}{\partial X}\right)^2 p^2{}_{0X} + \left(\frac{\partial U}{\partial Y}\right)^2 p^2{}_{0Y} + \left(\frac{\partial U}{\partial Z}\right)^2 p^2{}_{0Z} \tag{23}$$

Example. The area of a circle is to be derived from measurements made on its diameter, for which a series of readings gave $X_0 = 4.67 \pm 0.02$ in. as the mean value and its probable error. What will be the best estimate and its probable error for the area of the circle?

Since the area $U = X^2 \pi/4$, the best estimate for its value is obtained as $U_0 = \pi \times 4.67^2/4 = 17.1287$ in.^{2} with a probable error of $p_{0U} = (\partial U/\partial X)p_{0X}$ $= \pm(\pi X_0/2)p_{0X} = \pm(\pi \times 4.67/2)0.02 = \pm0.1467$ in.^{2}

If the aim of an experiment is to establish the value of an unknown quantity U with a *required degree of precision* from measurements made directly on the X, Y, and Z quantities, the precision necessitated in the determination of each of these latter quantities is indicated by equations 22 and 23. It may be seen, for instance, that the same value for the probable error in U_0 can be obtained by various combinations in the probable errors of the mean values X_0, Y_0, and Z_0. If the X, Y, and Z quantities are of different dimensions (one may be mass, the other time, etc.), a certain degree of precision may be more easily obtainable for one than for the other, and, even if they were the same, they are likely to affect the result in a different manner. The selection of the best combination to satisfy the correlations in equation 22 or 23 is the principal problem in the *planning of a precision experiment.*

Example. The value of g is to be determined from the pendulum formula $t = \pi \sqrt{l/g}$, by taking measurements on l and t. What are the fractional permissible errors in l and t in order that the resulting error in g should not exceed 1 per cent?

Denoting the probable error in g, l, and t by p_g, p_l, and p_t, we have from equation 23, on substitution of $g = \pi^2 l/t^2$,

$$p_g{}^2 = \left(\frac{\partial g}{\partial l}\right)^2 p_l{}^2 + \left(\frac{\partial g}{\partial t}\right)^2 p_t{}^2 = \left(\frac{\pi^2}{t^2}\right)^2 p_l{}^2 + \left(\frac{2\pi^2 l}{t^3}\right)^2 p_t{}^2$$

Dividing both sides by $g^2 = (\pi^2 l/t^2)^2$, we have the following relation between the fractional probable errors:

$$\left(\frac{p_g}{g}\right)^2 = \left(\frac{p_l}{l}\right)^2 + 4\left(\frac{p_t}{t}\right)^2$$

Thus, we find that, even if the determination of l could be made with such accuracy as to render the value of p_l practically equal to zero, in order to obtain the value of g within 1 per cent, the probable error in the determination of t should not exceed $\frac{1}{2}$ per cent of t.

7. Indirect Observations on More than One Unknown Quantity. In this case the object of measurement is to establish the most probable values of k unknown quantities, Q_1, Q_2, $\cdots Q_k$, from a set of n measurements, X_1, X_2, $\cdots X_n$, made on an X quantity that has a known functional relationship with the Q's. The results of such measurements can be stated in the form of n equations containing k unknowns, and, if $n > k$, in general, no set of the Q unknowns will satisfy these equations exactly.

When the X's are linear functions of the unknown Q's, and all the observed values, X_1, X_2, $\cdots X_n$, are of equal weight, the procedure of finding the most probable values for the Q's is as follows.

The relationship between the Q_1, Q_2, $\cdots Q_k$ unknowns and the measured X_1, X_2, $\cdots X_n$ quantities is defined now by the following *observation equations:*

$$a_1Q_1 + b_1Q_2 + c_1Q_3 + \cdots + k_1Q_k = X_1$$
$$a_2Q_1 + b_2Q_2 + c_2Q_3 + \cdots + k_2Q_k = X_2 \tag{24}$$

$$\cdot$$
$$\cdot$$
$$\cdot$$

$$a_nQ_1 + b_nQ_2 + c_nQ_3 + \cdots + k_nQ_k = X_n$$

Multiplying each of these equations by the coefficient of Q_1 in that equation, and then adding vertically the n equations, we get the *first normal equation.* The second normal equation is obtained in a similar manner by multiplying each of the observation equations by the coefficient of Q_2 in that equation and then summing up the n equations. If this operation is repeated k times, the result is the following set of normal equations:

$$(\Sigma a^2)Q_1 + (\Sigma ab)Q_2 + (\Sigma ac)Q_3 + \cdots + (\Sigma ak)Q_k = \Sigma aX$$
$$(\Sigma ab)Q_1 + (\Sigma b^2)Q_2 + (\Sigma bc)Q_3 + \cdots + (\Sigma bk)Q_k = \Sigma bX \tag{25}$$

$$\cdot$$
$$\cdot$$
$$\cdot$$

$$(\Sigma ak)Q_1 + (\Sigma bk)Q_2 + (\Sigma ck)Q_3 + \cdots + (\Sigma k^2)Q_k = \Sigma kX$$

where the summations denote the following expressions:

$$\Sigma a^2 = a_1{}^2 + a_2{}^2 + c_3{}^2 + \cdots + a_n{}^2$$

$$\Sigma ab = a_1b_1 + a_2b_2 + a_3b_3 + \cdots + a_nb_n$$

$$\Sigma aX = a_1X_1 + a_2X_2 + a_3X_3 + \cdots + a_nX_n, \quad \text{etc.}$$

The solution for the Q's from the previous normal equations indicates the most probable values of these quantities which we denote by Q_{01}, Q_{02}, Q_{03}, $\cdots Q_{0k}$. Substituting these in place of the Q's in the observation equations, we have the most probable values for the X's as X_{01}, X_{02}, X_{03}, $\cdots X_{0n}$.

$$a_1Q_{01} + b_1Q_{02} + c_1Q_{03} + \cdots + k_1Q_{0k} = X_{01}$$
$$a_2Q_{01} + b_2Q_{02} + c_2Q_{03} + \cdots + k_2Q_{0k} = X_{02} \tag{26}$$

$$\cdot$$
$$\cdot$$
$$\cdot$$

$$a_nQ_{01} + b_nQ_{02} + c_nQ_{03} + \cdots + k_nQ_{0k} = X_{0n}$$

The deviation, $\Delta_1 = X_{01} - X_1$, is called now an *adjustment,* which needs to be added to the observed quantity X_1 in order to derive its most probable value X_{01}. Similarly $\Delta_2 = X_{02} - X_2$ and $\Delta_n = X_{0n} - X_n$. It can be shown that the sum of squares of these deviations with respect to the $X_{01}, X_{02}, \cdots$ X_{0n} values is less than with respect to any other set of X quantities, or, in other words, the $X_{01}, X_{02}, \cdots X_{0n}$ quantities have the maximum combined probability of occurrence.

8. Adjustment of Conditioned Measurements. If there are n independent observations, $X_1, X_2, \cdots X_n$, which are related to a k number of unknowns, $Q_1, Q_2, \cdots Q_k$, and, at the same time, there is an l number of conditions which the Q unknowns have to satisfy among themselves, we speak of *conditioned measurements.* The simplest example of this kind is the case when independent measurements are made of the three angles of a triangle, α, β, and γ, which are known to be related by the condition $\alpha + \beta + \gamma = 180°$. In general, the measured values of these quantities, denoted by α_1, β_1, and γ_1, will not comply with the foregoing condition and will need adjustments for this purpose.

The most probable values of the unknowns, in the case when they are related in a linear manner to the measured quantities, which are assumed to be all of the same weight, can be determined in the following way.

The *observation equations* will be now:

$$A_1Q_1 + B_1Q_2 + C_1Q_3 + \cdots + K_1Q_k = X_1$$
$$A_2Q_1 + B_2Q_2 + C_2Q_3 + \cdots + K_2Q_k = X_2 \qquad (27)$$
$$\cdot$$
$$\cdot$$
$$A_nQ_1 + B_nQ_2 + C_nQ_3 + \cdots + K_nQ_k = X_n$$

At the same time the Q unknowns have to satisfy an l number of *condition equations:*

$$f_1(Q_1, Q_2, Q_3, \cdots Q_k) = 0$$
$$f_2(Q_1, Q_2, Q_3, \cdots Q_k) = 0 \qquad (28)$$
$$\cdot$$
$$\cdot$$
$$f_l(Q_1, Q_2, Q_3, \cdots Q_k) = 0$$

It may be seen that by substituting the condition equations into the observation equations the number of unknowns can be reduced to $m = k - l$, and the resulting *reduced observation equations* then can be written in the form:

$$a_1Q_1 + b_1Q_2 + c_1Q_3 + \cdots + m_1Q_m = X_1$$
$$a_2Q_1 + b_2Q_2 + c_2Q_3 + \cdots + m_2Q_m = X_2 \qquad (29)$$
$$\cdot$$
$$\cdot$$
$$a_nQ_1 + b_nQ_2 + c_nQ_3 + \cdots + m_nQ_m = X_n$$

The rest of the solution can be obtained in the same manner as outlined in the preceding article in connection with equation 24. From the reduced observation equations the normal equations are formed, the solution of which furnishes the most probable values $Q_{01}, Q_{02}, \cdots Q_{0m}$ of the m number of unknowns. By substituting these into the condition equations the rest of the Q values can be found.

The method is illustrated now in connection with the previously mentioned problem, where for the three angles of a triangle, α, β, and γ, independent measurements gave the values of α_1, β_1, and γ_1. The observation equations will be now:

$$\alpha \quad \cdot \quad \cdot = \alpha_1$$
$$\cdot \quad \beta \quad \cdot = \beta_1$$
$$\cdot \quad \cdot \quad \gamma = \gamma_1$$

The condition equation states that the exact (and also the most probable) values of these angles must be related as

$$\alpha + \beta + \gamma = 180°$$

Expressing γ from this last equation and substituting it in the foregoing, we have the reduced observation equations containing only two unknowns:

$$\alpha \quad \cdot \quad \cdot \quad = \alpha_1$$
$$\cdot \quad \beta \quad \cdot \quad = \beta_1$$
$$-\alpha \quad -\beta + 180° = \gamma_1$$

The corresponding normal equations will then be

$$2\alpha + \beta - 180° = \alpha_1 - \gamma_1$$

and

$$\alpha + 2\beta - 180° = \beta_1 - \gamma_1$$

The solution of these gives the most probable values for the angles α and β as

$$\alpha_0 = \frac{180° + 2\alpha_1 - \beta_1 - \gamma_1}{3}$$

and

$$\beta_0 = \frac{180° - \alpha_1 + 2\beta_1 - \gamma_1}{3}$$

which, in turn, on substitution into the equation of condition give for the third angle,

$$\gamma_0 = \frac{180° - \alpha_1 - \beta_1 + 2\gamma_1}{3}$$

Thus, we find that the Δ adjustments, that had to be added to the observed values, α_1, β_1, and γ_1, in order to obtain their most probable values that comply with the equation of condition, were

$$\Delta_1 = \Delta_2 = \Delta_3 = \frac{180° - \alpha_1 - \beta_1 - \gamma_1}{3}$$

BIBLIOGRAPHY

1. E. WHITTAKER and G. ROBINSON, *The Calculus of Observations*, Blackie & Son, 4th ed, 1944.   A classical treatise on numerical methods, including finite differences, solution of equations, numerical integration, theory of errors, and adjustment of observations.
2. A. G. WORTHING and J. GEFFNER, *Treatment of Experimental Data*, John Wiley & Sons, New York, 1943.   A textbook on the same topics as in Ref. 1, with numerous illustrations from the field of physical sciences.
3. M. MERRIMAN, *The Method of Least Squares*, John Wiley & Sons, 8th ed, New York, 1911.
4. T. W. WRIGHT and J. F. HAYFORD, *The Adjustment of Observations*, D. Van Nostrand Co., 2d ed, New York, 1906.   Deals extensively with geodetic work.
5. P. G. HOEL, *Introduction to Mathematical Statistics*, John Wiley & Sons, New York, 1947.   A textbook discussing methods of sampling, statistical hypotheses and analyses of experiments.
6. J. VOLGER, "On Estimation of Tenths," *Applied Sci. Research*, v A-1, n 3, pp 215–18, 1948.   Conclusions of this paper were quoted in footnote on page 1046.
7. B. EPSTEIN, "Statistical Aspects of Fracture Problems," *J Applied Physics*, v 19, pp 140–47, 1948.   Discusses several probability density functions, which may be used in the statistical interpretation of fracture data.

INDEX